D1067788

TEXTILE FIBERS

Matthews'

TEXTILE FIBERS

Their Physical, Microscopic, and Chemical Properties

SIXTH EDITION

Prepared by a Staff of Specialists under the Editorship of

HERBERT R. MAUERSBERGER

Secretary of Textile Book Publishers, Inc.
Director, Textile Department,
Fairleigh Dickinson College
Textile Consultant

JOHN WILEY & SONS, INC., NEW YORK
CHAPMAN & HALL, LIMITED, LONDON

Library of Congress Catalog Card Number: 54-6538

PRINTED IN THE UNITED STATES OF AMERICA

PREFACE

The first edition of this book, written by Dr. J. Merritt Matthews in 1904, was the first attempt that had been made to collect into one volume all the material then available for the study of textile fibers. At that time there had been only a small amount of chemical research on fibers; little was known of the action of the more modern chemical agents on the different ones. Many of the fibers that are familiar to us today had not even been heard of then, and many theories were accepted as true that have since been proved false. In the midst of these difficulties and uncertainties Dr. Matthews wrote a classic, a book that was the inspiration for much new research in this field. It was the only text and guide for many years.

The textile industry expanded so rapidly after the turn of the century that Matthews' subject matter had frequently to be rearranged, and each new edition contained more confirmed material. The fourth edition, his last, was published in 1924.

Today the textile industry is the second largest peacetime industry of the nation. Many laboratories throughout the country are conducting research on fibers now known and are constantly endeavoring to develop new ones. In this book we have tried to cover every available fiber of the animal, plant, and mineral kingdoms, and the synthetics. Although there still remain gaps in our fiber technology, the subject has expanded considerably since the brilliant pioneering of the original author so that now no one man can have a complete knowledge of its many facets.

Since the publication of the fifth edition in 1947 a tremendous advance has been made in the development of man-made fibers, and this division of fiber research continues to advance. This was one of the fundamental reasons for bringing out a sixth edition at this time. All the other material has been brought up to date by old and new contributors, each of whom is well known in his own field. Some material from previous editions has been retained and new information added. As editor-in-chief, I supervised the selection, revision, and arrangement of the material and wrote the chapters that are attributed to no other author. The entire book was carefully edited in an attempt to exclude overlapping material, contradictory statements, and unreliable data, as far as possible.

This book is not concerned with the analysis, testing, and processing of *fabrics*. It treats only of fibers and yarns and discusses their physical, chemical, and related properties. Production and trade statistics are included. Rubber yarns are not discussed, partly to save space and partly because they are not technically textile fibers. Brand names are included where necessary. Some of the illustrations were taken from previous editions; many were specially prepared by the chapter authors or obtained from authoritative sources. Botanical nomenclature of the plant fibers has been carefully coordinated in this edition.

The first chapter is introductory. The last three chapters cover identification methods, quantitative fiber analysis, X-ray identification, new in this edition, and testing methods.

This book is intended as a textbook for colleges and technical schools, and also as a reference book for all those concerned with the production, processing, conversion, and sale of yarns and fabrics of the different fibers now used in the apparel and related industries. The text is arranged in chapter groups which can be used as classroom assignments. For the benefit of layman and student alike, particular care was taken in the preparation of the subject index. Bibliographies at the end of each chapter and in footnote references give credit to the original researchers and indicate additional sources.

I wish to acknowledge gratefully the help of all the listed and anonymous contributors and collaborators as well as cooperating companies.

HERBERT R. MAUERSBERGER

New York, N. Y.
January 1954

COLLABORATORS AND CONTRIBUTORS

Herbert R. Mauersberger. Editor-in-chief. Director, Textile Department, Fairleigh Dickinson College, Rutherford, N. J. Textile expert and consultant. Formerly in charge of evening textile courses, Columbia University. Secretary of Textile Book Publishers, Inc.

John G. Albright, Ph.D. Professor and head of Physics Department, Rhode Island State College, Kingston, R. I.

Max Bachrach. Fur consultant. Lecturer at New York University, New York.

T. L. W. Bailey, Jr. Assistant Technical Director, Institute of Textile Technology. Formerly cotton technologist, Cotton Fiber Division, Southern Regional Research Laboratories, U. S. Department of Agriculture, New Orleans, La.

Louis C. Barail, Ph.D. Consulting biochemist and toxicologist, formerly bacteriologist for U. S. Testing Co.

Reginald J. Bray. Scientific Liaison Officer, International Wool Secretariat, London.

Charles J. Brick. In charge of Raw Silk Department, U. S. Testing Co., Hoboken, N. J.

E. R. Chatterton. Paper converting consultant, Delanco, N. J.

H. R. Childs. Tennessee Eastman Corp., Acetate Yarn Division, Kingsport, Tenn.

Charles F. Goldthwait. Senior cotton technologist, in charge of Modified Finishing Section, Cotton Chemical Finishing Division, Southern Regional Research Laboratories, U. S. Department of Agriculture.

John D. Guthrie, Ph.D. Chemist, Cotton Chemical Processing Division, Southern Regional Research Laboratories, U. S. Department of Agriculture, New Orleans, La.

A. N. J. Heyn, Ph.D. Professor (natural and synthetic fibers), Clemson Agricultural College, Clemson, S. C.

George H. Hotte. Manager, Synthetic Fiber Sales, National Aniline Division, Allied Chemical and Dye Corp.

Walter Krauss. Microscopist, Merchandise Testing and Development Laboratories, Sears, Roebuck & Co., Chicago, Ill.

Alfred R. Macormac, Ph.D. Chemist, U. S. Department of Agriculture, Food and Textiles Division, Beltsville, Md.

Bernice Montgomery. Bast and leaf fibers. Technical consultant and marketing adviser to growers and manufacturers; formerly technical expert for ramie to United Nations Technical Assistance Administration. Industry consultant to SCAP/GHQ, Tokyo, Japan, and UNRRS, Shanghai, China.

Ralph F. Nickerson, Ph.D. Research Department, Merrimack Division, Monsanto Chemical Co. Formerly Senior Industrial Fellow, Cotton Foundation Fellowship, Mellon Institute, Pittsburgh, Pa.

Tyler Stewart Rogers. Technical Director, Owens-Corning Fiberglas Corp., Textile Products Division, Toledo, Ohio.

A. S. Rossiter. Editor, *Asbestos Magazine,* Philadelphia, Pa.

Philip C. Scherer, Ph.D. Professor of Physical Chemistry, in charge of cellulose research, Virginia Polytechnic Institute, Blacksburg, Va.

Edward R. Schwarz. Professor of Textile Technology, in charge of Textile Division, Massachusetts Institute of Technology, Cambridge, Mass.

Harold DeWitt Smith, Ph.D. (deceased). Former technologist and treasurer, A. M. Tenney Associates, Inc., New York.

Werner von Bergen, F.T.I. Director of Research, Forstmann Woolen Co., Passaic, N. J.

W. Whitehead, Ph.D. Celanese Corp. of America, Inc., New York.

Arley C. Whitford, Ph.D. Research Director, Pinnellas Chemicals, Clearwater, Fla.

Cooperating Companies

American Cyanamid Co., Calco Chemical Division, Bound Brook, N. J. (*Fluorescence, birefringence, and staining*)

American Cyanamid Co., New Products Development Department, New York, and Stamford, Conn. (*X-51*)

Associated Factory Mutual Fire Insurance Cos., Factory Mutual Engineering Division, Boston, Mass. (*Flammability and fire risks*)

Carbide and Carbon Chemicals Co., division of Union Carbide and Carbon Corp., Textile Fibers Department, New York. (*Vinyon N and Dynel*)

Celanese Corp. of America, New York. (*Fortisan*)

The Chemstrand Corp., Decatur, Ala. (*Acrilan*)

E. I. du Pont de Nemours & Co., Inc., Textile Fibers Department and Patent Section, Wilmington, Del. (*Dacron, Orlon, and nylon*)

Firestone Plastics Co., Pottstown, Pa., division of Firestone Tire and Rubber Co. (*Velon*)

Owens-Corning Fiberglas Corp., Textile Products Division, New York. (*Fibrous glass*)

Reeves Brothers, Inc., New York. (*Polyethylene, Reevon*)

Rubberset Co., Salisbury, Md. (*Caslen*)

The Simco Co., Philadelphia, Pa. (*Static control*)

Textile Economics Bureau, Inc., New York. (*Statistics*)

Virginia-Carolina Chemical Corp., Richmond, Va. (*Vicara*)

CONTENTS

CHAPTER I

INTRODUCTION

The study of textile fibers has become a very intricate and exact science with many ramifications into the properties, sources, processing, and utilization of these fibers.

The history of fiber development has been a strange pattern of trial and error ever since fibers began to be used for making apparel. Climate seems to have had much to do with fiber utilization, since wool, hair, and fur fibers had great and continual development where the climate was variable or generally cold and where clothing was first worn to any great extent. In hot climates, the vegetable fibers were developed first, whereas expensive silks were used only in countries such as France and China where there were wealth, nobility, and privileged classes [1].

With the invention of machinery, fiber utilization became more rapid. Developments in cotton were greatly accelerated by the invention of the cotton gin. Wool and linen had no separation difficulty like that of cotton, which probably explains why most people believe that wool and linen were economically used for clothing long before cotton. Fulling of wool was practiced almost from the beginning. Coloring was done with natural dyes. Development of some fibers, such as acetate yarn, was delayed because of man's inability to dye them satisfactorily. Flax development was delayed because of the difficulty of degumming with sufficient thoroughness.

Cotton, in spite of its long existence, is still finding new uses, as Chas. K. Everett of the Cotton Textile Institute points out. He states in part: "We live in what is concededly the greatest transitional period in all history, whose very complexity makes intelligent planning as important as it is difficult." Political, economic, military, and trade conditions constantly alter fiber consumption and utilization. The totalitarian nations foresaw the necessity of building an economy based on blockade, an economy of self-sufficiency. This necessitated the invention of *ersatz* materials to take the place of natural fibers which were not produced within the totalitarian realm. Wool, silk, and cotton were affected seriously by these man-made fibers that could be produced quickly, cheaply, and more perfectly. Progress in making paper products at times encroached upon the development of nonwoven cotton products. Substitute products were invented and utilized to great advantage. In the words of David Cohn, author of *The Good Old Days*, "America has gone from cotton drawers to silk and rayon panties in one generation." New methods, new products, new machines, and new techniques continually displace the old, because of the profit motive, the motive of self-preservation, or "the motive of progress in terms of the promise of a fuller life," stated Chas. K. Everett.

This volume on textile fibers well depicts the progress that has been made in their economic utilization and technical development. Each fiber has been dealt with in regard to its historic origin, its development into a commercially usable fiber, its varieties or species, its grades, and its classification with botanical and commercial names. Availability and methods of production and preparation for market are duly considered, and prices are discussed with the aid of statistical tables, showing imports and exports by countries. The fiber properties in the raw and refined states are given in as great detail as our present state of technology permits. These properties are segregated into *three* distinct groups, namely, physical properties [2], miscroscopic characteristics, and chemical properties [3].

The utility of fibers, filaments, and yarns, both natural and man-made, as textile raw materials depends principally on the physical properties of the fibers, which include mechanical, thermal, optical, and electrical properties. Some of these physical properties of fibers are: molecular orientation, structure, length, density, fineness, elasticity, tenacity, breaking strength, ductility, moisture content, resiliency, pliability, spinnability, luster, extraneous physical impurities, elongation, creep, durability, permeability, combustibility, and electrical properties.

Although most fibers are used in the manufacture of fabrics and clothing, they have numerous other uses. For instance, the electrical industry employs fibers with high insulating qualities either inherent in the fibers or subsequently imparted to them. Other fibers find application in filling mattresses, pillows, and life preservers, where light weight, resilience, and buoyancy are required. Fibers such as wool are used in felts, because they mat readily. Furthermore, it is possible to endow natural fibers with new properties or to create new man-made fibers, filaments, and yarns which will serve specific purposes. Some instances are high-tenacity rayon for cord tires, nylon for parachutes, and Bubblfil for life rafts and preservers.

Before a fiber can be properly selected and its relative economic value and practical utilization can be determined, a careful study of all the physical properties, their terminology, definition, and interpretation under various conditions is essential.

Microscopy. Much progress has been made in the microscopy of textile fibers since 1925. Any study of textile fibers which does not consider the optical and microscopical aspects is incomplete. With the passing of time microscopy has become an important tool in testing, identification, and qualitative analysis of all textile materials. Throughout this book the microscopy of each fiber is dealt with in varying degrees, depending on how much research work has been done on each particular fiber. The purposes and aims achieved by such work and the technique and terminology employed are pointed out. The progress that has been made in microscopical work and research is amply demonstrated by the excellent photomicrographs in this book. They were carefully selected and especially prepared to serve their particular purpose in identification, examination, observance of normal and abnormal characteristics, quantitative and qualitative fiber analysis, measurement of fiber diameter, surface characteristics, and structure.

The use and selection of the proper microscope is a matter determined by practice, technical skill, and adaptation as well as application of basic principles.

It is not the purpose here to go into a detailed description of the microscope or of the many preparative techniques. It cannot be overemphasized, however, that a thorough knowledge of both is essential for the correct interpretation of the appearance of objects viewed in the microscope. Such is even more the case when really satisfactory photomicrographs are desired. In fact, it is the uncompromising verity of the combination of the microscope plus photography with its consequent dependence on superior technique that has led to so many improvements in this field. There are many excellent books on these subjects [4, 5, 6, 7, 8, 9].

Following is a partial list of subjects on which the microscope is an important tool for research and investigation: measurement of fibers, both length and diameter; identification; grading of fibers; study of linter; pigmentation; cross-sections of fibers; cause of damage, whether mechanical, bacterial, or fungic. In addition there are many strictly textile problems such as swelling, shrinking, felting, twisting, weaving faults, and knitting in which the microscope can be used. For many such investigations a low-power instrument, especially the Greenough binocular type, is ideal.

Aside from the determination of microscopic characteristics as such, much can be done in relating observations with the microscope with other physical data. All too often in the past, a single physical property has been taken as the criterion for the judgment of a fiber's worth. Many of these values are the average of a bundle of fibers. The microscope can frequently relate these values to a single fiber.

TRENDS IN FIBER CONSUMPTION

Figure 1 shows the mill consumption of raw fibers [10] in the United States from 1892 to 1948 in five-year averages. It should be noted from this chart that the total quantity of all fibers consumed by mills more than doubled between 1892 to 1919, rising from an average of 1.9 billion lb during 1892 to 1894 to an average of 4.3 billion lb during 1915–19. It then increased an average of 4.6 billion lb during 1935–39 and to an all-time peak of 7.5 billion lb in 1942, declining to about 7 billion lb in 1946, 1947, and 1948.

Cotton is the most important and is used in a quantity twice as great as that of all other fibers combined. It has comprised from 68 to 73 per cent of the entire fiber consumption in the United States since 1900, but in 1948, after a gradual decline, cotton consumption was only 64 per cent of the total consumption of all fibers, with wool 10 per cent, rayon 16 per cent, other synthetic fibers, flax, and silk 1 per cent or less, jute 2 per cent, hard fibers 6 per cent, and hemp a negligible percentage.

Rayon consumption has surpassed all other fibers in its continued upward trend since 1924. It has grown from 2.1 million lb in 1911 to 1149 million lb in 1948, or 16.4 per cent of the total raw fibers consumed in 1948. Rayons and acetate have been used in larger quantities than any other fiber except cotton during each year since 1937, except during 1941–43 when wool temporarily outranked them. See Figs. 1 and 2.

Figure 2 shows the production of viscose, acetate, and cuprammonium textile or nontire yarn, as well as viscose tire yarn, and viscose and acetate staple from 1920 to 1948 inclusive. Note the rapid and continual growth in the short span of years.

Other Synthetics. Until 1935 rayon was the only man-made fiber in production in the United States. Since then such fibers as nylon, Vinyon, glass, Saran, Orlon, Dacron, Vicara, etc., have come into production. Before 1940 consumption was negligible, but since then these fibers have comprised about 1 per cent of total raw fiber consumption. They are grouped together in Fig. 2; individual data are not available.

Peak quantities of raw jute were consumed by mills in 1905–09; flax in 1910–14; silk in 1925–29. Peak consumption of cotton occurred from 1940 to 1944 and of wool, rayon, and synthetic fibers during 1945 to 1948.

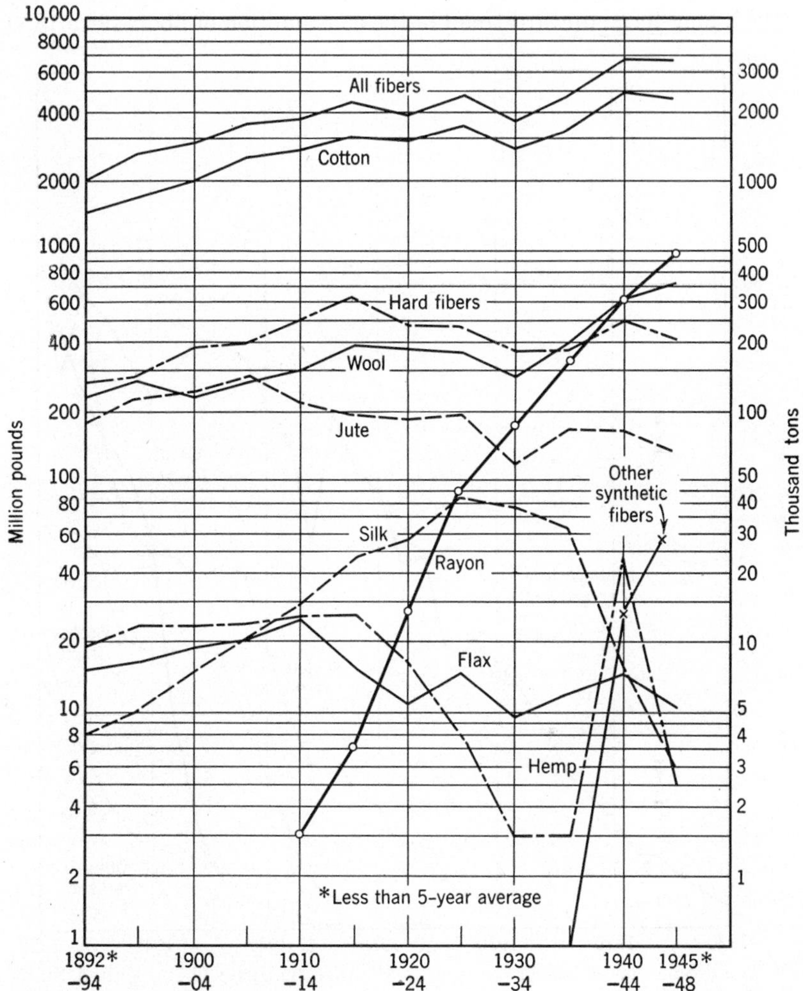

Fig. 1. Five-year averages for mill consumption of raw fibers, United States, 1892–48 [10]. Mill consumption of cotton and of all fibers in the aggregate increased rapidly from 1892 until the World War I period; increased only slightly between World Wars I and II; turned sharply upward with World War II; and leveled off during the postwar period. Peak quantities of raw jute were made available for mill use during 1905–09; of flax, 1910–14; and of silk, 1925–29. Peak mill consumption of cotton occurred during 1940–44, and of wool, rayon, and synthetic fibers during 1945–48.

Per Capita Consumption in the United States. There has been a continued, long-term, upward trend in the consumption of fibers since 1890,

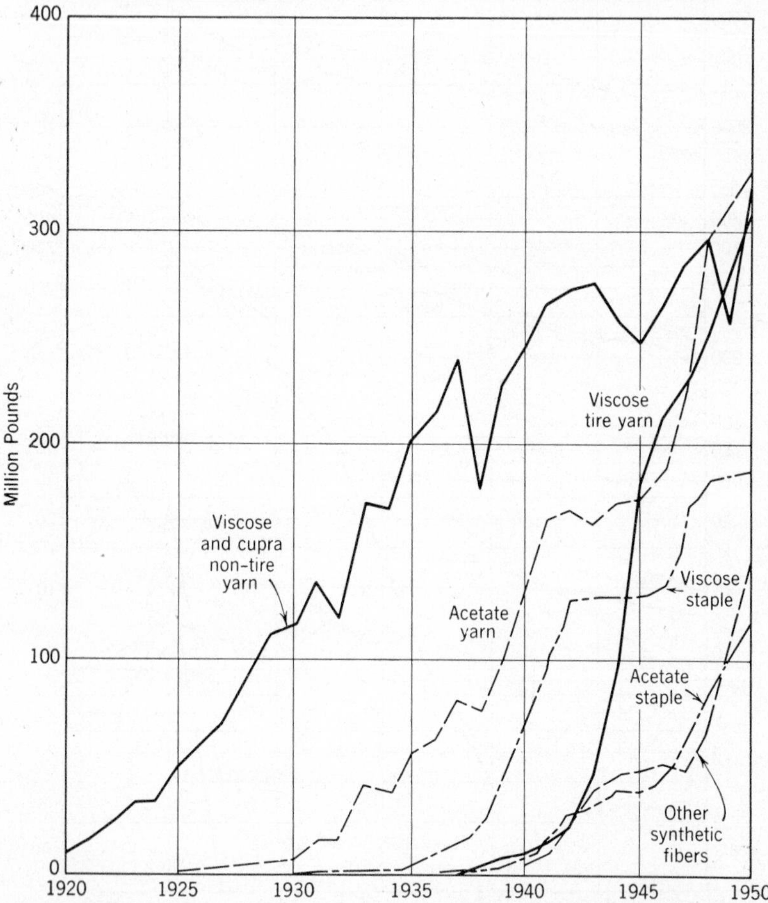

FIG. 2. Production of rayon by types and other synthetic fibers, United States, 1920–48 [10]. Production of all types of rayon and other synthetic fibers rose from minor quantities, from various years since 1920, to attain all-time output records in 1948, such as 313 million lb for nontire viscose yarn; 249 million lb for viscose tire yarn; 294 million lb for acetate yarn; 185 million lb for viscose staple fiber; 84 million lb for acetate staple fiber; and 71 million lb for other synthetic fibers.

but consumption rose no faster than the population from 1905 to 1939 and remained about the same for all fibers [10]. It rose tremendously during World War II, more rapidly than the population. See Fig. 3. It resulted in an increase from 41 lb per person per year to above 50 lb in the period from 1935 to 1939. In 1948 it was 49 lb per person, or about 10 lb less than the peak per capita consumption in 1941.

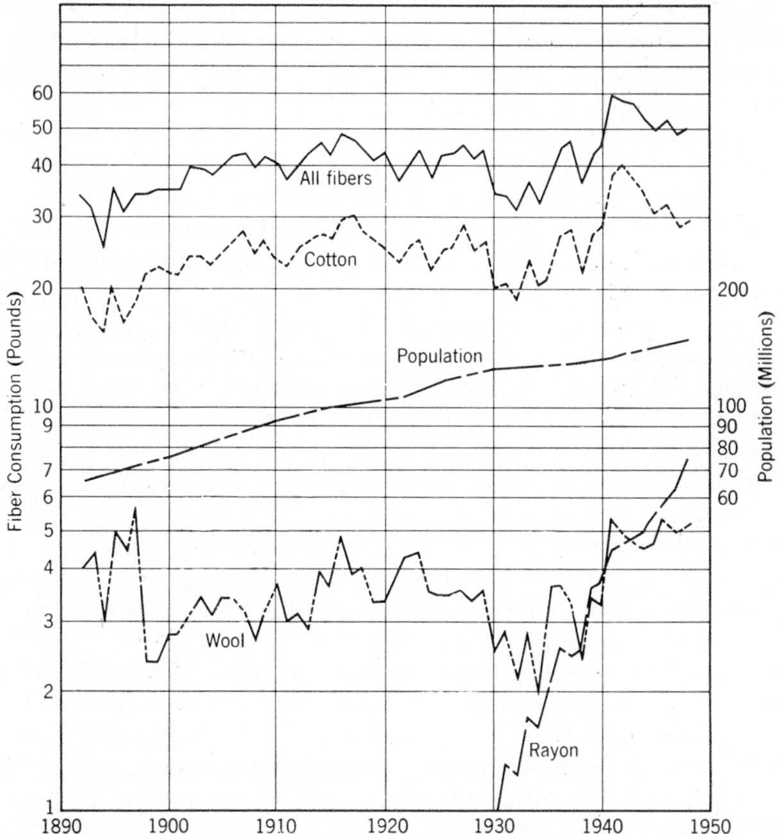

FIG. 3. Trends in the per capita quantities of all fibers, and of cotton, wool, and rayon, used by ultimate consumers, United States, 1892–1948 [10]. Per capita consumption of cotton, wool, and of all fibers failed to increase between 1910 and 1940, but increased rapidly to record levels during World War II. Since the war's end the per capita use of rayon and wool has been higher than ever before, while per capita use of all fibers and of cotton has been declining from the peak attained during the war.

Domestic or Foreign Origin. The entire supply of jute, hard fibers, and silk used by the ultimate consumers in the United States is of foreign origin; so also is nearly all the flax and, currently, a large portion of wool. On the other hand, nearly all the cotton, rayon, and, in 1948, hemp is produced domestically. The most important fiber of foreign origin consumed by final users in the United States, quantitatively, is jute. It comprised 47 per cent of the total fiber of foreign origin consumed during 1935–39 and 38 per cent during 1948. In comparison, wool comprised 11 per cent and 28 per cent; cotton 7 and 6 per cent; silk 4 and 1 per cent; flax 2 and 1 per cent; rayon 1 and 2 per cent; and hard fibers 28 and 24 per cent of the total fibers of foreign origin during 1935–39 and 1948, respectively.

Wool underwent the most outstanding change since World War II in our use of foreign fibers. Before the war, an average of about 178 million lb of foreign wool was used annually by final consumers as compared to a total of 538 million lb in 1948. Only 43 per cent of the wool finally consumed in the United States was of foreign origin during 1935–39, as compared to 73 per cent in 1948.

Imports vs. Exports. The foreign trade is of particular significance to the textile industry, since exports may constitute an important outlet for domestic production, whereas imports compete with the output of domestic mills for the domestic market. *Exports* [10] of principal fiber manufactures increased from an annual average of 148 million lb per year during 1935–39 to an annual average of 299 million lb during 1940–44, and to a record total of 847 million lb in 1947. Exports of fiber manufactures dropped to 565 million lb in 1948. About 67 per cent consisted of cotton manufactures, 3 per cent wool textiles, 18 per cent of rayon and acetate products, about 9 per cent of jute manufactures, and 3 per cent hard-fiber products.

Imports of textiles into the United States [10] were substantially larger than textile exports for 1922 through 1946, and 1948, and probably also were substantially larger than textile exports during the years before 1922. Annual averages for principal items declined from a peak of 909 million lb per year during 1925–29 to 665 million lb per year during 1930–34, then rose to 812 million lb during 1935–39. With World War II, there was a substantial reduction to a low point of 412 million lb per year during 1942, but after that date textile imports increased, the 1946 total of 769 million lb being the largest for any year since before 1940. The 1948 total, however, dropped to 733 million lb. Imports of principal fiber manufactures were equal in weight to 10 per cent of the total fiber consumption by ultimate consumers in 1946 and 1948 and to 15 per cent of the total in 1935–39.

Burlap and other jute products constitute the bulk of our textile imports, accounting for 84 per cent of the total during 1948 as compared with 6 per cent for hard-fiber products, 7 per cent for wool manufactures, 2 per cent for cotton textiles, and 1 per cent for manufactures of other fibers.

Consumption of fibers is, therefore, intimately connected with the clothing, housing, and industrial equipment needs of the country and is highly influenced by such factors as population growth, consumer income, and business prosperity. Considering that the population of the United States in 1948 was approximately 13 per cent higher than the average during the 1935–39 period, and assuming at least moderate prosperity in the years ahead, it can be reasonably expected that the total consumption of fibers by ultimate consumers will continue to be substantially greater than before World War II, even if it does not exceed the record levels reached during 1941–43.

UTILIZATION OF NEW FIBERS

J. Spencer Love, chairman of Burlington Mills, stated the following facts in his talk to the American Association of Textile Chemists and Colorists on October 18, 1951, regarding trends [11] in the consumption of new man-made fibers:

> We have come a long way in the man-made textile industry. It's only about a 25-year span that makes up our entire industry. . . . Nothing indicates the fascinating growth of the man-made fabrics industry more than the shift in fiber consumption in this country since 1925. In that year, cotton represented 86.6 per cent, wool 9.9 per cent, silk 1.9 per cent, and chemical fibers accounted for only 1.6 per cent. By 1940, cotton was at 81 per cent, chemical fibers had risen to 10 per cent, or second in rank, while wool stood at 8.4 per cent and silk 0.7 per cent. By 1950, the figures read 68.8 per cent for cotton, 21.8 per cent for man-made fibers, 9.3 per cent for wool and 0.08 per cent for silk. In the last 30 years, the use of rayon and acetate have risen from 8,700,000 lb to 1,200,000,000 lb. It is even more important to point out the spectacular rises that have taken place in the end-uses of rayon, acetate, and nylon fibers. In 1929, women's rayon suits were not even mentioned in the census. By 1950, over 40 per cent of all women's suits were made of rayon and acetate fibers. About 50 per cent of all women's skirts are now made of rayon and acetate fabrics. Over 70 per cent of all unit-price dresses use rayon and acetate. Over 75 per cent of all women's blouses are manufactured of man-made textiles.
>
> We all know about the spectacular growth rayon, acetate, and nylon have made in men's summer suits. Five years ago only 10 per cent of men's summer suits were made of these fibers. For the first time last year rayon, acetate, and nylon summer suits outsold tropical worsteds and worsted gabardines by 56 per cent compared to 40 per cent. As late as 1946, rayon and acetate fabric slacks accounted for about 25 per cent of the total trouser production. By 1950, there were more rayon and acetate fabric slacks made than wool (about 20,600,000 rayon to 19,100,000 wool). Rayon and acetate are used to great extent in bed blankets, rainwear, bathing suits, women's sportswear, men's underwear, carpets, rugs, and many prewar volume fields such as lingerie, hosiery, linings, decorative fabrics, and upholstery cloth, sweaters, dressing gowns, bathrobes, linens, and over-the-counter yard-goods.

C. W. Bendigo [12] of the New Product Division, American Cyanamid Co., had this to say on June 26, 1952, talking to the American Society for Testing Materials:

Between 1950 and 1953 the rate of production of all the newer synthetic fibers will increase 300 per cent with a total installed capacity of over 400,000,000 in place next year. By 1970, the rate for the noncellulosic synthetics should be near a billion annual pounds. During this same period, the production of cellulosic fibers should approximately double. President Truman's Materials Policy Commission has forecast United States fiber consumption at 7,500,000,000 pounds for 1975. If all the foregoing figures are correct, the evidence is that not only wool but also cotton will feel the impact of the synthetic fibers. There is no question that wool consumption will drop now that there are available in the United States several fibers with not only woollike properties but many points of superiority over wool. I am referring principally to the acrylic fibers including the polyesters.

In addition to rayon and acetate, there are at least ten other important synthetic fibers being produced in the United States. . . . These many new fibers are being produced in several different forms all of which adds to the large variety of materials the textile industry has to work with but which complicates any understanding of the significance of new fibers on the part of the consumer.

With so many new fibers and with their principal use being in blends, textile products will be engineered for specific performance characteristics and for ease of maintenance. There must be less emphasis on fiber content because fiber content can be misleading and is bound to be increasingly confusing. The significance of fiber content can be complicated by finishes that are applied to textiles. The current thinking in the industry is towards emphasis on performance and maintenance specifications and de-emphasis on fiber content.

The present price relationship between the various synthetic fibers is due for a change. Today the acrylic fibers Orlon and Acrilan are the highest priced, with nylon and Dacron somewhat lower. In the near future it can be expected that acrylic staple will be priced less than nylon and Dacron and eventually that the price of acrylic staple will be second only to cellulosic staples.

Synthetic fiber developments abroad parallel those in the United States to the extent that the increased rate in 1953 will be three times greater than the production in 1950. Today there are 29 foreign companies producing nylon fiber, 27 producing glass fibers, 9 producing polyvinyl chloride fibers, 6 producing polyvinyl alcohol types, and 4 foreign companies producing protein staple.

In the future in the United States, increases in rayon for industrial fabrics, increases in acetate for apparel, nylon for apparel and industrial, glass fibers for industrial uses, and in acrylics for the entire warmth field and for producing fabrics with ease of maintenance are foreseen.

TERMINOLOGY

Since textile raw materials are, of necessity and by definition, of fibrous nature, irrespective of their source, grade, or classification, the terminology employed in their manipulation should be considered. These terms can be used in the technical sense and also in the nontechnical sense. Improper use of these words causes confusion and misunderstanding.

Raw material has been defined as "material that has not been subjected to a [specified] process of manufacture." This term, of course, is relative in meaning with regard to textile fibers. Raw cotton is a raw material to the yarn spinner, whereas raw silk may be raw material to the knitter or weaver directly. Again, the material may be entirely in its raw or natural state; then again it may be partly processed, as in the case of flax and linen.

The word "textile" as an adjective requires some clarification. In the general and broad sense, the word "textile" comes from the Latin word *textilis* and the French *texere*, to weave, pertaining "to weaving or to woven fabrics; woven or capable of being woven; formed by weaving; that which is, or may be, woven; a woven fabric." Hence, textile raw materials are materials that can be converted into yarns and fabrics of any nature or character. Technically, they must be of spinnable length, since only then can they be made into spun yarns.

Fiber is raw material used in textile manufacturing. It is defined in the dictionary as "one of the delicate, threadlike portions of the tissues of a plant or animal." This is a general definition; textile technologists have defined a textile fiber as a "slender filament or fine strand of sufficient length, pliability, and strength to be spun into yarns and woven into cloth."

The word "fiber" is quite often used in this way: "Rayon is one of the textile fibers." Here, the word fiber is used generally to indicate a classification of textile fibers, whereas, when cotton fiber is defined by the technologist, he states "it is a very fine, much elongated, single cell seed hair, which grows on the outside of a cotton seed"; or, "the mature cotton fiber occurs as a hollow, collapsed, spirally twisted tube." The word "hair" has been used alternately with fiber in referring to both vegetable and animal fibers. The dictionary makes no clear distinction between hair and fiber.

The American Society for Testing Materials (A.S.T.M.) [13] defines hair as "a natural animal fiber other than sheep's wool or silk" and appends a note stating: "It is recognized that this definition implies a distinction between sheep's wool and the covering of other animals, notwithstanding similarity in their fiber characteristics. Thus, the crimped form and scaly structure are not confined to sheep's wool. It seems desirable in the textile trade, however, to avoid ambiguity by confining the term wool to the covering of sheep and to have available a general term for other fibers of animal origin. Normally, the less widely used fibers are known by name, for example, alpaca, mohair, etc., but collectively they are classed as hairs."

A "fibril" is a very small cell or fiber, a long cell or fiber of very small diameter, or a component of a cell wall. The length of a fiber is conveniently measurable in inches, whereas a fibril is measured in microns or millimicrons. A "filament" is a processed fiber of continuous length most conveniently measured in yards or meters. There may be only one (mono) or many (multi) filaments, as in a rayon or silk yarn. The basic difference between a fiber and a filament is one of length.

A.S.T.M. [13] defines a filament as "a variety of fiber characterized by extreme length" and appends a note stating that "the extreme length of filaments permits their being used in yarn without twist or with very low twist, and they are usually fabricated into yarn without the spinning operation required for fibers."

A yarn is a generic term, according to A.S.T.M., for "an assemblage of fibers or filaments, either natural or manufactured, twisted or laid together to form a continuous strand suitable for use in weaving, knitting, or otherwise intertwining to form textile fabrics." There are many varieties of yarns such as single yarn, ply yarn, novelty yarns, cords, twine, and sewing threads.

A thread is three or more yarns tightly twisted, singed, dyed, polished, and finished to fit into the eye of a needle or to be hand knotted, crocheted or tatted. The very extreme type of thread reaches into the area of cords and eventually ropes of all types.

These definitions constitute present usage of these words and include the fine distinctions that are made between them as well as their commercial and technological meanings.

Yarn Numbering Systems

Since there are many degrees of fineness in yarns made of many different fibers, twists, and weights, it becomes necessary to have a system of designating their size, yardage, number, or diameter. It is really a designation for the measure of their linear density. Linear density is defined as the mass per unit length expressed as grams per centimeter, pounds per foot, or equivalent, according to A.S.T.M. [13].

Two systems are in current use:

1. *Direct Yarn Numbering System.* This system is based on *weight per unit length* or specific linear density. The yarn number is equal to the observed linear density divided by the linear density of a number *one* yarn. A.S.T.M. states that direct yarn numbers have been recommended in a universal system and are commonly used for most yarn intermediates and in silk, jute, and man-made fiber industries.

2. *Indirect Yarn Numbering System.* This system is based on length per unit weight, and the numbers are the reciprocals of the specific linear density. They are commonly used in the asbestos, cotton, glass, linen, and woolen and worsted industries.

The numbers of cotton, jute, linen, woolen and worsted, spun rayon, and spun silk yarn are determined under standard atmospheric conditions, i.e., 70° F. and 65 per cent R.H., whereas the numbers of silk, viscose, and cuprammonium rayon yarns are based on commercial regain of 11 per cent. See Table 1. The number of acetate yarn is based on a commercial regain of 6.5 per cent.

The fineness of single yarns is defined below in the unit currently used for the common textile fibers. The definitions also apply to the equivalent single number of ply yarns.

Alpaca (hank): The number of 560-yd hanks per pound avoirdupois.
Asbestos (cut): The number of 100-yd lengths per pound avoirdupois.
Camel's hair (hank): The number of 560-yd hanks per pound avoirdupois.
Cashmere (hank): The number of 560-yd hanks per pound avoirdupois.
Cotton (hank): The number of 840-yd hanks per pound avoirdupois.
Glass (cut): The number of 100-yd lengths per pound avoirdupois.
Hemp (hank or lea):[1] The number of 300-yd hanks or leas per pound avoirdupois.
Jute (spyndle):[1] The weight in pounds avoirdupois of a spyndle of 14,400 yd of yarn expressed as pounds per spyndle.
Linen (hank or lea):[1] The number of 300-yd hanks or leas per pound avoirdupois.
Mohair (hank): The number of 560-yd hanks per pound avoirdupois.
Nylon (denier): The number of unit weights of 0.05 gram per 450-meter length.
Ramie (hank or lea):[1] The number of 300-yd hanks or leas per pound avoirdupois.
Rayon, continuous filament (denier): The number of unit weights of 0.05 gram per 450-meter length.
Rayon, spun (hank): The number of 840-yd hanks per pound avoirdupois. (Cotton count abbreviated cc.)
Silk, raw or thrown (denier): The number of unit weights of 0.05 gram per 450-meter length.
Silk, spun (hank): The number of 840-yd hanks per pound avoirdupois.
Vinyon (denier): The number of unit weights of 0.05 gram per 450-meter length.
Woolen (cut): The number of 300-yd cuts or hanks per pound avoirdupois; (run): The number of 1600-yd hanks per pound avoirdupois.
Worsted (hank): The number of 560-yd hanks per pound avoirdupois.

Systems for All Yarns

The *International metric system* is used for all kinds of yarn except fibrous glass fiber yarn (see Chap. XIX). The yarn count is the number of meters in 1 gram. No. 20 means that a length of 20 meters weighs

[1] Heavy flax, hemp, and ramie are sometimes numbered the same as jute; i.e., spyndle: The weight in pounds avoirdupois of a spyndle of 14,400 yd of yarn expressed as pounds per spyndle.

TABLE 1. Per Cent Regains Used in United States and Foreign Countries *

Textile Fibers	*U. S.*	*Italy*	*England*	*France*	*Switzerland*	*Germany*	*Spain*
Silk	11	11	..	11	11	11	11
Crepe Silk	..	13	..	..	..	..	..
Rayon							
Crepe rayon	..	11	..	..	..	..	..
Spun rayon	..	11	..	..	..	..	..
Floss rayon	..	14	..	..	..	..	..
Viscose rayon	11	11	..	..	11	11	..
Cuprammonium rayon	11	..	..	..	..	..	..
Acetate	6½	6	..	..	7	6	..
Cotton							
Cotton	8½	8½	..	8½	8½	..	8½
Mercerized cotton	8½	..	..	12	8½	..	9
Cotton yarns	7	..	..	8½	..	..	..
Cotton cloth	6½	..	..	..	..	..	..
Wool							
Wool	18¼	18½	..	..	17	18½	17
Spun wool	..	18¼	..	..	..	..	..
Combed wool	..	18¼	..	18¼	..	..	18¼
Treated wool	..	17	18	..	..	..	..
Scoured wool	13.6	18	17	17	17	11	..
Waste wool	16	12½	..	..	..	13¾	..
Shoddy wool	13	..	17	..	..	..	..
Partly scoured	..	..	..	18	..	..	..
Roving	..	..	..	18¼	..	..	..
Renaissance wool	..	..	..	17	..	..	..
Tops and ring laps	..	..	18¼	..	..	..	..
Noils (Schlumberger combing)	..	16	16	16	..	..	..
Noils							
Lister and	..	..	..	10 Lister	..	..	..
Noble combing	16	..	14	8 Noble	..	..	..
Combed in oil	..	..	19	19	..	..	..
Combed without oil	..	..	18¼	18¼	..	..	..
Carded yarns	17	..	17	17	..	..	..
Worsted yarns	..	..	18¼	18¼	18¼	18¼	..
Worsted yarn, Bradford (wet) spun	13	..	..	..	..	..	..
Worsted yarn, French (dry) spun	15	..	..	..	..	..	..
Worsted and woolen cloth	16	..	..	..	..	..	..
Uniform cloth without finishing	..	..	..	13	..	..	..
Lanital	..	17	..	..	17½	..	..
Linen	12	12	..	..	..	..	12¾
Jute	13¾	13¾	..	..	..	12	13¾
Ramie	..	..	..	..	..	12	..
Hemp	12	..	..	..	..	12	..
Nylon	4½	..	..	..	..	..	..
Orlon	1.5	..	..	..	..	..	..
Acrilan	1.7	..	..	..	..	..	..
Dynel	0.3–0.4	..	..	..	..	..	..
Dacron	0.4	..	..	..	..	..	..
Vinyon Staple HH	0.0–0.5	..	..	..	..	..	..
Vinyon N	0.3	..	..	..	..	..	..
Azlon	10	..	..	..	..	..	..
Glass	None	..	..	..	..	..	..
Saran	None	..	..	..	..	..	..
Polyethylene	None	..	..	..	..	..	..

* Courtesy U. S. Testing Co. [14] and *Textile World's* Synthetic Fiber Table (Sept. 1951).

1 gram (this measure was adopted by the Paris Conference of 1900). The *Typp system* is the number of thousand yards to 1 pound. The *Grex system* is based on the number of grams per 10,000 meters of yarn. Both are proposed by A.S.T.M.

MOISTURE AND MOISTURE REGAIN

Most textile fibers absorb more or less moisture from the surrounding atmosphere. The moisture present in a textile fiber or material is usually expressed (1) as a percentage of the original weight of the material or (2) of its oven-dry weight. In (1), it is generally referred to as *moisture content* or moisture "as is," "as received," or on a "wet" basis. In (2), it is referred to as *moisture regain* (frequently contracted to regain) or moisture on the "oven-dry," "moisture free," or "dry" basis.

Textile fibers vary widely in the amount of moisture they hold, absorb, or give up, as in drying. The amount of moisture a fiber will hold depends on the kind of fiber, its condition, i.e., loose or baled, yarn or cloth, and the humidity and temperature of the surrounding atmosphere. Moisture equilibrium is a condition reached by the fiber when it no longer takes up moisture from or gives up moisture to the surrounding air. Superficial equilibrium is reached rapidly, whereas stable equilibrium takes considerable time, especially if the surrounding air is motionless. Stable equilibrium is considered to be realized when successive weighings of a given fiber quantity do not show any progressive change in weight greater than the standard tolerances permitted for each textile material (see A.S.T.M. standards).

Abuses in connection with moisture content of commercial shipments of loose fibers, filaments, and yarns brought about the term Commercial Moisture Regain, which designates an arbitrary percentage, formally accepted by the trade as the regain to be used in calculating a commercial or legal weight of shipments or deliveries of any specific textile raw material. Various trade bodies have adopted arbitrary commercial regains, which are universally accepted by producers, dealers, shippers, and users alike. Table 1 shows the standard or accepted regains of many textile fibers for the United States and foreign countries [14].

Regains are not the same in all countries, nor are the regains of the same material under various conditions the same. It is noteworthy that standard regain of textile fibers ranges from a low of zero per cent to a high of 18½ per cent (wool). Table 1 is useful only in commercial transactions. It is to be assumed that the moisture content of the various textile fibers fluctuates with changing conditions. The data in Table 1 are based on an atmosphere of 70° F. and 65 per cent R.H. It is assumed that at this temperature and relative humidity textile materials are in their normal or standard condition of moisture. Table 2 gives

TABLE 2. WATER ABSORPTION OF TEXTILE FIBERS UNDER DIFFERENT CONDITIONS OF HUMIDITY AT 75° F.

Per Cent Rel. Humidity	*Cotton*	*Wool*	*Silk*	*Viscose Rayon*	*Acetate*	*Cupr. Rayon*	*Textile Nylon*
5	1.4	2.2	1.8	...	....	....	...
10	2.4	4.0	3.2	3.9	0.85	3.70	1.1
15	3.0	5.7	4.4	...	....	....	...
20	3.6	7.1	5.4	5.7	1.70	5.45	1.4
25	3.9	8.3	6.1	...	....	....	...
30	4.3	9.4	6.7	7.4	2.45	6.90	1.7
35	4.6	10.4	7.3	...	....	....	...
40	5.0	11.0	7.8	8.8	3.25	8.50	2.3
45	5.3	11.8	8.4	9.7	3.65	9.25	...
50	5.7	12.6	8.8	10.4	4.20	10.00	2.8
55	6.3	13.4	9.4	11.3	4.75	10.80	...
60	6.7	14.2	9.9	12.2	5.25	11.76	3.4
65	7.3	15.0	10.5	13.1	5.95	12.45	...
70	7.9	16.0	11.4	14.3	6.75	13.45	4.1
75	8.8	17.1	12.5	....	....	....	...
80	9.9	18.6	14.0	17.1	8.55	16.00	5.0
85	11.4	20.5	15.9	....	....	....	...
90	13.6	23.2	18.4	21.9	11.30	20.30	5.7
95	17.5	27.0	22.7	....	....	....	6.1

regain data under various moisture conditions at a constant temperature of 75° F.

DENSITY AND SPECIFIC GRAVITY

Density is mass per unit volume. It is usually expressed in grams per cubic centimeter or pounds per cubic foot. Specific gravity or specific weight is the ratio of the mass of a material to the mass of an equal volume of water; in other words it is the ratio of the weight of a fiber mass to the weight of an equal volume of water (at 4° C.). True fiber density is affected by molecular packing (crystallinity), orientation, and the atomic weight of the elements making up the molecule. Porosity, voids, lumen, and cracks may affect the apparent fiber density. All textile fibers except polyethylene are heavier than water. The lightest textile fiber is nylon, followed by Orlon, Dacron, and X-51, and the heaviest fibers are glass and asbestos.

Specific gravities of the important natural and man-made fibers, compiled from this book, are arranged alphabetically in Table 3.

TABLE 3. DENSITY OF TEXTILE FIBERS AT 25–30° C.

[From various sources.]

Natural Fibers	*Grams per cu cm*
Asbestos	2.2–2.6
Camel hair	1.32
Cotton	1.54–1.55
Hemp	1.48–1.49
Jute	1.48–1.50
Linen (flax)	1.50
Mohair	1.32
Ramie	1.51
Silk, raw	1.33–1.35
boiled off (degummed)	1.25
tussah	1.27
Wool	1.30
Man-Made Fibers	
Acetate, regular	1.33
saponified	1.50
Acrilan (Chemstrand)	1.35
Caslen (casein)	1.29
Cuprammonium rayon	1.52–1.54
Dacron	1.38
Dynel	1.31
Fiberglas (Vitron)	2.4–2.54
Fiber A	1.16
Fortisan	1.52
Nitrocellulose rayon	1.54
Nylon	1.14
Orlon	1.17
Permalon	1.72
Polyethylene	0.92
Saran	1.72
Velon	1.34
Vinyon E (elastic)	1.19
Vinyon N	1.35
Vinyon HST	1.35
Viscose rayon	1.52–1.54
Vicara	1.22
X-51 (Cyanamid)	1.17

CLASSIFICATION OF NATURAL FIBERS

According to a very complete compilation of M. Vernardin in his *Nomenclature Uselle des Fibres Textiles*, the number of plant fibers used by the human species is more than 550, and perhaps 700. Calculating in addition thereto the mineral fibers (asbestos) as well as the various packing materials, spun fibers, brush materials, animal hairs, and silk, the number of single substances would probably amount to 1000, if not more. Hence, textile fibers in general consist of a great number and a wide range of raw materials. For convenience of study, they may be divided into two broad divisions, namely, natural textile fibers and man-made or synthetic textile fibers.

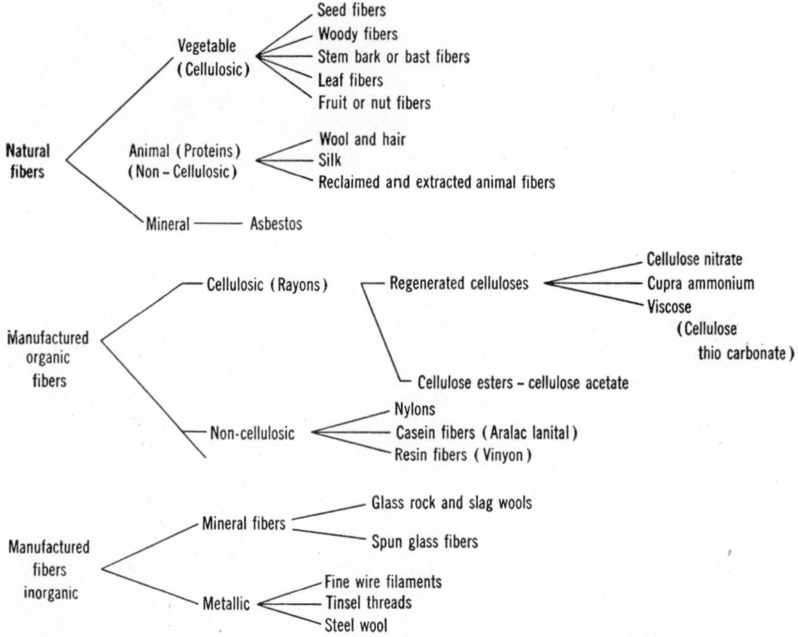

FIG. 4. L. A. Olney's tabulated classification of all textile fibers.

The natural fibers are generally subdivided into (*a*) animal fibers, (*b*) mineral fibers, and (*c*) vegetable or plant fibers. The A.S.T.M. revised compilation of natural fibers, which is quite comprehensive and the most complete in this country, attempts not only to list the fibers alphabetically but also to bring some semblance of order into the most common or preferred names, botanical nomenclature, and foreign equivalents. It is found in the Appendix of the *Standards on Textile Materials*, 1951 issue.

Various classifications for all natural fibers have been proposed and attempted from time to time. A favorite classification in tabular form [15] which is easily remembered and reconstructed by a student, for instance, is shown in Fig. 4.

CLASSIFICATION OF MAN-MADE FIBERS

The classification or grouping of man-made or synthetic fibers is much more difficult and cumbersome. Various such classifications have been proposed from time to time, but because of constant changes in this

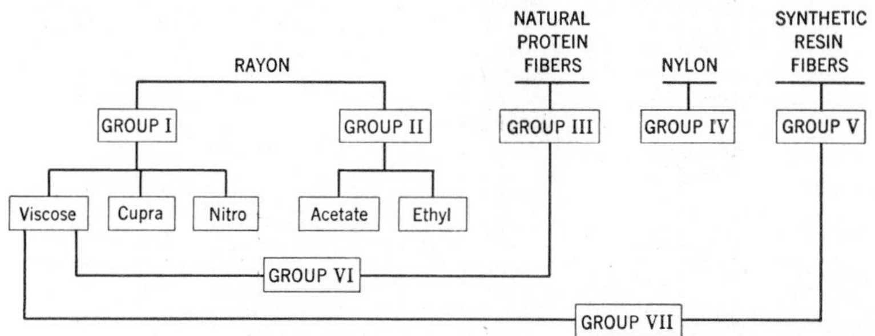

FIG. 5. Stanley Hunt's classification of man-made fibers (1939).

category such tabulations become quickly outmoded [16]. They have been attempted from various aspects. One offered by Stanley Hunt, of the Textile Economics Bureau [17], is shown in Fig. 5. It is based on fibers commercially available in 1939.

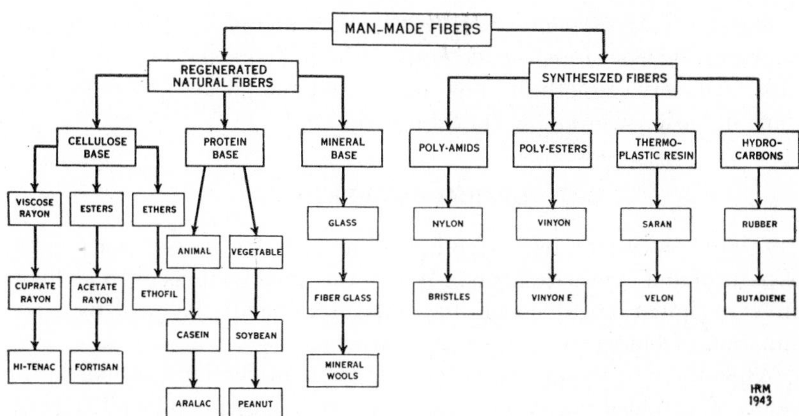

FIG. 6. Mauersberger's classification of man-made fibers (1943) proposed to the American Society for Testing Materials.

Another interesting breakdown of man-made fibers was submitted by H. R. Mauersberger to Committee D-13 of the A.S.T.M. in March 1943 and published in D-13 *Standards on Textile Materials* for 1943. This tabulation is shown in Fig. 6.

A chemical classification of man-made fibers prepared by Walter Krauss is based on an entirely different arrangement. It is shown in Table 4.

TABLE 4. Chemical Classification of Manufactured Fibers [18]

Source	Base	Type	Fibers
Natural sources	Cellulose base	Regenerated cellulose	Viscose rayon filaments and fibers.
			Cuprammonium rayon filaments and fibers
		Cellulose ester	Acetate filaments and fibers.
			Tri-acetate filaments and fibers.
			Ethyl cellulose rayon filaments and fibers.
	Protein base	Animal protein	Casein fibers.
			Fibroin fibers.
		Vegetable protein	Soybean fibers.
			Mazein fibers.
			Peanut fibers.
	Protein-like base	Chitin	Chitin filaments and fibers.
		Alginate	Alginate filaments and fibers.
	Inorganic base	Glass	Glass filaments and fibers.
		Metal	Metal threads and cut strips.
		Slag and mineral	Slag wool, rock wool.
Synthesized base	Polyamides	Nylon	Nylon filaments, bristles and fibers.
	Vinyl derivatives	Vinyl chloride and acetate	Vinyon.
		Vinylidene chloride	Vinylidene filaments.
		Vinyl butyral	
	Butadiene	Butadiene styrene	Synthetic rubber filaments.
		Butadiene acrylonitrile	Synthetic rubber filaments.

Note: This table includes all commercially and experimentally produced fiber types.

The A.S.T.M. *Standards on Textile Materials* of 1951 gives the list shown in Table 6 of man-made and synthetic fibers and monofilaments, which will serve to indicate how varied and complicated they have become in basic types and chemical description.

OPTICAL PROPERTIES

Table 5 shows the refractive indices and birefringence for a number of natural and synthetic fibers. Where the cross sections of some fibers are very similar, positive identification can frequently be made by determination of optical properties [20 and 20*a*].

While these techniques serve as positive identification methods in the hands of a trained microscopist, it is true that they are difficult to carry out in a practical way. It is necessary to have standardized liquids with different refractive indices so that the Becke method may be employed for determining the refractive index of the fibers under the polarizing microscope when the fibers are immersed in these various liquids. In use, when the microscope is focused up, the Becke line moves toward the medium of higher refractive index. If the fiber is mounted in a liquid of higher refractive index, it will move toward the liquid; see

TABLE 5. Optical Properties of Textile Fibers [20]

Fiber	*Refractive Indices* n_e	n_w	*Birefringence* $n_e - n_w$	*Reference*
Acetate	1.478	1.473	+0.005	[21]
Wool	1.556	1.547	+0.009	[21]
Cuprammonium rayon	1.548	1.527	+0.021	[21]
Viscose rayon	1.547	1.521	+0.026	[23]
Cotton	1.578	1.532	+0.046	[23]
Silk	1.591	1.538	+0.053	[21]
Ramie	1.596	1.528	+0.068	[23]
Flax	1.594	1.532	+0.062	[21]
Lanital	1.542+	1.542	+0.000	[24]
Aralac	1.537+	1.537	+0.000	[24]
Soybean	1.545+	1.545	+0.000	[24]
Ardil (peanut)	1.545+	1.545	+0.000	[24]
Zeolan	1.539	1.532	+0.007	[24]
Zein	1.536	1.532	+0.004	[24]
Cisalfa	1.546	1.533	+0.013	[24]
Slovlna	1.551	1.528	+0.023	[22]
Cotton mercerized under tension	1.566	1.522	+0.044	[23]
Cotton mercerized without tension	1.554	1.524	+0.030	[23]
Viscose (no skin)	1.549	1.523	+0.026	[24]
Viscose (thick skin)	1.541	1.516	+0.025	[24]
Lilienfield rayon	1.564	1.522	+0.042	[24]
Viscose (no skin)				
50% Godet stretch	1.554	1.526	+0.028	[24]
30% Godet stretch	1.552	1.526	+0.026	[24]
0% Godet stretch	1.548	1.526	+0.022	[24]
Vicara	1.536	1.532	+0.004	[22]
X-51 (staple)	1.515	1.518	−0.003	[22]
Orlon (staple)	1.515	1.517	−0.002	[22]
Acrilan (staple)	1.520	1.525	−0.005	[22]
Dynel (staple)	1.528	1.523	+0.005	[22]
Dacron (staple)	1.710	1.535	+1.115	[22]
Nylon (staple)	1.580	1.520	−0.060	[20]

Fig. 7. If the fiber is mounted in a liquid of lower refractive index, the Becke line will move toward the fiber; see Fig. 8.

These observations must be made in polarized light with the fiber positioned in the correct plane, since the refractive indices of fibers are generally different in each direction. The difference between the refractive indices in the two directions is the birefringence. The larger the birefringence, the greater the molecular orientation in the fiber. Re-

TABLE 6. MAN-MADE AND SYNTHETIC FIBERS AND MONOFILAMENTS [19]

Class or Basic Type [a]	*Generic Name*	*Species (Chemical Description)*
Acetate—*See* Cellulose Base Fibers		
Acrylonitrile—*See* Polyacrylic Fibers		
ALGINIC FIBERS		Metal salts of alginic acids [b]
Amino Acids—*See* Polyamide Fibers		
Azlon—*See* Protein Base Fibers		
Carboxymethyl Cellulose—*See* Cellulose Base Fibers		
Casein—*See* Protein Base Fibers		
CELLULOSE BASE FIBERS		
	1. Rayon (regenerated cellulose)	
	(*a*)	Cuprammonium process
	(*b*)	Denitrated nitrocellulose [b]
	(*c*)	Saponified cellulose acetate
	(*d*)	Viscose process
	2. Rayon, modified (regenerated cellulose plus other fiber-forming substances)	Viscose and protein [b]
	3. Estron (esterified cellulose)	Acetate
	4. Estron, modified (cellulose ester plus other fiber-forming substances)	Partially saponified acetate
	5. Cellulose ethers	
	(*a*)	Ethyl cellulose [c]
	(*b*)	Salts of carboxymethyl cellulose [c]
Cottonseed—*See* Protein Base Fibers		
Cuprammonium—*See* Cellulose Base Fibers		
Denitrated Nitrocellulose—*See* Cellulose Base Fibers		
ELASTOMERS		
	1. Natural rubber [d]	Polyisoprene
Estron—*See* Cellulose Base Fibers		
Estron, Modified—*See* Cellulose Base Fibers		
GLASS		Fused inorganic oxides
METAL FIBERS		Metallic elements and alloys
Nitrocellulose—*See* Cellulose Base Fibers		
Nylon—*See* Polyamides		
Peanut—*See* Protein Base Fibers		
POLYACRYLIC FIBERS		
	1.	Polymers of acrylonitrile
	2.	Copolymers of acrylonitrile and other monomers
POLYAMIDE FIBERS		
	1. Nylon	Linear polyamides made from
	(*a*)	Diamines and dicarboxylic acids
	(*b*)	Alpha, omega amino acids [b]
	(Polypeptide fibers)	Copolymers of simple alpha amino acids [c]
POLYESTER FIBERS		Polyesters made from
	1.	Dihydric alcohols and dicarboxylic acids [c]
	2.	Hydroxy acids [c]
POLYETHYLENE FIBERS		
	1. Polythene	Polymers of ethylene [c]
Polyisoprene—*See* Elastomers		
Polypeptide Fibers—*See* Polyamides		

TABLE 6. MAN-MADE AND SYNTHETIC FIBERS AND MONOFILAMENTS [19] (*Continued*)

Class or Basic Type [a] *Generic Name*	*Species (Chemical Description)*
POLYSTYRENE FIBERS [c]	
Polythene Fibers—*See* Polyethylene Fibers	
POLYURETHANE FIBERS	Polymers of diisocyanates and alcohols [c]
POLYVINYL FIBERS	
1.	Copolymer of vinyl chloride and vinyl acetate
2.	Copolymer of vinyl chloride and acrylonitrile
3.	After chlorinated polyvinyl chloride [b]
4. Saran	Copolymer of vinylidene chloride and other monomers
PROTEIN BASE FIBERS	
1. Azlon	
(*a*)	Modified protein from casein [b]
(*b*)	Modified protein from cottonseed [c]
(*c*)	Modified protein from peanuts [b]
(*d*)	Modified protein from soybeans [c]
(*e*)	Modified protein from zein (corn)
(*f*)	Modified protein from keratin (feathers) [c]
(*g*)	Modified protein from egg albumen [c]
Rayon—*See* Cellulose Base Fibers	
Rayon, Modified—*See* Cellulose Base Fibers	
Regenerated Cellulose—*See* Cellulose Base Fibers	
Rubber—*See* Elastomers	
Saponified Acetate—*See* Cellulose Base Fibers	
Saran—*See* Polyvinyl Fibers	
Soybean—*See* Protein Base Fibers	
STARCH FIBERS	
1.	Amylose acetate [c]
2.	Regenerated amylose [c]
Vinyl Acetate—*See* Polyvinyl Fibers	
Vinyl Chloride—*See* Polyvinyl Fibers	
Vinylidene Chloride—*See* Polyvinyl Fibers	
Viscose—*See* Cellulose Base Fibers	
Zein—*See* Protein Base Fibers	

[a] Only basic types are listed, trade-marked varieties are not included.

[b] Not manufactured commercially in the United States but available in commercial quantities abroad.

[c] Not manufactured commercially but available in experimental quantities or on a laboratory scale.

[d] Fibers have been made from other elastomers and thioplasts, especially during wartime when natural rubber was not available in adequate amounts.

fractive indices have therefore been of considerable value in studying fiber structure in addition to confirming the fiber identity.

Through such structure studies it is possible to get a better understanding why dyes do not penetrate or diffuse as rapidly through highly oriented cellulose as they do through a cellulose fiber of lower orientation. In other words, if a fiber is stretched, the orientation changes and the index of the fiber in this direction usually becomes greater than it

FIG. 7. Acrilan fiber mounted in liquid of higher refractive index than fiber.

FIG. 8. Acrilan fiber mounted in liquid of lower refractive index than fiber.

was before the stretching. There are some exceptions to this, but it has been found to be true generally, for example, in the Godet stretching of viscose rayon. See Table 6.

FLAMMABILITY AND COMBUSTIBILITY

With the exception of asbestos, glass, and the new synthetic fibers Saran, and Dynel, all textile fibers are highly combustible. Primarily they occur in a fine state of division and are easily ignited.

Flammability is defined by the Factory Mutual Engineering Division [25] as the relative ignitibility of a material and its liability to produce quick-spreading flash fires. Combustibility is the characteristic burning quality of a material, such as its intensity, persistence, or rate of burning. The term "combustible fibers," according to the same source, is intended to include the readily ignitible and freely burning fibers, commonly encountered in commerce, which are stored in relatively large quantities and which, when so stored, may present a considerable fire hazard. Such fibers are cotton, including linters and cotton waste, sisal or henequen, ixtle, jute, hemp, tow, cocoa fiber, oakum, kapok, Spanish moss, excelsior, regenerated cellulose, and Azlon, Dacron, and Orlon.

The density or compression to which baled stock has been subjected has a direct relation to the speed with which fire will consume the fibers. Highly compressed bales with densities of 35 to 40 lb per cu ft or more have greater thermal conductivity owing to the reduced size of air spaces in the bale, which give an insulating effect. Thus, a highly compressed bale will burn slower, will not retain heat as well, and is not so susceptible to fires of a burrowing nature as loosely compressed or picked stock. Highly compressed bales are not easily penetrated by water, and usually the salvage (or the recoverable portion) of such bales is greater. The available oxygen (air) necessary to support a fire or the penetration of air to aid a burrowing fire is inversely proportional to the compression.

The appendix of the booklet on *Standards of the National Board of Fire Underwriters* [26] gives the most up-to-date facts regarding the flammability or combustibility of textile fibers.

Ignition Properties

Regarding the ignition properties of various fibers, no definite information is available, although tests have been made by the fire resistance section of the National Bureau of Standards and others. However, the following is a good comparison between the various textile raw materials:

Cotton is highly combustible but not subject to spontaneous heating unless contaminated. Highly compressed cotton bales (density 35 to 40 lb per cu ft) will burn slower than loosely compressed or picked stock and have higher salvage value.

Cotton Shoddy Waste: Highly combustible, susceptible to spontaneous heating due to oil, metallic oxides in dye process, or metal oxide stains, which act as catalysts to oxidation.

Flax: Highly combustile and low salvage value.

Hemp (tow, sisal, henequen, ixtle): Highly combustile; heats spontaneously when wet; will reach maximum temperature in 5 days. No salvage value after 3 days. *Expands when wet.*

Jute (fiber, baled): Highly combustile; subject to spontaneous heating when wet; will reach maximum temperature in 5 days. Salvage value low.

Kapok (silk floss): Very highly combustible; not subject to spontaneous heating; high salvage value of baled stock; water resistant.

Manila (abacá): Highly combustible; not subject to spontaneous heating. High salvage value.

Spanish Moss: Highly combustible; not subject to spontaneous heating.

Wool: Not subject to flash fires. It is not easily ignited, but will continue to burn once ignited. Grease wool or oiled stock will burn slower than scoured wool and requires assistance from a more combustible source in order to maintain a flame. Scoured wool is not subject to spontaneous heating. High salvage value.

Bagged Fibers: Burlap jute wrappings present possibility of rapid flash fire.

Rayon: Considered quite similar to cotton in flammability, but tests show that viscose rayon is slightly more easily ignited than cotton. Loose viscose rayon burns faster than cotton fiber.

Acetate: Slightly less than cotton.

Vinyon: Low combustibility; high salvage value.

Nylon: Moderate combustibility; low salvage value.

Orlon: Same as cotton.

It will be noted from the above that the fibers most subject to spontaneous heating are hemp and jute.

Causes of Fires

Fires in all types of textile mills are caused principally by the following:

1. Faulty electrical equipment.
2. Friction, fiber-to-fiber or fiber on metal or metal-to-metal.
3. Foreign material in stock, i.e., metal, matches.
4. Smoking.

All of these causes call for constant supervision and control in order to minimize fire hazards. Losses from such fires run into many millions of dollars annually in the textile manufacturing industry.

Faulty Electrical Equipment. Motors, switches, fuses, lights, and wiring are a constant and major source of fires in textile mills. A Factory Mutual Engineering Division study of electrical fires in textile plants, and particularly in cotton mills, offers valuable suggestions as to where the greatest attention needs to be given to electrical maintenance. Thirty-three per cent of the fires studied started in motors. Thirty-two per cent involved control switches. Twenty-two per cent were in distribution circuits, including extension cords. The remainder involved improper fuse arrangements and the breaking of lamp bulbs, or overheating of combustibles in contact with them.

Friction. Poor machine adjustment is a principal cause of fiber chokes or metal-to-metal friction. Where friction fires persist, the services of a qualified lubrication engineer should be obtained. All reputable oil companies willingly furnish this service. Conditions should be checked to see that the recommendations are being followed.

Spontaneous Heating. This is an oxidation reaction occurring with some fibers, notably hemp and jute, if left in a confined damp condition. Spontaneous heating may also occur in fibers that have been treated with, or come into accidental contact with, oxidizable materials. The nature of all chemical treatments should be fully understood and temperature should be regulated to avoid the generation of excessive heat of reaction during the finishing of processed materials. Some of the more common causes of fires by spontaneous heating are accumulation of oily waste in uncovered receptacles and the use of oxidizable oils for batching stock. Oils such as cottonseed, lard, red oil, or in general most fixed oils, depending on their purity, have been the cause of numerous fires of this type. Spontaneous heating also comes from freshly carbonized stock after drying but before neutralizing; insufficient rinsing or finishing of sulfur-dyed stock; and insufficient cooling time, before packaging, of goods which have been subjected to elevated temperatures.

Dust and Lint. A problem in the processing of fibers which adds to the fire hazard is the accumulation of lint and dust around machinery and rooms. This condition is especially pronounced with short staple fibers and reworked stock. Lint not only adds to the fire hazard but also interferes with the normal operation of the machinery if allowed to accumulate excessively. Where machines are not equipped with lint collectors, a regular cleaning schedule is desirable.

If lint is allowed to accumulate excessively, a flash fire is apt to ensue. Dirty lint from floors and machines is subject to spontaneous heating and should be placed in covered metal disposal cans and removed to a safe place at least once a day. Reworkable waste should be processed in a separate unit so that any foreign material that might contaminate the waste and cause friction sparks may be removed before the stock enters the main preparatory processes.

Foreign Substances. Pins, nails, and bale ties mixed with the stock often come in contact with fast-moving machine parts and cause sparks or sufficient heat to ignite the fibers or yarns.

Magnetic separators and drop-out boxes will remove most foreign iron or steel objects, but their effectiveness depends on moving the stock through the opener machinery at the lowest practical speed. Besides helping to remove this major fire cause, early removal protects the machinery from serious damage by the "tramp" material. Magnetic separators should be properly installed ahead of fast-moving opener machinery to do their most effective work.

Fibers have a tendency to clog open bearings and wind on sprockets, bearings, and shafting, interfering with lubrication and normal operation and causing friction fires and excessive machine wear. This is especially true if excessive amounts of material are fed to machines at one time or if the machines are operated above rated speeds, as is common in some mills attempting extremely high production.

Smoking. This requires no discussion.

Storage. There are definite safeguards that can be followed in providing safe storage for raw textile fibers. The Factory Mutual Engineering Division [26] gives definite instructions on how textile fibers, yarns, and goods should be stored. Some fibers expand when wet, so due allowance should be made for protecting walls and piping. This is particularly necessary for jute storage. Table 7 shows a tentative classification, based on past experience, without determination of the actual physical properties of the materials regarding (1) absorption and swelling of the fibers and (2) affinity of material for water, and penetration of bales by water.

TABLE 7. COMMERCIAL FIBERS IN STORAGE GRADING OF CHARACTERISTICS AFFECTING SAFETY OF MATERIALS WHEN EXPOSED TO WATER

	1	*2*		*1*	*2*
Cotton	L *	L	Kapok	L	L
Cotton linters	L	M	Spanish moss	M	M
Cotton waste	M *	M	Hay	H	H
Sisal (ixtle, henequen)	H *	H	Excelsior	H	H
Jute, baled	H	H	Paper (print paper, in rolls)	L	L
Jute bags, baled	M	M	Paper (baled)	H	H
Jute bagging	M	M	Wool	M	M
Oakum	L	L	Silk	L	L
Hemp	H	H	Nylon	L	L
Tow	M	M	Rayon	M	M
Cocoa fiber	M	M			

* H, high; M, moderate; L, low.

Fiber Blending [26]. Fiber blending in textile mills is increasing extensively. This great increase in the use of rayon, especially at woolen and rug mills, is due not only to the scarcity and high cost of many grades of wool but also to the improved quality and physical structure of both viscose and acetate. From the economic angle alone, fiber blending appears destined to become increasingly important with most woolen mills. It is also currently reported that the wearability of textile materials has not been sacrificed by the use of blended fiber.

Fiber blending by the bin method introduces a number of additional fire hazards to the preparatory process when cellulosic base fibers (such as viscose rayon or saponified acetate) are used and should be avoided.

Most of the woolen and rug mills are at present installing modern blending equipment including baling presses, to safely handle such highly combustible fiber mixtures. It also appears certain that many of the mill operators do not appreciate the possible hazards because previous fire experience has been limited to handling comparatively safe wool fiber.

Because of these changing conditions, it will be necessary in many locations to reconsider important items such as the adequacy of water supplies for sprinkler systems and hose streams. Blending methods, housekeeping, first-aid fire equipment, training in fire fighting, and electrical and other important maintenance should be reviewed in order to provide proper safety measures to avoid large fire and use-and-occupancy losses. Due consideration must also be given to personal safety, particularly where blending in bins is performed on a large scale.

Additional hazards introduced by the use of rayon fiber should be discussed with top managements and, in the case of large organizations, these various conditions should be discussed with the research as well as the engineering departments. There have been several instances where valuable assistance has been given by research personnel, especially when new ideas are being developed.

Blending Methods. There are several methods of blending, some of which may offer excellent possibilities for control of the fire hazard as well as having advantages from the manufacturing angle. At present, chief concern is with blending bins poorly constructed to handle rayon-wool mixtures.

Accurate blending of the different type fibers is necessary for two main reasons: (1) to maintain yarn standards and (2) to obtain even, reproducible shades or dye lots. Although there are three methods for dyeing (1) stock, (2) piece, or (3) yarn, with blended fiber the popular method is to dye the individual fiber first (stock dyeing) and then mix by the picker-bin method. Recently, there is more attention being given to dyeing stock mixtures at one time, which tends to eliminate the number of picker bin operations. Baling of mixed stock (either dyed or undyed) instead of blowing to bins not only conserves factory space but also helps to lessen the fire hazard because baled fiber will not burn as rapidly as loose fiber.

In bin blending as practiced by carpet manufacturers, due consideration must be given to the necessity of preparing very large batches due to shade control requirements. For the present, individual studies to improve plant safety suggests submission of plant blending methods to the Insurance Engineering Division having jurisdiction, for consideration.

Housekeeping. Housekeeping in all preparatory operations such as opening, picking, blending, stock drying, and carding must be maintained at a high level with emphasis placed on overhead piping, beams, pneumatic conveyor ducts, etc., in order to minimize the possibility of flash fires spreading over lint accumulations.

Humidification. Humidification control at the highest maximum level (70–80 per cent on a basis of 70° F.) is an important condition to aid in preventing the ignition of fiber from incipient sources. While rayon is similar to cotton in combustibility, it retains a higher percentage of moisture under similar conditions than cotton, wool, or other textile fibers. This increased moisture absorption should be favorable to plant fire safety. The subject of humidity control should be discussed thoroughly with plant management as well as with research and engineering. One of the most important operations where moisture should be regulated would be stock drying, to insure that the fiber is not overdried.

STATIC ELECTRICITY

Causes and Effects [2]

Static electricity is often a severe production handicap in textile operations, made all the more serious by its common occurrence in both natural and synthetic materials and at many stages of processing. It can be produced to a varying degree on fibers, yarns, or cloth in motion, wherever they come into intimate contact with one another or with rollers, guides, or other surfaces, especially in a *dry* atmosphere. Some of the difficulties caused by static on the materials being processed are:

[2] Courtesy of Dolph Simons, The Simco Co., Philadelphia, Pa.

"ballooning" in warping; entangling or misalignment of yarns winding on a beam; riding of the warp yarns up the flanges of a beam; "fuzzing" of yarn during spinning; adhesion of fiber to fiber or fiber to metal and other surfaces; the familiar "shock" when one touches a material that has been pulled rapidly over a measuring or inspecting machine. These are common signs by which the presence of static is unconsciously or forcibly recognized. Naturally, these phenomena interfere with high-speed production and quality of merchandise, and create higher costs, discomforts to workers, to say nothing of possible fire hazards. The effects are particularly pronounced with synthetic materials such as acetate, Vinyon, Saran, nylon, Orlon, and Dacron, since these materials develop static more readily than the natural fibers. Hence, textile mill men are paying more and more attention to the causes and effects of, and remedies for, static electricity in processing.

Theory

The "contact theory" of the formation of static electricity is based on the electronic concept of the structure of matter, in which the atom is considered a definite aggregate of electricity. Each atom is composed of *three* types of fundamental particles: positively charged particles called *protons*, uncharged particles called *neutrons*, and negatively charged particles called *electrons*.

The protons and neutrons are grouped together into a relatively heavy and stationary nucleus, whereas the light, mobile electrons surround the nucleus and can be considered for graphic purposes like the planets of a solar system in which the nucleus serves as the sun. Under normal conditions the atom has the proper number of negatively charged electrons to balance exactly the positive charges of its nucleus, and it is then electrically neutral. A graphic representation of a neutral carbon atom is shown in Fig. 9.

A body composed entirely of electrically neutral atoms is uncharged. However, when two bodies are brought into intimate contact, electrons from each surface come within the sphere of influence of the atoms of the other. Electrons belonging to atoms in which the attractive force between them and their positive nuclei is weak are able to attach themselves to stronger positive nuclei. Hence, movement of electrons can take place between the contacting surfaces of the two materials; and, when separated, one surface will possess an excess of electrons and be negatively charged, the other will have a deficiency of electrons and be positively charged. This, then, is the mechanism by which textile materials, coming in contact with one another or with various parts of a machine, for instance, can become electrified. Pressure and friction magnify the effect by increasing the area and degree of contact. A material becomes charged positively or negatively according to its electrical relation with the substance with which it comes into contact, and the charges acquired in each case are, at least momentarily, equal and opposite to those on the other substance. Such charges can be measured with an electroscope or electrostatic voltmeter.

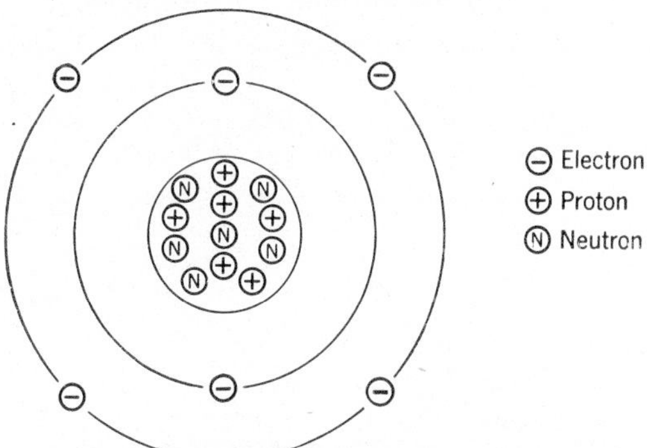

FIG. 9. Graphic representation of a carbon atom.

The electrical relationship among various materials which determines whether they will become positively or negatively charged can be illustrated by means of Table 8, called the contact-electrification series or

TABLE 8. ELECTROSTATIC SERIES OF FIBERS

Positive End	
Glass	Ramie
Human hair	Steel
Nylon yarn	Hard rubber
Nylon polymer	Acetate
Wool	Synthetic rubber
Silk	Orlon acrylic fiber
Viscose rayon	Saran
Cotton	Polythene
Paper	*Negative End*

the triboelectric series. Many experimenters have developed these series, and one set of results which includes many textile materials is given in Table 8. The series is determined by testing various substances in pairs and finding in each test which of the pair is charged positively and which negatively. The substances are then listed in an order such that, when any two are rubbed together, the one higher on the list acquires the positive charge.

It might be thought that the electrification series, in addition to indicating the polarity of the charges produced, would also be useful in predicting their magnitude. For example, it might be predicted from the series that, when rubbed against synthetic rubber, wool and nylon would generate almost equal amounts of charge, and that Orlon would generate almost none. Experiments made under carefully controlled conditions have disproved this assumption, and other factors have been investigated to help account for magnitude. See Table 9. Principal

TABLE 9. Electrostatic Voltages of Various Fibers against Synthetic Rubber

Fiber	*Voltage*
Cotton	50
Viscose rayon	100
Wool	350
Acetate	550
Vinyon N vinyl fiber	800
Silk	850
Orlon acrylic fiber	900
Nylon	1050

among these factors appears to be the relative ability of the material to hold a static charge. Textile materials are in general good insulators when dry, so that charges cannot flow through them as through metallic bodies. They can retain charges for long periods, and in making successive contacts the quantities of charge accumulated can become tremendous. The addition of moisture, on the other hand, increases the conductivity of the materials. Thus, their ability to hold charges can be directly correlated to their moisture regain. Since many synthetics have extremely low moisture regain (vapor absorbency), the magnitude of static charges which the synthetics develop is often much higher than would be expected from their positions in the electrification series.

Controlled tests, performed on textile fibers rubbed against synthetic rubber, give actual data on their relative electrostatic susceptibility. These are recorded in Table 9. A comparison of these experimental data with predictions of electrostatic susceptibility from moisture regain and from the electrostatic series gives concrete evidence that both, and probably other factors as well, influence the generation of static electricity. This comparison is tabulated in Table 10, in which the listings are in the order of increasing susceptibility.

Once a fiber, yarn, or cloth becomes charged, associated electrical phenomena come into play. It is well known that two bodies, both charged negatively or both charged positively, will *repel* each other. Ballooning

TABLE 10. Order of Electrostatic Susceptibility against Synthetic Rubber

Experimental	*Predicted from Moisture Regain*	*Predicted from Electrostatic Series*
Cotton	Wool	Orlon acrylic fiber
Viscose rayon	Silk	Vinyon
Wool	Viscose rayon	Acetate
Acetate	Cotton	Cotton
Vinyon N vinyl fiber	Acetate	Viscose rayon
Silk	Nylon	Silk
Orlon acrylic fiber	Orlon acrylic fiber	Wool
Nylon	Vinyon N vinyl fiber	Nylon

in warping is a good example in point. Moreover, two substances will attract when one is positive and the other negative. For instance, if a single synthetic yarn acquires a positive charge as it passes over a guide, a corresponding negative charge is produced, at least momentarily, on the guide. The first effect is the attraction between opposite charges, causing the yarn to stick to the guide. To overcome this attraction, tension is increased, which on delicate yarns results in breakage.

It is interesting to point out also, though the actual theory is quite involved, that charged yarns will tend to stick to almost any surface they happen to come in contact with, whether rough or smooth, whether conductive like metal or nonconductive like rubber, glass, Bakelite and porcelain. This characteristic represents the most serious single difficulty due to static with which the mill man has to contend. Typical operations on which a watchful eye should be kept for possible production disturbances are warping, slashing, winding, spinning, carding, gill reducing, drawing, twisting, weaving, knitting, tentering, and cloth examination or rolling.

Remedies

To avoid and combat the harmful effects of static electricity in textile operations, there are *two* methods of approach:

1. Encouraging dissipation or neutralization by the addition of opposite charges to surfaces from static eliminators.
2. Increasing the conductivity of materials through the aid of water vapor from humidifiers and atomizers, and by means of antistatic finishes.

Since under the contact theory of electrification described before both material and machine acquire charges, any method to remove them must deal with both machine and material. If a machine is insulated so that the charges on it cannot overcome the resistance of a possible path to earth, they will accumulate in the machine and greatly magnify any static troubles that are present. They can also cause further static charges to be generated on materials by a process called *electrostatic induction*. It is, therefore, necessary to ground all machines and thus permit any charges which could otherwise accumulate on the metal parts to dissipate to the ground. Grounding is accomplished by connecting a heavy wire from the machine frame to a water pipe or a well-grounded electrical conduit.

However, grounding does not eliminate the electrostatic charges on the materials being processed. As explained before, these are nonconductors of electricity, and charges will not flow through them to ground, particularly when they are dry. Some other remedy is therefore necessary. Static neutralizers or eliminators provide one commonly used and successful method. These neutralizers operate on the principle of ionizing the air, which means that they break atoms of the air into positive and negative parts. When a negatively charged material passes through the ionized region, positively charged ions in the air are attracted to its surface and combine with the negative charges (since opposite charges attract). Conversely, positively charged materials are neutralized by attracting negative ions from the air.

Electrically operated neutralizers usually consist of a small power unit and static eliminator bars. The power unit operates from a 110-volt a-c lighting circuit or from any other a-c line voltage, or it can be designed to go "on" and "off" with the machine. It supplies power to the applicator bars which are supported from the side frames across the machine in positions carefully selected with relation to where static gives trouble. The applicator bars ionize the air, providing a field containing both positive and negative electric charges capable of neutralizing any type of material which passes through the region, even at production speeds and under adverse weather conditions. Electric neutralizers have been greatly simplified, and a typical example is shown in Fig. 10.

A second type of static eliminator, *the radioactive type*, consists of a metal bar on which one surface is coated with a thin film of radioactive substance such as radium or polonium and overcoated with a protective film of another metal. The air in the vicinity of the bars is ionized by the bombardment of alpha particles emanating from the radioactive material. The advantage of this type of eliminator is its extreme simplicity and ease of installation. To avoid any harmful effects on personnel working with or around radioactive bars, manufacturers provide detailed instructions for locating, handling, cleaning, and using them.

The effective surface of the eliminator must be kept clean, since useful *alpha* radiation will not penetrate layers of lint or dirt.

Humidity is an extremely important means of reducing the generation of static charges. It should be pointed out that its effectiveness is not the result of a change in the conductivity of the air, since air remains an excellent insulator even though humidified and will not bleed off

FIG. 10. Static eliminator bar above doffer comb on card. (*Courtesy Simco Co.*)

electric charges from the surface of yarns and fabrics. However, if the material itself can be made slightly conductive by the absorption of moisture or by the deposition of a film of moisture on its surface, excess charges will be conducted through the material or along its surface to any metallic conductive parts of the machine and thence to the ground. This is another good reason why machine frames should be grounded.

Natural fibers will absorb moisture more readily than most of the synthetics and are therefore more easily treated by this method. Some of the synthetics, in fact, such as nylon, Orlon, Dacron, Velon, Saran, and acetate, have such low vapor absorbency that it is usually found necessary in some operations to use static eliminators regardless of, or in addition to, humidification. Another important consideration in applying humidification effectively is the frequent necessity of preconditioning the materials in the humidified atmosphere, since considerable time is required for unexposed layers on tightly wound bobbins or beams to absorb moisture.

Antistatic finishes provide another important method of increasing the conductivity of textile materials and thus preventing static difficulties. They may be applied as spin finishes to synthetics immediately after extrusion, may be incorporated in coning oil, or may be applied at other stages of processing by immersion or spraying. Discretion must be observed when using the finishes, however, since certain types carry with them the dangers of corrosion, dusting when dry, and bad effect on the the feel of yarn and fabric. Other types, satisfactory for one operation, may be detrimental for others by modifying the lubricity of the material to cause high backwinding tensions. Nevertheless, antistatic finishes are very helpful in many places, and extensive research is improv ing them.

EFFECT OF ULTRAVIOLET LIGHT

Ultraviolet light exists in sunlight, in carbon arc lamps, and in quartz mercury or sun lamps, which may come in contact with fibers and textile materials. It is used in detection of mildew, fluorescence, fiber identification, measurement of color fading, and checking certain types of fiber impurities. In ancient times, sun rays were employed extensively in bleaching linen and cotton fabrics by keeping the fabrics wet and exposed to the direct rays of the sun for weeks. The sun is the most effective and most efficient light source, and it is responsible for much of the fading of colors on textile fibers and materials.

Light is a form of energy and is probably electromagnetic in character. By light is meant not only what is visible but all energy radiated in the form of electromagnetic vibrations as well. There are two accepted theories of light, namely, the undulatory or wave theory and the electromagnetic theory, the latter originated by Maxwell. Light travels at the rate of 186,300 miles per second and is defined by its velocity, its wave lengths, and its frequency of vibrations of the wave per second. The waves range in length approximately from 3.9 to 7.6 ten-thousandths of a millimeter. They are usually stated in the Angstrom unit (A), which is equal to one one-hundred-millionth of a centimeter (10^{-8} cm) or approximately four-billionths of an inch.

The color impression produced by light varies with the wave length, and the brightness is proportional to the square of the amplitude of vibration. Waves of a similar character whose wave lengths are between 136 and 3900 A are ultraviolet rays or vibrations and are not perceptible to the eye, whereas visible light ranges from 3900 to 7700 A.

The ultraviolet rays are manifested by their photographic or other chemical action. Light waves exceeding 7600 A in length are the infrared rays, which can be detected by their thermal effects and are now utilized in textile drying. The most important phenomena of light are reflection, refraction, dispersion, interference, and polarization.

Visible light has been found one of the most potent agencies in the weathering or degradation of fibers and fibrous materials. This well-known fact is most commonly encountered in window curtains and draperies exposed to direct sunlight or to arc lamps or other illumination. The subject has been investigated by many scientists and chemists, who have proved, according to Barr [27] and to Waentig, that coarse fibers and yarns are less affected than fine fibers and yarns. Barr found silk to be more affected by light than cotton, but wool much less than either; rayon was affected less than cotton. Moisture, it is generally conceded, enhances the deteriorating influence of light, especially on wool and bast fibers. The purer the atmosphere, the less the destructive action of light.

It is quite generally conceded that the action of ultraviolet light during the sun bleaching of cotton leads to the production of photocellulose (which see). However, some insist that oxycellulose is formed first and then photocellulose, the formation of which does not involve oxidation. No matter which is the case, both involve a loss of strength and the development of reducing power. Cotton loses strength constantly up to about 40 per cent of its original strength. The rate of tendering is proportional to the intensity of the light. Bleached cotton tenders more rapidly than raw cotton. Spectrophotometric analysis has shown that all white and dyed fabrics are affected by sunlight, the white ones becoming increasingly yellow with increased exposure and the dyed ones fading in various degrees. Black clothing absorbs more of the sun's heat than white clothing.

Another angle of this subject is the degree to which clothing or fibrous textile material transmits ultraviolet rays or allows them to reach the body. Most investigators seem to agree that transmission depends less on the fiber than on the weave, texture, and thickness of the material. Several investigators found no difference in the transmission of ultraviolet radiation through bleached cotton, linen, viscose rayon, and acetate fabrics of the same weight. If there is any difference, it is too slight to be measured accurately.

FLUORESCENCE

Fluorescence is the emission of luminescent light by a substance only during the time that the substance is exposed to an exciting light source (e.g., ultraviolet). Fibers and fibrous materials, if carefully selected, may be treated with fluorescent chemicals or pigments, which in no way alter their life or durability. In ultraviolet light, certain stains, oils, dyes, and excrements in fibers may be studied and compared by means of their fluorescence. Animal fibers may be differentiated from vegetable fibers. Bleached cotton may be distinguished from bleached flax, and cotton and unbleached flax from hemp, for instance. Genuine camel hair fluoresces with a reddish gray-brown color and is easily distinguished from colored wool. Various cellulose fibers that have undergone different manufacturing treatments give different colors when they fluoresce. For instance, cuprammonium and viscose rayon scoured with 0.5 per cent solution of soap and an equal amount of ammonia show no change in fluorescence, whereas acetate so treated does show a change. Mildew not otherwise ascertainable may sometimes be detected in this manner [28].

PHOSPHORESCENCE

Phosphorescence or "afterglow" is the emission of visible light by a substance for a period of time after the exciting light is extinguished. Millson [28] states that exposure to ultraviolet rays will cause both organic and inorganic substances to phosphoresce. Textile fibers will phosphoresce for a short time after exposure to high-frequency ultraviolet rays. This is explained by Millson [28] thus: A light source, such as ultraviolet rays, builds up excessive energy within the atom and forces its electrons from one energy level to another. As these electrons return to their former levels, they release the excess energy in the form of visible light, which is phosphorescent and creates phosphorescence. Phosphorescence induced by visible light or ultraviolet rays is also called *photoluminescence* to distinguish it from phosphorescence induced by X-rays, cathode rays, or the rays from radium.

Millson [28] made some very interesting experiments regarding phosphorescence of textile fibers, using a 76-in. Skidmore cold quartz tube filled with a mixture of krypton, neon, and argon gases with a small amount of metallic mercury. No filter was used for phosphorescence observations, but for fluorescence a Corning No. 986 filter was employed. His data have been compiled in Table 11, which shows the fluorescence and phosphorescence of various undyed textile fibers arranged according to the duration of phosphorescence.

Table 11, page 39, demonstrates that textile fibers have fluorescence and that the time of phosphorescence ranges from a low of 5½ seconds in dull acetate to a high of 27½ seconds in mercerized cotton. Millson observed that a brighter tone and longer period of phosphorescence was

TABLE 11. PHOSPHORESCENCE AND FLUORESCENCE OF VARIOUS FIBERS

Fiber or Material	*Fluorescence Corning Filter #986*	*Color of Phosphorescence*	*Duration of Phosphorescence in Seconds*
Acetate, dull	Violet white	Colorless	5½
Human hair, dark brown	Dull greenish yellow	Colorless	5¾
Jute fiber, raw	Violet, white and buff	Colorless	6½
Human hair, auburn	Tan	Colorless	6½
Caroa fiber, raw	Bright bluish white	Yellowish white	7
Acetate, bright	Yellowish white, purple shadows	Colorless	7
Sisal fiber, raw	Bluish white	Colorless	9
Human hair, blonde	Bluish white, yellow and violet shadows	Colorless	9
Vinyon, bright	Yellowish white, purple shadows	Bright yellowish	10
Wool	Yellowish white	Colorless	12
Istle fiber, raw	Some blue and white, others buff	Yellowish white	12½
Rayon, viscose	White, violet shadows	Bluish white	12½
Wool, peroxide bleached	Bright bluish white	Yellowish white	13½
Viscose, dull	White, purple shadows	Colorless	14
Jute	Bluish white	Yellow	15
Sulfite pulp, bleached	White	Greenish white	15
Cuprammonium rayon (Bemberg), bright	Bright yellowish white	Colorless	15
Cuprammonium rayon (Bemberg), dull	Violet white	Colorless	16
Cotton linters, bleached	Bluish white	Yellowish white	17
Casein yarn (Aralac)	Bluish white	Bright yellow	17
Viscose, bright	Yellowish white, purple shadows	Colorless	19
Linen, bleached	Bluish white	Yellowish white	19
Cotton	Yellowish white	Yellowish white	20
Lanital	Yellowish white	Greenish white	21
Nylon, bright	Bluish white	Bright yellow	22½
Nylon, dull	Bluish white	Yellowish white	22½
Silk, pure, degummed	Bluish white	Bright yellowish white	23½
Cotton, mercerized	Reddish white	Yellowish white	27½

obtained with bone-dry samples. Damp or wet samples did not phosphoresce regardless of the incident radiation or length of exposure. Chemical damage, exposure to light, and other treatments often alter the fluorescence and phosphorescence of textile fibers. Partial saponification of undyed acetate can be detected by means of a change in its phosphorescence. Completely saponified acetate has a less violet-white fluorescence, and the phosphorescence is much brighter, distinctly yellower, and more persistent than that of unsaponified acetate (see Fortisan fiber).

Millson [28] states that exposure to light often causes a chemical change in textile fibers, which can be detected by its effect on the fluorescence and phosphorescence of the exposed area. It is well known that nylon and pure silk are sensitive to light, and it may be possible to determine the extent of damage by this means. All exposed areas showed a considerable reduction in the duration of phosphorescence. Millson also showed that cotton and viscose rayon reached a maximum of excitation at 1½ minutes, whereas acetate, nylon, silk, and wool show increases up to 3 minutes' exposure. He found also that both ether-extracted and untreated fibers gave about the same results.

Test data and experiments show that ultraviolet rays may be used in determining the identity of fibers, in detecting and identifying chemical damage or stains, and in checking the efficiency of various processes, including dyeing. Undyed fibers generally have a longer period of phosphorescence than dyed fibers. According to Millson [28] the phosphorescence of fibers colored with dyes which have a brilliant fluorescence was much weaker in intensity than the fluorescence. Again, Aralac and rayon fabrics incompletely desized phosphoresced 23 seconds, whereas completely desized they phosphoresced only 19 seconds. The amount of starch on a fabric influences the duration of phosphorescence. A cotton shirt phosphoresced only 30 seconds, whereas the heavily starched cuffs emitted light for 6 minutes and 35 seconds. One of the advantages of the use of ultraviolet rays is that tests can be made on fabrics or garments without removing samples or spoiling their appearance for further use.

HYDROGEN-ION CONCENTRATION [29]

*p*H is fundamentally based upon the electrolytic dissociation theory of Arrhenius. According to this theory, an acid, alkali, or salt when dissolved in water dissociates or breaks up into ions, which are atoms or groups of atoms carrying positive or negative charges of electricity. Most water-soluble inorganic compounds dissociate in water, many salts liberating both hydrogen and hydroxyl ions as a result of the ionization of the products of hydrolysis. The excess of one over the other determines whether the material is acid, alkaline, or neutral. An acid may be defined, therefore, as a substance yielding an excess of hydrogen ions; conversely a base produces an excess of hydroxyl ions. In the case of pure water a balance of H and OH ions exists and the substance is termed neutral.

Sørensen [29] introduced the method of expressing the hydrogen ion concentration in terms of the negative logarithm to the base 10. He called this the hydrogen exponent and gave it the symbol *p*H. This *p*H is the negative logarithm of the hydrogen ion concentration or the logarithm of the reciprocal of the hydrogen ion concentration.

The range of the present *p*H scale lies between 0 and 14; the midpoint of the range is 7, which is the *p*H of pure water and is the true neutral point [29]. Values below *p*H 7 indicate an increase in the hydrogen ion concentration, or an *acid* reaction. Values above *p*H 7 indicate that the hydroxyl ions predominate and, therefore, the solution is *alkaline*. In using the *p*H scale (Table 12) it is only necessary to keep in mind

TABLE 12. Hydrogen Ion Concentration Scale

pH Value		*Intensity of Acidity or Alkalinity*
0	Acid	10,000,000
1	Acid	1,000,000
2	Acid	100,000
3	Acid	10,000
4	Acid	1,000
5	Acid	100
6	Acid	10
7	Neutral	1 *
8	Alkaline	10
9	Alkaline	100
10	Alkaline	1,000
11	Alkaline	10,000
12	Alkaline	100,000
13	Alkaline	1,000,000
14	Alkaline	10,000,000

* The value 1 for *p*H 7 represents a concentration of H ions equivalent to 10^{-7}.

the fact that the acidity increases as the numbers decrease below 7 and the alkalinity increases as the numbers increase above 7.

Table 12 shows that a material having a *p*H of 5 has ten times the hydrogen ion concentration of one having a *p*H of 6. A *p*H of 4 likewise indicates ten times the hydrogen ion concentration of *p*H 5.

The fundamental reaction between acids and bases in aqueous solution [29] is between hydrogen and hydroxyl ions to produce water.

Whenever (H^+) is greater than (OH^-), that is, greater than 10^{-7} at 25° C., the solution is *acid*. Whenever (H^+) is smaller than (OH^-), that is, smaller than 10^{-7} at 25° C., the solution is *alkaline*.

The application of modern *p*H control in textile processing is most important and valuable. In the degumming of silk and the scouring of wool, the degree of emulsification and the extent of the removal of impurities increase with the *p*H. However, the *p*H cannot be too high or the material will be damaged. Safe values are dependent on temperatures. Sensitivity of cotton to high *p*H is less; hence kier-boiling is done with caustic alkali. Control of *p*H is essential in peroxide bleaching of straw, silk, wool, cotton, and rayon. The stability of emulsions used in silk-soaking processes depends on *p*H, as does the efficiency of soaking. In carbonizing of wool, where solutions of sulfuric acid are employed which tender and remove the cotton, the control of this acidity is essential. In dyeing of silk and wool *p*H control is important, because the affinity of acid dyes for these fibers increases as the *p*H decreases.

*p*H can be controlled with special test papers, which are easy to use but not very accurate. A more accurate method is the use of colorimetric indicators, which will give *p*H with an accuracy of 0.2. The most accurate and scientific control can be maintained with available electrometric instruments. Through *p*H control great savings in chemicals and materials can be attained, as well as greater uniformity of batches of fiber or material.

Electrophoretic Properties. According to Sookne and Harris [30] of the Textile Foundation, the isoelectric point of a substance is the hydrogen ion concentration at which the sum of positive and negative charges at the surface is equal to zero. They reported in 1944 [31] the measurements shown in Table 13, made by the electrophoretic method. The isoelectric point varies slightly with the concentration of the medium in which the measurements are made, even with usual systems like acetate and chloride solution.

TABLE 13. Isoelectric Point of Some Textile Fibers

Fibers	*Medium Used*	*Isoelectric Point*
Cotton	0.02 *M* * HCl-KCl Sol.	2.5
Nylon, stretched	0.02 *M* HCl-KCl Sol.	2.7
Nylon, unstretched	0.02 *M* acetate buffers	3.9
Wool	0.005 *M* acetate buffers	4.2
Silk fibroin	0.02 *M* acetate buffers	3.6

* *M* means molar.

Much of the confusion on this subject has arisen out of the assumption that the isoelectric and isoionic points are identical. The isoionic point is defined by Sookne and Harris [30] as the point at which dissociable groups of the substance combine equally and only with hydrogen and hydroxyl ions. It is identical with the isoelectric point only when the substance does not combine with ions other than hydrogen and hydroxyl. There are several methods by which the isoelectric point can be determined. One is titration, but only an electrokinetic method can determine it in every case. In some soluble proteins the two points are approximately the same.

The concept of the isoelectric and isoionic points, according to Sookne and Harris [30], can be utilized in practical wool processing. Since the isoionic point involves only the acidic and basic properties of the fiber, it should be considered in studying such wool processes as are related to these properties. Dyeing with soluble colors, felting, and removal of ash constituents from the fiber fall within this category; also, the swelling and tensile properties of wet fibers are functions of the state of their acidic and basic groups.

The isoelectric point, on the other hand, is concerned principally with the total net surface charge and is considered only in relation to processes involving either the removal or deposition of substances on the surface of the fiber, as in scouring and finishing. Scouring is facilitated when the charge on a fiber and the charge on the material being removed from the fiber are the same and therefore tend to repel each other. For example, dirt particles and particles of most inert substances carry negative charges. Obviously they are best removed from fibers which also have a large net negative charge. Similarly, the deposition of certain finishing agents on fibers or fabrics is best accomplished when the charges on the fibers and material to be deposited are of opposite sign.

MICROBIOLOGY [3]

Textile microbiology is an important part of industrial bacteriology and mycology [32, 33, 34, 35, 36, 37, 38, 39, 40, 41]. It deals with microorganisms, such as bacteria, fungi, and yeasts, which freely grow, under favorable conditions, on textile fibers and finished goods. All fibers of animal or vegetable origin are susceptible to bacterial or fungal attack, or both. Mineral fibers, such as asbestos, Vinyon, and the polyvinyls, are wholly resistant to microorganisms. Some others are not directly susceptible to microbiological disintegration. They are bacteria and

[3] Contributed by Dr. Louis C. Barail, consulting biochemist and toxicologist.

mold resistant when unfinished. However, as most dyes and finishes support bacteria and mold growth unless properly processed, these fibers when treated with such chemicals will secondarily be subjected to a similar contamination.

The severe requirements of the Pacific theatre of operations during World War II are largely responsible for the development of textile microbiology which took place during the war and subsequent years. They brought about an extensive study of the textile microorganisms in laboratories equipped with the best research instruments. They are responsible for the reconsideration of a great many germicides and fungicides which had been previously discarded, often without any valid reason. Such compounds were found, during these studies, to be of outstanding protective value. New specifications stimulated research in new improved products and were the basis for new developments in the chemical and bacteriological fields.

The importance of microbiology in the textile industry is now a well-established fact confirmed by the publication by government specialists of a statement to the effect that losses due to bacteria and mold growth in the textile industry are close to $1 billion a year.

It is not possible to enumerate and describe here all species of microorganisms that are responsible for the deterioration of textile fibers and finished goods. Only those most frequently encountered can be mentioned, and information will be given about ways and means of preventing and counteracting microbial attack. It is of prime importance to explain how microorganisms destroy textile fibers. The biochemical process which takes place is not well known outside of bacteriological circles. It is called an enzymatic action.

Enzymatic Action of Bacteria and Molds

Bacteria and molds do not digest animal or vegetable fibers the way moths or silverfish do. They produce enzymes which enable them to utilize best the nutritive value of the fibers, directly or indirectly. It is the chemical changes which occur at that time which cause the deterioration of the fibers. For instance, cellulose is transformed into glucose by two steps involving one enzyme each. *First*, cellulase converts cellulose to cellobiose; *second*, cellobiase converts cellobiose to glucose. Both enzymes are excreted at the same time by these microorganisms which destroy cellulosic materials. The reaction is as follows:

Cellulose
$(C_6H_{10}O_5)x$ + Cellulase

```
              ↓
          CH2OH              CH2OH                                  CH2OH
            |                  |                                      |
          HC-------+         HC-------+                             HCOH
            |      |           |      |                               |
          HCOH     |     +----CH      |                             HCOH
            |      |     |     |      |                               |
         HOCH      O     |   HOCH     |                            HOCH
            |      |     |     |      O + Cellobiase →                |
          HCOH     |     |    HCOH    |                             HCOH
            |      |     |     |      |                               |
          HC-------+     |   HOC------+                             HC=O
            |            |     H
            +------------+                                         Glucose
                                                                (2 molecules)
                   Cellobiose
             (Glucose-4-β-glucoside)
```

Similar reactions are found when other enzymes attack other cellulosic fibers, such as flax, ramie, hemp, sisal, jute, viscose, acetate, cuprammonium rayon, and many others, *or* protein fibers, such as wool (including cashmere, mohair, and other specialty fibers), silk, and protein synthetics.

Life and Reproduction

In order to excrete these enzymes in sufficient amounts to cause damage, bacteria and fungi require conditions of temperature, humidity, and light which have been established and vary with the species. Most textile microorganisms cannot live under a strong light. They thrive better in the dark. Some bacteria need oxygen (aerobes), some do not (anaerobes). Most microorganisms require a reasonable amount of moisture. They will not subsist on dry goods, but will proliferate on and cause damage on moist as well as wet materials. Bacteria live better at temperatures of 37° C. (98° F.) or slightly below. Molds fare better when the temperature is around 30° C. (86° F.). However, these figures should not be considered as limits, as some microorganisms can live at temperatures higher than those the human skin can stand (50° C. or 122° F.) and also in a home refrigerator (0–4° C. or 32–39° F.). Needless to say, when some of these conditions do not exist for natural or man-created reasons, the damage is usually limited.

Textile Bacteria

In the description of the bacteria which cause the deterioration of textile fibers, we have eliminated three categories of organisms:

1. Those which live *exclusively* in the soil and therefore destroy only fibers which come in contact with the soil.

2. Those which live *exclusively* on finishes, and therefore (*a*) cause only secondary damage to fibers, (*b*) do not feed on gray goods free from starch, gelatin or any other similar media.

3. Those which live *exclusively* in sea water and will not damage fibers in the absence of sea water.

Cellulose Bacteria. The eleven principal genera of bacteria which destroy cellulose by enzymatic action, as previously described, are listed in Table 14.

TABLE 14. PRINCIPAL BACTERIA THAT DESTROY CELLULOSE

Genus	*Species*
Angiococcus	*cellulosum*
Bacillus	*thermocellulolyticus*
Cellfalcicula Winogradsky	*viridis* *mucosa* *fusca* *
Cellulomonas	18 species
Cellvibrio Winogradsky	*Vibrio agar liquefaciens* †
Clostridium	*dissolvens* *carbonei* *cellulosolvens* *spumarum* *werneri* *omelianskii*
Cytophaga Winogradsky	*hutchinsonii* *lutea* *aurantiaca* *rubia* *tenuissima*
Polyangium cellulosum	*ferrugineus*
Sorangium	*cellulosum* *nigrum* *nigrescens*
Sporocytophaga Stanier	*myxococcoides* *congregata* *ellipsospora*
Streptomyces	*cellulosae* ‡

* Transforms cellulose into oxycellulose.
† Liquefies both cellulose and agar.
‡ Sometimes wrongly called *Actinomyces cellulosae* although it is a *Streptomyces*.

Protein Bacteria. There are six principal organisms:

Bacillus achromobacter
Bacillus aerobacter
Escherichia coli
Bacillus mesentericus
Bacillus proteus
Bacillus subtilis

Textile Fungi

In this nomenclature we are omitting those genera of fungi which grow only in the soil or on textile finishes. The name of each genus is followed by the letter "C" or "P," or both, indicating that the fungi destroy cellulose and/or protein. The numerous genera of fungi which disintegrate textile fibers can be divided into *two* categories: (1) the fungi non-pathogenic to man, and (2) the fungi pathogenic to man.

1. *Fungi Non-Pathogenic to Man.* These fungi are classified according to their morphologic characteristics and other properties, into *Fungi perfecti* and *Fungi imperfecti.*

The *fungi perfecti* comprise two orders:

A. Mucorales, genera { *Mucor* CP; *Rhizopus* CP; *Absidia* C }

B. Pyrenomycetes, genus *Chaetomium* C (28 species).

The *fungi imperfecti* comprise the single order of the *Hyphomycetales*, most important roster of textile fungi. Its principal genera are listed in Table 15 in alphabetical order to facilitate their identification. To each genus belong many species of fungi.

TABLE 15. Principal Genera of Textile Fungi

Alternarium CP	*Oidium* C
Aspergillus CP	*Oospora* P
Cephalosporium C	*Penicillium* P
Cephalothecium P	*Pullularia* C
Cladosporum—Hormodendron C	*Sporotrichum* C
Fusarium CP	*Stachybotrys* C
Helminthosporum C	*Stemphylium* C
Heterosporum C	*Torula* C
Metarrhizium CP	*Trichoderma* CP
Monilia CP	*Tricothecium* C
Myrothecium CP	

2. *Fungi Pathogenic to Man.* All fungi pathogenic to man destroy protein fibers when these fungi are in a suitable environment. Among them are the following genera:

Tricophyton, species { *gypseum*, *purpureum*, *sulfureum*, *schoenleini*, *violaceum*, *granulosum* }

Epidermophyton, species { *interdigitale*, *inguinale* }

Microsporum, species { *audouini*, *lanosum*, *fulvum* }

Monilia, species *albicans*

Mineral Fibers

Some of the mineral fibers are resistant to microorganisms: asbestos, Vinyon, and polyvinyls (Rhovyl, Fibrovyl, Thermovyl, and Isovyl). Needless to say, this immunity does not apply to any finishes or dye treatments given them; therefore, such fabrics may bear bacteria or mold spots. However, such spots on the surface can be removed by scouring off the dye or the finish so that there remains no apparent sign of degradation of the fiber itself.

Other mineral fibers show a great resistance to deterioration by microorganisms but often may become contaminated by attacked finishes or dyes and lose some of their properties. Some of these are nylon, Orlon, glass, Saran, Velon, Vinyon, Dynel, Dacron, and polyfiber. Finally, other mineral fibers do not seem to resist as well as those already mentioned when subjected to conditions highly favorable to the growth of microorganisms, principally bacteria; some of these are: Vinyon V, polyethylenes, acrylonitrile, Plexon, and polymethacrylonitrile.

Nature of Damages

Damages caused to textile fibers by microorganisms affect most of our senses. They can be seen, smelled, felt, and eventually tasted. The eye can detect discoloration of dyes, spots of various colors on materials, and even the growth itself. With the aid of the microscope the intensity of the growth and the depth and extension of the damage can be noted and measured.

The attack by microorganisms causes textile fibers to develop a musty odor and taste. The odor is well known and is readily detectable. The taste is eventually perceived on face towels, and on garments sucked by infants and babies.

The greatest evidence of deterioration is by touch: slimy feel and loss of strength. It is best illustrated when the material is submitted to a tensile strength test and shows a loss when compared with a control. When the tensile strength is greatly reduced, the goods are definitely unusable and unmerchantable. Damage by microorganisms also increases in the presence of organic matter after decomposition, such as perspiration, urine, blood, and feces, due to man, animal, or insect, as may occur in warehouses, ships, trains, cars, trucks, and many other places.

Protection and Prevention

There are several ways to prevent deterioration of fabrics by microorganisms. Some are temporary, like steam or hot-air sterilization; some are long-lasting and semipermanent.

Steam or hot-air sterilization kills all bacteria, fungi, and their spores. If the goods are wrapped before being sterilized, and sterilized as wrapped, the protection lasts as long as the wrapper is intact. It ceases as soon as the package is open because of contamination by human touch, contact with unsterile materials, as well as by contact with airborne bacteria and fungi.

The long-lasting means of protection are of a chemical nature. They consist in the impregnation of the fibers or finished materials with germicides and fungicides of high bactericidal and fungicidal value. The treatment can be applied to raw fibers, yarns, woven or knitted fabrics, or finished goods. It is always applied in the last rinse. Needless to say, it is also mandatory to treat dyes, finishes, paper cones, and wrapping materials to insure a complete protection of the treated goods and prevent secondary contamination.

Over 450 different formulas compounded for mildew and bacteria prevention have been tested. Very few of them can be considered as outstanding for performance, lack of toxicity and irritating properties, and absence of color and odor. When color and odor are not an obstacle, satisfactory compounds can be added to the list of recommended products. The germicides-fungicides for use in the textile industry can be divided into three principal categories: (1) chlorine and phenol derivatives; (2) salts of heavy metals; and (3) organic aromatics and miscellaneous.

In the *first* group can be found chloramine, ortho phenylphenol, pentachlorphenol and salts, dihydroxy dichloro diphenyl methane, parachlor meta xylenol, and many others.

The *second* group consists of inorganic and organic salts of copper, such as copper lactate, naphthanate, sulfate, 8-hydroxyquinolinate; of mercury, such as the numerous inorganic compounds, the impressive list of the efficient phenyl mercury salts, the pyridyl mercury salts; and also derivatives of zinc, chromium and cadmium.

The *third* group comprises compounds such as cresols, thymol, chlorthymol and other aromatics, and also iodine, bromine, formaldehyde, potassium permanganate, salicylanilide, and hydroxyquinoline.

To these three categories can also be added the group of resins and plastics which when incorporated into fibers that are made into articles such as towels and napkins render these materials mildewproof and also stainproof. A mere wiping with soap and water will remove all stains, including mildew spots growing on the soiled matter. Such goods remain mildew resistant for very long periods.

Testing Procedures

Fibers that have been treated to be mildew resistant can be tested according to a great many different methods. A biophysical method consists in using the property of mildew cells to fluoresce under ultraviolet radiations; therefore, mildew cells are easily and quickly detectable under Wood's light.

The only reliable quantitative methods are bacteriological. They all consist of the inoculation of supposedly treated textiles with various textile fungi or bacteria and incubation for various periods. Any of the previously mentioned bacteria or fungi can be used for the inoculation. The incubation is made at 37° C. for bacteria and at 30° C. for fungi. It can be conducted in broth, in agar, or in soil. It may last from 7 to 28 days or more. When made in soil, it is called *soil burial test*. Tensile strength tests are generally conducted after incubation.

The most common method for civilian use is the A.S.T.M. method Designation D684-45T, revised by the section on antiseptic finishes of Committee D-13. Various government agencies have specifications to be used to test various textile materials according to their nature, their intended use, and the mildewproofing compounds authorized in each case. After the unification of the Armed Forces took place, the number of the government specifications decreased considerably. A few important ones practically take care of all testing eventualities.

BIBLIOGRAPHY

1. Matthews, J. M., and Mauersberger, H. R., *Textile Fibers*, 5th Ed., John Wiley & Sons, New York, pp. 1–8 (1947).
2. Matthews, J. M., and Mauersberger, H. R., *Textile Fibers*, 5th Ed., John Wiley & Sons, New York, Chap. II (1947).
3. Matthews, J. M., and Mauersberger, H. R., *Textile Fibers*, 5th Ed., John Wiley & Sons, New York, Chap. III (1947).

4. ALLEN, R. M., *The Microscope*, D. Van Nostrand Co., New York (1940).
5. ALLEN, R. M., *Photomicrography*, D. Van Nostrand Co., New York (1941).
6. CHAMOT, E. M., and MASON, C. W., *Handbook of Chemical Microscopy*, 2nd Ed., John Wiley & Sons, New York (1938 and 1940).
7. COVINGTON, J. D., *Working with the Microscope*, McGraw-Hill Book Co., New York (1941).
8. MILLSON, H. E., and ROYER, G. L., "Microscopical Observations of Union Dyeing," *Am. Dyestuff Reptr.* (June 8, 1942).
9. SCHWARZ, E. R., *Textiles and the Microscope*, 1st Ed., McGraw-Hill Book Co., New York (1934).
10. MEADOWS, BARKLEY, "Trends in the Consumption of Fibers in the United States 1892–1948," *Agr. Econ. Bull. 89*, U. S. Dept. of Agr. (1950).
11. LOVE, J. SPENCER, "From Wonder Fiber to Wonder Fabric—A Challenge to Management," Leaflet, *Am. Assoc. Textile Chem. Colorists*, Burlington Mills Corp. (Oct. 18, 1951).
12. BENDIGO, C. W., American Society for Testing Materials (June 26, 1952), News Release, American Cyanamid Co., New Products Division, 30 Rockefeller Plaza, N. Y.
13. American Society for Testing Materials, Philadelphia, Pa., *Standards on Textile Materials*, Committee D-13 (Oct. 1951).
14. U. S. Testing Co., booklet on *Testing*. Regain table brought up to date (1949).
15. OLNEY, L. A., *Textile Chemistry and Dyeing*, Part I: "Chemical Technology of the Fibers," 7th Ed., Lowell Textile Associates (1942).
16. MAUERSBERGER, H. R., "Progress in New Synthetic Textile Fibers," A.S.T.M. *Bull. 121*, p. 25 (May 1943); A.S.T.M., Standards on Textile Materials, p. 351 (Oct. 1941); A.S.T.M., Standards on Textile Materials, p. 407 (Oct. 1943); *Ann. Rept., 1941, Smithsonian Inst.*, Appendix, pp. 211–223; *Ann. Rept., 1943, Smithsonian Inst.*, Appendix, p. 151; *Rayon Textile Monthly* (Nov. and Dec. 1940).
17. HUNT, STANLEY B., "Classification of Man-Made Fibers," *Textile Organon*, 10 (12), pp. 156–159, Textile Economics Bureau, Inc. (Nov. 1939).
18. KRAUSS, WALTER, by permission.
19. A.S.T.M. *Standards on Textile Materials*, Committee D-13 (Oct. 1951).
20. American Cyanamid Co., Calco Chemical Division, Bound Brook, N. J., *Calco Technical Bulletin 831*. "Identification of Synthetic Fibers by Microscopical and Dye Staining Techniques," G. L. Royer, p. 51 (1952).
20*a*. HEYN, A. N. J., *Textile Research J.*, **22,** 513 (1952).
21. Anon., *Rayon Textile Monthly*, **26,** 91 (May 1945).
22. MARSH, C., private communication.
23. PRESTON, J. M., *Trans. Faraday Soc.*, **29,** 65 (1933).
24. ROYER, G. L., and MARSH, C., *J. Soc. Dyers Colourists*, **63,** 290 (1947).
25. Factory Mutual Engineering Division, Assoc. Factory Mutual Fire Insurance Companies Bulletins (Nov. 1951).
26. National Board of Fire Underwriters, Pamphlet 44, *Storage and Handling of Combustible Fibers*, Appendix (Sept. 1941).
27. BARR, G., "The Action of Light on Textiles," *Trans. Faraday Soc.*, **30,** p. 284 (1924).
28. MILLSON, H. E., "The Phosphorescence of Textile Fibers and Other Substances," *Calco Tech. Bull. 753*, American Cyanamid Co. (1944).
29. SCOTT, W. W., *Standard Methods of Chemical Analysis*, 5th Ed., D. Van Nostrand Co. (1939).

30. Sookne, A. M., and Harris, M., "Electrophoretic Studies of Wool," *Am. Dyestuff Reptr.*, **28,** p. 593 (1939).
31. Harris, M., and Sookne, A. M., "Electrophoretic Studies of Wool," *J. Research Natl. Bur. Standards,* **23** (Oct. 1939), and correspondence with editor (March 1944).
32. Barail, Louis C., "A Suggested Method for the Thorough Testing of Antiseptic Fabrics," *Am. Dyestuff Reptr.* (Dec. 4, 1944).
33. Barail, Louis C., "Testing of Fungicidal Materials against Pathogenic Fungi," *Am. Dyestuff Reptr.* (Apr. 19, 1948).
34. McCulloch, Ernest C., *Disinfection and Sterilization,* Lea and Febiger, Philadelphia (1945).
35. Prescott, Samuel C., and Dunn, Cecil G., *Industrial Microbiology,* McGraw-Hill Book Co., New York (1949).
36. Smith, George, *An Introduction to Industrial Mycology,* Edward Arnold & Co., London (1946).
37. *Bergey's Manual of Determinative Bacteriology* (ed. by R. S. Breed *et al.*), Williams & Wilkins Co., Baltimore (1948).
38. Dubos, René J., *The Bacterial Cell,* Harvard University Press, Cambridge (1945).
39. Foster, Jackson W., *Chemical Activities of Fungi,* Academic Press, New York (1949).
40. Porter, John R., *Bacterial Chemistry and Physiology,* John Wiley & Sons, New York (1946).
41. Siu, Ralph G., *Microbial Decomposition of Cellulose,* Reinhold Publishing Co., New York (1951).

CHAPTER II

CELLULOSE: SOURCES, CONSTITUTION, AND CHEMICAL PROPERTIES

Philip C. Scherer

From the dawn of history to the present day, cellulose has played a very important part in the economic lives of the peoples of the world. Recorded history, as far back as that of the ancient Egyptians [39], has shown the use of cellulose fibers for clothing and, in the form of fibers from the papyrus plant, as paper. The ancient peoples made little improvement in the methods of extracting cellulose, all of their supply coming from the long fibers present in such plants as cotton, flax, ramie, and hemp.

The fact that cellulose was present in all vegetable matter [22] was recognized early in the nineteenth century, and since that time efforts have been made to obtain it in a pure form by chemical reagents. The first recorded experiments to obtain cellulose from raw vegetable products (such as wood and straw) were reported in 1846, using sodium hydroxide as the isolating agent [115]. In 1856 nitric acid was patented [109] for the extraction of cellulose. The important sulfite process of Tilghman [110] was introduced in 1867, and since then rapid strides were made in isolating cellulose in relatively pure form from practically all kinds of plant life.

Examination of various kinds of vegetable matter has shown that the amount of cellulose present varies greatly, depending upon the type of the plant. Cotton fibers give up to about 99 per cent, when purified, and flax and ramie average less than 30 per cent of usable fiber. The cellulose in various woods averages about 45 to 52 per cent, while straws and grasses yield smaller amounts. Examination of the isolated cellulose seems to indicate that, chemically at least, the material is nearly the same, regardless of the source. Development of this observation has shown that cellulose rarely occurs pure in nature, and other substances are always associated with it. Although many such substances have been recognized, it is possible to discuss only the most important types here.

SUBSTANCES FOUND WITH CELLULOSE

Lignin [34]. Lignin combines with cellulose in a manner, not yet clarified, to form woody tissue in the proportion of about 50 to 60 per cent of cellulose to roughly 20 to 30 per cent of lignin, depending upon the source. The composition of lignin has not yet been completely elucidated, but it appears to be a polymeric substance consisting of aromatic nuclei, methoxy groups, and possibly other kinds of groupings which render it chemically active. Although the manner of combination between cellulose and lignin is not clear, it generally requires the action of hydrolytic agents at high temperatures and pressures to liberate the cellulose from the combination. In addition to lignin and cellulose, vegetable matter usually contains small amounts of mineral ash, resins, sugars, and carbohydrates other than cellulose.

The combination of lignin and cellulose is widespread throughout the vegetable kingdom, but is most concentrated in the woody tissues of trees, where the lignin may form up to 30 per cent of the whole material. Smaller amounts are found in the woody parts of flax stems, cereal straws, and various grasses.

Pectins. Pectins [19], or materials closely related to them, are often found with cellulose. Cotton is perhaps the best known source of pectin. It contains between 0.4 and 3.0 per cent of pectic substances and 80 to 85 per cent of cellulose in the raw state.

Pectin in plants is not a single substance, but a complex series of carbohydrate derivatives containing galacturonic acid, associated with arabinose and galactose. It may exist either as the free acid, or in the form of a metal salt, or as the methyl ester. Pectic substances are further divided into *protopectin*, which is water-insoluble in the plant, but is rendered soluble by treatment with water, and salt solutions. *Pectin* is the water-soluble, methylated pectic substances obtained from protopectins. It is a group name for all pectic substances between protopectin and pectic acid. *Pectic acid* may be obtained by hydrolysis of pectin, resulting in the complete removal of the methyl ester group. In the plant cell walls pectin exists in the form of an insoluble calcium salt, or the salt of other metals.

Other carbohydrate compounds classed under the general name of *mucins* are also found associated with cellulose. Chemically, they are related to pentosans, which are combined with complex acids to form the mucins.

Fats and Waxes. Cellulose is also found closely associated with fats and waxes of various kinds. The best known example is probably cork

[124], which contains 2 to 3 per cent of cellulose along with a fatty compound, suberine. *Suberine* apparently is a mixture of complex esters and complex acids along with condensation products of such acids.

No cellulose, regardless of its source, consists of cellulose with only *one* of the above substances; it is usually a mixture of several of them. In wood, cellulose is chiefly found with lignin, *but* there are also present some pectic and adipic substances. In addition, all vegetable matter contains minerals, resins and gums, proteins, tannins, and carbohydrates other than cellulose.

In preparing a pure cellulose it is necessary to remove all the above; so the procedures used are adjusted to the type of matter to be removed. Since cellulose is sensitive to chemical reagents, the method of purification must be carefully standardized, if a uniform product is to be obtained. In order to base cellulose research on a common foundation, it is necessary to adopt a standard method for its preparation. The Cellulose Chemistry Division of the American Chemical Society [20] describes its preparation as follows:

PREPARATION OF STANDARD CELLULOSE

One hundred grams of Wannamaker's Cleveland raw cotton is mechanically freed from visible impurities and is then loosely packed into a nickel wire container of fine mesh. By means of a nickel chain passing through a hole in the center of the cover of a large beaker, the basket is suspended in a solution of 30 grams of NaOH and 15 grams of rosin dissolved in 3 liters of distilled boiling water. After 4 hr boiling, during which the container is agitated vertically, and the cotton is never allowed to rise above the surface of the liquid, the brown alkaline solution is displaced with hot distilled water run in through a syphon. This washing is continued until the solution is only slightly alkaline. The cotton is again heated for 15 min with 5 grams of NaOH in 3 liters of water (out of contact with air) and again washed with hot distilled water as before. This removes the rosin.

The sample is then immersed in cold water until the temperature is below 20° C. After it has been drained, it is bleached white by placing it for 1 hr in 3 liters of sodium hypochlorite solution containing 0.1 per cent available chlorine at 20° C. The cotton is then rinsed into a Buchner funnel and washed with distilled water for 10 min. This is repeated three times. During the final wash a saturated solution of sodium bisulfite is added, drop by drop, until the filtrate no longer colors starch-iodide paper. It is finally washed with distilled water, folded into a linen cloth, wrapped in filter paper, lightly squeezed, and dried in air, out of contact with fumes. If there is a slight trace of fat, it is removed with alcohol-benzene solution.

This process yields a cellulose which contains no fats, mineral substances, or nitrogen and its copper number is at a minimum. Corey and Gray [20] and Worner and Mease [20] have introduced modifications of this procedure, but they do not lead to significantly different results. Table 1 shows results obtained by this method, using a typical cotton.

TABLE 1. Purification of Cotton [82]

	Raw Cotton (per cent)	*Purified, Kier Boil (per cent)*	*Purified, A.C.S. Method (per cent)*
Cellulose	80 to 85	99.1 to 99.5	99.5 to 99.6
Wax, fatty acids	0.4 to 1.0	0.01 to 0.15	Nil
Ash	0.8 to 1.8	0.05 to 0.75	0.09
Pectins	0.4 to 1.1	Nil	Nil
Protein nitrogen	1.2 to 2.5	0.5 to 0.1	Nil
Pigment, resin	3 to 5	Nil	Nil
Moisture	6 to 8	Nil	Nil

PREPARATION OF CELLULOSE FOR INDUSTRIAL USES

Cellulose for industrial uses, other than for direct application in the textile field, comes from *two main* sources:

(*a*) Boll of the cotton plant (cotton linters).
(*b*) Wood (spruce, slash pine).

Cotton Plant. The boll of the ripe cotton plant [75] contains seeds to which are attached cotton fibers, ranging in size from short (average length of 0.2 in.), called *linters,* to long, single-celled fibers which may be as long as 2.5 in. (See Chapter V.) The seed cotton is subjected to a "ginning" process, which removes the long fibers suitable for spinning and leaves, still attached to the seed, the short *linters.*

The cleaned seeds are then passed to another "saw gin," where all the linters are cut in one passage and are called "mill run." The linters are passed once through the saws giving *first cut* linters and a second time to give *second run* linters. As many as seven different cuts are taken in removing the linters from the seeds. Both "mill run" and "first cut" linters are relatively long fibers and command a higher price in the market. The second and subsequent run linters offer a relatively cheap source of cellulose.

Purification. The cotton linters are dark in color and must be purified before use in industry. Mechanical impurities are removed by air separation. The linters are thoroughly wetted with a hot cooking solution and conveyed to the digestor. Here the air is dispelled and the stock cooked under pressure (out of contact with the air). The cooking solution consists of sodium hydroxide of about 3.5 per cent concentration. With the air excluded, little degradation of the linters occurs. At the end of this controlled cooking the linters are washed with pure water until free from chemicals and impurities.

The purified linters, free of oils, fats, and waxes, are now bleached and then washed to remove all traces of chemicals. After drying, the linters are ready for use in the rayon industry.

Wood. Wood [30] consists largely of lignin in combination with cellulose. It ranges in cellulose content, with the type of wood, from 40 to 60 per cent. The remaining components are carbohydrates other than cellulose (pentosans and hexosans), lignin, resins, fats, and inorganic constituents. To obtain pure cellulose from wood it is necessary to remove, by chemical reaction and solution, the other constituents with as little degradation of cellulose as possible. The several processes are divided into *two* main types. The *first* makes use of alkali to bring about liberation of the cellulose, and the *second* uses an acid for the same purpose. The alkaline processes are further subdivided, depending upon the type of alkali used, into the "soda" and the "sulfate." The acid method is confined to the use of sulfurous acid and its salts, although nitric acid has recently been successfully applied to the liberation of cellulose [97]. The degrading action of the acid process on the cellulose produced is generally less severe and for that reason it is preferred.

Soda Process. In this process, wood is subdivided mechanically into "chips" of about 3/8 to 7/8 in. in size and placed in a steel digestor which is provided with cooking liquor. This liquor consists of 6 to 8 per cent of sodium hydroxide obtained by causticizing soda ash, either fresh or recovered, with lime. The temperature of the mass is slowly raised either by blowing steam directly into the bottom of the vessel, or indirectly by heat interchangers. In about 2 hr the temperature is raised to about 165 or 170° C. and maintained 2 to 5 hr. The steam is now turned off and the pressure in the digestor reduced to less than 50 lb per sq in. The contents are blown into a large tank fitted with a false bottom, which drains the liquor off; the cellulose is then rinsed with pure water until all salts and impurities are removed.

Since the cooking never completely removes all the lignin, the fibers are still colored and require a chlorine bleach. After removal of the bleaching solution by washing, the pulp, suspended in water, is passed successively through pressure and drying rolls in a sheet-making machine to form coherent pulp sheets, about 0.035 to 0.040 in. thick. These are cut into convenient sizes, baled, and shipped to the rayon industry.

Sulfate Process. The type of pulp produced by this process is very similar to that of the soda cook since the cooking liquor used is alkaline in nature also. However, instead of using a liquor containing up to 8 per cent of free sodium hydroxide, as is done in the soda cook, a milder chemical solution is used. In the sulfate liquor only about 3 to 4 per cent of the total alkali is free sodium hydroxide and about 2.5 per cent is in the form of sodium sulfide.

Sodium sulfide is not added, as such, to the cook liquor but is formed during the recovery of waste liquor from the digestors. The waste, or "black" liquor, is evaporated and the resultant residue is mixed with sodium sulfate and burned in furnaces. Carbonaceous matter present during the ignition reduces the sodium sulfate to sodium sulfide. Any loss of alkali during the cooking process is made up in this way by the addition of sodium sulfate. The liquor resulting from the solution of the product from the furnaces is made up to the proper strength and used to cook the wood. The presence of the sodium sulfide appears to lessen the degrading of the cellulose and produces a strong pulp.

Sulfite Process. This process appears to produce a cellulose which has been degraded very little. This depends on the reactions taking place between the lignin, and other noncellulosic constituents of wood, and a solution of a metal bisulfite and sulfurous acid. The fundamental reaction is apparently one of conversion of the lignin to soluble lignin derivatives, leaving the cellulose unchanged.

Lignin itself is not soluble in water and is far from being a simple substance. Apparently, there are present in the lignin molecule aromatic nuclei which are related to coniferyl alcohol in general structure [34].

In the sulfite process the hydrogen-ion concentration (*p*H) present in the sulfite liquor is reduced, by common ion effect, on the addition of calcium, or other base. Under these conditions, the degrading effect of the cooking liquor on the liberated cellulose is milder than in the alkaline processes.

The mechanical steps involved in the debarking of wood, reducing it to chips, and grading the chips are already well described in good textbooks on the subject [30]. The main step in this process is the cooking of the chips with bisulfite liquor in steel digestors provided with an acid-resistant ceramic lining. A normal charge may run as high as 40 tons of chips and 50,000 gal of cook liquor. The digestor is charged with chips and liquor and the temperature slowly raised to 110° C. in about 2 hr after the start. The chips become completely penetrated by the liquor before the cooking temperature is reached.

The temperature is now rapidly brought to 135 or 140° C. and the pressure to about 75 lb per sq in., where they are maintained for 6 to 8 hr. Then the digestor contents are blown into the "blow pit," where a false bottom permits the spent cook liquor to drain off. The pulp is then washed thoroughly with volumes of clean water until all traces of salts are removed. Absence of inorganic ash in the final product depends largely upon the completeness of this washing.

The pulp, now freed from scale, knots, uncooked chips, etc., by screening processes, is thickened to about 18 per cent. The pulp still has a faint yellow or tan color which is removed by bleaching. The pulp, in suspension, is brought in contact with a solution of sodium, or calcium, hypochlorite under controlled conditions of temperature, concentration,

TABLE 2. CHEMICAL CHANGES IN WOOD DURING COOKING

	Alpha Cell %	*Lignin %*	*Pentosan %*	*Ether Sol. %*	*Alcohol Sol. %*	*Hot H_2O Sol. %*	*Total Sol. %*	*Ash %*	*Viscosity Poise*
			RAW WOODS						
Spruce	....	29.6	11.5	1.05	1.38	0.85	3.28	0.48	.....
Fir	....	28.8	8.3	0.94	2.52	2.28	4.35	0.59	.....
Beech	....	23.2	20.5	0.22	2.24	0.97	3.40	0.36	.....
Rock maple	....	23.8	16.5	0.25	3.64	0.34	4.21	0.48	.....
White birch	....	25.1	23.5	3.29	3.22	1.81	9.63	0.39	.....
White maple	....	27.8	18.0	0.35	2.78	2.13	5.08	0.32	.....
Yellow birch	....	23.0	19.0	0.54	2.14	1.39	4.13	0.44	.....
			UNBLEACHED SULFITE PULPS						
Spruce	88.6	1.2	4.5	1.1	0.60	0.50	....	....	100
Fir	88.8	1.1	4.1	1.3	0.80	0.60	....	....	90
Beech	87.2	1.3	6.8	0.45	0.32	0.30	....	....	19
Rock maple	87.5	0.9	7.2	0.3	0.27	0.72	....	....	20
White birch	88.2	1.5	9.3	2.6	0.58	0.67	....	....	25
Yellow birch	87.9	1.2	8.9	1.4	0.35	0.64	....	....	22
			BLEACHED SULFITE PULPS						
Spruce	89.1	....	4.2	0.50	0.42	0.40	....	....	15.0
Fir	89.4	....	3.8	0.48	0.39	0.51	....	....	12.5
Beech	88.8	....	6.1	0.42	0.30	0.48	....	....	2.5
Rock maple	88.6	....	6.2	0.30	0.24	0.63	....	....	2.8
White birch	89.4	....	7.2	2.40	0.50	0.30	....	....	3.0
Yellow birch	89.2	....	6.8	1.3	0.32	0.50	....	....	2.9
			PULPS PURIFIED BY ALKALINE BOIL						
Soft woods	95.1	....	1.80	....	....	....	....	....	8.0
Hard woods	95.7	....	2.8	....	....	....	....	....	5.0

pH and time. The oxidizing bleach converts lignin, and other colored substances, to soluble compounds which can be washed from the pulp.

Since cellulose is extremely sensitive to degradation by oxidation, great care must be used during bleaching if an undegraded product is desired. The pulp is again passed through a series of screens so as to remove very large, or very small, fibers and is then passed into a sheeting machine, which forms sheets of certain specified dimensions and thickness.

Table 2 gives recent values by Richter [90] on the chemical composition of the cellulosic materials during cooking. Wood is such a variable substance that the values represent an average. Any individual sample of wood might produce different percentages.

Table 3 shows a comparison of analyses of wood pulps [89] and of technically prepared cotton pulps.

TABLE 3. Per Cent Comparison of Wood Pulps and Cotton

	Low Alpha Wood Pulps	*High Alpha Wood Pulps*	*Cotton Linters Pulps*
Alpha cellulose	88.0 to 92.0	94.0 to 96.0	98.0 to 99.0
Beta cellulose	3.0 to 4.0	2.0 to 3.0	1.0 to 1.5
Gamma cellulose	4.0 to 9.0	1.0 to 4.0	0.0 to 1.0
Ash	0.03 to 0.10	0.04 to 0.08	0.07 to 0.12
Silica	0.003 to 0.005	0.003 to 0.005	0.05
Calcium	0.01 to 0.05	0.02 to 0.05	0.02
Iron, ppm	4 to 10	3 to 6	10 to 15
10 per cent KOH sol.	14 to 18	4 to 6	2 to 4
Ether extract	0.10 to 0.30	0.07 to 0.12	0.10 to 0.20
Cupra viscosity, cps	400 to 800	400 to 800	250 to 500

CHEMICAL CONSTITUTION OF CELLULOSE

Formula. The ultimate analysis of cellulose, regardless of the source, always shows the presence of 44.4 per cent carbon, 6.2 per cent hydrogen, and 49.4 per cent oxygen. This corresponds to an empirical ratio of six carbon to ten hydrogen to five oxygen, and the simplest formula for cellulose is written $(C_6H_{10}O_5)x$, where the evaluation of the factor x must await evidence as to molecular size. For many years it has been recognized that if cellulose is subjected to acid hydrolysis, a quantitative yield of glucose may be obtained. Experiments by Irvine and Hirst [55] and others have confirmed this point. It must be concluded, therefore, that the end product of cellulose hydrolysis is *glucose.* It follows that the structure of glucose must be the fundamental structure of the units from which cellulose is built up, and a knowledge of the glucose structure is then essential to that of cellulose. It was not until 1925 that Haworth [43] completely elucidated the structure of glucose as a six-membered ring instead of a five-membered ring as had been assumed previously. In accordance with this concept the two stereoisomeric forms of glucose are here represented in Fig. 1.

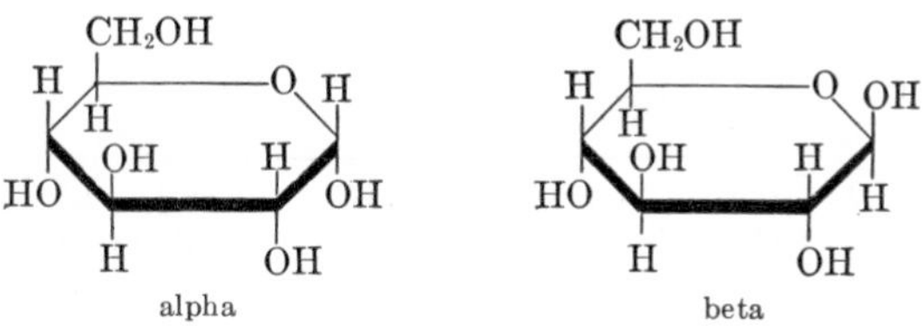

FIG. 1. Chemical structure of glucose.

The two forms differ only in that the alpha form has the 1,2,4-hydroxyl groups on one side of the ring plane with the 3,6-hydroxyl groups on the opposite side, while in the beta form the 2,4-hydroxyls are on one side and the 1,3,6-hydroxyls are on the other. The two forms may be accurately identified by their optical activity. Careful investigation of the hydrolytic products of cellulose by Freudenberg [34] and others has indicated that only the beta form of glucose is present and, therefore, only that form furnishes the building units for cellulose.

Cellobiose. Glucose has five hydroxyl groups, which can be esterified to give penta-acetates, or nitrates. When cellulose is acetylated, nitrated, or treated with sodium in liquid ammonia [91], there is evidence that it has at the most only three hydroxyl groups capable of reacting. It follows that during the combination of beta glucose units into cellulose, two hydroxyl groups on each unit must have reacted to furnish the means of combination. The obvious assumption is that water has been split out between two units to furnish an oxygen linkage. This is found when cellulose is treated with a mixture of acetic acid and sulfuric acid at 120° C. for a few minutes. The product from this acetolysis has been identified as *cellobiose,* a disaccharide, resulting from a hydrolysis which stops short of the complete separation of the individual units of cellulose and which must, therefore, still contain a two-unit linkage. This is typical of the whole cellulose structure.

By methylation and hydrolysis Haworth and Hirst [45] were able to show that cellobiose consists of *two beta glucose units* bound together by a 1,4-β glucosidic linkage. It follows that the glucose rings of which cellulose is composed must be bound together by an oxygen atom, one valence of which runs from the one-carbon atom of one ring to the four-carbon atom of the next unit. Work by Freudenberg [35] and by Karrer and Widmer [58] indicated that cellulose is composed largely of cellobiose units, and Freudenberg first suggested that cellulose is composed of long chains of glucose residues linked together as in cellobiose.

If two such cellobiose units are examined and an attempt is made to join them into a chain of four glucose units, it is apparent that there are several ways in which this can be done and still preserve the greatest symmetry.

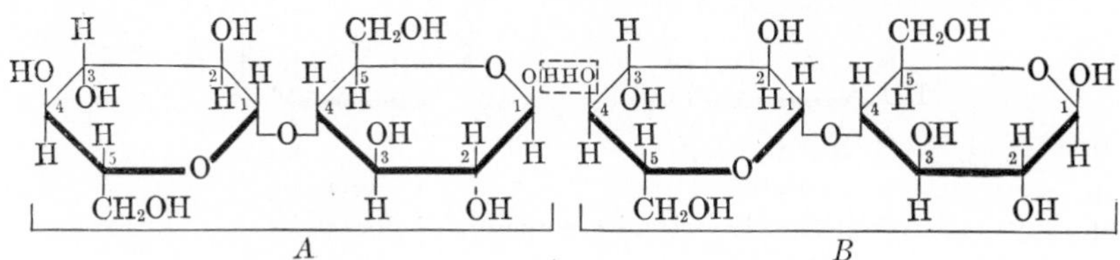

Fig. 2. Condensation of two cellobiose units.

In the arrangement given above, water splits out between the hydroxyl groups attached to the first carbon atom of one cellobiose unit and the number four carbon atom of the adjacent one. By a continuation of this type of combination a very long chain of anhydro-β-glucose units could be built up in which all of them would be united by 1,4 oxygen bridges. The same type of bridging then exists throughout the whole chain and all such bridges would be equally susceptible to hydrolysis. If this is true then only products with 1,4 unions should be found in the hydrolysis of cellulose. In no case has there been found a hydrolysis product of cellulose containing an oxygen bridge linking units in other than the 1,4 position.

If in the above formula the cellobiose unit marked *B* were reversed, water should split out between the one carbon of *A* and the one carbon of *B* and thus give rise to a 1,1 oxygen bridge. Such a linkage should be extremely sensitive to hydrolysis and would certainly never be found among the hydrolysis products. Further combination of the four-unit sugar to a longer chain could only occur through the two 4-carbon atoms and would, on a statistical basis, result in the production, somewhere in the chain, of at least some 4,4 oxygen bridges. Such bridges would be ether linkages and would be extremely resistant toward hydrolysis. As a result it would be expected that 4,4 bridges would exist, to at least some extent, in the hydrolysis products of cellulose if such a type of combination were possible. Since such products have never been isolated it is assumed that they do not exist in cellulose and that the anhydroglucose units, of which cellulose is composed, are all united by 1,4 oxygen bridges.

If the concept of cellulose as a chain of anhydro-β-glucose units bound together by 1,4 oxygen bridges is adopted it may be represented by the formula below:

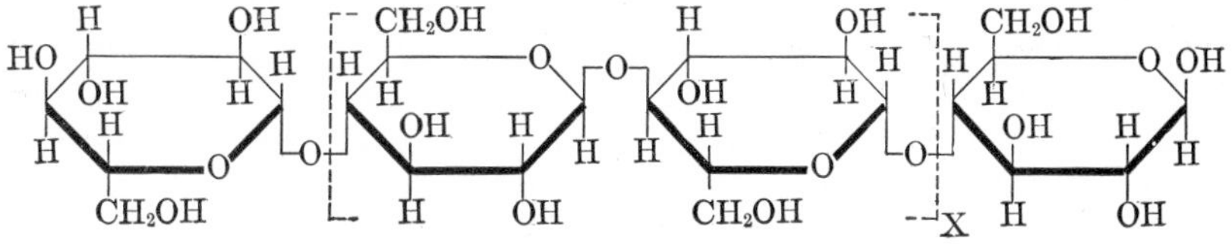

Fig. 3. Chemical structure of cellulose chains.

On exhaustive methylation of a compound of this type, all of the free hydroxyl groups are converted to OCH_3 groups and the resulting methyl cellulose is represented by the formula given above with all of the hydroxyl groups replaced by OCH_3.

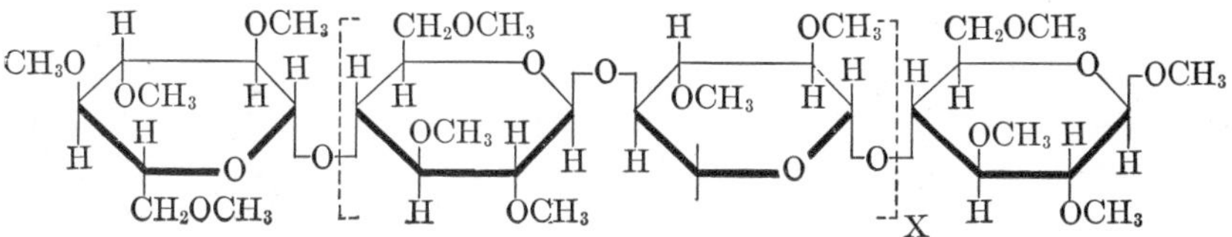

Fig. 4. Chemical structure of fully methylated cellulose.

METHYL CELLULOSE HYDROLYSIS

When methyl cellulose is subjected to hydrolysis the aldehydrol methoxy group on the one carbon of the glucose unit at the right extremity of the chain is readily converted to a hydroxyl group but none of the other methyl groups are removed. On continued hydrolysis the 1,4 oxygen bridges are broken to produce hydroxyl groups, the chain is destroyed, and 2,3,6-trimethyl glucose is formed from all units except that on the left hand end of the chain. Examination of this shows that there should be formed one molecule of 2,3,4,6-tetramethyl glucose for each chain of units so hydrolyzed. In experiments, carried out by Haworth and Machemer [44], small amounts of 2,3,4,6-tetramethyl glucose were isolated and confirmation of the formula in Fig 3 was obtained. The amounts so found were very small and corresponded to a chain containing at least 200 anhydroglucose units.

If the concept of cellulose as a chain of anhydro-β-glucose units is true, it should be possible to find, among the products of hydrolysis, fragments of the long chains all of which should show the typical structure. Among such products there have been found, in addition to cellobiose, a triose and a tetrose resulting from the decomposition of cellulose with hydrochloric acid [120]. Zechmeister and Toth [123] showed the presence of a cellosugar containing six glucose units among the decomposition products of cellulose. In no case was there found any other type of linkage except the 1,4 oxygen bridge between the glucose units. Further investigations carried on in the oligosaccharide series show that as the length of the saccharide chain is increased by one glucose residue, the optical rotation changes by a definite increment. On investigating this property, in the series produced from cellulose, no case of any other linkage than the 1,4-β linkage was found and it is very probable that cellulose has only this type of linkage throughout. Collateral evidence based on a study of the rate of hydrolysis also appears to confirm this.

Attempts to synthesize cellulose from glucose have been only partly successful. Freudenberg and Nagai [77], by the condensation of methylated glucoses, were able to obtain cellobiose and cellotriose, which are the same as those obtained by the decomposition of cellulose. Hibbert [52] synthesized a cellulose which is chemically the same as natural cellulose. The product also gives an X-ray pattern identical with that of natural plant cellulose. Since the bacteria used bring about a biochemical condensation of glucose units, this is confirmatory evidence for the concept of cellulose as *a condensation product of anhydroglucose units*, even though the actual mechanism of the condensation process is obscure.

The concept of pure cellulose as a chain of anhydro-β-glucose units united by 1,4 oxygen bridges is almost universally accepted by present-day chemists [84]. It satisfactorily explains the known chemical reactions of cellulose and also fits well the evidence obtained by X-rays and other physical means.

HOW NATURE PRODUCES CELLULOSE

For an explanation of the actual manner in which cellulose is produced in nature it is necessary to enter the realm of speculation and reasoning by analogy. It is known that plants imbibe water and salts through their root systems and carry these as sap to the leaf structure. There the water comes into contact with carbon dioxide, drawn from the air by respiration, and in the presence of chlorophyll and energy from the sun, a condensation apparently occurs resulting in the giving off of oxygen and the formation of glucose. Possibly the reaction is as follows:

$$H_2O + CO_2 \xrightarrow[\text{energy}]{} HCHO + O_2$$

$$6HCHO \xrightarrow[\text{energy}]{} \underset{\text{glucose}}{C_6H_{12}O_6}$$

The glucose, in solution, passes with the sap down into the cells of the plant where the transformation into cellulose probably takes place.

Hibbert [53] has suggested, in analogy with the known polymerization mechanism of ethylene glycol, that glucose, in an ethylene oxide equilibrium form, loses water and then undergoes polymerization into chains according to the following scheme:

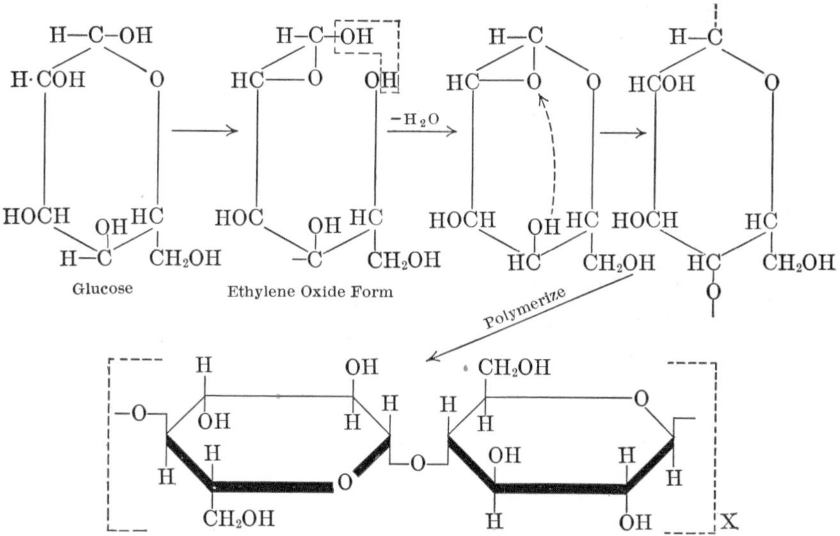

FIG. 5. Hibbert's theory of conversion of glucose to cellulose.

Even though none of the intermediate forms indicated above have been isolated, the mechanism postulated is quite logical and agrees well with known mechanisms, carefully elucidated by Carothers and others [13], in the case of synthetic polymers. The striking similarities between the synthetic polymers of known mechanism and cellulose are so great that it is probable that cellulose is built up by a similar mechanism. The way in which the individual chains are united in order to form the actual fiber and the length of the individual chain must rest on evidence other than chemical.

Molecular Weight. If the length of the individual chain of anhydro-β-glucose units is first considered, the field of molecular weights must be entered. For most organic compounds it is relatively easy to determine molecular weight, since available physical methods give reasonably accurate values. Among these are the cryoscopic methods in which the lowering of the freezing point or rise in the boiling point is measured. The measurement of osmotic pressure can also lead to a value for the molecular weight. All of these methods depend upon the ideal solution laws and are valid providing the molecular weight of the compound is not too great. For example, the osmotic pressure obeys the Van't Hoff equation in the region of low concentrations.

$$P = n/V \cdot RT$$

where P is the osmotic pressure, V is the volume of solution, n is the number of gram mols of the solute, R is the gas constant, and T is the absolute temperature. Since n equals w/M, where the weight of solute is w, and its molecular weight is M, and since c equals w/V is the concentration, the equation may be written as

$$P = RTc/M$$

Examination of this shows that the osmotic pressure is inversely proportional to the molecular weight. If the molecular weight is too large, as in the case of colloids, an extremely small osmotic pressure must be measured. The presence of even a very few ions from electrolytes would develop experimental errors, which would be very large relative to the total pressure measured. However, by adopting special methods it has been found possible to minimize such errors to an extent which permits the use of osmotic pressure determination for the measurement of molecular weight in many cases [106].

Since cellulose is soluble only in solutions of highly concentrated electrolytes, and always gives colloidal solutions, direct measurement of the molecular weight by cryoscopic methods is not very accurate. Cellulose derivatives, such as the acetate or nitrate, are quite soluble in certain organic solvents and therefore the molecular weights may be determined by the usual methods, although the results are never reliable since the solutions are colloidal, the weights very high, and the measurements therefore subject to error.

Possibly the most accurate method for determination of the particle or molecular weight is that of the ultracentrifuge as applied in the colloid range. This method was developed by Svedberg [107], and in it a solution of cellulose, or cellulose derivative, is centrifuged until the boundary between solution and pure solvent no longer changes. At this point an equilibrium has been set up between the centrifugal force acting toward the bottom of the vessel and the force of diffusion acting toward the top, from which the following equation may be derived [73].

$$M = \frac{2RT \ln C_2/C_1}{(1 - VS)x^2(r_2^2 - r_1^2)}$$

where M = molecular weight,
R = gas constant,
V = specific volume of particles,
x = angular velocity of rotation,
S = density of solvent,
C_2 = concentration at distance r_2 from center of rotation,
C_1 = concentration at distance r_1 from center of rotation.

Application of this method to cellulose and its derivatives has led to the values shown in Table 4.

TABLE 4. MOLECULAR WEIGHTS BY ULTRACENTRIFUGE

	Molecular Weight	*Number of Glucose Residues*	*Solvents*	*References*
Cotton	200,000 to 300,000	1,200 to 1,800	Cuoxam	63
Regenerated cellulose	90,000 to 110,000	555 to 680	Cuoxam	63
Acetate	50,000 to 250,000	175 to 360	Acetone	62
Nitrate	100,000 to 160,000	500 to 600	Acetone	62
Ethyl cellulose	125,000	540	Dioxane	62
Methyl cellulose	14,000 to 38,000	....	....	107

From these results it appears that cellulose disperses into a particle in solution in which anywhere between 1000 and 3000 anhydroglucose units are bound together. When the experiment is carried out in the ultracentrifuge it is found that solutions of cellulose do not give a sharp dividing line between solution and solvent; hence the particles do not all have the same molecular weight. Cellulose must be regarded as being made up of a homogeneous series of polymers, chemically the same, but differing in the degree of polymerization, and any weight determined by the above method is an average, or mean particle weight.

Particle Size. Further evidence as to the large particle size of cellulose is obtained by the method of Staudinger [101], who noted that the specific viscosity of solutions of substances of low molecular weight is independent of the molecular weight. On the other hand, the specific viscosity of substances with long chain molecules, such as paraffins and fatty acids, is proportional to the molecular weight of the substance. Based on these observations Staudinger derived an equation relating the molecular weight to the specific viscosity, which should apply to cellulose.

$$\frac{n_{sp}}{c} = K_m M$$

n_{sp} equals specific viscosity. This is the increase in viscosity of a solution compared with the viscosity of the pure solvent and may be written

$$n_{sp} = \frac{n_{solution} - n_{solvent}}{n_{solvent}} = \frac{n_{solution}}{n_{solvent}} - 1 = n_{relative} - 1$$

where c = concentration in fundamental mols per liter. In the case of cellulose $c = \frac{\text{weight per liter}}{162}$.

K_m = a constant for the particular polymeric substance.
M = molecular weight.

Values for the molecular weight of cellulose obtained by Staudinger and Feuerstein [103] and shown in Table 5 also indicate that cellulose is a highly polymerized substance.

TABLE 5. Molecular Weights by Viscosity

	Molecular Weight	*Glucose Units*
Cotton	327,000	2,020
Cotton linters	233,000	1,440
Wood pulp	113,000 to 146,000	700 to 900
Regenerated cellulose	49,000 to 81,000	300 to 500

In spite of the lack of a firm theoretical background the Staudinger method gives results which agree fairly well with those obtained by the centrifuge method and is much easier to carry out.

Other methods for the determination of molecular weights are capable of accuracy only on relatively highly degraded products, but they indicate that even such degraded substances consist of relatively large particles. Among such methods may be mentioned the determination of end groups by the method of Haworth [46], already mentioned, where the amount of 2,3,4,6-tetramethyl glucose is determined after methylation and hydrolysis; the determination of the reducing end group [6]; and the determination of free carboxyl end groups [93].

CELLULOSE A TRUE MOLECULE OR MICELLE

Cellulose Chain Construction. Whenever a large number of units is bound into a polymer there are at least two general ways in which such polymerization may take place. It is possible that in cellulose all 2000 units of the particle are in the form of a single chain 2000 units long and that when dispersion occurs, the colloidal particles are the same as the cellulose molecules. Every atom and every unit is united throughout the whole particle by primary valences. It is possible that the cellulose molecule is a short chain in which the units are bound by primary valences, and that the ultimate particle dispersed in solution is built up of a large number of the short chains held together by secondary valences.

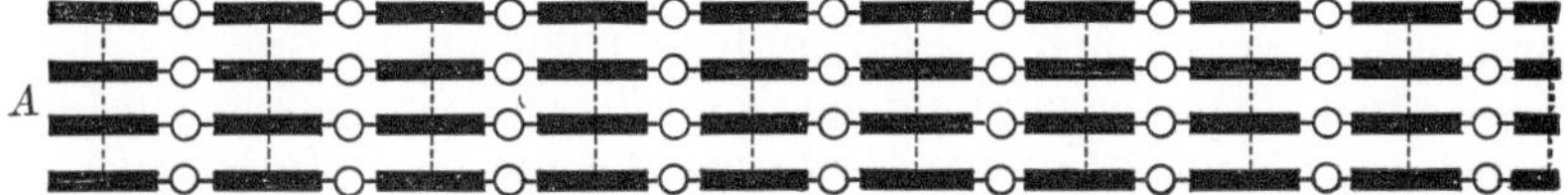

Fig. 6. Representation of structure of cellulose according to long-chain theory.

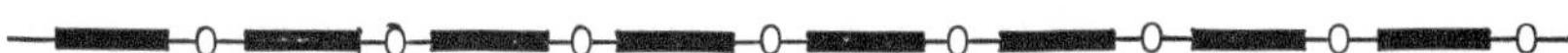

Fig. 7. Representation of single colloid particle of cellulose according to long-chain theory.

The ultimate colloid particle is composed of about 500 units in short chains held together in small bundles to form a micelle. In solid form the micelles are held to each other by tertiary forces, or cementing material. When dispersion occurs it takes place by separating the micelles to give particles of the same number of units as above, but held together by some secondary valences.

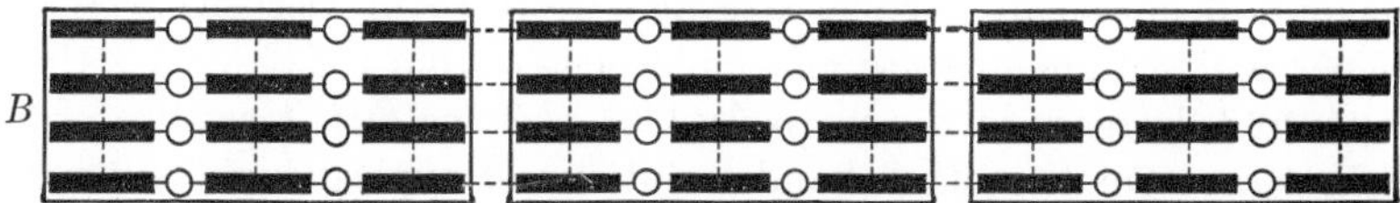

Fig. 8. Representation of structure of cellulose according to micelle theory.

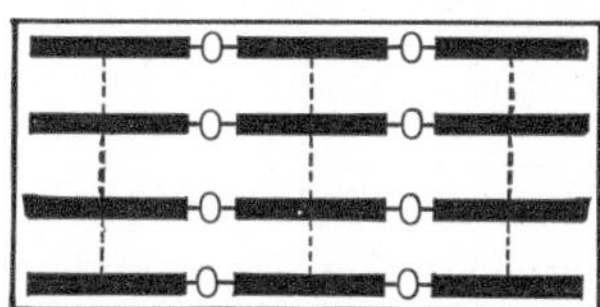

Fig. 9. Representation of single colloid particle of cellulose according to micelle theory.

In Case A, the particle is a *true molecule;* particle weight and molecular weight are the same. In Case B the particle weight is larger than the molecular weight since it consists of several molecules bound together by secondary valence. Since particle A is bound together wholly by primary valences between the glucose residues, its chain length could be reduced only by some reaction, or condition, supplying enough energy to rupture such primary valences. It follows that the viscosity of solutions of cellulose should be unaltered by any changes in conditions short of those capable of rupturing a primary bond, if the first structure is correct. Since particle *B* is held together by secondary valences, any change of condition of a solution containing such particles should reduce the viscosity of the solution provided sufficient energy is imparted to the particles to rupture a secondary valence. A solution of type *B* would require very much less energy for a reduction in viscosity than type *A*. In a discussion of Staudinger's work, Schulz [95] points out four possible ways in which a particle of type *B* could be ruptured with an accompanying decrease in particle weight and viscosity.

First, by varying the solvent a different state of dispersion could be reached for a particle of type *B* but not for *A*. Cellulose acetate gives the same molecular weight when dissolved in acetone, acetophenone, or benzyl alcohol [12]. Dobry [26] found the same result with cellulose nitrate in six different solvents, and it can be concluded from these studies that cellulose and its derivatives are probably of the *A* or *true molecule type.*

Second, molecules which are bound together with secondary valences are very sensitive to changes in temperature since such changes vary the energy content of the particle. If the energy of a particle is increased, it is possible that the secondary valences may be ruptured with an attendant decrease in particle size and decrease in viscosity. When 0.15 per cent sodium stearate solution is heated from 10° to 30° C., there is a tenfold decrease in the viscosity [36], *showing that it must be of the micelle type.* On the other hand, solutions of typical high polymers, among them cellulose and its derivatives, have specific viscosities almost independent of the temperature [102] except for slight variations due to the change in the state of solvation and in the viscosity of the solvent with the temperature. Again cellulose must be considered as a type *A* molecule.

Third, the amount and nature of electrolytes in solution determine the charge on the colloid particle. The stronger the charge, the greater the tendency to split into smaller particles, with a resultant lowering of the viscosity of the solution. Particles of the *B* type would therefore show a varying particle weight depending on the *p*H of the solution, while those of the *A* type would have particle weights independent of the *p*H. Svedberg [107] has investigated many colloids through different *p*H ranges and his results appear to indicate that the particle weights of true chain polymers, such as cellulose, are independent of the *p*H.

Last, type *B* particles, if subjected to a series of chemical changes should, owing to the changed nature of the secondary forces holding the chains together, change their particle weight. On the other hand, *A* type chains should undergo such a series of chemical changes, always provided that the reaction does not rupture 1,4 oxygen bridges between units, without a change in the particle weight. Despite very marked chemical changes in the nature of groups attached to the chain, Staudinger [104] found relatively no change in the particle weight of cellulose which had been converted to a triacetate, then regenerated to cellulose by saponification, and then methylated. Since the chain retained its particle weight through such a severe series of changes, it *is almost conclusive evidence that cellulose must be of the A type* and that the ultimate particle in solution is identical with the molecule.

From the evidence adduced above, cellulose may be considered a straight chain of anhydro-β-glucose units whose molecular weight depends upon the number of units in the chain. This number is not a constant value and so the molecular weight of cellulose is not a constant, but may vary over a very wide range of values. Cellulose must be regarded as a homologous series of polymers ranging in molecular weight from a very low value to one which may run as high as 450,000 or more. The distribution of these molecular weights in a given sample lies about an average value in a manner reminiscent of the Maxwell distribution law [72], and this average value varies depending upon the source and previous history of the sample involved.

PHYSICAL CONSTITUTION OF CELLULOSE

The manner in which the chains of anhydro-β-glucose units, which chemically form cellulose, are held together in order to form the actual microscopic fiber of cellulose is still a matter of controversy among cellulose chemists. There are three main theories, which have been advanced in order to explain the evidence obtained by physical and chemical means. *These are the Chain Theory, the Micelle Theory, and the Particle Theory.* They will be discussed after the available evidence has been presented.

Early investigations on cellulose [80] indicated clearly that cellulose possessed the properties of an anisotropic crystal, which behaved toward X-rays as a three-dimensional grating and thus indicated a certain regularity of internal structure. The first measurement of this regularity was made by Polanyi [87], who gave the size of the "unit cell" of cellulose, in Angstrom units, as:

a. Horizontal axis, 8.65 to 8.75 A.
b. Along fiber axis, 10.25 to 10.35 A.
c. At angle to *a*, 7.8 to 7.9 A.

From measurement of the angles between the planes he assumed the unit to belong to the rhombic-quadratic system, and calculated that four anhydroglucose units would fit in a unit cell. For many years this formed the basis for the concept of the molecule of cellulose as containing only four anhydroglucose units.

Sponsler and Dore [99], using the values for the diameters of the carbon, oxygen, and hydrogen atoms, and the normal interatomic distances between C—C, C—O, C—H, and O—H obtained by Bragg [11], calculated the size of the anhydroglucose units and found that an equivalent of four units fitted into the unit cell and that a chain of two glucose units fitted into the 10.3 A length of the cell. This led to their most important contribution, in the recognition of the fact that the unit cell was simply a "repeat" period along the fiber axis and that the long chains of cellulose extended through many unit cells. No discontinuities existed at the limits of the unit cells and therefore the molecules of cellulose contained many glucose units rather than four only.

Chain Theory. Cellulose chains are bound longitudinally by primary valences and laterally by secondary valences, which accounts for the greater thermal expansion of the fiber in a lateral direction and the greater swelling by solvents in this direction. Since any new groups introduced into the cellulose structure by chemical reaction would be expected to accommodate themselves in the spaces between the chains, the fact that cellulose can be esterified without loss of fiber form may also be explained on the above concept.

Meyer [78] summarized the available evidence from X-ray studies on cellulose and based his model for the cellulose crystal unit on the following data:

a. Each crystal unit is formed by five chains of anhydroglucose units running through the crystal, parallel to the fiber axis. One chain is located at each of the corners of the cell, and one runs through its center. The distances between the various atoms are C—C = 1.54 A; and C—O = 1.45 A.

b. The cell dimension along the *b* axis, parallel to the fiber axis, is 10.3 A and on the basis of the above interatomic distances can accommodate two anhydroglucose units. The dimension of 10.3 A does not represent a discontinuity separating one crystal cell from the next but is probably the result of a repetition of the cellobiose unit along the chains.

c. The cell dimension along the *a* axis represents two parallel chains united by secondary valences between hydroxyl groups. The distance between the hydroxyl groups of two chains in the *ab* plane is 2.6 A. The glucose rings lie very nearly parallel to the *ab* plane and

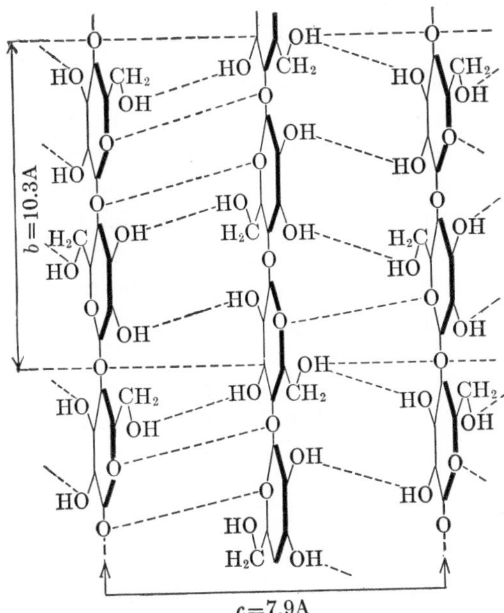

Fig. 10. Manner of combination of cellulose chains along b–c planes.

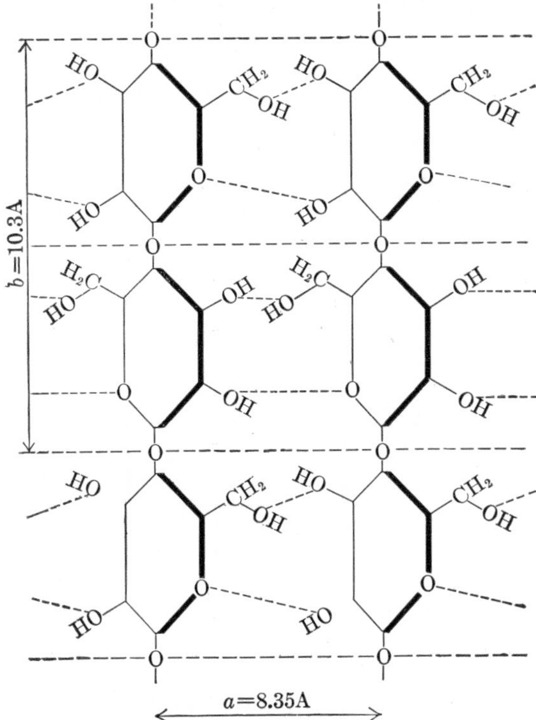

Fig. 11. Manner of combination of cellulose chains along a–b planes.

form a network which extends throughout the whole cellulose structure. This plane and those parallel to it in the fiber structure would be expected to reflect X-rays very strongly, and actual experiment shows a very marked reflection from the *ab* planes.

d. The cell dimension roughly perpendicular to the *ab* planes was found to be 7.9 A in the *c* direction. In this direction there is a chain of glucose units located at the center of the cell whose directional orientation is the reverse of the chains in the adjacent planes. The *ab* planes are at an average distance of 3.95 A from each other. The smallest distance between networks of *ab* planes, 3.1 A, is between the 5-oxygen atom of the first plane and the number 1 carbon atom of the second. The closest approach of two hydroxyl groups in two *ab* planes is 3.8 A. This distance is considerably greater than that for two hydroxyl groups along the *a* direction and therefore indicates that the binding force between *ab* planes is less than that between chains in any one *ab* plane. This is amply confirmed by X-ray studies of cellulose swollen by sodium hydroxide solution, which shows an extension of the lattice in the *c* direction and not in the others [2].

	Unmercerized	*Mercerized*
a	8.35 A	8.1 A
b	10.3	10.3
c	7.9	9.1

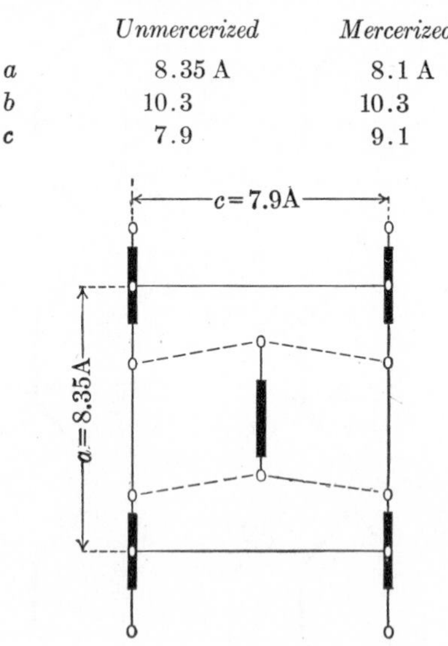

FIG. 12. Manner of combination of cellulose chains along *a–c* planes.

e. The angle between the *ab* planes and *bc* planes in the cell is 84° for the normal cellulose.

The model arrived at by Meyer, which is quite satisfactory for most purposes, may be represented as below.

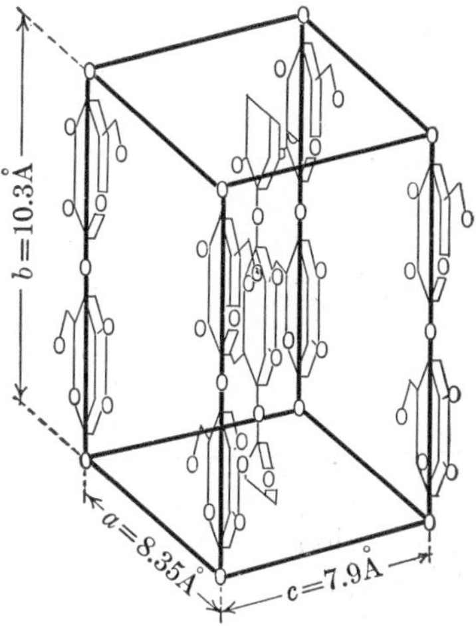

FIG. 13. Cellulose crystal unit according to Meyer. (Angle between faces is 84°.)

The concept of the crystal unit of cellulose as a repeat period occurring in long continuous chains of glucose residues which pass directly through many cells is quite in agreement with most of the available evidence. However, when an attempt is made to describe the manner in which the cells, or chains, are built up into actual macroscopic fibers, a divergence of opinion is found.

The long chains of glucose residues forming the cellulose molecule are held together by secondary valences. Apparently whenever two structures of similar energy exist so that a hydrogen atom can change its allegiance from an atom in one molecule to another atom in a second molecule merely as a result of a shifting of electrons, the two parts will be held together by "resonance" of the hydrogen atom between the two possible positions. Such resonance is common in many hydroxyl compounds such as water, alcohols, and phenols and may be represented as the possible existence of two molecules in two forms.

$$\begin{array}{cc} \mathrm{R} & \mathrm{R} \\ | & | \\ \mathrm{HO} & \mathrm{HO} \end{array} \quad \text{and} \quad \begin{array}{cc} \mathrm{R} & \mathrm{R} \\ | & | \\ \mathrm{HOH} & \mathrm{O} \\ + & - \end{array}$$

In this way the two molecules of ROH are held together by the hydrogen resonance bonding and it is possible to assume that two hydroxyl groups of two adjacent chains of cellulose are held together by a similar mechanism and that such a configuration represents a considerable bonding power. Anything which would interfere with this type of resonance, such as changing the nature of the OH group, or which would diminish the number of such points of union along the chains would permit the chains to move apart to an extent determined by the degree of weakening to which the bonding is subjected.

Micelle Theory With this concept of chain union it is easy to see how the idea of a cellulose fiber as simply a bundle of cellulose chains held together by secondary valences arose. The simple chain theory pictures the fiber as chains of as many as 2000 glucose residues held parallel to each other, and the fiber axis, by the secondary forces between the hydroxyl groups. However, according to this, the chains must be completely oriented throughout the whole bundle, and as a result, the X-ray patterns should show only a crystalline type of reflection. This is not the case since it has been estimated, from such diagrams [49], that only about 75 per cent of the cellulose consists of regularly arranged material and that the remainder is either an amorphous arrangement of cellulose or an amorphous cementitious material deposited in the structure. Early investigators [98] who examined the periodicity shown by the amorphous parts of cellulose concluded that the structure of cellulose which must be postulated to explain the amorphous portions could be similar to rectangular building units called "*micelles*." Each micelle consists of a bundle of 40 to 50 chains of glucose residues, each chain containing 100 to 200 glucose residues, and the micelle is held together by secondary valences acting between the chains of which it is composed. In order to build up the cellulose fiber from such micelles, many of them are assumed to be held together by either amorphous cementing material, or by tertiary forces similar in nature to van der Waals' forces.

Neither view in its simplest form is capable of explaining all of the phenomena associated with cellulose but a slightly modified form of the long chain theory appears to be gaining strength among cellulose chemists. Instead of assuming that the diffuse nature of the X-ray patterns indicates a measure of the crystallite size, it may be assumed that it indicates the appearance of irregularities in the orientation of the long chains which have the same effect on the X-ray diagram as the boundaries of the micelles would have. The structure of the cellulose fiber might then be represented as composed of long chains of glucose residues bound together by secondary valences but with the orientation of the chains only partly approaching perfection and interrupted at intervals by areas of random arrangement produced by the fact that cellulose must be formed in the presence of impurities and under variations in the conditions of formation as a natural process.

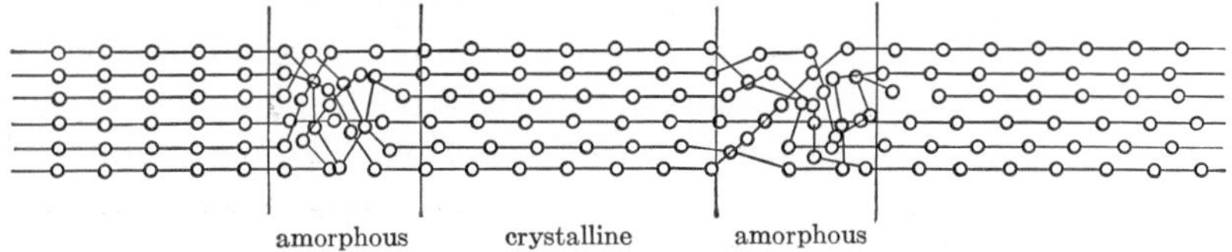

Fig. 14. Chain structure of cellulose showing long chains forming crystalline and amorphous regions.

There is some evidence [64] supporting this view and it is being rather widely accepted in spite of the difficulty of accounting for the X-ray data in a simple manner. The physical properties of the fibers are readily explained on the basis of the chain theory, whereas the micelle theory finds difficulty in explaining such things as the lateral swelling and axial shrinkage, the fact that chains of different length may all be esterified to the same degree, and that a uniform particle size is not obtained on dispersion of cellulose into solution.

Microfibrils. A further extension of the long chain theory [38] so as to explain the wide variation of the physical properties, such as tensile strength, elasticity, swelling, etc., with the source of the fiber has led to the concept that the macroscopic fiber is not one single bundle of chains. It is assumed that many long chains unite to form a submicroscopic bundle in agreement with the long chain theory. Many such chain bundles then unite into a *microfibril,* in which the chain bundles are held together in a roughly elliptical cross-section. There will exist between the chain bundles of the microfibril, a system of very fine capillaries into which only molecular solutions, or pure solvents, are capable of penetrating. In order to build up the macrofiber, many microfibrils are united into a bundle held together partly by cementitious material and partly by forces of a valence nature. Between the microfibrils there would exist capillary spaces much larger than those between the chain bundles and forming an interconnected series of capillaries throughout the macrofiber. Variations in lengths of the individual chains, in size of the chain bundles

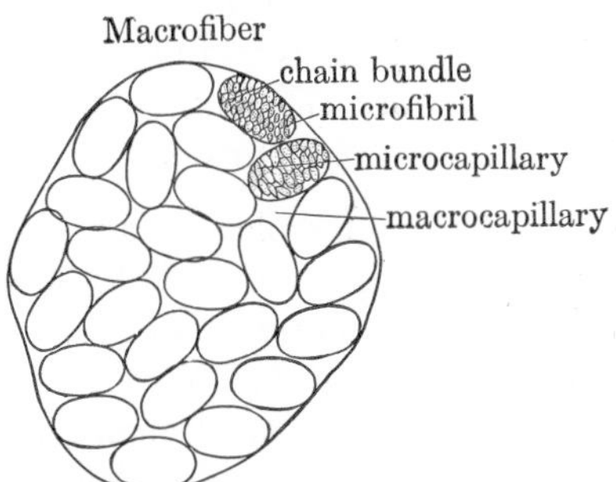

Fig. 15. Cross-section of cellulose fiber structure, showing designation of various parts.

and in the microfibrils would then account for the variations of the physical properties of cellulose from different sources. A cross-section of the structure might be represented as shown in Fig. 15.

This theory also accounts for the production of higher orientation by mechanical means, such as occurs during the stretch spinning of rayon, if it be assumed that regeneration of chains from solution results first in the formation of chain bundles, or of microfibrils. Such aggregates may then be oriented by the mechanical stretch in a manner previously assumed to take place with micelles.

Particle Theory. There is a third theory of the constitution of cellulose fiber which is based upon the work of Farr [31]. It is shown that small, uniform, ellipsoid particles about 0.00015 cm in length were formed in the living plant cell. By end to end aggregation of such particles into single chains, and by the union of such single strands, the microfibril is built up. The microfibrils are held together, as a macrofiber, by a pectinlike cementing material which constitutes about 3 or 4 per cent of the total mass. It is suggested that the particles account for the crystalline properties of cellulose, since they are capable of containing long oriented chains of 2000 or more glucose residues, and that the amorphous material accounts for the colloidal behavior. This theory appears to offer a mechanism for the formation of the macrofibers and seems to be based upon more direct experimental evidence than the previous ones. However, the fundamental concept of cellulose as a long chain structure held together by secondary valences is not altered and the impact of the newer theory on the explanation of the physical properties has not yet been fully worked out.

In this work the long chain theory will be used and the following assumptions will be made.

a. Cellulose molecules are chains of anhydro-β-glucose units which may run as high as 2000 to 3000 in a single chain.

b. All chains are not of the same length but every sample of cellulose contains chains of all sizes from a very low value to a very high value; the largest number of chains will have some average length, depending on the source and treatment of the material.

c. Cellulose molecular chains are oriented into bundles by resonance forces acting between the hydroxyl groups, but such orientation is not perfect since it is broken by areas of disorientation at intervals which depend upon the conditions of formation of the sample.

d. The bundles of cellulose chains are aggregated into microfibrils, again by secondary valences, in such a way as to leave a fine capillary network between the bundles. This fine capillary structure can be penetrated only by pure solvents, or molecular solutions.

e. The microfibrils are united into the macrofiber so as to form a coarse capillary network which can be penetrated by colloidal solutions.

f. The two capillary systems are interconnected to form a very complex structure which plays a large part in the phenomena of absorption and swelling.

ACTION OF REAGENTS ON CELLULOSE

General. When cellulose is brought into contact with various reagents there are several possible effects depending upon the nature of the reagent. It is possible that the reagent may merely penetrate the macrocapillary structure and relax the forces holding the microfibrils together so as to bring about a very limited swelling, or dispersion, of the cellulose fiber. Other reagents may be able to penetrate into the microcapillary spaces, thus causing relaxation of the forces holding the chain bundles and a deeper-seated swelling. Should the reagent be capable of penetrating between the chains themselves and breaking the secondary valences, a very marked swelling may occur which might extend to complete dispersion.

In all cases of penetration of the cellulose structure it is obvious that, with certain reagents, reaction with available hydroxyl groups might take place, or such reactions as hydrolysis or oxidation might occur. Where penetration is limited to the macrocapillary structure, any reaction would be limited to the chains forming the surface of the microfibril. If penetration between the chain bundles takes place, the reagent could bring about a more complete reaction since it could then react with the chains forming the surface of the chain bundles. When the reagent is capable of penetrating between the chains themselves, the reaction should proceed to completion on all the separate chains of the cellulose fiber.

The reactions of cellulose may be roughly classified into three main divisions: (1) those which result in a *swelling, or dispersion,* of the chains of cellulose without a decrease in the average length of the chains, or a change in the chemical nature of the groups on the chain, (2) those which result in a change in the average length of the chains *through degradation,* and (3) those which bring about a complete *change in the hydroxyl groups* into ester, or other groups. It should be recognized that no reactions belong entirely to any one of the above groups but that all reactions partake, to some extent, of all three classes. There are, however, certain typical reactions in each group, and a discussion of these will serve to illustrate the whole class.

Swelling or Dispersion Reactions [84]. One of the best-known effects of reagents on cellulose is the swelling brought about by solutions of sodium hydroxide. This was discovered by Mercer [76] and has been converted into the well-known process for the production of mercerized cotton. When cellulose fiber is immersed in sodium hydroxide of approximately 17.5 per cent concentration, the maximum swelling occurs transverse to the fiber axis and is accompanied by a shrinkage in length. Should the cellulose be a sample which had been degraded during preparation, complete dispersion into solution might take place.

Since sodium hydroxide solutions are capable of penetrating between the microfibrils, the first effect would be a relaxation of the forces holding them together. This would allow a swelling of the fiber and a slippage of the microfibrils, resulting in a readjustment of any longitudinal strain over all of the microfibrils instead of over only a few. The tendency would be to produce a fiber of greater tensile strength and so account for the observed increased strength of a mercerized fiber.

Sodium hydroxide solutions could also penetrate into the microcapillary spaces between the chain bundles and bring about a swelling of the microfibrils and a readjustment of the chain bundles within them. Any further swelling could only take place if the solution could penetrate between the chains themselves and break the secondary valences between the hydroxyl groups. That such penetration does occur is indicated by the degree of swelling, which is too large to be accounted for by any superficial effect, and also by the X-ray patterns of mercerized cellulose which indicate a separation of the chains and a distortion of the lattice. X-ray studies also show that, depending on the concentration of the sodium hydroxide, there is a conversion, to a greater or less degree, of the hydroxyl groups to ONa groups on the chains.

If water alone is used to swell cellulose, it has been found that the X-ray diagram is not altered and it must be concluded that the presence of NaOH is the cause of penetration between the chains. Neale [81] considers that the penetration and swelling of the chain bundles is the result of a Donnan membrane equilibrium. It is assumed that cellulose hydroxyl groups within the bundle membrane react with sodium hydroxide to form a sodium salt to an extent conditioned by the concentration of the alkali. The sodium salt then serves to produce a higher ionic concentration within the bundle than without, and the resultant osmotic pressure causes the introduction of water which distends the cellulose until the osmotic pressure is balanced by the cohesive forces of the remaining resonance bonds between the unchanged hydroxyl groups If the chains should be short, then the unchanged hydroxyl groups might be too small in number to overcome the dispersive force, and the whole structure could disperse into solution, as occurs in the case of a degraded cellulose.

A further effect when cellulose is treated with sodium hydroxide solution is the enhanced activity shown by the structure even after the alkali is completely removed. The absorption of water vapor, of alkalies, or of dyes is increased from 10 to 300 per cent, depending upon the concentration of the alkali used for mercerization. A mere increase of available surface cannot explain this large increase, particularly since the specific volume of a mercerized cellulose is very nearly the same as that of an unmercerized. It has been suggested that the presence of the highly charged ions of the alkali is able to exert a stronger attraction on the hydroxyl groups than can other hydroxyl groups and that therefore hydroxyl groups normally occupied in holding the chains together are swung out to the surface of the bundle by such attraction. On removal of the ions, not all of the hydroxyl groups return to their original inner positions, and the result is a higher concentration of hydroxyl groups on the surface of the chain bundles than normal and a resultant greater reactivity.

All alkalies show the same power of dispersion as sodium hydroxide except that the degree of their activity varies markedly with the order of the supposed hydration of their ions [17].

$$LiOH > NaOH > KOH > RbOH > CsOH$$

Strong organic bases of the tetraalkyl ammonium hydroxide [66] type produce marked swelling, which appears to be a function of the molecular volume of the base. Tetramethyl ammonium hydroxide mercerizes cotton, whereas the same concentration of tetraethyl ammonium hydroxide brings about complete dispersion.

The power of swelling cellulose and increasing its reactivity is not confined to alkaline substances, since solutions of many inorganic salts [59] are capable of doing so in nearly direct ratio to the supposed degree of hydration of their ions. Herzog and Beck [50] give the dispersive power of the ions in the following order:

$$NH_4 < K < Na < Li; \; Ba < Sr < Ca; \; \tfrac{1}{2}SO_4 < Cl < Br < I < CNS$$

Williams [119] advanced the theory that solutions of salts, particularly aqueous thiocyanates, could disperse cellulose completely only if the boiling point of the solution is between 135° and 150° C.; if the salt has a positive heat of dilution which is not more than 3500 cal; and if the viscosity of the solution is at least 3.3 times that of water. In order to possess such properties, it is obvious that the salt must have the power of absorbing water of hydration, but not so great an attraction for such water as to prevent its migration to the hydroxyl groups of cellulose. The boiling point fixes the quantitative relation between the salt and water at the optimum hydration. The viscosity indicates that the active swelling agent is the hydrated salt complex. Apparently the hydrated salt complex penetrates through the capillary structure into the chains where the water is transferred from the hydrate to the hydroxyl groups of the cellulose and so ruptures the hydrogen bonding as to bring about dispersion.

Zinc chloride solutions, in sufficient concentration, are also capable of dispersing, or swelling, cellulose, and considerable industrial use is made of such solutions in parchmentizing and in textile effects. Many other salts [21] bring about a partial dispersion although they have little industrial application.

A study of the swelling action of acids and their solutions is complicated by the fact that a very marked degrading action usually accompanies the swelling. In sulfuric acid [5] swelling begins when the concentration is above 50 per cent and solution occurs only in concentrations above 60 per cent. From such solutions it is impossible to recover the cellulose unchanged in nature, since degradation into products of low molecular weight takes place as a function of the time of contact. Very short contact time converts the cellulose into a swollen gel which, upon removal of the acid, reverts to a more or less transparent, hornlike substance called "amyloid." If this process is applied to paper, or fabric, a film of such amyloid is deposited on the surface to give a parchment effect. Much use is made of this treatment in the production of parchment paper, and in the production of fabric finishes which range from linenlike, through transparent, to a woollike appearance.

Concentrated hydrochloric acid [88] acts in a manner very similar to that of sulfuric acid, since it dissolves cellulose at a concentration greater than 39 per cent. Great degradation accompanies such dissolution. Nitric acid, phosphoric acid, and many other acids can also swell, and dissolve, cellulose at the proper concentrations.

Among the more important reagents bringing about swelling and ultimate dispersion of cellulose is a solution of copper oxide, or hydroxide, in aqueous ammonia. This reagent, first discovered by Schweitzer [96], has been developed into the cuprammonium process for the spinning of rayon and is considered in detail in the section of the text devoted to that process. Apparently the dispersion of cellulose by this reagent is due to the formation of a complex copper ammonia salt, $Cu(NH_3)_4(OH)_2$, which is stable only in the presence of excess ammonia. The solution of the salt penetrates into the microfibrils via the microcapillary structure and then reacts with some of the hydroxyl groups of the chains to set up a membrane equilibrium in the same way that sodium hydroxide does. Cuprammonium solutions are so easily prepared in a standard manner, and bring about relatively so small a degree of degradation, that they have been adopted for the standard determination of cellulose viscosity [16].

It should be recognized that in all of the above dispersion effects, the swelling of cellulose is accompanied, in part, by conversion of hydroxyl groups to other groups. Such conversion may be only temporary, but it plays a major role in the degree of swelling obtained. In many cases where the swelling is at all marked, there is also a simultaneous shortening of the cellulose chains, or degradation, to an extent which depends upon the nature of the reagent used. Accompanying the distortion of the cellulose lattice produced by swelling is an increased absorptive capacity and an increased reactivity probably due to the increased availability of hydroxyl groups.

Degradation Reactions. Whenever cellulose is brought into contact with reagents capable of penetrating it, the swelling so produced is usually accompanied by reactions which can alter the nature of the hydroxyl groups, or which are able to shorten the chains. Leaving the reactions which alter the hydroxyl groups for later consideration, it is found that degradation reactions are usually of two main types—hydrolysis and oxidation.

Whenever cellulose is brought into contact with acids or, more particularly, with their dilute solutions, the properties of the fiber are markedly altered. The name *hydrocellulose* was originally given to the product with the idea that a new derivative of cellulose is formed by the union of cellulose and water from the solution. The degree of modification of the properties depends on the time of contact, temperature, and concentrations employed, and is largely manifested by a decrease in the tensile strength, a decrease in the viscosity, and an increase in the reducing power of the cellulose material. The change in properties as a result of acid attack is so marked that hydrocellulose is defined in modern technology as "any preparation of cellulose (other than esters) the properties of which have been altered to a greater, or less, extent by the action of acids but in which the cellulose still retains its fiber structure" [74].

Cellulose, by virtue of its long chains of glucose residues, resists rupture of its fiber largely owing to the many secondary valence linkages between the chains. The longer the chains the more such secondary valences there are available to resist a strain applied to the structure and the greater the tensile strength. If any reaction reduces the length of the chains, there must be a corresponding reduction in the force required to pull them apart, and a reduction in the tensile strength takes place. The two situations may be represented as shown in Fig. 16.

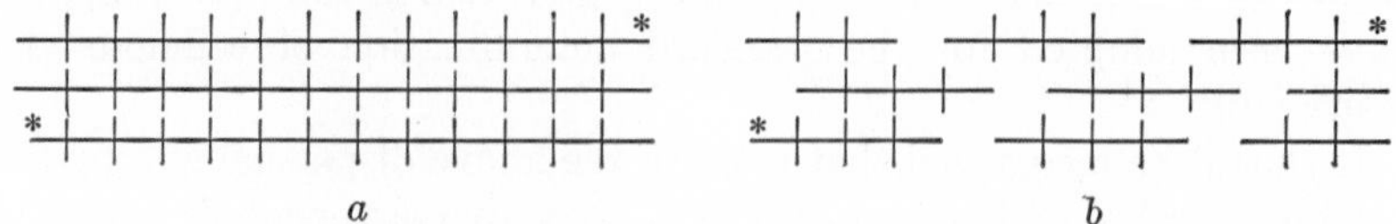

Fig. 16. Diagram showing effect of chain length on physical properties of cellulose.

In both figures the horizontal lines represent the chains. In *a* they are long and in *b* they are short. In both cases the short cross lines represent secondary valences. In *a* many secondary valences must be overcome before the starred ends of the structure can be pulled apart. In *b* the starred ends could be pulled from the structure by rupturing only relatively few secondary links and therefore a short chain should have only a fraction of the tensile strength of a long chain structure.

If reference is made to the chemical structure of a cellulose chain (Fig. 3) it may be seen that only one latent aldehyde group at the end of the chain (that on the number 1 carbon atom of the end unit) is capable of reverting readily to a true aldehyde group and so having reducing properties. A long chain would then have a reducing power corresponding to one aldehyde group per single chain. For example, if the chain had 2000 glucose units, then it would have one reducing aldehyde group per 2000 units. If the chain length were only 1000 glucose residues then the reducing power would be one aldehyde group per 1000

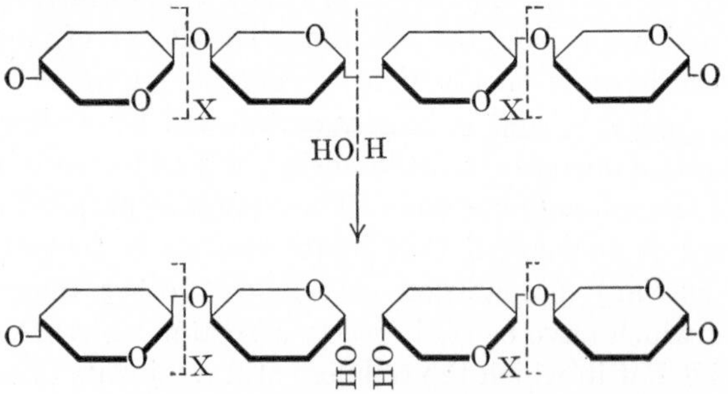

Fig. 17. Hydrolysis of cellulose.

units, or roughly double that of the first chain. It follows tnat with decrease in chain length the reducing power of the cellulosic material must rise to a maximum which may be assumed to correspond with that of glucose itself. This direct dependence of the reducing power on the chain length has led to the use of reducing power as a measure of the degree of degradation in the form copper number [16]. The copper number is defined as the grams of copper reduced from Fehling solution by 100 grams of the cellulose sample.

When acids react with cellulose a decrease in chain length is brought about by the hydrolysis of the 1,4 oxygen bridges between the glucose units, and such rupture forms an aldehyde group capable of reducing copper.

The reduction in viscosity of cellulose material by acid attack can also be readily explained by reduction in chain length owing to hydrolysis. If the viscosity is assumed, as in Staudinger viscosity law, to be largely due to the length of the chain unit in solution, it is obvious that the shorter the length of the chain the lower the viscosity of the solution.

A further effect of conversion to hydrocellulose is the increased solubility of the cellulose in solutions of sodium hydroxide. In shorter chain structures there are fewer hydroxyl bonds to bind the chains together, and in such cases the dispersion action of alkaline solutions already discussed may be great enough to bring about complete solution. The shorter chains of cellulose present in a sample may then dissolve and be removed by alkaline treatment. Whenever, therefore, the chains are shortened by hydrolytic attack an increased solubility in alkali should follow.

The various changes in properties of cellulose subjected to acid action are so related to each other that a common fundamental cause must underlie each. Whenever the viscosity of a cellulose sample is reduced by the acid action it is accompanied by a corresponding decrease in the tensile strength and a rise in the reducing power regardless of the conditions of the acid treatment. Such regularities appear in the curves [8]

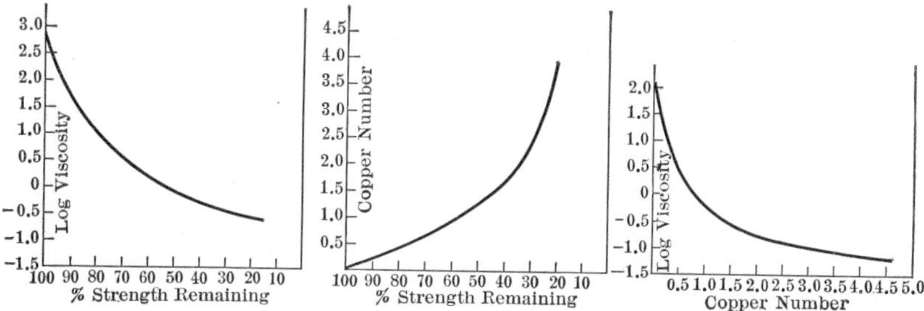

FIG. 18. Effect of hydrolysis on properties of cellulose.

shown in Fig. 18. The relation between the reducing power and viscosity is so regular that an equation may be used to define it.

$$NV^2 = 2.6$$

where N is the copper number and V is the logarithm of the relative viscosity. Such regularity may be explained only on the basis of a common cause, which is readily seen to be the reduction in the length of cellulose chains owing to hydrolysis by the acids.

As the acid degradation proceeds the properties of the cellulose change progressively until the material loses its fiber form and eventually approaches the properties of glucose, which is recognized as the end product of hydrolysis of cellulose. The changes in properties are in agreement with those found by Staudinger [105] in his study of the relation between physical properties and the chain length of cellulose. It may then be concluded that the conversion of cellulose into "hydrocellulose" must be a swelling, or dispersion, of the cellulose chains by penetration of the aqueous reagent between them, followed by an acid hydrolysis of the 1,4 oxygen bridges at random intervals along the chain. The extent of swelling and of hydrolysis is determined by the type of reagent and the conditions of its reaction.

It has been long recognized that cellulose is readily "tendered" when brought into contact with reagents of an oxidizing nature, and the name *oxycellulose* is given to a cellulosic material which has been acted upon by oxidizing agents but which still retains its fiber form. The ultimate products of oxidation are obviously carbon dioxide and water, so that oxycellulose represents an early stage in the process. If the reaction is allowed to proceed slowly, it is possible to study the changes in the properties of cellulose brought about by the oxidation. There is always a progressive loss of strength, a decrease in viscosity, a marked increase of absorptive power toward dyes, and an increase in copper number. Such changes are apparently dependent upon the time of attack and the nature of the reagent employed.

Examination of the products of oxidation has indicated that depending on the conditions of the reaction it is possible to produce two extreme types of oxycellulose [10]. One of these has markedly increased aldehydic properties shown by a high copper number, and the other has enhanced acidic properties but low reducing power. The increase in acidic nature is shown by an increased affinity for methylene blue. In each type of oxycellulose the progressive action of the reagent results in a regular increase in the copper number and methylene blue absorption along with a simultaneous decrease in the viscosity and in tensile strength and increase in solubility in alkali.

The type of oxycellulose depends on the nature of the oxidizing agent and the conditions under which it is used. In Fig. 19 curves are shown which give the effect of variation in *p*H on the oxidation of cellulose with hypochlorite solution [9]. From these it can be seen that acid oxidation favors the high reducing type, whereas the acidic type is favored by alkaline conditions.

Investigation of the action of potassium permanganate [27], of chromic acid [25], and of periodic acid [23] has thrown some light on the chemical

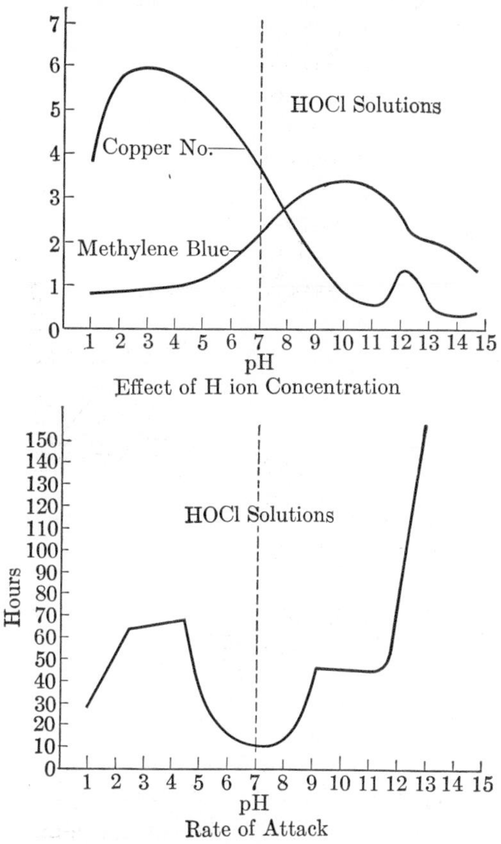

FIG. 19. Effect of *p*H on oxidation of cellulose.

changes involved in the formation of oxycellulose. In the case of periodic acid, Jackson and Hudson and others [56] were able to show that a glucose residue was broken between the two and three carbon with the formation of two aldehyde groups. Such a reaction would account for the high reducing type of oxycellulose and further oxidation could readily convert the aldehyde groups to carboxyl and so account for the acidic type. As shown by Evans and others [29] the oxygen bridge between the four carbon of the oxidized unit and the one carbon of the adjacent unit is very like the linkage occurring in the two glucosidoerythrose. Such a bridge is extremely sensitive to hydrolysis and might lead to rupture of the cellulose chain at the point of oxidative attack. It is apparent that such breakage of the chain must take place in order to account for the observed decrease in viscosity and strength. Further examination of the action of periodic acid on cellulose has shown that this reagent is able to disperse and attack the crystalline portion of the cellulose fiber [24]. Chromic acid, however, appears to attack only the amorphous portions of the fiber structure.

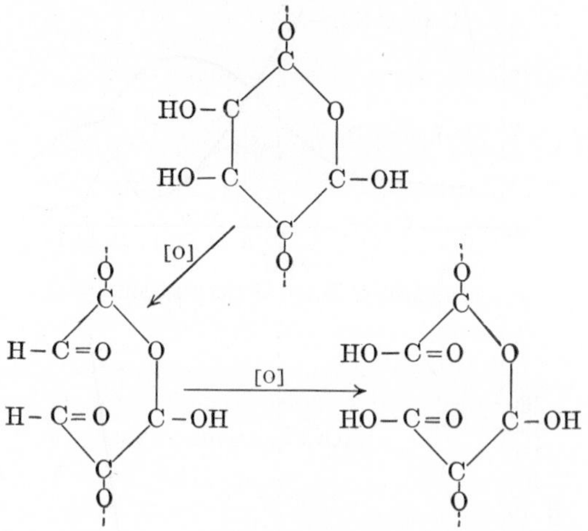

FIG. 20. Oxidation of cellulose, with formation of aldehydic and acid forms of oxycellulose.

Transformation of Hydroxyl Groups. Whenever hydroxyl groups of cellulose are changed into some other chemical grouping, the type of reaction involved is that of a normal organic alcohol and therefore such reactions depend upon the alcoholic nature of the hydroxyl groups of cellulose. Cellulose should then be capable of undergoing esterification, etherification, or xanthation. However, in the case of cellulose, all of the hydroxyl groups are not readily available for reaction, as in the case of ordinary alcohols, since many of them are bound by secondary valences to other hydroxyl groups of other chains. Any typical alcoholic reaction of cellulose can therefore only proceed to a degree, and at a rate, depending upon the availability of the hydroxyl groups. Any reagent not able to penetrate between the separate chains is not able to bring about a complete conversion but is limited by the degree of penetration. Since the ease of penetration of cellulose is increased when cellulose is swollen, those reagents react best which are able to swell cellulose as well as to react readily with hydroxyl groups. It is possible in many cases to combine a swelling agent for cellulose with the hydroxyl active reagent so as to bring about a swelling of the cellulose by the swelling agent which permits the entrance of the converting agent into the structure and a completion of the reaction. In most of the industrial processes for preparing cellulose derivatives, the cellulose is either first swollen by a pretreatment or is subjected to the combined action of swelling agent and reactant.

CELLULOSE ESTERS [1]

The typical alcoholic reaction whereby the hydrogen of the hydroxyl group of an alcohol and the available hydroxyl group of an acid form water and an ester is a characteristic reaction of cellulose also. However, the reaction of the hydroxyl groups of cellulose is impeded by the need of swelling and penetration, so that in many cases the conversion of all three hydroxyl groups of the glucose units is incomplete. Since the hydroxyl groups on the cellulose chains react completely at random, it is possible to get an infinite number of degrees of esterification up to a maximum of three ester groups per glucose unit. This maximum degree of esterification is rarely attained since, in the last analysis, the esterification reaction must be regarded as an equilibrium reaction which goes to an equilibrium condition, and never to completion except under extremely vigorous conditions. Both the availability of the hydroxyl groups and the esterification equilibrium are controlling factors in the degree of esterification.

Whenever a hydroxyl group is converted to an ester group the resonance bond with another hydroxyl group is altered in nature. When this alteration extends to a large enough number of such hydrogen bonds, the remaining bonds can no longer resist the dispersing effect of certain solvents and the ester becomes soluble in such solvents [100]. The completely insoluble cellulose becomes soluble in organic solvents, and the degree of esterification largely determines the solubility in the various solvents [18].

Cellulose Nitrates [122]. Cellulose nitrates, which were first prepared by Schönbein, have come to occupy an extremely important place in industry. They may be prepared by the action of concentrated nitric acid on cellulose since, as has already been shown, that acid is capable of penetrating into the chains of cellulose and acting directly on the hydroxyl groups. However, the reaction between cellulose and nitric acid soon reaches an equilibrium and the degree of nitration obtained is low.

$$\text{Cell. OH} + \text{HO}\cdot\text{NO}_2 = \text{Cell. O}\cdot\text{NO}_2 + \text{H}_2\text{O}$$

For every hydroxyl group esterified there is formed one mol of water and it is apparent that the presence of this water would largely influence the equilibrium. It has been shown [69] that the percentage of nitrogen in the product can range from a low of 6.5 per cent when 28.4 per cent of water is present to 13.65 per cent N when only 5.6 per cent of water is in the reaction mixture. It is obvious then that the degree of nitration may be largely controlled by adjusting the water content of the nitrating mixture. This is usually accomplished by introducing concentrated sulfuric acid as a dehydrating, and swelling, agent, which combines with the liberated water as soon as it forms to give inactive hydrates. In this way the equilibrium may be shifted toward the right and a cellulose nitrate of a high degree of nitration obtained.

Since the solubility of the nitrate varies with the degree of nitration, it is possible to prepare a nitrate of any desired solubility by controlling the degree of esterification through the amount of water in the reaction mixture. The relation between solubility and nitrogen content is given below [113].

TABLE 6. Solubility of Cellulose Nitrates, Per Cent

Nitrogen	*Acetone or Ethyl Acetate*	*Ether Alcohol*	*Ethyl Alcohol*
13.4 to 13.1	95 to 100	Insol.	Insol.
13.1 to 12.8	95 to 100	<30	Insol.
12.8 to 12.5	95 to 100	50 to 100	<10
12.5 to 12.0	95 to 100	95 to 100	<50
12.0 to 11.0	95 to 100	90 to 100	to 100
11.0 to 10.0	95 to 100	80 to 100	<50
10.0 to 9.0	30 to 90	30 to 90	Insol.
9.0 to 7.0	<30	<30	Insol.
7.0 to 3.0	Insol.	Insol.	Insol.

It can be seen that up to 7 per cent nitrogen the ester is insoluble in any of the above solvents; up to 9 per cent its solubility is very slight; above 10 per cent the solubility in acetone is complete but in ether alcohol it reaches a maximum at 12.5 percent and then decreases. The solubility in alcohol alone is never very great but its greatest range is between 11 and 12 per cent. It has become customary to classify the nitrates according to their solubility in ether alcohol solvent whereby "gun cotton" represents the nitrates practically insoluble in the mixed solvent and with a nitrogen content higher than 12.8 per cent. "Collodion" is defined as the group of nitrates showing complete solubility in the mixed solvent and having a nitrogen content of 11 to 12.5 per cent. "Celluloid" nitrates of less than 11 per cent but more than 10 per cent are those suitable for compounding with camphor, or other plasticizers, for use as a plastic. A theoretical nitrogen content of 14.2 per cent corresponds to complete nitration of all of the hydroxyl groups of cellulose but is only approached when very vigorous dehydrating agents are used in conjunction with nitric acid.

Attempts have been made to substitute phosphoric acid [7] for sulfuric acid in the nitrating mixture. Nitrates can be readily obtained but the process is accompanied by such strong dispersive action that the fiber form is lost. The phosphoric acid method appears to bring about a nitration with less degradation than with sulfuric acid. Acetic anhydride and acetic acid may be mixed with nitric acid to produce cellulose nitrates [112] which may be easily stabilized. High nitrogen contents are obtained when nitric acid and P_2O_5 are allowed to act on cellulose [65].

Esters of Other Inorganic Acids. Cellulose forms a series of esters with sulfuric acid under the proper conditions [111] corresponding in sulfur content to the series found in the nitrate. By direct action of sulfuric acid, the disulfate is the highest product obtained and appears to consist of a highly degraded material. When cellulose is treated with SO_3, either as a gas or in CS_2 solution, a potassium salt of the trisulfate may be isolated in which the cellulose is apparently highly degraded, since saponification does not regenerate cellulose but gives sugars. Chlorosulfonic acid in pyridine gives a cellulose sulfate whose barium salt may be isolated, and from which a cellulose can be regenerated in only a slightly degraded form. In general, the degradation during esterification does not proceed very far unless the degree of esterification is high.

Many methods [108] have been devised for the formation of cellulose phosphates, but the knowledge available about the esters is extremely limited and as yet no industrial use has developed for them.

In addition to the esters already described, the literature contains references to the sulfide [86]; alkylated carbonic [51]; thionyl, phosphoryl, and sulfuryl esters [42].

Cellulose Formate. Cellulose reacts directly with formic acid in the presence of catalysts such as HCl, H_2SO_4, and $ZnCl_2$ to give formates. Apparently the function of the catalyst is to bring about an opening up of the cellulose chain structure so as to make the hydroxyl groups available for reaction rather than to remove the water from the reaction mixture. A dispersed cellulose will be esterified with formic acid alone but a native, or undispersed, cellulose requires the presence of a swelling agent before reaction [37]. The conversion is never complete since the theoretical formate content of a triester is 56.1 per cent but the highest degree obtained by special treatment is only about 50 per cent [114].

When the diformate is formed it is found to slowly decompose in the atmosphere with a decrease in formate content to about 11 per cent. The formates are soluble in pyridine and formic acid but are insoluble in most usual organic solvents. An acetone soluble formate can be prepared [14] by special treatment of the cellulose with formic acid in the presence of chloracetic anhydride.

Cellulose Acetate [94]. Probably the most important organic ester of cellulose is the acetate, since it forms the basis of a rayon industry and has also entered the field of plastics under many different trade names. The reaction producing the acetate is a typical esterification reaction since it involves the conversion of the hydroxyl groups of cellulose into acetyl groups through an equilibrium reaction which is shifted toward completion by the presence of dehydrating catalysts. The esterification is also governed by the rate of diffusion of the reagent into the cellulose structure and conditions which bring about a swelling cause a more rapid progress of the reaction.

In general, cellulose acetate is prepared by treating cellulose with a mixture of acetic acid, acetic anhydride, and concentrated sulfuric acid as a catalyst [28]. After a short period, at low temperature to avoid degradation, the cellulose dissolves completely and may be precipitated by pouring into water. After washing, the "primary" acetate is obtained as a white, fibrous powder which is soluble in chloroform, acetic acid, and pyridine, but insoluble in acetone. Films and filaments formed from solutions of the primary acetate are quite brittle and generally unsatisfactory. It was not until methods of converting the primary acetate to a "secondary" form were found [79] that cellulose acetate became of industrial importance. Such conversion consists partly in hydrolyzing the primary acetate with dilute mineral acids so as to produce an acetyl content in the range of 35.8 per cent to 41.5 per cent, in which range the material is soluble in acetone. Along with the adjustment of the acetyl content, the hydrolytic action appears to degrade the very long chains down to an average size, and to dissolve out any very short chains present. The secondary acetate therefore is not only acetone soluble, but consists of a more nearly uniform chain distribution than in the primary form. This uniformity of chain size permits the formation of films and filaments of desirable properties.

Other Organic Esters [116]. Other esters of cellulose with organic acids have been prepared according to the general methods which apply. When the propionic ester [118] is formed the same method may be used as for the acetate. The higher fatty acids, however, require generally the use of the acid chloride instead of the anhydride [70]. Another method which serves to produce esters of the higher fatty acids, and of aromatic acids, is the use of chloracetic anhydride as an impeller [15], causing esterification by acids which had been previously considered inactive. Among the esters which have been prepared, and investigated, are those of all the saturated fatty acids up to the stearate. With increasing length of carbon chain in the esterifying acid, the dependence of the viscosity of solutions on the size of the particle decreases [32*a*]. In the higher esters the solubility appears to be determined largely by the nature of the esterifying group, and the esters are soluble in solvents in which the lower esters are insoluble. The tensile strength of the esters decreases and the extensibility increases with increasing length of the acid chain.

Esters of the various hydroxy acids have been prepared [54] as have those of dicarboxylic acids [71], carbamates [48], and unsaturated fatty acids [32], benzoates [3], furoates [61], naphthenates [60], phthalates [83], cinnamates [33], and many others.

It is possible to partly esterify cellulose with one acid and then complete the esterification with a second acid so as to form "mixed" esters [41]. Inorganic esters such as the nitrate may be prepared having an acetic acid content as high as 32.3 per cent and a nitrogen content of 13.7 per cent. Such esters can be made by the simultaneous action of the nitrating and esterifying reagents under the proper conditions. Mixed organic esters can be prepared by the simultaneous action of a mixture of anhydrides and chlorides of the acids to be introduced. Another method for preparing mixed esters consists in treating an organic ester with another organic acid whose ionization constant is higher than the original esterifying acid [117].

Among the more important esters of cellulose must be classed the cellulose ester of dithiocarbonic acid whose sodium salt forms the cellulose xanthate which, in solution, is the "*viscose*" from which viscose rayon is spun. The existence of a definite cellulose dithiocarbonate, under the industrial conditions for the manufacture of viscose, has not been completely proved but there exists little doubt that at least some of the available hydroxyl groups have been converted to xanthate groups by the action of caustic soda and carbon disulfide on cellulose [47] according to the following reaction:

$$\text{Cell. OH} + \text{NaOH} = \text{Cell. ONa} + H_2O$$

$$\text{Cell. ONa} + C_2S = \text{Cell. O}\cdot CS_2Na$$

The industrial development of this compound, which has been enormous, is discussed more fully in another section of this text.

CELLULOSE ETHERS [4]

Cellulose, by virtue of its alcoholic properties, is able to form ethers with alcohols, or alcohol derivatives, by two general methods; first, the action of esters of inorganic acids, such as alkyl halides, or sulfates, directly on cellulose, and second, by converting the cellulose to soda cellulose and then reacting thereon with alkyl halides, or sulfates. These general methods also serve to form the aryl ethers of cellulose.

$$\text{Cell. OH} + CH_3Cl \rightarrow \text{Cell. OCH}_3 + HCl$$

$$\text{Cell. ONa} + CH_3Cl \rightarrow \text{Cell. OCH}_3 + NaCl$$

One of the great technical advantages of ethers is their great stability toward hydrolysis by either acid or alkaline solutions, a property not shared by the cellulose esters. This difference might be predicted from the known differences in properties of esters and ethers in general.

Methyl cellulose and ethyl cellulose are prepared by the same methods [68], generally by the action of the alkyl sulfate, or chloride, on soda cellulose. When the chlorides are used, the reaction is carried out in an autoclave at temperatures between zero and 25° C. for the methyl ether, and 70° to 80° C. for the ethyl.

The solubility of both ethers is a function of the degree of etherification, since when the methoxy content is above 32 per cent, or higher than the dimethyl ether, the material is soluble in organic solvents and insoluble in water. Methoxy content of 22 to 26 per cent gives an ether soluble in water, whereas ethers with about 5 per cent methoxyl are soluble only in 5 to 12 per cent NaOH solutions. The same variation in solubility is noted in the case of the ethyl ethers. Five per cent ethoxy gives ethers soluble only in alkalies, 27 per cent ethoxy content ethers are soluble in water, and those with more than 40 to 48 per cent are soluble in a wide range of organic solvents. Complete etherification in the case of methyl cellulose would correspond to 45.58 per cent methoxyl, and in the case of the ethyl ether to 54.87 per cent ethoxyl. Commercially no attempt is made to obtain the triethers since they are obtained only with great difficulty and the lower degrees of etherification possess the more desirable properties from an industrial point of view.

A very large number of cellulose ethers have been prepared and their properties studied; the reader is referred to the literature.

An exception to the usual resistance of cellulose ethers to hydrolysis is found in cellulose methylene ether, which results from the action of formaldehyde on cellulose. Such ethers are in general stable in alkali but are readily hydrolyzed by acids. When cellulose is treated with formaldehyde in the presence of sulfuric acid, or when soda cellulose is acted upon by methylene sulfate [40], a product is obtained which may contain as high as 17 per cent of combined formaldehyde. The chief interest of this ether lies in the fact that it can be made in situ on the fiber and the conversion of some of the hydroxyl groups of the cellulose tends to increase the resistance of the fiber to creasing, to increase the wet strength, and to increase the elasticity of the filaments. Water-repellent and crease-resistant fibers are being made by this process.

In addition to the simple ethers of cellulose it is also possible to prepare mixed ethers [121] in which two or more different alcoholic groups have been introduced into the cellulose chains to form a distinct compound. Profound modification in the properties of the ethers can be obtained in this way. The methods for preparing such ethers are the general ones and apply to alkyl or aryl ethers alike.

If cellulose can be partly etherified, leaving one or more hydroxyl groups still available for reaction, it is possible to esterify one or more of the remaining hydroxyls and so obtain a mixed ether-ester [71] whose properties are generally the resultant of the effects of the substituent groups. The reverse process by which a partial ester of cellulose is etherified usually cannot be carried out since the ester group cannot resist the hydrolyzing action of the etherifying reagents and so is lost.

NITROGENOUS DERIVATIVES

Many attempts have been made to introduce nitrogen into the molecule of cellulose in the hope of influencing the affinity of the structure for certain dyes. If cellulose is allowed to react with *p*-toluene sulfochloride, a toluene sulfonic acid ester of cellulose results.

$$\text{Cell. OH} + \text{Cl}\cdot\text{O}_2\text{S}\cdot\text{C}_6\text{H}_4\cdot\text{CH}_3 = \text{Cell. O}\cdot\text{O}_2\text{S}\cdot\text{C}_6\text{H}_4\cdot\text{CH}_3 + \text{HCl}$$

It was found [57] that such esters will decompose in the presence of ammonia and primary and secondary amines to give a cellulose in which some of the hydroxyl groups are changed to amino groups.

$$\text{Cell. O}\cdot\text{O}_2\text{S}\cdot\text{C}_6\text{H}_4\cdot\text{CH}_3 + \text{NH}_2\cdot\text{H} = \text{Cell. NH}_2 + \text{HO}_3\text{S}\cdot\text{C}_6\text{H}_4\cdot\text{CH}_3$$

In this way 0.7 to 0.8 per cent of amino nitrogen could be introduced into the cellulose, which is sufficient to profoundly affect the dyeing properties. The product contains about 3 per cent of sulfur and is therefore not a pure amino derivative.

By the direct action of sodium, or sodium amide, in liquid ammonia on cellulose nitrate [92], a cellulose amine may be prepared in which amino nitrogen is present to the extent of 8.3 per cent. The product is a brown amorphous powder which is very soluble in water.

Nitrogen [85] is usually introduced in industry by (*a*) esterifying, or etherifying, with nitrogenous acids or alcohol derivatives, (*b*) esterifying, or etherifying, with reagents containing nitro groups, which may then be reduced to amines, (*c*) using halogen-containing reagents and then converting the halogen groups to the amino, or (*d*) by introducing ether, or ester, groups containing nitrile groups which can readily be converted to amines.

If the sodium salt of cellulose dithiocarbonic acid, or viscose, reacts with sodium chloracetate [67], cellulose xanthacetic acid is formed.

$$\text{Cell. O}\cdot\text{CS}_2\cdot\text{Na} + \text{Cl}\cdot\text{CH}_2\cdot\text{COONa} = \text{Cell. O}\cdot\text{CS}_2\cdot\text{CH}_2\cdot\text{COONa} + \text{NaCl}$$

On treatment of this with a primary or secondary amine a cellulose thiourethane is formed.

$$\text{Cell. O}\cdot\text{CS}_2\cdot\text{CH}_2\cdot\text{COONa}+\text{H}_2\text{N}\cdot\text{C}_6\text{H}_5=\text{Cell. OCS}\cdot\text{NH}\cdot\text{C}_6\text{H}_5+\text{HS}\cdot\text{CH}_2\cdot\text{COONa}$$

The urethanes so formed are claimed to possess markedly improved properties for certain purposes, and their preparation by other methods is in the course of investigation.

Limitations of space have prevented the full presentation of all the chemistry of cellulose. For a more extended treatment the reader is referred to several texts on the subject [125].

REFERENCES IN TEXT

1. Anderson, B., *Modern Plastics*, **19**, 5, 88, 90 (1942); Purves, C. B., *Tech. Assoc. Papers*, **25**, 718 (1942).
2. Andress, K. R., *Z. physik. Chem.*, **B4**, 190 (1929); Katz, J. R., *Trans. Faraday Soc.*, **29**, 279 (1933); Sisson, W. A., *J. Phys. Chem.*, **40**, 343 (1936); Sobue, H., *Bull. Tokyo Un. Eng.*, **8**, 381 (1939).
3. Atsuki, K., and Shimoyan, K., *Cellulose Ind.* (Tokyo), **2**, 336 (1926).
4. Bass, S. L., and Young, A. E., *Modern Plastics*, **19**, 5, 90 (1941); Wolfram, M. L., and Morgan, H., *Tech. Assoc. Papers*, **25**, 706 (1942); Gordon, R., *Rev. Current Lit.*, **15**, 85 (1942).
5. Bechamp, A., *Ann. chim. phys.*, **48**, 458 (1856); Speitel, R., *Bull. soc. ind. Mulhouse*, **100**, 109 (1934); Bouchonnet, A., Jacquet, A., and Mathieu, M., *Bull. soc. chim.*, **47**, 1265 (1930).
6. Bergman, M., and Machemer, H., *Ber.*, **63**, 416 (1930); Mease, R. T., *J. Research Natl. Bur. Standards*, **22**, 271 (1943); Montonna, R. E., and Winding, C. C., *Ind. Eng. Chem.*, **35**, 782 (1943).
7. Berl, E., and Ruff, G., *Ber.*, **63**, 3212 (1930); *Cellulosechemie*, **14**, 115 (1933).
8. Birtwell, C., Clibbens, D. A., and Geake, A., *J. Textile Inst.*, **17**, 145 (1926); Musser, D. M., and Engel, H. C., *Paper Trade J.*, **114**, 15, 29 (1942); Unruh, C. C., and Kenyon, W. O., *J. Am. Chem. Soc.*, **64**, 127 (1942); Harris, M., *J. Research Natl. Bur. Standards*, **27**, 449 (1940).

9. BIRTWELL, C., CLIBBENS, D. A., and GEAKE, A., *J. Textile Inst.*, **16,** 13 (1925); CLIBBENS, D. A., and RIDGE, B. P., *J. Textile Inst.*, **18,** 135 (1927); NABAR, G. M., SCHOLEFIELD, F., and TURNER, H. A., *J. Soc. Dyers Colourists*, **51,** 5 (1935); *ibid.*, **53,** 5 (1937).
10. BIRTWELL, C., CLIBBENS, D. A., and RIDGE, B. P., *J. Textile Inst.*, **16,** 13 (1925)
11. BRAGG, W. H., *X-Rays and Crystal Structure*, Bell & Sons, London (1912).
12. BUCHNER, E. H., and SAMWEL, P. J. P., *Trans. Faraday Soc.*, **29,** 32 (1933); STAUDINGER, H., *Ber.*, **67,** 96 (1934); STAUDINGER, H., and MOHR, R., *J. prakt. Chem.*, **158,** 233 (1941).
13. CAROTHERS, W. H., and HILL, J. W., *J. Am. Chem. Soc.*, **54,** 1579 (1932); CAROTHERS, W. H., U. S. Pat. 2,130,948 (1937); MARK, H., *High Polymers*, Interscience Pub., N. Y. (1943); MARK, H., *Am. Scientist*, **31,** 2, 97 (1943).
14. CLARKE, H. T., and MALM, C. J., U. S. Pat. 1,880,420 (1932).
15. CLARKE, H. T., MALM, C. J., and STINCHFIELD, R. L., Brit. Pat. 313,408 (1927); U. S. Pat. 1,880,808 (1932).
16. CLIBBENS, D. A., and GEAKE, A., *J. Textile Inst.*, **19,** 77 (1927); HARRIS, M., et al., *J. Research Natl. Bur. Standards*, **27,** 449 (1941); HATCH, R. S., HAMMOND, R. N., and MCNAIR, J. J., *Tech. Assoc. Papers*, **25,** 426 (1942); ZIMMERMANN, A., *Melliand Textilber*, **23,** 73 (1942).
17. COLLINS, G. E., *J. Textile Inst.*, **16,** 123 (1925); HEUSER, E., and BARTUNEK, R., *Cellulosechemie*, **6,** 19 (1925).
18. COLTOF, W., *J. Soc. Chem. Ind.*, **56,** 363 (1937).
19. Committee of American Chemical Soc., *J. Am. Chem. Soc.*, **49,** Proc. 37 (1932); GLENN, J., *Bull. Natl. Formulary Comm.*, **9,** 18 (1940); OLSEN, A. F., *Am. J. Digestive Diseases Nutrition*, **7,** 515 (1940); LEGER, F., and LAROSE, P., *Can. J. Research*, **19B,** 61 (1941).
20. Committee of American Chemical Soc., *Ind. Eng. Chem.*, **15,** 748 (1923); COREY, A. B., and GRAY, H. L., *Ind. Eng. Chem.*, **16,** 853 (1924); WORNER, R. K., and MEASE, R. T., *J. Research Natl. Bur. Standards*, **21,** 609 (1938).
21. COUNCLER, E. C., *Chem.-Ztg.*, **24,** 368 (1900); SCHERER, P. C., *J. Am. Chem. Soc.*, **53,** 4009 (1931); FRANKE, H., *Z. ges. Textil-Ind.*, **13,** (1933); DOBRY, A., *Bull. Soc. Chim.*, **3,** 312 (1936).
22. CROSS, C. F., and BEVAN, E. J., *Cellulose*, Longmans, Green, London (1895).
23. DAVIDSON, G. F., *J. Textile Inst.*, **32,** 109 (1941); RUTHERFORD, H. A., MINOR, F. W., and HARRIS, M., *J. Research Natl. Bur. Standards*, **29,** 131 (1942).
24. DAVIDSON, G. F., *J. Textile Inst.*, **32,** 109, 132 (1941); NICKERSON, R. F., *Ind. Eng. Chem.*, **34,** 1480 (1942).
25. DAVIDSON, G. F., *J. Textile Inst.*, **32,** 132 (1941); BROWNSETT, T., and DAVIDSON, G. F., *J. Textile Inst.*, **32,** 25 (1941).
26. DOBRY, A., *Compt. rend.*, **199,** 289 (1934).
27. DOREE, C., and HEALEY, A. C., *J. Soc. Dyers Colourists*, **49,** 290 (1933); ELBEY, A., *Indian Textile J.*, **58,** 369 (1941).
28. EICHENGRUEN, A., and BECKER, F., *J. Soc. Chem. Ind.*, **22,** 961 (1903).
29. EVANS, W. L., *J. Am. Chem. Soc.*, **52,** 294 (1930); **53,** 4384 (1931); **58,** 2388 (1936); DAVIDSON, G. F., *J. Textile Inst.*, **25,** 174 (1934); **29,** 195 (1938); BROWNSETT, T., and CLIBBENS, D. A., *J. Textile Inst.*, **32,** 57 (1942).
30. Exec. Com. Pulp and Paper Ind., *Manufacture of Pulp and Paper*, Vol. III, McGraw-Hill (1937); SUTERMEISTER, E., *Chemistry of Pulp and Paper Making*, John Wiley & Sons (1941).

31. Farr, W. K., *J. Phys. Chem.*, **42,** 1113 (1938); *Boyce Thompson Inst. Prof. Papers*, **10,** 71, 127 (1938); *Nature*, **146,** 153 (1940).
32. Favorskii, A. E., *Compt. rend. acad. sci. U.R.S.S.*, **32,** 630 (1941).
32a. Fordyce, C. R., Salo, M., and Clarke, G. R., *Ind. Eng. Chem.*, **28,** 1310 (1936).
33. Frank, G., and Mendrzyk, H., *Ber.*, **63,** 875 (1930).
34. Freudenberg, K., *Ann. Rev. Biochem.*, **8,** 81 (1936); Freeman, R. D., and Peterson, F. C., *Ind. Eng. Chem. Anal. Ed.*, **13,** 803 (1941); Lautsch, W., *Brennstoff-Chem.*, **22,** 265 (1941); Hibbert, H., *Ann. Rev. Biochem.*, **11,** 183 (1942).
35. Freudenberg, K., *Ber.*, **54,** 767 (1921).
36. Freundlich, H., and Jores, H. J., *Kolloid Z.*, **22,** 16 (1929).
37. Frey, A., and Elod, E., *Z. angew. Chem.*, **48,** 579 (1930); Sihtola, H., *Suomen Kemistilekti*, **14,** 15 (1941); Schramek, W., *Deutsche Textilwirt.*, **9,** 1, 2 (1942).
38. Frey-Wyssling, A., *Protoplasma*, **27,** 372 (1937); Boulton, E., and Morton, J. H., *J. Soc. Dyers Colourists*, **56,** 145 (1940); Kuhnel, *Cellulose-chem.*, **19,** 52 (1941); Kratky, O., *Holz Roh- u. Werkstoff*, **4,** 8, 12 (1941); *Kolloid Z.*, **98,** 170 (1942).
39. Glazier, S., *Historic Textile Fabrics*, Scribner (1923).
40. Goetze, K., and Reiff, A., *Zellwolle, Kunstseide, Seide*, **46,** 331 (1941).
41. Hagedorn, M., and Möller, P., *Cellulosechem.*, **12,** 29 (1931); Fordyce, C. R., and Meyer, L. W. A., *Ind. Eng. Chem.*, **32,** 1059 (1940).
42. Harrison, W., Brit. Pat. 192,173 (1921); Carré, P., and Mauclère, P., *Compt. rend.*, **192,** 1567 (1931).
43. Haworth, W. N., *Nature*, **116,** 430 (1925); *J. Chem. Soc.*, **128,** 89 (1926); *Helv. Chim. Acta*, **11,** 534 (1928).
44. Haworth, W. N., and Machemer, H., *J. Chem. Soc.*, **134,** 2372 (1932); Freudenberg, K., and Blomqvist, C., *Ber.*, **68B,** 2070 (1935).
45. Haworth, W. N., and Hirst, E. L., *J. Chem. Soc.*, **119,** 193 (1921); *J. Chem. Soc.*, **129,** 2436 (1927).
46. Haworth, W. N., *J. Chem. Soc.*, **134,** 2270 (1932); Hess, K., *Ber.*, **73,** 505 (1940).
47. Hayford, W. H., *Rayon Textile Monthly*, **21,** 685 (1940).
48. Hearon, W. M., Hiatt, G. D., and Fordyce, C. R., *J. Am. Chem. Soc.*, **65,** 826 (1943).
49. Herzog, R. O., *Kolloid Z.*, **39,** 98 (1926); Astbury, W. T., and Wood, F. C., *J. Textile Inst.*, **23,** 17 (1932).
50. Herzog, R. O., and Beck, F., *Z. physiol. Chem.*, **111,** 287 (1920).
51. Heuser, E., and Schneider, G., *Ber.*, **57B,** 1389 (1924).
52. Hibbert, H., *Can. J. Research*, **5,** 580 (1931).
53. Hibbert, H., *Can. J. Research*, **8,** 103, 192, 199 (1933).
54. Hoppler, F., *Chem.-Ztg.*, **66,** 132 (1942).
55. Irvine, J. C., and Hirst, E. L., *J. Chem. Soc.*, **121,** 1585 (1922); Monier-Williams, G. W., *J. Chem. Soc.*, **119,** 803 (1922).
56. Jackson, E. L., and Hudson, C. S., *J. Am. Chem. Soc.*, **58,** 378 (1936); **59,** 944 (1937); **60,** 989 (1938); Davidson, G. F., *J. Textile Inst.*, **31,** 81 (1940); *J. Soc. Dyers Colourists*, **56,** 58 (1940).
57. Karrer, P., *Helv. Chim. Acta*, **9,** 592 (1926); Sakurada, I., *J. Soc. Chem. Ind. Japan*, **32,** 11B (1929).
58. Karrer, P., and Widmer, F. R., *Helv. Chim. Acta*, **4,** 174 (1921).

59. Kasbekar, G. S., *Current Sci.*, **9,** 411 (1940); Haller, R., *Z. Textil.-Ind (Klepzig's)*, **44,** 645 (1941).
60. Kita, G., and Mayume, T., *Cellulose Ind.* (Tokyo), **2,** 31 (1926); *Kunststoffe* **16,** 167 (1926).
61. Kobe, K. A., and Montonna, R. E., *J. Am. Chem. Soc.*, **53,** 1889 (1931).
62. Kraemer, E. O., *Ind. Eng. Chem.*, **30,** 1200 (1938).
63. Kraemer, E. O., and Lansing, W. D., *J. Phys. Chem.*, **39,** 753 (1935).
64. Kratky, O., *Kolloid-Z.*, **84,** 149 (1938); **86,** 245 (1939); **88,** 78 (1939); Mark, H., *Chem. Revs.*, **26,** 169 (1940); Lieser, T., *Ann.*, **548,** 195 (1941).
65. Lenze, F., and Rubens, E., *Chem. Zentr.*, **1,** 2993 (1931).
66. Lieser, T., *Ann.*, **528,** 276 (1937); Brownsett, T., and Clibbens, D. A., *J. Textile Inst.*, **32,** 32 (1941).
67. Lilienfeld, L., U. S. Pats. 1,674,401 to 1,674,405 (1928).
68. Lorand, E. J., *Ind. Eng. Chem.*, **30,** 527 (1938); Ellsworth, D. C., and Hahn F. C., U. S. Pat. 2,249,754 (1941).
69. Lunge, G., and Bebie, J., *Z. angew. Chem.*, **14,** 86 (1901); Lunge, G., *J. Am. Chem. Soc.*, **23,** 527 (1901).
70. Malm, C. J., and Clarke, H. T., *J. Am. Chem. Soc.*, **51,** 274 (1929); Hagedorn, M., and Möller, P., *Cellulosechem.*, **12,** 29 (1931).
71. Malm, C. J., and Fordyce, C. R., *Ind. Eng. Chem.*, **32,** 405 (1940).
72. Mark, H., *Tech. Assoc. Papers*, **24,** 217 (1941).
73. Mark, H., *High Polymers*, Vol. II, p. 302, Interscience Pub., N. Y. (1941).
74. Marsh, J. T., and Wood, F. C., *Introduction to Chemistry of Cellulose*, p. 209, Van Nostrand (1942); Nickerson, R. F., *Ind. Eng. Chem.*, **33,** 83 (1941); Yackel, E. C., and Kenyon, W. O., *J. Am. Chem. Soc.*, **64,** 121 (1942); Ott, E., *High Polymers*, Vol. V, p. 88. Interscience Pub., N. Y. (1943).
75. Mauersberger, H. R., and Schwarz, E. W. K., *Rayon and Staple Fiber Handbook*, 3rd Ed., p. 79 (1939); Bieber, G. D., *Chem. Met. Eng.*, **48,** 92 (1941).
76. Mercer, J., Brit. Pat. 13,296 (1850); Marsh, J. T., *Mercerizing*, Chapman & Hall, London (1941).
77. Meyer, K. H., Hopff, H., and Mark, H., *Ber.*, **62,** 1103 (1929); **63,** 1531 (1930); Freudenberg, K., and Nagai, W., *Ann.*, **494,** 63 (1932); Kuhn, W., *Ber.*, **63,** 1503 (1930).
78. Meyer, K. H., and Misch, L., *Ber.*, **70,** 266 (1937); *Helv. Chim. Acta*, **20,** 232 (1937); Mark, H., *Chem. Revs.*, **26,** 169 (1940).
79. Miles, F. D., U. S. Pat. 838, 350 (1906).
80. Nageli, C., *Die Stärkekörner*, Schultub, Zurich (1858); Gilson, E., *La Cellule*, **9,** 337 (1893); Ambronn, H., *Kolloid-Z.*, **9,** 147 (1911); Preston, R. D., *Trans. Faraday Soc.*, **29,** 65 (1933).
81. Neale, S. M., *J. Textile Inst.*, **20,** 373 (1929); *Trans. Faraday Soc.*, **29,** 228 (1933); Thompson, L., *Textile Recorder*, **58,** 35 (1940).
82. Nickerson, R. F., *Ind. Eng. Chem.*, **32,** 1454 (1940); Nickerson, R. F., and Leape, C. B., *Ind. Eng. Chem.*, **33,** 83 (1941).
83. Nikitin, N. I., and Korchemkin, F. I., *Bull. acad. sci. U.R.S.S.*, **245** (1940).
84. Ott, E., *High Polymers*, Vol. V, p. 256.
85. Peacock, D. H., *J. Soc. Dyers Colourists*, **42,** 53 (1926); Levi, C., *Boll. assoc. ital. chim. tessili color.*, **6,** 80 (1930); Riesz, E., *Bull. soc. ind. Mulhouse*, **99,** 349 (1933).
86. Plauson, H., Brit. Pat. 183,908 (1921).
87. Polanyi, N., *Naturwissenschaften*, **9,** 288 (1921).

88. Pope, W. J., and Huebner, J., *J. Soc. Chem. Ind.*, **22,** 70 (1903); Hibbert, H., *J. Soc. Dyers Colourists,* **46,** 294 (1930); Fredenhagen, K., and Cadenbeck, G., *Z. angew. Chem.*, **46,** 113 (1933); Schluback, H. H., *Z. angew. Chem.*, **47,** 132 (1934); Bernoulli, A. L., and Stauffer, H. S., *Helv. Chim. Acta,* **23,** 627 (1940).
89. Ott, E., *High Polymers,* Vol. V, p. 811 (Emil Kline).
90. Richter, G. A., *Ind. Eng. Chem.*, **33,** 75, 1518 (1941).
91. Scherer, P. C., and Hussey, R. E., *J. Am. Chem. Soc.*, **53,** 2344 (1931); Schorigin, P., *Ber.*, **69,** 1713 (1936); Schützenberger, P., *Ann. Chem. Phys.* (4), **21,** 235 (1870).
92. Scherer, P. C., and Feild, J. M., *Rayon Textile Monthly,* **22,** 10 (1941).
93. Schmidt, E., *Cellulosechem.*, **13,** 129 (1932); Nickerson, R. F., *Ind. Eng. Chem.*, **34,** 1480 (1942); Heyman, E., and Rabinov, G., *Trans. Faraday Soc.*, **38,** 209 (1942); Weber, O. H., *J. prakt. Chem.*, **158,** 33 (1941).
94. Schultze, G., *Kunststoffe,* **31,** 23 (1941); Yarsley, V. E., *Brit. Plastics,* **13,** 352, 424, 487 (1942); Hearon, W. M., Hiatt, G. D., and Fordyce, C. R., *J. Am. Chem. Soc.*, **65,** 829 (1943).
95. Schulz, G. V., *Chem.-Zeit.*, **64,** 285 (1937).
96. Schweitzer, D., *J. prakt. Chem.*, **22,** 109 (1857); Kuhn, R., *Kunstseide,* **20,** 364 (1938); Rogovin, Z., *Uspekhi Khim.*, **9,** 737 (1940).
97. Simoda, I., and Kono, M., *Cellulose Ind.* (Tokyo), **16,** 328 (1940); **17,** 233 (1941).
98. Sisson, W. A., *Textile Research,* **5,** 119 (1935); **6,** 143 (1936); Kratky, O., and Mark, H., *Z. physik. Chem.*, **B36,** 129 (1937); Bredée, H. L., *Kolloid-Z.*, **94,** 81 (1941); Lyons, W. J., *Sci. Monthly,* **54,** 238 (1942); Kenney, A. W., *Tech. Assoc. Papers,* **25,** 722 (1942).
99. Sponsler, O. L., and Dore, W. H., *J. Gen. Physiol.*, **9,** 677 (1926); *4th Colloid Symposium Monograph,* (1926); Hess, K., and Trogus, C., *Z. physik. Chem.* (Bodenstein Festband), 885 (1931).
100. Spurlin, H. M., *J. Am. Chem. Soc.*, **61,** 2224 (1939); Sheppard, S. E., and Newsome, P. T., *J. Phys. Chem.*, **39,** 143 (1935).
101. Staudinger, H., *Naturwissenschaften,* **22,** 747, 813 (1934); *Cellulosechem.*, **20,** 1 (1942); Staudinger, H., and Nuss, O., *J. prakt. Chem.*, **157,** 283 (1941); Jurisch, J., *Chem.-Ztg.*, **64,** 269 (1940).
102. Staudinger, H., *Hochmolekular Verb.* (Berlin), pp. 204, 410, 471, 509 (1932); Dobry, A., *Kolloid-Z.*, **81,** 190 (1937); Boissonas, C. G., and Meyer, K. H., *Helv. Chim. Acta,* **20,** 783 (1937).
103. Staudinger, H., and Feuerstein, K., *Ann.*, **526,** 72 (1936); Staudinger, H., *Papier-Fabr.*, **36,** 474 (1938); *J. prakt. Chem.*, **156,** 11 (1941); Kraemer, E. O., *Ind. Eng. Chem.*, **30,** 1200 (1938); Golova, O. P., and Nikolaeva, I. I., *Compt. rend. acad. sci. U.R.S.S.*, **29,** 582 (1940).
104. Staudinger, H., and Husemann, E., *Ann.*, **527,** 195 (1937); Staudinger, H., and Mohr, R., *J. prakt. Chem.*, **158,** 233 (1941); Kraemer, E. O., *J. Franklin Inst.*, **230,** 664 (1940).
105. Staudinger, H., and Sorkin, M., *Ber.*, **70,** 1565 (1937).
106. Steurer, E., *Z. physik. Chem.*, **A190,** 1 (1941); Mark, H., *High Polymers,* Vol. IV, p. 13, Interscience Pub., N. Y. (1942).
107. Svedberg, T., *Chem. Revs.*, **20,** 81 (1937); *Svensk Papperstidn.*, **45,** 444 (1942); *The Ultracentrifuge,* Clarendon, Oxford (1940).
108. Tanner, W. L., U. S. Pat. 1,896,725 (1933); Hagedorn, M., and Guehring, E., U. S. Pat. 1,848,524 (1932).

109. THORPE, J. F., *Dictionary of Applied Chemistry*, Vol. I, p. 460, Longmans, Green, London (1905).
110. TILGHMAN, B. C., U. S. Pat. 70,483 (1867).
111. TRAUBE, W., BLASER, B., and LINDEMANN, E., *Ber.*, **65**, 603 (1932).
112. TROGUS, C., *Ber.*, **64**, 405 (1931).
113. ULLMAN, M., *Enzyk. der Tech. Chem.*, **5**, 96 (1917); WADANO, M., *Kolloid-Z.*, **93**, 324 (1940); KRAUS, A., *Nitrocellulose*, **12** (1941).
114. UEDA, Y., and HATA, K., *J. Cellulose Inst.* (Tokyo), **4**, 1 (1928).
115. VON MEYER, E., *History of Chemistry*, Macmillan (1906).
116. WARWICKE, J., *Rev. Current Lit. Paint, Color, Varnish and Allied Ind.*, **36**, 9 (1943).
117. WEBBER, C. S., and STAUD, C. J., U. S. Pat. 1,785,466 (1931).
118. WERNER, K., *Chem.-Ztg.*, **65**, 467 (1941).
119. WILLIAMS, H. E., *J. Soc. Chem. Ind.*, **40**, 221T (1921).
120. WILLSTÄTTER, R., and ZECHMEISTER, L., *Ber.*, **46**, 722 (1913); BERTRAND, G., and BENOIST, S., *Bull. soc. chim.*, **33**, 1451 (1923); IRVINE, J. C., and ROBERTSON, G. J., *J. Chem. Soc.*, **128**, 1488 (1926).
121. WOOD, F. C., *J. Soc. Chem. Ind.*, **50**, 411 (1931); HAGEDORN, M., and MÖLLER P., *Cellulosechem.*, **12**, 29 (1931).
122. WORDEN, E. C., *Technology of Cellulose Esters*, Estanbach, Pa. (1921); FABEL, K., *Nitrocellulose*, **12**, 103, 147 (1941); GORDON, R., *Rev. Current Lit. Paint, Color, Varnish and Allied Ind.*, **35**, 85 (1942).
123. ZECHMEISTER, L., and TOTH, G., *Ber.*, **64**, 854 (1931).
124. ZETSCHE, F., and ROSENTHAL, G., *Helv. Chim. Acta*, **10**, 346 (1927).
125. MARSH, J. T., and WOOD, F. C., *Introduction to Chemistry of Cellulose*, Van Nostrand (1942); HEUSER, E., *Cellulose Chemistry*, John Wiley and Sons (1944); OTT, E., *High Polymers*, Vol. V, Interscience Pub., N. Y. (1943).

CHAPTER III

COTTON: HISTORY, GROWTH, AND STATISTICS

R. F. Nickerson

History

Man learned to utilize the fine-textured fiber yielded by the cotton plant perhaps about 5000 years ago and there is inconclusive evidence of even earlier use. Gulati and Turner [1] in 1929 published a summary of their observations on some bits of cotton fabric and string which were found by archeologists at a site in the valley of the Indus in Sind (India). A probable date of 3000 B.C. was estimated for the period of the site. The samples were decomposed by molds but appeared to have been dyed with a vegetable pigment of the madder type. These authors also cited inconclusive evidence that cotton was grown and used in Middle Egypt about 12,000 B.C., before flax was known. Nevertheless, India is generally recognized as the cradle of the cotton industry.

India. The use of cotton in India dates back to prehistoric times, and it is often referred to as early as 800 B.C. in the ancient laws of Manu. It may be stated that from 1500 B.C. to about the beginning of the sixteenth century, India was the center of the cotton industry, and the cloth which was woven in a rather crude and primitive manner was of exceptional fineness and quality.

The earliest mention of cotton appears to be in the *Asvaláyana Sranta Seitra* (about 800 B.C.). The *Books of Manu* state that the sacrificial thread of the Brahmin had to be made of cotton (karpasi), that the theft of cotton thread was punishable by fines, and that rice-water (starch?) was used in the weaving. In the Hebrew *Scriptures* cotton is mentioned by the name *Kirbas* (or *Karpas*), as in the description of green draperies at the palace of Susa (*Esther* 1, 6). Among the Latin authors of the Augustan age curtains and tents of *carbasa* are frequently mentioned.

Reference to the use of cotton as a textile fiber is to be found in the writings of Herodotus (445 B.C.): "There are trees which grow wild there (India), the fruit of which is a wool exceeding in beauty and goodness that of sheep. The Indians make their clothes of this tree-wool." The same writer also refers to the clothing of Xerxes' army as being composed of "cotton fiber." Theophrastus (350 B.C.) gives a definite statement as to the manner in which the cotton plant was cultivated in India.

The use of cotton was evidently known to the Greeks soon after the invasion of India by Alexander, though this does not signify that the Greeks themselves either grew the cotton plant or engaged in the manufacture of the fiber into clothes. Aristobulus, a contemporary of Alexander, mentions the cotton plant under the name of the "wool-bearing tree," and states that the capsules of this tree contain seeds which are taken out, and the remaining fiber is then combed like wool. Nearchus, an admiral of Alexander, about 327 B.C., says: "There are in India trees bearing, as it were, bunches of wool. The natives made linen garments of it, wearing a shirt which reached to the middle of the leg, a sheet folded about the shoulders, and a turban rolled around the head. The linen made by them from this substance was finer and whiter than any other."

Two Arabian travelers of the Middle Ages, writing of India, said: "In this country they make garments of such extraordinary perfection that nowhere else are the like to be seen; these garments are woven to that degree of fineness that they may be drawn through a ring of moderate size." Marco Polo, about A.D. 1298, mentioned India as producing "the finest and most beautiful cottons that are to be found in any part of the world." Tavernier, in his *Travels*, said of India that some calicoes were made so fine that one could hardly feel them in the hand, that thread, when spun, was scarcely discernible, and that the rich had turbans of so fine a cloth that thirty ells of it weighed less than four ounces.

The superior fineness of some Indian muslins, and their quality of retaining, longer than European fabrics, an appearance of excellence has occasioned the belief that the cotton fiber from which they are woven is superior to any known elsewhere. The excellence of these Indian muslins must be wholly ascribed to the skillfulness and patience of the workmen in the different processes of spinning and weaving. The very fine muslins which thus attest the efficiency of some of the East Indians, and which have been poetically described as "webs of woven wind," are, however, viewed as curiosities even in the country of their production, and are made only in very small quantities.

Egypt. There is evidently a good deal of confusion among the early writers respecting the terms used for "flax" and "cotton," and it may be that the ancient Egyptians were better acquainted with the use of the cotton fiber than is generally supposed; it is probable that the cotton plant was grown there at a very early date. Herodotus states that the Egyptian priests wore linen clothes, but Pliny refers to them as also wearing cotton material, and Philostratus supports this latter statement. The words translated as "linen" do not always refer to the fiber of which the cloth was made, but often have reference to the general appearance of the material; therefore, cloth made from either flax or cotton alone, or mixed, was called linen. Even the fact that all Egyptian mummy cloths so far examined appear to consist of flax is no argument against the probable use of cotton by these people; it only proves that flax alone was employed for certain religious purposes, and cotton, wool, and silk may have been in common use for clothing.

Italy. The cotton plant does not appear to have been cultivated in Italy until some time after the beginning of the Christian era, although a knowledge of the fiber and a probable use of the cloth made from it was known to them a long time previously. Cotton cloth was probably used for clothing by the Romans prior to A.D. 284. The real introduction of the cotton plant into Europe and the manufacture of the fiber into cloth was due to the Mohammedans, who spread this knowledge throughout the countries bordering on the Mediterranean Sea during the period of their widespread conquests. Abu Zacaria Ebn el Awam, a Moorish writer of the twelfth century, gives a full account of the proper method of cultivating the cotton plant, and mentions that cotton was cultivated in Sicily.

Spain. The first European country to manufacture cotton goods appears to have been Spain. A rather ambiguous passage in the *Historia Critica de España* indicates that the manufacture of linen, silk, and cotton existed in Spain as early as the ninth century. De Marles states that cotton manufacture was introduced into Spain during the reign of Abderahman III, in the tenth century, by the Moors. In the fourteenth century Granada was noted for its manufacture of cotton. A commercial historiographer of Barcelona states that one of the most famous and useful industries of the city was the manufacture of cotton; its workers were united in a guild in the thirteenth century.

China and Japan. Cotton was introduced into China and Japan from India, but its adoption by these countries was slow. It was not until the seventeenth century, during the reign of Tokugawa, that the cultivation of cotton became general in Japan. A great deal of cotton is now grown in Korea (Chosen), having been introduced into that country from China about 500 years ago. The Korean cotton is of longer staple and of better quality than the Chinese cotton, as the soil and climate in Korea are better adapted to its growth. In the seventh century the cotton plant was used as an ornamental shrub in Chinese gardens; and it was not until about A.D. 1000 that the plant was commercially grown in China.

Cotton was probably introduced into China at the time of the conquest of this country by the Tartars, but it was not until about A.D. 1300 that the fiber was cultivated for manufacturing purposes. Marco Polo (Book II, Chap. 24) gives no account of the culture of cotton in

China, except in the province of Fo-Kien, but speaks of silk as being the customary dress.

England. Since those remote times the cotton fiber has played a prominent part in human history and economics. Cotton fabrics were among the wonders that attracted European adventurers and tradesmen to the East during the Dark Ages and, later, the demand for cotton goods was responsible in no small measure for inventions that ushered in the Industrial Revolution.

There is much uncertainty as to when the manufacture of cotton was first introduced into England; the first authentic record is in Robert's *Treasure of Traffic*, published in 1641. England first came into prominence as a cotton manufacturing country in 1635, the supply of the raw fiber being obtained from the East. Long previous to this, however, England, as well as other European countries, had imported cotton goods (calicoes, etc.) from India by way of Venice.

The influence of this trade is still apparent in English words like damask (from Damascus), calico (from Calicut in the East Indies), and muslin (from Mosul in Mesopotamia).

The introduction of the cheaper fabrics was vigorously opposed in England as being destructive of the woolen industry. By an Act of 1720 the use and wear in England of printed, painted, or dyed calicoes was prohibited.

The Americas. Crawford [2] has prepared an excellent discussion of the history of cotton in the New World. It has been established with reasonable certainty that cotton was being used by the Mayas in Central America by 632 B.C. Fabrics did not preserve well in this climate and dates are, therefore, difficult to ascertain. For this reason the art may have been well advanced long before the date indicated. Crawford also has included in his book an interesting chronology of cotton developments.

Among the Mexicans cotton was found to be the chief article of clothing, as these people did not possess either wool or silk and were not acquainted with the use of flax, although the plant grew in their country. Among the presents sent by Cortez to Charles V of Spain were many fabrics made from cotton. In Peru cotton was also in use from an early date, and at the time of Pizarro's conquest of that country in 1522 the inhabitants were clothed in cotton garments; cotton cloths have also been found on Peruvian mummies of a very ancient date. Furthermore, the cotton plant is indigenous to Peru and from it is obtained a special variety known as Peruvian cotton. According to Bancroft, the first attempt toward cotton cultivation in the American colonies was in Virginia, during Wyatt's administration, in 1621. In 1733 the cultivation of cotton was started in Carolina, and the following year in Georgia. In 1748 the first consignment of Georgian cotton was sent to England. In 1758 white Siam cotton was introduced into Louisiana. In 1784 fourteen bales of cotton arrived in Liverpool from America, of which eight bales were seized on the grounds that so much cotton could not have been produced in the United States. In 1786 the black-seeded cotton from the Bahamas was introduced into Georgia. The first mill in the United States for the manufacture of cotton goods appears to have been erected at Beverly, Mass., in 1787.

Terminology

The English word "cotton" is derived from the Arabic *Katán* (or *qutn, kuteen*), though it is claimed this name originally denoted flax. The word *linon* was itself at one time used to denote cotton, and even at the present time cotton fibers are spoken of as *lint*. In early times it was used to denote a particular texture rather than to describe a distinct fiber. For instance, "Manchester Cottons" (1590) was a name for a certain woolen fabric.

The various names given to the cotton fiber in different countries are given in Table 1:

TABLE 1. Names for Cotton in Various Languages

Country	*Names for Cotton*
India	Pucu
Spain	Algodon
Yucatan and ancient Mexico	Ychcaxihitvitl
Tahiti	Vavai
France	Coton
Italy	Cotone
Germany	Baumwolle
Persia (Iran)	Pembeh or poombeh
Arabia	Gatn, kotan, kutn, katán, qutn, or kuteen
Cochin China	Cay haung
China	Hoa mein
Japan	Watta ik or watta noki
Siam (Thailand)	Tonfaa
Hindustan	Nurma
Mysore and Bombay	Deo kurpas and deo kapas
Mongolia	Kohung
Greece	Vamvax

Growth

Cotton, a vegetable seed fiber, consists mainly of cellulose, especially after purification treatments such as soda-boiling and bleaching. About 10 per cent of the weight of the raw fiber is lost as a result of the removal of wax, protein, pectates, and other constituents. The purified fiber is nearly pure cellulose, a condensation product of glucose, and it is this natural polymer that gives cotton its important properties. (See Chapter II.)

Cotton is a hair attached to the seed of several species of the genus *Gossypium,* which belongs to the natural order of Malvaceae. The cotton plant is a shrub, which reaches the height of 4 to 6 ft. It is indigenous to nearly all subtropical countries, though it is best capable of cultivation in warm, humid climates where the soil is sandy, and in the neighborhood of the sea, lakes, or large rivers. It appears to thrive most readily in North and South America, India, China, Russia, and Egypt; it is also cultivated in Australia, but not as yet to any great extent; appreciable quantities are grown along the coasts of Africa; that grown in Italy and Spain is practically negligible as far as commercial considerations are concerned, but Bulgaria and Turkey produce some. In addition to the numerous varieties of cultivated cottons, there are various wild cotton plants met with in many parts of the world. With respect to the detailed botany of these wild plants, the reader is referred to Sir George Watt's *The Wild and Cultivated Cotton Plants of the World* [3] and, especially, to S. C. Harland's *Genetics of Cotton* [4]. As to the general characteristics of wild cottons, they all have a red-colored woolly coating on the testa of the seed. In some varieties this assumes the condition of a short dense velvet, called the *fuzz.* In others, there are two coats of fiber, an under-fleece (the fuzz) and an outer coat or floss. In the third class there is no fuzz, but a distinct floss.

While the cotton plant grows well in warm climates, its commercial cultivation is somewhat limited. The principal cotton-producing regions are Egypt, southern United States, India, Brazil, the western and southern coasts of Africa, and the West Indies. Large amounts of white cotton are raised in China and the U.S.S.R. but much of it is used in these countries.

Planting begins at various times in different regions, depending on the climate. The seasons are, in North America, from the middle of March to the middle of April; in Egypt, from the beginning of March to the end of April; in Peru and Brazil, from the end of December to the end of April; in India, China, and Russia, from April to August.

In the United States, India, and Egypt the cotton plant is an annual, but in tropical climates it is often a perennial plant that assumes a tree-like form. However, the plant is frequently treated as an annual even in the latter regions to assure quality and maintain productivity.

The portion of the world lying between the equator and the 34th degree of latitude presents the most suitable conditions for the cultivation of "Sea Island" and American Upland cottons, a mean yearly temperature of 68 to 86° F. being required. Indian cotton is best cultivated in zones where the temperature in winter does not fall below 50° F., nor in summer rise above 77° F. In the United States the cotton plant is cultivated up to 37° north latitude. The best fiber, Sea Island, was formerly obtained along the eastern coast, including the states of Florida, Georgia, and South Carolina. Highest quality fiber is now grown in the Mississippi Delta and the West Indies. The better grades of Indian and Egyptian cottons are coastal growths. In China and Japan cultivation reaches as far north as 41°, and in the European Black Sea region to 46°.

Cotton Growing Practice

Cotton growing practices differ widely throughout the world cotton belt, even within a given district. The type of cotton being grown, whether American Upland, Egyptian, or Indian black soil variety, and local soil and climatic conditions, as well as local conditions, seem to be major factors governing the choice of method.

Cotton requires from 6 to 7 months of warm or hot weather, plenty of sunshine, and appreciable amounts of moisture for optimum development. An average of 3 to 5 in. of rain a month during the stages of active growth is favorable for American Upland, with a dry season desirable to check vegetative growth as the crop approaches maturity.

The culture of cotton is clean and may be either deep or shallow, depending on the kind of land. The ground is usually bedded up to provide a warm seedbed in the cool early spring and the seed drilled in. When the young plants become sufficiently large, they are thinned to distances of 8 to 14 in. and weeds and grass are kept in check with hoe, cultivator, and plough. The soil crust is generally broken after each rain to preserve the moisture and inhibit fungus growth.

In a period of 8 days to 2 weeks after the planting, young shoots appear above the ground in the form of hooks. A few hours later the seed end of the stalk rises out of the ground and discloses two leaves folded over and closed together. The leaves and stem of the young plant are smooth and oily, possess a fleshy color, and are extremely tender. Shortly afterward the plant begins to straighten itself and deepen in color, or, rather, changes to a light olive green, while the two leaves gradually separate. Further development is rapid and proceeds as in other plants.

Before the plant attains its full height it begins to throw off flower-stalks, or "squares," which, when perfectly formed, are small in diameter and of considerable length; on the extremity of these stalks the blossom pods or "forms" after a time appear, encased in three leaf sheaths or calyxes, with fringes of various lengths. Gradually this pod expands until it attains the size of a bean, when it bursts and displays the blossom. This blossom in full development lasts for about 24 hr, when it begins to revolve imperceptibly on its axis and in about a day's time twists itself completely off. When the blossom has fallen, a small dark green three- or five-celled triangular capsular pod forms, which increases in size to that of a walnut. Meantime the seeds and fibers have been formed inside this boll. At complete maturity the fiber expansion causes the boll to burst into sections, in each cell of which, and adhering firmly to the surface of the seeds, is a tuft of the downy material, cotton.

The time between planting of seed and flowering of the plant ranges from 80 to 110 days, and between flowering and the opening of the boll 55 to 80 days. The long fine varieties take longer to mature. The mature fiber is picked as soon as possible after the boll opens to minimize deterioration of the fiber by light and moisture.

Picking in America is done almost exclusively by hand. Mechanical pickers have been tried but they have not been very successful, the chief difficulty being that the crop does not mature all at once and the picker must select only the ripe bolls. Mechanical pickers also have the disadvantage of collecting large amounts of trash.

In west Texas much cotton is gathered by a process known as "snapping" or "sledding." The crop there rarely matures before the first frost, which causes the whole crop to open at once. After the leaves, killed by the frost, fall off, nothing remains on the stalk but the bolls which are stripped off with a "sled." With extra cleaning equipment sledded cotton produces a lint lower in grade than hand-picked cotton, but otherwise quite merchantable. A "sled" is a kind of large coarse rake which, in combination with a wagon or other large receptacle, is drawn or pushed through the field. The teeth of the rake or comb are so spaced that the plant stalks, but not the bolls, can pass through. There are a number of modified and refined variations of this crude apparatus which saves much of the labor of hand-picking.

Cotton Ginning

Cotton as it is picked in the field still contains the seed and is known as "seed cotton." The fiber constitutes about one-third of the total weight of seed cotton, the remainder being seed. The proportion of lint to seed cotton varies considerably with the different varieties and is usually smaller for fine cottons.

Ginning is accomplished commercially with either a "saw" gin, used mainly for intermediate and short staple cottons, or a "roller" gin for long staple cottons. Roller ginning is slower and more expensive than saw ginning, production per unit being in the ratio of about 1 : 10, but it eliminates damage to the long fibers. The lower output and greater expense of roller ginning preclude its application to the great volume of shorter cottons.

In American commercial practice a wagon containing about 1500 lb of seed cotton is placed under a suction flue in which the cotton is borne by an air current directly to cleaning machines attached to the gin stands. From the gin the lint travels pneumatically to a condenser located above the press or baling box into which it is subsequently permitted to drop. It is settled into the press box with a mechanical "tramper." When the press box is filled, it is moved under the press where the lint is compressed and the baling operation completed.

The bale as finished at the gin is rectangular with dimensions of about 54 × 27 × 46 in., a density of about 13 lb per cu ft, and a net weight of 478 lb. The six metal ties weigh about 9 lb and the jute or cotton wrapping about 12 lb. These low-density bales are often further compressed at concentration points, the density of export bales being about 32 lb per cu ft and of standard or railway bales about 28 lb per cu ft.

The saw gin consists of a seed roll box or hopper for holding the seed cotton; one side of this box is a grate composed of steel bars, through the intervals of which a number of thin steel disks, notched on the edge (saws), rotate rapidly. The fibers are caught in the notches or teeth of these disks and thus pulled from the seeds. The latter, as they are cleaned, fall down through a slit below the grate. The fibers are carried off the revolving saws by means of an air current or a rapidly rotating cylindrical brush. The ginned cotton fiber is technically known as "lint."

In Upland or ordinary American cotton, the seeds are not entirely freed from fiber by ginning, there remaining more or less short fiber together with a fine undergrowth of fiber, amounting on an average to about 10 per cent of the total weight of the seed. At the present time these seeds are further delinted by passing through specially constructed gins. The fiber obtained is known as "linters." It is widely used both as a filler in mattresses and upholstery and, after purification, as chemical or rayon pulp. It is the raw material for much nitrocellulose and cellulose acetate as well as for best quality rayons and newer cellulose plastics.

These ginning processes represent only the bare essentials of the usual procedure. Sledded or snapped cotton must be passed through extractors or hull separators, which are intended to remove the burrs (outer shells of bolls) from the seed cotton. Most gins are equipped with cleaners designed to effect a partial separation of the fine leaf and trash from the seed cotton. Many ginneries have installed driers where the fiber is conditioned to the proper moisture content as a part of its preparation. The U. S. Department of Agriculture recommends that seed cottons up to 1⅛ in. in length contain not more than 12 per cent moisture and longer cottons not more than 8 per cent of moisture for proper ginning.

Types of Available Cottons

The cotton of commerce can be classified into *three* general groups on the basis of fiber length, fiber fineness, and geographical region of growth as follows:

Type 1. Long, fine strong fibers of good luster, staple length from 1 to 2½ in. It includes Egyptian and Sea Island cottons, i.e., varieties probably derived from the botanical species, *Gossypium barbadense* and *G. purpurascens*.

Type 2. Intermediate cottons of somewhat coarser texture and shorter length, staple from ½ to 1⁵⁄₁₆ in. The principal member of this group is American Upland, i.e., *G. hirsutum*, the most important of the cotton-yielding plants.

Type 3. Short, coarse fibers of no luster that range in staple length from ⅜ to 1 in. These are mainly the Indian or Asiatic cottons, species: *G. herbaceum* and *G. arboreum*.

Cottons of the first type are most valuable, the most difficult to produce, and are the least abundant. Most of the world's supply is raised in Egypt, southern United States including California, and islands of the West Indies. Cottons of this type are employed in the manufacture of hosiery, fine broadcloths, and fine strong yarns, which are mercerized or converted to threads or closely woven fabrics.

The intermediate types represent the bulk of commercial cottons, are somewhat coarser, shorter, and less lustrous. They are grown principally in North and South America, although the aggregate produced in various other parts of the world is not inappreciable. They are lower priced than the long staple group and consequently are the raw material for a wide variety and large volume of textile products.

The third type includes the short coarse varieties of cotton, which are produced mainly in India and China and to a lesser extent in Turkey, Iran, Iraq, Turkestan, southeastern Europe, and southern Africa. While much of this kind of cotton is converted to fabrics of lower quality, it is also especially suitable for blending with wool, and for the manufacture of carpets and cotton blankets. In the latter products harsh cottons give thick, lasting naps or piles.

The more common varieties of cotton available in the world's markets are very similar in general physical appearance. Many possess characteristic features, which are worthy of careful study and comparison. While the different varieties may look more or less alike, they nevertheless exhibit great differences in qualities and properties, which should be fully recognized by the manufacturer. It requires a highly trained and experienced person to grade properly the different qualities or "character" of cotton for manufacturing purposes. The greater part of this skill is acquired from intimate knowledge of manufacturing requirements, but often can be supplemented with fiber examinations under the microscope as well as strength and fineness determinations.

Important Commercial Varieties

The more important commercial varieties are listed and discussed in the order of decreasing fiber lengths and fineness below:

Sea Island Cotton. This variety is perhaps the most valuable of all the different species. It was of particular importance in the lace industry and in the pneumatic tire industry. Owing to the ravages of the boll weevil, production fell steadily until by 1923 the quantities ginned were too small to be recorded in government statistics. A decade later production had increased enough that the recording of statistics was again resumed. Faster-developing strains now are somewhat more resistant to plant disease. While these newer strains represent some sacrifice in the quality of the original Sea Island, this variety may again become an outstanding article of commerce.

Sea Island cotton was used mostly for the production of fine yarns, from 120's to 300's count. The "count" or size of cotton yarn means the number of 840 yard hanks contained in 1 lb. The size 120's means cotton yarn that has 120 hanks of 840 yards in 1 lb, or 100,800 yards. Sea Island was introduced into the United States in 1786, and was first grown on St. Simons Island, off the coast of Georgia. It appears to have been brought from the island of Angulla in the Caribbean Sea to the Bahamas, and from there to the coast of Georgia. From St. Simons culture extended to the Sea Islands of Charleston, where the finest varieties were grown. Very fine staple was also grown along the coast of East Florida. Sea Island cotton may be cultivated in any region near the sea, the principal requisite being a hot and humid climate, but the results of acclimatization indicate that the humid atmosphere is not entirely necessary if irrigation is employed. Sea Island requires a great deal more moisture than the Upland cottons; in fact, moisture is an all-important factor in the quality of the staple. Dry years give a poor staple and wet years a good staple.

Cultivation of Sea Island cotton is no longer confined to the islands, and a definite statement as to staple length cannot be made since this differs from place to place and variety to variety. Lint lengths up to $2\frac{3}{8}$ in. have been observed [4]. Much Sea Island which averaged $1\frac{3}{4}$ in. was grown in the West Indies. The American Sea Island ranges from $1\frac{5}{16}$ to $1\frac{13}{16}$ in. mostly between $1\frac{1}{2}$ and $1\frac{11}{16}$ in.

Sea Island produces a smaller yield per acre than other varieties grown in the United States, but the greater value of this fiber has partly compensated for the low yield. Formerly, the average yield was about 100 lb of lint per acre and the ginning outturn was about 25 per cent. A normal crop was 90,000 to 110,000 bales with nine-tenths coming from Georgia and Florida. In 1939 about 2200 bales ranging in staple length from $1\frac{5}{16}$ to $1\frac{3}{4}$ in. were produced at an average yield of 70 lb of lint per acre. In 1942 the yield was approximately 69 lb per acre. By 1948 production had fallen to 6 bales.

Egyptian Cotton. Makko-Jumel, the first variety of cotton grown in Egypt on commercial scale, went through many changes and evolutions, and gradually changed in color to a yellowish brown, the new variety being known as *Ashmouni*, from the valley of Ashmoun. The following is quoted from the American Cotton Handbook [5]:

> In general, the cottons from Egypt are so outstanding in volume and value that they must be considered the most important of the importations. Their qualities can best be appreciated after a study of the Egyptian cotton-growing area and the conditions which prevail there. As there is a tariff of 7¢ [1] per lb on cotton of $1\frac{1}{8}$ in. or more in length (effective June 18, 1930), these cottons must be of outstanding value to warrant the added cost landed in this country . . .
>
> The Egyptian cultivated area is well over 8,000,000 acres in the valley of the Nile River. The area is divided into two parts: *the Delta,* a triangular tract roughly bounded by Alexandria, Port Said, and Cairo, and *the Upper Valley,* a narrow strip of land bordering the Nile from Cairo, south to Assouan.
>
> The entire Egyptian cotton production depends upon irrigation from the waters of the Nile. An enormous dam at Assouan, about 600 miles south of the Mediterranean, backs up water as much as 182 miles. By holding water during the freshet season, this system regulates the water to maintain a flow during the dry season sufficient to supply vegetation and produce good crops.
>
> The triangular shape of the Delta is the result of using territory within reach of the various canals taking water from the Nile at Cairo. This territory is all lowland, some even below sea level, with an annual rainfall of from 1 to 8 in. The soil is very rich and the cultivation is very intensive. In order to maintain certain qualities in the Egyptian crop, the government has regulated the types of cotton permissible in some areas. Here, as in the United States, depreciation of some varieties has resulted from growing several varieties within one area. As deterioration of long staple cotton greatly reduces its value, it is being avoided as much as possible.

[1] The current tariff is $3\frac{1}{2}$¢ per lb for $1\frac{1}{8}$- to $1\frac{11}{16}$-in. cotton; no duty on staple longer than $1\frac{11}{16}$ in.

Upper Egypt, or the Upper Valley, is a narrow strip of land bordering the Nile from Cairo southward to Assouan. Cotton is grown more extensively in the northern half of this area, especially from Assiut to Cairo. There is practically no rainfall and many of the types of cotton that grow in the Delta do poorly here. This is so true that in the area from Cairo to Assiut, *Ashmouni* is the only cotton grown. South of Assiut, the variety *Giza* 3 has been commonly grown in recent years. The acreage planted to cotton in the Upper Valley is usually *about half that of the Delta plantings*.

While the rainfall in Egypt is low, the relative humidity is higher than would be expected. During the cotton growing season, there is usually a rising relative humidity, starting at about 60 per cent and increasing to 75 per cent in the more humid area and ranging about 40 per cent to 60 per cent in the drier area in the Upper Valley [6] . . .

With close government supervision, the varieties of cotton grown in Egypt are few. The disastrous results of mixing varieties being recognized, the government has passed stringent regulations to prevent mixing seed and at the same time has made extensive efforts to propagate and distribute pure strain seed suited to the needs of the community . . . Table 2 gives the recognized varieties in commercial cultivation at present and some details regarding their origin and characteristics.

TABLE 2. VARIETIES OF EGYPTIAN COTTONS

Date	*Color*	*Staple (inches)*	*Name*
1868	Dark tan	1⅛	Ashmouni
1918	Dark tan	1⅛	Zagora
1927–30		1 3/16	Giza 3
1907	Light tan	1⅜	Sakellarides
1927	Dark tan	1½	Maarad
1930	Light tan	1⅜	Giza 7
1931	Very light tan	1⅜	Sakha 4
1937	Dark tan	1⅜	Wafir
1938	Dark tan	1½	Malaki
1940	Medium tan	1⅜	Karnak

The *Ashmouni* variety has been so extensively grown in the Upper Valley for so many years that any cotton called "Uppers" is expected to be Ashmouni unless otherwise specified. It is a brown cotton and is decidedly short. However, it is grown in great volume and is so dependable that it has a considerable market. Since the decline in the quality of *Sakellarides*, considerable Ashmouni-type cotton has been grown in the southern Delta under the name of "*Zagora*." For statistical purposes, these two are usually grouped together. Another cotton grown in the Upper Valley, especially south of Assiut, is *Giza 3*. This cotton is a little longer and finer than Ashmouni and produces a higher yield. The actual volume is still small.

For many years, *Sakellarides* was the outstanding and typical Delta cotton. Several strains of Sakellarides have been developed by the government stations in an effort to maintain high qualities. However, as commercial Sakellarides became less satisfactory, other varieties were developed and introduced in an effort to get an equal or better cotton. "*Maarad*" was developed from American Pima seed and "*Giza 7*" from Ashmouni. "*Sakha 4*" was developed from Sakellarides

The varieties *Wafir*, *Malaki*, and *Karnak* are all rather new and until September, 1940, were called "Giza 12," "Giza 26," and "Giza 29," respectively. Several other strains are being developed by the Ministry of Agriculture and they may become important later. In all these strains, long staple is *not the only important factor*. It has been shown that fiber fineness is very important, and that a finer cotton, even though shorter, may be spun to a finer count than a coarse, long cotton. Yield, of course, must not be sacrificed too much in securing length and fineness or the loss in volume will more than offset the gain in the other qualities.

Egyptian cottons, as a class, are not so fine as Sea Islands, but are superior to American Uplands for goods that require a smooth finish and a high luster. A contributing factor in the demand for these cottons is the strong, silky staple which is particularly suitable for the manufacture of sewing thread, yarns for mercerizing, fine underwear, and fine broadcloths. Upward of 200,000 bales a year were imported by the United States prior to 1931, but as a result of a high tariff on cottons over 1⅛ in. in length, imports had fallen to 50,000 to 70,000 bales a year just before the war.

The soft nature of the Egyptian cottons and the fact that they possess a brown color probably indicate that they are really of Sea Island origin, but there is no evidence to show whence their deeper coloration than Sea Island arose.

It is interesting to note that yarn of Egyptian cotton is finer than that of the same count made from American Upland cotton. The fibers of the former are narrower, which, together with their greater flexibility, permits their being more closely twisted and thus yielding a finer, more compact yarn.

Pima and "S×P." The production of irrigated cottons in western and southern United States has increased rapidly since the growth of Egyptian cottons was first undertaken in these areas in 1903. About 1908 *Yuma* cotton was developed from Egyptian *Mit Afifi* and from this *Pima* was selected in 1910. By 1920, Pima was the only variety of American-Egyptian type and remained so until 1934 when "S×P," a new strain, was obtained from a cross between Pima and Egyptian *Sakellarides*. The American-Egyptian crop increased to about 90,000 bales by 1920 but has since decreased. According to Pressley, Whittaker, and Barr [7], S×P production averaged 24,300 bales for the 8 years ending 1937–38. The fiber was of good grade and staple with a yield of about 250 lb per acre. Production of American-Egyptian cottons in 1941 was 57,929 bales, was down to 4000 bales in 1949 but rose to 59,000 bales in 1950 when it was not under acreage control.[2]

S×P is said to be slightly coarser than Pima, somewhat lighter in color, and shorter in staple, but this has not been confirmed. It gives a higher yield per acre than Pima, develops earlier, and seems to produce a slightly stronger yarn.

[2] "Crops in Peace and War," *Yearbook of Agriculture*, U.S.D.A. (1950–51).

American-Egyptian cotton is usually medium to high grade and ranges in staple length from 1½ to 1⅝ in. These cottons were developed for use by the pneumatic tire industry but are used principally in dress goods and specialties. Acreage was about equally divided between Pima and S×P in 1938.

The yields of American-Egyptian cottons are low compared with the yields of Upland grown under similar conditions. The latter averages about 500 lb per acre in the irrigated regions of Arizona, New Mexico, and California and about 280 lb per acre where it is rain-grown in its normal habitat in Texas and other cotton states. Unless, therefore, a high premium is paid for the American-Egyptian, its production is not profitable.

Other Long Staple Cottons. A number of other varieties of the same species (*G. barbadense*) as Sea Island cotton are grown commercially but in smaller quantities than those mentioned above. This group includes smooth Peruvian, rough Peruvian, and Tanguis. Tanguis was developed in 1918 and in 1933 comprised 92 per cent of the Peruvian crop, with Pima ranking second [8]. The production of rough Peruvian has been decreasing rapidly. The lint of Tanguis is not as long as of some of the other varieties and, being rather coarse, is used for the same purposes as long staple Upland [4, 8]. Ishan cotton grown in Nigeria belongs to the Peruvian group and is believed to be a transitional form between the tree type and the annual type, Sea Island [4]. The lint is rather short and coarse. In the *G. barbadense* group there are also perennial types which may grow into large trees 15 to 20 ft high and which produce a short, coarse staple up to 1¼ in. in length. "Kidney" cotton is in this class as also are "Aspero" of Peru, "Vergara" of Central Colombia, and "Criollo" of Minas Geraes, Brazil [4].

A distinctly separate species (*G. purpurascens*) known as the Bourbon group is the basis of the cotton-growing industries of Haiti, the Atlantic region of Colombia, Carriacou (West Indies), and part of North Brazil [4]. Typically, it is a perennial capable of living for 20 years or more. While the lint varies considerably in quality, some strains produce a staple of 2 in. with a fineness equaling Sea Island. Mongrelization of Bourbon stock with Upland cotton has occurred to an appreciable extent.

Upland Cottons. The group of cottons comprising the species *G. hirsutum* and generally known as Uplands was described as follows by Harland [4]:

> The cotton-growing regions of the southern United States, Turkestan, South Brazil, Uganda, South and West Africa, Queensland, Mesopotamia and parts of China, India, and Manchuria cultivate this species. Thus the greater proportion

of the cultivated cotton of the world is *G. hirsutum*. According to Vavilov [9, 10], this species originated in Central America, probably in southern Mexico. It is an annual cotton, flowering under optimum conditions in 7–8 weeks from sowing. Under wild conditions it would probably not survive competition with other species, and it is thus essentially a species of cultivation. It exists in innumerable forms, for a description of a large number of which the reader is referred to Tyler [11].

It is now adapted for annual cultivation in subtropical regions, for which it has obviously been selected from some more primitive stock by human agency. Physiologically it is characterized by being practically nonphotoperiodic, in which it differs strongly from the more southerly *barbadense* group. The lint length varies from ½ to about 1⁵⁄₁₆ in.

Most American cottons belong to this group, ranging in staple length from ¾ to 1⅜ in. and in diameter from 15 to 22 μ (0.0006 to 0.0008 in.). The average American Upland cotton was just over 1 in. in staple length in 1941 [12] and slightly above 1¹⁄₃₂ in. in 1949 (Table 14).

Table 3 is reproduced from a recent publication [5] and shows the varieties of cotton commonly grown here with details as to their staple length (in 32nds in.), per cent ginning outturn, bolls per pound, and date and place of origin. The samples have been arranged in the order of their length for convenience.

The *Agricultural Yearbook* [8] for 1937, which contains summary accounts of the origin and properties of many of these varieties as well as of some varieties developed from them, is recommended for more detailed information.

The quality of American cottons has improved materially since 1930, when it showed an alarming retrogression in staple length. This decline in staple was the result of efforts to minimize boll weevil losses through the growing of short staple, quickly maturing varieties. Since that time the percentage of the American crop with staple length under ⅞ in. has fallen appreciably.

More and more Upland cotton is being grown in the irrigated cotton regions of Arizona, California, and New Mexico, over 700,000 bales in 1939. Staple length ranged from 1 to 1⁷⁄₃₂ in. The yield per acre in these areas is extremely high compared with Upland raised under rain-grown conditions, but for many purposes irrigated cotton is inferior to rain-grown, being more irregular in staple, and often wastier and weaker. Nevertheless, production had risen to over 1,500,000 bales in 1950.

Upland types of cotton are raised commercially in Mexico, the better staple types being grown in the Mexicali district (lower California) and medium to short staples in other districts.

In Argentina the cotton-growing industry is probably based on Upland or strains of Upland origin. The Chaco territory produces most of the

TABLE 3. Details for Commonly Grown American Upland Varieties

Names	Staple 32nds	Output (per cent)	Bolls per lb	Origin	
				Year	State
Half and Half	24 to 28	40 to 45	65 to 70	1906	Ga.
Wannamaker Cleveland	28 to 30	37 to 39	65 to 70	1908	S. C.
Piedmont Cleveland	28 to 30	34 to 36	65 to 70	1914	Ga.
New Boykin	28 to 31	37 to 40	75 to 80	1913	Tex.
Trice	28 to 32	31 to 33	74 to 84	1906	Tenn.
Dixie Triumph	28 to 32	33 to 35	65 to 75	1908	S. C.
Cook	28 to 32	35 to 38	70 to 85	1912	Ala.
Toole	30	35 to 37	65 to 75	1907	Ga.
Oklahoma Triumph	29 to 32	34 to 36	70 to 90	1914	Okla.
Kasch	30 to 32	38 to 41	45 to 60	1912	Tex.
Lone Star	31 to 33	38 to 41	45 to 60	1904	Tex.
Dixie 14	31 to 33	34 to 38	65 to 70	1920	S. C.
Rowden	30 to 33	34 to 37	50 to 65	1890	Tex.
Mebane	30 to 34	37 to 40	50 to 65	1882	Tex.
Station Miller	32	32 to 36	60 to 65	1926	Miss.
Acala 5	32 to 34	33 to 37	65 to 75	1914	Okla.
Mexican Big Boll	32 to 34	34 to 37	60 to 65	1917	N. C.
Delta and Pine Land 10	32 to 34	33 to 36	70 to 80	1920	Miss.
Cleveland 5	32 to 34	36 to 40	65 to 70	1921	S. C.
Delta and Pine Land 8	32 to 34	36 to 38	70 to 80	1921	Miss.
Arkansas Rowden 40	32 to 34	32 to 36	55 to 70	1921	Ark.
Stoneville	32 to 34	33 to 36	70 to 80	1923	Miss.
Cleveland 884	32 to 34	36 to 38	65 to 70	1923	S. C.
Acala 8	34 to 38	35 to 38	60 to 70	1914	Okla.
Delfos	36 to 38	31 to 34	75 to 85	1916	Miss.
Express	36 to 38	32.5	75 to 80	1921	Miss.
Lightning Express	36 to 38	32 to 34	75 to 85	1922	S. C.
Missdel	37 to 38		68 to 78	1916	Miss.
Wilds	38 to 44	31 to 34	60 to 75	1919	S. C.
Delta type Webber	38 to 44	31 to 33	60 to 65	1915	S. C.

Argentine crop. The Chaco type that predominates is a hardy variety yielding a staple of 7/8 to 1 3/32 in. It is believed to be derived from an American Upland introduced early in the present century.

The southern states of Brazil have increased their production of cotton enormously since 1920. Much of this increase has occurred in the State of São Paulo. This southern area raises Upland varieties almost exclusively. The Brazilian Federal and State Governments have been active in cotton improvement through importation of better American varieties and through selection from local varieties. Eighty per cent of the Brazilian crop ranges in staple length from 7/8 to 1 3/32 in. with about 20 per cent 1 1/8 in. or longer. The character of Brazilian cottons is said to be less satisfactory than of American cottons of the corresponding lengths. American varieties imported by Brazil for breeding purposes include Sunbeam, Upright, Cleveland, Durango, Webber, and Russell, which have become hybridized among themselves and possibly also to some extent with native tree cottons.

Cotton production in the U.S.S.R. fell from over 1,000,000 bales in 1910 to about 50,000 in 1920. The volume then increased markedly and in 1940 reached 4,000,000 bales. The Soviet crop is confined largely to Turkestan, Transcaucasia, and the Uzbek Republic and is principally from a variety called Navrotsky, developed from Russell, an American Upland variety. Strains of King and Mebane Triumph have also been adapted to the Asiatic environment. The staple of Soviet Upland ranges from 7/8 to 1 3/32 in. Some longer Egyptian strains have been adapted to Transcaucasia and the Tadzhik and Turkmen Republics of central Asia, where they are now enjoying some success. U.S.S.R. production was estimated at 2,700,000 bales in 1949.

The commercial cottons of Uganda are Uplands derived from stocks brought from the United States during the last two decades. These adapted varieties produce a staple of 7/8 to 1 1/16 in. Small quantities of American Upland are also raised under rainfall conditions in the southern provinces of the Sudan and in the Nuba Mountains.

American Upland varieties introduced in Korea in 1906 now serve as the basis for about 75 per cent of the crop. Cultivated chiefly in the southern half of the peninsula, these varieties yield a staple ranging from 7/8 to 1 1/16 in. Manchuria raises in the southern part of the country small quantities of cotton that originated from American Upland seed. About 90 per cent of the Manchurian crop comes from coarse, native types.

Coarse, short cottons predominate in India, but staple improvement efforts are being rewarded with an increasing proportion of medium staple growths. The latter, ranging from 7/8 to 1 in., now constitute approximately one-third of the Indian crop. In two of the four regions that produce medium staple, namely Bombay and the Punjab, acclimatized Uplands are widely grown. Uplands were introduced in India as early as 1825, when both Georgia and New Orleans varieties were grown, but the former was successful in perpetuating itself. Mixing with native varieties did not occur and by the turn of the century, when breeding work was undertaken, the Upland strains were well adapted and relatively pure. Since 1900 Upland varieties, imported from the United States, have had some success but only after several years' acclimatization and only in certain areas.

Adapted strains of the Upland varieties Acala and Trice were distributed to farmers in China in 1923. The Trice strain was found to be especially good in regions away from the coast and in the North, because of its early maturity.

Short Staple Cottons

The greater part of the commercial cottons of India and China are short, coarse, Old World types that belong to the species *G. arboreum* and *G. herbaceum*. Harland [4] states that strains of the former are widely distributed in India, Malaya, and South China, with some spreading westward into Abyssinia and the Sudan, and that strains of the latter species are grown throughout India but are typical of northwest India, Turkey, Persia (Iran), Iraq, Turkestan, southeastern Europe, and southern Africa. The species *G. herbaceum* is an annual and *G. arboreum* is both an annual and a perennial.

Two-thirds of the Indian crop is estimated to range in staple length from ⅜ to ⅞ in. and is suitable for spinning counts only as high as 16's. One native variety, Surat 1027 ALF, is an exception, yielding yarns as high as 34's in count. The native varieties are cultivated in central India, Central Provinces, Berar, Bengal, and Assam.

"Kumpta" cotton is a trade name for native varieties of the *G. herbaceum* species in Bombay that have been developed to good yield and disease resistance. Surat 1027 ALF, mentioned above, originated from a cross between a Kumpta strain and another *G. herbaceum* variety known as "Ghogari." Other varieties of *G. herbaceum* now being grown are Gadag No. 1 and Wagad 8. In the Broach area of Bombay a wilt-resistant variety known as BD8 (Broach, *G. herbaceum* × Deshi 8, *G. neglectum*) has been developed.

A native cotton called Million Dollar was the best among domestic varieties cultivated in China before World War II. It was selected from a field near Woosung, Shanghai, in 1919 and carried through further selections in 1920 and 1921. Its superiority over other native growths in 1935 was indicated by the fact that the mills were paying a premium of more than 20 per cent for it. Like other Old World types, Chinese cottons are coarse, harsh, and short. Much of China's large crop was used domestically by hand manufacture and for the padding of clothing; however, in the textile mills it was suitable only for coarse goods and wool mixtures. In consequence, China was forced to import American and Indian cottons to provide her mills with fiber of the quality needed for manufacturing. Cotton improvement work was placing China on the way to supplying her own needs when the war came in 1937.

Rare Varieties

The number of different cultivated varieties and strains of both the Old and New World species is extraordinarily large. In addition there are countless wild cottons of both types as well as of other species [13]. Watt [3] described many of the wild cottons but his classification of them was arbitrary and is not accepted at the present time [4]. More than 1200 different strains of cotton were under cultivation in experimental plots at the Delta Experiment Station, Stoneville, Miss., in 1937. Many of these were strains being propagated for breeding purposes.

The *American Cotton Handbook* [5] reproduced an interesting example of the origin of commercial varieties of cotton. The following quotation and Fig. 1 are taken from that source:

> The chart below illustrates the development of a series of varieties of cotton showing how new varieties are derived from older varieties by selection or crossing. The chart shows most of these new varieties as *selections* from Mebane, which was

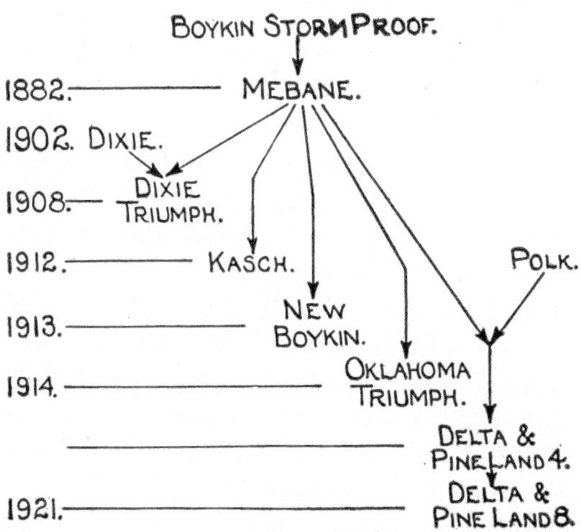

FIG. 1. Origin of commercial varieties of cotton.

a selection from Boykin Storm Proof in 1882. It also shows how two varieties were obtained by *cross-breeding* Mebane with other varieties. This chart was developed from data in a paper by H. B. Brown, chairman of the subcommittee on cotton registration for varietal standardization of the American Society of Agronomy.

Lints of various colors are known and some are grown experimentally. Green-, orange-, and brown-tinted cottons are under small-scale cultivation but are not yet of commercial interest. The Soviets claim development of a black lint that does not require dyeing. According to Conrad [14], the wax content of lint from a variety of Arkansas green lint is 14 to 17 per cent as against 0.4 to 0.7 per cent for most cottons. Hopi cotton, a native variety that the Hopi Indians in Arizona have used for centuries, has lately become of interest. This variety is short but very fine. The United States Department of Agriculture has undertaken the development of a Hopi-Acala cross.

Botanical Classifications

The genus *Gossypium,* which includes the cultivated cottons, is a member of the sub-tribe Hibisceae in the natural order of Malvaceae. Truly wild forms of cotton also belong to this genus, whose members are native to tropical and subtropical regions of both the Eastern and the Western Hemisphere. The name *Gossypium* was adopted by Linnaeus, who established the genus. The most important contributions to the taxonomy were made by Parlatore (1866), Todaro (1878), Watt (1907), Zaitzev (1928), and Harland and his coworkers (1926–35). The boundaries of the genus are still not known with certainty but, according to Harland [4]:

> It is unlikely that any species at present (1938) accepted as members of the genus will have to be removed to other genera, though it is highly probable that some species at present assigned to other genera will ultimately find a place in the genus *Gossypium.*

The knowledge necessary for an adequate taxonomic classification of *Gossypium* has existed only since about 1924, when Denham in England, Nikolajeva in Russia, and Longley in America discovered almost simultaneously that cultivated Old World and New World cottons have 13 and 26 haploid chromosomes, respectively. Zaitzev's original classification (1928) based on this fundamental difference has been criticized by Harland [4], who proposed a classification now widely accepted in principle. Kearney [13] has presented a modification which follows the main lines of Harland's classification but differs in details.

In Harland's scheme, the genus *Gossypium* is classified broadly according to chromosome number, genetical behavior, and geographical distribution, and more narrowly according to morphological and physiological characteristics. The more important characters employed for this purpose are as follows:

a. Degree of pittedness of bolls.
b. Arrangement of filaments.
c. Photoperiodic reaction.
d. Habit.

Harland's classification is given below:

Section 1. The 26 Chromosome Group

A. New World (cultivated and wild):
  1. Upland group, *G. hirsutum*, Linn.
  2. Bourbon group, *G. purpurascens*, Poir.
  3. Punctatum group, *G. punctatum*, Sch. et Thon.
  4. Peruvian group, *G. barbadense*, Linn.

B. Polynesian (wild):
  1. *G. tomentosum*, Nutt. (Hawaiian Islands).
  2. *G. taitense*, Parl. (Fiji Islands, etc.).
  3. *G. darwinii*, Watt (Galapagos Islands).

Section 2. The 13 Chromosome Group

A. Old World (wild and cultivated):
  1. *G. arboreum*, Linn. (Asia and Africa).
  2. *G. herbaceum*, Linn. (Asia and Africa).

B. Old World (wild):
  1. *G. anomalum*, Wawra et Peyr. (Africa).
  2. *G. stocksii*, M. Mast. (India).

C. New World (wild):
  1. *G. davidsonii*, Kell.
  2. *G. thurberi*, Tod. (= *Thurberia thespesioides*, A. Gray).
  3. *G. harknessii*, Brandg.
  4. *G. amourianum*, Kearney.
  5. *G. aridum*, Skovsted (nov. comb.) (= *Erioxylum aridum*, Rose and Standley).

D. Polynesian (wild):
  1. *G. klotzschianum*, Andss.

E. Australian (wild):
  1. *G. sturtii*, F. v. M.

Harland noted that this classification representing 18 species does not provide for some of the species admitted by other workers. These exclusions were made either because particular cases were so close to accepted species as to merit only sub-specific or varietal rank, or because insufficient knowledge was available to establish valid relationships. The following species were incorporated with other species:

1. *G. hirsutum* probably includes *G. mexicanum*, Tod.
2. *G. purpurascens* includes *G. schottii*, Watt and *G. morelli*, Cook.
3. *G. punctatum* includes *G. ekmanianum*, Wittmack and *G. hopi*, Lewton.
4. *G. barbadense* includes *G. mustelinum*, Miers, *G. microcarpum*, Tod., *G. peruvianum*, Cav., *G. vitifolium*, Lamk., and *G. lapideum*, Tussac (= *G. brasilense*, Macf.). The exclusion of *G. kirkii*, M. Mast., and *G. drynarioides*, Seem., formerly classified as members of the genus, was made definite.

The general description of the genus *Gossypium* given below is quoted from Harland [4].

> Habit ranges from that of a herbaceous plant to a sub-arboraceous shrub or small tree. Main stem round and characterized by a lower zone with monopodial branches and an upper zone with sympodial branches. Flowers are cream, yellow, red or purple, and are borne on sympodial branches. Bracteoles three, large or small, cordate, toothed or entire. Calyx truncate or five-toothed. Staminal column bearing indefinite filaments, below naked or with anthers to the apex. Ovary 2–5 locular, seeds per loculus indefinite. Style glandular, club-shaped or clavate shortly into as many lobes as loculi in the ovary. Capsule with loculicidal dehiscence. Seeds subglobose or angular, covered with one or two layers of unicellular convoluted hairs: albumen thin, membranous or absent; cotyledons strongly folded. Glands nigro-punctate distributed over the whole plant. Leaves entire or 3–9 lobed.
>
> Eighteen or more species distributed in the tropics and sub-tropics of America (N. & S.), Africa, Asia, and Australia.

Harland's general description of the Upland group [4] (*G. hirsutum*) is as follows:

> Habit sympodial, the first fruiting branch being produced at nodes 6–10. Boll pale green and with glands buried beneath surface, more often round than long; sometimes very large. Anthers early bursting. Filaments long at top and middle of column, shorter at base. Pollen medium yellow or medium cream. Leaf only shallowly cut into 3–5 lobes. Corolla usually widely expanded, cream, spotted in some types but usually devoid of spot.

The geographical distribution of this species is discussed in another section.

Harland [4] and Kearney [13] have pointed out that the evidence of cotton having been cultivated prehistorically in both the Old World and the New is now convincing. The different chromosome numbers indicate that it was domesticated independently from different wild species in the two hemispheres. Within and near the tropics of the two centers there are many forms growing without cultivation that are long-lived and often reach the size of small trees. Although many of these have been described as species, Kearney considered them to be relics of ancient cultivation rather than truly wild and indigenous forms. Further evidence of this origin is the fact that there exist in many parts of Africa and Polynesia apparently wild cottons of American relationship, which must have been introduced there by man.

Kearney [13] also stated that the ancestry of species now under cultivation may never be determined. Difficulties in the way of such determination are

a. The antiquity of the domestication of cotton.

b. Its wide distribution in and near the tropics in prehistoric times.

c. The ease with which seed, remaining viable for several years, can be transported from place to place.

d. The facility with which plants escape from cultivation and become established as long-lived perennials in warm countries.

e. The extensive cross-compatibility in the genus which is favorable for the production and maintenance of hybrids between species.

Furthermore, the crossing of two species, such as Sea Island and Upland, produces a multitude of peculiar-appearing plants in the second generation that might well mislead the systematic botanist. Thus, while a large number of "species" has been tabulated and named, it is doubtful at the present whether or not more than 25 or 30 can be ranked as true species.

The Grading of Cotton

The need for a system of grading cottons becomes apparent when it is realized that manufacturing requirements are widely different for various products and that cottons vary in quality from year to year even though the same seed may be planted in the same locality. Weather conditions at the time of harvest influence the quality as also does the subsequent handling at the gins. The American crop is raised on some 1,250,000 farms and in most cases the producers are free to select their own seeds. The result is that the crop must be evaluated, bale by bale, for qualities not related to staple length. This evaluation is known as "grading," and by it an equitable basis of settlement is sought for both the purchaser and the producer. Grading also describes the cotton and makes buying and selling easier, where there are no samples.

In recent years the one-variety community has gained considerable impetus in the United States. This movement has been encouraged by the Government and by some of the mills in the cotton belt that wanted to assure themselves of a supply of suitable cotton in their immediate vicinities. The advantages of the system are that cross-breeding is reduced and that an appreciable amount of the same cotton is available in one small area. In addition, mixing of lint and seed at the gins becomes relatively unimportant.

The grades employed for American Upland cotton are as follows:

1. Middling fair.
2. Strict good middling.
3. Good middling.
4. Strict middling.
5. Middling.
6. Strict low middling.
7. Low middling.
8. Strict good ordinary.
9. Good ordinary.

In an average season this range of grades covers practically all of the white cottons grown. The grade names containing the word "strict" are known in the trade as *half* grades; the others are *full* grades. "Middling," as the name indicates, is the middle or basic grade, and is the grade upon which the market quotations are based. All grades above middling bring a higher price, and all below middling bring a lower price. Many more grade names are used by the trade in the large spot markets to describe the different classes of colored cottons. The grades of white cotton, however, are the foundation of all these other classes. When the cotton is not white, its nature is indicated by adding the words "spotted," "tinged," or "stained," as the case may be, to its grade.

There are a number of terms employed in the grading and selection of cotton which require explanation. A good glossy, full-bodied fiber, which has been well-ginned and packed, will reflect light well. "Blush" is sometimes used to describe this character. "Tinged, "spotted," and "stained" explain themselves, as do also "musty," "sandy," and "leafy." "Musty" cotton is caused by dampness, and the unmistakable musty smell is a sure indication of an excess of moisture. "Sandy" cotton is readily detected by holding a sample up to the light and gently shaking it; the fine particles will sometimes fall like a miniature cloud; by passing the palm of the hand over the place where the samples have lain on paper, sand can always be detected if present in any quantity. "Soapy" and "waxy" are used to describe the sensations experienced when cotton with these characteristics is passed through the fingers. "Green" cotton is cotton which has been picked early. It may be unripe or insufficiently aged and may contain large amounts of natural moisture. It is not suitable for spinning. "Staple" cottons are generally understood to be 1⅛ in. or longer.

The grade of cotton, as the term is most widely understood, is composed of three factors:

a. Color. Color may be described in terms of three attributes, hue, brilliance, and chroma. Hue is defined as the name of the color; brilliance as the lightness or darkness of a color; and chroma as the intensity, strength, or degree of color.

b. Foreign Matter.[1] The term "foreign matter" as here employed refers to parts of the cotton plant such as broken leaves, stems, bracts, or burr, which in greater or lesser degree normally pass through the processes of picking and ginning and are thus retained in the ginned lint.

c. Preparation. This is a term used to describe the degree to which the normal fiber length is maintained or the regularity with which the individual fibers are laid together in ginning, and the relative "nappiness" of the cotton. *Poor* preparation is evidenced by an appearance of roughness or stringiness. A somewhat rougher preparation is normally found in long-staple cotton than in short-staple cotton. Hence, standards for the preparation of cotton of a staple length of 1⅛ in. or longer have been prepared and promulgated tentatively.

Color

The normal color of raw cotton is a light to dark cream, depending on the variety, weather, and soil conditions. When cotton is left too long in the field, the "bloom" is lost and the color changes to a "dead" or bluish white, reducing the grade appreciably. A rain may change a good middling to middling "tinged" or middling "stained," according to the kind of soil and the quantity of rain. Weather-tinged and weather-stained cottons are often a "gray" or bluish color, and, when not grown on sandy land, generally contain mud spots. The action of frost on the late bolls before they open also causes spots, tinges, or stains, depending upon the amount of colored cotton that is mixed with the white. This "frost" cotton has a yellowish or buff color, and may be weaker than other tinged cotton because the bolls were forced open before the fiber was fully developed.

Cotton picked while wet with dew or soon after rain will contain an excess of moisture. This may cause mildew and give the cotton a *bluish cast.* A bale of cotton left exposed to the weather in the gin yard very often has a mildewed outer surface or plate, and a sample drawn from near the surface of such a bale may not afford a fair representation of its color,

The United States Official Cotton Grades, as well as other grade standards, require that cotton grading strict good middling or above

[1] The term "foreign matter" as used here does not refer to pieces of stone, iron, or other foreign objects occasionally found in falsely packed bales. *Editor.*

should be of a bright creamy or white color, and free from any discoloration. A definite or fixed color is not absolutely required in the grades below strict good middling. For example, a middling may be creamy or dead white, and the same sample might grade below or above middling, accordingly as it contained more or less impurities. Below strict low middling, however, the creamy color or bloom is lost, since climatic and soil conditions that lower the grade to this extent also affect the color, giving a dead white, a gray, or a reddish or dingy cast to the lower grades, although they pass commercially as *white cotton*.

The above variations in color can be seen when the cotton is placed in a north light. Out of doors, the examiner turns his back toward the sun, so that his line of vision will be parallel to the rays of light. The best light may be had on a clear day between the hours of 9 a.m. and 3 p.m. It is sometimes hard to judge the color of cotton on a cloudy or partly cloudy day because of reflected light. This difficulty is frequently experienced along the coast, where the reflection may be even more troublesome when grading is done near large bodies of water. "Extra white" cotton, which is produced for the most part in the dry areas of Texas, has almost no pigment, is exceptionally white, and is of the highest color grade.

"White" cotton has a light creamy appearance due to fiber pigments. It may also be an extra white cotton contaminated with enough fine foreign matter, such as dust, to reduce it in the color scale.

"Spotted" cotton is that which has been discolored with brown spots as a result of contact with wet bolls, leaves, or stems. The brown discolorations are distinctly separated and in a white cotton give a spotted appearance.

"Tinged" cotton contains more extensive brown discoloration than spotted grades. The color is more uniformly distributed than in the spotted sample.

"Yellow stained" cotton is almost completely discolored and gives a mottled, tan appearance. Such stains are often difficult to remove during processing and consequently the grade is reduced.

Foreign Matter

Inevitably, foreign matter finds its way into the seed cotton. Hand-picked cotton is usually higher in grade than mechanically picked, because the human picker exercises greater care. The amount of "leaf, dirt, and sand" in a sample often depends upon the weather. Usually there is very little leaf when the cotton is picked before the vegetation is killed by frost. The first picking of a field nearly always yields a higher grade than subsequent pickings. Sand and dust get into the cotton, some naturally, some during the picking. Wind and rain are the natural causes of dust and sand in the bolls. Many of these impurities may be taken out at the gins by the use of cleaners. Fifty pounds or more can very often be extracted from one bale of low-grade cotton. *Two* types of leaf contamination are recognized, (1) "fine," "pin," or "pepper" leaf, which is light and highly fragmented and therefore relatively difficult to separate from the cotton during manufacture, and (2) "large" leaf, which is coarser and usually is easier to remove.

"Broken bolls" consist of pieces of the burr which formed the outer shell of the boll and may appear in lint that has been picked hastily or carelessly. The white membranous inner coating of the burr is called "*shale.*"

"Broken twigs" are leaf or plant stems which are coarser and less brittle than leaf particles and are generally easy to separate from the lint during processing, but nevertheless increase the percentage of mill waste.

"Seed" refers both to small undeveloped seeds that may carry a fine coating of fuzz and to fragments of mature seed, cut or torn out in the ginning. The former are called "motes" and are found to some extent in all cottons, the number depending upon the variety and weather conditions during growth and maturation of the cotton. "Cut seeds" are caused by fast ginning with a hard roll and by broken or bent gin-saw teeth that strike the grate-bars. Because they have long fibers attached to them, cut seeds adhere strongly in the cotton and may appear as dark spots in the finished goods. Such fragments as are removed during manufacture carry the long fibers with them and increase the amount of waste.

Preparation

The preparation is an estimate of the uniformity of sample, of gin damage to the fiber, and of "napping" and "nepping" caused by ginning. Properly ginned cotton is uniform and not matted, while a poorly ginned sample is tangled and ropy in behavior. The latter is said to have a "rough appearance."

"Naps" are matted portions of fiber that are stringy or ropy. They are caused either by excessive moisture in the cotton during the ginning or by faulty equipment. While immature fibers in the cotton may tend to nap, stringy cotton may sometimes be caused by a wrong adjustment of the brushes that remove the lint from the gin saws. The fibers in these strings do not separate very easily and cause mill waste.

"Neps" are small tangled fiber clumps that have the appearance of white flecks about 0.04 in. in diameter. They are caused by dull saws, by dampness in the cotton, and by a high percentage of immature fibers.

They can be seen when a thin layer of the sample is held toward the light. Cut fibers show in bunches as V-shaped kinks and give the sample a rough appearance. A detailed discussion of naps, neps and motes has been presented by Pearson [15].

Universal Standard Grades

The U. S. Department of Agriculture has set up standards [16] to be used in grading, because there frequently are differences of opinion as to the grade of a particular cotton when various factors are balanced. A series of "Universal Standard Grades for American Upland Cotton" was promulgated, and in 1941 there were 32 recognized grades. Thirteen of these are in "Practical Forms," i.e., in large boxes with 12 separate samples of cotton of a given grade, including the accepted variations within the grade. The cotton samples in each "Practical Form" are chosen to be representative of all American cottons. Since 1924 they have been called "Universal Standards," and have been accepted by the world's larger cotton markets.

The following discussion is based on U.S.D.A. publications [5, 16, and 17].

The 32 Universal Standard grades are shown below. Those shown in bold face type are the 13 for which practical forms are available. The others are called "Descriptive" grades. The grades shown above the horizontal lines may be delivered on future contracts, while those below may not [17].

TABLE 4. Thirty-Two Universal Standard Grades for Cotton

Gray	*Extra White*	*Main Grades*	*Spotted*	*Tinged*	*Yellow Stained*
		No. 1, or middling fair			
		No. 2, or strict good middling			
GMG	GMEW	**No. 3, or good middling**	GMSp.	**GMT**	GMYS
SMG	SMEW	**No. 4, or strict middling**	SMSp.	**SMT**	SMYS
MG	MEW	**No. 5, or middling**	MSp.	**MT**	MYS
	SLMEW	**No. 6, or strict low middling**	SLMSp.	**SLMT**	
	LMEW	**No. 7, or low middling**	LMSp.	**LMT**	
	SGOEW	**No. 8, or strict good ordinary**			
	GOEW	**No. 9, or good ordinary**			

Because of the importance of preparation and the impracticability of trying to include variations in preparation in the regular practical forms, a set of nine tentative practical forms have been prepared for the long-staple Upland cottons. Three grades are shown, Strict Middling, Middling and Strict Low Middling, with three grades of preparation for each, A, B, and C.

"*Preparation A* is free from perceptible gin cut fibers, and from neps, naps, stringy cotton, etc. The surface of the sample is relatively smooth with the fibers laid evenly. *Preparation B* is slightly rough, with the fibers showing some irregularity in their alignment with each other, and a slight amount of neps and naps. The crop of long staple cotton is predominantly B, and B is therefore ordinarily regarded as 'normal preparation for cotton having a staple length of 1⅛ inches and longer.' . . . *Preparation C* shows considerable roughness with both neps and naps prominent through the sample [16]."

When a sample of cotton has the color of one grade, the foreign matter of a second and the preparation of a third or any other similar combination, the grade is determined by an average of these factors. The general rule of the Secretary of Agriculture is:

"American Upland cotton which in color, leaf and preparation is within the range of the standards established by this notice, but which contains a combination of color, leaf and preparation not within any one of the definitions herein set out, shall be designated according to the definition which is equivalent to, or if there be no exact equivalent is next below, the average of all the factors that determine the grade of the cotton: *Provided,* That in no event shall the grade assigned to any cotton or sample be more than one grade higher than the grade classification of the color or leaf contained therein [16]."

A study of the practical forms for white Upland cottons shows that the differences in dirt content for the grades above Middling are slight and that from Middling grade down, the quantity of discoloration and dirt increases very rapidly. This is generally borne out by the differences in prices for the various grades. An illustration of this is shown in the following table, giving the prices for the various white grades as of June 7th, 1941:

Grade	*MF*	*SGM*	*GM*	*SM*	*M*	*SLM*	*LM*	*SGO*	*GO*
Price	13.77	13.71	13.65	13.53	13.20	12.69	11.88	11.18	10.71
Reduction *		0.06	0.06	0.12	0.33	0.51	0.81	0.70	0.47

* Reduction from price of next better grade.

It is of interest to note how the differences between grades above middling are fairly uniform but how those below Middling gradually increase.

AMERICAN-EGYPTIAN COTTON, having been ginned on roller gins, having an entirely different natural color, and being grown under such different conditions, requires an entirely separate grading system. Names, such as "Fancy," "Extra Choice," etc., after the old Sea Island grades, were used at first for American-Egyptian cotton, but the present system of numbers (1941) was promulgated in 1918 and the standards were revised in 1923, 1930, and 1931. This system uses the numbers one to five to designate the standard grades available in the practical forms. Grades 1½, 2½ and 4½ are between the full numbers. The lowest number represents the best grade and the half numbers are poorer than the number preceding. The same grade standards are used for Pima and S×P.

The characteristics of Sea Island cottons are so different from either Upland or American Egyptian that separate grades are necessary for this crop, also. Before the first World War, Sea Island cottons were graded on an independent commercial system. In 1918, the Secretary of Agriculture promulgated a series of grades for this crop, but with its disappearance from commercial production, no attention was paid to them. However, with the recent production expanding, the Secretary has had a new set of grades promulgated which became effective August

10, 1939. In this system, there are six full grades numbered 1 to 6, for which there are practical forms, and five half grades, which are descriptive. The lowest number represents the best grade.

"STAPLE" is the average length of fibers in a given cotton. However, this is not a mathematical or statistical average. The *Handbook for Licensed Classifiers* [18] defines staple as: *the length by measurement of a selected portion of the fibers, which, although every sample contains fibers of many different lengths, by custom is assigned to a sample or bale as a whole.* To the inexperienced person, this may seem to leave a great deal of leeway with respect to "a selected portion," but note that this is assigned "by custom." Men hoping to be cotton classers spend months, if not years, becoming thoroughly conversant with what to select to agree with established custom. One point frequently overlooked in discussion on staple is that the length assigned to a cotton is not arbitrarily taken, but is that length which a manufacturer uses in determining the proper machinery adjustments.

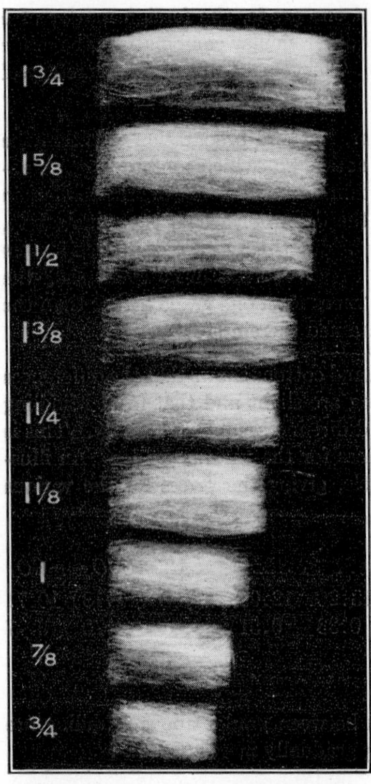

Fig. 2. A photographic representation of the official cotton standards of the United States of those lengths of staple for which types are available for distribution, each respective length as shown being obtained from the original type bale. (U. S. Dept. Agr., Bur. Markets.)

There have been many attempts to perfect some mechanical device which would precisely measure the length of cotton fibers but none of these has been able to do the work as rapidly and successfully as a competent classer. In "drawing a staple," a sample like that used for grading is broken open and fibers are drawn from one portion to make a small rectangular tuft about one half an inch wide. In preparing the tuft, the fibers are fairly well straightened and parallelized to make as uniform a density as possible. While many classers measure cotton to the nearest sixteenth of an inch, differences of a thirty-second of an inch are recognized by the U. S. Department of Agriculture.

Figure 2 illustrates staples for which official standards are available.

Staple and Price. Staple length, as might be expected, exerts a pronounced influence on the price of cotton just as grade does. A price schedule called "basis" is set up which indicates the premiums or deductions for different grades and staples in relation to the market quotation for middling $^{15}\!/_{16}$ in. Basis is fairly constant over a period of time but may be altered by unusual demands for supplies of different grades and staples. The basis for spot cotton at Memphis in "points" (0.01¢) on

October 9, 1952, is shown in Table 5. Actual prices can be calculated from the New York December futures price of 37.83¢ on October 9, 1952.

TABLE 5. Spot Cotton at Memphis in Points Off and On

Lengths (inches)	*S.M.*	*Mid.*	*S.L.M.*
13/16	300 off	375 off	425 off
7/8	200 off	225 off	325 off
29/32	125 off	150 off	275 off
15/16	50 off	75 off	250 off
31/32	35 off	60 off	235 off
1	10 on	25 off	200 off
1 1/32	35 on	even	150 off
1 1/16	115 on	65 on	100 off
1 3/32	200 on	125 on	40 off
1 1/8	335 on	235 on	60 on
1 5/32	610 on	485 on	160 on
1 3/16	860 on	710 on	335 on
1 7/32	1160 on	1010 on	510 on
1 1/4	1460 on	1260 on	685 on

It can be seen that the higher grades and longer staples bring the greater premiums ("on"). Thus, strict middling 1 1/4 in. cotton was quoted at 52.43¢, while strict low middling 13/16 in. had a value of 33.58¢.

Grade and value do not run parallel except for cottons that have the same qualities of staple; that is to say, the cotton merchant must rate the strength, length, pliability, cling, and evenness of the staple as well as the grade. It was shown in the preceding paragraphs that regular commercial practice involves a reduction in price as the grade becomes lower. This price reduction is justified both by the lower quality of the fiber itself and by higher percentages of waste in conversion shown by the lower grades. The variation in amount of waste with grade, the composition of mill wastes for middling and strict low middling cottons, and waste variation from mill to mill are shown in Tables 6, 7, and 8 prepared by the Cotton Textile Institute [19].

TABLE 6. Waste Removed from Six Different Grades of Cotton

Grades	*Number of Samples*	*Average Picker and Card Waste (per cent)*
G.M.	83	6.71
S.M.	183	6.99
M.	118	7.59
S.L.M.	66	9.38
L.M.	33	10.61
S.G.O.	22	13.11

TABLE 7. Types of Waste Removed from Middling Cotton *

Types of Waste	Mill Number			
	1	2	3	4
	Per Cent	*Per Cent*	*Per Cent*	*Per Cent*
Bagging and ties	4.25	4.25	4.25	4.25
Picker motes	2.42	2.22	2.04	2.17
Card strips	4.01	3.56	3.25	2.51
Card motes and fly	1.07	1.02	1.24	1.30
Card sweepings	0.63	0.63	0.68	0.67
Dust flue	0.22	0.16	0.23	0.24
Spinning sweeps	0.71	0.68	0.66	0.58
Clearer waste	0.21	0.16	0.13	0.25
Soft thread	0.56	0.54	0.35	0.87
Spindle bands	0.09	0.09	0.04	0.08
Twister sweeps	0.29	0.25	0.40	0.43
Total	14.46	13.56	13.27	13.35

* Average for 52 weeks. Carded yarn mill.

TABLE 8. Waste Removed from Strict Low Middling Cotton *

Types of Waste	Mill Number		
	1	2	3
	Per Cent	*Per Cent*	*Per Cent*
Bagging and ties	4.80	4.80	4.80
Picker motes	1.50	1.26	1.20
Picker sweeps	0.08	0.04	0.12
Card flat strips	2.60	3.08	2.90
Card cylinder and doffer strips	0.88	0.74	0.72
Card motes and fly	1.80	1.70	1.71
Card sweepings	0.94	1.07	1.00
Spinning sweeps and clearer waste	1.21	1.43	1.24
Weave sweeps	0.66	0.75	0.81
Soft thread	0.64	0.39	0.48
Weave room hard waste	0.29	0.18	0.20
Slasher hard waste	0.27	0.52	0.32
Spooler hard waste	0.55	0.54	0.38
Total	16.22	16.50	15.88

* Average for one month. Weaving mill on print cloth.

Thorough knowledge of the amount of waste given by different qualities of cotton is important to the cotton buyer in the evaluation of a sample of cotton.

Cost of Fiber Preparation

The demand for cotton as indicated by the market price of strict middling appears to vary with general business activity over a period of years. In other words, price statistics show clearly that cotton is consumed most rapidly at the peaks in business cycles. Except for a break to nearly $2.00 a lb during and directly after the War between the States and for another to 40¢ a lb at the close of World War I (1919–24), the average price of cotton has fluctuated continuously between 5 and 20¢ a lb for almost a century. Early in 1951 it was 41¢ per lb.

The cost of fiber preparation, that is, picking, ginning, and baling and, in some cases, compressing, is somewhat less variable, although it does differ from year to year and locality to locality. The cost of picking in the United States has ranged from an approximate base rate of 50¢ to $2.50 (in 1950) per 100 lb of seed cotton; the actual rate is determined by local conditions such as the availability of pickers and the heaviness of the cotton stand. Ginning costs have risen from about $5.00 a bale in a decade to $10.50 in 1950 with some local variations. In the same period the farm price of cotton has ranged from 5½ to 43¢ a lb. These figures refer to Upland cotton and *saw ginning.* The cost of roller ginning long-staple Pima and S×P was about double that of saw ginning during the same period. This higher cost indicates the relative difference between *roller* and *saw* ginning.

Seed cotton as it arrives at the gin represents about one part lint and two parts seed. A common practice followed by small cotton producers is to leave their seed with the ginner, who sells the seed to an oil mill, deducts the ginning charges, and returns the balance to the farmer. The higher cost of ginning in Texas and other states in the western part of the rain-grown cotton belt has been attributed to the more elaborate equipment required and to the fact that the cotton frequently has more trash and is more difficult to gin. Local custom also plays a part in ginning. In some sections, particularly the Southeast, the ginning cost is a flat rate based on a 500-lb gross weight bale; in Georgia and Louisiana, it is a fixed rate per 100 lb of lint with or without an extra charge for bagging and tie bands; in the Western regions, costs are calculated on the weight of seed cotton.

Government Supervision

Governmental interest in the cotton industry has increased as the cotton problem has become more acute. A Cotton Futures Act became law in 1916 by which official grades were established as standard in the United States, and the preparation and distribution of these standards was reposed in the Division of Cotton Marketing. It was also given the authority to settle cotton classing disputes. In 1919 it became mandatory that all cotton delivered on future contracts be classed by government-appointed classers.

The Cotton Standards Act, passed by Congress in 1923, made mandatory the use of *Official Cotton Standards* when spot cotton was bought and sold under the grade names of the standards. "Spot cotton" is any cotton not bought or sold on a future contract. The grade standards, after a complete revision in 1935, are still in force.

The cotton industry was at a very low ebb in 1933. The New York spot market price of middling ⅞ in. cotton was about 5¢ a lb, the lowest in nearly a century. The average income per farm family in the cotton belt that year was $232, the lowest in 30 years and less than half the normal. The short-lived National Recovery Act undertook to control textile mill output, hours of labor, and wages. Minimum wages were established as $12.00 per week in the South and $13.00 in the North for a 40-hr week.

The Agricultural Adjustment Administration was established by Congress and its purpose as regards cotton was to reduce production and to raise prices. The former was to be effected by a curtailment in acreage, the latter by a cotton loan and processing tax. As a result 10,500,000 acres were withheld from production in 1933–34 and the crop reduced by an estimated 4,500,000 bales. The price of cotton rose from 6.5 to 9.7¢ per lb.

Garside [20] has prepared a very able discussion of the economic legislation pertaining to cotton, covering the Agricultural Adjustment Act, Commodity Credit Corporation, Soil Conservation, etc., to which the reader is referred.

Availability

Cotton is raised in more than 50 different countries but the bulk of the world's supply comes from a few major producers, of which the United States is the largest. In many of the countries where the cotton crop is small, estimates of cotton production are lacking or inaccurate because an unknown part of the crop never reaches the market. It is used by the producers or converted by primitive methods for local consumption.

It does not seem likely that world production data are influenced seriously by the lack of reliable figures from the smaller producers. Many of the countries included in the group of cotton producers have a yearly crop of only a few bales. The industrial and exporting countries do keep fairly accurate records; hence the supply of commercial cottons can be established with reasonable assurance of exactness. For example, although there are about 1,250,000 cotton farms in the United States and the cotton eventually goes into countless different outlets, a very close approximation to the crop can be made from ginnings. There are only about 9200 gins, and it is relatively simple to make an appraisal as the cotton flows through this restricted channel. Both the U. S. Census Bureau and the U. S. Department of Agriculture accept the ginners' figures as accurate.

Sources. World production statistics may be somewhat misleading in that they do not differentiate cottons of different grades and values. The different local practices in baling are overcome, however, by a conversion of production figures to bales of 478 lb net weight. The U. S. Department of Agriculture makes several forecasts of the American crop during the progress of the season. These estimates are based on acreages, field inspections, weather conditions, and other factors and are usually very close to the actual crop as determined from ginnings.

World production statistics are published by several agencies including the U. S. Department of Agriculture and the New York Cotton Exchange. The U. S. Department of Commerce records all exports and imports of cotton as well as processing information it receives from American manufacturers. The National Cotton Council of Memphis, Tenn., has recently undertaken the analysis and publication of data on the use of cotton. Most of their data appear in miscellaneous publications. The *Year Book* and *Transactions* of the National Association of Cotton Manufacturers (Boston) regularly estimate spinning data, while the *Bulletin* of the International Federation of Master Cotton Spinners supplies biennial figures on the world's cotton spindles.

Prices. It has already been indicated that the price of cotton appears to fluctuate around 10¢ a lb. Table 9 contains estimates of the average price of spot cotton at New York for the decade preceding the year given.

TABLE 9. AVERAGE PRICE OF NEW YORK SPOT COTTON BY DECADES, 1800 TO 1950

	Cents		*Cents*		*Cents*
1800	35	1860	11	1920	19
1810	25	1870	100	1930	22
1820	20	1880	19	1940	11
1830	14	1890	11	1950	33
1840	13	1900	8		
1850	9	1910	10		

These averages fail to show the wide price fluctuations that occurred within the different decades. A cotton price chart by years with the

TABLE 10. COTTON PRODUCTION IN SPECIFIED COUNTRIES AND WORLD, 1930 TO 1950

[Thousands of running bales.]

Year	United States	Mexico	Argentina	Brazil	Peru	Egypt	Anglo-Egyptian Sudan	Uganda [1]	Belgian Congo	China [2]	India [3] and Pakistan	U.S.S.R.	Turkey	Other Countries	Estimated World Total [4]
1930–31	13,932	178	139	483	271	1,715	106	158	67	2,301	4,373	1,587	74	502	26,200
1931–32	17,097	210	169	555	234	1,317	206	174	40	2,824	3,353	1,845	91	467	27,850
1932–33	13,003	102	150	481	242	1,027	121	247	64	2,720	3,898	1,816	94	485	24,450
1933–34	13,047	260	200	1,014	278	1,777	135	239	82	2,981	4,274	1,887	128	618	26,920
1934–35	9,636	223	295	1,328	342	1,566	228	212	105	3,243	4,065	1,687	174	706	23,810
1935–36	10,638	315	373	1,757	393	1,769	201	269	124	2,667	4,962	2,250	241	871	26,830
1936–37	12,399	397	144	1,817	386	1,877	268	283	147	3,870	5,312	3,400	236	954	31,500
1937–38	18,946	341	237	2,075	376	2,281	264	349	188	3,556	4,914	3,700	299	1,104	38,630
1938–39	11,943	307	327	1,989	396	1,728	263	253	172	2,301	4,315	3,800	306	990	29,090
1939–40	11,817	312	362	2,141	378	1,801	245	252	204	1,883	4,195	4,000	300	1,076	28,966
1940–41	12,566	302	232	2,507	383	1,900	247	310	205	2,354	5,182	3,000	218	1,177	30,580
1941–42	10,744	375	373	1,844	329	1,735	247	198	208	2,406	5,192	[5]	268	3,481	27,400
1942–43	12,817	435	498	2,089	322	877	271	94	235	[5]	4,005	[5]	231	5,466	27,340
1943–44	11,427	520	535	2,700	289	740	196	159	141	500	4,249	2,000	217	[5]	26,800
1944–45	12,230	472	332	1,626	325	962	313	228	168	1,600	3,693	[5]	225	952	24,785
1945–46	8,852	434	297	1,350	327	1,082	187	191	174	1,820	3,610	1,700	166	854	21,044
1946–47	8,574	407	314	1,300	321	1,257	220	194	176	1,925	3,557	2,240	204	830	21,519
1947–48	11,658	484	412	1,715	307	1,320	215	134	181	2,150	3,525	2,600	218	835	25,754
1948–49 [6]	14,649	570	420	1,500	310	1,845	257	310	218	2,120	2,710	2.600	309	995	28,813
1949–50 [6]	15,921	980	590	1,360	275	1,805	275	260	220	1,700	3,720	2,700	445	1,190	30,941

Note: Totals include estimates for minor producing countries and allowances for other figures not available. [1] Exports; [2] Including Manchuria; [3] Including Burma; [4] Including China; [5] Not available; [6] Preliminary.

Source: U. S. Dept. Agr. and International Cotton Advisory Committee, as compiled in 1948–52 Year Books and Basic Data Sheets of N. Y. Cotton Exchange.

TABLE 15. Trading in Cotton Futures *

Seasons	*Volume of Trading in All U. S. Cotton Futures Markets* † *(million bales)*	*Government Stock July 31* *(million bales)*
1929–30	101.7	1.3
1930–31	74.5	3.4
1931–32	65.0	2.4
1932–33	87.6	2.2 ‡
1933–34	72.4	3.0
1934–35	46.9	5.1
1935–36	39.6	3.2
1936–37	54.2	1.7
1937–38	47.3 §	7.0
1938–39	37.9	11.0
1939–40	42.9	8.7

* Source: U. S. Dept. Agr.

† New York, New Orleans, and Chicago.

‡ Stock May 30; July 31 stock not available.

§ Figures previous to November 1937 did not include passouts, which it is understood account for approximately 25 per cent of the total.

TABLE 16. Cotton Exports, in Thousands of Running Bales *

Seasons	*Exports*	*Seasons*	*Exports*	*Seasons*	*Exports*
1790–91	(†)	1910–11	8026	1940–41	1112
1800–01	32	1920–21	5745	1941–42	1125
1810–11	124	1930–31	6760	1942–43	1480
1820–21	250	1931–32	8708	1943–44	1139
1830–31	554	1932–33	8419	1944–45	2007
1840–41	1060	1933–34	7534	1945–46	3613
1850–51	1855	1934–35	4799	1946–47	3545
1860–61	615	1935–36	5973	1947–48	1968
1870–71	2923	1936–37	5440	1948–49	4748
1880–81	4453	1937–38	5598	1949–50	5771
1890–91	5850	1938–39	3327		
1900–01	6807	1939–40	6192		

* Source: U. S. Dept. Commerce.

† Less than 500 bales.

Note: Includes linters 1790–1911.

United States population depends, cotton is an enormous economic force in the national well-being. The loss of American export markets as a result of the increase in cheaper foreign growths and the rise in the use of synthetics fostered by "nationalistic self-sufficiency policies" of some of the big importing countries had, prior to World War II, produced a crisis in the American cotton industry. It was temporarily alleviated by the artificial price-control measures adopted by the government but may reappear.

There were and still are reasons for the maintenance of cotton production even at subsistence price levels. It is the traditional crop of the South, and its culture is known and understood, whereas substitute crops represent an unknown risk to the producers. In addition, cotton is not a perishable crop. Complete crop failure has never occurred, and a certain percentage of the expected yield is usually realized. Thus, the future crop can be mortgaged and cotton on hand can be held for a favorable market. However, post-war conditions and government policies are bound to play a dominating role in the cotton economy of the future and no forecast of trends is possible.

Markets and Marketing. The marketing of cotton includes all transactions that occur between ginning and acceptance at the mill. Cotton reaches the mill through a variety of different channels, some of which are mentioned below. Although some cotton is bought by the ginners, most of the crop is still owned by the producers after it is ginned. The producer may dispose of his cotton by exchanging it for other necessities at the general store; or he may sell it to a private dealer; or, in the case of the cooperative, his cotton is pooled and sold through the farm organization. A small fraction of the crop passes directly from the farm to mill; a mill representative may purchase from the farmer or the mill may encourage the growth of the types of cotton it needs in its immediate vicinity through seed distribution and the promise of premiums.

Normally cotton is purchased at the farm by the cotton merchant or is sold through a broker. From these dealers it passes to the large wholesale houses or to the mills. The merchant usually tries to accumulate a sufficient stock of the different types—100 bales or more—to fill expected mill orders or to handle in blocks in the open market.

The world's large cotton markets are in New York, Liverpool, New Orleans, Memphis, and Houston, with smaller markets in many other cities. From these markets cotton passes again to jobbers, supply merchants, and factors, and thence to the mills. Thus, cotton may pass through the following channels:

1. Farmer to local merchant.
2. Local merchant to central market merchant.
3. Central market merchant to New York broker.
4. New York broker to mill.

Futures contracts are made in the United States only at New York, New Orleans, and Chicago. They cover the purchase or sale of definite amounts of cotton for delivery at some future date. Since 1940 the United States Cotton Futures Act has required that no cotton below Low Middling White, Good Middling Tinged, or Good Middling Stained may be delivered on a futures contract. The futures market has evolved as a means of distributing cotton rather than as a means of supplying cotton; that is, it permits the owner of a supply to sell contracts against it and the processor to buy contracts which will supply the cotton at some future time. The entire crop is ready for market between Sept. 1 and Dec. 30 and, being seasonal, necessitates a system that will distribute it uniformly. All cotton sales except those on futures contracts are "spot" sales. A bale of "spot" cotton may be anywhere and may be delivered at any time. These sales do not involve any particular cotton, and most of it goes to manufacturers. The transfer of cotton from a local merchant to a large dealer is spot sale.

Spot cotton and future cotton remain fairly parallel in price although futures are usually somewhat lower; that is, allowance must be made for the accumulation of storage, insurance, and interest charges on the cotton during the life of the contract. The practice of buying or selling futures as a protection is known as "hedging." Thus, if a cotton dealer or large producer has a supply of cotton he may sell futures to protect his holdings against sharp price declines. He sacrifices the possibility of greater profit from a price rise to gain partial or complete insurance against a decrease. A mill may buy futures at the time of making a sale of cloth to protect the market.

Eric Alliot [21], president of the New York Cotton Exchange, described the hedge in these words:

> By the use of time contracts, planters, factors, merchants, importers and exporters, and mills are able to insure or "hedge" themselves against violent or rapid changes in the price of raw materials.
>
> A time contract is exactly what the term implies. In the case of cotton, it is a contract entered into for six, nine or twelve months in advance of the date the buyer and seller agree upon for the delivery and receipt of units of 100 bales of cotton. Cotton merchants are among the largest users of time contracts. Through the use of . . . time contracts, hundreds of millions of dollars worth of cotton is purchased from the farmers who produce it and distributed throughout the world at profit margins so small as to appear almost ridiculous when compared with the margins necessarily required in many other industries.

The trend to less trading in futures is attributed to government activities of one kind or another. The pegging of prices and the rise in volume of government-owned stocks have reduced the likelihood of sharp price changes and perhaps have obviated some of the need for hedging practices.

Price Fluctuations. The following discussion is taken from the *American Cotton Handbook* [5].

The price of cotton is primarily set by the laws of supply and demand and the crop is much too large to be artificially held far from the natural price. Even with the resources of the U. S. Government supporting them, the various efforts to peg the price of American cotton have not been successful. This is *partly* because of the enormous volume of capital necessary to hold a given price, and *partly* because there are enough other countries, where cotton may be produced, who take advantage of any artificial maintenance of the price to help complicate the problem. Spot quotations come from the various spot markets of the cotton belt and from the various mill centers. Spot prices differ, *partly* because some markets use different bases for quotation and, *partly,* because of the costs of transportation to the consuming localities. These prices are what buyers will give and sellers will take, balanced one against the other.

Future quotations come from the three cotton exchanges. In the *North,* the New York figures are most commonly used, while in the *South,* New Orleans figures are more commonly given. These represent what the market value of the cotton at the various months is likely to be. Sometimes, differences represent only the carrying charges from one month to another. In other cases, the quotations are influenced by the prospect of a poor or a bumper crop, by the possibility of accumulation due to lack of consumption, by damage from weevil or an early frost. However, the future quotations set only the price for Middling cotton. If deliveries are made, this figure is modified by the differences obtained from the ten spot markets for New York and Chicago and from the local differences for New Orleans.

Exports

About two-thirds of the American cotton crop is consumed at home. The remainder must be sold abroad as raw cotton or as finished goods if only a protective carry-over from season to season is to be maintained. Table 16 shows the course of American cotton exports during the last century and a half.

There is visible an appreciable decline in American export shipments between the middle 1920's and the onset of World War II. As has already been indicated, this decline has been favored by domestic crop restrictions, artificial prices, and the increase in foreign growth.

A breakdown of export data since 1932 is shown in Table 17. For the most part, exports as here shown are credited to the country where the cotton is unloaded, which may or may not be the country of ultimate destination. For example, in former seasons, a large portion of the cotton here shown as being exported to Germany was forwarded from German ports to other European countries.

The United Kingdom has taken nearly 2,000,000 bales of this cotton every year since 1920. Prior to 1933 Germany was receiving about 1,500,000 bales annually; exports to Germany then fell to approximately 300,000 bales in 1938–39. The average annual exports to other European countries during the 1920–40 period were roughly as follows:

	Bales
France	700,000
Italy	600,000
Spain *	250,000
Belgium	170,000
All others	500,000

* Except during the Revolution 1936–39.

TABLE 17. Season Exports of American Cotton by Countries *

(World War years omitted)

[In thousands of running bales, counting round as half bales; linters not included.]

Country	1933–34	1934–35	1935–36	1936–37	1937–38	1938–39	1939–40	1947–48	1948–49	1949–50
Great Britain	1270	741	1416	1171	1569	412	1924	257	742	584
Continent:										
Belgium	123	99	159	159	200	92	183	50	147	186
Denmark	49	50	50	59	69	61	59	3	28	32
France	712	370	685	663	713	353	677 †	206	653	766
Germany	1364	381	821	690	807	431	21	247	484	733
Holland	116	59	71	89	128	76	159	33	184	249
Italy	666	492	384	415	539	301	591	67	622	718
Norway	9	9	12	12	12	14	26	3	16	8
Poland	228	202	253	177	259	212	6	47	89	45
Portugal	52	43	46	35	25	4	32	..	..	..
Russia	59	111	..	..	..	..	..	0	26	0
Spain	274	241	210	..	..	16	291	3	68	62
Sweden	72	79	83	84	85	91	181	6	..	28
Other continent	6	9	8	20	32	34	54	53	225	227
Total	3730	2145	2782	2403	2869	1685	2280	718	2542	3054
Asia:										
Japan	1856	1537	1518	1566	708	876	950	448	623	885
China	389	112	47	27	91	97	414	293	277	127
India	17	40	8	13	148	2	81	20	2	398
Other	..	..	..	..	..	..	..	63	78	250
Total	2262	1689	1573	1606	947	975	1445	824	980	1660
The Americas:										
Canada	266	225	246	304	244	228	413	136	293	272
Mexico	24	16	23	27	43	53	63	..	..	..
Other	..	..	..	..	..	..	..	14	115	117
Total	290	241	269	331	287	281	476	150	408	389
All others	..	..	..	..	..	..	..	19	62	79
Grand total	7552	4816	6040	5511	5672	3353	6125	1997	4748	5771

* Source: New York Cotton Exchange, and *Cotton Quarterly Statistical Bulletin.*

† Of this total, it is estimated that approximately 30,000 bales were diverted to Great Britain.

Exports to China have varied widely from 1,100,000 bales in 1931–32 to 14,000 in 1936–37. From 1925 to 1937 Japan took between 1,000,000 and 2,300,000 bales of American cotton a year with a sharp decline in the succeeding years. Canada received more than 200,000 bales a year up to 1939.

Imports

It may seem somewhat anomalous that the United States with a huge surplus of cotton for export should also import appreciable quantities of foreign growths. The extent of this trade is shown in Table 18.

TABLE 18. Cotton Imports *

[Equivalent 500-lb bales.]

Seasons	*Total*	*Egypt*	*China*	*Peru*	*India*	*Mexico*	*All Other Countries*
1949–50	255,000	132,400	......	21,400	83,800 †	17,200	200
1948–49	176,600	95,800	......	5,000	47,700 †	23,900	4,200
1947–48	244,600	88,200	......	24,300	99,100 †	18,500	14,500
1939–40	168,114	67,178	......	1,045	85,116	12,568	2,207
1938–39	149,780	47,727	25,620	545	49,923	21,809	4,156
1937–38	159,015	43,499	16,491	744	48,040	43,598	6,643
1936–37	253,034	75,268	51,438	1,740	79,115	27,391	18,082
1935–36	154,817	65,602	25,914	1,125	57,655	3,387	1,134
1934–35	107,031	71,176	3,185	1,192	24,903	5,137	1,438
1933–34	148,116	96,523	18,321	3,644	25,987	2,652	999
1932–33	130,429	67,800	50,788	6,053	4,895	8	885
1931–32	131,569	81,091	7,191	3,528	17,513	20,641	1,605
1930–31	107,529	22,902	31,177	2,373	34,218	15,126	1,733
1929–30	378,107	215,181	44,034	19,427	58,449	39,323	1,693
1928–29	457,804	296,286	34,857	17,353	54,424	52,009	2,875
1927–28	338,226	201,856	62,888	23,319	25,663	22,843	1,657
1926–27	400,983	231,767	33,466	20,877	18,892	93,272	2,709
1925–26	325,511	238,620	22,452	16,637	22,143	23,553	2,108
1924–25	313,328	190,313	33,703	13,389	28,147	44,384	3,392
1923–24	292,288	164,152	45,118	19,928	34,419	27,062	1,609
1922–23	469,954	329,335	50,239	21,186	22,124	45,679	1,391
1921–22	363,465	233,729	15,563	38,753	10,348	53,637	11,435
1920–21	226,341	87,168	14,722	22,597	8,489	88,155	5,210
1919–20	700,214	485,004	57,185	63,426	14,358	65,343	14,898
1918–19	201,585	100,006	10,871	25,230	2,893	54,434	8,151
1917–18	221,216	114,580	38,964	19,692	7,096	35,726	5,158
1916–17	291,957	199,892	36,063	11,069	3,860	32,858	8,215
1915–16	437,574	350,796	35,792	10,909	4,214	30,098	5,765

* Source: U. S. Dept. Commerce; *Cotton Quarterly Statistical Bulletin.*

† Includes Pakistan.

It is immediately apparent that imports represent largely types of cotton not grown in this country, namely, long-staple Egyptian and harsh Indian and Chinese cottons. The effects of the high tariff on imports of long staple that went into effect in 1931 are clearly visible in the drastic curtailment of Egyptian imports. The tariff also reduced the total of American imports, since Egyptian cotton represented a large part of the normal imports.

Consumption

Much information on the final uses of cotton is available in the Biennial Census of Manufacturers of the U. S. Dept. of Commerce. In addition, the National Cotton Council of America has published a series of excellent cotton use summaries since 1942 [22]. These tabulations cover the 1939–49 period and contain consumption data for more than

TABLE 19. Principal Uses of Cotton

	1939		1949	
	Bales	*Per Cent of Total U. S. Consumption*	*Bales*	*Per Cent of Total U. S. Consumption*
Automobiles	633,100	8.75	627,380	7.86
Shirts	463,520	6.45	534,330	6.70
Bags	458,760	6.39	404,230	5.07
Sheets	433,120	6.03	449,460	5.62
Cordage and twine	357,340	4.96	137,420	1.72
Piece goods	331,670	4.60	....	....
Towels	303,400	4.21	248,470	3.12
Trousers	284,720	3.95	380,110	4.76
Men's overalls	232,000	3.22	114,190	1.43
Men's underwear	209,850	2.92	240,650	3.02
Blankets	180,440	2.51	135,040	1.69
Women's dresses	175,100	2.43	215,850	2.70
Draperies and upholstery	154,240	2.14	387,750	4.73
Rugs and carpets	148,450	2.06	181,650	2.18
Curtains	130,270	1.81	91,260	1.14
Shoes	107,800	1.50	147,190	1.84
Women's underwear	104,140	1.45	59,370	0.74
Men's socks	98,000	1.36	153,020	1.92
Bedspreads	94,240	1.31	198,420	2.48
Medical uses	87,500	1.22	131,500	1.65
Apparel uses	2,731,280	37.8	2,748,910	34.5
Household uses	1,808,120	25.1	2,116,420	26.5
Industrial uses	2,677,150	37.1	2,446,180	30.7
Total	7,216,550		7,982,440	*

* Accounts for 92 per cent of domestic consumption.

Source: "Cotton Counts Its Customers," National Cotton Council of America, Memphis, Tennessee.

100 final uses and subuses of cotton. The amounts of cotton consumed in 20 leading uses are tabulated in Table 19 for 1939 and 1949.

The data bring out in a striking way the diversity of uses to which cotton is put. The largest single use in 1939 represented less than 10 per cent of total U. S. consumption and only about 5 per cent of the U. S. crop. Cotton's economic position appears to reside in its versatility and diversification, for the complete loss of any one of the many small use outlets would not be disastrous. On the other hand, such diversification of a single fiber must eventually operate against it in as much as it cannot be expected to compete in all uses with synthetic specialties. Nevertheless, the ingenuity of science will be taxed for many years before the natural fiber is surpassed in many uses. In volume and importance to mankind cotton truly is "the foremost fiber of the world" [23].

REFERENCES IN TEXT

1. Gulati, A. N., and Turner, A. J., *J. Textile Inst.*, **20,** T1 (1929).
2. Crawford, M. D. C., *Heritage of Cotton*, G. P. Putnam's Sons, N. Y. (1924).
3. Watt, Sir G., *The Wild and Cultivated Cotton Plants of the World*, Longmans Green & Co., London (1907).
4. Harland, S. C., *The Genetics of Cotton*, Jonathan Cape, London (1939).
5. *American Cotton Handbook*, Textile Book Publishers, Inc. 2nd revised edition (1949).
6. "Cotton Production in Egypt," U. S. Dept. Agr., *Tech. Bull. 451* (Oct. 1934).
7. Pressley, E. H., Whittaker, R., and Barr, G. W., *Ariz. State Bull. 167*, pp. 39–77 (1940).
8. "Plant Breeding and the Cotton Industry," U. S. Dept. Agr., *Yearbook Separate 1578*, Washington (1937).
9. Vavilov, N. I., *Bull. Applied Botany Plant Breeding* (*U.S.S.R.*), **16** (2), 1 (1926).
10. Vavilov, N. I., *Intern. Kong. Vererb. Wiss.*, **5** (Ver. 1), 342 (1928).
11. Tyler, F. J., *Bull. U. S. Bur. Plant Ind.*, p. 163 (1910).
12. "Cotton Quality Statistics," U. S. Dept. Agr., Washington (Dec. 1942).
13. Kearney, T. H., "Relationships of the Cultivated and Wild Cottons of the World," U. S. Dept. Agr., Bur. Plant Ind. (1936).
14. Conrad, C. M., *Science*, **94,** 113 (1941).
15. Pearson, N. L., U. S. Dept. Agr., *Tech. Bull. 396* (Nov. 1933).
16. "Classification of Cotton," U. S. Dept. Agr., *Pub. 310* (May 1938).
17. "Handbook for Cotton Classers," U. S. Dept. Agr. (Sept. 1940).
18. "Handbook for Licensed Classifiers," U. S. Dept. Agr., Bur. Agr. Econ. (Aug. 1931).
19. Cotton Textile Inst., private communication from J. T. Wigington.
20. Garside, A., *American Cotton Handbook* (see ref. 5).
21. Alliot, E., newspaper release, New York (Aug. 14, 1943).
22. Horne, M. K., Jr., and McCord, F., "Cotton Counts Its Customers," Natl. Cotton Coun., Memphis (1942 et seq.).
23. Hildebrand, J. R., "The Foremost Fiber of the World," *Natl. Geographic Mag.* (Feb. 1941).

CHAPTER IV

COTTON FIBER: MICROSCOPIC CHARACTERISTICS

T. L. W. Bailey, Jr.[1]

The microscope has proved itself a most valuable tool in the study of fibers. It makes possible the study of size, shape, color, structure or markings, physical properties, and behavior on chemical treatment. Microscopical analysis of cotton fibers embraces many fields. The examination of surface characteristics is of utmost importance, but measurements of length, diameter, and area may be made with great accuracy. The action of chemical reagents can be followed; cross-sectional characteristics may be compared; unusual structures, pigmentation, natural deformities, and mechanical damage may be observed.

With the aid of unique methods it is possible to examine the cotton fiber from all perspectives: longitudinally for width and convolutions and for surface features; transversely for shape, wall thickness, and lumen size. These various characteristics can be emphasized by choice of the proper technique—staining, swelling, cross-sectioning, mounting, or lighting. A combination of several of these methods is usually employed.

Special methods of illumination may be employed to bring out the desired features. Transmitted light is generally used, as the cotton fiber is both colorless and transparent, and its internal structure can be seen readily. By reflected light, however, the surface characteristics can be observed more clearly and irregularities of shape and form studied to better advantage. Oblique illumination is sometimes an advantage. By the use of special condenser arrangements "dark ground" illumination is produced, in which the cotton fiber appears self-luminous against a black background. Surface details, such as pits and markings, are most clearly seen by dark field methods. The object under investigation should never be studied by dark ground illumination alone, however, since false interpretations may result. The use of this method in conjunction with the usual examination by transmitted light will frequently

[1] Director of Industry Relations, Institute of Textile Technology, Charlottesville, Virginia; formerly Cotton Technologist, Southern Regional Research Laboratory, U. S. Department of Agriculture, New Orleans, Louisiana.

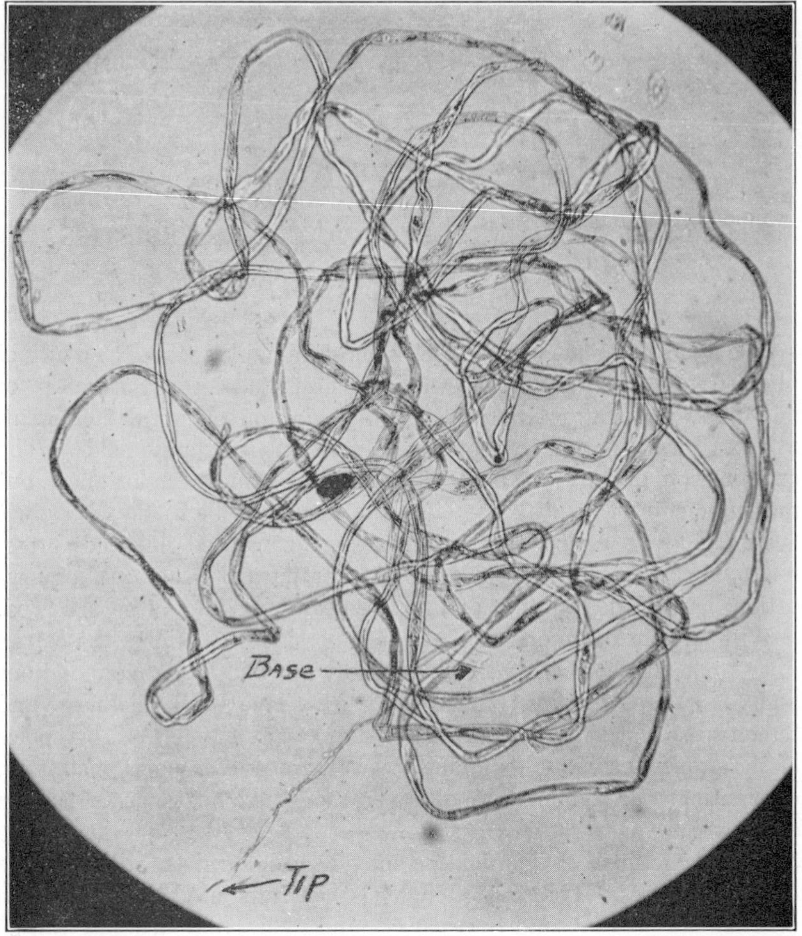

Fig. 1. Portrait of a single cotton fiber, complete from base to tip. Actual fiber length 1¼ in. ×80. (*Bailey.*)

show additional points of interest and aid in a correct evaluation of the fiber under study.

General Longitudinal Appearance

The characteristics of the cotton fiber are so pronounced as to distinguish it readily from all other fibers. It is a single cell and when examined under the microscope appears as an irregularly twisted and collapsed, flattened tube, with a central canal, or lumen throughout its length (Fig. 1). In natural unbroken fibers the attenuated tip portion does not show any lumen.

The Base (Fig. 2). Technically, a cotton fiber is an elongated epidermal cell, the basal portion of which extends into one layer of cells on the surface of the seed coat. The part of the fiber which extends below the surface of the seed coat is usually a very thin membrane. Pearson and Smith [1] reported that the bases of mature fibers dissected

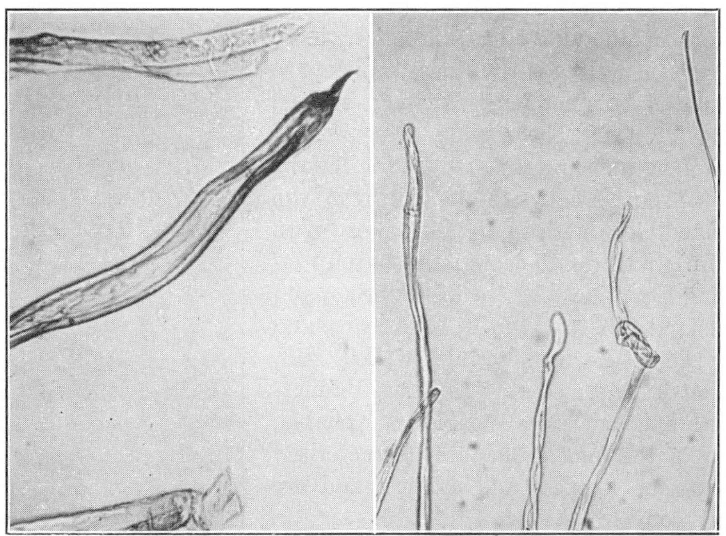

FIG. 2. Fiber bases and tips. *Left,* upper and lower fiber torn from epidermis of seed. *Middle,* fiber showing remains of membrane formerly attached to seed. *Right,* long needle-shaped closed tips, from same fibers as left view. ×250. (*Bailey.*)

from the seed coat have various irregular shapes ranging from those which are cone-shaped or cylindrical to those resembling an hourglass. However, as the fiber is removed from the seed, the fragile portion beneath the surface is generally torn or broken and this rupture is readily distinguished from breaks at any other point along the fiber length (Fig. 3).

The Body. Except for the base and tip, the mature fiber is essentially the same throughout its length. The body of the fiber is characterized by its thickened wall and central canal. The spirals or convolutions are distinct twists about the longitudinal axis of the fiber, and the direction of the helix is frequently reversed. The body of the fiber constitutes the greatest part of its length (Fig. 4).

The Tip (Fig. 2). The distinguishing features of the tip of the fiber are the absence of both lumen and convolutions. It is further differentiated by a tapered rodlike end. In some fibers these attenuated portions are of considerable length.

Dimensions. The greatest dimension of the fiber is its length, which ranges from 1000 to 4000 times that of its width (Fig. 1). Fiber lengths have a wide range in any given single sample. Cottons of different types, moreover, have different length distributions, which are designated commercially by their various staple lengths. Three wide categories of staple length are represented by the following: (*a*) short Asiatics (½ to ⅞ in.); (*b*) the intermediate American Upland types (¾ to 1½ in.); and (*c*) the long staple group including Egyptians, American-Egyptian, and Sea Island (1½ to 2½ in.). The coarse and short fibers are usually thick-walled, stiff, and harsh; intermediate lengths are thinner-walled and are more flexible and pliable; fibers of the long group are characterized by extreme fineness and softness and are highly convoluted (Fig. 4, part *c*).

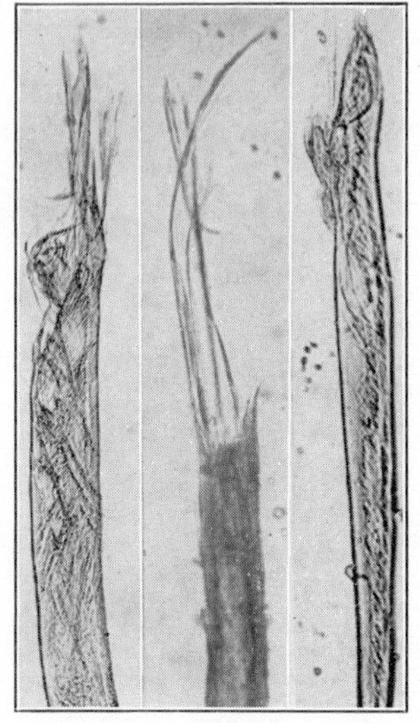

Fig. 3. Broken fibers from tensile break. Note irregular break of fibrils. ×250. (*Bailey.*)

General Cross-Sectional Appearance

The most striking characteristic of cross-sections of cotton fibers is the variability of every dimensional feature. Karrer and Bailey [2] classified fibers with respect to cross-sectional shape into three categories—*circular*, *elliptical*, and *linear*. The general geometric shape for the most mature fibers is elliptical to circular; for the less thickened fibers, flat and rectangular, with rounded corners. Immature fibers are often U-shaped in cross-section, because of the tendency of thin-walled fibers to fold or curl on themselves, and frequently are so entirely collapsed that their cross-sections show no lumen (Fig. 5).

Clegg [3], as well as others, pointed out that, for a given type of cotton, the original diameter of the living fiber varies within relatively narrow limits. During maturation cell walls vary considerably in degree of thickening. This gives rise to the extreme variability in both size and shape often observed in commercial lint. Occasionally, samples of unusual uniformity in cross-sectional features are encountered (see Fig. 6).

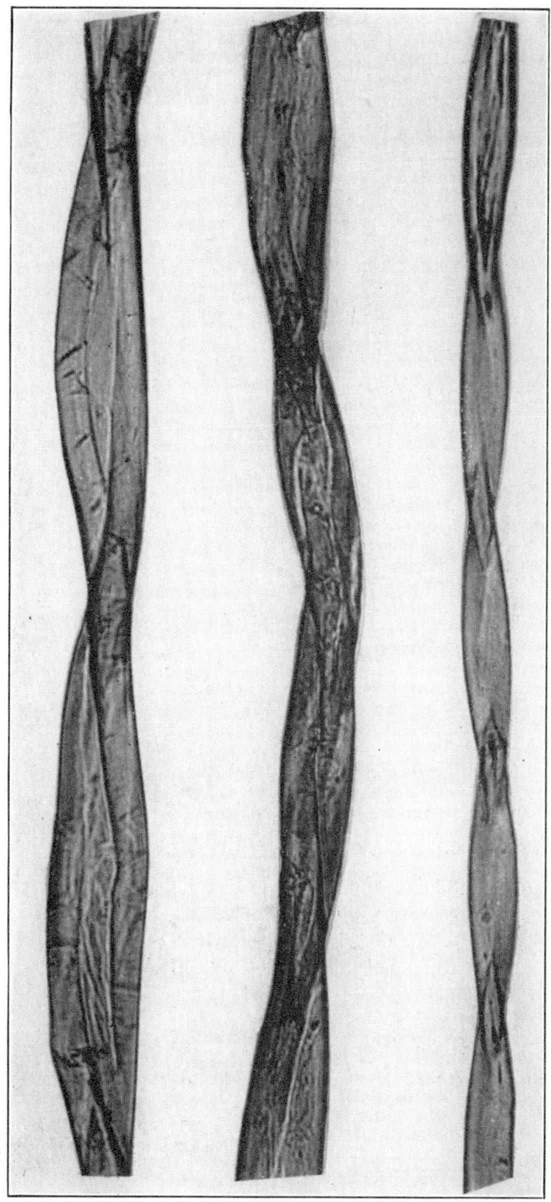

Fig. 4. Mid-portions of mature cotton fibers of different growths. *a*, Very coarse Asiatic with long low-angle convolutions; *b*, American Upland, with intermediate features. *c*, Fine Sea Island with short steep-angle convolutions. ×475. (*U. S. Dept. of Agric.*)

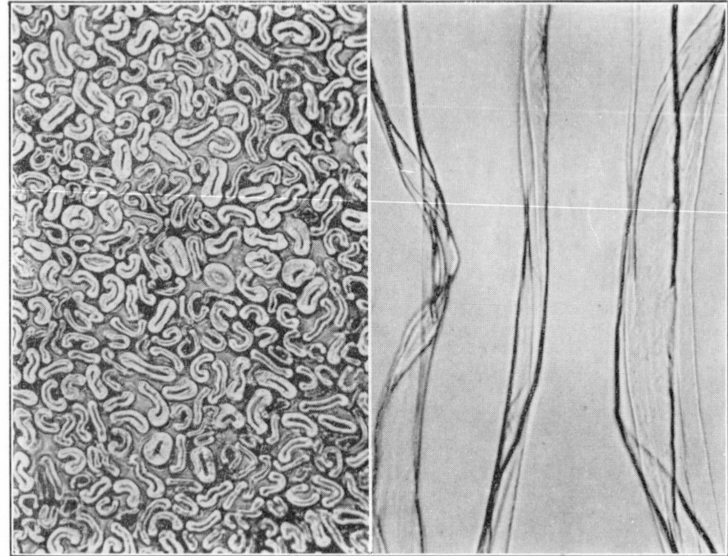

Fig. 5. Cross-section and longitudinal views of irregular and immature fibers. *Left,* variability of cross-sectional shapes, wall thicknesses, and cell sizes. *Right,* typical immature or "dead" cotton fibers. (Compare with Fig. 6.) ×250. (*Bailey.*)

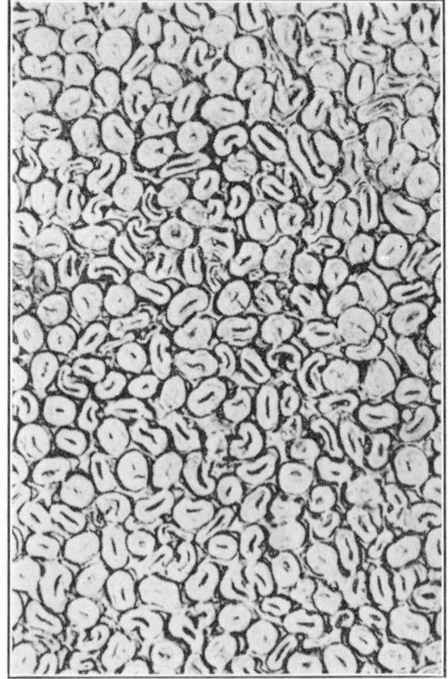

Fig. 6. Cross-section of sample of unusual uniformity as to cross-sectional features. (Compare with Fig. 5.) ×250. (*Bailey.*)

Detailed Structure (Fig. 7). The body of the fiber may be divided into the following main parts: (*a*) primary wall, (*b*) secondary wall, and (*c*) lumen. The outside of the fiber is covered with a thin film of cuticle, which consists of wax and pectic material and some encrusting mineral matter.

The Primary Wall and Cuticle. Nickerson [4] states that the structure of the cuticle and primary wall is not precisely known. The cellulose of the primary wall appears to be composed of tiny threads or fibrils

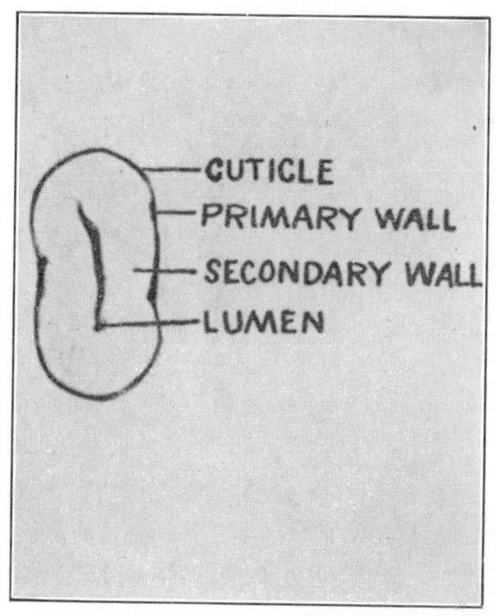

FIG. 7. Cross-section of single cotton fiber, showing its parts. ×1000. (*Bailey.*)

that resist the action of acids and the usual solvents for cellulose. Hock and Harris [5] suggest that its structure differs somewhat from that of the cellulose of the secondary wall. Studies by Berkley [6] showed that the cellulose of the primary wall lies transverse to the fiber axis. This is not in complete agreement with work reported by Sisson [7]. Sisson observed random orientation of the cellulose of the fibers until the twenty-fifth day after flowering.

The Secondary Wall. The secondary wall of the fiber is composed of successive layers of cellulose, deposited on the inner side of the primary wall without altering the original cell diameter. These layers are not readily observed in untreated cross-sections but are clearly visible in properly swollen material. Balls [8] was first to observe that these layers were associated with the intermittent development of the secondary wall; he referred to these formations as *daily growth rings*. Later Kerr

[9] reported experiments which demonstrated the effect of fluctuations in temperature and light with the formation, size, and pattern of ring formation. Kerr states that each lamella consists of *two* rings, one compact and one porous. These two rings constitute a daily growth

Fig. 8. Cross-section of swollen single fiber, stained to show growth rings. (*Kerr.*)

ring (Fig. 8). Hock, Ramsay, and Harris [10] observed these structures both in swollen cross-sections and in longitudinal sections (see Fig. 9). Balls and Hancock [11] pictured each growth ring as a separate cylinder or shell of cellulose.

This laminated structure of the secondary wall is further divided into tiny threadlike components called "fibrils" (Fig. 10). The fibrils are aligned side by side in each lamella and follow in a spiral path about the longitudinal axis of the fiber. The direction of the twist of the fibrils often reverses within the same lamella. Early observations by Balls [12] indicated that the fibrillar reversals coincide with the reversals in the exterior convolutions. These observations have been confirmed by several investigators. With the aid of micromanipulative methods,

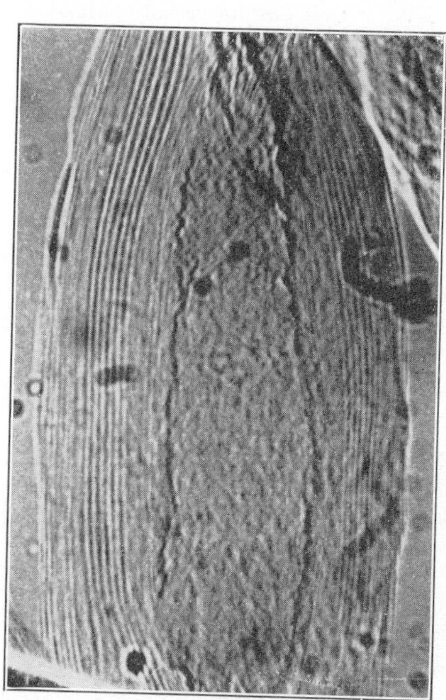

Fig. 9. Depectinized cotton fiber swollen in cuprammonium hydroxide solution to show striations. ×500. (*Hock.*)

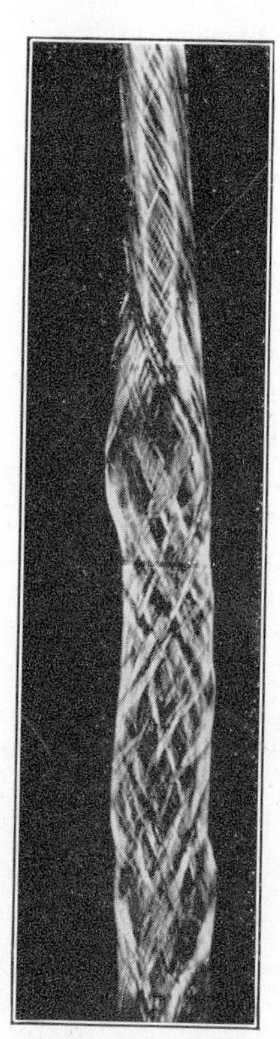

Fig. 10. Fibril structure of cotton fiber. Approx. ×800. (*Courtesy E. R. Schwarz.*)

Hock and coworkers studied the fibrillar structure in swollen fibers and dissected them one from another.

The size of the fibrils has not been definitely established. Different fibril sizes have been reported by a number of independent investigators. Table 1 includes the source, size, and pertinent remarks on this subject.

Barnes and Burton [13] employed the electron microscope to investigate the size of cellulose fibrils. Direct comparisons between visual light

TABLE 1. Source, Size, and Remarks on Fibril Sizes

Sources	*Size in Microns*	*Remarks*
Balls and Hancock [11]	0.4	Diameter.
Herzog and Jancke [14]	0.3 to 0.5	Diameter.
Frey-Wyssling [15]	0.4	Diameter.
Seifriz and Hock [16]	1.4	"Primary Fibrils."
Do.	0.1 to 0.3	"Secondary Fibrils."
Farr and Eckerson [17]	1.1 x 1.5	"Ellipsoidal Particles."
Bailey [18]	3 to 4	"Unit Fibrils" visually estimated range.
Bailey and Brown [19]	0.93 to 0.96	Diameter.
Do.	1.0 to 1.5	Height.
Freudenberg [20]	....	No consistent size and grade down to the limits of microscopic resolution.
Bailey and Kerr [21]	....	
Anderson and Moore [22]	....	
Anderson and Kerr [23]	....	

microscope photomicrographs and the electron micrographs (Fig. 11) of mechanically disintegrated cotton fibers were observed. These pictures were used to assist in the proper interpretation of the size of

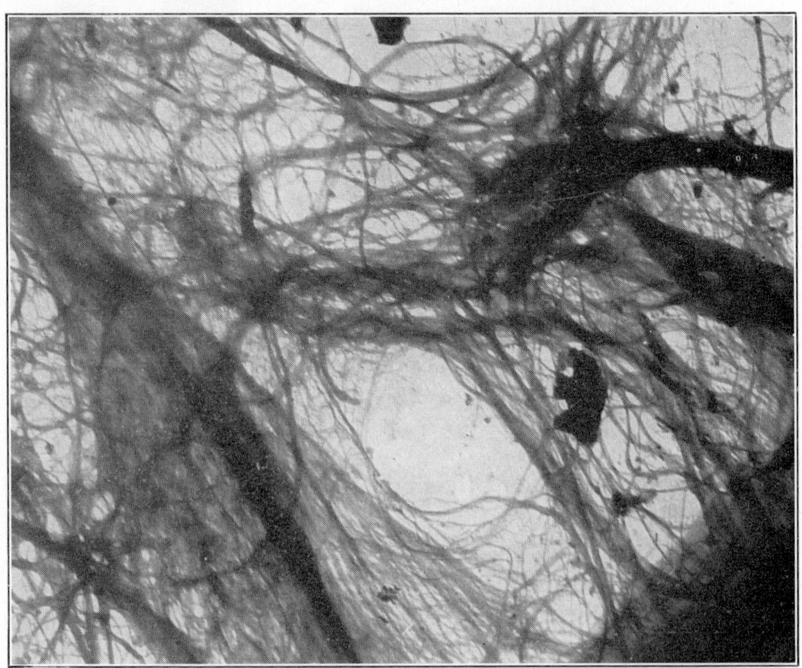

Fig. 11. Mature cotton fibers mechanically disintegrated in water. ×7500. (*Stamford Research Labs., American Cyanamid Co.*)

cellulose fibrils. The results of these observations are quoted in part as follows:

> The use of any optical instrument for the study of objects so small that they are comparable to or smaller than the limit of resolving power of the instrument is complicated by many factors. Among these is the fact that the depth of focus of the high-resolving-power objectives is of necessity so small (down to 0.06 μ for a theoretical resolving power of 0.15 μ) that it is practically impossible to focus sharply at any one time more than a few scattered particles out of a given field... Inasmuch as cellulose fibrils and crystallites or particles have been reported to have diameters ranging from 0.1 to 1.4 μ, and since the limit of resolution of the best visible light microscopes is also of this same order of magnitude, we have believed that some of the chief characteristics of many published photomicrographs of cellulose have been determined by diffraction effects.
>
> The smallest objects shown by the electron microscope fail to show up in the photomicrographs.
>
> It is impossible to estimate accurately the size or the shape of such small objects from a study of their optical images.
>
> Many types of inhomogeneities, such as the crossing or branching of filaments whose diameters are far below the limits of resolving power of the visual microscope, are blown up by diffraction effects into rounded images which in some cases are many times too large. Similarly, minute objects or isolated bits of debris appear also as rounded and enlarged images.

In order that the fine structural arrangement of the internal complexities of the secondary wall of the cotton fiber may be studied, samples have been swollen in a number of different reagents. For swelling transverse sections Balls [8] used carbon disulfide and sodium hydroxide; Hock [10] and coworkers used trimethylbenzylammonium hydroxide in some experiments. Kerr [9], Hock [5, 10], Anderson and Moore [22], Anderson and Kerr [23], and Farr [32] employed cuprammonium hydroxide as the reagent for use in studying the structure of the secondary wall.

When treated with this solution and examined under the microscope, the fiber is seen to swell, but not uniformly; it seems that at regular intervals there are annular sections which do not swell. The result is that the fiber assumes the form of a distended tube tied at intervals somewhat after the manner of a string of sausages (Fig. 12). Höhnel considers these ligatures as merely parts of the cuticle; he explains their formation by the fiber swelling so considerably as to rupture the undisturbed cuticle, which in places adheres to the fiber in the form of irregular shreds which are difficult to see. In other places, where the rupture occurs obliquely to the length of the fiber, the cuticle becomes drawn together in annular bands surrounding the fiber, whereas between these rings the much-distended cellulose protrudes in the form of balloons (Fig. 13). The inner membrane or canal, which persists after the remaining fiber has dissolved, is an exceedingly thin tissue of dried protoplasm which was contained in the living fiber.

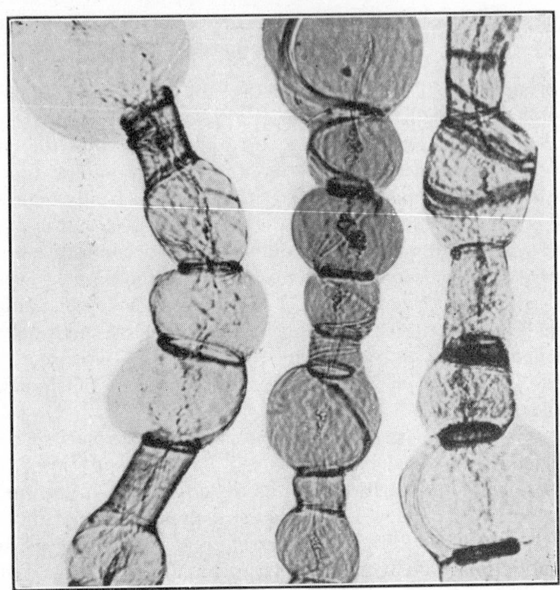

Fig. 12. Cotton fibers swollen in cuprammonium solution to produce balloon effect. ×250. (*Bailey.*)

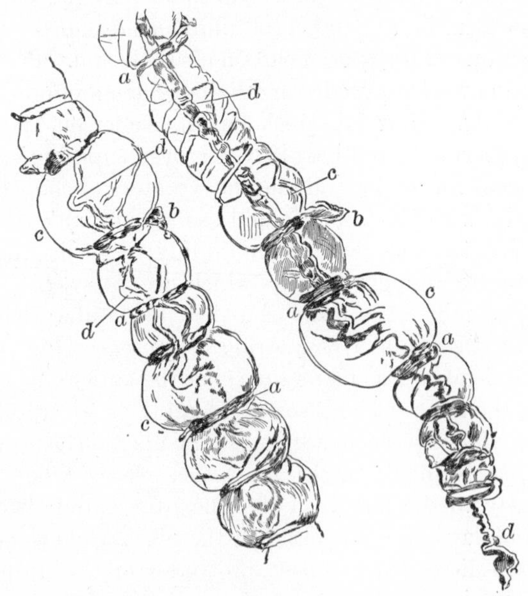

Fig. 13. Appearance of cotton fiber on treatment with Schweitzer's reagent. (*After Witt.*) *a*, Transverse ligatures of disrupted cuticle; *b*, irregular shreds of cuticle torn apart; *c*, swollen mass of cellulose; *d*, walls of internal canal.

This membrane, apparently consisting of dried albumen, like the cuticle remains undissolved after the solution of the cellulose in either ammoniacal copper oxide or concentrated sulfuric acid. As the fiber in dissolving becomes shortened by 40 to 60 per cent, its contents assume a peculiar appearance, exhibiting "crisscross" markings by reason of the folds that are formed.

When the fiber has become much swollen by the action of the reagent it begins to dissolve, whereupon the walls of the central canal are seen quite prominently; the dissolving action proceeds rapidly, but apparently there is a thin cuticular tissue surrounding the fiber, which resists the action of the solvent for a much longer time than the inner portion. The walls of the central canal also resist the action of the liquid to even a greater extent than the external tissue; the annular contracted ligatures also persist after the rest of the fiber has dissolved.

Investigations by Hock and coworkers [10] in a detailed study of the cause and formation of balloons in raw and depectinized fibers gave some interesting results. It was found that there was a relationship between the optical differences in polarized light (Fig. 31) and fibril reversals on the one hand and balloon formation on the other. Previous work indicated that the primary wall played an important part in the formation of balloons. When fibers from which the wax and pectic substance had been removed were placed in cuprammonium hydroxide solution the swelling took place unevenly along the axis. The "ballooned" portion of the fiber almost invariably occurred between the points at which the fibrils reversed, whereas the reversal points themselves formed the constrictions between adjacent balloons. Depectinized fibers which show no reversals usually swelled without the formation of balloons. It has been recognized that the primary wall is responsible, at least in part, for the formation of balloons. When young fibers with little secondary wall development were placed in the solution, relatively little swelling took place.

The Lumen and Protoplasmic Residue. The lumen of the fiber varies in dimensions over a wide range. Mature fibers may be so fully developed as to almost completely close the lumen, appearing as solid rods without any central canal. On the other hand, very immature fibers are so entirely collapsed (Fig. 5) that the wall practically adheres to itself. In cross-section the lumen in these fibers appears as a very thin line. Another worker noted the existence of uncollapsed fibers with unusually large lumens. Karrer and Bailey [2] reported fibers with extreme lumen size, the variation in cross-sectional area ranging from 4 sq μ to 84 sq μ.

The lumen is often partly filled with material (Fig. 14), which is thought to be merely the remnant of protoplasm left when the fiber dried

poor spinning quality. Further peculiar shapes in fibers are the distinct warts, knots, knees, or elbows, along the fiber length which are referred to as "abnormalities" (Fig. 16). The cause of these deformations is not fully understood; but it has been suggested that they are the result of pressure in the boll during late stages of boll maturation. Farr [24] in a study of fiber abnormalities and density of the fiber mass within the boll observed that few abnormalities were found in fibers from cotton with less boll density than from cotton with greater boll density during later stages of boll development. Farr suggests that this is one of the important factors causing the number of abnormalities found in the samples studied.

Fiber Development

Microscopical examination of the ovules before fertilization of the blossom shows the outer layer to be composed of undifferentiated epidermal cells. The period immediately following fertilization is one of rapid growth in the epidermal layer. This is characterized by cell division rather than merely enlargement of the cells. Newly divided epidermal cells become differentiated by outward elongation to form young cotton fibers. This elongation proceeds for a number of days, dependent to some extent on variety, climate, and seasonal conditions. Balls [12] in studies of Egyptian cottons observed that the outward extension continued for as long as 25 days. During this stage of develment the fiber consists only of a thin primary wall with nucleus and cytoplasm.

After the cells attain approximately full length, secondary growth by deposition of layers of cellulose on the inside of the primary wall commences. The secondary wall continues to thicken until the boll matures. The period of secondary thickening may vary considerably, owing to variety, season, and other factors (Fig. 17). Later studies on different species and varieties, including American-Egyptian, American Upland, and Indian, have, in general, confirmed the observation made by Balls [8].

Anderson and Moore [22], in studying the development of the secondary wall, grew cotton plants under constant light and temperature and found that no growth rings were developed in the wall. By alternating the light periods with 12 hr of darkness, rings were formed, although during the experiment the temperature was held constant. Kerr [9] found evidence to indicate that a relationship existed between the warmer temperature during the day and the distinct formation of rings.

In connection with the investigation of fiber development and cellulose orientation, Berkley [6] reported the relationship of wall development

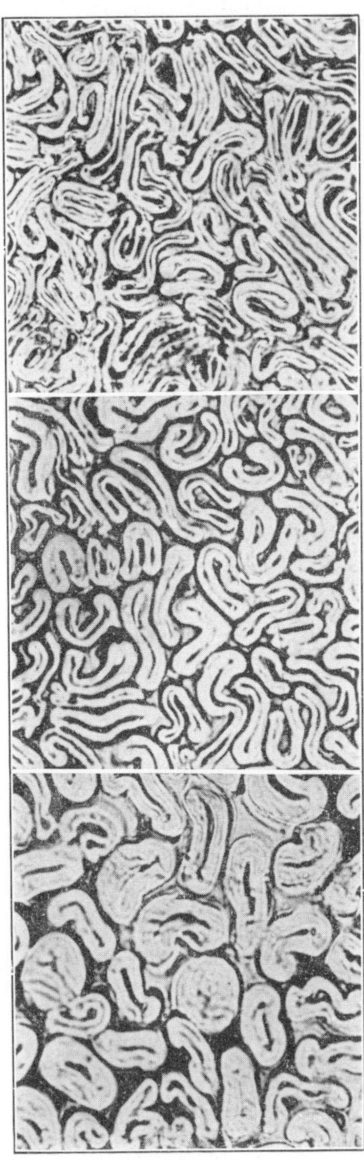

FIG. 17. Fiber development at different ages. *Top,* 28 days after flowering. *Middle,* 32 days after flowering. *Bottom,* approximately mature, 47 days after flowering. ×500. (*Bailey.*)

to strength of fibers. The tensile strength of the young fibers rapidly increases with the formation of the secondary wall and reaches a maximum about the thirty-fifth day after flowering.

In most Upland varieties, after the true lint is removed by ginning, there remains about the seed a woolly covering of short fibers, about ¼ in., known as "linters" or fuzz fibers. Fibers of this nature appear in varying amounts among the lint fibers in ginned cotton (Fig. 18). These are outward protuberances from the epidermal layer of the seed, but differ in microscopical appearance from true lint hairs. Studies by Lang, as reported by Brown [25], indicate that in the fuzz-seeded varieties the fuzz fibers arise from the epidermal layers about 6 days after the true fibers have emerged. Most true lint fibers are white, but the fuzz fibers range in color from green to yellow, buff, or gray. These fibers are usually coarse and thick-walled and when examined microscopically have a number of twisted enlarged areas, or abnormalities. Although the tip is somewhat tapered, fuzz fibers do not have such long attenuated tips as are usually found in true fibers (Fig. 18).

Reporting on studies of imperfections found in cottons, Pearson [26] pointed out the presence of fuzz fibers entangled with normal fibers to form small imperfections generally called "neps." The number of such fibers in ginned lint is determined partly by the variety and closeness with which the cotton is ginned. Pearson further states that abnormalities do not seem to be of importance in nep formation.

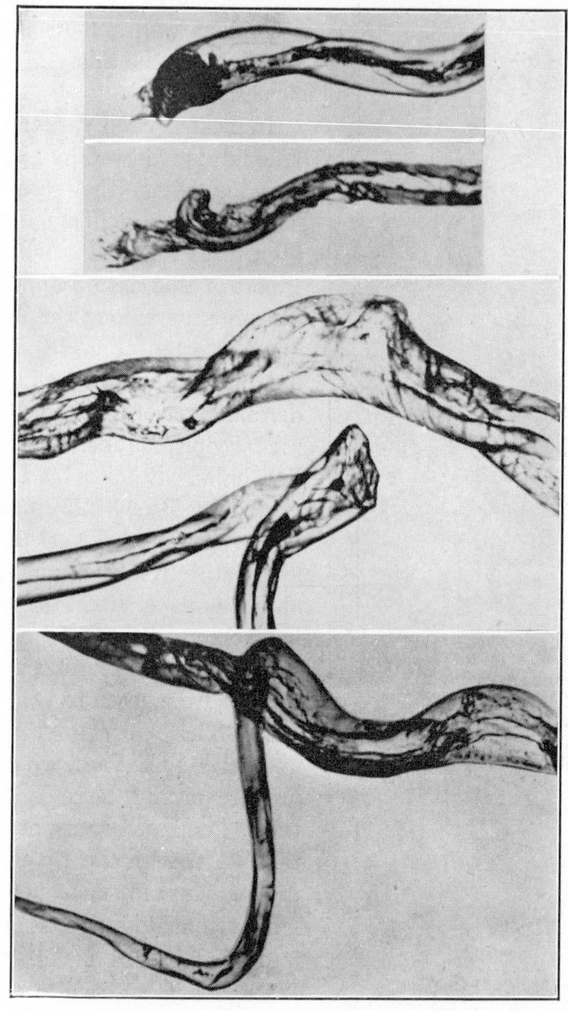

FIG. 18. Linters or fuzz fibers. *Top,* bases. *Middle,* body and abnormality. *Bottom,* twisted tip. ×250. (*Bailey.*)

Damaged Fibers

Microscopical examination of fibers for effects of damage is of considerable value not only as a means of detecting the type of damage, but as an aid in the improvement of processing to minimize damage. Practically any sample of commercial lint contains some form of fiber

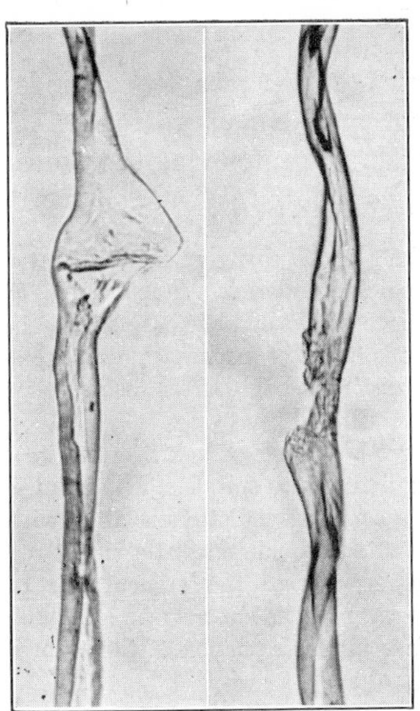

Fig. 19. Mechanical damage: bruised and cut fibers. ×250. (*Bailey.*)

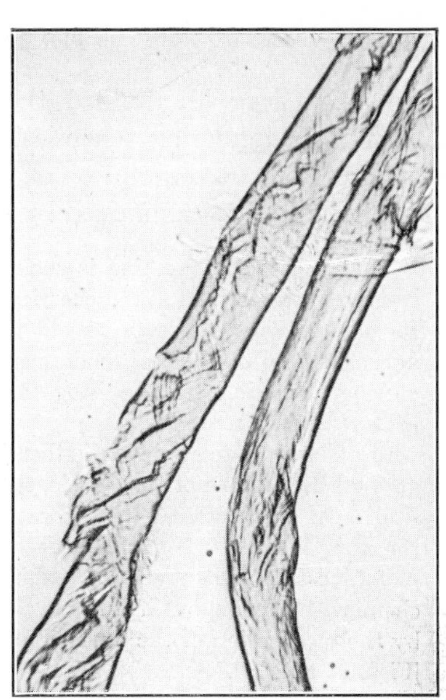

Fig. 20. Chemical damage: overbleached fiber. ×250. (*Bailey.*)

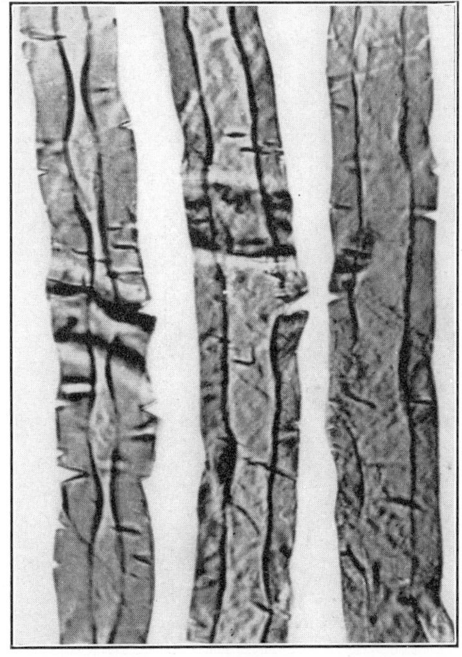

Fig. 21. Chemical damage: excessive heat. Fibers swollen to show breaks in cuticle and wall. ×250. (*Bailey.*)

damage. Clegg [3] divided the forms of damage into three kinds: Mechanical tendering, chemical tendering, and biological tendering. Classification and description of tendering damage employing the Congo Red method are summarized by Clegg [27] as follows:

> (i) Mechanical tendering is sufficiently obvious to be easily recognisable and can be distinguished from chemical and biological tendering. Some forms of fungal tendering, however, except for the presence of the hyphae, are similar in appearance to mechanical tendering. The various forms of mechanical damage—cutting, abrasion and bruising—are usually distinguishable from each other [Figs. 3 and 19].
>
> (ii) Chemical tendering, whether by heat, over-bleaching or acid, results in a gradual breakdown of the cuticle, shown by a splitting into spirals. The effect is similar in all cases and these three forms of damage are indistinguishable, with the exception of strong acid tendering which results in a characteristic bright red blotchiness. Light tendering exhibits similar features to the other forms of chemical tendering but if it has occurred on the yarn or cloth it may be identified by the localisation of the tendering to the surface fibres or portion of these fibres [Figs. 20 and 21].

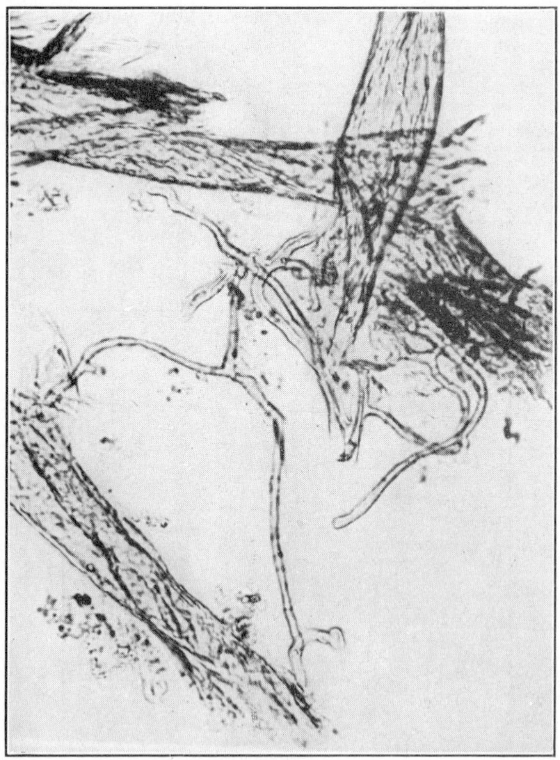

FIG. 22. Biological damage: damage by fungi. ×250. (*Bailey.*)

(iii) Biological tendering, whether by mildew or bacteria, may bear a general resemblance either to mechanical or to chemical tendering, but the disintegrated appearance of the fibres and tendency for the fibres to break up along the quick spirals, together with the presence of hyphae or bacteria are distinguishing features [Figs. 22 and 23].

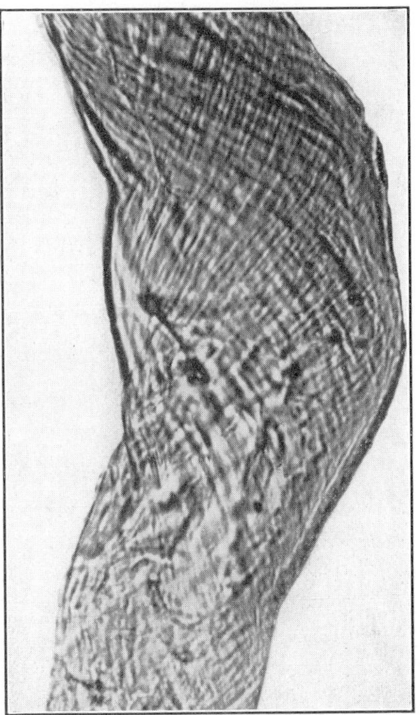

Fig. 23. Biological damage: damage by microorganisms. Note breakdown of fibrillar structure. ×500. (*Bailey.*)

TYPICAL FEATURES OF DIFFERENT COTTONS

Any sample of cotton of one type may contain fibers widely variant in microscopical features from those of another sample of the same general type. However, each general category, such as Asiatic, Short Upland, Fine Upland, Egyptian, or Sea Island, usually has an average distribution of microscopical features sufficiently marked to distinguish its members from those of another type. It is not always possible, however, to identify specifically the individual types by microscopical study alone. The finer Upland strains may have dimensions approaching those of the coarser Sea Island strains; conversely, in special cases, the finer Asiatics may have features resembling those of the coarser Upland varieties.

In Table 2, Von Bergen and Krauss [30] report the fiber width measurements of five various types of cottons.

TABLE 2. Width Measurements of Cotton Fibers

Types	*Number of Fibers*	*Average Width (microns)*	*Coefficient of Variation (per cent)*	*Dispersion Range (microns)*
Sakellarides	200	16.4	18.7	8 to 26
American Egyptian	300	16.2	20.9	6 to 26
Fine American Upland	200	17.1	22.4	8 to 27
Coarse American Upland	200	19.2	21.2	8 to 30
Indian	400	21.2	18.8	10 to 33

In the same publication further data on microscopical .dimensions were stated.

TABLE 3. Average Cross-Sectional Features of Cottons in Four Ranges of Fineness

Samples	Areas μ^2			Diameters μ				Ratio Major/Minor	Av. Wall Thickness μ
				Lumen		Fiber			
	Total	Lumen	Net	Major	Minor	Major	Minor		
Very fine	98.90	10.54	88.38	9.77	1.20	16.73	6.20	3.07	2.50
Fine American Upland	155.26	11.89	143.37	10.92	1.05	20.02	7.83	2.77	3.39
Coarse American Upland	230.05	19.02	211.04	14.22	1.55	24.97	9.49	2.90	3.97
Very coarse Asiatic	374.26	27.49	346.78	12.53	2.24	27.26	14.57	2.07	6.17

Sea Island Cotton

The chief points in which Sea Island cotton differs from other cottons are in its length, fineness, and number and uniformity of convolutions. Sea Island fiber is noticeably soft and is usually of a creamier color than Upland varieties. In cross-sectional appearance the fibers exhibit the usual shapes but are considerably smaller in dimensions than those of most cotton samples. Generally, Sea Island samples contain more thin-walled flattened fibers than are encountered in cottons of shorter staple. Samples grown in a number of localities and under different conditions show varying degrees of fineness and maturity. Fig. 24, *A* is somewhat representative of the finer and longer Sea Island types.

Egyptian Cottons

Microscopical examination of cross-sections reveals a similarity between Egyptian and Sea Island cottons. In general, the cell wall diameter is small, there are few circular fibers, and a large percentage of elliptical formations. Fibers of the Egyptian varieties, like those of Sea Island, are long and soft, but as a group Egyptians are not as fine or as long as the Sea Island group. The creamy yellow coloring is more pronounced in the Egyptian than in the Sea Island types. Transverse view of a typical Egyptian cotton is shown in Fig. 24, *B*.

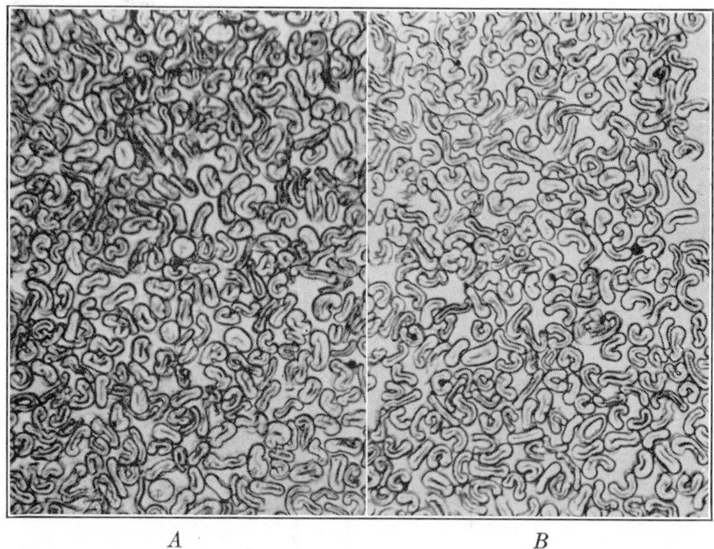

A *B*

FIG. 24. Cross-sections of fine cottons. *A*, Sea Island. *B*, Egyptian. ×250. (*Bailey*.)

American Upland Cotton

Cross-sectional photomicrographs of two Upland cottons are reproduced here to represent a coarse and a fine cotton from this group (Figs. 25, *A* and 25, *B*). These samples were selected as having normal characteristics: the finer sample those of the longer staple cottons grown in the Delta region, and the coarser sample those of cottons from the short-staple Upland area.

Asiatic Cotton

Samples of Chinese and Indian are used as illustrative of this group of short coarse cotton. The cross-sectional features of these samples are very thick walls and mostly elliptical or circular shapes (Figs. 26, *A* and

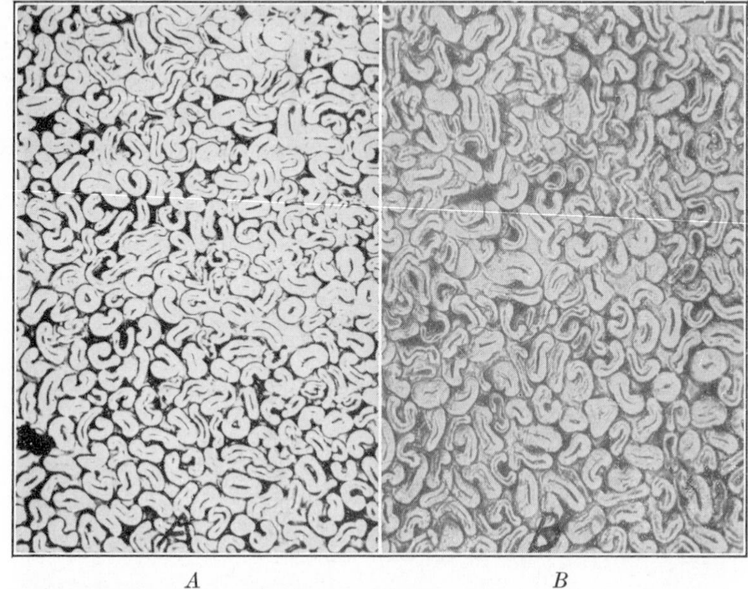

A B

Fig. 25. American Upland cottons. *A*, Delta. *B*, Upland. ×250. (*Bailey.*)

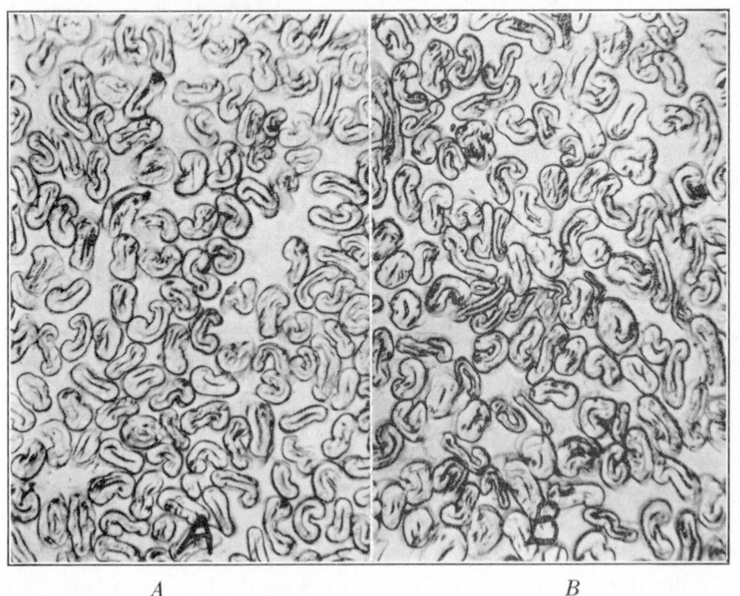

A B

Fig. 26. Asiatic cottons. *A*, Indian. *B*, Chinese. ×250. (*Bailey.*)

26, *B*). The wall thickness of the Asiatic cottons is considerably greater than that of most other types. The number of convolutions per unit fiber length is fewer, and they usually form long open spirals, as contrasted with the tight spirals of Sea Island and Egyptian varieties.

Peruvian Cotton

One of the coarser types of cotton is the Peruvian. It differs from most other coarse types in that it is generally longer than other cottons of

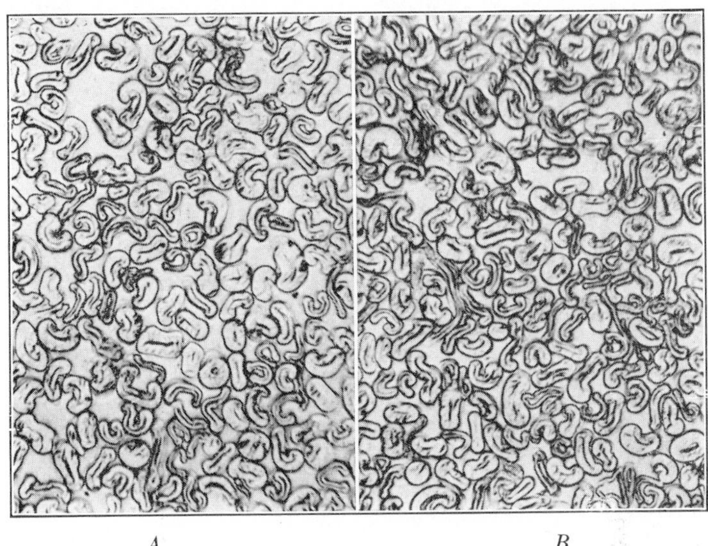

A *B*

FIG. 27. South American cottons. *A*, tree cotton from Brazil. *B*, Peruvian cotton. ×250. (*Bailey*.)

such coarseness. Examined microscopically, the fibers are thick-walled, relatively uniform in shape and size, with few immature or thin-walled fibers (Fig. 27, *B*). Rough Peruvian has a wiry harshness somewhat like coarse wool. Some fibers appear rod-shaped, with long slow spirals. In cross-section the walls are thickened, so as to entirely fill the lumen. Smooth Peruvian and rough Peruvian are very similar in microscopical features. Tree cotton (Maco) from Brazil is another example of harsh, coarse, thick-walled cotton (Fig. 27, *A*).

Colored Cottons

Brown and green lint cottons are of interest mainly because of their color. The brown lint cotton (Fig. 28) does not differ appreciably from other fibers of comparable fineness and length except for the pronounced pigmentation. Some fibers are deeply colored, the central canal often being entirely filled. The green lint on the other hand is very lightly pigmented. All distinctly "green" samples examined in cross-section by the author have been very uniformly colored and also very immature

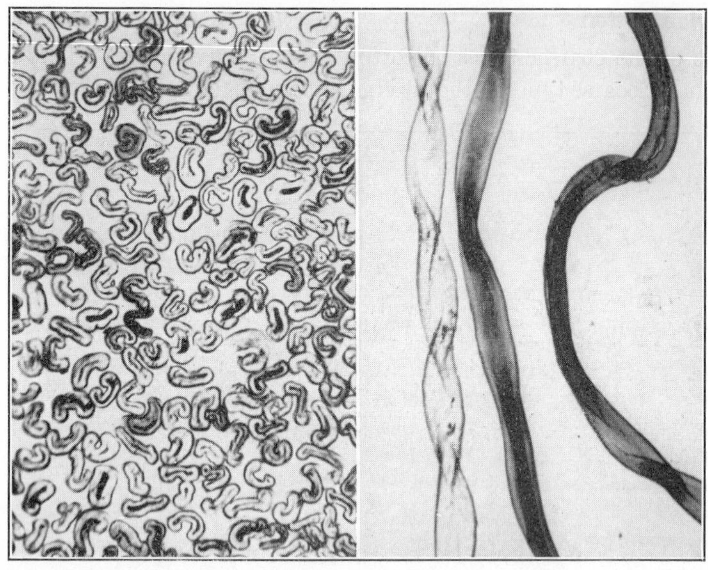

FIG. 28. Brown lint cotton. *Left,* cross-sectional view. *Right,* longitudinal view. ×250. (*Bailey.*)

as regards cell-wall development (Fig. 29). (Note magnification of cross-sectional view ×500 to shcw extremely collapsed fibers.)

Microchemical Reactions

With iodine and sulfuric acid cotton fibers swell and become blue. In raw cotton the protoplasmic residue in the lumen and parts of the cuticle, which contain encrusting materials, are colored yellow by this treatment.

The most characteristic of the microchemical reactions for cotton is the "ballooning" with ammoniacal copper solution previously described (Figs. 12 and 13). Another convenient and similar swelling reagent for the study of cotton fiber structure is trimethylbenzylammonium hydroxide. If ruthenium red is used with this reagent or with cuprammonium hydroxide the cuticle, lumen wall, and protoplasmic remains in the fiber can be stained red or purple, revealing their structure in relation to that of the cellulose cell wall, which remains unstained.

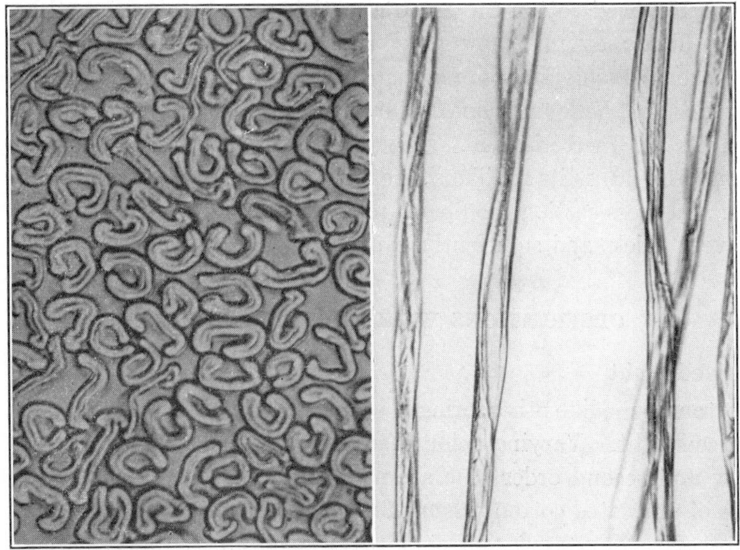

Fig. 29. Green lint cotton. *Left*, cross-sectional view. ×500. *Right*, longitudinal view. ×250. (*Bailey.*)

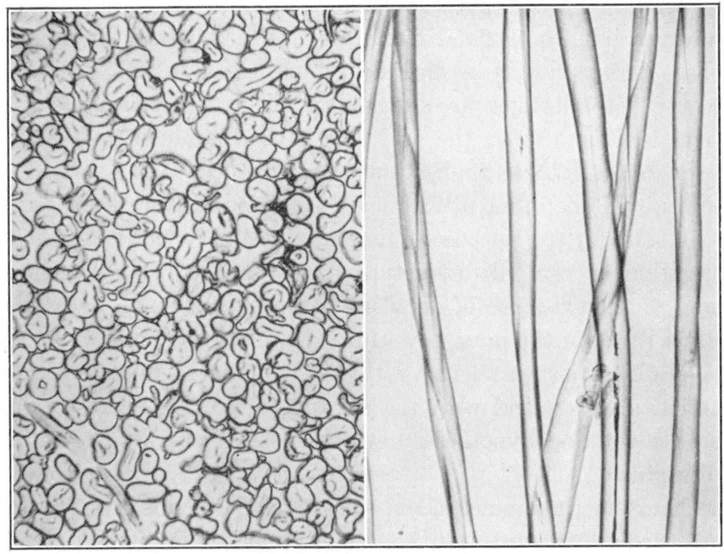

Fig. 30. Mercerized cotton. *Left*, cross-sectional view. *Right*, longitudinal view. ×250. (*Bailey.*)

With bleached cotton the external cuticle may be absent, and hence such a fiber may not show any "ballooning." Likewise, mercerized fibers are so evenly swollen throughout by the treatment with sodium hydroxide that ballooning does not occur, the cuticle having already been dissolved by mercerization. The chief characteristic of mercerized cotton (Fig. 30) is its rodlike shape, with complete absence of convolutions. In cross-section the fibers are for the most part circular, the cell wall very thick, and sufficiently swollen to practically close the lumen.

OBSERVATIONS WITH OTHER EQUIPMENT

Polarized Light

Cotton fibers, like other forms of cellulose, exhibit double refraction in polarized light. Varying color effects are obtained, but second order yellow and second order blue are most prominently the characteristic colors of untreated cotton, when a first order selenite plate is used in the microscope. These color effects may be reversed by rotating the fiber through 90° (Fig. 31). The colors, blue and yellow, seem to alternate down the length of the fiber. This is interpreted by Farr [28] as due either to differences in thickness of cellulose or to differences in orientation of cellulose units or both. The fibril reversals found in cotton may be shown strikingly by polarized light. Surface details and markings may be observed clearly by dark-field illumination [31] (Fig. 32).

Because all textile fibers are more or less anisotropic, polarized light is a powerful tool for use on the problems of the fine structure of fibers. Schwarz [29] cites three applications of microscopy with polarized light to the study of fibers: the utilization of polarized light for the identification of fibers, for the purpose of determining fiber quality, and for the investigation of the microstructure. By the use of this technique, evidence of the existence of details of structure too small to be visible directly with even the most powerful light microscope may be studied. These observations correlated with those made by means of X-ray diffraction analyses and with the aid of the electron microscope may serve as a working hypothesis toward the understanding of ultimate fiber structure.

The X-ray method, an excellent summary of which is given by Mark and Meyer [33], is most valuable when applied to a bundle of fibers. In this way an over-all average result is obtained for a large number of fibers. The X-ray method is not easily suited to the study of single fibers.

Electron Microscope

A new and more powerful research instrument, the electron microscope no doubt will play an important role in the ultimate unraveling of

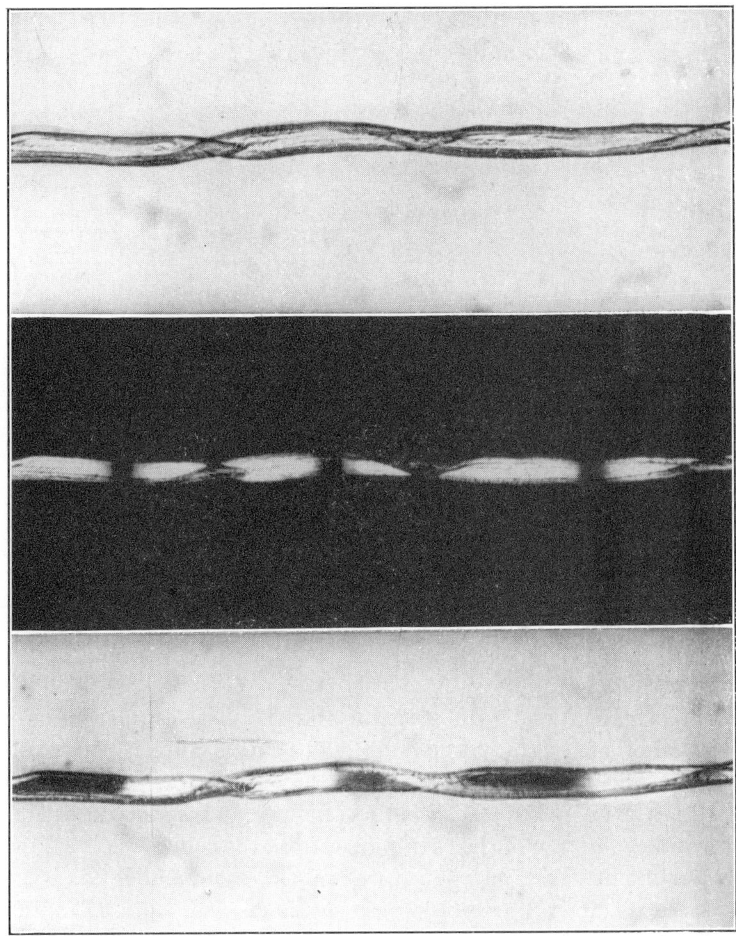

FIG. 31. Raw mature fiber mounted in water and photographed under various lighting conditions. *Top,* ordinary light, showing convolutions. *Middle,* between crossed Nicols, showing bands of extinction, where fibrillar orientation is reversed. *Bottom,* between crossed Nicols with selenite plate, showing differences in color in regions adjacent to extinction bands. ×180. (*Hock.*)

the fine structural details of cotton fiber. Barnes and Burton [13] have reported work with the electron microscope, in which are shown electron micrographs of mechanically disintegrated cotton fibers (Fig. 11) compared with similar photomicrographs made with the optical microscope to show the fine structure of cotton fibers.

The electron micrographs show fine fibrillar structures which cannot be resolved with the optical microscope. They indicate that the ultimate fibril, which constitutes a structural element in the cell wall lamella, is a much finer unit than has previously been reported. Further

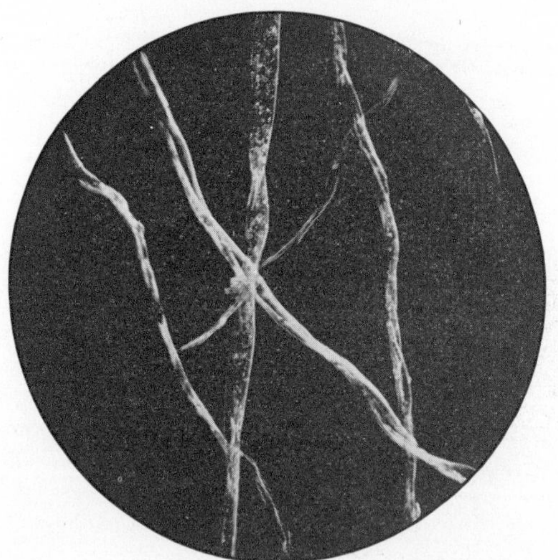

FIG. 32. Effect produced on fibers by dark ground illumination. Note surface detail. (*Schwarz.*)

research investigations with electron and X-ray instruments and the correlation of such data will undoubtedly lead to a much better understanding of the cotton fiber than we now have.

The optical microscope has pointed the way and is still an invaluable aid toward evaluation of the cotton fiber from the commercial and industrial standpoint. The gross features of the cotton fiber, its varietal differences, its dimensions, cross-sectional shape, and degree of maturity, as well as its response to chemical treatment, are essential details in its proper utilization and processing.

REFERENCES IN TEXT

1. PEARSON, N. L., and SMITH, W. S., U. S. Dept. Agr., Mimeographed report Feb. 1941, Washington, D. C.
2. KARRER, E., and BAILEY, T. L. W., JR., *Textile Research*, **8**, 381 (1938).
3. CLEGG, G. G., *J. Textile Inst.*, **23**, T35–T54, illus. (1932).
4. NICKERSON, R. F., *Ind. Eng. Chem.*, **32** (11), 1454–1462 (1940).

5. Hock, C. W., and Harris, M., *J. Research Natl. Bur. Standards*, **24,** 743 (1940)
6. Berkley, E. E., *Textile Research*, **9,** 355 (1939).
7. Sisson, W. A., *Contrib. Boyce Thompson Inst.*, **9** (3), 239–248 (1938).
8. Balls, W. L., *Proc. Roy. Soc. London*, **B90,** 542–555 (1919).
9. Kerr, T., *Protoplasma*, **27,** 229 (1937).
10. Hock, C. W., Ramsay, R. C., Harris, M., *J. Research Natl. Bur. Standards*, **26** (1940).
11. Balls, W. L., and Hancock, H. A., *Proc. Roy. Soc. London*, **B93,** 426–440 (1922).
12. Balls, W. L., *Studies of Quality in Cotton*, Macmillan Co., London (1938).
13. Barnes, R. B., and Burton, C. J., *Ind. Eng. Chem.*, **35,** 120 (1943).
14. Herzog, R. O., and Jancke, W., *Z. Physik.*, **3,** 196 (1920).
15. Frey-Wyssling, A., "Die Stoffausscheidung der höheren Pflanzen," J. Springer, Berlin (1935).
16. Seifriz, W., and Hock, C. W., *Paper Trade J.*, **102,** 36–38 (May 7, 1936).
17. Farr, W. K., and Eckerson, S. H., *Contrib. Boyce Thompson Inst.*, **6,** 189–203 (1934).
18. Bailey, A. J., *Paper Ind.*, **17,** 735–739 (1936).
19. Bailey, A. J., and Brown, R. M., *Ind. Eng. Chem.*, **32,** 57 (Jan. 1940).
20. Freudenberg, K., *J. Chem. Education*, **9,** 1171 (1932).
21. Bailey, I. W., and Kerr, T., *J. Arnold Arboretum*, **16,** 273–300 (1935).
22. Anderson, D. B., and Moore, J. H., *Am. J. Botany*, **24,** 503–507 (1937).
23. Anderson, D. B., and Kerr, T., *Ind. Eng. Chem.*, **30,** 48–54 (1938).
24. Farr, W. K., *Boyce Thompson Inst.*, **6** (4), 471–478 (1934).
25. Brown, H. B., *Cotton*, 2nd Ed., McGraw-Hill Book Co., N. Y. (1938).
26. Pearson, N. L., "Neps and Similar Imperfections in Cotton," *U. S. Dept. Agr. Tech. Bull. 396* (1933).
27. Clegg, G. G., *J. Text. Inst.*, **31** (5), T49–T68 (May 1940).
28. Farr, W. K., and Clark, G. L., *Contrib. Boyce Thompson Inst.*, **4** (3), 273–295 (1932).
29. Schwarz, E. R., *Textile Research*, **7,** 271–287; **8,** 310–326 (1937).
30. Von Bergen, W., and Krauss, W., *Textile Fiber Atlas* (1942).
31. Schwarz, E. R., *Textiles and the Microscope*, McGraw-Hill Book Co., N. Y.-London (1934).
32. Farr, W. K., *J. Phys. Chem.*, **42** (8) (1938).
33. Mark, K. H., and Meyer, H., *Der Aufbau der hochpolymeren organischen Naturstoffe*, Akad. Verlag. Leipzig (1930).

BIBLIOGRAPHY

Alexander, Jerome, "Textile Fibers (Chemical and Physical Aspects)," *Ind. Eng. Chem.*, **31,** 630 (May 1939).

Allen, R. M., *The Microscope*, D. Van Nostrand Co., N. Y. (1940).

Clark, George L., *Applied X-Rays*, McGraw-Hill Book Co., N. Y.-London (1940).

Gage, S. H., *The Microscope*, Comstock Publishing Co., Ithaca, N. Y. (1936).

Heermann, P., and Herzog, A., *Mikroskopische und mechanish-technische Textil-untersuchungen*, 3rd Ed., Julius Springer, Berlin (1931).

Herzog, A., and Koch, P. A., *Fehler in Textilien*, 1st Ed.. publ. by Melliand Textil-berichte, Heidelberg (1938).

Hock, C. W., and Harris, Milton, "Microscopic Examination of Cotton Fibers in Cuprammonium Hydroxide Solutions," *J. Research Natl. Bur. Standards*, Res. Paper No. 1309, **24,** 743 (June 1940).

Hooper, Florence E., "Disintegration of the Cell Membrane of the Cotton Fiber by a Pure Culture of Bacteria," *Contrib. Boyce Thompson Inst.*, pp. 267–275 (Apr.-June 1939).

McClung, C. E., *Handbook of Microscopical Technique*, Paul B. Hoeber, Inc., Harper & Bros., N. Y.-London (1939).

Morey, D. R., "Relation of Orientation to Physical Properties of Cottons and Rayons," *Textile Research*, **V** (11), 483–492 (1935).

Osborne, G. Gordon, "Observations on the Structure of Cotton," *Textile Research*, **V** (6), 275–297; (7), 307–325 (1935).

Preston, J. M., *Modern Textile Microscopy*, Emmott & Co., Ltd., London W. C. 2 (1933).

Prindle, Bryce, "Cotton Fiber: Methods of Microbiological Analysis," *Textile Research*, **IV** (9), 413; (10), 438; (12), 555; **V** (1), 11 (1934).

Prindle, Bryce, "Growth of Mildew Organisms in Raw Cotton at 25° C. and Relative Humidities of 70 to 95 Per Cent," *Textile Research*, **VII** (11), 413; (12), 445 (1937).

Prindle, Bryce, "Method for the General Histological Examination of Normal or Mildewed Cotton Fibers," *Textile Research*, **VI** (11), 481 (1936).

Prindle, Bryce, "Microbiology of Textile Fibers—Raw Cotton," *Textile Research*, **V** (12), 542; **VI** (1), 23 (1935).

Schwarz, E. R., *Textiles and The Microscope*, McGraw-Hill Book Co., N. Y.-London (1934).

Schwarz, E. R., and Shapiro, L., "Cotton Fiber Maturity (Polarized Light and Cross Section Studies)," *Rayon Textile Monthly* (June, July, August, September 1938).

Skinkle, J. H., *Textile Testing—Physical, Chemical, and Microscopical*, Chemical Publishing Co., N. Y. (1940).

Skinkle, J. H., and Olney, L. A., *Elementary Textile Microscopy*, Howes Publishing Co., N. Y. (1930).

Strang, P. M., "Some Phases of Cotton Character," *Am. Wool Cotton Reptr.* (Sept. 17, 1942).

Von Bergen, Werner, and Krauss, Walter, *Textile Fiber Atlas*, American Wool Handbook Co., N. Y. (1942).

CHAPTER V

COTTON FIBER: PHYSICAL PROPERTIES

R. F. Nickerson

Fiber Growth

The cotton fiber, as the term is generally understood, is a hair which grows out of a single epidermal cell in the cottonseed coat. Fiber formation begins during or shortly after the flowering of the plant and continues for 40 to 60 days, depending on the species and environmental conditions. As a result of the classical investigations of Balls [1] on Egyptian cotton and more recent studies of Anderson and Kerr [2] on Upland, fiber growth is known to occur in two fairly distinct stages:

The first stage, the primary wall formation, requires between 13 and 20 days [3], during which the thin, outer fiber envelope emerges from the parent cell. This cell wall pushes rapidly out and attains the mature length of the fiber by the end of the first phase. Thus, both the ultimate fiber length and breadth are determined long before maturity.

The second growth stage occupies another 30 to 50 days [4] and corresponds to secondary wall formation. During this phase an inward thickening of the fiber occurs as successive layers of cellulose are deposited. The mechanism of cellulose formation and deposition is not yet known. Finally, a period of dehydration occurs (15 to 25 days), during which the more or less tubular fiber collapses and a residue of proteinaceous solids is deposited in the lumen. The latter substances, as part of the cell sap, probably play a role in the metabolism of the living cell.

Balls believed that secondary wall thickening is a stepwise process and that the successive layers of cellulose in a fiber cross-section are daily growth rings, which represent the rapid synthesis and deposition of cellulose during sunlight hours. Although controversy centered around this hypothesis, it appears to be confirmed by Anderson and Kerr [2]. These investigators employed artificial conditions and showed that growth rings were not formed when the plant received continuous illumination at a constant temperature.

Kerr [5] stated that two lamellae are formed each day during secondary wall deposition, one spongy and one compact, and that diurnal temperature fluctuations are probably responsible in large part for growth-ring formation. Hock and his collaborators [4] agreed with Balls and Kerr

[5] that growth rings are probably formed at the rate of one compact and one porous ring a day, until growth ceases. (See Fig. 8, Chapter IV.)

Fiber diameter is undoubtedly a varietal characteristic, whereas wall thickness seems to be a function of maturity, according to Peirce and Lord [6], who reported a study of fiber cross-sections. Since fiber diameter is a species and varietal characteristic, it makes possible the selection and reproduction of desired types. The observations on wall thickness are in accordance with the growth mechanism outlined above for, if secondary wall formation should cease before average wall thickness is reached, a thinner-than-average fiber wall may result. Immature or thin-walled fibers are probably formed in this way. Hock *et al.* [4] indicated that growth-ring deposition may not proceed to the same extent in all fibers; in other words, natural variation is operative.

Fiber Shape

A typical, mature raw cotton fiber is a flattened tube; examined under the low-power microscope it is a long, twisted ribbon with slightly thickened edges. The basal fiber end is open and irregular, where it is torn from the seed coat in ginning, while the tip is closed, symmetrical, and tapered. There are many individual deviations from this typical fiber such as the more or less unflattened, tubular shapes that characterize extremely thick walled fibers, particularly those of Asiatic origin, and abnormalities such as forked, branched, and bulged tips. Pearson [7] and Osborne [8] have discussed many kinds of irregularities. (See also Figs. 1, 2, 4, 16, 18, 19, Chapter IV.)

Fibers of different species and varieties of cotton range in length from 1000 to 4000 times their breadths, with values of 1200 to 1500 for the more common types. Actually, fiber breadth has only limited significance inasmuch as it may not reveal the amount of functional substance the fiber contains. In other words, both fiber breadth and wall thickness must be known if the dimensions are to have meaning.

Convolutions

The number of twists or half-convolutions in raw cotton fibers varies widely (Fig. 4, Chapter IV). Immature fibers are practically nonconvoluted, while mature fibers of the same variety may be highly convoluted. Bowman [9] gave the following table of estimates of average number of half-convolutions per inch for different classes of cotton.

TABLE 1. Half-Convolutions per Inch in Different Cottons

Cotton	Half-convolutions	Cotton	Half-convolutions
Sea Island	300	American	192
Egyptian	228	Indian (Surat)	150
Brazilian	210		

Adderley [10] stated that cottons of various types have from 20 to 100 half-convolutions per centimeter, i.e., 50 to 250 per in. Osborne [8] gave as a range of lengths for convolutions 10 to 12,700 μ, noting that they are alternately in "S" and "Z" spirals for different, irregular distances. From measurements of clinging power based on the pulling of single fibers from pads of parallel fibers, Adderley [10] concluded that minimum slippage obtains when adjacent fibers contain 150 to 175 half-convolutions per inch. Navkal and Ahmad [11] have discussed the effect of convolutions on the length and strength of cotton fibers.

It was once thought that fiber convolutions were produced by the flow of cell sap back into the seed at maturity. An explanation more consistent with present knowledge is that convolutions are caused largely by strains and by inequalities and peculiarities in the fine structure. The fiber lumen contains a residue of nitrogenous substances. It has been suggested [12] that fiber weight per inch may be estimated from the nitrogen content of the sample.

Thin-Walled Fibers

Any sample of cotton is likely to contain fibers varying appreciably in wall thickness. Three classes of fibers have been recognized by the Shirley Institute in England, namely, thin, medium, and thick-walled. Thin-walled fibers are often called "immature" fibers, the terms being used interchangeably in U. S. Department of Agriculture publications. In general, thick-walled fibers have well-defined convolutions and the fiber wall is relatively thick compared to ribbon width; thin-walled fibers are more or less transparent, nonconvoluted, and ribbonlike, and have little secondary-wall deposition. Medium-walled fibers are intermediate. The American tendency is to distinguish only thin-walled fibers from the others. "Dead cotton," as the term is generally understood, probably refers to extremely thin walled fibers. For obvious reasons precise definitions of terms are lacking.

Thin-walled fibers usually constitute from 20 to 40 per cent of Upland cottons as well as of other species. Pearson's studies [7] indicate that thin-walled fibers are present in a large proportion of the neps in raw cotton and also tend to knot up much more readily than medium and thick-walled fibers. Clegg and Harland [13] stated that a distinction must be made between immature fibers and dead fibers, the latter appearing as tangled clumps on the surface of the cloth. The difference between these two types of fibers may be one of degree and definition.

The presence of up to 50 per cent of thin-walled or immature fibers in a cotton does not seem to influence fiber-bundle strength [3] or yarn strength, even though the individual fibers may be weaker than the medium- and thick-walled. Because they are thin, immature fibers pack more numerously in a unit cross-sectional area and in the aggregate approach the strength of the thick-walled fibers. Nevertheless, high percentages of thin-walled fibers, as indicated by "neppiness" in raw cotton, are undesirable and may reduce the grade of the cotton, aside from increasing both the amount of waste and the number of neps in the goods. It is also questionable whether or not immature fibers are as durable as the thick-walled.

The behavior of immature fibers in cuprammonium reagent, described by Hock, Ramsay, and Harris [4], is in sharp contrast to that of mature fibers. The latter swell, writhe and twist, and form "balloons," whereas immature fibers swell little in the reagent, undergo few visible changes, and leave the undissolved wax and pectic materials in the original tubular shape of the primary wall. Thus, immature fibers can be distinguished from the mature. Mature and immature fibers may also differ in their dye affinity so that neps in the cloth may be conspicuously lighter or darker than the fabric.

Immature and mature fibers do not look alike in polarized light when a first-order selenite plate is used with microscope (see Chapter IV). Unlike mature fibers which exhibit varied color effects, the immature fibers are brilliantly and uniformly colored [14]. Strang [15] has presented some excellent photomicrographs in color of immature fibers, and Schwarz and Hotte [16] have suggested a method of determining immature fibers which is based on color differences of mature and immature fibers in polarized light. These color effects are discussed in Chapter IV.

STRUCTURAL COMPOSITION

The cotton fiber may be regarded as composed of three more or less distinct parts: the *cuticle*, the *primary* wall, and the *secondary* wall (see Fig. 7, Chapter IV).

Cuticle

Many investigators do not make a distinction between the cuticle and the primary wall. Osborne [8] summarized information on the subject as follows:

> Although closely and firmly moulded to the primary wall during growth, it is not an integral part of it. The primary wall may just be resolved for inspection by critical magnification while the cuticle many times thinner, is not detectable in this manner. This accounts for the fact that lack of knowledge of this part of the fibre is greater than for the other components, and is most regrettable, for, as the cuticle plays a major part in the surface attributes of the hair, it has a corresponding influence on spinning and yarn properties.

Primary Wall

From the flowering of the plant to the onset of secondary wall formation, cotton fibers consist of a thin primary wall enclosing protoplasm. Studies of the primary wall are usually made on fibers at this stage of development. In ordinary light, primary wall material exhibits no evidence of structure. In polarized light unstained young fibers show no detectable birefringence, according to Hock, Ramsay, and Harris [4], but when a selenite plate is interposed between the Nicols prisms they produce faint color, indicative of a transverse orientation of the cellulose framework. When such young fibers are treated with cuprammonium reagent, the cellulose dissolves and leaves waxes and pectic materials in the outline of the fiber. Purified before treatment with the reagent, these young fibers dissolve completely (see Figs. 12 and 13, Chapter IV).

Chemical identification tests and X-ray examinations concur with other evidence that the primary wall is largely cellulose in the form of transversely oriented threads [4]. The bulk of the pectic and fatty matter is located in or on this network. Compton and Haver [17] showed that waxes and pectates accumulate rapidly during the period of primary wall formation.

The crisscrossed network of transversely oriented cellulose threads has been described by Balls [1], Anderson and Kerr [2], and Berkley [18], in addition to Hock and his coworkers [4]. It is of interest to note that since cellulose has its maximum strength in the direction of its orientation, these circularly disposed threads are arranged to produce high peripheral strength and consequently to restrict lateral fiber swelling. This arrangement also makes the primary wall weaker in the lengthwise direction of the fiber and may account for the low strength per square inch of young fibers. (See Fig. 10, Chapter IV.)

Secondary Wall

The secondary wall of a mature fiber is practically pure cellulose and probably represents about 90 per cent of the fiber weight [8]. This wall is lamellate as a result of the nature of fiber development. Actually, the secondary wall consists of many tiny threads of cellulose, called fibrils, laid side by side to form the ring-shaped lamellae. (See Fig. 10, Chapter IV.) The fibrils in a lamella appear to follow a helical course around the lumen with frequent reversals in direction. The fibrils of some lamellae seem to spiral in one direction, other lamellae in the reverse direction, both making an acute angle with the fiber axis. Striations due to this crossing of fibrils of different lamellae can be discerned with the microscope, particularly when the fiber is swollen. The evidence is fairly conclusive that the larger part of the fiber convolutions occur between the abrupt reversals in fibrillar orientation. Diagrammatic representations of fiber structure have been given by Anderson and Kerr [2], by Berkley [3], and by others.

The size of the fibrils has not been established with any certainty. Estimates of diameter range from 0.1 to 1.4 μ [19, 20]. According to Barnes and Burton [21], who made a simultaneous study of mechanically disintegrated fibers with the optical and the electron microscopes, part of the variation in estimates may be attributed to diffraction effects. That is, the optical microscope causes appreciable distortion of the image at the magnifications which must be employed. Electron photomicrographs show that a fine fibrous structure of cotton is readily visible at magnifications of $\times 6000$ (see Chapter IV). It is possible, therefore, that the fibril has no definite width but varies widely with the sample and method of preparation. Further investigations with the electron microscope may extend present knowledge of fine fiber structure considerably.

The structure of fibrils, like that of fibers, probably involves two distinct regions: surface and internal. Since fibrils appear, under the optical microscope, to be discrete entities, it is likely that their surfaces oppose the cohesion which would cause a fusion into an undifferentiated mass. At any rate, fibrils can be caused to separate from young fibers by mechanical treatment, such as by pressing, and from mature fibers by the action of the papermaker's beater. A layer about 0.2 μ thick is said to separate the lamellae [22].

The fine structure of fibrils is, for all practical purposes, the fine structure of native cellulose [23]. For a description of the chains of condensed glucose and crystallite structure see Chapter II, "Cellulose." Frey-Wyssling [24], Mark [25], and others have prepared diagrams which indicate the probable arrangement of elementary chain molecules. Some of the possible molecular phenomena involved in fiber structure and properties as explained by Kratky [27] and Mark [28, 29] are described in a summary [26] from which Table 2 was taken.

TABLE 2. Physical Properties of Unmodified Cotton Fibers

Property	*Relative Amount*	*Possible Determinative Factors*
Rigidity (torsonial)	High	Rigid molecules, extensive crystallization.
Resistance to bending	High	Same.
Plasticity	Low	Large intermolecular forces.
Extensibility	Low	Stretched molecules, high crystallinity and orientation.
Resiliency	Low	High molecular interaction.
Dry tenacity	Fairly high	Good molecular and crystallite orientation.
Wet tenacity	High	High degree of polymerization.

Tensile Strength

Strength is one of the most important attributes of cotton and in respect to this property it stands between wool and silk. The load required to break single cotton fibers varies widely and appears to depend on the thickness of fiber wall and the amount of prior damage and cellulose degradation. Mature fibers of the coarse, heavy-walled type are strongest, ranging in strength from 9 to 13 grams per fiber. Mature fibers of the intermediate and fine types range in strength from 4 to 9 grams. Thin-walled fibers of any species or variety are generally weak, their strength varying appreciably.

Clegg [30] investigated the breaking strength of single fibers and observed that the individual values were highly variable and did not correlate with either fiber diameters or number of convolutions. Within the same variety, fiber strength seemed to be related to wall thickness. An average breaking load of about 5.5 grams (1/5 oz) was observed for a number of varieties, even though cross-sectional areas ranged from 120 to 270 sq μ. By calculation from these data tensile strengths of about 60,000 lb per sq in. can be obtained for the finer fibers and about 30,000 lb for the coarser. These values do not agree with Chandler bundle strength measurements discussed below.

The integration of single fiber measurements as a means of determining tensile strengths in pounds per square inch may not yield reliable values for several reasons. (1) Appreciable errors may be made in the estimates of fiber strengths and cross-sectional areas. (2) Each individual fiber breaks at its weakest point and, consequently, the integration yields as a sum the minimum strength of all fibers, a condition not realized in bundles or in yarns. (3) A large number of fibers must be broken and measured before a representative set of data is obtained.

In practice, tensile strengths based on bundles of parallel fibers are less tedious to determine experimentally, are more representative of the way cotton is used, and may be made with smaller errors. That is, if a section of cotton yarn is regarded as a bundle of fibers, it is highly improbable that the weakest portion of each fiber occurs in the same yarn cross-section. It is more likely that the weaker and stronger portions of the fibers are randomly distributed so that at any place in the yarn the stronger parts of some fibers are reinforcing the weaker parts of others. Because the bundle strength simulates conditions of use, is determined from a relatively large and representative sample, and can be obtained readily, it is now employed almost exclusively in fiber evaluation tests.

The modified Chandler Method for determining bundle strengths was developed and improved over a period of years by the U. S. Department of Agriculture [31]. In practice a small bundle of parallel cotton fibers is closely and tightly wrapped with a stout thread, so that only a small section in the middle of the bundle remains exposed. The bundle is so placed in closely spaced jaws that the break occurs in the exposed region and fiber tensile strength is calculated from breaking strength and cross-sectional area. Considerable specialized technique and equipment are required if reliable data are to be obtained, and careful examination of the published descriptions [32] is recommended. However, attention is directed to the fact that the bundle breaks at a predetermined spot and consequently the resulting value represents average fiber strength. A newer and more rapid method due to Pressley [33] is gaining favor and has recently been adopted by the U. S. Department of Agriculture.

Chandler bundle strengths of normal cottons range from 60,000 to 120,000 lb per sq in. [31], the coarse cottons generally tending toward the lower limit and the very fine toward the higher limit. The bulk of commercial cottons falls between 70,000 and 90,000 lb per sq in. A few illustrative data are given in Table 3; more extensive information on strength and other fiber properties of different species and varieties of cotton is given later in this chapter.

TABLE 3. PHYSICAL DATA ON SEVEN COTTONS GROWN AT STONEVILLE, MISS. [12]

Variety	*Crop Season*	*Staple Length (in.)*	*Weight per Inch (micrograms)*	*Chandler Bundle Strength (lb per sq in.)*
Half and half	1937	7/8	5.71	68,100 ± 700
Rowden	1938	1	4.97	80,600 ± 900
Wilds No. 5	1937	1 3/32	4.46	82,300 ± 900
Acala	1938	1	4.13	81,700 ± 600
Express	1938	1 1/32	4.06	80,500 ± 800
Delfos	1938	1 1/32	3.05	73,900 ± 400
Sea Island *	1938	1 1/4	2.98	96,000 ± 1600

* This sample was not as long and strong as typical Sea Island.

It is apparent that the longer and finer cottons tend to be stronger than the coarser and shorter cottons. The proportionally higher strengths of the fine cottons have been ascribed by Mann and Peirce [34] to a skin effect. They stated:

> It is generally known that thin filaments are proportionately stronger than thick ones, the surface layers than internal layers . . . The strength of the cotton hair may be regarded as due to two elements, an outer layer relatively more elastic and constant with a varying amount of internal thickening of more imperfect elasticity.

A more direct expression of this idea is that while the fibrils of the secondary wall may account for a large part of the fiber strength, there is a relatively large disparity between the lengths of the inner and outer layers of fibrils. That is, the axial fibrils coil around a short radius, the outer fibrils around a longer radius. In the fine, long cottons the disproportion in fibril lengths is a minimum and a load falls more evenly on the entire fiber cross-section.

The degree of orientation of crystallites in the fiber direction has been shown by Berkley and Woodyard [35] to be directly related to the Chandler bundle strength, provided the cotton is undegraded. They made X-ray photographs of bundles of intact fibers and determined the 40 per cent angles. They also obtained Chandler bundle strength data on the same cottons. Forty-eight different cottons photographed without tension yielded a correlation coefficient of −0.82 between bundle strength and 40 per cent angle, while 30 samples photographed with tension gave a correlation coefficient of −0.95. It is apparent, therefore, that crystallite orientation is an important factor in fiber strength.

The weakness of thin-walled fibers has already been mentioned. Berkley [3] has presented data on Chandler bundle strength and percentage of thin-walled fibers, as shown in Table 4.

TABLE 4. Variation of Chandler Bundle Strength with Percentage of Thin-Walled Fibers

Age of Secondary Wall (Days)	*Per Cent of Thin-Walled Fibers*	*Chandler Bundle Strength (1000 lb per sq in.)*
9	91.9	53.2
12	66.8	70.9
18	33.8	79.4
23	29.7	80.0
28	22.3	78.8
46	31.4	82.6

These data show both the rapid development and the strengthening influence of secondary-wall cellulose.

The strength of individual cotton fibers as well as of yarns is influenced to an appreciable extent by relative humidity. Fiber strengths increase with rising relative humidity in the lower range, but do not respond in most cases to increases in relative humidity beyond 60 per cent. It has been estimated that fibers saturated with water are about 20 per cent stronger than air-dry fibers [36]. The relationship of strength to fiber moisture content is discussed in a subsequent section.

Tensile Strength of Cotton Yarns. Cotton yarns are highly complex in structure and behavior. Yarn is one of the most important forms in which cotton is used, but many practical differences exist among yarns and cottons. A variety of combinations of yarn counts and twist factors are in common use, the combination being determined by the cotton and the purpose of finished textile. Hence, the present discussion must be held to a few fundamental features.

Yarn strength is essentially the resultant of the constituent fibers and of their relationship to each other in the aggregate. When yarn strength is represented as a percentage of the actual fiber strength, values as low as 10 to 20 per cent are not uncommon. It would be completely erroneous, however, to assume that the bulk of the fibers was inactive.

Slippage of fibers is undoubtedly among the more important factors involved in yarn strength. Clegg [37] evolved a staining technique which, it was claimed, permitted the differentiation of cut and broken fibers from tip and basal ends in a broken section of yarn. A 36's Sakellarides yarn with 20 turns per in. showed 70 per cent of broken fibers, whereas a 20's Surat yarn contained only 40 per cent. Clegg was not able to correlate fiber strength with yarn strength, partly because averages of individual fiber breaks were employed. Fiber bundle strengths would have been superior to average fiber strengths for the purpose. Nevertheless, appreciable fiber slippage occurs and potential fiber strength is dissipated in this manner.

There are other factors which influence yarn strength. If every fiber in a yarn is considered held in place by the contacts with adjacent fibers, evidently fiber length, yarn density, amount of entanglement, relative surface area, and coefficient of friction all come into play. Yarn density is determined by the forces that press the fibers together.

The forces resulting from contacts that hold a fiber in place, or restrain it, vary from zero at each end to a maximum somewhere near the middle of the fiber. That is, the restraining force at any point is the sum of the contact forces between that point and the less securely held end of the fiber. With short fibers the lightly held end portions represent a high proportion of the total length and, consequently, the total restraint on the fiber, as well as the maximum value, is correspondingly reduced. As a result slippage is pronounced and the yarn is weak. Calculations based on cotton fiber length-frequency distributions suggest that, for cotton having an average fiber length of 1½ in., about 30 per cent of the fiber strength might be lost, whereas an average fiber length of ¾ in. might involve a 50 per cent loss under comparable conditions.

Yarn twist causes the fibers to lie in spirals, and, since fiber stresses are in the fiber direction, fiber strength is not fully utilized. Conrad and Berkley [38] have shown that the twisting of fibers on themselves lowers fiber strengths appreciably, an influence that may assert itself in axial yarn regions. The portion of the fiber strength that cannot be realized in the yarn because of the spiral arrangement of fibers is not completely lost. Radial forces press the fibers together, increasing friction and raising the density of the yarn. The radial pressure increases with increasing helix angle and binds the bundle more securely together. Twist multiplier is approximately proportional to this helix angle. It is said [38, 39] that the proportion of fiber strength actually realized can be predicted approximately from the product of fiber strength and the cosine of the angle of twist, i.e., from the vector component of fiber strength in the yarn direction.

Twist has two apparent effects—one tending to reduce the proportion of fiber strength realized, the other tending to increase yarn strength by pressing the fibers together. These opposing effects do not change at similar rates as the twist multiplier is changed. The strengthening influence predominates at low twist, the weakening effect at high twist. In consequence, there is an intermediate, optimum twist multiplier, which corresponds to maximum yarn strength. In the region of optimum twist, the fibers are bound tightly together, and the loads they can carry are limited by their strengths.

The twist multiplier corresponding to maximum yarn strength is determined largely by fiber length; but other factors, such as fiber strength, fineness, friction, convolutions, flexibility, and length-frequency distribution, also play a part. Hence, for a given cotton there is an optimum twist multiplier and a maximum yarn strength.

Fine yarns are inherently weaker than coarse yarns. This can be ascertained readily from count-strength products for the same cotton [40]. The reason seems to be that fine yarns have a higher surface-to-volume ratio than coarse yarns. Fibers in the yarn surface make fewer contacts with adjacent fibers and have less radial pressure exerted against them. This effect is sometimes obscured by the fact that only the long, strong cottons can be spun to fine counts.

Data have been presented [40] which indicate that cotton tire cord is more sensitive to fiber strength than single yarns are. It was also observed that tire cord is stronger in proportion to its size than a single yarn is to its size.

In general about half the potential fiber strength can be realized in a well-made yarn. A mill-run 16/4/3 tire cord (S/S/Z twist) made from $1\frac{1}{16}$ in. cotton averages 40,000 lb per sq in. conditioned (6.5 per cent regain) and 35,000 lb per sq in. oven-dry. These values are based on cord having a stretch of 6.6 per cent at the 10-lb load conditioned and 6.0 per cent at the 10-lb load oven-dry. The following data were given by Barker [41], who cited Sommer as his authority.

TABLE 5. RELATIONSHIP OF "SUBSTANCE" STRENGTH TO YARN STRENGTH

Fibers	Substance Strength *		Yarn Strength		Ratio of Yarn Strength to Substance Strength × 100
	Breaking Length (kg)	Elongation (per cent)	Breaking Length (kg)	Elongation (per cent)	
Cotton	25.0	6 to 7	12 to 15	3 to 6	45 to 60
Wool	8.5	35 to 40	4.2 to 5.0	40	50 to 55
Ramie	33.0	2.7	15	2.6	45
Flax	52.0	1.6	20	1.5	38.5
Hemp	55.0	1.6	20	2.0	36
Nettle	24.8	2.5	8.5	2.4	35
Jute	32 to 34	0.8	11.5	1.5 to 2.0	35

* "Substance" strength is the equivalent of fiber strength.

Since the elongation value for cotton yarn in the above table is extremely low, it must be assumed that some sort of stretching treatment was employed to produce high density.

The strength of raw cotton yarns can often be increased perceptibly by solvent extraction of the natural fiber wax [42], or by kier-boiling which achieves the same result. Conversely, the addition of wax lowers yarn strength. Vincent [43] claimed that treatment of yarn with dilute sulfuric acid prior to kier-boiling increases the strength of the finished yarn.

An extensive program of cotton spinning tests has been conducted by the Agricultural Marketing Administration of the U. S. Department of Agriculture. Many data on species, varieties, grades, staple length, and fiber strength, as well as the characteristics of yarns spun from them, have been published. Upland cottons are usually compared as 22's yarns spun to optimum twist multiplier. Table 6, typical of published results, is self-explanatory.

Table 7, compiled from similar published data [44, 45, 46], illustrates the relationship between fiber properties and yarn strength.

It is apparent that strict relationships between yarn and fiber characteristics do not exist, although fairly high correlations between fiber and yarn strengths have been obtained under favorable conditions. The above data indicate that the shorter, coarser, and weaker cottons produced the weaker yarns. It is generally found that strong yarns can be obtained from the long, fine, strong cottons. Since length, strength, and

TABLE 6. CLASSIFICATION, SPINNING TEST RESULTS, AND CERTAIN FIBER CHARACTERISTICS OF SEVEN 1940 COTTONS [44]

Item	*Miller*	*Deltapine 12*	*Deltapine 14 [44–51]*	*Stoneville 2B*	*Delfos 6*	*Delfos 4729*	*Delfos 588*
Classification:							
Grade	M	SLMBrt.	M	M	SLMBrt.	SLMBrt.	SLMBrt.
Staple length (ins.)	1 1/32	1 1/16	1 1/16	1 1/16	1 3/32	1 3/32	1 1/8
Spinning test results:							
Picker and card waste (%)	7.53	7.48	6.69	7.71	8.58	9.18	9.08
Remarks *	Average	Very low	Very low	About average	Slightly low	About average	About average
Yarn skein strength (lb):							
22's	99.1	107.8	112.4	110.9	105.4	103.7	109.8
60's	24.8	29.7	32.4	33.1	30.6	29.7	31.4
Skein strength index †	98.2	102.6	106.2	104.9	96.4	94.0	95.2
Yarn appearance grade ‡							
22's	B	B	B+	B+	B−	B	B−
60's	C+	C+	C+	C+	C	C	C
Fiber characteristics:							
Upper quartile length (in.)	1.147	1.250	1.256	1.307	1.339	1.352	1.410
Weight per inch (micrograms)	4.73	3.89	4.14	3.78	3.87	3.65	3.49
Thin-walled fibers (%)	29.8	32.9	28.7	31.6	33.1	31.5	31.3
Tensile strength (1000 lb per sq in.)	68.4	71.2	71.8	77.2	69.8	73.0	71.8
X-ray 40% angle (degrees)	38.4	40.4	37.5	35.6	40.6	40.0	39.2
Outstanding features	Very weak	Weak, slightly fine, large angle	Weak fiber	Slightly fine	Very weak, large angle	Weak, large angle, slightly fine	Weak fiber

* Based on average waste percentage previously found in similar tests of these grades.

† Based on 3 counts after correcting for differences attributed to upper quartile length (1935–1936–1937 Regional Variety Series = 100).

‡ In accordance with yarn standards developed at the Laboratory. For 22's yarn B+ is good, B is acceptable, and B− is poor. Corresponding cottons when made into 60's are generally about 2/3 of a grade lower.

TABLE 7. COMPARATIVE AVERAGE FIBER AND YARN PROPERTIES OF INTERMEDIATE AND LONG STAPLE COTTONS

Item	*Stoneville, Miss., Cottons*	*Texas Cottons*	*Long Staple Cottons* *
Crop year	1940	1940	....
Upper quartile mean length, in.	1.295	1.202	1.469
Classer's staple length, in.	1 1/16	1 1/16	1 7/16
Weight per inch, micrograms	3.94	4.32	3.14
Thin-walled fibers, per cent	31	29	27
Fiber tensile strength, 1000 lb per sq in.	71.9	81.3	79.7
Skein strength of 60's yarn, lb	30.2 †	28.5 †	49.5 ‡
Number of cottons averaged	7	15	15

* Egyptian, Peruvian, American-Egyptian, and Upland.
† Carded.
‡ Combed.

fineness are usually associated in cottons, it is not feasible to isolate any one factor.

Turner [47] discussed the foundations of yarn strength and yarn extension, noting, in addition to the factors already mentioned, that variations in twist and count and imperfect mixing and "lie" of fibers give imperfect yarns. Sullivan [48] has presented a theoretical approach to yarn strength problems which is worthy of mention as is the influence of fiber length outlined by Köhler [49]. Campbell [50] has confirmed the relationship between fiber length and twist multiplier, finding higher factors necessary for the shorter cottons. The relationship between strength and fatigue of fabrics has been ably discussed by Busse [51] and his collaborators. Concerning the marked upward convexity of the load-extension relation for "open" or soft yarns, Brown, Mann, and Peirce [52] stated:

> The tension forces the fibers into contact and straightens them out in the direction of the yarn, so producing a structural extension which is added to that of the fibers themselves. When the latter are in close contact, their own extension only is recorded.

The same idea is implied in the observation of Gurney and Davis [53], that true yarn elasticity is determined by the fibers, elongation by the twist.

Fiber stiffness has a direct bearing on yarn strength, as can be demonstrated readily. An oven-dry yarn may be as much as 30 per cent weaker than the same yarn normally conditioned. Oven-dry fibers are somewhat weaker than conditioned fibers, but this difference does not entirely account for the loss of yarn strength. For example, fibers do not appear to gain appreciably in strength as relative humidity exceeds 60 per cent [52], and yet a yarn may continue to gain strength up to complete saturation [54]. Since water is a softener or plasticizer of cellulose, it is highly probable that fibers swell and soften in proportion to their moisture content and are then compressed under applied stresses. A compressed or compact aggregate of slightly swollen fibers represents a more efficient utilization of frictional effects. Moist fibers also stretch more readily than dry fibers; hence, better equalization of internal yarn strains may occur under humid conditions than at complete dryness. Improvements in the dry strength of yarns or cords can be obtained through treatments that reduce elongation and increase yarn density. Fiber-to-fiber contacts, thereby established, may be maintained to an appreciable extent in the dry yarn or cord.

It is evident that, with the same cotton, yarn and cord strengths can be augmented by changes in friction at fiber surface, by increases in yarn density that create more fiber-to-fiber contacts, and by improvements in product uniformity that raise the average strength level. Other factors being the same, cottons of uniform fiber length should be superior to non-uniform cottons of the same classer's length. However, despite the strength increments that can be obtained from shorter cottons by such devices, there is little doubt that the long cottons with their fineness and high fiber bundle strengths can be expected to yield the stronger yarns.

Staple Length

The staple lengths of the various species of cultivated cotton are given in a general way in Chapter III, as is the official definition of staple length. The purpose of this section is to present specific data on staple length and on other fiber characteristics.

It should be understood that, at maturity, the fibers attached to a single cottonseed vary considerably in length. There are, in fact, two groups of fibers that must be distinguished in many species—the longer textile fibers or "lint" and an undercoat of coarse, short fuzz fibers that remain on the seed after the ginning. The latter fibers become "linters."

A number frequency distribution of fiber lengths in a sample generally forms a skew curve which may vary considerably in skewness from one cotton to another. Fiber arrays can be prepared with a Suter-Webb Sorter, a double set of combs which yield fibers in intervals of staple length. The groups of fibers obtained can be counted or weighed [32]. Hertel [55] has recently developed the "Fibrograph," a photoelectric scanning device, which gives a rapid cumulative estimate of fiber

Table 8. Classification and Certain Fiber Characteristics of Different Upland Cottons of the Same Staple Length, Crop Year 1940 *

Variety	Location of Growth	Grade	Staple length (inches)	Upper Quartile length (inches)	Weight per inch (micro-grams)	Immature Fibers (per cent)	Tensile Strength per Square Inch † (1000 lb)	X-Ray 40% Angle (degrees)	Outstanding Features
Cook Wire Grass	Headland, Ala.	M	7/8	0.944	5.11	25.8	77.8	34.8	About normal.
New Boykin	Temple, Tex.	SLM	7/8	0.982	4.74	32.8	77.8	34.8	About normal.
Furguson 406	Temple, Tex.	LM	7/8	0.962	5.38	26.8	75.6	36.8	Coarse, slightly weak.
Rowden (Malone)	Greenville, Tex.	M	29/32	1.047	5.59	21.1	82.6	35.6	Mature, coarse.
Buckellew Mebane	Temple, Tex.	SLM	29/32	1.017	5.14	26.4	72.2	37.5	Weak.
Watson	Temple, Tex.	SLM	29/32	1.005	5.21	28.3	70.0	37.8	Weak.
Bryant Mebane	Temple, Tex.	LM	29/32	0.997	4.90	23.1	77.8	35.4	About normal.
Watson	Greenville, Tex.	M	15/16	1.065	4.92	33.0	70.6	39.6	Weak.
Sharp	Greenville, Tex.	M	15/16	1.131	5.16	29.4	76.0	35.7	Slightly weak.
Mebane 140	Chillicothe, Tex.	M	15/16	1.029	5.20	27.9	79.4	34.0	About normal.
Lankart	College Sta., Tex.	SLM	15/16	1.163	4.60	31.3	80.4	36.5	About normal.
Sunshine	College Sta., Tex.	SLM	15/16	1.073	5.54	27.8	71.4	34.2	Coarse, weak.
Cliett	Temple, Tex.	SLM	15/16	1.048	5.11	30.9	78.0	35.6	About normal.
Mebane (A. D. Estate)	Temple, Tex.	SLM	15/16	1.041	4.67	30.8	80.4	33.5	About normal.
Sunshine	Temple, Tex.	SLM	15/16	1.118	5.32	27.5	71.2	37.0	Coarse, weak.
Shafter Acala	Temple, Tex.	SLM	15/16	1.074	4.55	34.8	81.0	35.6	About normal.
Roldo Rowden	Temple, Tex.	SLM	15/16	1.034	5.44	27.2	77.4	31.2	Coarse, fair strength, small angle.
Acala-Cody Lentz	Victoria, Tex.	SM	31/32	1.090	4.11	28.8	87.8	31.8	Good strength, rather small angle.
Acala-Hasselfield	Victoria, Tex.	SM	31/32	1.095	4.32	31.7	80.4	34.8	About normal.
Acala-Rogers 111	Victoria, Tex.	SM	31/32	1.092	4.10	30.0	90.2	29.9	Excellent strength, small angle.
Acala-Tex. Rogers	Victoria, Tex.	SM	31/32	1.149	4.11	30.0	86.8	32.6	Good strength.
Furguson 406	Greenville, Tex.	M	31/32	1.035	4.92	23.7	69.6	38.2	Mature, very weak.
Hog Round	Greenville, Tex.	M	31/32	1.086	5.11	22.3	76.8	35.8	Mature, slightly weak.
Qualla	Greenville, Tex.	M	31/32	1.101	5.01	22.7	77.0	37.9	About normal.
Station Strain 21–24	Tifton, Ga.	M	31/32	1.079	5.36	25.2	81.2	32.0	Good strength, coarse, small angle.
Cook 144	Prattsville, Ala.	M	31/32	1.088	5.21	26.5	80.2	36.0	Coarse.
Watson	College Sta., Tex.	SLM	31/32	1.049	4.74	31.4	68.8	39.1	Very weak.
New Boykin	College Sta., Tex.	SLM	31/32	1.065	4.73	29.9	71.2	38.2	Weak.
Mebane (A. D. Estate)	College Sta., Tex.	SLM	31/32	1.120	4.76	26.6	77.8	36.7	About normal.
Lankhart	Temple, Tex.	SLM	31/32	1.068	4.53	32.0	84.2	34.2	Good strength.
Deltapine A (DPL 11-A)	Temple, Tex.	LM	31/32	1.069	4.51	27.8	84.6	32.8	Good strength.
Nucala	Greenville, Tex.	M	1	1.099	5.09	25.7	86.0	34.0	Good strength.
Lone Star D-2	Greenville, Tex.	M	1	1.118	5.16	24.2	79.0	35.4	About normal.
Watson	Chillicothe, Tex.	M	1	1.087	4.96	30.8	69.6	40.7	Very weak, large angle.

Stoneville 2B	Rocky Mount, N. C.	M Lt. sp.	1	1.094	4.45	29.4	78.7	35.2	About normal.
Cook 144	Auburn, Ala.	SLM Brt.	1	1.095	5.32	22.5	79.0	34.7	Coarse, mature.
Roldo Rowden	College Sta., Tex.	SLM	1	1.106	5.53	22.9	81.8	34.7	Coarse, mature.
Rogers Acala	Temple, Tex.	SLM	1	1.116	4.15	27.4	93.0	28.2	Excellent strength, small angle.
Stoneville 2B	College Sta., Tex.	SLM	1 to 1 1/32	1.199	4.24	26.3	86.4	31.6	Good strength, small angle.
Coker 100-2	Rocky Mount, N. C.	M+	1 1/32	1.127	4.60	29.9	74.1	36.4	Rather weak.
Lone Star P4-1-64	Greenville, Tex.	M	1 1/32	1.172	4.80	24.2	78.2	35.5	About normal.
Coker Clevewilt 7-2	Florence, S. C.	M	1 1/32	1.080	4.21	40.9	84.9	32.4	Immature, strong.
Dixie Triumph 25	Clemson, S. C.	M	1 1/32	1.125	4.40	26.7	72.5	37.8	Weak.
Rogers Acala	College Sta., Tex.	M−	1 1/32	1.208	3.99	28.3	87.6	32.1	Good strength.
Stoneville 2B	Statesville, N. C.	M Lt. sp.	1 1/32	1.122	4.25	33.8	81.8	32.2	Average strength, small angle.
Mebane (A. D. Estate)	Chillicothe, Tex.	M Lt. sp.	1 1/32	1.127	5.14	22.3	76.8	38.0	Slightly weak.
Qualla	Chillicothe, Tex.	M Lt. sp.	1 1/32	1.196	4.88	23.6	69.2	40.7	Very weak, large angle.
Wann. Cleve. Wilt R	Tifton, Ga.	SM	1 1/32+	1.183	4.19	36.1	75.9	35.8	Slightly weak.
Shafter Acala	Victoria, Tex.	SM	1 1/32	1.172	3.94	32.7	80.6	37.8	Fine fibered.
Coker 100-3	Florence, S. C.	SM	1 1/32	1.177	4.27	33.2	87.8	32.0	Very strong, small angle.
Stoneville 2B	Florence, S. C.	SM	1 1/32	1.177	4.50	34.3	90.3	30.2	Excellent strength, small angle.
Deltapine 12	Tifton, Ga.	SM	1 1/32	1.160	3.93	42.4	73.4	37.4	Immature, weak.
Deltapine 12	Florence, S. C.	SM	1 1/32	1.067	4.67	35.3	82.6	34.3	Slightly immature.
Deltapine A (DPL 11-A)	College Sta., Tex.	SLM Brt.	1 1/32	1.198	4.46	25.7	79.2	36.1	About normal.
Shafter Acala	College Sta., Tex.	SLM Brt.	1 1/32	1.200	3.80	31.6	77.8	38.0	Fine fibered.
Washington	College Sta., Tex.	SLM Brt.	1 1/32	1.196	4.12	30.7	80.6	33.6	About normal.
Coker 100-2	Statesville, N. C.	SLM Lt. sp.+	1 1/32	1.108	3.85	35.0	74.5	34.8	Slightly immature and weak, fine fiber.
Shafter Acala	Greenville, Tex.	M	1 1/16	1.230	4.12	27.7	76.0	38.0	Slightly weak.
Washington	Greenville, Tex.	M	1 1/16	1.167	4.44	36.7	84.0	29.9	Good strength, small angle.
Coker Clevewilt 7-2	Tifton, Ga.	M	1 1/16	1.104	3.92	41.6	76.9	35.7	Immature, slightly weak.
Stoneville 2B	Greenville, Tex.	M	1 1/16	1.206	4.23	31.9	88.4	32.0	Very good strength.
Rogers Acala	Chillicothe, Tex.	M Lt. sp.	1 1/16	1.236	4.08	26.9	89.6	33.2	Very good strength.
Dixie Triumph 12	Florence, S. C.	SM	1 1/16	1.160	4.54	29.0	84.2	32.0	Strong, small angle.
Shafter Acala	Chillicothe, Tex.	SM Lt. sp.	1 1/16	1.255	4.07	34.4	87.8	40.0	Very good strength, large angle.
Wann. Cleve. Wilt R	Florence, S. C.	SM	1 1/16−	1.083	4.69	30.0	89.1	32.4	Very strong.
Coker 100-3	Tifton, Ga.	SLM	1 1/16	1.187	3.45	44.6	78.3	36.0	Very immature, very fine.
Coker 100-3	College Sta., Tex.	LM+	1 1/16	1.218	4.25	32.8	78.6	37.6	About normal.
Stoneville, 2B	Tifton, Ga.	M	1 3/32	1.187	3.67	41.6	76.1	33.4	Immature, slightly weak.
Coker's 4 in 1-4	Tifton, Ga.	M	1 3/32	1.251	3.49	42.1	69.1	38.3	Immature, weak.
Coker's 4 in 1-4	Florence, S. C.	M	1 3/32	1.180	4.19	33.3	84.8	33.8	Strong.
B. A. R. (Kekchi)	Greenville, Tex.	SLM	1 3/32	1.250	4.51	27.6	85.8	32.6	Good strength.
Marett's White Gold	Clemson, S. C.	M	1 1/8	1.231	4.32	29.3	74.9	35.8	Slightly weak.
Deltapine 12	Statesville, N. C.	M	1 1/8−	1.202	4.70	28.4	66.7	41.4	Very weak, large angle.
Coker 100-3	Statesville, N. C.	M Lt. sp.	1 1/8	1.276	4.48	25.3	64.7	38.7	Very weak.
Coker Clevewilt 7-2	Statesville, N. C.	SM	1 1/8	1.286	4.48	26.5	71.8	38.2	Weak.
Stoneville, 2B	Statesville, N. C.	M	1 5/32	1.237	4.34	30.5	70.5	36.4	Weak.
Coker's 4 in 1-4	Statesville, N. C.	M	1 5/32	1.247	4.20	26.2	66.5	39.7	Very weak, large angle.
Wann. Cleve. Wilt R	Statesville, N. C.	M	1 5/32	1.213	4.68	22.9	70.3	39.4	Weak, large angle, mature.

* The above tests were made in the laboratories of the Agricultural Marketing Administration, Cotton Branch, at College Station, Texas, and at Clemson College, S. C., in cooperation with the Agricultural and Mechanical College of Texas and Clemson College.

† Differences between means of approximately 2700 lb are required for significance (odds of 19 to 1) and of 3500 lb to be highly significant (odds of 99 to 1).

lengths. Length values are obtained from a tracing by graphical analysis. (See Chapter XXII.)

Definition. Staple denotes the length of a certain group of fibers in a ginned sample and is generally understood to mean an intermediate length, which is exceeded by 25 to 35 per cent of the fibers. That is, it is approximately the mean length of the longer half of the fibers or the upper half mean length. Cottons 1⅛ in. or longer in staple length are called staple cottons.

Character of Cotton

There are factors other than staple length grouped under the term "character" which may influence the utility of a cotton to a high degree. Nevertheless, staple length is extremely important, because it is easily recognized and other fiber properties are often associated with it.

Spinning and fiber tests conducted mainly by the U. S. Department of Agriculture have yielded an enormous number of data during the last few years. A table containing fiber data representing a wide range of cottons is given below. This table was condensed from a compilation by J. T. Wigington of the Cotton Textile Institute from results reported by the Agricultural Marketing Administration of the U.S.D.A.

Table 8, herewith, is of interest from several points of view. (1) It shows how the properties of the same variety may vary from location to location in the same year. (2) The differences in upper quartile length at the same staple length illustrate how the regularity of fibers may vary from variety to variety; staple length is approximately equal to upper half mean length. (3) It shows a good range of staple lengths and finenesses, the latter being represented by fiber weights per inch, for the bulk of American Upland cottons. (4) It indicates the complicated relationships that exist among staple length, fineness, immature fibers, tensile strengths, and X-ray 40 per cent angles.

A similar table for some long staple cottons, recently prepared by the Food Distribution Administration of the U. S. Department of Agriculture [46], is shown below. Comparison of Tables 8 and 9 brings out in a striking way the fineness of the latter group and suggests that on the average the X-ray 40 per cent angles are somewhat lower for the long cottons. Low angle correlates with high tensile strength.

The lengths of fibers attached to a single seed are variable, the longest fibers occurring at the chalazal end, the shortest at the narrow or micropylar end. The undergrowth of short fuzz fibers that is found in many species, particularly in *G. hirsutum*, usually consists of coarse, nonconvoluted fibers varying in length up to one quarter inch.

TABLE 9. COTTON CLASSIFICATION AND FIBER TEST RESULTS FOR CERTAIN AMERICAN, EGYPTIAN, SUDAN, AND PERUVIAN LONG-STAPLE COTTONS

Place Grown and Variety	Classification		Fiber Test Results				
	Grade *	Staple Length (inches)	Upper Quartile Length (inches)	Fineness (weight per inch, micrograms)	Thin-walled Fibers (per cent)	Chandler Strength per Sq. In.† (1000 lb.)	X-ray Angle (degrees)
Pecos, Tex.: ‡							
S × P	1	1 9/16	1.559	2.82	31	74.0	35.6
Wilds 13	M	1 7/16	1.415	3.60	29	80.9	34.8
Sacaton, Ariz.: ‡							
SP × Sak 35 §	1½	1 7/16	1.558	2.77	27	84.2	29.6
S × P (S. Farm)	2	1½	1.657	2.95	25	73.6	34.3
S × P	2	1½	1.602	2.77	25	78.0	33.8
Wilds 13	M−	1 5/16	1.405	3.31	31	83.2	30.3
Egypt: ‖							
Giza 7	1	1⅜ +	1.266	3.66	21	80.7	31.8
Karnak	1½	1 7/16	1.422	2.88	25	83.9	30.4
Maarad	2	1 7/16	1.497	2.90	29	78.7	35.3
Malaki	2	1 7/16	1.354	2.85	26	82.6	29.8
Sakha 4	1½	1 7/16	1.348	2.82	28	80.0	30.2
Sudan: ‖							
Sudan L	1	1 7/16	1.499	3.50	25	82.2	31.0
Sudan S	1½	1 7/16	1.515	3.05	25	79.3	31.2
Peru: ‖							
Pima	1	1½	1.657	2.83	26	78.5	34.6
Tanguis	GM sp.	1¼	1.275	4.32	26	75.5	34.8

* Grades are based on the standards for American-Egyptian cotton with the exception of the Wilds 13 and Tanguis varieties, which are based on grades for American upland cotton.
† Differences between means of approximately 2700 lb are required for significance (odds of 19 to 1).
‡ 1942 crop.
§ This variety is in the developmental stage and seed is not ready for general distribution.
‖ Test samples taken from commercial bales.

Fiber Fineness

The preceding tables emphasize the wide variation in weight fineness between varieties. Attention has already been directed to the fact that ribbon width is also an important characteristic. The finer cottons usually have narrower ribbon widths. A method of determining weight fineness is covered by a specification of the American Society for Testing Materials [32]. A method for geometric fineness determinations has been developed by Karrer and Bailey [56]. The latter utilize a microscopic technique. Hertel [57] has evolved a method for determining fineness based on the surface area per gram of fibers; surface area is estimated from the resistance of the sample to the flow of air.

The wall thicknesses of different types of cotton range from 0.35 to

15.5 μ according to Clegg [58] and Karrer and Bailey [56]. Ribbon widths are said to range from 11.9 to 20.3 μ. The thickest part of a fiber is not at the base (as might be expected) but toward the middle. The tip end is usually gently tapered and the basal end only slightly less thick than the middle portion.

Fiber Uniformity

Cotton cannot be considered a uniform material even though a sufficiently large number of fibers may have a characteristic average behavior. Each fiber must be regarded as an individual with its own characteristic length, strength, fineness, and other traits. For this reason sampling methods are extremely important and test data must be handled by statistical methods.

A comparison of the staple lengths and upper quartile lengths of varieties shown in Tables 8 and 9 indicates that the longer cottons tend to be more uniform in length than the shorter ones. That is, the staple lengths appear to approach the upper quartile lengths more closely in the longer cottons. The varying percentages of immature fibers also indicate the nonuniformity of wall thicknesses for the same variety in different locations. Similarly, strength and X-ray angle vary from location to location for the same variety. In addition to these variations there are considerable differences between cotton grown from the same seed in the same location from year to year.

Uniformity in the physical properties of fibers within a variety is unquestionably desirable. It is also highly probable that the more uniform cottons are superior for spinning purposes. Cotton buyers include uniformity in their classing evaluation of samples. Much cotton breeding work is being done to improve the uniformity of cotton fibers.

Porosity

The cotton fiber is somewhat porous and, consequently, exhibits capillary effects to a high degree. The origin of the porosity and capillarity appears to be in the porous parts of growth rings and in closely knit fibrillar network, which expose relatively large surfaces and create many elongated interstitial capillaries. The fibrils themselves are probably dense as a result of the crystalline nature of cellulose and also nonporous. The crystalline part of the structure may constitute 90 per cent or more of the fiber [26, 59]. The arrangement of denser fibrils in the fiber might be visualized as analogous to the packing of fibers in a well-made yarn.

Exact data on porosity are difficult to obtain experimentally. Rough estimates of the unoccupied space in fibers range from 20 to 41 per cent of the fiber volume, with the fine cottons somewhat more compact than the coarse varieties [60]. It is possible to make some interesting calculations. If the fiber cross-section is considered to be an ellipse with semi-major and semi-minor axes, a and b respectively, in the ratio of 2 : 1, then the cross-sectional area is πab, or in the case of a fiber of average ribbon width 20 μ, area is $\pi \times 10 \times 5$. The volume of a meter length of such a fiber in cubic millimeters would be

$$\pi(1000)(0.01)(0.005) = 0.05\pi = 0.157 \text{ mm}^3$$

The weight of this meter of fiber on the basis of an average fiber weight of 17×10^{-4} mg per cm would be

$$(100)(17 \times 10^{-4}) = 17 \times 10^{-2} \text{ mg.} = 0.17 \text{ mg}$$

The specific volume of cellulose, that is, the volume occupied by 1 gram, does not vary much from 0.640; hence the minimum volume necessary to contain the mass is

$$(0.64)(0.17) = 0.109 \text{ mm}^3$$

From these two volume estimates, it is perceived that unoccupied space constitutes 31 per cent of the total fiber volume in this example. However, the lumen is generally small, representing about one-third of the unoccupied space [56], and consequently, the pore space is largely between the fibrils as capillaries of small average diameter. By means of a calculation similar to the above it can be shown that a cylinder of yarn represents approximately 50 per cent fiber substance and 50 per cent air space. It was pointed out in the section on tensile strength that this air space is in part responsible for lowered yarn strength through fiber slippage. The pore space in fibers permits considerable permanent fiber elongation.

Luster

The natural luster of cotton fibers seems to be determined by two factors, namely, fiber shape and natural fiber polish. Adderley [61] stated that luster does not depend upon hair weight, length, diameter, or "fineness" and is not related to convolutions. Rather, it depends upon the ratio of the semi-major and semi-minor axes of the elliptical fiber cross-section; the lower the ratio, the higher the luster. In other words, the highest luster would be found in a fiber of circular cross-section. He attributed the higher luster of mercerized fibers to their rounder shapes as compared with the unmercerized. American cottons were said to have low luster.

Foster [62] concluded that the dominating influence in luster is the external fiber surface and that geometric shape is of secondary importance. In the luster of yarns, fiber length may have a role. Adderley [63] suggested that when two cottons of the same luster are employed, the longer cotton yields the more lustrous yarn. It is possible that the long fibers produce this effect by reason of a more parallel arrangement in the yarn.

Elongation and Elasticity

It is general practice to express the elastic properties of matter in terms of stress, the force per unit area tending to produce a deformation, and of strain, the resulting deformation. Changes in length and in volume as well as shears or twists produced by applied stresses are all included in the elastic properties. Mann and Peirce [34] defined the following three types of strains that occur in cotton:

"Elastic strains are proportional to the stress which produces them, are independent of time or past history of the material, and disappear with removal of the stress.

"Epibolic strains increase with time at a decreasing rate, attain a final equilibrium, and eventually disappear or decrease gradually to a small value after the removal of the stress. This type of strain produces the so-called elastic after-effect or manifests itself in the time decrease in the torsional couple of threads under moderate twist.

"Ductile strains are characterized by a semi-viscous flow proceeding indefinitely with time, are irreversible, and lead eventually to attenuation and rupture.

"In a material such as cotton these three types of strain are appreciable, the proportion of each in a given strain depending on the manner in which the strain was produced."

The extension of single fibers at rupture is determined by moisture content and is about 7 per cent under ordinary conditions but their elasticity is imperfect; i.e., they fail to regain their original lengths when the stretching stress is removed. Collins [64] demonstrated this effect in a study of the relationship between time and stress-strain. He observed that the rate of extension of cotton fibers in water gradually slows down during the first 30 to 150 min, and a pseudo-equilibrium condition is reached. His explanation of this phenomenon was that the stress causes a slow collapse of the fibers, the fibrils become closer packed, and the pore space between them disappears. When this occurs, the effective friction between fibrils increases rapidly. After attaining the pseudo-equilibrium condition, fibers become more truly elastic but continue to show a slow extension until a true equilibrium condition, corresponding to a balance between the applied stress and the opposing frictional forces, is established after 5000 to 10,000 min. The elastic recovery of fibers so treated is much more uniform than the original extension. The recoverable part of the elongation probably represents the true elasticity of the fibrils, the nonrecoverable part, the straightening and denser packing of fibrils. Steinberger [65] made similar observations on fiber behavior.

The above experimental findings indicate that determinations of a Young's modulus (elastic modulus) of cotton fibers mean little unless the exact history of the sample is known. Young's modulus is defined as the ratio of the stretching stress per unit of cross-sectional area to the elongation per unit length produced. According to Barratt [66] and to Brown, Mann, and Peirce [52], fibers at the breaking point yield Young's moduli of 2 to 8×10^{10} dynes per cm^2; during recovery from an applied stress the Young's modulus is only about one-third of this value as a result of the more or less permanent stretch.

The stress-strain relation for single fibers is roughly a straight line when the fibers contain little moisture, and it has been noted that Hooke's law is valid under such conditions. In other words, the elongation of dry fibers is approximately proportional to the load.

Moisture

Moisture has a singular effect on the strength and extension of cotton fibers. Brown, Mann, and Peirce [52] made a careful study of the breaking loads and stress-strain relations of cotton fibers at different relative humidities (R.H.) and made the following observations:

> Average fiber elongation at the breaking point rises continuously from about 5.3 per cent at 10 per cent R.H. to about 9.5 per cent at 100 per cent R.H.; the breaking load increases as the R.H. is raised to 60 per cent, at which it reaches a constant value and becomes independent of humidity. With fiber elongations plotted as ordinates, the load-elongation curves are convex upward, the higher the humidity, the greater is the convexity. The steeper initial slopes of these curves are attributed to the straightening of fibrils, the lesser final slopes to the true stretching (about 3 per cent) of fibrils. Greater amounts of absorbed moisture progressively reduce the cohesion between fibrils and permit them to straighten more and more. In dry fibers where fibril cohesion is high, the elongation is largely accounted for by true fibril extension. The increase of fiber strength with relative humidity is explained by the more uniform distribution of stresses; the fibrils are equalized in tension by the straightening and stretching effects. The latter effects are appreciable only when R.H. exceeds 50 per cent according to Steinberger [65].

These observations on fiber behavior seem in good agreement with X-ray evidence of increased orientation resulting from the wetting and pulling of fibers (fibril straightening) as observed by Sisson [67], with Collins' [64] work on stress-strain equilibrium, and with the observation of Clegg and Harland [60], that convolutions originating in spiral inequalities of fibrils are pulled out by tensions or removed by prolonged aqueous swelling.

The elongation of yarns is even more complex than that of fibers. Yarn extension probably involves fiber slippage, collapse of fibers into free spaces in the yarn, and changes in the spiral angles of fibers in the yarn as well as the fibers themselves. The true elasticity of yarns is said to be determined by the fibers, the elongation by the twist. The reader is referred to the general discussion of yarn strength in a preceding section for more detailed treatment of the subject.

Rigidity

The modulus of rigidity or shear modulus is another elastic property of considerable importance. It is defined as the ratio of the tangential or torsional force per unit area to the angle of shear or twist produced. In the case of a single cotton fiber, a torsional force would create a direct pull on fibrils that spiral in the direction of the force and a compressing or straightening of the reversed fibrils. Where the angles of the fibrils to the central axis of the fiber are large or the number of fibril lamellae is appreciable (as in short-stapled, thick-walled fibers), large torsional forces would be required to produce a displacement. In cotton spinning and twisting operations this rigid behavior is extremely significant.

Peirce [68] found that mean rigidities of cottons range from 0.010 to 0.111 dyne per cm^2 and tabulated the following data on varieties:

TABLE 10. Rigidities of Various Cotton Fibers

Varieties	*Length* (*cm*)	*Rigidity* * (*dynes per sq cm*)	*Weight* (*10^{-6} grams*)
Sea Island	4.2 to 5	0.010 to 0.021	5.9 to 6.7
Egyptian nubarri	3.6	0.024	6.3
Egyptian affifi	3.1	0.032	5.6
Peruvian hybrid	2.9	0.063	7.7
Trinidad native	2.6	0.045	4.9
Upland Memphis	2.6	0.039	5.3
American	2.4	0.061	5.6
Upland	2.3	0.045	5.0
Pernams	2.2	0.071	6.7
Indian Bharat	1.7	0.111	5.8

* The rigidity of the fiber is the torque, or twisting force, in the fiber when one cm is given one complete twist.

Correlations between rigidity and other fiber characteristics indicated that rigidity varies with the shape, conditions of growth, and, largely, with the wall thickness of fibers. The high rigidity of thick-walled fibers suggests why coarse cottons must be more highly twisted than fine cottons to produce yarns of the same size.

Peirce also furnished the following physical factors for the cotton fiber, that may be calculated approximately from the staple length:

Staple length	L (in cm)
Fiber mass	5.8×10^{-6} gram
Mass per centimeter	$(5.8/L) \times 10^{-6}$ gram
Wall cross-section	$(3.9/L) \times 10^{-6}$ sq cm
Rigidity	$0.3/L^2$ dynes cm^2
Breaking load	$20/L$ grams
Fibers in yarn section	$1000L/N$ or $(L''/4N) \times 10^4$
Initial couple in yarn	$300t/LN = 300p/L\sqrt{N}$

The density of the cotton fiber is assumed as 1.51.[1] N is the count of the yarn; L'' is the staple length in inches; t is the twist, and p the spinning factor $t/\sqrt{N}$.

Temperature and humidity have pronounced influences on fiber rigidity or stiffness to bending [69]. At room temperature the rigidity of a cotton fiber is six times as great in dry air as in a water-saturated atmosphere; at constant moisture regain, rigidity decreases as temperature rises. The cotton fiber is about one-tenth as rigid a structure as a glass fiber of similar dimensions.

Plasticity

The plastic properties of cotton, that is, the tendency of cotton to be deformed permanently by stresses or to behave like a highly viscous liquid, play a prominent part in its textile utilization. Actually, cotton cellulose may be relatively nonplastic, but it is capable of acquiring semi-permanent "sets" to an appreciable extent.

Peirce [70] investigated the plasticity of cotton in a newly twisted yarn. The untwisting or restoring forces in the yarn appeared to decrease with time according to a logarithmic function. This decay of the torsional restoring forces is indicative of plastic changes, or the substitution of "epibolic" and "ductile" strains for the purely elastic ones. In other words, the setting of yarn twist results from a plastic decay of elastic couples generated in the fibers by the yarn twist; most of this change takes place in one day. The restoring forces never vanish completely but diminish to residuals, which vary with the amount of twist introduced. The decay of untwisting forces is most rapid and complete in highly twisted yarns; loose or soft yarns retain a high proportion of elastic couples. According to Steinberger [65], the extension of single

[1] The value assumed by Peirce is somewhat lower than more recent estimates.

fibers with time is also logarithmic and, thus, may be of the type involved in the setting of yarn twists.

Cotton fibers exhibit a large increase in plasticity under humid heat. In fact, processes included under the term "schreinering" are defined as those which depend on the increase in plasticity of cotton fibers as they swell in water vapor at elevated temperatures. It appears, however, that the plasticity is highly dependent on moisture, since dry fibers are practically nonplastic. It is indicated in the following paragraphs that water may be regarded as a plasticizer for cotton.

The observed plasticity seems to involve the same factors that operate in fiber elongation, i.e., the porosity and the movement of fibrils under stresses. Strains normally present in fibers disappear when the fibers are subjected to prolonged soaking in cold water or to short treatment with hot water. It is entirely possible that the apparent plasticity of cotton involves strain development and that these strains can be removed under suitable conditions. In other words, the fiber is practically nonductile. The following paragraphs are quoted from a recent discussion [26] of plastic behavior.

> The sorption of water by cotton causes lateral fiber swelling, lowers rigidity, and increases strength, extensibility, and plasticity. Moisture desorption has the reverse effects.
>
> Assuming that cotton takes up water in two ways—by chemical association with glucose units and by condensation in structural capillaries—Peirce [71] considered fiber properties to be influenced largely by α-phase moisture and noted a linear decrease in rigidity as calculated amounts of combined moisture increased. Entropy calculations substantiate the view that a part, at least, of the moisture sorbed by cellulose is in chemical association.
>
> The amorphous network of cellulose appears to be extremely hygroscopic in comparison to the crystallites, whose X-ray diffraction pattern persists unaltered through treatments with water. Stamm and Millett [72] found total surface areas of about 2×10^3 sq cm per gram of oven-dried cotton and 3×10^6 sq cm per gram of cotton suspended in aqueous medium.
>
> The suggestion of Baker, Fuller, and Pape [73], that water acts as a plasticizer, particularly for partial esters of cellulose, seems equally applicable to unmodified cotton. That is, water may reduce the forces of association among cellulose molecules, *first*, by combining with and deactivating hydroxyl groups, and *secondly*, by increasing intermolecular distances. In other words, water may rupture or weaken hydroxyl-hydroxyl cross linkages between sections of cellulose molecules in the noncrystalline regions of the fiber. This action would be tantamount to a conversion of cohesive, high-density cellulose to a lower density and more labile condition and would be in agreement with the large internal area changes noted above.
>
> As has been indicated, moisture seems to exert its effects mainly in the noncrystalline fiber areas. Thus, the deactivation of hydrogen bonds would lead to swelling and enlargement of amorphous regions, principally as a result of involvement of mesomorphous fringes between the truly amorphous and truly crystalline

components. The reversible changes in fiber properties as moisture is sorbed and desorbed would be a direct consequence of the swelling and corresponding changes in structure.

The following data are a practical illustration of some moisture effects on cotton cord:

	Per Cent Stretch at 10-Lb Load	*Breaking Strength, Lb*
Conditioned *	12.66	19.51
Oven-dry	9.92	15.40

* Moisture content, about 7 per cent.

It can be seen that, at constant stretching stress, oven-dry cord has a much lower extensibility than conditioned cord. The lower strength of the dry cord may have *two* causes: an increased rigidity of dry fibers that opposes stretch and prevents compression to a denser and stronger cord, and the lower strength of dry fibers themselves. The lower strength of dry fibers may result from decreased plasticity and extensibility that retard crystallite orientation and equalization of stresses. In short, moisture desorption may promote a true crystallization that makes fibers more rigid, less plastic, and less extensible.

It might be added that the high-density, low-stretch tire cord in more common use at the present time has an oven-dry/conditioned strength efficiency of 0.93 to 1.00, the actual value depending on the stretch. Such cord has a stretch at the 10-lb load of 5 to 7 per cent conditioned, and often a slightly higher stretch when oven-dry. The greater strength efficiency of these cords may be attributed largely to their higher density which, in turn, assures good fiber-to-fiber contact under both conditions. In the high-stretch cords there can be a substantial change in helix angle of fibers near the cord breaking point. This change probably occurs to a lesser degree under dry conditions and tends to increase the difference in breaking strengths.

Durability

The cellulose molecules in cotton are extremely long and are probably tied into the moisture-impervious crystallites at frequent intervals. Cotton also is relatively pure in its native state and can be brought to a high degree of purity by mild treatments. The absence of extractable short chains of glucose residues and the freedom of purified cotton from degrading components make the fiber extremely durable. Other factors that probably contribute to fiber durability are high wet strength and the relatively high crystallinity.

Absorbency

Raw cotton has a deposit of natural wax and other substances, notably calcium and magnesium pectates, on or in the primary wall that make it water-repellent. In the raw state, it is wet very slowly by distilled water at room temperature, but somewhat more rapidly at elevated temperatures. The substances which impart water-repellency are readily removed by kier- or soda-boiling and the normal cream color by a subsequent mild bleaching. Cotton purified in this manner is practically pure cellulose and wets almost instantaneously with water. All of the surfaces of cellulose are studded with hydroxyl groups, which have excellent affinity for water and are preferentially wet by this solvent.

The U. S. Pharmacopoeia has established standards for absorbent cotton and specifies methods to be used for assay. U.S.P. absorbent cotton shall (*a*) be insoluble in ordinary solvents, (*b*) have not more than 0.2 per cent ash, (*c*) contain no residual acid or alkali, no dyes, less than 0.07 per cent of ether extractables, and less than 0.25 per cent of water extractables, (*d*) consist of fibers of certain lengths, (*e*) retain at least 24 times its own weight of water at 25° C., and (*f*) be packaged and sterilized in an approved manner.

Good grades of absorbent cotton retain from 24 to 27 times their own weight of water when tested as prescribed and immersion times range from 3 to 6 sec.

There is evidence, however, that modifications of the cotton, probably by surface oxidation, may increase the time of immersion enormously. Tests of absorbent cottons aged in the package indicate that 36 hr or even longer may be required for wetting [74]; when the time of immersion exceeds 15 min., the water-retention of cotton seems to exhibit a slight increase. Kohman [75] demonstrated that partly oxidized paper is *hydrophobic*, being preferentially wetted by benzene, while the untreated paper is *hydrophilic*.

Moisture Relations

The moisture content of a cotton sample at equilibrium is dependent primarily upon temperature and relative humidity and secondarily upon several other factors. It may be expressed either as percentage moisture content or as percentage moisture regain. The moisture content represents that fraction of the sample which is moisture or, in other words, is calculated on the basis of the moist weight of the sample. It is much more common practice to employ moisture regain, i.e., to express the moisture as a percentage based on the bone-dry weight of the cotton.

The adsorption of water vapor by cotton, being dependent on the relative vapor pressure of water in the environment, changes continuously with a changing environment and it is obviously necessary to exclude from this discussion all but equilibrium values. Four hours is generally sufficient for ordinary cotton yarns or fabrics to reach moisture equilibrium or to be "conditioned" to standard textile testing conditions of 70° F. and 65 per cent relative humidity. That is, the exchange of moisture vapor between the conditioning atmosphere and the sample practically ceases after about 4 hr, but due allowances must be made for unusually heavy yarns and for poor circulation of the atmosphere.

The primary influence of relative humidity at constant temperature on moisture regain is shown by the data in Table 11, observed by Stamm and Woodruff [76].

TABLE 11. Moisture Regain of Cotton Linters at 20° C.

Relative Vapor Pressure	*Adsorption (per cent of oven-dry weight)*	*Desorption (per cent of oven-dry weight)*	*Adsorption/Desorption Ratio*
0.10	2.1	2.5	0.84
0.20	3.2	3.8	0.84
0.30	3.9	4.6	0.85
0.40	4.75	5.6	0.85
0.50	5.6	6.6	0.85
0.60	6.7	7.8	0.86
0.70	8.0	9.2	0.87
0.80	9.9	11.4	0.87
0.90	13.0	14.9	0.87
0.95	16.9	18.0	0.88

The data above were obtained on cotton linters but do not differ significantly from the following data of Urquhart and Williams [77].

TABLE 12. Moisture Regains of Cotton Yarns

Relative Vapor Pressure	*Grey (per cent)*	*Water-Boiled (per cent)*	*Soda-Boiled and Bleached (per cent)*
	Adsorption		
0.198	3.27	3.23	3.01
0.394	5.00	4.91	4.61
0.591	7.16	6.91	6.59
0.773	9.59	9.14	8.73
0.897	14.85	14.10	13.78
0.959	20.65	18.82	18.63
	Desorption		
0.958	22.19	19.64	19.71
0.888	16.34	15.13	15.08
0.777	12.33	11.71	11.57
0.588	8.62	8.40	8.21
0.425	6.22	6.18	5.94
0.226	3.96	4.00	3.73

A considerable hysteresis effect in moisture regain is apparent, that is, at a given relative vapor pressure and temperature two reproducible values are obtainable. The higher (desorption) value is obtained when equilibrium is reached through loss of moisture by the cotton and the lower (adsorption) value, when equilibrium is attained through a gain in moisture by the sample. This hysteresis is characteristic of normal cellulose materials and has been investigated by Urquhart [78] and a number of other workers [79]. Temperature has a much smaller influence on regain than does relative humidity.

In addition to temperature and humidity, several other factors appear to be involved in moisture regain. Cotton variety and growth region do not seem to be correlated with regain, although the latter may exhibit some variation from sample to sample. The previous history of the cottons does seem to play a part. Urquhart and Williams [80] and Houtz and McLean [81] have shown that desiccation at elevated temperatures (110° to 150° C.) causes a semipermanent decrease in moisture vapor adsorption capacity. The reduction is especially pronounced when the dried sample is conditioned at low humidities, amounting to about 30 per cent, and is least at high humidities, being about 10 per cent. However, if the cotton is treated with hot water or steam and allowed to dry at room temperature, it recovers its normal hygroscopic properties.

Deformations of fibers also appear to alter the moisture vapor uptake of cotton. For example, it was shown recently that the desorption moisture content of cotton yarn is considerably depressed when the yarn is placed under a stretching stress. The following data obtained on carefully prepared, parallel skeins of yarn is illustrative. The loose skeins were first saturated with water vapor and then transferred to standard textile testing conditions (21° C. and 65 per cent relative humidity) to attain equilibrium. During the latter stage one skein was allowed to remain loose, the other was placed under a tension corresponding to 60 per cent of its breaking strength.

TABLE 13. Effect of Stress on Moisture Regain

Condition of Yarn During Desorption	*Equilibrium Moisture Content (per cent)*
Unstressed	8.78
Under 60% load	8.19

The observed reduction in moisture retention may originate in the alignment and compression of structural elements.

Chemical treatments cause appreciable changes in moisture vapor adsorption. Mercerization with tension generally increases the equilibrium moisture content at standard conditions in the ratio of about 1.4 to

1 over unmercerized cotton. Mercerization without tension produces even higher moisture regains at standard conditions. It is well established that the moisture content at standard conditions of mercerized cotton varies as the concentration of caustic employed.

Basic dyes appear to lower the moisture content of cottons by a greater amount than would be expected from a simple loading effect [80].

Preceding sections of this chapter show how fiber strengths and elongations vary with moisture content. The following data observed by Peirce and Stephenson [54] indicate the manner in which cotton yarn properties vary with relative humidity—in other words, with moisture uptake. It is apparent that both strength and extension are influenced by humidity, but the latter is specially responsive.

TABLE 14. VARIATION OF YARN STRENGTH AND EXTENSION WITH HUMIDITY

[Averages of 100 single thread tests; original lengths, 20 in.]

Relative Humidity (per cent)	*Yarn Strength (grams)*		*Yarn Extension (mm)*	
	50's	*32's*	*50's*	*32's*
Dry	160.0	168.0	22.0	21.0
30	186.1	207.4	22.9	24.6
50	195.3	233.3	28.7	30.9
70	207.4	245.3	30.7	33.3
85	213.9	246.1	35.4	37.8
92	217.3	252.6	35.3	37.4
100	217.6	251.4	34.5	38.8

Some of the water molecules adsorbed by cotton are held very tightly, probably in association with hydroxyls. The last traces of water are very difficult to remove for this reason. Stamm and Hansen [82] have calculated that cotton holds water with 17 per cent greater force than water holds water. The two-phase water adsorption theory of Peirce [72] has already been mentioned. According to this concept part of the adsorbed water is combined with the cellulose, while the remainder is held by capillarity. The properties appear to be influenced more by the combined water than by the capillary water.

MISCELLANEOUS PHYSICAL PROPERTIES

As a result of its unique structure, the cotton fiber is highly pliable. While the long chain length may be important, it is not unlikely that the subdivision into fibrils, the presence of a lumen in the fiber, and the existence of a continuous external fiber sheath are the dominant factors in this respect. Some of the coarser and stiffer fibers, like ramie, being more highly oriented, are much less pliable than cotton and tend to fracture during processing and use or to become brittle with age.

Cohesiveness of fibers is recognized by the cotton classer as the feel or drag he experiences during stapling. It is one of the factors on which he bases his estimate of suitability. Fiber fineness and convolutions undoubtedly are important attributes and, together with moisture content, may determine cohesiveness to a large extent through the relative fiber-to-fiber contact areas. Finer cottons are less rigid than the coarser and moist fibers are more plastic than dry ones. The combination of fineness and moisture yields a tractable fiber that can be molded readily to the proper configuration in a yarn.

Compressibility also may be determined in a similar way by fineness and plasticity. Thus, the wet-twisting processes employed in the production of dense, strong yarns may have their origin in these effects. Conversely, the coarse, harsh or rigid fibers are most suitable for naps and felts, where matting together is undesirable. Bone-dry fibers represent maximum rigidity and lowest compressibility.

Hygienic Qualities. Cotton is an excellent hygienic material because in purified form it contains no protein, it can be sterilized without danger of disintegration, and it bleaches to a clear white. Its wet strength and launderability also contribute to its usefulness as do its lack of taste, odor, and water extractives.

Specific Gravity

Cotton has a specific gravity of approximately 1.58, corresponding to a specific volume of roughly 0.63. Specific volume is the volume occupied by 1 gram of the material. The specific volume also varies somewhat with the nature of the displacing fluid employed in the determination. Stamm and Hansen [82] gave a value for specific gravity of 1.585, which corresponds to a specific volume of 0.63 for cotton in helium. Larger molecules than helium, or fluids like water that interact with the cellulose, tend to give low values of specific gravity.

Davidson [83] measured the specific volume of cotton in helium and in water and from his data calculated the amount of swelling at different temperatures. His calculations indicate that the swelling of cotton in water varies considerably, exhibiting a minimum at about 50° C. The investigations of Collins [84] suggest that the lateral swelling of cotton by water produces about a 20 per cent increase from the bone-dry fiber diameter, corresponding to a 40 per cent increase in volume; at the same time fiber length changes only 1 to 2 per cent.

Electrical Properties

The electrical conductivity of cotton appears to vary as relative humidity and electrolyte content. Pickard [85] noted that a 20-fold increase in the electrical resistance of cotton could be produced by extraction of the raw fiber with boiling water. It is not unlikely that salts associated with fiber growth are removed by such extraction. Basic dyes also appear to lower electrical resistance, perhaps through a reduction in hygroscopicity.

Murphy [86] reported that in a-c conduction cotton may be considered to act as an electrolytic cell in parallel with a dielectric, water paths forming the electrolyte. As humidity rises, a-c conductivity rises rapidly. Studies of moisture content and electrical resistance led Walker [86] to the conclusion that the previous history of the sample is highly important and that high temperature drying of wet cotton alters the relationship of hydroxyl groups as compared with slow drying. In a later paper Walker [87] noted that slightly more than 1 per cent of water is necessary to form a monomolecular layer on all internal fiber surfaces and proposed a theory to explain the dependence of electrical properties of textiles upon their moisture-adsorbing properties.

Electrostatic charges play an important role in fiber behavior during manufacture; and the control of electrostatics is both necessary and difficult. Bullock [88] tabulated the following electrostatic series:

1. Fur
2. Flannel (wool)
3. Ivory
4. Glass
5. Cotton
6. Paper
7. Silk
8. Paraffin wax
9. Ebonite
10. The hand
11. Metals
12. Sulfur
13. Celluloid
14. Rubber tubing

Of any two members of the series in rubbing contact, the *first* is said to become positively charged with respect to the *second*. For example, cotton becomes positively charged with respect to metals on which it rubs during fabrication. High humidity usually facilitates the leakage of such charges. Alexander [89] believed that electronic molecular fields are involved in the strength of yarns and threads, but this has not been established.

Spinnability

A list of the factors contributing to spinnability cannot yet be prepared, because the subject is so complex. Fineness is undoubtedly extremely important and yet is not a sufficient criterion. The lack of methods and knowledge, which would permit the determination of intrinsic values by simple laboratory tests, places tremendous responsibilities on cotton classers and buyers. It has led also to the institution of practical small-scale spinning tests as the best method of ascertaining spinnability. In the latter respect the work of Campbell [40, 50] is noteworthy and should be consulted. Spinning tests are now being conducted under government auspices [44, 45, 46].

Special Properties and Defects

Cotton is highly resistant to degradation by heat and can be ironed at very high temperatures. Among its important defects some of which future research may correct are its "limpness" when it is wet, its tendency to crease easily and become rumpled, and its tendency to be attacked by fungi (mildewing), with loss in strength under moist conditions. At present these defects are generally outweighed by the durability and long, flexing life of cotton and by its high resistance to drastic treatment such as constant laundering. In respect to the latter property it is supreme among cellulosic fibers.

REFERENCES IN TEXT

1. Balls, W. L., *Development and Properties of Raw Cotton*, Black, London (1915).
2. Anderson, D. B., and Kerr, T., *Ind. Eng. Chem.*, **30**, 48 (1938).
3. Berkley, E. E., *Textile Research*, **9**, 355 (1939).
4. Hock, C. W., Ramsay, R. C., and Harris, M., *J. Research Natl. Bur. Standards*, **26**, 93 (1941).
5. Kerr, T., *Protoplasma*, **27**, 229 (1937).
6. Peirce, F. T., and Lord, E., *J. Textile Inst.*, **30**, T173 (1939).
7. Pearson, N. L., U. S. Dept. Agr., *Tech. Bull. 396* (Nov. 1933).
8. Osborne, G. G., *Textile Research*, **5**, 275 (1935).
9. Bowman, F. H., *Structure of the Cotton Fiber*, Macmillan, Manchester (1908).
10. Adderley, A., *Shirley Inst. Mem.*, **1**, 151 (1922).
11. Navkal, H., and Ahmad, N., *J. Textile Inst.*, **28**, T307 (1937).
12. Nickerson, R. F., Fontaine, T. D., and Leape, C. B., *Textile Research*, **11**, 154 (1941).
13. Clegg, G. G., and Harland, S. C., *J. Textile Inst.*, **14**, 125 (1923).
14. Pattee, C. L., *Textile World*, **84**, 2012 (1934); *Textile Research*, **6**, 87 (1935).
15. Strang, P. M., *Am. Wool and Cotton Reptr.*, **56** (38), 9 (1942).
16. Schwarz, E. R., and Hotte, G. H., *Textile Research*, **5**, 370 (1935).
17. Compton, J., and Haver, F. E., *Contrib. Boyce Thompson Inst.*, **11**, 105 (1940).
18. Berkley, E. E., *Am. J. Botany*, **29**, 416 (1942).
19. Bailey, A. J., and Brown, R. M., *Ind. Eng. Chem.*, **32**, 57 (1940).
20. Barrows, F. L., *Contrib. Boyce Thompson Inst.*, **11**, 161 (1940).
21. Barnes, R. B., and Burton, C. J., *Ind. Eng. Chem.*, **35**, 120 (1943).
22. Wergin, W., *Naturwissenschaften*, **26**, 613 (1938).
23. Nickerson, R. F., *Ind. Eng. Chem.*, **32**, 1454 (1940).

24. Frey-Wyssling, A., *Submikroskopische Morphologie*, Gebrueder Borntraeger, Berlin (1938).
25. Mark, H., *J. Phys. Chem.*, **44**, 764 (1940).
26. Nickerson, R. F., *Ind. Eng. Chem.*, **34**, 1149 (1942).
27. Kratky, O., *Angew. Chem.*, **53**, 153 (1940).
28. Mark, H., *Nature*, **144**, 313 (1939).
29. Mark, H., *Ind. Eng. Chem.*, **34**, 449 (1942).
30. Clegg, G. G., *Shirley Inst. Mem.*, **2**, 357 (1923).
31. Richardson, H. B., Bailey, T. L. W., and Conrad, C. M., U. S. Dept. Agr., *Tech. Bull. 545* (1937).
32. Am. Soc. for Testing Materials, D-13, Spec. D-414-40T, Sect. 23.
33. Pressley, E. H., *ASTM Bull.*, **118**, 13 (1942).
34. Mann, J. C., and Peirce, F. T., *Shirley Inst. Mem.*, **5**, 7 (1926).
35. Berkley, E. E., and Woodyard, O. C., *Ind. Eng. Chem.*, Anal. Ed. **10**, 451 (1938).
36. Obermiller, J., and Goertz, M., *Melliand Textilber.*, **7**, 163 (1926).
37. Clegg, G. G., *Shirley Inst. Mem.*, **5**, 223 (1926).
38. Conrad, C. M., and Berkley, E. E., *Textile Research*, **8**, 341 (1938).
39. Anon, *Textile Recorder*, **41** (Aug. 15, 1923).
40. "Tests of Irrigated and Rain-Grown American Upland Cotton," U. S. Dept. Agr., Agr. Marketing Admin. (May 1941).
41. Barker, S. G., *J. Textile Inst.*, **30**, P273 (1939).
42. Knecht, E., and Hall, W., *J. Soc. Dyers Colourists*, **34**, 220 (1918).
43. Vincent, P. D., *Shirley Inst. Mem.*, **3**, 125 (1924).
44. "Results of Tests of Seven Cottons Grown at Stoneville, Miss., 1940," U. S. Dept. Agr., Agr. Marketing Admin. (May 1942).
45. "Results of Fiber and Spinning Tests of Some Varieties of Cotton Grown in Texas, Crop of 1940," U. S. Dept. Agr., Agr. Marketing Admin. (Dec. 1941).
46. "Comparative Manufacturing Performance and Fiber Properties of Certain Long-Staple Cottons," U. S. Dept. Agr., Food Distrib. Admin. (July 1943).
47. Turner, A. J., *J. Textile Inst.*, **19**, T268 (1928).
48. Sullivan, R. R., *J. Applied Phys.* (March 1942).
49. Köhler, S., *J. Textile Inst.*, **25** (4) (April 1934).
50. Campbell, M. E., *Textile Research*, **8**, 263 (1938).
51. Busse, W. F., Lessig, E. T., Loughborough, D. L., and Larrick, L., *J. Applied Phys.*, **13**, 715 (1942).
52. Brown, K. C., Mann, J. C., and Peirce, F. T., *J. Textile Inst.*, **21**, T186 (1930).
53. Gurney, H. P., and Davis, E. H., *J. Textile Inst.*, **21**, T463 (1930).
54. Peirce, F. T., and Stephenson, R. J., *J. Textile Inst.*, **17**, T645 (1926).
55. Hertel, K. L., *ASTM Bull.*, **118**, 25 (1942).
56. Karrer, E., and Bailey, T. L. W., *Textile Research*, **8**, 381 (1938).
57. Hertel, K. L., *Textile Research*, **10**, 510 (1940), U. S. Pats. 2, 352,835–6, July 4, 1944.
58. Clegg, G. G., *Shirley Inst. Mem.*, **5**, 223 (1926).
59. Goldfinger, G., Mark, H., and Siggia, S., *Ind. Eng. Chem.*, **35**, 1083 (1943).
60. Clegg, G. G., and Harland, S. C., *Shirley Inst. Mem.*, **2**, 353, 370 (1923).
61. Adderley, A., *Shirley Inst. Mem.*, **3**, 105 (1924).
62. Foster, G. A. R., *Shirley Inst. Mem.*, **5**, 1 (1926).
63. Adderley, A., *Shirley Inst. Mem.*, **4**, 121 (1925).
64. Collins, G. E., *Shirley Inst. Mem.*, **3**, 271 (1925).

65. Steinberger, R. L., *Textile Research*, **6**, 325 (1936).
66. Barratt, T., *J. Textile Inst.*, **13**, T17 (1922).
67. Sisson, W. A., *Contrib. Boyce Thompson Inst.*, **9**, 239 (1938).
68. Peirce, F. T., *J. Textile Inst.*, **14**, T7 (1923).
69. Peirce, F. T., *Shirley Inst. Mem.*, **3**, 353 (1924).
70. Peirce, F. T., *Shirley Inst. Mem.*, **2**, 278 (1923).
71. Peirce, F. T., *J. Textile Inst.*, **20**, T133 (1929).
72. Stamm, A. J., and Millett, M. A., *J. Phys. Chem.*, **45**, 43 (1941).
73. Baker, W. O., Fuller, C. S., and Pape, N., *J. Am. Chem. Soc.*, **64**, 776 (1942).
74. Beal, G. D., Mellon Institute, Pittsburgh, Pa., unpublished work.
75. Kohman, G. T., *Ind. Eng. Chem.*, **31**, 807 (1939).
76. Stamm, A. J., and Woodruff, S. A., *Ind. Eng. Chem.*, Anal. Ed., **13**, 836 (1941).
77. Urquhart, A. R., and Williams, A. M., *J. Textile Inst.*, **17**, T38 (1926).
78. Urquhart, A. R., *J. Textile Inst.*, **20**, T125 (1929).
79. Walker, A. C., *J. Textile Inst.*, **24**, T145 (1933).
80. Urquhart, A. R., and Williams, A. M., *Shirley Inst. Mem.*, **3**, 49 (1924).
81. Houtz, C. C., and McLean, D. A., *J. Phys. Chem.*, **45**, 111 (1941).
82. Stamm, A. J., and Hansen, L. A., *J. Phys. Chem.*, **41**, 1007 (1937).
83. Davidson, G. F., *Shirley Inst. Mem.*, **6**, 41 (1927).
84. Collins, G. E., *J. Textile Inst.*, **21**, T311 (1930); **30**, P46 (1939).
85. Pickard, E., "Research in the Cotton Industry," Shirley Inst., Didsbury, Manchester (1926).
86. Murphy, E. J., and Walker, A. C., *J. Phys. Chem.*, **32**, 761 (1928).
87. Walker, A. C., *Textile Research*, **7**, 229, 289 (1937).
88. Bullock, H. L., *Ind. Eng. Chem.*, **33**, 1119 (1941).
89. Alexander, J. H., *Ind. Eng. Chem.*, **31**, 630 (1939).

CHAPTER VI

COTTON FIBER: CHEMICAL PROPERTIES

CHARLES F. GOLDTHWAIT AND JOHN D. GUTHRIE

Chemical Composition

Although the chief component of cotton fiber is cellulose, any of the constituents commonly found in plant cells may be present in small amounts. These are frequently called impurities, but their influence on the processing and usefulness of the fiber necessitates their consideration. The composition of typical mature cotton fiber is given in Table 1.

TABLE 1. CHEMICAL COMPOSITION OF COTTON FIBER

	Per Cent Dry Basis *		
Constituents	*Typical*	*Low*	*High*
Cellulose	94.0	88.0	96.0
Protein (N × 6.25)	1.3	1.1	1.9
Pectic substances	0.9	0.7	1.2
Ash	1.2	0.7	1.6
Wax	0.6	0.4	1.0
Malic, citric, and other organic acids	0.8	0.5	1.0
Total sugars	0.3		
Pigment	Trace		
Other	0.9		

* Moisture about 8 per cent regain.

Cellulose. The cellulose content of raw cotton fiber ranges from 88 to 96 per cent of the dry weight [38, 153, 166], a content higher than that of any other large commercial source. Scoured, bleached, and dried cotton fabric is approximately 99 per cent cellulose. The variation in cellulose content of raw cotton fiber is due to soil, climate, variety of cotton, and other factors which prematurely interrupt its growth.

Low cellulose content usually indicates a high proportion of thin-walled immature fibers, which contain a high proportion of noncellulosic substances. Diverse values may be due also to uncertainty in the analytical methods for the determination of cellulose. These methods are usually based on the extraction of all other substances from the cotton with sodium hydroxide [100], monoethanolamine [139], or chlorine followed by sulfurous acid [51], and determination of the residual cellulose by weighing or by wet oxidation with sulfuric acid-dichromate mixture [150]. Low values may result from the solution of small quantities of cellulose, or high values may result from incomplete removal of noncellulosic material. A steady loss of cellulose, amounting to 0.3 per cent per hr when cotton is boiled with 1 per cent sodium hydroxide, has been reported [189].

Wax. The crude material extracted from raw cotton fiber [1] by chloroform, carbon tetrachloride, benzene, or other organic solvents is usually called wax. Cotton wax may be classed with the plant cuticle waxes and is somewhat similar in X-ray diffraction pattern [73] and other properties to carnauba wax. It is likely that many of the alcohols, acids, and other compounds isolated [30, 59, 61, 62] from cotton wax are really mixtures. Chibnall and others [19] concluded that montanyl alcohol and gossypyl alcohol are mixtures of C_{28}, C_{30}, and C_{32} alcohols, and that cotton wax contains all the primary alcohols ($C_nH_{2n+1}OH$) and normal fatty acids ($C_nH_{2n}O_2$) having even numbers of carbon atoms from C_{24} to C_{34}.

The alcohol present in the largest amount is probably *n*-triacontanol, ($C_{30}H_{61}OH$) and the acid present in the largest amount is probably *n*-tetracosanoic acid ($C_{24}H_{48}O_2$). Small amounts of fatty acids, probably palmitic ($C_{16}H_{32}O_2$), stearic ($C_{18}H_{36}O_2$), and oleic ($C_{18}H_{34}O_2$), are found. The wax also contains small amounts of sitosterol and its glucoside, sitosterolin. Other constituents reported to be present are: glycerol, resinous material, amyrin ($C_{30}H_{50}O$), and hydrocarbons, including a solid, probably heptacosane [30].

Cotton wax can be fractionated on the basis of solubility in petroleum ether into cotton wax *A* (more soluble fraction, about 70 per cent) and cotton wax *B* (less soluble fraction, about 30 per cent). Clifford and Probert [30] give the following values for the wax from Mississippi Delta cotton: Wax on the dry cotton, 0.49 per cent, melting point 76.5° C., density 0.976, acid value 29, saponification value 57, saponification value after acetylation 137, acetyl value 84, iodine value 27, unsaponifiable matter 68 per cent, and acetyl value of unsaponifiable material 123. They call attention to the presence of a large proportion of free wax alcohols and the comparative absence of wax esters.

A genetic strain of cotton having a green-colored lint has been found to contain 14 to 17 per cent of wax [36]. This wax has a melting point of 85 to 95° C., considerably higher than wax from ordinary cotton

[1] Unspun, native cotton fiber without any treatment beyond ginning and mechanical cleaning.

fiber. The fibers of this strain of cotton are thin-walled, and the possibility of combining the high-wax character with the desirable characters of commercial cotton in order to make cotton a commercial source of wax appears to be remote, from the standpoint of genetics [39].

A proposed method for estimation of wax in cotton fiber is to extract with 95 per cent alcohol in a Soxhlet extractor, mix with and transfer to chloroform by dilution with water in a separatory funnel, wash the chloroform with water to remove nonwax substances, evaporate the chloroform, and weigh the residue [37]. This method has the advantage of rapid and complete extraction of the wax and insures the separation of wax from other substances that may be extracted from the cotton. Isopropyl alcohol may be substituted for ethyl alcohol in this method [99]. Wax values obtained on cotton tendered with vapors of hydrochloric acid have been shown to be invalid [107].

Most cotton which is spun contains its natural wax. Dewaxed cotton does not spin well [102]. The wax undoubtedly has desirable lubricating properties for spinning but may interfere with the fullest development of strength in yarns and fabrics, by contributing to fiber slip [152]. Conversely, increases of as much as 25 per cent in tensile strength have been reported when yarn or cord made of raw cotton was extracted with solvents such as benzene, or subjected to other processes to remove wax [94, 182].

Pectin. The typical, mature cotton fiber contains from 0.6 to 1.2 per cent pectin according to the best estimations available. The amount reported depends somewhat on the method of determination. Extraction of the pectin from the fiber with hot ammonium oxalate or citrate solutions, followed by precipitation as calcium pectate, gives values of about 0.7 per cent [35, 80], and determinations based on the evolution of carbon dioxide from the uronic acid groups of the pectin when boiled with hydrochloric acid give values of about 1.2 per cent [174]. Most of the pectin is localized in the primary cell wall, where it may be identified by staining with ruthenium red [89]. Available evidence indicates that pectin occurs in the fiber as insoluble calcium, magnesium, and iron salts [174]. Pectic acid has been isolated from the cotton fiber [80] and identified by its specific rotation of $+225.4°$ in 0.1 N sodium hydroxide, titration equivalent of 201, carbon dioxide yield of 21.8 per cent, and mucic acid yield of 44 per cent. These values are similar to those found for pectic acid from citrus fruits. Arabinose and xylose have been reported from cotton fiber pectin [20].

Practically all the pectin is removed from the cotton fiber by kier boiling, owing to the formation of pectic acid salts and to decomposition, but it is not readily removed by water alone. Tensile strength of the fiber and fluidity in cuprammonium hydroxide are not greatly altered by the removal of pectin [106].

Protein. According to Ridge [141], the total nitrogen content of raw cotton of American origin is 0.21 per cent, whereas Egyptian cotton contains 0.30 per cent. If this is considered to be all protein nitrogen, the values may be multiplied by the conventional 6.25 to give 1.3 and 1.9 per cent protein, respectively. It is likely, however, that part of the nitrogen in the fiber is nonprotein. The raw cotton fiber gives the xanthoproteic test with concentrated nitric acid followed by aqueous sodium hydroxide, and also Millon's reaction for tyrosine. The protein occurs chiefly in the central cavity or lumen of the fiber [64]. The nitrogen is readily removed from the cotton in the bleaching process. No important change in nitrogen content is observed subsequent to a mild alkali boil. As a means of controlling the bleaching operation analytically, the estimation of nitrogen is, therefore, of little value [141]. The nitrogen content of scoured cotton is about 0.035 per cent.

The brown coloring matter of cotton and the dark brown color of kier liquors are associated with proteins in the discussions of a number of writers. This is, no doubt, due to the influence of the observations of Schunk [148] that brown materials containing 5 to 6 per cent nitrogen could be obtained from kier liquors. Leucine or tyrosine was reported in this material and histamine has been isolated in crystalline form in extremely small quantities from cotton dust collected from card rooms in connection with investigations of the cause of "stripper's asthma" [82].

Ash and Its Constituents. A typical sample of raw cotton contains about 1.2 per cent of ash [93, 114, 117, 116] of approximately the composition given in Table 2.

TABLE 2. Composition of Ash of Cotton Fiber

Substance	*Per Cent*	*Substance*	*Per Cent*	*Substance*	*Per Cent*
K_2O	34	Al_2O_3	2	CO_2	20
CaO	11	SiO_2	5	Cu	Trace
MgO	6	SO_3	4	Mn	Trace
Na_2O	7	P_2O_5	5		
Fe_2O_3	2	Cl	4		

Recorded variations may be due to the presence of sand, soil, and dust in the cotton, to faulty methods of analysis, and to variations arising from soil, climate, and variety of cotton. Fargher and Probert [63] give the average ash content in per cent of dry weight of combed raw cotton grown in different parts of the world as shown in Table 3.

TABLE 3. Ash Content of Various Cottons

Type of Cotton	*Per Cent Ash*
North American	1.17
South American	1.16
American, grown in India	1.25
American, grown in other countries	1.47
Egyptian	1.20
Indian	1.28
Sea Island	0.98

Kearney and Scofield [97] found the average ash content of cotton taken from unopened bolls to be 1.17 per cent of the dry weight. One gram of cotton-fiber ash will neutralize 13 to 16 ml of normal acid. About 85 per cent of the ash may be removed from the fiber by extraction with water, but most of the calcium, iron, and aluminum remain in the fiber [171]. The ash content of cotton after scouring and bleaching is usually negligible. The fact that washing cotton with water greatly increases its electrical resistance by removing most of the soluble potassium and sodium salts has made possible its adoption as a substitute for silk in textile insulation of telephone cord, wire, and cable [170].

The phosphorus content has received considerable attention. Geake [68] found the following average values, expressed as per cent P_2O_5, for the phosphorus content of raw cotton: American, 0.05; Sea Island, 0.07; Sakellarides, 0.12; Egyptian other than Sakellarides, 0.09; South American, 0.07. Comber waste, which is composed of the shorter fibers, may contain as much as 0.17 per cent P_2O_5. According to Calvert [14] the phosphorus compounds present in cotton are readily extracted with water. Pons found 0.028 per cent total phosphorus and 0.015 per cent of phosphate phosphorus in a sample of raw cotton [134].

Pigment. The nature of the pigment which is responsible for the faint creamy color of raw cotton is not known. According to Oparin and Rogowin [130] it is at least genetically related to chlorogenic acid, a condensation product of caffeic acid and quinic acid. It is possible that cotton fibers may contain some of the flavone pigments found in cotton flowers [164]. Cotton fiber increases in color or chroma after storage periods of 2 to 5 yr [128]. Highly colored cottons are known, mainly brown and green. The green color fades quickly upon exposure to light or weather, but some of the browns are fast. Although most of the naturally colored cottons are inferior to ordinary varieties, several brown strains have satisfactory maturity and strength [172].

Other Constituents. The presence of a galactoaraban has been demonstrated in raw cotton fiber. This is accompanied by traces of rhamnose

TABLE 4. PHYSICAL DATA AND CHEMICAL CONSTITUENTS OF RAW COTTONS AS PERCENTAGE OF DRY WEIGHT

Variety	*Crop Season*	*Staple Length (in.)*	*"Fineness"* * *(cm/mg)*	*Bundle Strength (lb per sq in.)*	*Wax (%)*	*Pectate (%)*	*Organic-Ammonia Nitrogen (%)*	*Total Nitrogen (%)*	*Phosphorus. (%)*	*Weight Loss During Kier-Boil (%)*	*Ash (%)*	*Ash Alkalinity* † *cc. N* H_2SO_4
Half and Half	1937	7/8	441	68,100 ± 700	0.44	0.43	0.132	0.140	0.020	7.0	1.01	13.0
Rowden	1938	1	461	80,600 ± 900	0.60	0.58	0.127	0.129	0.020	7.1	1.14	14.2
Wilds-5	1937	1 3/32	565	82,300 ± 900	0.70	0.60	0.147	0.144	0.020	7.8	1.11	14.6
Acala	1938	1	610	81,700 ± 600	0.75	0.69	0.165	0.172	0.020	8.0	1.20	13.6
Express	1938	1 1/32	621	80,500 ± 800	0.90	0.77	0.168	0.168	0.019	8.2	1.17	14.8
Delfos	1938	1 1/32	826	73,900 ± 400	0.87	0.71	0.172	0.174	0.019	8.6	1.26	15.4
Sea Island	1938	1 1/4	847	96,000 ± 1600	0.89	0.76	0.232	0.234	0.022	8.5	0.80	16.3

* The reciprocal of the more usual fiber-weight-per-centimeter.

† Defined as milli-equivalents of sulfuric acid to neutralize one gram of ash.

and inositol [76]. Raw cotton fiber contains about 0.8 per cent of organic acids, exclusive of pectic acid, of which about 0.5 per cent is 1-malic acid and 0.07 per cent is citric acid. Both of these acids have been isolated in crystalline form from raw cotton fiber [115]. The amount of organic acids including pectic acid is approximately equivalent to the ash alkalinity of raw cotton fiber. Cotton may acquire an alkaline reaction due to the action of microorganisms prior to picking [113]. The vitamins biotin, pyridoxime, and thiamine have been found in cotton batting [142]. The folic acid content of raw cotton is 0.028 gamma per gram [155].

Relation Between the Chemical Composition of the Fiber and Its Physical Properties. Nickerson, Fontaine, and Leape [129] have determined the various groups of constituents found in raw cotton on seven samples selected for different degrees of fineness. Their work is one of the few instances where most of the constituent groups for which analytical methods are available have been estimated on the same group of samples. They found that wax, pectin, and nitrogen tended to increase in amount with increasing fineness of fiber. Their data are given in Table 4. See also Heyn [88]. Additional rather complete analytical data on a series of samples of raw cotton were published in 1951 [116].

Chemical Changes in the Developing Fiber. Cellulose has been detected microscopically in the 2-day-old fiber [3] and by X-ray analysis in the 6- to 10-day-old extracted fiber [156, 85]. However, during the elongation stage in the development of the fiber, the cell wall is composed chiefly of noncellulosic substances such as pectin. The young 20- to 25-day-old fiber contains about 6 times as much nitrogen [92] and about 3 times as much pectin [173, 32], as the mature fiber. At this stage the sugar content may be 25 per cent or more on the dry basis [17, 33]. The sugars found are glucose, fructose, and a pentose [34]. Starch grains have been identified microscopically in the immature cotton fiber [3]. Coincident with the start of thickening and deposition of cellulose in the secondary wall at about the 25th day, the pectin, nitrogen, and sugar contents of the fiber fall abruptly during a period of 10 to 15 days to nearly the composition of the mature fiber and then slowly until the boll opens. Any condition that interrupts or hinders the process of development results in the final fiber being thin-walled and high in pectin, nitrogen, and sugar.

Extraction of Cotton with Various Solvents

Raw cotton loses 1.4 to 4.2 per cent of its dry matter when extracted with water at 20° C. (68° F.) and somewhat larger amounts at higher temperatures [60]. Typical data are shown in Table 5.

TABLE 5. WATER EXTRACTION OF COTTON AT VARIOUS TEMPERATURES

	20° C. 68° F.	25° C. 77° F.	40° C. 104° F.	60° C. 140° F.	90° C. 194° F.	Pressure, 20 Lb at 125° C. 257° F.
American	...	2.4	...	...	...	4.2
American Upland	1.4	...	1.6	1.7	2.3	...
Egyptian	...	3.1	...	...	...	4.2
Indian	...	3.3	...	...	...	5.3
Indian Broach	3.1	...	3.5	3.7	3.8	...

Hydrochloric and sulfuric acids of about 0.1 N concentration have solvent action similar to water but extract more ash, about 97 per cent of the total, and more nitrogenous material. Within the limits set by possible tendering of the cotton, acids do not hydrolyze the wax. Treatment with water or dilute acids may render the wax more readily removable by boiling alkali. Steeping in such acid prior to boiling may liberate fatty acids from calcium and magnesium soaps, thought to be present in raw cotton, making them more readily removable, and is believed to finish to a whiter fabric than steeping in water alone. The effects of steeping upon the removal of wax by subsequent boiling [58] are illustrated by Table 6.

TABLE 6. AMOUNT OF WAX PRESENT IN COTTON

Variety of Cotton	Kind of Scour with 1 Per Cent of NaOH for 6 Hr	Residual Wax, Per Cent		
		Not Steeped	Steeped in Water	Steeped in 0.2 N H_2SO_4
Texan	Open kier	0.36	0.22	0.18
Texan	20 lb pressure	0.20	0.15	0.11
Sakellarides	Open kier	0.40	0.26	0.22
Sakellarides	20 lb pressure	0.26	0.19	0.18
Averages		0.31	0.21	0.17

Commercial Purification of Cotton

The term "bleaching" is usually used in the industry in a broad sense for the purification of cotton goods.[2] The usual purpose of a bleach is

[2] Cotton yarn, thread, or cloth, when ready for bleaching, is called gray goods. Yarn and thread usually consist of raw cotton modified only by the mechanical

not merely whitening but, of equal importance, the removal of natural wax and any other material that may interfere with wetting and absorbency as in surgical cottons, or with the penetration and fixation of dyes and print colors.

The so-called impurities are mainly noncellulose constituents of cotton, warp size used to facilitate weaving and consisting typically of starch with an oil or fat softener, and motes.[3] The motes are difficult to break down and may have more to do with determining details of the processes than the natural impurities of the fiber.

The bleaching of piece goods is by far the largest application of the purification of cotton. There are many variations in the practice of commercial bleaching, with a strong trend for a number of years from the so-called chlorine bleach with caustic kier boil and hypochlorite to the continuous peroxide process.

Bleaching usually begins with singeing by passing the cloth rapidly over red hot metal plates, rollers, or free gas flames to burn off loose fiber ends or fuzz. Overheating has the effect of slight oxidation [27]. The goods are quenched with water or, frequently, with dilute sulfuric acid which is utilized in the next step in the process.

Steeping and Desizing. The next step in most bleaching processes is steeping or desizing. Steeping by standing for a few hours after squeezing from dilute sulfuric acid, say 0.5 per cent, may cause desizing by hydrolysis of starch, but some bleachers consider the effects on the natural cotton impurities to be the more important. Solubilizing of the starch can also be effected by suitable commercial enzymes. Such desizing, as well as the acid treatment, should be followed by thorough washing before the next step.

Alkali Boiling. The purpose of the alkali boil is to scour or to clean. It is usually less expensive to remove impurities than to try to whiten them without removal, and if this is done the white bleached goods will be less likely to turn yellow upon storing.

Kier liquors usually consist of 1 to 2 per cent caustic soda solution. In textile work, percentages are sometimes calculated on the weight of goods and may appear in the literature in that form. A normal procedure would be to boil for 8 hr at 15 lb pressure with sufficient liquor to cover the goods completely.

The removal of wax is not complete, although it is one of the main objects of the process. Boiling raw cotton containing 0.76 per cent wax

treatment. Sometimes, however, a very small amount of mineral oil is added in the spinning mill. Cloth usually contains warp sizing in addition.

[3] In the classification of cotton [165] the term "motes" means immature and undeveloped seeds; in the textile trade the term means bits of the cotton plant and fragments torn from seeds during ginning.

with 1 per cent sodium hydroxide for 5 hr at atmospheric pressure reduced the wax content to 0.31 per cent whereas boiling at 2.5 times atmospheric pressure for 2 hr reduced the wax content to 0.26 per cent [103]. According to Fargher and Higginbotham [60], experimentally scoured cotton contained about 0.2 per cent wax, whereas technically scoured cotton contained about 0.3 per cent. Apparently the scouring process removes wax from the surface of the fiber since boiled cotton wets readily. There is probably some saponification of wax and of other fatty matter present and the resulting small amounts of soap may contribute, as the boil proceeds, to the emulsification of the wax. See also [18].

Since oxidation of the cotton by atmospheric oxygen can take place in the presence of hot caustic alkali, the air in a kier is displaced by steam before the kier is put under pressure. However, a normal kier liquor is believed to acquire reducing capacity early in the process, as is well illustrated by its known tendency to reduce vat dyes if present in goods being boiled. Much of the actual removal of impurities is effected in the washing after boiling. A less severe type of kier boil at atmospheric pressure may be employed for yarn or piece goods.

Bleaching by Chlorine. The bleaching proper is effected by oxidizing agents which attack remaining impurities and make them white or facilitate their removal in the washings. Chlorine bleaching, by release of nascent oxygen through the use of sodium hypochlorite, is the most common. When time, temperature, concentration, and pH of the bath are properly controlled there is relatively little oxidation of the cotton itself during a normal bleach. (See [120] for more details.) Washing follows the bleaching to remove the residual chemicals and such oxidized impurities as will wash out. Goods from the chlorine bleach are usually given a light sour with sulfuric acid, washed, and frequently given a bath of dilute sodium bisulfite to remove residual traces of chlorine. Sulfurous acid may be used as both sour and antichlor. All chemicals must be thoroughly washed out.

Bleaching by Peroxide. Bleaching with hydrogen peroxide [120] as the active agent is being practiced to an increasing extent. A batch process has steps similar to those already described, through a regular pressure boil. Then the bleaching can take place in a hot alkaline peroxide solution in the same kier followed by a thorough washing. Advantages are less pulling and handling of the cloth, softer goods, and saving of time.

In the continuous peroxide process [120, 175], the goods, singed and desized, in open width or rope form, enter a saturator where the cloth takes up a controlled amount of sodium hydroxide solution. Details differ with weight and character of goods. In a representative process the cloth moves at 100 yd per min, passes through a heater at 210° F., and is run hot into a *J*-box through which it moves in 1 hr. It is then washed well, saturated with the required amount of alkaline hydrogen peroxide at ordinary temperatures, enters another *J*-box (hot) for 1 hr, and is finally washed well at 160° F., to emerge fully bleached in a little over 2 hr (from the time of desizing).

Kettering and Kraemer published [101] the results of a detailed critical comparison of the properties and quality of goods bleached by (*a*) the chlorine bleach by the caustic kier boil and hypochlorite, (*b*) kier boil and peroxide, and (*c*) the continuous peroxide method. Fabrics from *a*, and from *b* and *c* were found equal in whiteness. The continuous peroxide gave slightly better results than the chlorine bleach in terms of other fabric properties. Possibilities of damage through hydrolysis and oxidation of the cellulose of the cotton are discussed briefly in the section "Degradation of Cotton," below, and also in Chapter II. The principles of bleaching are treated by Marsh [110]. Commercial practice is outlined in the *American Cotton Handbook* [120], and modern installations are frequently described in the trade press.

Swelling

Swelling phenomena of cellulose in general, particularly with active swelling agents, are discussed in Chapter II. Specific applications of swelling to cotton are found in the next five sections and under "Mercerization."

Swelling by Water Vapor. Cotton increases in volume upon absorbing moisture from the atmosphere. Therefore, all ordinary cotton is normally slightly swollen. Swelling increases with humidity and may cause tightly constructed cotton goods to become harder or stiffer and to change in dimensions. Reverse changes take place when the humidity is decreased.

The swelling of soda-boiled cotton [4] in terms of percentage of the dry volume is of similar order to moisture [133] regain as shown in Table 7.

TABLE 7. Moisture Regain and Swelling of Dry Cotton

Moisture Regain (*per cent*)	*Swelling* (*per cent*)
1.09	0.51
5.32	5.64
6.67	7.44
8.03	9.51
17.79	24.22

[4] The term "soda-boiled cotton" used in the British textile literature refers to cotton which has been given a boil with caustic alkali.

Similar data are available [31] for mercerized Sea Island cotton hairs. The swelling of cotton by water vapor is utilized in the aging of prints. Dry, freshly printed fabric is treated in an atmosphere of steam, usually to bring about a chemical reaction, and particularly to moisten the cloth and swell the fibers to facilitate penetration and dyeing within the printed areas. Meggy [118] has reported a study of the mechanism of this process, with special reference to vat dyes.

Some cotton finishing depends mainly upon swelling by moisture, with heat and mechanical pressure to shape the fibers and cloth surfaces. The Schreiner calender is an example of the plastic behavior of cotton under such conditions. The cloth passes between a gas-heated steel roll, engraved with fine parallel lines or striations, and a soft lower roll. The lines become impressed on the cloth and are immediately set by drying, thus imparting a soft sheen or luster by reflection from their minute flat surfaces.

Swelling in Water. Upon wetting, cotton fibers swell in volume owing almost entirely to increase in cross-sectional area; the swelling in length is usually not more than 1 per cent. Various figures have been reported for swelling, viz., 50 per cent [41], 40 to 42 per cent [182*a*], 33.5 per cent [44], and for mercerized cotton 46 and 44.5 per cent [44]. Later figures are 21–34 per cent with an average of about 30 per cent [122]. Retention of water upon centrifuging, sometimes called imbibition, gives values which serve as rough measures of swelling. Retentions determined [135] with water whose surface tension was reduced to 36 dynes by a wetting agent are shown in Table 8. Swelling of cotton in water is the subject of a bibliography [143].

TABLE 8. Imbibition of Various Fibers Compared

Fibers	*Grams Water per 100 Grams Cellulose (per cent)*
Viscose rayon	92–97
Cotton	47
Mercerized cotton	49
Acetylated cotton	22–26
Nylon	12

Swelling of fibers by water has a commercial application in tightly woven fire hose which does not require a rubber lining. Cotton does not swell enough normally, but yarn mercerized at high tension [132] has been proposed to replace the usual linen in such hose. Upon wetting, it quickly swells and stops leakage through the hose wall.

Cotton fibers tend to elongate slightly upon wetting, but yarn and cloth tend to shrink. If shrinkage is desired it can be brought about by simple wetting. Sanforizing is a widely used method for preshrinking cotton goods [120] to reduce subsequent shrinking to the extent of less than 1 per cent.

Swelling by Concentrated Solutions. Cotton may be swollen to great increases in volume by concentrated solutions of certain acids, salts, and bases. The action of these swelling agents is usually associated with the sorption of highly hydrated ions. The fiber strength is diminished, but the cotton does not lose its apparent (microscopic) homogeneity. (See Mercerization.)

Swelling by Acids. The principal interest in swelling by acids has been in connection with special cotton finishes [111, 112, 146]. Sulfuric acid at various concentrations swells cotton. Sellars and Vilbrandt [151] obtained results resembling the effects of mercerization with caustic soda, viz., improvement in luster, increase in strength, and greater dye absorption. These were in general agreement with the results of other investigators. The most favorable action was at 62.5 per cent within ½ to 2 min, below 68° F. Parchmentizing begins at 69 per cent, but 78 per cent acid for 15 sec at 50° F. is usual for this purpose [112].

When swelling is great there will be a tendency toward a high activity ratio, and a large residual swelling, as measured by retention of water in the centrifuge, after the swelling agent is washed out. When sulfuric acid solutions of 63.4 per cent and 68.5 per cent were used the retentions were 128 and 254 per cent, respectively, as compared with 50 per cent of the dry weight of cotton for water alone. Drying after washing reduced retentions to 57 and 150 per cent [112].

Strong sulfuric acid is used as the basis of several special cotton finishes. A momentary treatment is sometimes used to increase the transparency of cotton, and various strengths of acid have been suggested. It is always a matter of treatment for seconds and at low temperatures. Methods employing strong sulfuric acid have been operated especially under patents owned by the Heberlein interests (Swiss), sometimes combined with treatment with strong caustic soda. Details of the processes actually used have not been made public. The finishes vary greatly and have been characterized by such terms as "transparent," "linenlike," and "wool-like." A specific example is the permanent organdie finish which upon washing and ironing recovers its stiffness without starch. Marsh [111] gives an extensive review of numerous methods of applying strong sulfuric acids in cotton finishing.

Acid finishes have been considered objectionable because hydrolytic degradation sets in quickly, and very close control of the process is required. Various additions have been proposed to slow the action of the sulfuric acid in order to reduce the tendency to damage.

Effects resembling those of mercerization with caustic soda can be obtained with nitric acid [112] of 70 to 71 per cent strength, and a definite compound with cellulose is believed to be formed under suitable conditions. Processes in this field for finishing cotton have been reviewed by Marsh [111]. Strong solutions of hydrochloric, phosphoric, and other inorganic acids also have swelling effects on cotton.

Swelling by Salts. Effects resembling mercerization are obtained with calcium thiocyanate solution of 60 per cent concentration [112]. Parchmentizing and dissolving occur under other special conditions. Zinc chloride swells cotton and is used in the so-called vulcanizing process for making hard board for electrical insulation. It has been proposed also for swelling effects in cotton finishing [111, 112]. Various other salts swell cotton, such as lithium bromide, sodium mercuric iodide, potassium iodide, and barium iodide. Mercerizing effects have been claimed for sodium sulfide [112].

Swelling by Bases. The most important swelling of cotton by a base is mercerization by sodium hydroxide, discussed below. Hydroxides of other alkali metals swell cotton and have mercerization effects as summarized in [109, 112, 167]. Cotton swells little in concentrated aqueous ammonia.

Cuprammonium solution has been tried in various ways to produce highly lustrous and strong yarns and fabrics, and special finishes [111], but it is not widely used. The old Willesden finish, produced by a surface action of cuprammonium solution on cotton goods, and originally intended for waterproofing, also imparts resistance to biological rotting. Such treatment with the cuprammonium produces partly dissolved cellulose on the cloth surface, which is pressed into the goods and dried in. However, the tendency of the chemical to dissolve the cotton makes it difficult to employ such finishes.

Cellulose can be swollen and dissolved by a number of organic bases, but few data are available on their specific effects as swelling agents for cotton [86, 112]. Lieser [108], in his work on various quaternary ammonium and similar bases, found that there is swelling in aqueous solutions up to some narrow range of concentrations where the cellulose dissolves, and then there is only swelling again at still higher concentrations. Trimethylbenzyl ammonium hydroxide is a swelling agent with mercerizing properties at 1.9 *N*, but at 2.11 *N*, or about 35 per cent, it becomes a very effective solvent for cotton [112, 131]. For theories and discussions of the mechanism of swelling see Ott [131], Stamm [160], Meyer [121], and Hermans [84].

Mercerization

John Mercer in 1844 performed the classical experiment of filtering strong caustic soda solution through cotton cloth, and noted that the cloth swelled and shrunk. Nearly 50 years later it was noticed that when the cloth was prevented from shrinking a high luster developed. The basis for these effects, which underlie commercial mercerization, is the swelling of the cotton fiber. Attention will be given mainly to the swelling rather than to technical details of processing. Among the best general references are Clibbens [23], Edelstein and Cady [53], Valko [167], and Marsh [109].

For scientific purposes, it is no doubt best to define mercerized cotton as cotton which shows the X-ray diffraction diagram of mercerized or regenerated cellulose, which Meyer [121] calls an allotropic modification of native cellulose. In the commercial treatment of cotton, the term "mercerization" is usually limited to the process for producing permanent luster or other effects of swelling by caustic soda.

Much scientific work has been done on cotton while it is free to shrink in the caustic alkali. This is in contrast to nearly all commercial work where the cotton is not allowed to shrink to any extent, and may be mercerized with applied tension or stretch.

When normal unrestrained cotton fibers are treated with caustic soda of mercerizing strength, the swelling causes almost complete disappearance of the lumen and convolutions. Studies on the mercerization of single fibers of cotton have been valuable in showing what cotton tends to do under different conditions of treatment. Available data have been reviewed by Valko [167] and by Marsh [109]. There were different amounts of shrinkage under different conditions, the maximum being about 17 per cent loss of length [16]. There were increases in cross-section of 75 to 80 per cent at ordinary mercerizing concentrations [183]. Increase in volume accompanying treatment with 14.3 per cent and stronger caustics was reported to be 177 $\pm$ 8 cc per 100 grams of cotton, as determined by the centrifugal method, or a swelling to nearly four times the original volume [41]. Similar experiments on cloth showed that it swelled only about half as much, owing to the restricting effects of yarn and fabric structure.

The behavior of cotton fibers upon mercerization when not complicated by yarn or cloth structure is given by Schubert [147], abstracted by Valko [167] and by Ott [131]. Fibers were first allowed to shrink, then measured and brought back to normal length, and held there while the caustic was being washed out. With Mako cotton there was a maximum shrinkage of 19 per cent in 14 per cent sodium hydroxide (by weight) and a general progressive change of properties until this critical concentration was reached. Fiber strength increased by about 25 per cent, elongation at the break dropped by about a third, luster increased to a maximum, and mercerization was nearly complete as shown by

X-ray analysis. All these properties remained practically constant through higher concentrations up to at least 31 to 32 per cent. When fibers were mercerized with tension to prevent shrinkage the transformation to the mercerized form was not complete until the concentration was about 17 per cent, the highest fiber strength and the lowest elongation also being reached at this point.

Cotton fiber structure as well as the cellulose submicroscopic structure cause several variations in the mechanism of swelling. Below 8 or 9 per cent the alkali is believed absorbed by the noncrystalline material and crystal surfaces [121], with little swelling and little transformation to the mercerized form. Up to about 11 per cent, swelling takes place inwardly into the lumen [16, 22]. Swelling and transformation continue up to 13 or 14 per cent concentration, about the point of maximum swelling where curves representing mercerizing effects frequently show a sharp change of direction. The rather definite limitation of swelling that begins at this concentration is set by the primary wall and greatly facilitates control of the practical process of mercerization, because the fiber does not continue to swell excessively under accidental adverse conditions, such as delay during the process. At higher concentrations the crystalline portion is all of the mercerized type. Cotton is completely converted within a few seconds in 18 per cent caustic soda.

Commercial mercerization usually represents only a partial conversion to actual mercerized cellulose, but this seems to make no difference for the ordinary mercerized finish. The conversion may be partly prevented by heat or tension; or there may be reversion by too hot washing, but there is little indication of any adverse effect on luster.

The sorptive properties of natural cotton are increased by mercerization because the hydroxyl groups upon which they depend have been made more available or accessible. For normal mercerized goods the ratio is about 1 : 1.25, but for cotton mercerized without tension it may be 1 : 1.5 or higher. Reactivity ratios are similar.

Voluntary commercial standards [124] show such a difference where 7 and 8.5 are accepted as the base regain percentages for unmercerized and mercerized yarns respectively. These are the approximate values for cotton stored at 70° F. and 65 per cent R.H.

Mercerized cotton has the well-known reputation of dyeing a darker shade than unmercerized. Usually such comparisons are based on dyeing at the same time in the same bath by the ordinary method for direct dyes. Unmercerized yarn, yarn mercerized at normal length, and yarn fully shrunk in the caustic will dye to three different depths, but, since the apparent depths of color are partly determined by optical effects, the appearance of the three is not in strict accordance with the amounts of dye absorbed, or the absorption ratios of the yarns. Mercerized cotton also dyes more rapidly [9].

Shrinking and Luster. The shrinking in length of a fiber upon mercerization is, no doubt, due partly to its spiral structure and partly to the netlike submicroscopic structure which appears to make the fiber expandable in diameter at the expense of length. Shrinking of yarn and cloth is more complicated. Swelling of fibers in the spiral yarn structure also tends to increase the yarn diameter, which causes sharper twist angles and contraction in length.

When mercerized with tension, the swollen fiber takes on a smooth cylindrical form which is retained after washing and drying. Luster is due primarily to reflection from large groups of the smoothed fiber surfaces, the high lights being brought out by contrast with less bright areas. Although luster is reported to follow roundness of fiber (Chapter V) it can be increased by impressed flat surfaces, such as a Schreiner finish. The subject of luster has been reviewed by Buck and McCord [12].

Commercial mercerization consists essentially of putting yarn or cloth under restraint from any considerable shrinkage, impregnating with caustic soda solution, frequently assisted by prewetting or the addition of a wetting agent to the caustic soda, washing, neutralizing of residual alkali, washing and drying, accompanied by such tension or stretching as is required to prevent loss of yardage. Usual conditions are 20 to 25 per cent caustic acting for 0.5 to 2 min at room, or slightly higher, temperature, but there are endless possible variations in time, temperature, concentration, purity of the caustic, and possible changes in washing, shrinking, and stretching. Impurities and other additions to the bath reduce the amount of swelling.

Yarn is usually mercerized for luster and increased dyeing capacity. Cloth is mercerized for dye economy and brightness of shade; for luster and sometimes to obtain a more sheer appearance; to help set the finished width, sometimes in conjunction with Sanforizing; and to help cover extremely thin-walled cotton by swelling it so that it will dye more nearly like the rest of the piece. It seems to have been rather generally concluded that the gain in strength from mercerizing yarn, frequently 15 or 20 per cent, arises entirely from increase in compactness of structure and fiber cling. Schubert's results [147] indicate, however, that true gains in fiber strength may contribute to the added yarn strength.

Tests for Mercerized Material. The identification and evaluation of mercerized material usually depend upon visual observation of luster supplemented by an absorption test. All tests are preferably made in comparison with known similar material, both mercerized and unmercerized. The microscope can be used to distinguish mercerized cotton (see Chapter IV).

The simplest absorption test is to make comparative direct dyeings in the same bath. Mennel's test [119] exaggerates the darker dyeings of mercerized cotton. Iodine and other absorption tests are covered by Marsh [109]. Clibbens and Geake [27] have studied irregularities and testing of mercerized yarns and present unusual dyeing tests, which are especially useful in showing defects in mercerizing, or variations such as are found in a series of experimental results. Edelstein [52] has developed a modification of Neale's barium absorption test [125], which has the advantage (over tests depending upon color) that it can be applied directly to most dyed goods. The deconvolution count [15] utilizes an estimate of the amount of visual change in short lengths of cotton fibers for conclusions regarding their mercerization. Degree of mercerization depends upon so many factors that it is comparative only.

Sorption

Sorption of Gases and Vapors. Many of the sorption effects of cellulose have been specifically determined for cotton. Stamm [160] attributes to Davidson an estimate that air is adsorbed by cotton to the extent of 0.023 cc per gram of dry cotton under normal conditions, but without indicating whether the proportions of oxygen and nitrogen are the same as in the atmosphere. Heertjes [83] estimates the amount for mercerized cotton to be 0.029 cc per gram at 20.6° C. (68.9° F.) and 0.008 cc per gram at 59.2° C. (138.4° F.).

Large amounts of the vapors of some organic liquids and of volatile chemicals may be taken up by cotton. Brimley [10] reported in round numbers the amounts taken up from saturated vapors in the presence of air at room temperature. (See Table 9.)

TABLE 9. Sorption from Saturated Vapors by Bleached and Unbleached Cottons

Liquids	*Unbleached (per cent)*	*Bleached (per cent)*
Water	18 to 20	19 to 20
Glacial acetic acid	18 to 20	17 to 19
Absolute alcohol	3 to 3.5	8.5 to 9
Carbon disulfide	1.5 to 2	1.5 to 2
Benzene	1.5 to 2	1 to 2
Ether	7 to 7.5	7 to 7.5
Nitrobenzene	1.5 to 2	1.5 to 2
Acetone	2 to 2.5	6.5 to 7

The marked difference in the absorption of absolute alcohol and acetone by bleached and unbleached cotton was not explained. Data on sorption of vapors by cotton, taken from those selected by Stamm [160] from the literature, are presented in Table 10.

TABLE 10. VAPOR SORPTION OF COTTON UNDER VARIOUS CONDITIONS

Vapors	*Temperature* °C.	°F.	*Pressure, Cm of Hg*	*Relative Vapor Pressure, Per Cent*	*Sorption, Per Cent by Weight*
Hydrochloric acid	22	71.6	5.4		0.8
Hydrochloric acid	22	71.6	70.2		2.0
Sulfur dioxide	22	71.6	76.0		5.0
Ammonia	22	71.6	76.0		4.0
Methyl alcohol	30	86.0		100.0	11.2
Ethyl alcohol	30	86.0		100.0	8.6
Propyl alcohol	30	86.0		100.0	5.0
n-Butyl alcohol	30	86.0		100.0	1.5

Air-dried cotton immersed in organic liquids, then dried to constant weight at 105° C. (221° F.), retained considerable amounts [181] of the liquids. (See Table 11.)

TABLE 11. RETENTION OF VARIOUS LIQUIDS BY COTTON

	Per Cent
Methyl alcohol	0.80
Ethyl alcohol	1.60
Propyl alcohol	1.60
n-Butyl alcohol	1.72
Diethyl ether	0
Benzene	0.24
Gasoline	0
Benzene-ethyl alcohol 2 to 1	2.31
Benzene-ethyl alcohol 1 to 2	1.26

In extracting cotton with solvents, in exceptional cases the cotton may weigh more afterward instead of less, owing to retention of solvent, so that the extract cannot be determined directly by loss of weight. The theories and methods of measuring adsorbed materials on cotton have been reviewed by Stamm [160], Salley [145], Sheppard and Newsome [154], and Babbitt [4].

Sorption from Aqueous Solutions. Cotton adsorbs strong acids and bases from dilute solutions and may hold them very tenaciously. Therefore, for a volumetric determination, it is advisable to titrate an aqueous extract in the presence of the cotton [42].

The action of dry heat upon cotton containing small quantities of dilute sulfuric acid results in a fixation of acid on the cotton accompanied by degradation [25]. Such fixed or combined sulfuric acid is not entirely removed from cotton by boiling with 1 per cent sodium hydroxide. Methods have been given [25] for determining acid in cotton, which will include such combined acid. (See Degradation.)

Caustic soda frequently contains iron dissolved from iron equipment [45]. Cotton can adsorb such iron and has been used to purify concentrated caustic soda solutions. Iron may be deposited on cotton during mercerizing, but is usually taken out by the sulfuric acid sour. Swelling and mercerization furnish other examples of sorption and its effects.

Mordanting. A mordant is a substance which can be fixed upon a fiber and, in turn, serves to fix a dyestuff which would not otherwise dye the fiber or would not dye it so satisfactorily.

Metallic mordants, although extensively used in the past in fixing dyes on cotton, are relatively unimportant.

Mineral khaki is applied like a mordant which serves as its own coloring medium, by the precipitation in the fiber of hydroxides, hydrated oxides, or other complexes of chromium and iron from suitable salts. It is very fast to washing but not to acids. Its application has had very critical study [6, 136]. The mineral color imparts some resistance to mildewing but not enough to serve as a mildew or rotproofing agent. Introduction of copper [95] increases the mildew resistance but detracts from resistance to weathering.

Cotton has the property of readily absorbing tannic acid or tannin from solution. After fixing by some salt of antimony or iron, the tannin serves as a mordant for basic dyes which are used for unusually bright or deep shades. The practical application and many precautions are described in Whittaker and Wilcock [177]. The general procedure is to soak cotton in a solution containing an amount of tannin suitable for the required depth of dyed shade for an hour or two at 40° C. (104° F.); to squeeze evenly without any washing; to fix with tartar emetic or some double salt of antimony that breaks down readily to the oxide; and then to wash well and dye. The sorption of tannic acid by cotton and subsequent fixation of dye are attributed [167] to strong van der Waals' forces of attraction.

Direct and sulfur dyes also serve as mordants for basic dyes which may be applied to dyeings by "topping" to obtain brightness. The same principle is used in a synthetic mordant best known under the name "Katanol," a phenolic condensation product containing sulfur, which is applied like a direct dye and is virtually a dye without color which requires no further fixing to serve as a mordant for basic dyes.

Dyeing. Direct cotton colors have the property of substantivity, or dyeing directly without a mordant or other special process. This property is shared by the Indigosols, the leuco vat and sulfur colors, and by dye components like the "naphthols," all of which are positively absorbed by cellulose.

Direct dyes tend to form aggregates in solution but they are largely in monomolecular form in the hot dye bath, and are adsorbed on cellulose as dye ions. According to modern views they are held to the cellulose at hydroxyl groups by hydrogen bonds [167]. Available evidence suggests [168] that aggregation of dye within the fiber, or formation of multimolecular layers, takes place under some conditions as dyeing proceeds.

Water-swollen fibers contain pores of some such radius as 20–30 A, large enough to admit dye molecules, and possibly much larger openings. The absorptive surface available for dyeing in swollen cellulose is on the order of 3×10^5 sq cm per g. Dyeing is essentially adsorption; and dye molecules, of such representative dimensions as 30 A × 8 A × 3 A, which have access by diffusion through the network system of openings to the internal surface of the fiber, are apparently well distributed over crystal surfaces as well as through the porous amorphous portion. They cannot penetrate crystalline regions. Boulton and Morton [9] suggest that each type of cellulose, such as native cotton, mercerized cotton, and different rayons, has a rather specific fraction of noncrystalline cellulose available for dyeing, but it would seem that crystal surfaces must account for a large part of it.

Mercerized cotton dyes a darker shade than unmercerized cotton, apparently because many more hydroxyl groups become available on crystal surfaces; there is usually also an increase in noncrystalline material; and the optical properties are changed.

The mere presence of cotton in a dye solution is not sufficient for dyeing. When dyeing does take place, it continues to an equilibrium between the dyed cotton and the dye bath if conditions are not disturbed. Ordinary dyeing depends upon a balance of effects but is controlled mainly by heat and the addition of sodium chloride or sulfate.

Heat may make the dye more readily available for absorption by promoting disaggregation. The salt does not normally have a salting out effect but may act to increase the charge upon the fiber by the absorption of cations, which may attract dye anions. Since the discussion above is greatly oversimplified attention is called to four summaries on the theory or mechanism of dyeing [9, 144, 167, 168].

Most commercial direct dyeing is done under such conditions that it depends upon rate of dyeing, and equilibrium is very seldom reached.

There is probably more difficulty from salt control than from any other variable in the process, and the amount of salt should be governed by the salt sensitivity [176, 177] rather than the amount of the dye. The temperature needs careful control, according to the dye selected and to its behavior with salt. Complete wetting and effective movement of goods through dye bath or dye solution through the goods are essential. Nearly all dyeing has to be done with dye mixtures in "compound" shades. Since the dyestuffs compete for available absorbing positions within the cotton, dyes are used which behave as nearly alike as possible in the dyeing process.

The behavior of reduced leuco vat dyes appears to be fundamentally similar to that of direct dyes, with a strong tendency to very high substantivity and low diffusion speed. Difficulties in dyeing are related to the fact that the normal hydrosulfite vat contains very high concentrations of sodium ions, more than are common with direct dyes.

Cotton can be dyed to all degrees of fastness but not necessarily to the fastest shades in complete lines of colors. Generally speaking, the fastest dyes are insoluble. Some direct dyes can be improved by after-treatment of the dyed goods, but the special classes of colors and special methods of application required for the best fastness are beyond the scope of this book. For data on the principles and methods of practical dyeing see Whittaker and Wilcock [177].

Partial Chemical Derivatives of Cotton

Chemical derivatives, for the present purpose, are limited to compounds formed from cotton without loss of fibrous form and textile characteristics, but with new chemical properties. They result from typical cellulose reactions which, however, proceed only to limited degrees and do not seriously weaken or deform the fibers. The reactions are usually those that take place at hydroxyl groups, such as formation of esters and ethers. Hence the new properties obtained may be due to blocking some of the hydroxyl groups, thus interfering with the normal absorption capacity of cotton or its normal reactivity, or to the introduction of new substituent groups.

The earlier interest in partial chemical derivatives of cotton arose from the desire to make certain threads in a piece of cloth dye differently from the rest, or resist dyeing entirely, in order to produce new color effects when the whole piece was dyed.

Esters. If an esterification reaction on cotton can be controlled, and stopped after it has gone part way to completion, a virtually new fiber may result, for example, a partial acetate. According to Rheiner [140] bleached cotton yarn will acetylate overnight at room temperature in a mixture of 50 parts of acetic anhydride, 40 parts of glacial acetic acid, and 10 parts of zinc chloride, changing to approximately the composition of a monoacetate while remaining in the form of an acceptable textile yarn. More rapid methods are also possible [40, 71].

Such partially acetylated cotton yarns and fabrics will color with the special dyes used on acetate rayon but will resist most direct cotton dyes. They have low moisture contents under normal conditions, have high electrical resistance [126], and are highly resistant to heat. For example, in ordinary oven tests at 160° C. (320° F.) acetylated cottons retained 70 per cent or more of their strength after 7 days, whereas untreated cottons retained only 50–55 per cent after 1 day [40]. Similar materials were equally resistant in dry or in moist atmospheres [91]. They withstand for long periods of time degradation by microorganisms during immersion in sea water or burial in soil, which will rapidly decompose normal cotton [50, 162].

The acetylation reaction seems to proceed readily through the amorphous parts of the fiber and probably to the crystalline surfaces [70]. With care to avoid degradation, about half the hydroxyl groups can be reacted without loss of fibrous form or serious loss of fiber strength. Higher fibrous acetates can be made by acetylating in an inert medium like benzene which is not a solvent for cellulose acetate [112]. Most of the desirable properties are pronounced upon the substitution of about one-third of the hydroxyl groups of the cellulose.

Acetylated cottons containing 30 and 60 per cent of "combined acetic acid" are made commercially in England as Cotopa 30 and Cotopa 60 [127]. Cotopa 60, called triacetylated cotton, is reported to have lost very little of the original cotton strength and elasticity.

There seems to be no reason why cotton cannot be combined with almost any esterifying or etherifying agent with enough conversion of the more accessible groups to form a partial ester or ether with new properties contributed by the new compound while retaining the fiber characteristics of the original cotton.

There are special problems in conducting such reactions, as compared with ordinary organic chemistry. For example, in the partial acetylation of cotton yarn or cloth the catalyst must not cause serious hydrolysis and loss of strength in the cotton. Reactions with cotton yarn or cloth in the form of alkali cellulose, from preparation with caustic alkali, may be complicated in practical application by serious shrinkage in length or width of the goods.

An ester, known as immunized cotton because it resists dyeing, is prepared by the action of *p*-toluenesulfonyl chloride [5, 187] on alkali cellulose. To avoid shrinking during the process, the alkali cellulose is prepared from alcoholic caustic alkali. A patent proposes the use of hot aqueous caustic alkali, which has little shrinking effect [161]. This ester when prepared entirely in nonaqueous solutions is supposed to form as an outside layer around the cotton fiber. Several papers contain data on this and some other partial esters [21, 140, 187].

Phosphorylated cotton, a partial cellulose phosphate in the form of its ammonium salt, may be made by curing cotton with a solution of phosphoric acid and urea at about 150° C. for a short time [67]. This material contains 2 to 4 per cent phosphorus and is flame resistant, but the process lowers the strength and impairs the wear resistance of the fabric. Phosphorylated cotton loses its flame resistance when washed in alkaline detergents or in sea water because of cation exchange of ammonium ions for sodium ions. The use of phosphorylated cotton as a cation-exchange material has been proposed [96].

Ethers. Cotton fibers can be partly converted to ethers, but special methods for accomplishing this seem to be of greater interest than the more familiar reaction of alkyl halides on alkali cellulose.

Ethylene oxide dissolved in carbon tetrachloride reacts with cotton cloth containing caustic soda to produce partial conversion to hydroxyethyl ether [105]. With suitable neutralizing and finishing methods, stiffened and transparent fabrics like organdie, linen finish, and printed damask effects can result, according to the specific conditions employed.

The partial conversion of cellulose to methylene ether by reaction with formaldehyde has been the subject of many patents referring particularly to rayon but often including cotton. Cotton becomes crease resistant; it acquires changed dyeing properties and probably other useful properties not yet fully explored. An —O—CH_2—O— group may form between different cellulose chain molecules in the fiber or form a ring within one chain and possibly within one glucose unit. The reaction, which is based on the use of an acid catalyst, can be performed in different ways [69, 184, 185]. Crease resistance may also be obtained by similar reactions involving urea-formaldehyde resins [11].

Velan and Zelan, commercial agents for imparting water repellency, which contain stearamidomethylpyridinium chloride, react with cotton to form a partial stearamidomethyl ether of cellulose [48, 149]. About one anhydroglucose unit out of 150 is modified in this way, but this is sufficient to make the cotton water repellent. Partial carboxymethylation of cotton produces fibers, yarns, and fabrics having high swelling capacity [137]. Cotton yarn that dissolves in water has been made by carboxymethylation [138] and by oxidation with nitrogen dioxide [98].

Certain dyes may be attached to cotton by ether linkage [75] to obtain outstanding washfastness.

Amino Derivatives. The introduction of amino groups into cotton imparts the capacity of dyeing with the acid wool colors which have slight affinity for cotton but give brighter shades than the usual cotton colors. Amino groups may be introduced into cotton by the mere addition of amino compounds or by combining amino groups to the cotton by chemical reactions. For example, ethylenimine imparts acid-dyeing properties to cellulose [66] chiefly by polymerizing on the fibers, although a portion of the ethylenimine may combine chemically with the cellulose. A process for aminizing cotton by reacting it with 2-aminoethylsulfuric acid in the presence of sodium hydroxide to make a partial aminoethyl ether of the cellulose has been described [74], and the use of aminized cotton as an anion-exchange material has been proposed [90].

Many patents on various chemical modifications of cellulosic fibers are discussed in Worden [188] and in Faust [65]. Summaries are available on such subjects as crease resistance, water repellency, dye fixation, and the basifying or animalizing of cellulose fibers, i.e., their modification to respond to acid dyeing [18, 78, 158, 186].

Degradation of Cotton

Cotton is normally very stable under the usual conditions of storage, manufacture, and use, but its chemical constitution allows attack which may result in degradation. This is usually due to oxidation, hydrolysis, or both. A general discussion of the action of hydrolytic and oxidizing agents on cellulose and an explanation of the terms "oxycellulose" and "hydrocellulose" are found in Chapter II.

Measures of Degradation. Degradation of cotton is measured by the following tests:

1. Breaking or tensile strength.
2. Cuprammonium viscosity or fluidity [1, 2, 26, 56], a measure of average molecular chain length of the cellulose.
3. Nitrate viscosity or fluidity [46]. This test does not break alkali-labile oxygen linkages present in cellulose modified by oxidizing agents.
4. Copper number [24, 87], a measure of aldehydic reducing groups present in modified cellulose.
5. Methylene blue absorption [47], usually considered to be a measure of acidic carboxyl groups present in modified cellulose.
6. Alkali solubility [8], usually considered to be a measure of short-chain cellulose molecules.

The references cited may be consulted for details of the more commonly used procedures. The most nearly quantitative of these measures of degradation is the viscosity or fluidity in cuprammonium solution. An interpretation of its significance [56] is given in Table 12.

TABLE 12. VISCOSITY IN CUPRAMMONIUM SOLUTIONS

Classes	*Fluidity 20° C. (68° F.) in Reciprocal Poises*	*Comments*
1	1 to 5	Very mildly scoured and bleached cottons.
2	5 to 10	Normally scoured and bleached cottons.
3	10 to 20	Significant loss in strength due to processing.
4	20 to 30	Overbleached, with serious loss in tensile strength.
5	30 to 40	Incipient loss of fibrous structure due to chemical attack.
6	40 or above	Highly degraded by chemical attack to products described as oxy- and hydro-celluloses.

Fluidity under comparative conditions may be proportional to loss of strength but fluidities of a variety of products may not have any such definite relationship.

Effect of Storage. Storage under normal warehouse conditions has little effect on the properties of cotton. Unpublished analyses by J. H. Kettering showed that values for copper numbers, alkali solubilities, and fluidities in cuprammonium hydroxide of cotton known to have been stored in a bale for at least 50 years differed only slightly from the average of those obtained from a crop not over 3 years old. A sample of cotton found in a cliff-dweller grave and estimated to be nearly 600 years old had a tensile strength only 21 per cent less than the average of two samples of similar cotton grown recently by the Hopi Indians [81].

Effect of Heat. The thermal decomposition of cellulose has been reviewed by Heuser [86]. Cotton, raw or purified, usually shows no visible change with rise of temperature until about 248° F. is reached. At this temperature, it sometimes develops a yellowish color after 5 hr [77]. However, a small but significant increase in cuprammonium fluidity and in copper number occurs between 212 and 248° F. and, in fact, exposure for several weeks at 194 to 203° F. is said to produce detectable alterations. Cotton yarns and fabrics show little or no change in strength when heated for 5 hr at 248° F., but at temperatures much above this permanent loss of strength takes place [163]. At 284° F. a distinct yellowish brown color develops [77], and at 354° F. marked rises in cuprammonium fluidity and in copper number occur. Almost complete loss of strength results from heating for a few hours at 465° F.

The action of heat is due in part to that of oxygen, losses of strength being less in its absence [163].

Some of the results of the research on drying by Wiegerink [178, 179, 180], which covered the effects of various temperatures and humidities on cotton yarns, are shown in Table 13.

TABLE 13. EFFECT OF HEAT AND HUMIDITY ON COTTON YARNS

Types of Yarn	Temperatures		Breaking Strength in Per Cent of Original after Heating for the Following Periods and Per Cent Absolute Humidities *					
	°C.	°F.	1.5 hours			6 hours		
			1%	56%	96%	1%	56%	96%
Raw cotton yarn, water washed	105	221	95	89	93	94	92	95
	125	257	89	98	96	88	93	92
	150	302	94	91	89	89	89	84
Purified cotton	105	221	99	100	91	95	93	87
	125	257	100	93	87	92	85	78
	150	302	94	79	82	84	68	58
Mercerized cotton	105	221	92	92	92	108	105	94
	125	257	92	88	92	99	100	88
	150	302	90	87	88	92	91	89

* Actual per cent by volume of water vapor in the system. The corresponding relative humidities are: For 105° C., 1, 48, and 79 per cent; for 125° C., 0.5, 24, and 42 per cent; for 150° C., 0.2, 12, and 20 per cent, respectively.

Wiegerink's experiments showed that purified cotton is slightly more unstable to moist heat than either raw or mercerized cotton, that moisture favors degradation by heat, and that heat has only a small effect until 257° F. is exceeded. Cuprammonium fluidities of the heated cottons were in general agreement with the breaking strength values. Heating may reduce the capacity of cotton for absorbing moisture. For example, after heating for 6 hr at 302° F. cotton regained 6.3 per cent moisture as compared with a normal value of 7.2 per cent.

Effect of Light. The literature on the action of light on cellulose, including cotton, has been reviewed by several writers [13, 54, 55, 72, 131]. Knowledge on this subject is incomplete, but the main action is generally considered to be an oxidation by atmospheric oxygen promoted by the ultraviolet portion of sunlight. There is considerable evidence that the visible violet and blue rays also have some action. The degradation of cotton by light is increased by high temperature and high humidity. Cotton degraded by light has a lowered breaking strength and responds to chemical tests for degradation.

Degradation of cotton by sunlight or by ultraviolet light of a wave length of 3400 A or longer is inhibited or retarded by lack of oxygen when exposures are made in atmospheres of nitrogen, hydrogen, carbon dioxide, or in a vacuum. Cotton cellulose is degraded by ultraviolet light of a wave length less than 3400 A even in the absence of oxygen, but this short-wave ultraviolet light is not present in sunlight at the earth's surface [49].

The effects of light and of total exposure to weather may be very serious. For example, Grimes [72] reported that commercial bleached and dyed cotton goods exposed horizontally, in the open, to Texas summer sun (not weather) lost various amounts of strength up to more than 50 per cent in 375 hr in actual sunlight.

Unbleached (gray) materials are usually more resistant to sunlight than bleached goods. The presence of metals, for example copper and manganese, and of some other substances may promote oxidation of the cotton. A group of vat dyes, mainly oranges and yellows, has been conspicuous for abnormal fading and tendering actions [159, 177]. Numerous results have been given in terms of cuprammonium fluidity as well as in loss of strength.

Cotton is protected from deterioration by light by some dyes, pigments, and other substances, including a number of direct cotton colors, lead chromate, chromium hydroxide, and tannic acid.

Oxidation During Cotton Bleaching. The possibility of degradation while purifying or bleaching has already been mentioned. The chlorine bleach is usually performed with alkaline solutions and is readily controlled so that there is no excessive oxidation of the cotton. Particular care may be necessary under some conditions because sodium hypochlorite solutions are most active when neutral [29, 123]. If the initial alkali in the system becomes neutralized the cotton may be more easily damaged. Other conditions which can cause oxidation and tendering of the cotton are too high concentration or temperature, or too long a time of treatment. Peroxide bleaching has been considered less liable to cause damage to the goods than chlorine bleaching, but this is largely a matter of careful control.

It has been shown [29] that cotton overbleached by hypochlorite did not deteriorate in sunlight any more rapidly than normally bleached cotton, as judged by changes in copper numbers.

Degradation by Acids. Under some conditions even very dilute solutions of common inorganic acids like hydrochloric, sulfuric, and phosphoric act on cotton to reduce the strength and increase the cuprammonium fluidity and the copper number. Definite relationships exist between the changes in strength, fluidity, and copper number irrespective of the mode of acid treatment. (See Chapter II.) Acids act on the cellulose of cotton through hydrolysis of some of the glucosidic linkages in the chain of anhydroglucose units, thus producing shorter chains.

The effects of acids of different concentrations have been determined under many conditions largely with reference to preparing hydrocelluloses. Cuprammonium fluidities determined after immersion in acid solutions of 0.001 *N* to 0.1 *N* concentrations, and in salt solutions have been reported [28]; also many data are available from a more varied group of acids and conditions of treatments [7].

Percentages of tendering have been recorded for treatments with various acids of 0.1 *N* and 2 *N* concentrations for lengths of time up to 1 hr at 140° and 212° F. [43]. For example, boiling bleached cotton cloth for 1 min in 0.1 *N* sulfuric acid (about 0.5 per cent) caused 12 per cent loss of strength, whereas heating for an hour at 140° F. reduced the strength by only 5 per cent. Boiling cotton with 0.01 *N* sulfuric or hydrochloric acid for 1 hr will reduce the breaking strength about 20 per cent [51]. Vincent [169] has reported data for yarn treated with sulfuric acid of 10 to 70 per cent concentrations, and from tests made after kier boiling such acid-treated yarns. Organic acids, such as acetic acid, by virtue of their low ionization, have much less action on cotton than the inorganic acids, but acetic acid at 0.1 *N*, or about 0.6 per cent, caused 5 per cent tendering in 15 min at 212° F. Nonvolatile organic acids have a tendering action if dried into the fabric.

When washing acid-treated cotton goods, for example after souring, the last traces of acid wash out with great difficulty. When bleached soured cotton has been thoroughly washed with distilled water it should contain less than 0.02 per cent of sulfuric acid, and the presence of any greater quantity in tendered material indicates acid damage, probably during drying [25]. Coward, Wood, and Barrett [43] concluded that 0.01 per cent acid can cause appreciable tendering if dried in at 248° F.

and that 0.05 per cent of hydrochloric acid will cause serious tendering at 212° F. when dried into the fabric while held between hot copper plates for 10 min.

Acid salts may dissociate while on cotton and the liberated acid cause tendering. The presence of a high concentration of salt may accentuate the effect of a very small amount of acid.

Lawrance [104] treated cotton yarn with dilute sulfuric acid and dried it without washing. Time and temperature of both treatment and drying were varied. The percentage reductions of the breaking strengths of the yarns are given in Table 14.

TABLE 14. Per Cent Reduction of Strength Due to Acids

Temperatures of Drying		Temperature, Time, and Concentration of Acid							
		20° C. 16 hr		38° to 40° C. 1 hr		58° to 60° C. 1 hr		100° C. 1 hr	
°C.	°F.	0.01 N	0.005 N	0.01 N	0.005 N	0.01 N	0.005 N	0.01 N	0.005 N
20	68	2	0	6	0	8	5	11	7
40	104	6	0	9	4	14	7	17	10
60	140	19	4	22	8	25	10	28	15
80	176	59	27	62	33	70	37	77	45
100	212	67	40	72	45	78	49	84	56

Acid at a concentration of 0.01 N or less has only a slight immediate effect on cotton, provided the drying takes place at room temperature, but it may lead to tendering during subsequent use or storage.

When cotton with a high copper number due to the action of acids or oxidizing agents is boiled with dilute alkali, the copper number is greatly decreased. This is probably due to the solution of short-chain degraded portions of the cellulose or to the conversion of aldehydic groups to carboxyl groups. Cotton damaged by oxidation usually shows further reduction of tensile strength and further increase in cuprammonium fluidity on boiling with alkali, whereas cotton damaged by acids does not [51].

Action of Microorganisms

Many microorganisms attack cotton. Numerous fungi cause mildew, with discoloration from pigments in the organisms, weakening or rotting of the fiber, and a musty smell. Certain bacteria also cause microbiological rotting and appear to be its main cause under waterlogged conditions. Most fungi reproduce by means of spores, largely distributed through the air, and present wherever cotton is likely to be found.

"Cavitoma," the alteration of fiber properties, characterized by bacteria and fungus inside cotton fibers, as well as on the outer surfaces, has been widely reported [79] as causing fiber damage in manufacturing and as capable of affecting quality of cotton goods.

Microorganisms and their deterioration of cellulose are treated exhaustively by Siu in a book [157] based on cotton, where references to all branches of the subject can be found. In it he indicates something of the millions of dollars worth of loss from microbiological destruction of cellulosic textiles, particularly outdoor fabrics including fishing gear and textiles in use by the armed services. Deterioration is especially serious in tropical countries.

All raw cotton contains constituents which serve as food for the fungi which appear as mildew; it also contains mineral substances which promote their growth. Capacity to support mildew is measured fairly closely by soluble reducing constituents, represented by "soluble" copper number [57]. The presence of nutrients such as starch also promotes mildew; removing starch and noncellulose constituents by scouring makes cotton much more resistant. Nevertheless, the organisms can obtain their necessary carbon from the cotton cellulose.

Mildew tends to grow on cotton in atmospheres of high relative humidity, when moisture regains exceed 8–9 per cent and temperatures reach 80–90° F.

As fungi and bacteria grow on cellulose, they secrete chemical substances called enzymes which attack it by microbiological hydrolysis and convert it to soluble sugars that serve as food for the organisms. Although their mode of action is not known, the enzymes appear to attack amorphous cellulose more readily than crystalline. Bacteria may ultimately reach the lumen of the cotton fiber; fungi frequently penetrate the cell wall quickly and grow in the lumen.

Fabrics degraded by weathering with little attack by mildew are characterized by high cuprammonium fluidity; but if cotton is equally degraded (in terms of loss of strength), mainly by action of microorganisms, it undergoes almost no increase in fluidity, an observation not yet fully explained.

The almost universal method of protecting cotton from attack is that of adding substances which either inhibit further development or kill the organisms. One of the most promising agents is copper-8-quinolinolate; others widely used are copper naphthenate and polychlorphenols. The use of these and many others has been reviewed by Siu [157].

Another possibility for protection is that of chemical modification of the cotton by partial substitution of its hydroxyl groups to render it unsuitable for microorganisms, or less readily available to them. Examples are partial acetylation, recognized [50] long ago as capable of imparting a high degree of rot resistance, for months instead of days or weeks [70]; and partial methylenation where formaldehyde chemically combined into the cotton imparts an appreciable degree of rot resistance. The explanation of such effects is not complete, but factors contributing to them have been considered in the literature [70, 157].

There is no best way of testing a treated fabric for resistance to deterioration by microorganisms except exposure under the actual conditions of service. This is frequently impossible, and it is usually desirable to make a more rapid test. Among the most common is a pure-culture type of test, in which *Chaetomium globosum* is the preferred organism. Siu [157] discusses both pure and mixed culture methods. Burial in composted soil remains, however, about the most drastic and most popular method. Strips of cloth are buried either horizontally or vertically in an active soil, usually capable of destroying cotton within 1 week; the strips are removed at suitable intervals for tests for breaking strength. A standard method is available [2]; also a detailed discussion of the factors involved in such a test [157].

REFERENCES IN TEXT

1. American Chemical Society Committee on Viscosity of Cellulose, *Ind. Eng. Chem.*, Anal. Ed., **1,** 49–51 (1929).
2. American Society for Testing Materials, *ASTM Standards on Textile Materials*, Philadelphia (1951).
3. Anderson, D. B., and Kerr, T., *Ind. Eng. Chem.*, **30,** 48–54 (1938).
4. Babbitt, J. D., *Can. J. Research*, **20** (Sec. A), 143–172 (1942).
5. Bernoulli, A. L., and Stauffer, H., *Helv. Chim. Acta*, **23,** 627–649 (1940).
6. Bertolet, E. C., *Am. Dyestuff Reptr.*, **32,** P214–P219, P226–P227 (1943); **33,** P21–P24 (1944).
7. Birtwell, C., Clibbens, D. A., and Geake, A., *J. Textile Inst.*, **17,** T145–T170 (1926).
8. Birtwell, C., Clibbens, D. A., and Geake, A., *J. Textile Inst.*, **19,** T349–T364 (1928).
9. Boulton, J., and Morton, T. H., *J. Soc. Dyers Colourists*, **56,** 145–159 (1940).
10. Brimley, R. C., *Nature*, **114,** 432 (1924).
11. Buck, G. S., Jr., and McCord, F. A., *Textile Research J.*, **19,** 216–247 (1949).
12. Buck, G. S., Jr., and McCord, F. A., *Textile Research J.*, **19,** 715–754 (1949).

13. Cady, W. H., *Am. Dyestuff Reptr.*, **27,** P325–P327 (1938).
14. Crace-Calvert, F., *J. Chem. Soc.*, **20,** 303–305 (1867).
15. Calvert, M. A., and Clibbens, D. A., *J. Textile Inst.*, **24,** T233–T254 (1933).
16. Calvert, M. A., and Summers, F., *J. Textile Inst.*, **16,** T233–T268 (1925).
17. Caskey, C., Jr., and Gallup, W. D., *J. Agr. Research*, **42,** 671–673 (1931).
18. "Celltex," *Silk and Rayon*, **15,** 444–446, 490–492, 576–578, 603, 626–628, 652 (1941).
19. Chibnall, A. C., Piper, S. H., Pollard, A., Williams, E. F., and Sahai, P. N., *Biochem. J.*, **28,** 2189–2208 (1934).
20. Chilikin, M. M., and Rozova, Z. S., *J. Applied Chem.* (U.S.S.R.), **10,** 709–715 (1937).
21. Chippindale, E., *J. Soc. Dyers Colourists*, **50,** 142–149 (1934).
22. Clegg, G. G., *J. Textile Inst.*, **31,** T49–T68 (1940).
23. Clibbens, D. A., *J. Textile Inst.*, **14,** T217–T249 (1923).
24. Clibbens, D. A., and Geake, A., *J. Textile Inst.*, **15,** T27–T38 (1924).
25. Clibbens, D. A., and Geake, A., *J. Textile Inst.*, **18,** T168–T174 (1927).
26. Clibbens, D. A., and Geake, A., *J. Textile Inst.*, **19,** T77–T92 (1928).
27. Clibbens, D. A., and Geake, A., *J. Textile Inst.*, **24,** T255–T272 (1933).
28. Clibbens, D. A., and Little, A. H., *J. Textile Inst.*, **27,** T285–T304 (1936).
29. Clibbens, D. A., and Ridge, B. P., *J. Textile Inst.*, **18,** T135–T167 (1927).
30. Clifford, P. H., and Probert, M. E., *J. Textile Inst.*, **15,** T401–T413 (1924).
31. Collins, G. E., *J. Textile Inst.*, **30,** P46–P61 (1939).
32. Compton, J., *Contrib. Boyce Thompson Inst.*, **11,** 403–420 (1941).
33. Compton, J., and Haver, F. E., Jr., *Contrib. Boyce Thompson Inst.*, **11,** 105–118 (1940).
34. Compton, J., and Haver, F. E., Jr., *Contrib. Boyce Thompson Inst.*, **11,** 281–290 (1940).
35. Conrad, C. M., *Textile Research*, **7,** 165–174 (1937).
36. Conrad, C. M., *Science*, **94,** 113–114 (1941).
37. Conrad, C. M., *Ind. Eng. Chem.*, Anal. Ed., **16,** 745–748 (1944).
38. Conrad, C. M., and Kettering, J. H., "Do Grades of Cotton Reflect Cellulose Deterioration? A Study of the 1937 Crop," Washington, U. S. Agricultural Marketing Administration and Bureau of Plant Industry, 15 pp., mimeographed (May 1942).
39. Conrad, C. M., and Neely, J. W., *J. Agr. Research*, **66,** 307–312 (1943).
40. Cooper, A. S., Jr., Voorhies, S. T., Jr., Buras, E. M., Jr., and Goldthwait, C. F., *Textile Ind.*, **116** (1), 97–102; 194, 195 (1952).
41. Coward, H. F., and Spencer, L., *J. Textile Inst.*, **14,** T32–T45 (1923).
42. Coward, H. F., and Wigley, G. M., *J. Textile Inst.*, **13,** Trans. 121–126 (1922).
43. Coward, H. F., Wood, F. C., and Barrett, F. L., *J. Textile Inst.*, **14,** T520–T528 (1923).
44. Davidson, G. F., *J. Textile Inst.*, **18,** T175–T186 (1927).
45. Davidson, G. F., *J. Textile Inst.*, **23,** T95–T133 (1932).
46. Davidson, G. F., *J. Textile Inst.*, **29,** T195–T218 (1938).
47. Davidson, G. F., *J. Textile Inst.*, **39,** T65–T86 (1948).
48. Davis, F. V., *J. Soc. Dyers Colourists*, **63,** 260–263 (1947).
49. Dean, J. D., Fleming, C. M., and O'Connor, R. T., *Textile Research J.*, **22,** 609–616 (1952).

50. Dorée, C., *Biochem. J.*, **14,** 709–714 (1920).
51. Dorée, C., *The Methods of Cellulose Chemistry*, 2nd Ed., D. Van Nostrand Co., N. Y. (1946).
52. Edelstein, S. M., *Rayon and Synthetic Textiles*, **32,** (10), 62 and 64 (1951).
53. Edelstein, S. M., and Cady, W. H., *Am. Dyestuff Reptr.*, **26,** P447–P460 (1937).
54. Egerton, G. S., *J. Soc. Dyers Colourists*, **65,** 764–780 (1949).
55. Ellis, C., Wells, A. A., and Heyroth, F. F., *The Chemical Action of Ultraviolet Rays*, Reinhold Publishing Corp., N. Y. (1941).
56. Fabrics Research Committee, Dept. Scientific and Industrial Research, "Viscosity of Cellulose Solutions," H. M. Stationery Office, London (1932).
57. Fargher, R. G., *J. Soc. Dyers Colourists*, **61,** 118–122 (1945).
58. Fargher, R. G., Hart, L. R., and Probert, M. E., *J. Textile Inst.*, **18,** T29–T45 (1927).
59. Fargher, R. G., and Higginbotham, L., *J. Textile Inst.*, **15,** T419–T433 (1924).
60. Fargher, R. G., and Higginbotham, L., *J. Textile Inst.*, **17,** T233–T246 (1926).
61. Fargher, R. G., and Probert, M. E., *J. Textile Inst.*, **14,** T49–T65 (1923).
62. Fargher, R. G., and Probert, M. E., *J. Textile Inst.*, **15,** T337–T346 (1924).
63. Fargher, R. G., and Probert, M. E., *J. Textile Inst.*, **17,** T46–T52 (1926).
64. Fargher, R. G., and Withers, J. C., *J. Textile Inst.*, **13,** T1–T16 (1922).
65. Faust, O., *Celluloseverbindungen und ihre besonders wichtigen Verwendungsgebiete*, 2 vols., Edwards Bros., Ann Arbor, Mich. (1943).
66. Fink, H., Bitterfeld, W. K., and Stahn, R., U. S. Pat. 2,097,120 (1937).
67. Ford, F. M., and Hall, W. P., U. S. Pat. 2,482,755 (1949).
68. Geake, A., *J. Textile Inst.*, **15,** T81–T93 (1924).
69. Goldthwait, C. F., *Textile Research J.*, **21,** 55–62 (1951).
70. Goldthwait, C. F., Buras, E. M., Jr., and Cooper, A. S., *Textile Research J.*, **21,** 831–840 (1951).
71. Goldthwait, C. F., McLaren, J., and Voorhies, S. T., *Textile World*, **96** (2), 115–117, 212, 216 (1946).
72. Grimes, M. A., *Texas Agr. Expt. Sta. Bull. 474* (1933); *Bull. 506* (1935); *Bull. 538* (1936).
73. Gundermann, J., Wergin, W., and Hess, K., *Ber.*, **70B,** 517–526 (1937).
74. Guthrie, J. D., *Textile Research J.*, **17,** 625–629 (1947).
75. Guthrie, J. D., *Am. Dyestuff Reptr.*, **41,** P13–14, 30 (1952).
76. Guthrie, J. D., and Reeves, W. A., *Textile Research J.*, **20,** 859–861 (1950).
77. Haas, H., "Beitrag zur Kenntnis der Einwirkung der Wärme auf die Baumwolle," dissertation, Würzburg (1935).
78. Hall, A. J., *Can. Textile J.*, **58** (No. 6), 34–36, 50–51; (No. 8), 35–38, 50 (1941).
79. Hall, L. T., and Elting, J. P., *Textile Research J.*, **21,** 580–590 (1951).
80. Harris, S. A., and Thompson, H. J., *Contrib. Boyce Thompson Inst.*, **9,** 1–5 (1937).
81. Haury, E. W., and Conrad, C. M., *Am. Antiquity*, **3,** 224–227 (1938).
82. Haworth, E., and MacDonald, A. D., *J. Hyg.*, **37,** 234–242 (1937).
83. Heertjes, P. M., *Rec. trav. chim.*, **60,** 689–699 (1941).
84. Hermans, P. H., *Physics and Chemistry of Cellulose Fibres*, Elsevier Press, New York (1949).
85. Hess, K., Kiessig, H., Wergin, W., and Engel, W., *Ber.*, **72B,** 642–652 (1939).
86. Heuser, E., *The Chemistry of Cellulose*, John Wiley & Sons, N. Y. (1944).
87. Heyes, T. F., *J. Soc. Chem. Ind.*, **47,** 90T–92T (1928).

88. HEYN, A. N. J., *Textile Research J.*, **19,** 711–714 (1949).
89. HOCK, C. W., and HARRIS, M., *Textile Research,* **10,** 323–333 (1940).
90. HOFFPAUIR, C. L., and GUTHRIE, J. D., *Textile Research J.*, **20,** 617–620 (1950).
91. HONOLD, E., POYNOT, J. M., and CUCULLU, A. F., *Textile Research J.*, **22,** 25–29 (1952).
92. IVANOVA, V. T., and KURENNOVA, A. M., *Trans. Middle Asiatic Sci. Inst. Cotton Culture, Ind. Irrigation Bull. 50,* 57–71 (1931); *Chem. Abst.*, **26,** 5988 (1932).
93. JACKSON, C. T., "Chemical Analyses of Cotton Soils—Analyses of the Ash of the Cotton Plant," Rept. of Commiss. Patents, 1857, Washington, pp. 296–304 (1858).
94. JACOBY, R. W., U. S. Pat. 1,398,378 (1921).
95. JARRELL, T. D., STUART, L. S., and HOLMAN, H. P., *Am. Dyestuff Reptr.*, **26,** 495–500, 519–523 (1937).
96. JURGENS, J. F., REID, J. D., and GUTHRIE, J. D., *Textile Research J.*, **18,** 42–44 (1948).
97. KEARNEY, T. H., and SCOFIELD, C. S., *J. Agr. Research,* **28,** 293–295 (1924).
98. KENYON, R. L., HASEK, R. H., DAVY, L. G., and BROADBOOKS, K. J., *Ind. Eng. Chem.*, **41,** 2–8 (1949).
99. KETTERING, J. H., *Ind. Eng. Chem.*, Anal. Ed., **18,** 275 (1946).
100. KETTERING, J. H., and CONRAD, C. M., *Ind. Eng. Chem.*, Anal. Ed., **14,** 432–434 (1942).
101. KETTERING, J. H., and KRAEMER, R. M., U. S. Dept. Agr. *Tech. Bull.*, 941 (1947).
102. KNECHT, E., *J. Textile Inst.*, **2,** 22–29 (1911).
103. KOLLMANN, L., *Melliand Textilber.*, **19,** 269–271 (1938).
104. LAWRANCE, W. A., *Can. Chem. J.*, **3,** 329–331 (1919).
105. LAWRIE, L. G., REYNOLDS, R. J. W., and WARD, D., *J. Soc. Dyers Colourists,* **56,** 6–17 (1940).
106. LEGER, F., and LAROSE, P., *Canadian J. Research,* **19B,** 61–64 (1941).
107. LESSLIE, C., HAGAN, L., and GUTHRIE, J. D., *Anal. Chem.*, **21,** 190–191 (1949).
108. LIESER, TH., *Ann.*, **528,** 276–295 (1937).
109. MARSH, J. T., *Mercerising,* Chapman and Hall, Ltd., London (1941); D. Van Nostrand Co., N. Y. (1942).
110. MARSH, J. T., *An Introduction to Textile Bleaching,* Chapman and Hall, Ltd. London (1946).
111. MARSH, J. T., *An Introduction to Textile Finishing,* Chapman and Hall, Ltd., London (1947).
112. MARSH, J. T., and WOOD, F. C., *An Introduction to the Chemistry of Cellulose,* 2nd Ed., Chapman and Hall, Ltd., London (1942); D. Van Nostrand Co., N. Y. (1942).
113. MARSH, P. B., GUTHRIE, L. R., and BUTLER, M. L., *Textile Research J.*, **21,** 565–579 (1951).
114. MCBRYDE, J. B., and BEAL, W. H., "The Cotton Plant. Its History, Botany, Chemistry, Culture, Enemies, Uses," U. S. Dept. Agr., *Bull. 33,* 81–142 (1896). (Early series, Office of Exp. Stations.)
115. MCCALL, E. R., and GUTHRIE, J. D., *J. Am. Chem. Soc.*, **67,** 2220–2221 (1945).
116. MCCALL, E. R., and JURGENS, J. F., *Textile Research J.*, **21,** 19–21 (1951).
117. MCHARGUE, J. S., *J. Am. Soc. Agron.*, **18,** 1076–1083 (1926).
118. MEGGY, A. B., *J. Soc. Dyers Colourists,* **59,** 192–196 (1943).
119. MENNELL, H., *J. Textile Inst.*, **17,** T247 (1926).

120. Merrill, G. R., Macormac, A. R., and Mauersberger, H. R., *American Cotton Handbook*, 2nd Ed., Textile Book Publishers, Inc., N. Y. (1949).

121. Meyer, K. H., *Natural and Synthetic High Polymers*, 2nd Ed., Interscience Publishers, N. Y. (1950).

122. Moore, A. T., Scott, L. W., deGruy, I. V., and Rollins, M. L., *Textile Research J.*, **20**, 620–630 (1950).

123. Nabar, G. M., Scholefield, F., and Turner, H. A., *J. Soc. Dyers Colourists*, **53**, 5–26 (1937).

124. Natl. Bur. Standards, Commercial Standard CS11–41; 2nd Ed., Aug. 1, 1941.

125. Neale, S. M., *J. Textile Inst.*, **22**, T349–T356 (1931).

126. New, A. A., *Electrical Communications*, private publication issued quarterly by International Standard Electrical Corp., N. Y., **13**, 216–225, 359–379 (1935); **14**, 213–231 (1936).

127. New, A. A., *J. Soc. Dyers Colourists*, **57**, 197–198 (1941).

128. Nickerson, D., "Color Stability in Raw Cotton: II, Storage Tests," Washington, D. C., U. S. Dept. Agr. Marketing Service, 16 pp., processed (1941).

129. Nickerson, R. F., Fontaine, T. D., and Leape, C. B., *Textile Research*, **11**, 154–157 (1941).

130. Oparin, A., and Rogowin, S., *Melliand Textilber.*, **11**, 944–946 (1930).

131. Ott, E., *Cellulose and Cellulose Derivatives*, Interscience Publishers, N. Y. (1943).

132. Pickard, R. H., *J. Textile Inst.*, **34**, P95–P102 (1943).

133. Peirce, F. T., and Lord, E., *J. Textile Inst.*, **30**, T173–T210 (1939). (See Davidson's data, p. T193.)

134. Pons, W. A., Jr., and Guthrie, J. D., *Ind. Eng. Chem.*, Anal. Ed., **18**, 184–186 (1946).

135. Preston, J. M., and Nimkar, M. V., *Bull. Inst. Textile de France No.* 18, 53–58 (1950).

136. Race, E., Rowe, F. M., and Speakman, J. B., *J. Soc. Dyers Colourists*, **57**, 213–223, 257–264 (1941); **58**, 32–36, 161–162 (1942).

137. Reid, J. D., and Daul, G. C., *Textile Research J.*, **18**, 551–556 (1948).

138. Reid, J. D., Daul, G. C., and Reinhardt, R. M., *Textile Research J.*, **20**, 657–659 (1950).

139. Reid, J. D., Nelson, G. H., and Aronovsky, S. I., *Ind. Eng. Chem.*, Anal. Ed., **12**, 255–259 (1940).

140. Rheiner, A., *Angew. Chem.*, **46**, 675–681 (1933).

141. Ridge, B. P., *J. Textile Inst.*, **15**, T94–T103 (1924).

142. Robbins, W. J., and Ma, R., *Torrey Bot. Club Bull.*, **69**, 184–203 (1942).

143. Rollins, M. L., Fort, H. H., and Skau, D. B., *Cellulose Water Relations: A Selected Bibliography with Special Reference to Swelling of Cotton, Etc.*, Library List No. 44, U. S. Dept. Agr. Library, Washington, D. C. (1949).

144. Rose, R. E., *Am. Dyestuff Reptr.*, **31**, P204–P211 (1942).

145. Salley, D. D. J., *Textile Research*, **5**, 493–508 (1935).

146. Schorger, A. W., *Chemistry of Cellulose and Wood*, McGraw-Hill Book Co., N. Y. (1926).

147. Schubert, C., Dissertation, Technische Hochschule, Dresden (1932).

148. Schunck, E., *Chem. News*, **17**, 118–119 (1868).

149. Schuyten, H. A., Weaver, J. W., Frick, J. G., Jr., and Reid, J. D., *Textile Research J.*, **22**, 424–432 (1952).

150. Segal, L., Tripp, R. C., Tripp, V. W., and Conrad, C. M., *Anal. Chem*, **21**, 712–718 (1949).

151. Sellars, W. B., and Vilbrandt, F. C., *Am. Dyestuff Reptr.*, **17**, 645–649, 685–695 (1928).
152. Sen, K. R., and Ahmad, N., Indian Centr. Cotton Comm. *Tech. Lab. Tech. Bull.* [*B*] *No. 25*, 24 pp. (1938).
153. Shaposhnikov, V. G., and Tikhvins'kiĭ, V. M., *Mem. Inst. Chem. Tech. Acad. Sci. Ukr. S.S.R.*, *No. 2*, 43–50 (in English, 50–51) (1937).
154. Sheppard, S. E., and Newsome, P. T., *Ind. Eng. Chem.*, **26**, 285–290 (1934).
155. Sherwood, M. B., and Singer, E. D., *J. Biol. Chem.*, **155**, 361–362 (1944).
156. Sisson, W. A., *Contrib. Boyce Thompson Inst.*, **8**, 389–400 (1937).
157. Siu, R. G. H., *Microbial Decomposition of Cellulose*, Reinhold Publishing Corp., New York (1951).
158. Society of Chemical Industry, Reports of the Progress of Applied Chemistry, Issued annually by Soc. Chem. Ind., London.
159. Society of Dyers and Colourists, Symposium on Photochemistry in Relation to Textiles, *J. Soc. Dyers Colourists*, **65**, 585–788 (1949).
160. Stamm, A. J., "Colloid Chemistry of Cellulosic Materials," U. S. Dept. Agr. *Misc. Pub. 240* (1936).
161. Stocker, E., U. S. Pat. 1,895,298 (1933).
162. Thaysen, A. C., Bunker, H. J., Butlin, K. R., and Williams, L. H., *Ann. Applied Biol.*, **26**, 750–781 (1939).
163. Tiltman, A. H., and Porritt, B. D., *India-Rubber J.*, **76**, 245–248 (1928).
164. Turner, H. A., *Textile Mfr.*, **57**, 106–107 (1931).
165. U. S. Bureau of Agricultural Economics, "The Classification of Cotton," U. S. Dept. Agr. *Misc. Pub. 310* (1938).
166. Vadimovich, I. I., *Mem. Inst. Chem. Tech. Acad. Sci. Ukr. S.S.R.*, *No. 7*, 83–94 (in English, 94–95) (1938).
167. Valkó, E., *Kolloidchemische Grundlagen der Textilveredlung*, Julius Springer, Berlin (1937).
168. Vickerstaff, T., *The Physical Chemistry of Dyeing*, Interscience Publishers, Inc., N. Y. (1950).
169. Vincent, P. D., *J. Textile Inst.*, **15**, T281–T290 (1924).
170. Walker, A. C., *Bell Telephone System Tech. Pub.*, Monograph B-999, or *J. Applied Phys.*, **8**, 261–268 (1937).
171. Walker, A. C., and Quell, M. H., *J. Textile Inst.*, **24**, T131–T144 (1933).
172. Ware, J. O., *J. Amer. Soc. Agron.*, **24**, 550–562 (1932).
173. Whistler, R. L., Martin, A. R., and Conrad, C. M., *Textile Research*, **10**, 449–452 (1940).
174. Whistler, R. L., Martin, A. R., and Harris, M., *Textile Research*, **10**, 269–279 (1940).
175. White, E. D., *Textile World*, **101** (10), 118–119 (1951).
176. Whittaker, C. M., *J. Soc. Dyers Colourists*, **58**, 253–256 (1942).
177. Whittaker, C. M., and Wilcock, C. C., *Dyeing with Coal-Tar Dyestuffs*, 5th Ed., Baillière, Tindall & Cox, London (1949).
178. Wiegerink, J. G., *J. Research Natl. Bur. Standards*, **24**, 639–644 (1940).
179. Wiegerink, J. G., *J. Research Natl. Bur. Standards*, **24**, 645–664 (1940).
180. Wiegerink, J. G., *J. Research Natl. Bur. Standards*, **25**, 435–450 (1940).
181. Wiertelak, J., and Garbaczówna, I., *Ind. Eng. Chem.*, Anal. Ed., **7**, 110–111 (1935).
182. Wilkie, J. B., *Textile Research*, **3**, 347–363 (1933).

182*a*. Willows, R. S., and Alexander, A. C., *J. Textile Inst.*, **13,** Trans. 237–240 (1922).

183. Willows, R. S., Barratt, T., and Parker, F. H., *J. Textile Inst.*, **13,** Trans. 229–236 (1922).

184. Wood, F. C., *J. Soc. Chem. Ind.*, **50,** 411T–418T (1931).

185. Wood, F. C., *J. Soc. Chem. Ind.*, **52,** 33T–34T (1933).

186. Wood, F. C., *J. Textile Inst.*, **30,** P142–P149 (1939).

187. Woodhead, A. E., *J. Soc. Dyers Colourists*, **46,** 69–74 (1930).

188. Worden, E. C., *Technology of Cellulose Ethers*, 5 vols., Worden Laboratory and Library, Millburn, N. J. (1933).

189. Worner, R. K., and Mease, R. T., *J. Research Natl. Bur. Standards*, **21,** 609–616 (1938).

CHAPTER VII

THE BAST FIBERS[1]

BERNICE MONTGOMERY

Bast fibers are obtained from the stalks of dicotyledonous plants. The fibers occur in that portion of the fibrovascular area, generally termed the phloem, located around the woody, central portion and just under the outer bark or cuticle of the stalk. The so-called "true" bast fibers, which comprise most of the group, occur in bundles, i.e., aggregates, of sclerenchymatous (thick-walled) cells, with the ends overlapping so as to produce continuous filaments throughout the length of the stalk. In a few plants from which bast fiber is obtained, the fibers are interlaced through the length of the stalk.

The bast bundles of fibers are held in place by the cellular tissue of the phloem and by gummy and waxy substances that also hold the fibers to each other within the bundles. The function of the bast bundles is to give strength to the stalk of the plant. With two exceptions, all the most important bast fibers are utilized commercially in the form of full-length bast bundles, the bundles after removal from the plant being termed "strands," or in commercial trade simply "fiber." The two exceptions are flax, the individual fibers of which are separated during the spinning process for fine yarns, and ramie, the individual fibers of which are separated before any yarn preparation and spinning takes place.

Bast fibers are also termed "soft fibers," the principal textile fibers in this group being jute, flax, ramie, sunn, kenaf, urena, and nettle. Some bast fibers, however, are harsh and stiff, e.g., *Sesbania exaltata*, sometimes termed Colorado River "hemp."

Many of the plants furnishing bast fibers are closely related. All except two of the most important belong to the order Malvales. These include jute, ramie, hemp, kenaf, urena, and nettle. Flax belongs to the order Geraniales, sunn to the order Rosales. A listing by botanical

[1] The author wishes to express her gratitude to Mr. Elton G. Nelson, agronomist, U. S. Department of Agriculture, who drew upon his knowledge of bast and leaf fibers to give valuable assistance by making suggestions concerning presentation of material and by reviewing the manuscript.

orders and families for bast fibers is given at the end of the chapter. The large number of plants included in the bast fiber group represents, in relation to the number that are cultivated and processed on a commercial scale, a very rich potential supply of textile fiber. As methods of cultivation and processing are improved, many of these plants will undoubtedly be utilized to a greater extent.

The relative importance of each of the bast fibers on the basis of world production is given in Table 1.

TABLE 1. Relative Importance of Bast Fibers on Basis of World Production

(Thousands of short tons)

	Period		
Bast Fiber	*1951*	*1950*	*Average 1934–38*
Jute	2190	1840	1712
Flax	915	881	869
Hemp	390	360	495
Sunn	99	100	111
Ramie	11	10	90
Kenaf	60	60	60
Urena	30	30	neg.
Nettle	neg.	neg.	neg.
All others	neg.	neg.	neg.

neg. negligible.
Note: Figures for jute have been adjusted to omit estimated production of kenaf.

JUTE

Nomenclature. Jute is the internationally recognized name of bast fiber obtained from stalks of plants of the genus *Corchorus* of the Tiliaceae family. The principal species grown for commercial fiber are *capsularis* and *olitorius.* Each species has a large number of varieties. There are a number of other species, most of which are to be found only in a wild state, from which fiber is utilized for textiles and cordage on a local basis. These include *acutangulus* (syn. *fuscus*), Asia; *aestuans,* tropical America; *hirsutus,* West Indies; and *siliquosus,* tropical America. *Decemangulatus,* formerly considered a species, is now generally accepted as a synonym for *olitorius.*

The word "jute" apparently is adapted from a word used to designate the plant in Orissa Province, India, and which has been variously anglicized as "jhout," "jhat," "jhut," and "jute." The date of its in-

Fig. 1. Jute plants. This view is of plants at a corner of the field, which accounts for the branchiness of the plants in the outside rows. Such plants are frequently left standing to produce seed (see section on "Cultivation"). (*Courtesy Embassy of Pakistan, Washington, D. C.*)

troduction into the Western Hemisphere has not been fixed, but it probably occurred sometime during the seventeenth or eighteenth century. There is no common vernacular word used to designate the plant or fiber in the Indo-Pakistan subcontinent where most of the world's supply of commercial jute is grown. The words "pat," "pata," and "patua" are most frequently used, and are derived from the Sanskrit word "patta," meaning cloth. In the Philippines, plants and hence fiber from the genus *Corchorus* are termed "saluyot."

The so-called Bimli "jute" and Mestha pat "jute" are not jute but fiber from the plant *Hibiscus cannabinus;* occasionally fiber from *Hibiscus sabdariffa* is also designated by these terms. Tientsin "jute," Ch'ing ma "jute," and much of the Chinese "jute" are fiber from the plant *Abutilon theophrasti* (syn. *avicennae*). Java "jute" is fiber from the plant *Hibiscus sabdariffa.* Broom "jute" is fiber from *Sida rhombifolia.* Congo "jute" is fiber from *Urena lobata;* Cuban "jute" is fiber from *Urena lobata* or *U. sinuata.*

Plant. Plants of the genus *Corchorus* are herbaceous annuals. The species *C. capsularis* and *C. olitorius,* when grown for fiber, have tall, straight, slender stalks. Height of the plants ranges from 5 to 16 ft, with an average of 10 to 12 ft. See Fig. 1. Diameter of the stalks is about ½ to ¾ in. Leaves, which appear on the upper part of the stalk, when the plant is grown for fiber, are borne alternately, are a light to medium green, lanceolate shape, 4 to 5 in. long, and about 1½ to 2 in. wide on the upper or widest portion, with serrated edges, the two serrations at the base of the leaf terminating in slender filaments. Flowers are small with five pale yellow petals and are borne, usually singly, from short stalks growing from the axils of the leaves. Seeds are small and numerous.

Principal differences between the two species *C. capsularis* and *C. olitorius* are summarized in Table 2. See also Fig. 2.

History. Use of fiber from plants of the genus *Corchorus* for fabrics and cordage is of great antiquity. The jute plant generally thought to be *C. olitorius* is mentioned for its food uses in the Bible, Job 30:4, as well as in ancient Egyptian and other early literature of the Mediterranean area. This may indicate that the genus originated in the Mediterranean area and was brought to the Indo-Pakistan subcontinent in prehistoric times. Its use as a textile fiber by the peoples of the Mediterranean area is somewhat obscure, though it may well have been used for the "sackcloth" of ancient times. It is possible that the plant, which in the Mediterranean area is only 4 to 5 ft tall, did not yield sufficient fiber to make it of unusual interest for this purpose

TABLE 2. PRINCIPAL DIFFERENCES BETWEEN *C. capsularis* AND *C. oliotorius*

Point of Difference	*C. capsularis*	*C. oliotorius*
Shape of seed pods (see Fig. 2)	Globular or round.	Long, approximately cylindrical.
Color of stalk bark	Light green to purple, bark on green stalks being thicker than that of purple stalks.	Light green to reddish pink
Resistance to effects of waterlogging	Good after plants reach 5 ft. Can be grown on high and low lands.	Very little until ready for cutting.
Fiber	White, though dependent upon cleanness of retting water. Finer, though usually shorter, than fiber from *C. olitorius.*	Golden yellow to slate brown, though color depends upon cleanness of retting water. Usually more lustrous, stronger, and more easily separated from stalk than fiber from *C. capsularis.*
Flavor of leaves	Bitter	Sweet

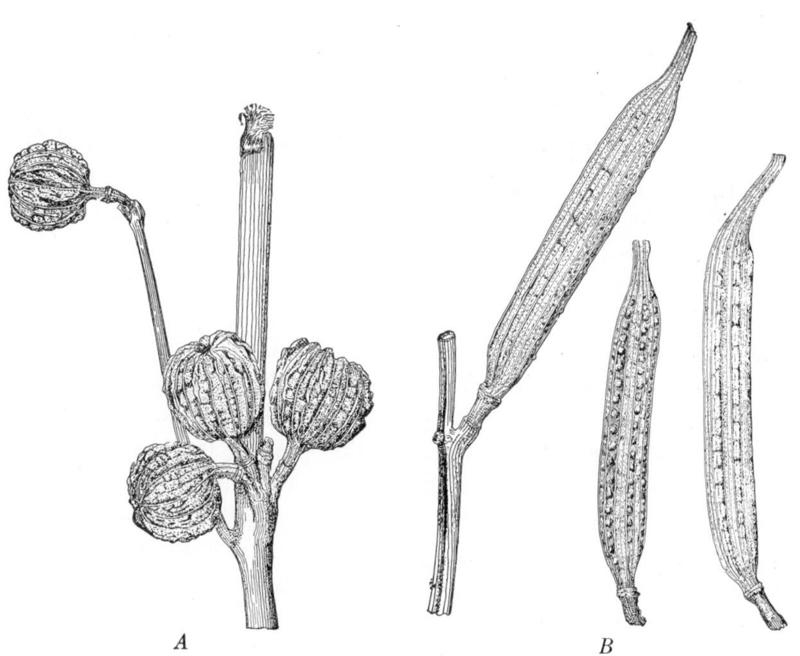

FIG. 2. *A,* Seed-vessels of *Corchorus capsularis; B,* seed-vessels of *Corchorus olitorius.* (*Bull. U. S. Department of Agriculture.*)

but that, when it began to grow in the warm, moist climate of Asia, the greater height of the stalks resulted in its utilization as a fiber plant. Ancient literature from Asia makes frequent mention of the fiber for textile use.

Exports of gunny [2] bags in 1746 and in 1755 from India to England are the first recorded instances of any jute products being sent to the Western Hemisphere in modern times. The first shipment of jute fiber from India was made in 1791 to England, and small shipments were made frequently thereafter. During 1796–97, 65 tons of fiber were exported from India, 6 to the United States, 19 to England, and 40 to Germany.[3] Primary use of this fiber was for cordage.

Jute was first spun experimentally in England at Abingdon, Oxfordshire, in 1820. As a result of the Napoleonic Wars, which disrupted supplying of hemp and flax fibers from Russia, the spinning mills at Dundee, Scotland, were especially interested in obtaining fiber from a new source. In 1822, Thomas Neigh, a Dundee merchant, persuaded one of the Dundee mills to try spinning jute fiber. It was not until 1832, however, that yarn was successfully manufactured. The first satisfactory results were obtained by mixing jute with hemp and flax fibers, but gradually skill was developed for spinning all-jute yarns. By 1850 jute spinning was beginning to be well established, some 15,000 short tons of fiber being imported into Dundee during that year. The Crimean War in 1853, which cut off supplies of hemp and flax fibers from Russia, gave impetus to the use of jute, and, by 1860, Dundee imported 40,000 short tons. The Civil War in the United States in 1861–65 disrupted supply of low-priced cotton and provided an added impetus to the use of jute. Dundee imports in 1871 were more than 113,000 short tons.[4]

Because of its very low price and availability in large quantities, acceptance and use of jute fiber and its products expanded rapidly. In 1855, the first spinning mill was established in India, and in 1859 the first power looms were installed for weaving bag fabrics. The number of spindles and looms increased steadily; by 1939 India had 68,400 looms, 57 per cent of the world's total. In 1951 a total of 68,620

[2] Probably derived from the words "gania," "ganja," or "goni," which are anglicized versions of an Indian word for hemp (*Cannabis sativa*).

[3] "The Golden Fibre," M. Aslam Hayat, Publications and Foreign Publicity Dept., Government of Pakistan, Karachi (1949).

[4] "Jute," *Board of Trade Working Party Repts;* H.M. Stationery Office, London (1948).

looms was reported.[5] Construction of spinning and weaving mills was begun in East Pakistan in 1951. By 1952 two mills were in operation and others were under construction. The Pakistan Government has announced a goal of 6000 looms for 1957.

The first European mill was established in France in 1857, and in 1861 a mill was established in Germany. By 1890 mills had also been established in Belgium, Austria, Italy, Spain, Poland, Czechoslovakia, and Russia. Spinning and weaving mills were established in Latin America during the first half of the twentieth century. Currently Brazil, with more than 30 mills, is the largest producer for this area. Chile has 3 mills.

The first jute mill in the United States was set up in 1848 in Ludlow, Massachusetts, for weaving yarn imported from Dundee. Spinning machinery was installed in the Ludlow mill by 1850. Subsequently other mills were established for both spinning and weaving. The low price of Indian woven jute fabrics, however, made it more profitable to confine activities of the United States mills to spinning yarns for special purposes, and the weaving equipment fell into disuse or was sold. The United States Census of Manufactures, 1947, shows 35 establishments in the United States engaged in the manufacture of products from jute fiber.

World Production. Jute is one of the world's most important fiber crops, being exceeded in quantity only by cotton. Most of the world's supply is produced in East Pakistan (East Bengal, all provinces, with Mymensingh, Rangpur, Dacca, Faridpur, Tippera, Jessore, and Pabna Provinces accounting for most of the production) and in India (West Bengal, Cooch Behar, Tripura State, Bihar, Assam, and Orissa). Brazil, which began growing jute about 1900, is the only other country producing a significant amount. Plans have been announced to increase the Brazilian crop.

The plant is grown for fiber in other countries, but only small quantities are produced. Argentina began growing jute on an experimental basis in 1942. Annual production in Iran averages 2000 to 4000 short tons. Nepal formerly produced 10,000 to 12,000 short tons annually; 1952 production was approximately 6000 to 7000 short tons. Thailand produces 2000 to 3000 short tons annually. French Indochina, usually producing less than 500 short tons a year, increased production to 5000 to 8000 short tons during the period 1941–45; current production is less

[5] "Report of the Committee for Year Ended 31 December, 1951," Indian Jute Mills Association, Calcutta (1952).

than 500 short tons. Formosa, pre-World War II, produced an average of 15,000 short tons annually, production amounting to about 33,000 short tons in 1938; in 1952 production was approximately 9000 to 10,000 short tons. China produces about 1000 short tons annually. Japan during the 1930's produced more than 1000 tons annually (*C. capsularis*), production having been increased to 11,000 short tons in 1940, when acreage declined because of need for food crops; current production is less than 1000 short tons.

TABLE 3. WORLD PRODUCTION OF JUTE FIBER

(Thousands of short tons)

	Jute Year				
Country	*1952–53*	*1951–52*	*1950–51*	*1949–50*	*Average 1934–38*
Pakistan ‡	1364.5	1266.2	1201.5	666.6	1742.0
India ‡	939.0	937.6	660.2	617.8	
Brazil	30.0	25.0	20.0	20.0	†
Nepal	*	*	*	*	11.5
Formosa	*	*	*	*	14.9
Japan	†	†	†	†	1.3
Other countries	*	*	*	*	2.0
Total	2360.0	2250.0	1900.0	1315.0	1771.7

* Not available. Estimate included in total.
† Less than 500 short tons.
‡ Includes small quantity of kenaf fiber (*Hibiscus cannabinus*), termed mestha pat.

Sources

1949–53: Pakistan, "Monthly Summary of Jute Statistics, December 1952," No. 60, The Directorate of Jute Prices, Government of East Bengal, Department of Commerce, Labour, and Industries, Narayanganj, Dacca, Pakistan (1953).

India, "Monthly Summary of Jute and Gunny Statistics," August 1952, No. 89, and February 1953, No. 95, Indian Jute Mills Association, Calcutta (1952 and 1953, respectively).

Brazil, Formosa, Nepal, Japan, and other countries—Estimates on basis of best available data.

1934–38: "Statistics on Jute and Jute Manufactures," H. G. Porter and M. R. Cooper, U. S. Dept. Agr., Washington (1945).

World production data are given in Table 3 for the jute years[6] 1952–53, 1951–52, 1950–51, 1949–50, and for the 5-year average 1934–

[6] Though jute is planted and harvested within the calendar year, production is measured and commercial transactions conducted on the basis of a jute year running from July 1 to June 30, since jute harvest customarily begins on July 1 in the Indo-Pakistan subcontinent.

38. Largest production on record was for the jute year 1940–41, when more than 2.6 million short tons were produced. Data for the 1952–53 jute year show that production approached the 1940–41 level, and when final figures are available (they usually are at the end of the following jute year) production may even exceed the 1940–41 crop, as some estimates indicate that the Pakistan crop for 1952–53 may be as high as 1.6 or 1.8 million short tons. It is expected, however, that the crop for the 1953–54 jute year will be smaller than that for 1952–53 as a result of a carryover of 260,000 short tons of Pakistan jute stocks at the end of the 1951–52 jute year, which, together with the large crop for 1952–53 will probably also result in a substantial carryover of stocks at the end of the 1952–53 jute year. It has been stated that plantings for the 1953–54 jute year in Pakistan are expected to be curtailed below those of previous seasons, primarily to further the program for increased cultivation of food grains throughout Pakistan and to avoid incurring excessive surpluses of fiber. Official estimate for area to be planted has not been announced; informal estimates indicate a decrease of from one-third to three-fourths from the 1952–53 area.

Utilization. The principal use of jute has been for bagging and wrapping fabrics for agricultural products, giving it a close and important relationship to the economy of world food supply. Other consumer and industrial uses include yarns for carpet backing, wire rope centers, fuses, electrical insulations, tying and wrapping twines and cordage, linoleum backing, brattice cloth for mines, tarpaulins, padding cloth, roofing materials, carpets, and rugs. Jute waste is also utilized for such items as oakum and padding. In Germany, Italy, and Yugoslovia, a process was developed, during the 1920's and 1930's, which, by treating jute waste with a strong solution of caustic soda, resulted in a fiber that could be blended with wool. Various trade names were given this fiber, which was used for the manufacture of very inexpensive clothing fabrics.

Obvious economic reasons require that yarns and fabrics for uses such as those listed above be made from a low-cost fiber which is available in large quantities. For many years jute fulfilled these requirements. Dislocation of supply and demand during World War II and subsequent changing economic and political conditions have, however, disrupted jute's position in world textile markets, to some extent. Until 1952 supply was below demand, partly because of a large backlog of demand accumulated during World War II, partly because demand for bagging and wrapping fabrics has increased in ratio to expanding world economy, partly because of an increase in demand resulting from the Korean War, and to some extent because supply was disrupted when partition of India and Pakistan occurred in 1947 as Pakistan produces most of the raw fiber and India had, at that time, almost all the baling and shipping facilities for exporting jute. Government crop controls regulating amount of land planted to jute have also influenced supply.

During the period of unusually high demand, prices rose to approximately seven times the average price prevailing during the 1930's, partly because of increased export duties placed on both raw jute and on manufactured goods by the principal producing areas, partly as a result of inflation, and, in some measure, as a result of a favorable supplier's position in relation to demand. The low supply of jute in relation to demand, together with the high prices, resulted in the use of other materials for bagging and wrapping fabrics to a greater extent than ever before. Some of these uses developed, of course, during World War II when the available jute supply had to be channeled to war needs. They have continued and expanded because of the postwar supply and price situation. Also, facilities for handling bulk shipments have been increased; therefore, some of the need for bagging fabrics has decreased. The governments of all countries where large quantities of bagging and wrapping materials are used are actively encouraging the growing of crops from which can be produced low-cost fiber in large quantities for these uses.

All these factors have inevitably affected jute's position in world textile markets. In the first half of the calendar year 1952, it became apparent that, though total demand for baling and wrapping fabrics was, and is still, heavy, it was not sufficiently acute to result in purchases in world markets of raw jute and jute manufactures at the price levels then prevailing. To stimulate sales, prices of Pakistan jute for export were decreased. By July 1952, prices were 35 to 40 per cent below the January 1952 level. The decline continued after July, but at a slower rate, the total decrease by the end of 1952 being about 50 per cent of January 1952 price levels. On July 1, 1952, Pakistan reduced the export duty charged all countries on raw jute by more than 50 per cent as a further means of stimulating trade. In March 1953, Pakistan removed the export licensing fee which had been in effect since 1951 on jute sold to India. The decrease in export prices resulted in a decrease in prices paid growers to a level which the growers stated was almost one-third below costs of growing jute, especially for the lower qualities. This slowed the harvesting and movement of jute to market. To overcome the situation which had developed, controlling agencies in Pakistan plan to curtail plantings for the 1953–54 jute year. This will, it is believed, result in a supply small enough to obviate the need for pricing fiber for export at a level that would result in a loss to the grower and/or the exporter but large enough approximately to meet demand. The extent to which this plan will be successful as well as the manner in which the other factors will affect the future position of jute in world textile markets is impossible to determine at this time because of the many ramifications with which the situation is involved.

Data showing quantity of jute and principal jute manufactures exported by the Indo-Pakistan subcontinent for the jute years 1951–52, 1950–51, 1949–50, and average for 1934–38 are given in Table 4. These

TABLE 4. Exports of Raw Jute and Principal Jute Manufactures from Indo-Pakistan Subcontinent

(Thousands of short tons)

	Jute Year and Area									
	1951–52			*1950–51*			*1949–50*			*Average 1934–38*
Item	*Total*	*India*	*Pakistan*	*Total*	*India*	*Pakistan*	*Total*	*India*	*Pakistan*	*Indo-Pakistan Area*
Raw jute	640	*	640	842	1	841	464	119	345	845
Principal jute manufactures, total	861	861	0	781	781	0	707	707	0	951
Bags, exported as such	567	567	0	443	443	0	414	414	0	532
Cloth, exported as such	294	294	0	338	338	0	293	293	0	419

* Less than 500 tons.

Sources

1949–52: "Monthly Summary of Jute Statistics, July 1952," No. 55, Directorate of Jute Prices, Department of Commerce, Labour, and Industries, Government of East Bengal, Narayanganj, Dacca, Pakistan (1952).

"Monthly Summary of Jute and Gunny Statistics, January 1953," No. 94, Indian Jute Mills Association, Calcutta (1953).

1934–38: "Statistics on Jute and Jute Manufactures," H. G. Porter and M. R. Cooper, U. S. Dept. Agr., Washington (1945).

data obviously exclude export of raw jute from Pakistan to India. Prior to 1949, more than one-half of total raw jute produced on the Indo-Pakistan subcontinent was consumed in the mills in India for export as jute manufactures. Beginning with the jute year 1948–49, exports of raw jute from Pakistan to India were, in thousands of short tons, as follows: 1948–49, 782; 1949–50, 332; 1950–51, 512; and 1951–52, 336.[7] Consumption of raw jute, both Indian and Pakistanian, by Indian mills was: 1948–49, 1241; 1949–50, 993; 1950–51, 1050; and 1951–52, 1137.[8]

Raw jute exports from the Indo-Pakistan subcontinent go to more than 50 countries, with the United Kingdom and European countries taking most of the total. The United Kingdom, France, Germany, Italy, and Belgium, in the order named, take the largest amounts, together accounting for two-thirds of the total in the 1951–52 jute year. United Kingdom took approximately 17 per cent of total, France 16 per cent, Germany 13 per cent, Italy 10 per cent, and Belgium 9 per cent. Other important European consumers were the Netherlands, Poland, and Portugal, together accounting for 7 per cent of the total. The United States, in 1951–52, took 5 per cent of the total, Brazil more than 3 per cent, Japan slightly more than 3 per cent, U.S.S.R. 3 per cent, and South Africa more than 2 per cent. The export pattern for raw jute, post-World War II, has been influenced to a greater extent than usual by the foreign currency situation prevailing in the various countries, especially with respect to "hard" and "soft" currencies. During the period 1949–51, difficulties encountered in trade negotiations between India and Pakistan over nondevaluation of Pakistan currency also influenced the export pattern, exports to Europe and other areas rising while consumption of Pakistan raw jute by Indian mills decreased. More than two-thirds of the jute cloth, exported as such, goes principally to North America, with South America taking about one-sixth of the total. Exports of bags are quite widely distributed but with Africa, the Middle East, Australia, and the West Indies taking more than half the total.

Data on United States imports, by principal items, are shown in Table 5 for 1949–51 and the 1934–38 average. Raw jute imported is chiefly of a high quality for special yarns, Tossa being preferred. Burlap[9] is the jute manufacture imported in largest quantity, India

[7] "Monthly Summary of Jute Statistics, July 1952," No. 55, Directorate of Jute Prices, Department of Commerce, Labour, and Industries, Government of East Bengal, Narayanganj, Dacca, Pakistan (1952).

[8] "Monthly Summary of Jute and Gunny Statistics," July 1951, No. 76, and July 1952, No. 88, Indian Jute Mills Association, Calcutta (1951 and 1952 respectively).

[9] Burlap is the name given in the United States to a cloth termed "hessian" in India and the United Kingdom, a coarse, plain-weave jute fabric made with single

TABLE 5. UNITED STATES IMPORTS OF RAW JUTE AND JUTE MANUFACTURES FROM ALL SOURCES

(Thousands of short tons)

	Calendar Year			
Item	*1951*	*1950*	*1949*	*Average 1934–38*
Raw jute	109	87	69	81
Jute manufactures				
Subtotal	256	302	285	316
Burlap	167	209	223	256
Bagging for cotton bale covering	36	28	27	11
Bags	10	14	9	21
Other	43	51	26	28
Grand total	365	389	354	397

Source: Data published by the U. S. Dept. of Commerce, Washington, D. C.

having supplied more than 90 per cent of the total until 1950. In 1950, India supplied 87 per cent of the total and in 1951 83 per cent. The balance came from European mills, Belgium supplying the largest amount from this area, 5 per cent of the total imported in 1950 and almost 4 per cent in 1951. Decreased burlap supply from India was largely due to disruption of movement in fiber from East Pakistan to India, as a result of problems of exchange arising in 1949 when the Indian rupee was devalued and the value of the Pakistanian rupee was maintained.

During the 1930's, more than three-fourths of imported burlap was used for bag manufactures, about half the balance going to the furniture and automotive industries, largely for upholstery uses. This distribution pattern was markedly changed during World War II and continues to vary largely because of high prices and, to some extent, shortness of supply in relation to demand.

Cultivation. The plants grow best in a rich sandy loam. The area should be well drained, though some varieties are suited for growing on lowland areas. Fiber from plants grown in these lowland areas, however, is harsh and "mossy" at the bottom. Rainfall for the area should average not less than 3 to 4 in. per month during the growing season. A relative humidity range of 65 to 90 per cent is most beneficial to the

yarns. Burlap is also sometimes used in the United States to designate any jute sacking or bagging fabric, except heavy jute fabric used for baling cotton.

crop. Temperature should be warm to hot, the most satisfactory range being 80 to 100° F.

The new, rich, alluvial soils brought down by the Ganges and Brahmaputra Rivers and their tributaries have proved ideal for growing jute in India and East Pakistan. This area, about 5000 square miles, extends from southeastern Nepal and from Bihar and Assam in India down through the provinces of East Pakistan and through West Bengal and Orissa in India. The farmers, called "raiyats," depend largely upon this new soil, brought down by the rivers when in flood, for fertilization. On the high lands where this silt is not deposited, fertilizer is required. Cattle manure and commercial fertilizer are used when they are available and the farmers able to afford them.

Land is prepared by plowing and then harrowing until well pulverized. These cultivating operations, as well as all others used for jute are, currently, primitive. Bullocks are used to draw plows and harrows. All other operations are done with hand labor.

Seed, in the past, has usually been obtained by the farmers from plants grown on the edges of the fields or plants left to nature. Unfortunately, this has meant that in some areas little attention has been paid to selection of seed from varieties which show the most desirable characteristics for fiber production. The seed is sown broadcast, about 10 to 12 lb per acre of *C. capsularis* and 8 to 10 lb per acre of *C. olitorius,* and covered by means of a wooden drag or harrow. Sowing begins, depending upon location, in the middle of February and is completed by the end of May.

Weeds must be pulled by hand, since the custom of sowing seed broadcast does not permit the use of even a small cultivating and weeding machine that can be operated by one person. The fields require weeding two or three times before plants attain sufficient growth to shade the ground. When the plants are about 6 to 10 in. high they are cultivated by means of a hand rake. At this stage they are thinned to allow 6 in. between plants of *C. capsularis* and 8 in. between those of *C. olitorius.* Proper thinning insures straight, even stalks with minimum branching, which are most suitable for fiber production. Just before the rainy season begins, weak plants are usually pulled from the fields. Fiber is extracted from these plants and is termed "bach pat," that is, "rejected jute."

In Brazil, "the most important areas of jute production are on overflow 'Varzea' soils, alluvial soils along the Amazon River from Santarem to Manaos and along the Solimoes to the Peruvian border. The greatest concentration of plantations is around Santarem, Jurity,

Obidoes, Parintins, and Manaos. Jute production also has been introduced into South Brazil in the State of Espirito Santo. The methods used . . . are very primitive. The native clears the land and at the end of the dry season burns the clearing. Seed is then broadcast on soil that has no preparation. No labor is involved from seed sowing to harvesting. The rains start the germination. . . . The field may be planted to jute a second and third time before weeds and grass prevent further culture and require the undertaking of a new clearing. In the Amazon basin two crops of jute may be produced a year."[10]

Harvesting. Harvesting, in the Indo-Pakistan area, begins in July and ends in October. Plants are usually ready about 120 days after seed is sown. There are three plant stages for harvesting: (1) when in flower; (2) just after flowers are shed and fruit has begun to set; and (3) when fruit is fully developed. At the first stage, fiber is finer and lighter in color than at other stages, but total yield is consequently less. At the third stage, the total yield in pounds is greater but the fiber is coarser and of a darker color, hence is of less value. Harvesting, therefore, is generally done at the second stage, though in order to distribute labor supply, it usually begins at the first stage.

Cutting the stalks, that is, harvesting, is done by hand with a sickle. In the high land areas, the stalks are tied into small bundles and stacked on the field for 2 days, during which time the leaves fall off the stalks onto the ground. Stacks are covered with straw or palmyra leaves as sunlight on the stalks will cause discolored fiber. In lowland areas, where water is standing on the fields, jute is cut in the water, several layers being laid one over the other. In 5 or 6 days, leaves will have become detached from the stalks.

Yield per acre is about 29,000 to 30,000 lb of green stalks. Yield of dry fiber averages 4 to 5 per cent of green weight or approximately 1200 to 1400 lb of fiber per acre. Many farmers with adequate fertilizer, skillful cultivation, and favorable growing conditions obtain larger yields.

In Brazil harvesting is done by hand cutting, about 120 days after sowing, and must be done before flood waters, resulting from the rainy season, rise to cover the field. Total annual yield for two crops is about 1000 lb per acre.[10]

Retting, Stripping, and Washing. Retting is the process by which the fiber, which is just under the bark of the stalk, is prepared for removal from the stalk. Essentially it consists of soaking the stalks

[10] "Status of the Fiber Plant Industry in Latin America," Brittain B. Robinson et al., Pan American Union, Washington (1947).

in water until the effect of bacterial action makes it possible to free the fiber easily from the stalk and subsequently wash it clean of gummy substances and any bits of bark and stalk that may remain on it.

The operation, in India and Pakistan, consists of immersing bundles of stalks in water, still or running. Slowly moving water is generally preferable because retting occurs more evenly throughout the bundle of stalks and also because of the possibility of bundles being carried away in fast-running water. Water should have a temperature of not less than 80° F. It must also be of sufficient depth to prevent bundles of stalks from touching bottom as this prevents even retting and causes discoloration of fiber. It is important that the water be clean. Muddy water discolors the fiber. The water should also be free of minerals, especially iron, which discolor fiber. To insure complete immersion, bundles of stalks are usually weighted. Wood, stones, plants, or clods of grass and earth are placed on top of the bundles. Clods are most unsatisfactory as earth discolors the fiber. In some areas, before the bundles of stalks are immersed, the root, that is, bottom, ends of the stalks are placed in water for a few days. This gives a more even ret throughout the stalk, since the bottom ends are heavier and require longer to ret than the balance of the stalk.

Retting is completed in from 10 to 20 days, depending upon temperature of water, condition of stalks, and other related factors. During retting, frequent checking is done to observe progress. Proper retting is, obviously, very important. Under-retting results not only in difficulty in removing fiber from stalk but also in gums remaining on fiber, which makes it harsh and causes fibers to stick to each other. Over-retting results in weak fiber, with little or no luster.

When the ret is completed fiber is stripped from stalks. Workmen, standing in the water, pick up a few stalks from a bundle, break the pith, that is, woody central portion, of each stalk at a point about 8 to 10 inches from the bottom end, work the ends of the fiber loose from each stalk, and then, taking hold of the ends of the fibers, jerk the stalks back and forth until the full length of the fiber strands is freed. A wooden paddle is often used to pound bottom ends of stalks before breaking pith, to loosen fiber and to facilitate freeing the ends. Another method of stripping, which results in better fiber though it is more costly because of the greater amount of labor required, is to remove the fiber strands from each stalk separately, by running the stalk between the fingers or between pieces of bamboo or wood set into a frame. This work is usually done by women, either at home or on the banks of the retting area. A third method of stripping is to hit stalks against bamboo poles set into the retting water until the fiber strands are freed. In a fourth method, used principally in Orissa, stalks are hit against the surface of the water until the fiber is loosened. The stalks are then dried, the pith broken in several places, and the fiber strands are removed from the stalk. This method produces a less desirable quality of fiber. Still another method is by pounding the stalks with wooden mallets; this is used principally for over-age or very woody stalks at the end of the season.

The pith is dried and used for fencing, thatching, and fuel. Sometimes it is burned and the ashes used as fertilizer.

The fiber strands, immediately after they are freed from the stalk, are washed repeatedly in clear water to free them from gum and any pieces of bark and wood remaining on them. They are then hung on poles or spread on the ground to dry. Drying in the shade is preferable as strong, hot sunshine may cause discoloration.

Brazilian-grown jute, as well as jute grown in other areas, is processed in much the same manner as jute from India and Pakistan.

Marketing and Grading. In the Indo-Pakistan area, growers usually sell their fiber to small middlemen, "beparis," who do not own go-downs (warehouses) and frequently act as moneylenders. Sometimes large growers act as middlemen, purchasing fiber from nearby small growers. The bepari takes the fiber to collecting centers, sorts it into grades, rolls it into drums of about 80 lb each, and sells it to a buying firm, "mahajan," whom he represents and whose go-down he uses. The mahajan may also buy fiber through "farias," who go from one small grower to another, buying fiber on a commission basis. The mahajan reassorts fiber by grades, bales it into "kutcha" (sometimes anglicized as "kucha" and "kacha"), bales, each weighing approximately 280 pounds and loosely pressed, and sells it to exporters or mills through a commission agent, known as an "aratdar." Sometimes the functions of the mahajan and aratdar are combined; sometimes functions of exporter or mill are also combined with this organization. The aratdar transports the fiber to an export baling center or to mills. If the fiber is to be exported, it is again sorted by grades and rebaled; these bales, known as "pucca" bales, are tightly pressed and weigh 400 pounds each. If necessary, the fiber, before baling, is given a kind of hackling by having the bottom ends thrown, but not drawn, over coarse pins to separate them into finer strands and to remove bits of bark and shive; hand labor is used for this operation. The bottom ends of the fiber, usually being rather coarse and rough (termed "mossy" or "flaggy"), are generally cut off before hackling to make fiber length and quality more uniform; occasionally tip ends are also cut; hand labor is also used for this operation. The pieces cut off the bottom ends, and tops, are known as "cuttings."

Principal markets for the sale of raw jute for export are at Dacca and Narayanganj, East Pakistan, with principal port of shipment at Chittagong and Chalna. The market at Calcutta, India, which formerly was the largest, is being maintained, though currently the quantity of fiber being exported there is negligible. Almost all the available jute fiber in India is being channeled to Indian mills for export as jute manufactures. Prices of raw jute quoted on the Dundee and New York markets are based on prices from the Pakistan and Indian markets. All prices are spot. Trading in futures was stopped in 1948, reopened on April 26, 1952, on the Calcutta market, and closed on December 18, 1952.

There are no jute fiber grades and grade designations clearly defined on an overall basis and acceptable to and understood by all parties, from grower to manufacturer of jute products. This has resulted in the use of many grade designations, having little basis for comparability.

The first grading given the fiber as it leaves the grower relates to color, luster, length, texture, and general condition. Terms generally used are, in a descending order: Top, Middle, Bottom, and Cross Bottom. The amount of moisture in the fiber is also a point considered; the amount acceptable on loose fiber and fiber made into drums and subsequently into kutcha bales is based principally upon opinion or personal judgment of buyer and seller. Moisture content to 12 per cent is accepted on fiber in pucca bales.

As the fiber progresses from bepari to mahajan and aratdar, it is given further quality designations, relating to the species of the plant, the district in which it was grown, as well as care and method used in processing. Principal terminology in general use for these designations, together with brief description of each, is given in Table 6. These designations are used for loose fiber or fiber made into drums and/or kutcha bales. An idea may be obtained of the approximate relationship of these designations, often termed "varieties," from the standpoint of money value by minimum prices set by the government of Pakistan for 1950–51 jute year. These show for White jute: District, 1 rupee less per maund (82.28 lb) than Jat; and Northern, 1 rupee less than District. For each of these "varieties," Middles were 2 rupees less than Tops, Bottoms 5 rupees less than Tops and Cross

TABLE 6. PRINCIPAL TERMINOLOGY USED TO DESIGNATE QUALITY OF JUTE FIBER PRODUCED IN INDO-PAKISTAN SUBCONTINENT

(Used for loose fiber or fiber made into drums or kutcha bales)

Species and Name	*District in Which Grown*	*Description of Fiber*
C. capsularis		
White jute		
Jat (sometimes termed Narayanganj or Dacca)	East Bengal in districts of Mymensingh, Dacca, and Tippera, along the Brahmaputra River.	Finest quality, strong, clean, lustrous, with firm even fiber strands and waxy texture.
District (sometimes termed Serajgunge)	East Bengal in districts west of Dacca and areas west of Brahmaputra River and adjacent to districts producing Jat.	Approximately medium quality. Somewhat softer in texture than Jat.
Northern (sometimes termed Uttarya)	North Bengal in districts lying north of the Ganges and west of the Jumna Rivers.	Soft in quality. Is pit-retted and, as season progresses, quality declines due to deterioration in cleanness of water.
Western (sometimes termed Bihar)	Purnea district of Bihar.	Soft fiber, tends to be weak and discolored.
Assam	Assam and in East Bengal, district of Sylhet.	Quality varies due to methods of processing.
Orissa	Orissa.	Quality frequently low due to shorter fiber and methods of processing.
Dowrah	Some areas of Bakarganj and Faridpur.	Fiber generally strong but harsh and discolored.
Jungli	West Bengal in Murshidabad and Malda.	Fiber soft and heavily rooted.
C. olitorius		
Tossa jute		
Jat	Same areas producing White Jat.	Highest quality. Fiber very strong, clean, lustrous, even and golden to slate brown.
District	Faridpur and to some extent in Khulna and Nadia districts.	Quality below that of Jat. Color brownish red to golden yellow.
Northern	Rajshahi, Murshidabad, Pabna and Bogra.	Soft in quality, color somewhat lighter than District.
Daisee jute		
Jat	West Bengal, Howrah, Hooghly, Burdwan, and Midnapore.	Fiber lustrous with good length, color usually grey, texture somewhat soft. Is said to be highly flexible and hence to permit higher degree of twist.
District	24 Paragnas, Nadia, Jessore, and Khulna.	Somewhat similar to Northern Tossa but color varies, generally being dark because of lack of cleanness of water.

Sources

Jute and Substitutes, Nabaran Chandra Chaudhuri, W. Newman and Co., Calcutta (1933).

"The Golden Fibre," M. Aslam Hayat, Publications and Foreign Publicity Dept., Government of Pakistan, Karachi (1948).

Conferences with jute dealers and exporters in Dacca, Narayanganj, and Calcutta.

Bottoms 7 rupees less than Tops. An extra 2 rupees was added for Tossa for all designations. It should be noted that these differences relate to growers' prices.

Grading the fiber for export, that is, for pucca baling, introduces different quality terminology, which is termed "marks," and varies with each exporter in relation to the species and quality of fiber used to make up bales for each of his marks. A mark usually consists of various symbols and letters intended to designate species, quality, and color of fiber, as well as names of merchant and/or baler. The kind and quality of fiber which an individual merchant or baler decides to put into a bale under any one mark is governed, of course, basically by the class of jute manufacture for which he hopes to sell the fiber. Marks, of which there are more than 2000, are registered with a trade association which publishes, usually annually, a list of all registered marks. The association also establishes "public marks," which any exporter may use but which, however, are seldom used.

It should be noted that the quality designations used by the exporter for fiber made into pucca bales are different from those used for loose or kutcha baled fiber. They may be those of the individual exporter or those used by a number of exporters. Quality designations used by many exporters and which were established originally by the London Jute Association, are as follows, in a descending order, for each species of jute:

White jute— Firsts
Lightnings
Hearts
Tossa jute— 2s/3s (that is, half seconds and half thirds)
4s
5s
Daisee jute—2s/3s
4s
5s

These qualities may have the initials "LJA" preceding them to indicate that the quality is intended to conform to the standards set by the London Jute Association. Or each of the qualities may be separated into additional qualities. Terminology in general use for these additional qualities includes the following: "good," "mill," and "grade," in a descending order, for each of the qualities of white jute, e.g., good firsts, mill firsts, and grade firsts, good, mill, and grade lightnings, and good, mill, and grade hearts (the term "grade" is principally in use for jute sold to the United Kingdom and to European countries);

"dacca" and "district" for each of the qualities of tossa (used in the United States), e.g., dacca tossa 2s/3s, or 4s, or 5s, etc., or good and grade for each of the qualities of tossa (in use in the United Kingdom and in European countries), e.g., good tossa 2s/3s, or 4s, or 5s, etc.; and "good" and "grade" for each of the qualities of daisee. The degree to which quality of fiber packed under the quality designations mentioned above is identical between exporters depends upon care with which individual exporters or balers sort and pack fiber and, to some extent, upon competition and quality of each year's crop; comparability may be close or may vary considerably. The quality designations mentioned above are some, as is stated, that are in general use. There are many others in use by various exporters and/or balers, many of which are related to the quality designations in general use. Exporters customarily offer a guarantee with respect to kind and quality of fiber being sold under a mark, as it relates to kind and quality of fiber under that same mark in preceding seasons. Also, many exporters indicate comparability of their marks with those of other exporters. It is obvious, however, that there exists a large number of qualities and of quality designations for pucca bales for export sale.

In addition to the grades discussed in the foregoing paragraphs, there are several others, used largely for internal trade in the Indo-Pakistan area and for some specialized uses. Among these are: "Reject," previously mentioned; "Hubbi-jubbi," meaning an assortment of odds and ends; and "Garsat," meaning unassorted.

Brazilian-grown jute is not exported; it goes directly to the mills from the growers. There is no system of grading in general use in Brazil nor in the other countries where jute is grown.

Characteristics. The fiber, when properly grown, retted, and washed, is fairly lustrous and has moderate strength. Tests made by Schiefer [11] for cordage fibers showed high-grade jute, on the basis of a 15-in. bundle of fibers weighing 5 grains, to have a dry breaking strength of 53 lb; wet breaking strength of 44 lb; and, after a 100-hr exposure in a twin arc Weatherometer, 41 lb. Elongation, in the same series of tests, was 1.7 ($\pm$0.07) per cent. This lower elasticity gives jute an advantage as a bagging material as it means that loaded bags have less tendency to shift about when stacked than bags made of fibers with greater percentage of elongation.

Jute may be dyed, though care must be taken to insure penetration and to prevent injury to the fiber. Because of its naturally darker

[11] "Machines and Methods for Testing Cordage Fibers," Herbert F. Schiefer, RP1611, Natl. Bur. Standards, U. S. Dept. Commerce, Washington (1944).

color, jute must be bleached before dyeing, unless very dark shades are wanted. Bleaching also requires considerable care.

Commercial jute fiber consists of strands, i.e., bast bundles of individual fibers with ends overlapping so as to produce continuous filaments throughout the length of the stalk. The individual fibers are

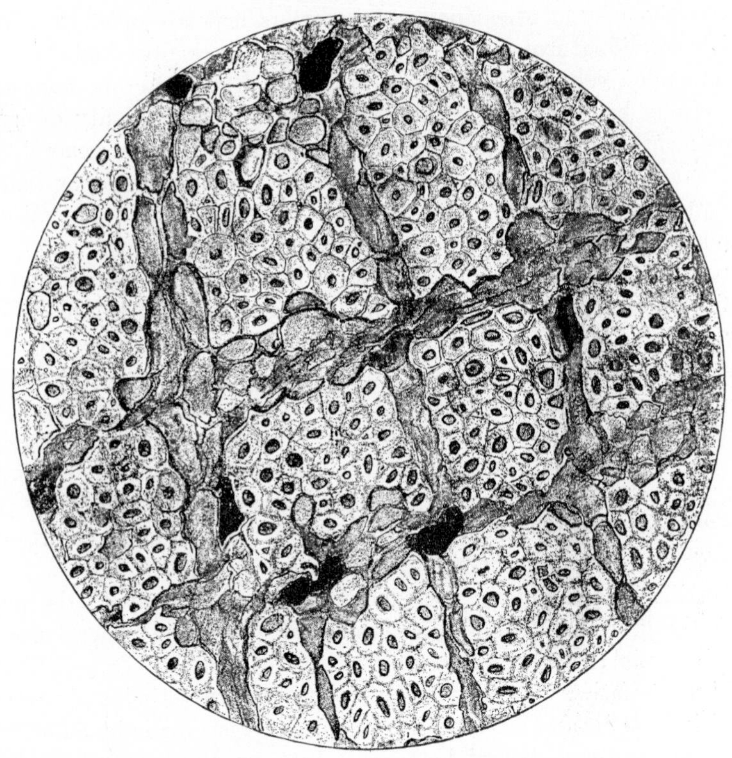

Fig. 3. Cross-section of jute bast bundles as they appear in stalk, surrounded by cellular tissue. (*Cross and Bevan.*)

held together by gums, waxes, and lignin. As is characteristic for bast fibers, these bast bundles occur around the woody core and just under the bark of the stalk. Figure 3 shows a cross-section of several of these bast bundles as they appear before removal from the stalk, the bundles being surrounded by cellular tissue. It is this cellular tissue that is removed by the retting and washing processes, leaving the bast bundles more or less intact. The ends of some of the individual fibers in the bundle become loosened during processing, resulting in a varying amount of "hairiness" on the strand. This hairiness, together with the substances holding the bast bundles together, causes commercial jute fiber to be somewhat harsh or rough to the touch.

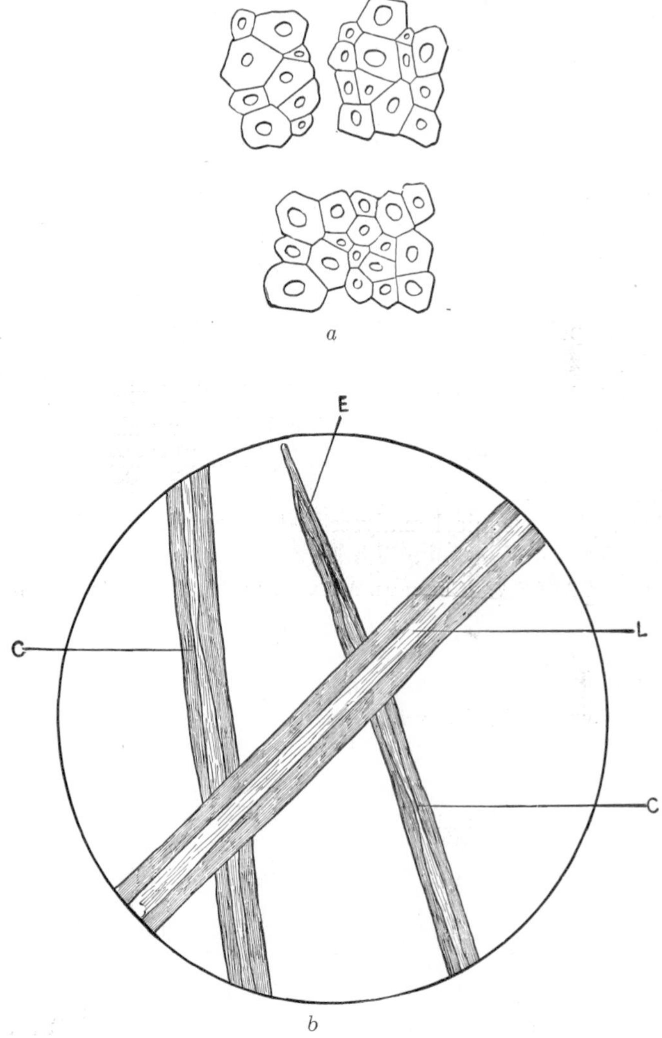

Fig. 4. Jute fiber (×300). *a,* Cross-sections (*Cross and Bevan*). *b,* Longitudinal views; *L,* lumen; *C,* constrictions in lumen; *E,* end of fiber (*Matthews*).

These are very useful qualities, however, for many bagging and wrapping purposes, as they tend to prevent slipping, provide some loftiness or resiliency in the yarns and fabrics, and make the fabric less likely to rip when snagged. On the other hand, they also cause jute yarns and fabrics to be unsuitable for a few bagging and wrapping uses, notably for certain foodstuffs, as the individual fiber ends break off, causing a shedding of small pieces of fiber.

Individual fiber cells, according to Vétillart, range from 0.06 to 0.20 in. in length and average 0.08 in. Diameter ranges from 20 to 25 μ and averages 23 μ. Some studies show slightly greater range in lengths. The surface of the cell is generally smooth with only occasional nodes or cross-markings. The cross-section of the fiber is polygonal in shape with sharply defined angles. Cell walls are thick. The lumen is large, and the cross-section is oval. Longitudinally, the lumen is irregular, with occasional sharp constrictions. Toward the end of cell, the lumen thickens, resulting in the cell wall becoming very thin. Cell ends are tapering to pointed. The cell is surrounded by a thin median layer of lignin.

Figure 4 shows cross-sections and longitudinal views of individual fiber cells. Cross-sections of individual fibers are also shown in Fig. 3, which also shows the thin median layer of lignin surrounding individual fiber cells.

Table 7 gives chemical analyses of three specimens of jute fiber.

TABLE 7. CHEMICAL ANALYSIS OF JUTE (PER CENT)

Components	*Nearly Colorless Specimen*	*Fawn-Colored Specimen*	*Brown Cuttings*
Ash	0.68	.....	.....
Water (hygroscopic)	9.93	9.64	12.58
Aqueous extract	1.03	1.63	3.94
Fat and wax	0.39	0.32	0.45
Cellulose	64.24	63.05	61.74
Incrusting and pectin matters	24.41	25.36	21.29
Total	100.68	100.00	100.00

The ash of jute consists principally of silica, lime, and phosphoric acid; manganese is nearly always present in small amounts. Ash content in completely dry jute ranges from 0.6 to 1.75 per cent.

According to Cross and Bevan, jute fiber may be regarded as an anhydro-aggregate of three separate compounds:

a. A dextrocellulose allied to cotton.

b. A pentacellulose yielding furfural and acetic acid on hydrolysis.

c. Lignone, a quinone which is converted by chlorination and reduction into derivatives of the trihydric phenols.

Jute fiber, being lignocellulose, when treated with reagents, shows the following microchemical properties: (*a*) iodine and sulfuric acid results in a yellow color; (*b*) dilute chromic acid, to which a little hydrochloric acid has been added, results in a blue color; (*c*) chlor-iodide of zinc results in a yellow color; (*d*) ferric ferricyanide results in a deep blue, owing to deoxidation of ferric compound by the lignone; (*e*) ammoniacal solution of copper oxide causes fiber to swell considerably but does not readily dissolve it.

FLAX

Nomenclature. Flax is the designation given in English-speaking countries to bast fiber from the plant *Linum usitatissimum* of the Linaceae family, as well as to the plant itself. There are a large number of species of the genus *Linum* only a few of which are cultivated for fiber, and these, with the exception of *L. usitatissimum,* to a very limited extent. *L. angustifolium* is generally considered to have been cultivated for the longest time; some authorities believe that this is the species cultivated by the Swiss Lake Dwellers and by the ancient Egyptians.

The word "flax" is derived from "fleax," Anglo-Saxon, and "flachs," Old High German. Although the word "flax" is understood in most countries, the word "linen" is more widely used both to designate the plant as well as the fiber. In English-speaking countries, "linen" is generally used to designate the yarns and fabrics made from flax fiber. Origin of the word "linen" predates written history. It appears in the language of almost every European country: in Anglo-Saxon as "līn," in Dutch as "linnen," in Old Norse and Middle High German as "līn," in German as "lein" or "leinen," in Gothic as "lein," in Latin as "linum," in Greek as "linon," in Lithuanian as "linai," in Ireland as "llin," in French as "lin," in Italian and Spanish as "lino," and in Russian as "lyen." Words used in the Near East and Egypt to designate the plant and its fiber or products vary. One of the most common Hebraic terms is anglicized as "pishtāh"; the Arabic as "kotla," and the Persian as "katan."

Plant. The plant *L. usitatissimum* is an annual. Varieties grown for fiber have straight, slender, pale-green stalks and being planted close together have branches only at the top. Their height is 3 to 4 ft, and the diameter of the stalk is about 0.10 to 0.15 in. Varieties grown for seed are characteristically shorter and more branching and are spaced farther apart to encourage added branching and increase seed production. Leaves are borne alternately on the stalk, are very small, lanceolate in shape, and light green. Flowers appear on stems growing out from the tips of the branches, are about ½ in. across, have 5 petals, and are sky blue, though some varieties have white flowers and some pink. Flowers are complete, having both staminate and

FIG. 5. Fiber flax plants. (*Courtesy U. S. Dept. Agr.*)

pistillate parts in the same flower. Seeds are small and numerous and are borne in small, 5-lobed globular capsules. See Fig. 5.

History. Flax fiber appears to be one of the oldest, if not the oldest, fiber utilized in the Western Hemisphere for cordage and fabrics, the antiquity of its use in this area corresponding to the antiquity of use of ramie fiber in the Eastern Hemisphere. The flax plant also appears to have been grown in the Eastern Hemisphere since very ancient times but principally for oil from the seeds. Use of fiber from the flax plant is of such great antiquity and so widespread among many countries that the plant and its products have come to have symbolic values in the cultural life of many nations.

Among the earliest evidences of the use of flax are traces of cordage and fabric found among the artifacts of the Swiss Lake Dwellers of prehistoric times. It apparently has been used for untold centuries in the countries of the Near East. There is some thought that the plant may have originated somewhere in the alluvial soil area of the Caucasus. The antiquity of its use by the Egyptians as well as by the Hebrews, the Persians, the Arabs, and other people of these areas is well known and widely described. Biblical literature, and the writings, wrappings of mummies, and pictures found in ancient Egyptian tombs, provide evidence that flax spinning and weaving had reached a high degree of perfection thousands of years ago.

Utilization of flax products is mentioned in the most ancient literature and folk tales of European countries, of England, Scotland, and Ireland, of the Scandinavian countries, and of Russia, though methods of spinning and weaving were apparently considerably more crude than those used in Egypt and the Near East. As the civilized nations of the Mediterranean area expanded their territorial and trade boundaries, knowledge of improved methods of manufacture was also spread. The Phoenicians are thought to have dispersed this information as they extended their trade routes around the Mediterranean and up the west coast of Gaul to Britain, several centuries before the Christian Era. One of the principal items in Phoenician trade was fine linen from Egypt. Expansion of the Roman Empire furthered exchange of knowledge of manufacture. The Moors are said to have brought improvements in linen manufacture to Spain during the Middle Ages.

The modern phase in the utilization of flax fiber may be said to have begun in the seventeenth century. The linen industry in Holland expanded, utilizing flax fiber and yarn from the German states, which had long supplied these items to neighboring countries. The industry began to expand in Ireland, England, and Scotland during this period, largely as the result of immigration of thousands of skilled Flemish and French linen workers who left their native countries to escape religious persecution. The Flemish had been noted for several centuries for their fine linen products, made principally from native flax, the cities of Bruges and Ypres being especially outstanding. France was also well known for production of large quantities of fine linens from native fiber. Some of the yarns and fabrics made by the French became known by the names of places where they were made and these names are part of today's textile industry, though generally used now to designate fabrics made from cotton fiber, e.g., cambric, lawn, and lisle.

The industry in England, prior to the seventeenth century, had been developing slowly, partly because competition from the wool industry meant that only small quantities of flax were raised in England. With the influx of skilled workers, fiber for the expanding industry was imported, principally from Russia, where it had been grown for many centuries. Export of Russian flax had been handled by the Finns for more than 800 years when, in the sixteenth century, the English began to participate in the trade.

The Irish flax industry received an impetus not only from Flemish and French emigrants but also because the English Government encouraged the growth of the linen industry, especially in Northern Ireland, while at the same time discouraging the wool industry there to prevent competition. The flax industry in Scotland had developed steadily until the seventeenth century when a severe setback occurred as a result of actions taken by the English Government. To prevent competition with English wool trade, Scottish woolens were barred from England; the Scottish then withheld raw wool from England; and the English in turn prohibited importation of Scottish linen. The Scottish linen industry began to revive, however, during the early part of the eighteenth century, after union of the two countries.

Flax has been cultivated for fiber in Argentina on an experimental basis since 1900. Brazil has grown fiber flax for many years but only on a small scale. Chile has also cultivated flax, for fiber, for many years, though on a small scale. The first flax spinning mill was established in 1941. Peru has grown flax for fiber on a commercial scale since 1939 with some degree of success, after considerable discouragement in the initial stages of the project due principally to inexperience and high incidence of disease. The first spinning and weaving mill was established during the 1940's.

Fiber flax has been grown on a commercial basis in Japan since 1900, in Hokkaido, the northernmost island. The first mill was established in 1913.

The early American colonists brought flax seed and spinning and weaving equipment with them. Many attempts were made to stimulate the cultivation of flax and its processing on a large scale. Invention of the cotton gin in 1793, however, lowered cost of cotton processing with a subsequent rapid expansion of that industry, and flax fiber growing and processing declined. Most of the flax currently grown in the United States is seed flax for production of linseed oil.

World Production. Before World War II, more than 70 per cent of the world's total supply of flax fiber was produced in Russia, cultivation centering in the western regions of European Russia, the central industrial region and the upper Volga areas, with some production also in the north, Ural, and Western Siberia areas.[12] Production was greatly reduced during the war because heaviest yield areas were invaded and wartime shortages handicapped production in uninvaded areas. Highest recorded production of Russian-grown flax fiber was in 1913, when 850,000 tons were produced. Postwar boundaries of Russia include the three Baltic republics which produced considerable quantities of flax fiber before World War II. Production in these areas also decreased during the war period. Postwar production for all these areas has increased, but, on the basis of best available information, has not reached prewar levels.

Production in other European countries, after wartime decreases, has risen back to prewar levels. Partly as a result of strong export demand for linen goods and partly as a result of encouragement given growers by the Flax Act of 1949, production in Northern Ireland has increased to almost three times prewar levels. This figure combined with that of the Irish Republic is still below the annual production of the eighteenth century for both the Irish Republic and Northern Ireland. Highest yields were in 1853, 49,600 tons, and 1864, 72,200 tons; both resulting from wartime demands for fibers. Production in 1890 was 22,400 tons, declining thereafter, except for increases during World Wars I and II.[13] Production in Egypt in response to wartime demand increased to 20,000 tons in 1942, but there was a postwar decline. Fiber flax production in Japan increased during the period 1938–45, the highest yield being in 1944 when more than 8000 tons of potential fiber was grown. Because of lack of transportation and wartime shortages in mills, much of the fiber grown during the 1938–45 period was not scutched and brought to the mills until after 1947. Postwar cultivation has been below prewar because food crops have brought greater returns to the farmers.

Production in Argentina rose to more than 3000 tons in 1944–45 but declined thereafter. Principal areas of production in Brazil are in the states of Parana, Santa Catarina, and Rio Grande do Sul, the most

[12] "A Survey of Soviet Russian Agriculture," Lazar Volin, U. S. Dept. Agr., Washington (1951).

[13] "Bast and Leaf Fibres," A. J. Turner, *J. Textile Inst.*, **42** (8), Manchester (1951).

important being Parana.[14] Total annual production is less than 1000 tons. Fiber flax is grown in Chile in the southern section of the Central Valley.[14] Present production is about 1000 tons. Most of Peru's fiber flax is grown in the Sierra region.[14] Highest production was in 1942–43 when more than 3000 tons each of fiber and tow were produced; present production is about one-third of this figure.

United States fiber flax production increased rapidly in response to wartime demand, to more than 5000 tons (line and tow) in 1942, but declined thereafter. Current production is about 500 tons annually. Almost all of this is produced in the state of Oregon.

In addition to flax fiber, a quantity of flax straw is produced for export in that form. Principal exporting areas are France, with 44,800 short tons in 1949 and 68,300 in 1950, and Netherlands, with 66,000 short tons in 1949 and 68,300 in 1950. All of this was imported by Belgium for processing in the River Lys area.

Data on world production by chief producing countries are given in Table 8. "Other countries" include production for Australia, Canada, New Zealand, Scandinavian countries, European countries other than those listed, China, Uganda, Kenya, and South American countries.

Utilization. With the exception of the United Kingdom (especially Northern Ireland) and Belgium, the largest part of world flax fiber production is spun and woven in countries where it is grown, chiefly for home consumption. Northern Ireland is the largest exporter of flax manufactures, utilizing a considerable quantity of fiber imported from Belgium, much of which is grown in France and the Netherlands and imported into Belgium in the form of straw. The United States manufactures only a small quantity of flax fiber; in addition to the quantity grown, imports of fiber (line and tow) average a little more than 2000 tons annually, Belgium and Luxemburg being the chief suppliers. Chief United States manufactures are industrial sewing thread, fish nets, and fire hose.

Because present methods of growing and processing flax fiber are costly in relation to those for many of the other fibers, the total amount of flax used is comparatively small; as late as the end of the eighteenth century it was one of the most widely used fibers in the Western Hemisphere. Principal uses are consumer fabrics and industrial sewing threads, twines, fire hose, and special fabrics where need for strength and resistance to effects of moisture justifies additional cost. Processes have been in existence for many years for utilizing flax tow

[14] "Status of the Fiber Plant Industry in Latin America," Brittain B. Robinson et al., Pan American Union, Washington (1947).

is pumped into the tank to cover the stalks. This temperature of water is maintained throughout the ret. Quality of water is important; it must be clean and free from minerals, especially iron, which would stain or discolor the fiber. The water penetrates to the inner part of

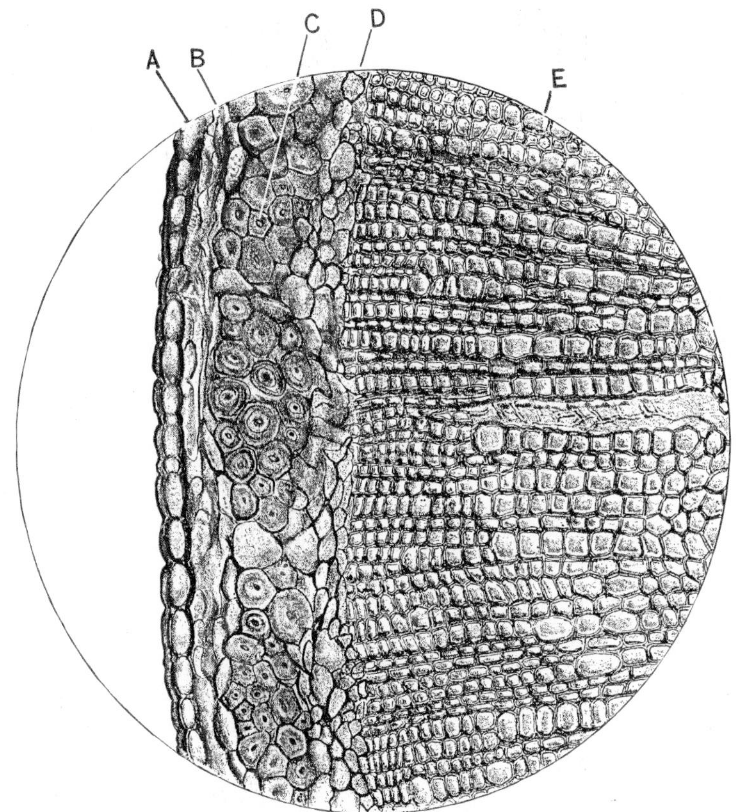

Fig. 6. Cross-section of portion of flax stalk. *A,* Bark or cuticle; *B,* phelloderm; *C,* bast bundles of fibers; *D,* cambium; *E,* xylem or wood. (*Cross and Bevan.*)

the stalk via small flaws in the cuticle or bark, causing the inner cells to swell and burst cuticle. This in turn increases moisture absorption and permits greater penetration of bacteria, which act on pectins in the substances surrounding the fiber bundles, changing them into soluble sugars.

During the first 6 or 8 hr of the ret, dirt and coloring matter are usually dissolved off the fiber. If water is changed after this period, the resulting fiber will be cleaner. This first period of retting is termed the "leach." As fermentation progresses, acids are formed in the water which are harmful to fiber. These are generally neutralized by allowing a slow trickle of water to run off and replacing it with fresh water; aeration is sometimes used. Retting is complete when fiber separates readily from stalk. Time required for tank retting is about 4 to 6 days; for rivers and ponds time required may be as long as 2 weeks, depending upon temperature of water.

Retting in river, bog holes, ponds, or dams is done in the same manner as in tanks but cannot be controlled as well. Stones, wood, and sometimes clods of earth and grass (unsatisfactory, as fiber is discolored from the earth) are used to weight the bundles of stalks.

Double-retting consists of removing the fiber from the tank when the ret is about half complete, drying straw in sun and air, beginning the ret again in a few months, and continuing the ret until completed. This results in very gentle retting action on fiber and hence good quality. The method is practiced in Courtrai, Belgium, which is famous for superior quality of fiber.

Waste retting water has toxic elements, harmful to fish in concentrated quantities, and should be aerated or impounded for a time before being released into stream or river. It is rich in chemicals, and farmers in some areas are reported to make use of it, after neutralizing with lime or chloride of lime, as a liquid fertilizer.

After the ret is complete, bundles of stalks, which are now termed "straw," are dried, usually by standing in small shocks in open, grassy fields. Mechanical drying is also used, though some authorities believe this to be detrimental to quality. Mechanical driers that will give uniform, generally acceptable results will do much to improve the economy of the flax industry. By producing continuous drying facilities, mechanical driers will eliminate the seasonal stoppages necessitated by outdoor drying. When the straw is dry, it is stored in sheds or weatherproofed stacks to cure for at least 1 month, preferably longer. During curing, the fiber is said to become stronger. Bast bundles are reported to be more easily freed from bark and woody portions of stalk, with less waste of fiber, when straw is cured. In many areas the cycle of production is to allow bundles of fiber to cure through winter before retting and then to cure straw through another winter before next operation takes place. In the United States curing is not generally used. Instead care is taken to scutch when humidity is high.

In Germany, a process was developed during the 1940's for washing the straw immediately after ret is complete, then running straw through squeeze rolls to remove excess moisture, after which it is dried. Resulting straw and fiber are said to be lighter in color and of better quality than straw and fiber not receiving this treatment.

Scutching. This is the process which frees the bast bundles by removing the bark and woody portions of the stalk, sometimes termed "shive" or "boon." Like other operations in the flax industry, methods and equipment vary, depending upon customs and mechanization available in an area.

The dried and cured bundles of straw first have root ends evened, an operation termed "butting." This is done by hand or in a machine, which by vibration arranges straw so that the root ends are even. The shive is next broken, either by hand by hitting the straw at intervals along its length with a specially shaped thin piece of wood, or by running the straw through a machine termed a "breaker," the most common method. There are a number of breaking machines on the market; all operate on essentially the same principle, that is, straw passes between fluted rollers which break shive in a great many places throughout its length.

The broken pieces of shive are next removed from the bast bundles. This is done on a machine termed a "scutching mill." Hand scutching, done by beating the pieces of shive from the bast bundles with a wooden "scutching blade," sometimes known as a "swingling tool," is rare. The scutching mill, of which there are a number of models on the market, removes the pieces of shive from the fiber bundles by bringing straw into contact with wide flat blades which scrape or beat off the shive. Blades are set at an angle on spokelike arms, arranged in a circle, the whole rotating at a fairly high rate of speed; on some mills blades are of wood, on others of steel; the number varies from four to six. An efficient scutching mill will remove shive from the fiber bundles with a minimum of fiber waste, leaving the bundles clean and undamaged. This fiber is termed "scutching line."

In many European areas, in most parts of the United Kingdom, and in the United States, modern machines which combine breaking and scutching in one continuous operation are used. These machines operate on the same principles as separate breakers and scutchers and obviously result in higher productivity with lower labor costs than when the work is done on separate machines.

The waste from the first scutching, consisting of pieces of shive and short pieces of fiber beaten off in the process, is run through a tow cleaner, which operates on the same general principles as a scutching mill, in order to recover the tow fiber. In some scutching plants, this operation is repeated a second time. Fiber recovered in this manner is termed "scutching tow," tow first recovered being of a higher quality than the second. Scutching tow is sometimes made into coarse yarns; sometimes it is utilized for paper. Waste resulting from the last scutching consists of very short fiber and shive. It is run through a "shaker" machine which separates the pieces of shive from the short fibers by a shaking motion. These short fibers are occasionally used for coarse yarns, more frequently for paper making. The pieces of shive are customarily used for fuel to heat the retting water; in some areas they are made into other products such as wallboard.

After scutching, line fiber is generally hackled by hand on coarse steel or wooden hackle pins. This operation removes the shorter line fibers and makes the line fiber somewhat softer. The resulting waste fiber is termed "combings," in some areas "coarse hackling tow."

Weight of scutching line and tow fiber averages from 12 to 18 per cent of weight of dried and cured straw after deseeding, or from 2 to 5 per cent of green weight of pulled plants. Hodge of Belfast cites the data in Table 10. Green weight of plants is about twice that of dried weight.

TABLE 10. CONSTITUENTS OF DRIED FLAX PLANT

Item	*Percentage of Total*
Seed	11.7
Seed pods	13.3
Loss in retting and curing	18.7
Loss in scutching	47.3
Fiber	9.0
Total	100.0

A process has been developed for breaking and scutching green flax and was used during World War II in an effort to shorten time of processing. Results were not as satisfactory as with conventional methods, and the process is being continued only on an experimental basis.

There are no grade standards and designations which are recognized and used throughout the industry for scutched fiber and tow. Almost all fiber and tow is bought on basis of submitted samples. Some suppliers have their own grade designations, which their customers recognize. In Oregon, in the United States, flax fiber is graded into 5 classes, designated in an ascending order as 1X, 2X, 3X, 4X, and 5X, which relate to color, luster, length, and general condition.

Spinning. Fiber upon reaching the mill is inspected and, depending upon the product to be made, may be again sorted for quality. It may also have bottom and top ends cut off, by machine, as cutting strand into three sections permits mixing fiber for spinning more evenly, with respect to diameter of fiber, and results in smoother yarn. Fiber from the bottom end of the stalk is heavier and somewhat harsher than that in the middle; from the top of the stalk, fiber is finer but not as even.

Fiber is next machine hackled, which is a kind of combing operation to separate long and short fibers and also to remove any bits of shive which may still remain on fiber. Resulting long fiber is termed "line"; shorter fiber, "hackling tow." Yarns are spun from tow as well as from line fibers, the tow being given additional carding and combing to remove bits of shive and broken or rough fibers.

Spinning operations consist of forming a sliver on a series of drawing frames, forming a roving on one or more roving frames, depending upon the fineness of the yarn, and then spinning the yarn on a ring, flyer, or gill spinning frame, depending upon product being made. Wet spinning is used to obtain finer, more even yarns. A small trough of hot water (temperature may be 150 to 200° F., depending upon fiber and yarn being spun) is attached to the spinning frame, and the roving passes through this water before it is spun. The hot water softens gums holding individual fibers together, allowing fibers to be spun into a more even, finer yarn. Yarn is dried on bobbins after spinning. Gummy substances, depending upon the product being made, may be removed from yarn or from fabric after weaving by boiling and bleaching.

Characteristics. Raw fiber, when properly processed, is creamy white, the color varying with the skill and quality of retting and other processes. The fiber is naturally highly lustrous because it contains about 1 per cent wax. This wax imparts suppleness to fiber, hence is important in preparation and spinning; if there is too little wax, the fiber is harsh and brittle, if too much, the fiber sticks to rollers of machines. The wax, which varies in color with the fiber from which it is obtained, has a rather unpleasant odor. Its melting point is 142.7° F. and its specific gravity at 60° F. is 0.983. According to Hoffmeister, this wax consists of 81.32 per cent of unsaponifiable waxy matter and 18.68 per cent of saponifiable oil. Of the latter, 54.49 per cent is free fatty acid. The unsaponifiable waxy matter has a melting point of 154.4° F. and apparently is a mixture, the principal constituent resembling ceresin. Ceryl alcohol and phytosterol are also present. Saponifiable matter appears to contain small quantities of soluble fatty acids as caproic, stearic, palmitic, oleic, linolic, linolenic, and isolinolenic.

Flax is very strong. One test series cited from *Transcriptions of the Faraday Society* [15] showed flax to have a tensile strength from two to three times that of cotton. It is highly absorbent and has good resistance to effects of moisture and mildew. Fabrics made from it launder well. It may be dyed readily, though care must be taken to insure complete penetration, and it takes special finishes, such as crease resistance, well.

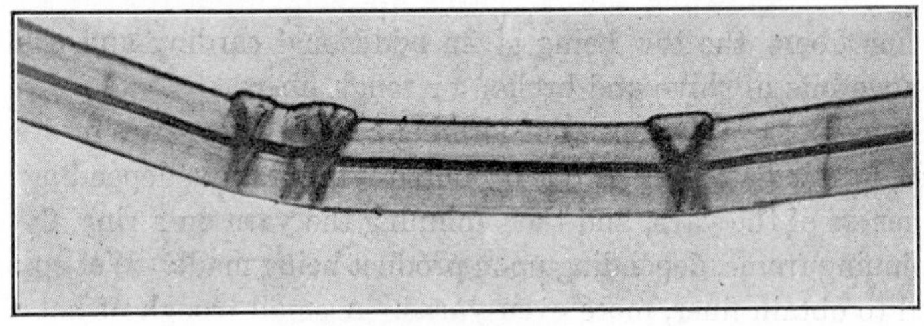

FIG. 7. Flax fiber showing X-shaped transverse nodes stained with chloroiodide of zinc. (*Herzog.*)

Commercial flax fiber is in strands, that is, fiber bundles, ranging in length from 6 to 40 in., with the average at about 15 to 25 in. These fiber bundles are made up of a large number of individual cells, held together by a gummy substance, which has a large proportion of pectin in it. Retting dissolves the cellular tissue and most of the gummy substances holding bast, that is, fiber, bundles in place in the stalk. Subsequent breaking and scutching operations tend to separate these bundles into somewhat smaller bundles. The individual or ultimate cells are not generally separated further for coarse yarn, beyond the partly split bundles resulting from hackling. For fine yarns, individual fibers are separated by wet spinning, that is, by immersing roving in hot water before the final spinning operation. This is not a complete separation, as the hot water only softens gummy substances holding individual fibers together, allowing the spinning machinery to rearrange them as the yarn is formed.

Measurements of individual fiber cells made by various authorities vary, probably because of the large number of varieties of *L. usutatissimum* and varying growing conditions. Average length appears to be

[15] *Flax and Its Products,* Textile Foundation, Washington (1942).

1.00 to 1.25 in., and average diameter 15 to 18 μ. Matthews gives a length range of 0.43 to 1.49 in. and a diameter range of 11 to 20 μ; Herzog, 0.15 to 2.60 in. in length and 12 to 26 μ in diameter; and Vetillart, 0.16 to 2.60 in. in length and 15 to 37 μ in diameter.

The shape of the cell is cylindrical, with a smooth surface, except for transverse nodes which are frequently in the form of an X (see Fig. 7). The cross-section of the mature fiber is round to polygonal, the cell walls are thick, the lumen very small but well defined, and the

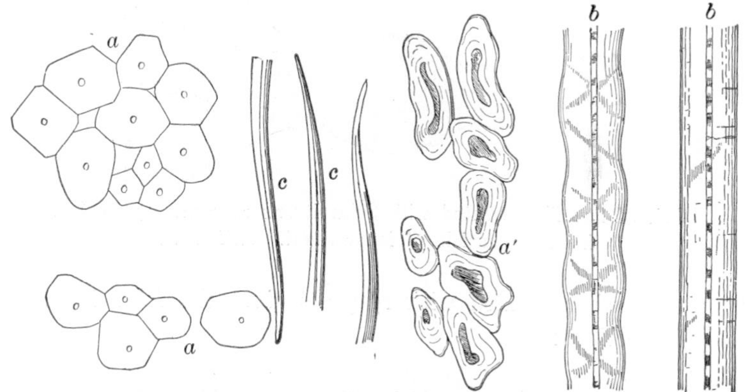

Fig. 8. Flax fibers (×400). *a, a'*, Cross-sections; note larger lumens in *a'* (immature fiber); *b,* longitudinal views; *c,* ends. (*Cross and Bevan.*)

ends of the fiber are pointed with lumen disappearing near the end. The cross-section of immature or "unripe" fiber is oval to ribbonlike, with large lumina running across the broad width of the cell, cell walls being correspondingly thinner. See Fig. 8.

Analysis (H. Müller) of chemical components of two specimens of fiber are given in Table 11.

TABLE 11. Chemical Components of Raw and Boiled Flax Fiber

Component	*Raw Flax (per cent)*	*Boiled Flax (per cent)*
Water (hygroscopic)	10.70	8.65
Aqueous extract	6.02	3.65
Fat and wax	2.37	2.39
Cellulose	71.50	82.57
Ash (mineral matter)	1.32	0.70
Intercellular matter	9.41	2.74
Total	101.32	100.70

Boiled-off and bleached fiber, on a dry basis, is almost pure cellulose. Though raw flax fiber is also generally considered nonlignified, Höhnel is of the opinion that very short sections with lignified cross-walls occur between long sections with walls of pure cellulose. Herzog determined the lignin in raw fibers from different parts of the plant by the methyl oxide method; he found end fibers from the root contained 3.8 per cent lignin; from the middle of the stalk, 2.36 per cent; and from the tip of the stalk, 1.65 per cent.

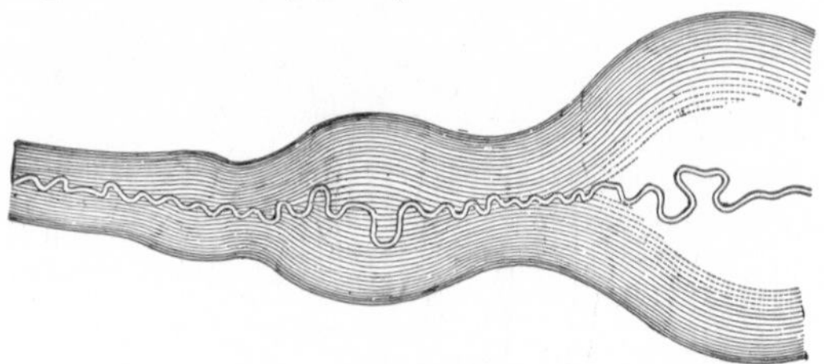

Fig. 9. Cell of flax fiber treated with Schweitzer's reagent. (×400.) Showing insoluble cuticle of inner canal. (*Wiesner.*)

The fiber when treated with reagents gives the following microchemical reactions:

Boiled but unbleached—tincture of madder gives an orange color. Fuchsine, followed with ammonia, gives a permanent rose color.

Boiled and bleached—iodine and sulfuric acid give a blue color. Schweitzer's reagent causes fiber to become quite swollen; inner layers of cell withstand action longest (see Fig. 9).

RAMIE

Nomenclature. Ramie is now, in the Western Hemisphere, the generally accepted designation for fiber obtained from just under the bark of the stalk of the stingless nettle plants of any species of the genus *Boehmeria.* The word comes from an ancient Malayan word, which is anglicized as "rami" (pronounced rahmee). Early designations in the United States and Europe, still in limited use and referring primarily to ramie products from China, are China grass (crude fiber), grass linen, and grasscloth. Some of the many designations in use in other parts of the world are: China—tchou-ma, chu-ma, ch'u, tsu, dzi; India—rhea, pooah, puya, kunkhoora, kunchoor, kurkunda; Malaya and Indonesia—rami, calooee; Indochina—pan, goni; Philippines—amarai; Japan—karamushi, karoa, mao, tsjo.

The ramie fiber-bearing plant belongs to the Urticaceae, that is, nettle, family and was classified by Linnaeus in 1737 as *Urtica nivea*. A few years later Gaudichaud named the genus which includes ramie plants *Boehmeria* in honor of George Rudolph Boehmer, giving the ramie fiber-bearing species the name of *Boehmeria nivea*. William Roxburgh, after studying fiber and plants sent him from Sumatra during the period 1800–1805, named the plant *Urtica tenacissima*. About 1836–1840, study of fiber from plants found growing in Assam, India, and which the natives called "rhea," showed it to be identical with that from the plants named by Gaudichaud and Roxburgh, though the leaves of the "rhea" plants in some areas had green undersides instead of silvery-white ones like the plants of Gaudichaud and Roxburgh. Largely as a result of information published by Sir William Hooker, during the period 1850–1855, the term *Boehmeria nivea* has been used to designate the species of which the leaves have silvery-white undersides and the term *Boehmeria tenacissima* to designate that of which the leaves have green undersides. *Nivea* is the species cultivated most extensively for commercial fiber. Many other species have been discovered and classified, most of which are to be found only in a wild state. The number in the Eastern Hemisphere has been stated at various figures from 100 to 200. Classification of many species is still in dispute. Some botanists and other authorities maintain that many of the classified species should be reclassified as varieties of *Boehmeria nivea*. It has been reported[16] that "information is available on at least 13 species" in the Western Hemisphere, only one species being reported as growing in the United States, "*Boehmeria cylindrica*, which occurs as far north as Maine and Southern Canada . . . a perennial herb, grows 1 to 3 ft tall and is found in most soils." In many areas of the Orient, *Boehmeria nivea* is given a further general classification as "white bark" and "green bark." The stalk of the former is a somewhat lighter green in color than the latter and generally contains finer and a larger amount of fiber; hence it is most widely grown for commercial purposes.

Description of Plant. The ramie plant *Boehmeria nivea* (Fig. 10) is a perennial which sends up large numbers of straight slender stalks (approximately 16 to 20 per sq ft). These grow to a height of 5 to 8 ft with a diameter varying from ½ to ¾ in. The leaves, which appear on the upper part of the stalk, are approximately heart-shaped, about 2 to 5 in. wide and 4 to 6 in. long. The edges are finely serrated. The

[16] "Ramie Production in Florida," U. S. Dept. Commerce, U. S. Dept. Agr., and Univ. of Florida, Everglades Expt. Sta., Washington (1948).

upper part of the leaves is a brilliant, medium green and the underside is silvery-white. The flowers have been described [16] as "greenish-white in color . . . borne in declinate clusters in the axils of the leaves.

FIG. 10. Ramie plants (*Boehmeria nivea*) growing on plantation in Florida. (*Courtesy Newport Industries.*)

Pistillate and staminate flowers are generally found on the same stalk, the former on the upper part of the stalk and the latter on the lower part." The seeds, which are produced in great numbers, are very small, said to average 3 or 4 million per lb. The root system of the plant consists of storage roots, small fibrous feeding roots, and rhizomes (sometimes termed reproductive or lateral roots).

History. The use of the fiber for textile purposes predates written history in the Far East. One of the oldest known written references dating 600 B.C., or earlier, is in the Chinese classic, *The Book of Odes*. The fiber is mentioned in ancient Indian literature, e.g., the drama *Sacantala,* by Kalidassa, written about 400 A.D. The date of introduction of ramie textiles into the Western Hemisphere has not been fixed. Cloth found on some of the Egyptian mummies of the predynastic period (5000 to 3300 B.C.) has been classified as ramie. There is also evidence from the literature of the periods that such fabrics were known to a limited extent in the ancient Mediterranean area as well as in Europe of the Middle Ages. In the Western Hemisphere, some of the twines used by the North American Indians in ancient times for fastening spear and knife blades to shafts or handles, for bowstrings and for packlines, have been identified as ramie.

The modern phase in the history of ramie may be said to have begun in 1690, when a Dutch botanist, George Eberhard Rumpf, found the plants growing in the East Indies and named them *Ramium majus.* Plants for the botanical gardens were brought to Holland in 1733, France in 1844, Germany in 1850, Kew Gardens in London in 1851, and Belgium in 1860. Plants of Far Eastern ramie were first brought to the United States in 1851 from Java by Dr. George C. Schaeffer of the U. S. Patent Office, and planted in the Botanical Gardens in Washington. By the end of the nineteenth century, ramie seed and/or plants had been transported to most of the areas where it is being grown today.

Crude fiber and fabrics were regularly brought in small quantities from the Far East to the Western Hemisphere beginning with the eighteenth century. The first successful processing of crude fiber in the Western Hemisphere was in Holland, about 1845, with fiber from Java. By 1890, small mills had been established in England, France, Germany, and Austria. It was not until the beginning of the 1930's, however, that production of goods on a commercial scale could be said to have been firmly established, the principal mills being located in Germany, Japan, England, France, and Switzerland.

In the United States, a small amount of fabric and other products have been produced and the fiber used for blending purposes since the early part of the twentieth century. Since 1945 the number of mills in the United States using ramie, in some form, has been steadily increasing. One complete mill, that is, a mill performing all processing from the crude fiber through weaving, has begun operations on a commercial scale.

A history of ramie fiber, however brief, would be incomplete without some mention of the promotional schemes in which the fiber has been involved during the past 200 years. The great antiquity of the use of the fiber and its unusually satisfactory performance for some purposes have made it what might be termed a natural selection for promotional purposes with little or no reference to expenditure of skill, time, and money necessary to establish an economically sound basis for the enterprise. These projects were doomed to failure from the beginning. The need for increasingly efficient processing methods and machinery has also often served as a basis for promotional activities, giving rise to the development of projects involving the use of newly devised methods and/or machinery which had not been given a sufficient trial to determine their practicability; many of these projects have also failed. Reports of these failures have, at times, almost obscured those ventures, which, as a result of considerable amounts of hard work, patience, and money have been and are continuing to be successful.

World Production. Crude fiber is produced in Asia (Burma, China, India, Indochina, Thailand, South Korea, and the Straits Settlements); Australia; the Philippine Islands; Indonesia; Ceylon; British North Borneo; the Marianas Islands; the Ryukyu Islands; Formosa; Japan; Africa (Algeria, Belgian Congo, French Cameroons, Egypt, Kenya, and Libya); Europe (France, Italy, and Spain) and U.S.S.R.; North and Central America (the United States [Florida and very small amounts in Alabama, California, Louisiana, Mississippi, and Texas], Mexico, Guatemala, El Salvador, British Honduras, and Yucatan); Cuba, Haiti, Jamaica, Trinidad, and Martinique; and in South America (Argentina, Brazil, and Peru). In most of these areas, fiber is produced for home consumption or only on an experimental basis.

Data on world production of crude fiber, estimated on the basis of the best information available in the absence of formal, statistical records of production, are shown in Table 12 for 1951, 1952, and for the average during the 1930's. Current fiber production for commercial use is greatly below demand. Plantings made, or in process of being made, indicate that production will increase considerably.

Utilization. Chief products manufactured from ramie are twine for fish nets, industrial sewing threads, industrial packings, canvas, fire hose, filter cloths, upholstery fabrics, and clothing and household furnishing fabrics. Some of the shorter fiber strands and processing and spinning waste are used for the manufacture of paper. In the United States most important uses are industrial packings and upholstery

TABLE 12. Estimated World Production of Crude Ramie Fiber

(Short tons)

Areas	*1952* Total	*1952* Commercial Use	*1951* Total	*1951* Commercial Use	*Average during 1930's* Total	*Average during 1930's* Commercial Use
Total	11,000 [a]	5,000 [a]	10,000 [a]	4,000 [a]	90,000	28,000
China	n.a.	n.a.	n.a.	n.a.	75,000	25,000
Japan	1,800	1,700	1,400	1,300	1,000 [b]	900
Philippine Islands	500	500	200–500	200–500	700 [c]	700
United States	1,500	1,500	1,200	1,200	neg.	neg.
All others	7,400	1,500	6,900–7,200	1,000–1,300	13,000	1,400

n.a. Not available. neg. Negligible.

[a] Excluding production from China, for which data are not available.

[b] Peak year 1941, 5600 tons.

[c] Peak year 1941, 1500 tons.

fabrics, the latter generally being made of ramie blended with another fiber. Data concerning amount of fiber used for principal manufactures are not available.

Principal barrier to more extensive utilization of ramie fiber in recent years has been low supply of crude fiber. Post-World War II, very high prices, approximately six to nine times those of the 1930's, resulting from high demand and low supply, have also served to discourage wider use of the fiber.

Cultivation. Ramie plants grow best in a warm, moist climate, tropical, subtropical, and temperate, where winter temperatures are above freezing though there are varieties that are grown in areas with freezing winter temperatures as far north or south as 40° latitude, only one crop a year being obtained. In temperate and subtropical zones best results are obtained at altitudes of less than 1000 feet above sea level; in tropical areas satisfactory results may be obtained at altitudes as high as 4000 or 5000 ft, if temperature, amount of sunshine, and moisture are suitable. Rainfall should average not less than 3½ to 4 in. per month and be fairly evenly distributed throughout the year as periods of drought or heavy rains damage the plants. Irrigation is used in some areas to supplement rainfall. The area should be free of strong winds, preferably with winds of less than 20 mph. Strong winds cause the stalks to rub against each other, damaging the fiber. The preferred soil is a moderately rich loam, loose and friable, and well drained. The last point is important, as the roots die quickly if water stands on them. Fertilization depends upon the composition of the soil; the quantity required is in proportion to the number of crops harvested annually. Propagation is usually by means of cuttings from the rhizomes.

Strong, well-established plants are uprooted, the rhizomes are immediately cut into 5- to 6-in. lengths, and are planted as soon as possible after cutting in trenches 4 to 5 in. deep. In some areas, where hand labor is used for planting, the cut pieces of rhizome are sprouted before being planted to insure viability. Plants usually appear 7 to 10 days after planting. Ramie is also grown from seed and from cut pieces of the stalk. Seeds require more labor and seldom breed true, and are used chiefly in experimental work for developing new varieties. Cut pieces of the stalk require more planting labor than cuttings of rhizomes as there will be more dead pieces or "skips" to be replaced in the field after planting unless the cuttings are first rooted and then transplanted. In some areas stalks are bent to the ground and covered at intervals with earth; when the covered parts have developed roots, stalks are cut into pieces and planted in the fields.

Methods of cultivation vary in relation to local customs, labor costs, and degree of mechanization available in an area. In the United States, on large plantations, agricultural machinery is used for almost every cultivating operation. Stalks sent up by the new, young plants are cut every 2 to 4 months and allowed to remain on the field until the root system spreads out and becomes strongly established. Elapsed time required for this is from 9 months to 2 years, depending principally upon the climate and upon the spacing used for initial planting. When the root systems are well established, a crop may be harvested during the warm growing season on the average of once every 60 days, and the plants will continue to produce stalks with good-quality fiber for a period of 5 to 15 years, depending upon growth conditions in the area. After this period, roots become matted and overcrowded and only thick, short stalks with coarse fiber result. In tropical areas, roots require pruning between rows every 12 to 18 months to prevent root matting and overcrowding; by the end of 5 years, roots in the centers of the rows will have become matted and the field will require replanting. In areas where only one crop a year can be harvested, rootstock needs replacing only every 20 to 30 years since growing conditions are not favorable in these areas and roots do not become matted as quickly. In areas where the plant is grown on a commercial scale, it is apparently bothered by few pests and diseases, and these not to a significant degree, as they are readily controlled.

Ramie is ready for harvesting for optimum quality of fiber when the lower part of the stalk turns a yellowish, light brown, when the lower leaves begin to turn yellow and are easily detached, and when the tips of the new stalks just begin to appear above ground. Harvesting is done by cutting the stalks close enough to the ground to insure maximum stalk length and prevent stumps from sprouting but high enough above ground to prevent damage to the tips of the new stalks. This work is generally done by hand; in the United States machinery is used.

Production of crude fiber (that is, fiber after it is removed from the stalk and dried) per acre varies considerably in relation to climate and soil, skill of cultivation, and efficiency of fiber removal from the stalk, the figures stated for various areas in the world ranging from 100 to 3000 lb per acre. Data from the United States, the Philippine Islands, and Japan show that, when ramie is grown on a commercial scale, total annual yield of green stalks and leaves per acre range from 25,000 to 50,000 lb in climates where three crops a year are harvested, and 50,000 to 100,000 lb in climates where five crops a year are harvested. The yield of crude fiber from these quantities of green material ranges from 1000 to 1800 lb per acre in three-crop areas and 1800 to 2800 lb per acre in five-crop areas.

Decortication. Decortication is removal of fiber from the stalk and affects both the quality and the quantity of crude fiber obtained. Decortication was formerly entirely a hand operation, and utilization of the fiber on a commercial scale made little progress. Individual ramie fibers occur in the form of bast bundles with the ends overlapping so as to produce continuous filaments throughout the length of the stalk. They are held in place and to each other by gums, waxes, and pectins. Decortication frees the fibers in the form of fiber strands, i.e., the continuous filaments which are made up of bundles of individual fibers, by removing the bark and woody part of the stalk, termed the "shive," and of a portion of the gums, waxes, and pectins, which are usually designated as "gum." Decorticated fiber strands are generally termed "crude ramie fiber." See Fig. 11.

In areas where hand decortication is still practiced each area has its own individual way of performing the work. Basically, the operation in most areas consists of either peeling or beating the bark, with the fiber adhering to it, from the stalk when freshly cut or after drying. The stalk may or may not be soaked before the bark is removed. The fiber is then freed from the bark by alternate soaking and scraping. Before decortication, leaves are removed from the stalks, either by hand or by running long bamboo poles up and down the stalks before cutting. Fresh or salt, still or running, and cold, warm, or hot water is used, depending upon local custom. Tools used for scraping are abalone shells, specially prepared pieces of bamboo, and bronze or iron knives, and the operation is done either by holding the scraper in the palm of one hand with the edge against a guard placed on the thumb or by holding the scraper against a block of wood by hand or with a crude mechanism. Beating is done by flailing stalk or bark against wooden or rock surface or by pounding with wooden paddles or mallets. Drying of fiber is by sun or air. Both sun and dew

FIG. 11. Cross-section of ramie stalk. Outside lighter-colored area is the bark, consisting of cork or cuticle and phelloderm. The black dots enclosed by this area are the fibers. Inside the fiber area is the woody part of the stalk consisting of the phloem, the cambium, and the xylem layers. The very light-colored area in the center is the pith.

bleaching are used. To bleach the fiber still more, the Chinese in many areas use the fumes from burning charcoal or sulfur. The result is the so-called "white" fiber. In some areas, notably southeast Asia and Indonesia, bark is scraped from the length of the stalk, leaving the fiber adhering to the stalk, which is then washed and dried. After drying fiber is peeled from the stalk in the form of strands. To prevent damage to the fiber during the scraping operation, plant is allowed to mature botanically, that is, to flower and seed, so that the bark may be thick and firm. The resulting fiber is coarse, and, in areas where this method of fiber removal is used, fiber is generally used for twines and not for weaving fabrics.

Literally thousands of machines for decortication have been developed in various countries since 1800 when ramie began to arouse interest for commercial use. In the United States alone, more than 2000 patents have been issued. The first fairly successful machine was a small portable type, patented in France in 1896. This machine, of which some models are in use, was patterned after the raspador, a machine invented by a Spanish Franciscan friar for removing fiber from the leaves of sanseviera, agave, and similar plants. The basic principle of the raspador consists of first crushing the leaf (or, in the case of ramie, the stalk), and then holding it, by mechanical means, against the scraping action of blades set at intervals in the outer circumference of a rotating wheel. The tip end of the leaf, or ramie stalk (which must first be defoliated), is inserted first and the fiber freed for about half its length, when the leaf, or stalk, is pulled from the machine. The butt end is then fed into the machine until the remaining length of fiber is freed, when it is pulled from the machine and hung up to dry.

A large stationary machine, patented in Germany in 1933, primarily for decorticating sisal, was readily adapted for ramie. This machine, still in use, utilizes the basic principle of the early raspador and frees the full length of the fiber in one continuous operation by bringing alternate halves of the fiber length against one of two sets of rotating blades. A stream of water is played on the fiber as it is freed. Before being fed into the machine, stalks must be defoliated, topped, and butted. A small portable machine now in wide use was patented in Japan in 1947, and utilizes the basic principle of the early raspador, freeing the full length of the fiber in a continuous operation with one set of rotating blades and eliminating the need for defoliation. A companion machine, intended to be used with the decorticator for brushing the fiber after decortication and drying, was patented at the same time.

Several machines have been developed in the United States since 1940, and are in use in various areas. These machines also utilize the basic principle of the early raspador and include both the small portable or semiportable type as well as the large stationary type. Experimental work is being done in the development of harvester-decorticators.

The efficiency of the machines varies. Quantity of crude fiber yield from the larger machines ranges from 2½ to 3½ per cent on the basis of total weight of green stalks and leaves, and from the smaller machines 2½ to 6 per cent.

Grades. After decortication, crude fiber is dried in kilns or in sun or open-air sheds, then, if intended for commercial use, baled for shipment, the size of the bales varying, according to local custom, from 100 to 500 lb. Ramie fiber is sold almost entirely on the basis of submitted sample, there being no generally adopted grading standards. Qualities principally considered are length and cleanliness of fiber, date of crop, and moisture content. A few fiber brokers and one or two growers have their own grading standards, which their customers recognize. The Philippine Islands has officially adopted a set of grading standards for crude fiber. These are based on efficiency of fiber removal; general quality of fiber, especially with respect to pliability and color; and length. The grades are, in a descending order: RD-A Special; RD-1 Good; RD-2 Fair; RD-3 Shorts; RD-Y Damaged; RD-O Strings; RD-T Tow; RD-W Waste, with subclassification for length as follows: Extra Long, Very Long, Long, Normal, and Short.

Degumming. Degumming the fiber, as the name implies, means completing the removal of the gums, waxes, and pectins remaining on the crude fiber after decortication and which, if left on the fiber, render it brittle and weak. Proper degumming separates the individual fibers and leaves them in a soft, clean state with their strength and other characteristics intact. Maintenance of production of degummed fiber of a uniformly good quality requires considerable skill because the crude fiber varies in quality from area to area and season to season. The successful accomplishment of the degumming operation, like decortication, was formerly a major barrier to commercial use of ramie fiber.

In areas of the world where the fiber is processed by hand, degumming is accomplished by repeatedly soaking, scraping, washing, and sun-drying the fibers. In some areas, lye, made from ashes, or lime is used in the soaking water. Degumming on a commercial scale is customarily done by the mills which spin the fiber. There are two basic methods for commercial degumming: bacteriological and chemical. The former has received much attention, but, so far, no bacteriological process has appeared that will, on a commercial scale, degum successfully the full length of the crude fiber strand.

The chemical process of degumming consists of boiling the fiber in a chemical solution, usually made with caustic soda. The amount of chemical used depends largely upon the quality of the crude fiber and the quantity of bark and shive and gum on it. Residual bark and shive and gum on commercial fiber on today's market ranges from 50 to 15 per cent of total weight of crude fiber, most frequently ranging from 40 to 25 per cent. For crude fiber with a 30 per cent residual bark and shive and gum content, an amount of caustic soda equal to approximately 5 or 6 per cent of the dry weight of the fiber is added to enough water to make a solution with a total weight of either 5 or 6 times the weight of dry fiber. A reducing agent, usually sodium sulfite, is also added to the solution. A wetting agent is added to the degumming solution or the fiber is soaked in water for 24 hr before boiling. Cooking, i.e., boiling, in most plants is done in open vats. Length of cooking time varies in relation to equipment and method, the more usual time being somewhere between 1 and 4 hr. After cooking the fiber is rinsed, neutralized, washed, and centrifuged several times, then oiled and dried. In some plants the fiber is bleached before oiling. Chemical degumming can be done with pressure kiers, but this equipment is not used extensively. Experiments are being conducted in the United States with a continuous system for chemical degumming and subsequent operations, using the principle of the counterflow system.

Fiber Preparation and Spinning. Methods of ramie fiber and yarn preparation are widely diversified, whether the operations are done by hand or on a commercial scale by machinery. The machinery is principally adapted from that designed for handling other fibers; hence equipment varies from mill to mill to a greater degree than is usual in the textile industry. Existing yarn preparation equipment used for commercial production, both in the United States and elsewhere, is limited as to the length of fiber that can be utilized. Ramie fibers, after degumming, therefore, must be prepared by having their lengths reduced to those suitable for the equipment being used. This is done either by stapling or by mechanically sorting into basic length groups. The sorting method, which approximates carding and combing, produces the strongest and smoothest yarns, more nearly realizing the strength potentialities of the fiber. This operation, in the United States, is done chiefly on machinery which has been adapted from that used for wool and for cotton fibers; elsewhere, adaptations of machinery for flax and for spun silk are also used.

Subsequent yarn preparations for the longer fibers are, in the United States, usually done on an adaptation of some of the machines used for wool fibers; in other areas adaptations of machinery designed for flax or spun silk fibers are also used. Yarn preparation for the shorter fibers are usually done on machinery adapted from the cotton system.

Dry spinning with ring spindles is used in the United States and also chiefly in other areas. Although the size of the yarn spun in greatest quantity in all areas, for commercial purposes, is 56 to 60 lea (20.00 to 21.43 cotton count or 295 to 276 Grex), dry spinning with long draft ring spindles can also be used to produce finer yarns, some mills regularly producing yarns of size 180 lea (64.28 cotton count or 93 Grex). Twisting of plied yarns is done on conventional types of machinery.

On the basis of average quality of crude fiber on today's market and efficiency of degumming and preparation and spinning equipment in use, the following average production results may be obtained, crude fiber to yarn, in terms of percentages of weight of crude fiber: Crude fiber—100 per cent; degummed fiber—70 per cent; prepared fiber, on basis of mechanical sorting by lengths—63 per cent; and yarn—60 per cent.

Fiber Characteristics. Ramie fiber is naturally very white and does not change color upon exposure to sunlight. It is highly lustrous and has an exceptionally high resistance to the effects of bacteria and fungi, including mildew. Yarns and fabrics made from it are highly absorbent and dry quickly. One series of tests with yarns[17] showed, upon total immersion, 100 per cent water absorption in 10 min and 195 per cent in 72 hr. Fabrics were equally absorbent, depending upon construction and finish. The fiber takes dyes readily, although care must be taken to insure complete penetration. Fabrics are easily laundered, requiring no special care, and showing only minor strength loss after repeated washings.

Specific gravity of the fiber ranges from 1.50 to 1.55 and averages 1.51. The fiber denier ranges from 4.5 to 10.5, with an average of 6 to 7 for fiber from the middle section of the stalk. Fiber at the butt end of the stalk is 45 to 50 per cent heavier and at the tip end 25 to 30 per cent lighter than fiber from the middle section. The tensile strength is very high, ranging from 27 to 55 g with an average of 35 and 45 g. Tenacity, i.e., breaking strength in grams per denier, ranges from 3 to 9 with the average at 6 to 7. Wet strength is 140 to 160 per cent of strength at standard atmosphere, on the basis of immersion of 1 sec to 24 hr. Elongation ranges from 2 to 10 per cent and averages 3 to 4 per cent.

A comparison of tensile strengths of ramie, cotton, and flax yarns, of the same size, is shown in Table 13.

Ramie yarns show satisfactory strength when knotted or looped. Results from one study are shown in Table 14. The flexing quality is also satisfactory. Yarns show about four times that of cotton yarns and two times that of flax yarns.

[17] "Ramie Today," Harold T. Coss and James L. Taylor, Ga. Inst. of Tech., State Engineering Expt. Sta., Atlanta, **X** (14), Circular (Aug. 1948).

TABLE 13. Comparison of Breaking Strengths of Yarns of Same Size

Test Group	Tensile Strength: Ramie Compared with Cotton (Cotton Yarns = 100)	Tensile Strength: Ramie Compared with Flax (Flax Yarns = 100)
Group A [a]		
Ramie stapled to 2″; Cotton 1″ staple		
Singles yarn	117	n.t.
6-ply	140	n.t.
Group B [b]		
Ramie fibers cut into 15″ lengths; cotton staple not stated, 6-ply yarn	194	n.t.
Group C [c]		
Ramie long fiber, range 4″ to 12″, average 5″ to 6″; cotton staple not stated; flax, line fiber; singles yarn	300 to 500	200 to 250
Ramie short fiber, range 1¾″ to 3″, average 2″; cotton staple not stated; flax, tow fiber; singles yarn	120 to 140	110 to 115

n.t. Not included in tests.

[a] "Ramie Today," Harold T. Coss and James L. Taylor, Ga. Inst. of Tech., State Engineering Expt. Sta., Atlanta, **X** (14), Circular (Aug. 1948).

[b] "Ramie Production in Florida," U. S. Dept. Commerce, U. S. Dept. of Agr., and Univ. of Florida, Everglades Expt. Sta., Washington (1948).

[c] Studies made by Japanese ramie mills (1947–1950).

TABLE 14. Knot and Loop Strengths of Ramie and Cotton Yarns

Arrangement of Yarns	Strength in Terms of Tenacity of Straight Yarns: Ramie	Strength in Terms of Tenacity of Straight Yarns: Cotton [a]
Straight	100	100
Looped	92 [b]	54 [b]
Knotted	96	84

[a] Ramie and cotton yarns same size; ramie fiber stapled to 2″ length and cotton fiber 1″ staple. Yarns conditioned to 50 per cent R.H. and 75° F.

[b] Approximate. Computed by using twice the tenacity of straight yarn as a base, since a two-yarn system exists across the span of the break test.

Source: "Ramie Today," Harold T. Coss and James L. Taylor, Ga. Inst. of Tech., Atlanta, **X** (14), Circular (Aug. 1948).

The individual bast cells are unusually long, ranging from ½ to 20 in. and averaging 5 to 6 in. Width ranges from 25 to 75 μ, averaging 30 to 50 μ. The shape of the mature cell is approximately cylindrical, with almost no twist. The surface is characterized by small nodelike ridges and striations which sometimes result in cross-sections of the fiber being termed polygonal. The cell walls are thick and the lumina well defined. Immature fiber is ribbonlike, varying from a rather flat to an elliptical shape, and has a small amount of twist. Cell walls are thin and lumina flat and undeveloped, extending across the long width of the fiber. The fibers end in a rounded point, the cell walls being thickened and the lumen almost disappearing. See Figs. 12 and 13.

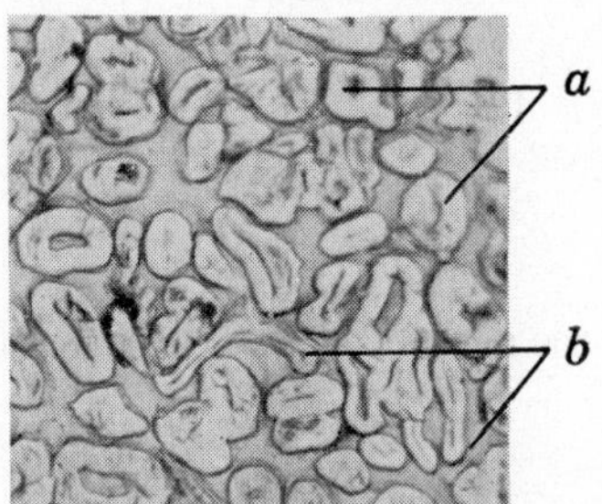

Fig. 12. Cross-section of ramie fiber, ×180. *a,* Mature fibers; *b,* immature fiber. (*Ramie Today, op. cit.*)

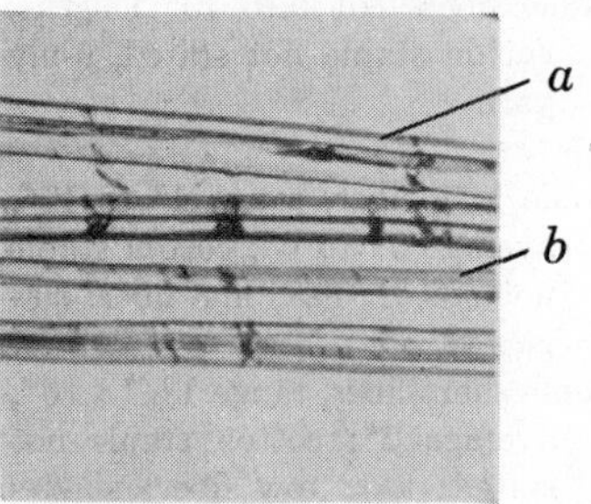

Fig. 13. Longitudinal view of ramie fiber, ×172. *a,* Mature fiber; *b,* immature fiber. (*Ramie Today, op. cit.*)

Chemical analyses show a high percentage of cellulose. Table 15 gives data on two analyses of decorticated, *not degummed,* fiber, on a dry basis.

TABLE 15. Chemical Components of Decorticated Ramie Fiber

	Per Cent of Component	
Components	*Haitian* [a]	*Japanese* [b]
Ash	2.05	3.15
Aqueous extract	6.90	6.89
Fats and waxes	0.22	0.22
Cellulose	83.32	83.09
Pectins and other intercellular material	7.51	6.65
Total	100.00	100.00

[a] "Ramie Today," Harold T. Coss and James L. Taylor, Ga. Inst. of Tech., Atlanta, **X** (14), Circular (Aug. 1948).

[b] Studies made by Japanese ramie mills (1947–1950).

Properly degummed fiber, dry basis, is 96 to 98 per cent α-cellulose, with very little or no trace of lignin. Iodine and sulfuric acid, when applied to degummed fiber, give a clear blue stain, and aniline gives no color. In an ammoniacal solution of copper oxide, the fiber swells considerably but does not dissolve. It gives a blue coloration with chloriodide of zinc reagent and rose red with chloriodide of calcium.

HEMP

Nomenclature. Hemp is the name designating fiber obtained from the stalk of the hemp plant *Cannabis sativa,* an annual of the Moraceae family. It is sometimes called the "true hemp," as the fiber had such widespread usage for textiles and especially for cordage, in Europe and other parts of the Western Hemisphere, that, when other fibers were introduced, beginning with the seventeenth and eighteenth centuries, they were generally given the name "hemp," preceded by an adjective or noun, usually to indicate their places of origin. A list of these fibers is included at the end of this section. Even today, a large segment of the trade in cordage fibers, notably the British, uses the word "hemp" in a categorical sense, with two subcategories: "hard hemp," under which are included the leaf or structural fibers used for cordage, and "soft hemp," under which are included some of the bast fibers, especially those used for cordage.

Plant. The hemp plant, when grown for fiber, has tall, slender, medium-green stalks, averaging 7 to 10 feet in height and about ½ in. in diameter. The plant is also grown for oil seed and, in some areas, for its narcotic properties, when, being planted at wider intervals than for fiber, the plants are heavily branched. Leaves, which are alternate except near the top of the plant, have comparatively long stems and are bright green and digitate, with five or seven lobes, usually five, each leaflet narrow, with serrated edges and tapering to a point. Staminate and pistillate flowers, which are greenish-yellow and small, are borne on separate plants, staminate appearing in drooping panicles and pistillate in bushy, spikelike racemes. (See Fig. 14.)

History. Use of the plant for fiber, which predates written history, apparently originated in Asia or the Near East. Records indicate that the fibers were used in China and in Persia and other parts of the Near East from prehistoric times. Hemp is the oldest textile fiber used in Japan. Cultivation of the plant for fiber spread to many of the Mediterranean countries of Europe, notably Italy, during the early centuries of the Christian Era and expanded through Europe during the

rows, with a space of about 5 in. between rows and about 3 in. between plants. Methods of land preparation and cultivation vary widely, depending upon customs and equipment available for the area. In the Far East and some parts of Russia and Europe, hand labor predominates. In Italy, cultivation is partially mechanized. In the United States, cultivation is highly mechanized.

Harvesting. Stalks are ready for harvesting when the lower leaves just begin to turn yellow. Northern varieties usually require about 80 to 90 days from sowing and southern varieties from 110 to 120 days. Male plants are ready for harvesting usually 1 to 2 weeks before female plants. In some areas where hand labor is used, male plants are pulled, or cut, first and female plants harvested at a later date. In some of these areas, when seed is wanted for oil, female plants may be allowed to remain uncut until seed ripens, a practice which results in coarse, heavy fiber. In other areas where hand labor is used and in areas where machinery is used for harvesting, cutting is done at a time when it is judged the best quality of fiber will result from both male and female plants at the same cutting. This, of course, results in a mixture of some coarse fiber from those male plants which are past the best harvesting stage, and some very fine fiber from those female plants which have not reached the best harvesting stage. In the United States, approximate stage for harvesting is when the male plants are in full flower and shedding pollen.

Preparation of Fiber and Grading. Methods of separating the fiber from the stalks also vary widely. Dew retting is used in many areas, including the United States. Snow retting is used in a few areas. In other areas, the stalks, after being butted and topped, are water retted in bogs, ponds, or tanks, either when freshly cut or after they have been sun dried. Water for retting should be clean and free of chemical impurities that might stain or discolor the fiber. Determination of the time when retting is finished is also of great importance. When fiber will slip easily from the stalk, the ret is complete. Under-retting results in rough, broken fiber and over-retting in weak fiber.

After retting, stalks are dried either by air or mechanically. The bark with the fiber adhering to it is then removed from the stalk by peeling by hand, by pounding with wooden mallets or between wooden blocks, or by running the stalks through a breaking machine. In some growing areas the bark is next removed from the fiber by hand scraping; in others bark is removed from the fiber by machine scutching in a manner similar to that used for flax. In other areas, machinery which combines the breaking and scutching operation is used. After scutching, that is, removal of bark, the hemp is usually dressed, generally a hand operation, to insure thorough cleaning of the fiber, by pulling the fiber strands between a wooden blade and block or between a dull knife and a padded block. The fiber is then softened by "beetling," which consists of pounding it, by hand or by running it through a stamping or rolling machine. In the United States, machinery is used for all these operations.

Yield of prepared fiber per acre varies widely, ranging from 200 to 1000 lb, depending upon area, efficiency of cultivation, and method of fiber preparation. Highest yield per acre is in Italy, where the average is 1100 lb. In the United States average yield is 850 lb per acre. The variety grown affects the yield, northern varieties yielding less than southern varieties.

There are no generally recognized grading standards in use for hemp. The fiber is purchased principally on the basis of samples. Some dealers have their own grades, which their customers recognize. In the United States, growers in each state follow grading standards for that state; these are based on color, length, texture, cleanness, and strength and are usually designated by the name of the state followed by a numerical indication of the grade. The Conzorio Nazionale Canapa, the national agency charged with collection and sale of hemp in Italy, has established a detailed grading system for Italian hemp based on length, color, texture, cleanness, strength, area where grown, system of processing used for fiber removal, and purpose for which hemp will be used. The Conzorio Nazionale Canapa also fixes prices, establishes allocation of fiber for domestic use and for export trade, supervises negotiation of export agreements, and sponsors research for improved cultivation and processing methods. It developed in 1947 from an amalgamation of two associations, one of growers and one of workers, which had been formed in 1946. These associations were formed to replace the Federcanapa which had operated from 1936, when government controls over hemp production and distribution were first instituted, until 1944. Originally the Federcanapa was under the control of the Ministry of Agriculture and Forests, but, with the outbreak of World War II, control was transferred to the Ministry of Industry and Commerce. Control measures for the 1945–46 crop were under the responsibility of the Allied Commission.

Characteristics. The fiber, if carefully prepared, is very light-colored and quite lustrous. Generally, however, the commercial fiber is pale grey, yellowish, greenish, or dark brown, depending upon variety and method of preparation. Fiber strands range from 40 to 80 in. in length. Strength is good. Tests of cordage fibers conducted by Schiefer[21] showed that Wisconsin Line No. 1 hemp fiber had 72 per cent of the dry breaking strength of abacá, grade J2 Davao, and 87 per cent of that of sisal, grade 3L, two of the strongest cordage fibers in use.

Individual cells are quite long, ranging, according to Vétillart, from 0.20 to 2.16 in., and averaging 0.59 to 0.98 in. The shape is cylindrical with surface irregularities in the form of frequent joints, longitudinal

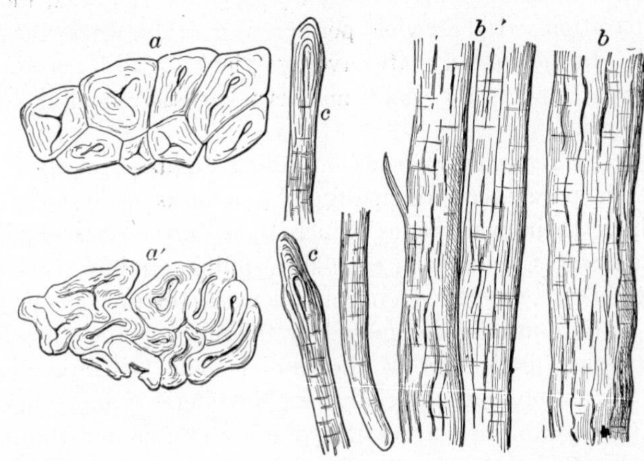

FIG. 15. Hemp fibers. *a, a'*, Cross-sections; *b, b'*, longitudinal views; *c*, ends. (*Cross and Bevan.*)

fractures, and swollen tissues. The cross-section is polygonal with rounded edges. The diameter is markedly uneven, ranging from 16 to 50 μ, and averaging 22 μ. Occasional fragments of parenchymatous (i.e., spongy or porous) tissue are attached to the outer surface of the fiber cell. The cell walls are thick. The lumen is broad and rather flat, becoming very small toward end of cell. Cell ends are blunt, irregularly shaped, and occasionally show lateral branches. (See Fig. 15.)

Table 17 shows Müller's analysis of a sample of the best Italian hemp.

Hemp gives the following microchemical reactions: (*a*) with iodine-sulfuric acid reagent, bluish-green coloration; (*b*) with chloriodide of zinc, blue or violet with traces of yellow; (*c*) chloriodide of calcium, rose red with traces of yellow; (*d*) ammoniacal fuchsine solution, pale-

[21] "Machines and Methods for Testing Cordage Fibers," Herbert F. Schiefer, Natl. Bur. of Standards RP1611, U. S. Dept. Commerce, Washington (1944).

TABLE 17. CHEMICAL ANALYSIS OF HEMP

Components	*Per Cent*
Ash	0.82
Water (hygroscopic)	8.88
Aqueous extract	3.48
Fat and wax	0.56
Cellulose	77.77
Intercellular matter and pectin bodies	9.31
Total	100.82

red coloration; (*e*) with Schweitzer's reagent fibers swell irregularly with a characteristic appearance (Fig. 16) and dissolve almost completely, leaving only the fragments of parenchymatous tissue; (*f*) hydrochloric acid and caustic potash give a brown coloration; (*g*) ammonia produces a faint violet. The fiber appears to be a mixture of cellulose and lignocellulose, the latter being responsible for the yellow to yellowish-green coloration with aniline sulfate and a greenish color with iodine and sulfuric acid.

Hemp is at times difficult to distinguish from flax. Major points of difference follow: (1) cell ends of hemp are blunt and show lateral branches, which are never present on flax fiber; (2) hemp fiber, when treated with iodine-sulfuric acid reagent exhibits a stratified appearance of the cell wall and a bluish-green coloration; flax gives a characteristic blue color; (3) fibers of hemp are less transparent than those of flax, and the interior canal is more difficult to distinguish because of numerous striations on surface; (4) appearance of cross-sections is different for the two fibers; (5) parenchymatous tissue which is frequently found attached to hemp

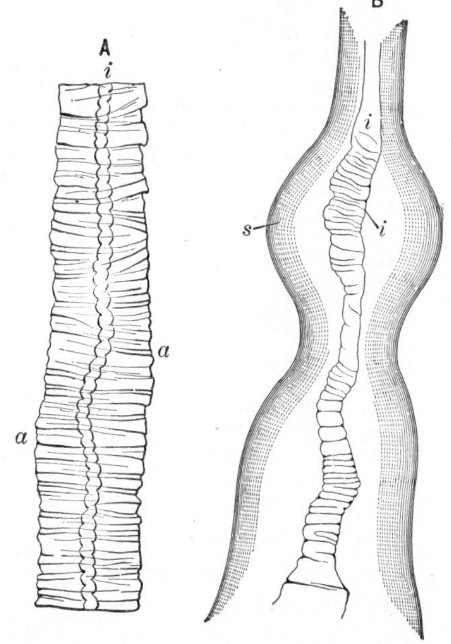

FIG. 16. Hemp fibers treated with Schweitzer's reagent. *A*, Strongly lignified fiber; *B*, fiber free from ligneous matter; *i*, skin of inner canal; *a*, external ligneous tissue; *s*, swollen cellulose. (*Wiesner.*)

TABLE 18. Names Used in Trade including Word "Hemp" but Representing Fibers from Plants Other than *Cannabis sativa*

Trade Name	*Botanical Name*
African bowstring "hemp"	*Sansevieria metallica*
Agrimony "hemp"	*Eupatorium cannabinum*
Ambari "hemp"	*Hibiscus cannabinus*
Benares "hemp"	*Crotalaria juncea*
Blackfellow's "hemp"	*Commersonia fraseri*
Bombay "hemp"	*Crotalaria juncea*
Bowstring "hemp"	*Sansevieria roxburghiana* and *S. zeylanica*
Brown "hemp"	*Crotalaria juncea*
Calcutta "hemp"	*Cochorus capsularis*
Ceylon bowstring "hemp"	*Sansevieria zeylanica*
Colorado River "hemp"	*Sesbania exaltata*
Conkanee "hemp"	*Crotalaria juncea*
Cretan "hemp"	*Datisca cannabina*
Cuban "hemp"	*Furcraea cubensis*
Deccan "hemp"	*Hibiscus cannabinus*
False "hemp"	*Rhus typhina*
False sisal "hemp"	*Agave decipiens*
Florida bowstring "hemp"	*Sansevieria metallica*
Gambo "hemp"	*Hibiscus cannabinus*
Guinea bowstring "hemp"	*Sansevieria thyrsiflora* (syn. *guineensis*)
Guinea "hemp"	*Hibiscus cannabinus*
Haiti "hemp"	*Furcraea gigantea*
Ife "hemp"	*Sansevieria cylindrica*
Indian "hemp"	*Apocynum cannabinum*
Indian "hemp"	*Crotalaria juncea*
Itarsi "hemp"	*Crotalaria juncea*
Jubbulpore "hemp"	*Crotalaria juncea*
Kaffir "hemp"	*Grewia occidentalis*
Kudzu "hemp"	*Pueraria thunbergiana*
Madras "hemp"	*Crotalaria juncea*
Manila "hemp"	*Musa textilis*
Mauritius "hemp"	*Furcraea gigantea*
Musk "hemp"	*Hibiscus abelmoschus*
New Zealand "hemp"	*Phormium tenax*
Pangane "hemp"	*Sansevieria kirkii*
Perini "hemp"	*Hibiscus cannabinus*
Pita "hemp"	*Yucca species*
Puya "hemp"	*Maoutia puya*
Queensland "hemp"	*Sida rhombifolia*
Rajmahal "hemp"	*Marsdenia tenacissima*
Rangoon "hemp"	*Laportea gigas*
Roselle "hemp"	*Hibiscus sabdariffa*
Sann "hemp"	*Crotalaria juncea*
Sisal "hemp"	*Agave sisalana*
Somaliland bowstring "hemp"	*Sansevieria eherenbergii*
Sunn "hemp"	*Crotalaria juncea*
Swedish "hemp"	*Urtica dioica*
Tampico "hemp"	*Agave heteracantha*
Water "hemp"	*Eupatorium cannabinum*

TABLE 21. COMPARISON OF SELECTED PHYSICAL FACTORS FOR KENAF WITH THOSE OF ROSELLE, URENA, AND JUTE

(Basis 15-in. bundles of fiber weighing 5 grams)

		Fiber				
Item	*Unit*	*Kenaf*	*Roselle*	*Urena*	*Jute, High-Grade*	*Jute, Low-Grade*
Fineness of fiber	1000 ft/lb	270	287	540	880	490
Breaking strength						
Dry	Pounds	44	46	30	53	43
Wet	Pounds	40	47	35	44	36
Dry, after exposure in twin-arc Weatherometer for 100 hours	Pounds	42	33	23	41	29
Flexural endurance						
At 50% of original strength	Cycles	200	400	430	420	560
At strength of 20 lb	Cycles	150	450	300	710	620
Elongation at rupture						
Dry	Per cent	1.7	1.7	0.9	1.7	1.3
Wet	Per cent	2.1	1.8	1.3	1.5	1.3

Notes: Published results show a ± figure for each of the figures given in the above table; these have been omitted here to conserve space.

Country of origin or quality of fiber not indicated for kenaf, roselle, or urena.

Source: "Machines and Methods for Testing Cordage Fibers," Herbert F. Schiefer, Natl. Bur. of Standards RP1611, U. S. Dept. Commerce, Washington (1944).

fiber, when treated with iodine or sulfuric acid, is somewhat similar to that shown by sunn fiber. The median layer of lignin surrounding the kenaf cell wall shows a much darker color reaction than the inner layers of the cell wall.

URENA

Nomenclature and History. Urena fiber is obtained from just under the bark of the stalk of the plant *Urena lobata,* a member of the Malvaceae family. The name "urena" is derived from the Malayalam word "uram," which is used to designate the plant on the Malabar coast of India. Though the name "urena" is coming into general use in export trade in the fiber, both the plant and the fiber have many names in the various areas where it grows wild or is cultivated. These include: in Brazil, uacima, uacima roxa, or guaxima; in Cuba, malva blanca or Cuban "jute"; in other parts of South America and the

West Indies, aramina, bamia, bolo bolo, cadillo, candilla, candillo, carrapicho, cousin rouge, grand cousin, grand mahot cousin, guaxima roxa, guaxima vermehla, guiazo, ottoto grande, paka, and toja; in the United States, Caesar weed; in India, East Pakistan, and southeast

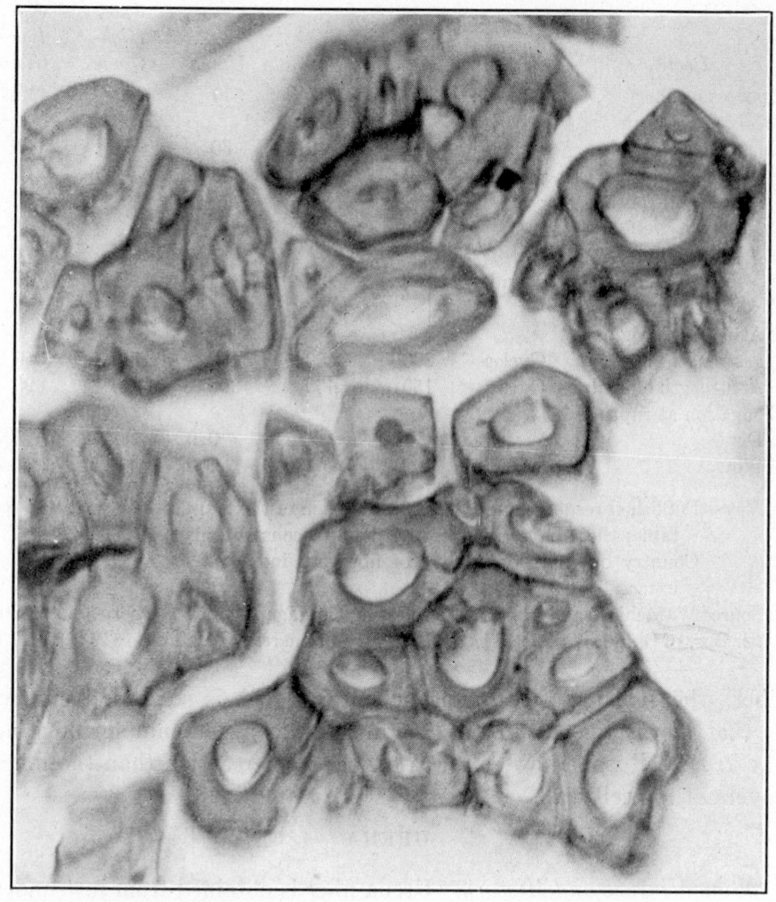

FIG. 19. Kenaf fiber, cross-section (×800). (*Courtesy George Moro.*)

Asia, bun (ban) ochra; in Indonesia, pulut and various other vernacular names; in Yorubaland, Africa, aka-ire; in the Belgian Congo and French Equatorial Africa, Congo "jute."

Urena grows wild, sometimes becoming a noxious weed, in tropical and temperate zones in South and North America, Asia, Indonesia, the Philippines, Madagascar, and Africa. It is cultivated to a small extent in Brazil, India, and Madagascar, and to a much larger extent in the Belgian Congo and in French Equatorial Africa. Principal areas in which fiber is produced are Brazil, where plants growing in a wild state are utilized for most of the production, Belgian Congo, French Equatorial Africa, India and some parts of Asia, the Philippines, Indonesia, Africa, and also in Madagascar, where, as in Brazil, plants growing in a wild state are utilized for most of the production.

Another species, *U. sinuata* (known in Cuba as Cuban "jute" and in Bengal as kunjia) grows wild and/or is cultivated on a very small scale in the West Indies and in tropical Asia Fiber is similar to that from *U. lobata*. Some authorities classify *U. sinuata* as a variety of *U. lobata* instead of as a separate species.

The use of urena fiber in Brazil is of great antiquity, the principal producing areas being Espirito Santo, which accounts for about three-fourths of the total, and Para, Rio de Janeiro, and São Paulo. The use of urena fiber in most of the other areas where the plant grows also covers a long period of time. The first attempt to cultivate the fiber on a commercial basis in the Belgian Congo was made in 1926 but met with no success. A second attempt was made in 1929, by a Belgian textile firm, in the Province of

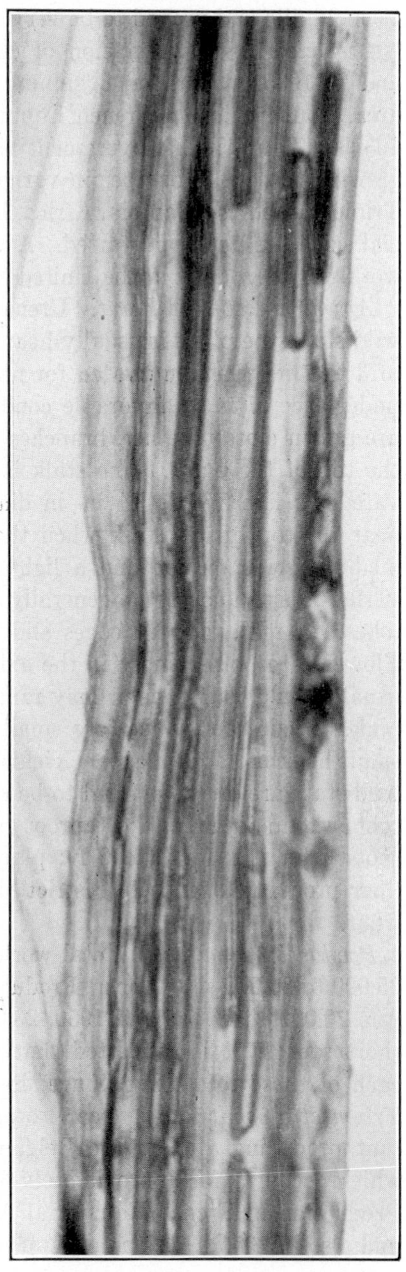

FIG. 20. Kenaf, longitudinal view of fiber (×500). (*Courtesy George Moro.*)

Leopoldville and proved to be very successful; by 1932 the government was sponsoring an expansion of cultivation in the Leopoldville area and in 1935 encouraged beginning of cultivation in the Stanleyville area. Cultivation in French Equatorial Africa was begun during the 1930's. The British Government has sponsored experimental trials of growing the plant for fiber in various areas, including British Guiana, Trinidad, and the Gambia, Africa, but so far cultivation on a commercial scale has not been started. A very minor amount of experimental work has been done in the United States.

Appearance of the Plant. Urena is a herbaceous perennial. In the wild state, the plant is usually heavily branched and grows to a height of 3 to 7 ft; when cultivated for fiber, height ranges from 10 to 12 ft, under exceptionally favorable conditions to 15 ft, and because plants are grown close together, branches are negligible and occur only near the top of the plant. The stalk is a medium green and, when cultivated for fiber, ½ to ¾ in. in diameter. Leaves, which occur only near the top of the stalk when the plant is cultivated for fiber, are medium green on top and a lighter green on the underside and are varied in size and shape, generally being somewhat round with 3 or 5 lobes and with serrated edges and measuring 1 to 2 in. by 2 to 3 in. Flowers are borne singly in the axils of the leaves, are 5-petaled and usually pink, though color may range from reddish violet to white and pink. Seeds are moderately small and are characterized by having small hooklike appendages. Yields of seeds from plants growing in a wild state are large but tend to be sparse from cultivated plants. The root system is large, the taproot being 8 to 18 in. long with lateral roots extending for 3 to 6 ft; planting close together as is done for fiber production tends to restrict size and area of root system somewhat.

Production and Use. Total world production is estimated at about 25,000 to 30,000 short tons. Production in the Belgian Congo for 1949 was 20,000 short tons, in 1950, 23,000 short tons and in 1951, 22,000 short tons;[24] it is estimated that approximately 4000 short tons of each of these totals was punga fiber (*Cephalonema polyandrum* and *Triumfetta semitriloba*) (see also pp. 343 and 351). The most important producing area in the Belgian Congo is the Leopoldville area, which accounts for approximately 85 per cent of the total production. Production in French Equatorial Africa was 1000 short tons in 1950 and also in 1951;[24] the amount of punga fiber (*Triumfetta cordifolia*)

[24] "Monthly Bulletin of Agricultural Economics and Statistics," I: 1, Food and Agricultural Organization of the United Nations, Rome (1952).

ranges from 9 to 27 μ, averaging 13 μ. The lumen is irregular, mostly rather broad and not so large as the lumen of individual fibers of jute. With iodine and sulfuric acid, urena fiber gives a yellow color, aniline also gives a deep yellow, indicating strong lignification. Schweitzer's reagent produces strong swelling of cell wall. Cells often show parenchymatous (spongy) tissue, containing crystalline deposits. Ash of the fiber shows aggregates of calcium carbonate, a feature which distinguishes it from jute.

NETTLE FIBER

Nomenclature. Nettle fiber is obtained from three species of the stinging nettle, *Urtica dioica, U. urens,* and *U. pilulifera,* of the family Urticaceae. *U. dioica* is a perennial; the other two species are annuals. *U. dioica,* which is also known as the "great nettle," yields the largest amount of fiber but the fiber is of large diameter and with very thin cell walls. *U. urens,* which is known as the "small nettle," has a small yield of fiber. The fibers from both *U. urens* and *U. pilulifera* are much smaller in diameter than fibers from *U. dioica* and have thick cell walls, resembling flax fibers to a great extent. Nettle fibers are cultivated in some parts of Germany and in the province of Picardy in France.

History. Savorgnan states that the nettle is known as Swedish hemp and that the plant has long been cultivated in Sweden for the production of fiber employed in the making of cordage and sailcloth. Ancient records note the use of nettle fiber in Germany and Russia. It was also known in Italy and France during the Middle Ages. An encyclopedia of the eighteenth century contains an article on the production and use of nettle fiber and states that it was manufactured into yarn in Germany. About the same period experiments with nettle fiber were carried on in France and Belgium. At the beginning of the nineteenth century there was a permanent trade in nettle goods carried on in France, Germany, and Sweden. Current world production is small; data are not available, either by country or area to show quantity of production.

Cultivation. Cultivation of nettle plants is similar to that given flax plants. During the past century, there have been numerous attempts to cultivate and use nettle fiber on a commercial scale, including those of Bartolini in Tuscany, 1809; Edward Smith in England, 1810; and Withlow in the United States, 1814. Among those who engaged in this work it is necessary to include a number of Frenchmen, the Abbé Rozier, 1793; Chalumeau, 1803; Chaumeton, 1818; Lardier, 1820; Chatin, 1861; Eloffe, 1869; Barot, 1891; d'Astanieres, 1894; and Michotte, 1895. The Abbé Provenchir, 1862, reported that the nettle was used in Canada in the manufacture of cloth and cordage. Experiments in nettle culture have been made for some years on Russian plantations. The late G. S. Smith of Martock, England, carried out long experiments on nettle fibers, and his records disclose that they were used by the natives on the slopes of the Pyrenees Mountains as a substitute for flax.

Fig. 22. Nettle fiber.

Fiber Preparation. Freeing the fibers from the woody core of the stalk is done either by dew or water retting or by mechanical decortication. Chemical boiling, similar to the degumming operation used for ramie fiber, is then necessary to free the fibers from the outer bark . After drying, following the boiling operation, the fiber is hackled or combed and oiled to soften it. According to Grothe, yield from green bark to combed fiber (filasse) is: green fiber, 100 lb; dry fiber, 46 lb; degummed fiber, 32 lb; and combed fiber, 20 lb.

Fiber Characteristics. Combed fiber strands are from 3 to 4 ft in length. The fiber, if properly prepared, is soft and flexible and a yellowish white. Method of preparation affects color; if retted in standing water or dew retted the fiber is usually a dirty gray. Individual cells of *U. dioica* range in length from 0.16 to 2.16 in. (Vetillart) and from 20 to 70 μ in diameter. According to Höhnel, the microscopic characteristics of the fiber show very irregular and unevenly marked, creased, and, in part, ribbonlike forms. The lumen is small to medium-sized and often contains a yellow substance. Ends are tapered, rounded, and often split or forked. Cross-section is oval, flattened, or even has the walls turned in an elliptical shape. Cell walls are thick and stratified, inner layers frequently being marked radially. See Fig. 22.

The fiber appears to have a high percentage of cellulose, with occasional traces of lignin on the surface. It gives the following microchemical reactions: (*a*) with iodine-sulfuric acid reagent, blue coloration; (*b*) with ammoniacal fuchsine solution, no coloration; (*c*) with sulfate of aniline, no coloration; (*d*) with chloriodide of zinc, bluish-violet coloration; and (*e*) with chloriodide of calcium, rose-red coloration.

MISCELLANEOUS BAST FIBERS

Bast fibers in the following list are almost all of small importance, except as they add to the world's total supply of textile fibers. Comparatively few of them are cultivated, fiber being obtained from plants growing in a wild state. This list should not be considered as a complete list of all plants yielding bast fibers for textile purposes throughout the world. There are, in various areas, other plants from which bast fiber is utilized to some extent and which will become better known as knowledge of fibrous plants continues to increase.

For the plants included in this list, the following information is given: botanical name, genus and species, with common name, if generally known, in parentheses immediately following; area or areas where plant grows or is grown; and a brief description of the plant's habitat, the plant, its fiber, and principal uses.

Abroma augusta (abroma, devil's "cotton," Indian "flax"; in the Philippines, anabo and various other vernacular names; in Indonesia, kaworo and kapasan). Tropical Asia, Philippines, and Indonesia, and has been introduced into tropical Africa. Plant 3 to 5 ft, perennial. Leaves and stalks covered with hairs which are irritating to skin of workers handling plant. In favorable climate yields 2 to 3 crops of fiber annually. Fiber utilized principally from plants growing in wild state; small cultivations made in Africa, especially Belgian Congo and Uganda. Fiber obtained by retting in manner similar to that used for jute; yields vary from 100 to 2600 lb per acre per year, depending upon whether obtained from plant in wild or cultivated state. Fiber strands vary in length from 2 to 5 ft and in color from creamy white to golden brown, are lustrous, and are said to have strength approximately the same or somewhat less than that of kenaf fiber. Results of experiments indicate abroma fiber could be spun on jute machinery in mixture with jute.[28] Fiber used by natives, in some areas where plant grows, for hand-spun twines and hand-woven fabrics.

Abutilon theophrasti (syn. *avicennae*) (Indian mallow, Tientsin "jute," ch'ing ma "jute," Chinese "jute"). Tropical and warm areas,

[28] "*Abroma Augusta* Fiber from Uganda," R. H. Kirby, Bull. Imp. Inst., XLVI: 2–4, H.M. Stationery Office, London (1948).

Asia. Plant 3 to 4 ft high. Fiber from stalks, white, glossy, moderately strong, and apparently consisting of cellulose and lignocellulose. Used for cordage, coarse fabrics, and paper. *A. incanum.* Mexico. Fiber said to be strong. Natives use it for cordage. *A. indicum, A. graveolens, A. muticum,* and *A. persicum* (syn. *polyandrum*). Tropical Asia. Fiber long, soft, similar to hemp. Used for cordage. *A. longicuspe* (zada buack). Abyssinia. Used for cordage. *A. angulatum.* Tropical Africa. Used for cordage. *A. bedfordianum.* Tropical America and Africa. Used for cordage.

Acacia leucophloea (piland bast). Tropical Asia. Tree. Fiber from bast of inner bark, moderately strong. Natives use it for cordage.

Adansonia digitata (boabab tree). Tropical Asia. Tree. Fiber from bast of inner bark, moderately strong. Natives use it for cordage.

Apocynum cannabinum (Indian "hemp," dogbane). North America. Plant, 2 to 3 ft high. Fiber from bast in stalk, strong and soft, somewhat similar to flax. Used by American Indians for cordage. *A. venetum* (kendir or kendyr fiber). Eastern Asia to eastern Europe, especially southeastern Asia, China, and southern Russia. Plant. Fiber from bast in stalk, said to be strong and soft. Used for cordage and fabrics.

Aquilaria agallocha. India, East Pakistan, and Burma. Tree. Strips of bark used for ropes, not considered to be very strong. *A. malaccensis* (alim, kepand, and various vernacular names). Indonesia. Similar to *A. agallocha.*

Artocarpus elastica (kerbang, terep, and various other vernacular names). Indonesia and Malaya. Tree. Fiber obtained from bark, usually by pounding and washing; used either in the form of strips or of sheets for fabrics for clothing, bandages, and house construction, and for tying, wrapping, and fish-net twines.

Asclepias syriaca. North and South America, Europe, Africa, Asia. Plant. Bast fiber from under bark of stalks. Natives use it for cordage. *Note:* Fiber is also obtained from seed pod; see Miscellaneous Plant Fibers, Chapter IX. *A. incarnata* (swamp milkweed). North America. Similar to *A. syriaca.* *A. fruticosa.* South Africa. Similar to *A. syriaca.*

Bauhinia racemosa (malu creeper). Southeast Asia. Vine. Bast fiber from under bark. Said to be very strong. Natives use it for cordage. *B. vahli* (malu creeper). Similar to *B. racemosa.*

Brachystegia spicaeformis, B. tamarindoides, and other species (m'changa, mecomba, or m'donde). East Africa. Tree. Fiber from inner bark, which is removed in sheets, scraped, pounded, and dried.

When used as fabric, sheets are strong lengthwise but weak crosswise. Fiber cut in strips from sheets for cordage and yarn. Strong when wet but brittle when dry. Natives use it for cordage and for sacking fabrics.

Broussonetia papyrifera (tapa cloth fiber, also kapa or masi). South Pacific Islands, Japan, and China. Tree, better known as paper mulberry tree. Natives of South Pacific remove bast fibers from under bark, clean, and dry. Several layers of fiber are laid down to form a large sheet with an even surface, wetted, and allowed to remain overnight. They are then pounded with a wooden mallet until a fabric sheet is formed. Sheets have moderate strength and may be bleached, dyed, or printed. In Japan, fiber is made into paper, then cut into strips, twisted to form filling yarn, hemp or silk being used for warp yarns. Höhnel reports individual fibers 0.24 to 0.59 in. long and about 25 to 35 μ in diameter with lumen small and difficult to distinguish because at intervals it is filled with yellowish material. Fibers are of *two* shapes: thick and ribbonlike, the latter exhibiting some twist. Ends of thick fibers are small and pointed; of ribbonlike fibers, broad and rounded. Fibers often show presence of small prismatic crystals of calcium oxalate.

Calotropis gigantea (yercum). Asia. Plant. Fiber from bast in stalk, white, strong, and said to be about 11.8 in. long and 210 μ in diameter and to contain about 77 per cent cellulose. Natives use it for cordage. *Note:* Fiber is also obtained from seed pods of *C. gigantea* as well as other species of *Calotropis*. See Chapter IX. Seed fiber is also termed "yercum"; other names given to seed fibers are: ak, akund, madar, and mudar. These names are also used interchangeably to designate bast fiber from plants of this genus.

Cephalonema polyandrum (punga, a native name used in equatorial Africa to designate fiber from several plants). Tropical West Africa, especially Belgian Congo. Plant, 8 to 12 ft high. Bast fiber from stalks. Used for coarse fabrics similar to those made from jute, and for cordage. Approximately 4000 tons are said to have been exported from Belgian Congo in 1950, and also in 1951, principally to Belgium, with small quantity to United States.

Chonemorpha macrophylla (bangi and other vernacular names). Indonesia (East Java). Climbing shrub. Fiber obtained by scraping bark from stalks, drying, and then peeling off fiber strands. Used for fish nets and said to have good strength in either fresh or salt water.

Commersonia fraseri (Blackfellow's "hemp"; tie plant). Australia. Small tree. Fiber from under bark, dark in color. Used by natives for cordage and matting. *C. echinata* (syn. *bartramia*). Australia and Indonesia. Similar to *C. fraseri;* fiber darker. Natives use it for fishing and hunting nets.

Couratari tauari (and other species) (tauari fiber, also many native names). South and Central America. Tree, various species ranging in height from 20 to more than 100 feet. Laminated whitish inner bark stripped off in thin sheets, scraped, and dried. Sheet may be wetted and pounded together or cut into strips and twisted into yarn. Natives use sheets as clothing and for household fabrics. Twisted strips are used as cordage, especially for caulking boats. Thin sheets are used for cigarette paper.

Cryptoslegia grandiflora (rubber vine). Tropical Africa and India. Woody vine. Fiber from vine stems used for cordage. Cultivated to a very limited extent in some parts of India.

Cytisus scoparius (broom fiber, sometimes Spanish broom). Southern Europe, principally. Fiber from stalk. Used principally for cordage.

Daphnopsis guacacoa (guacacoa in Cuba). Tropical America and West Indies. Tree. Bark used for rope. Another species, *D. occidentalis,* also occurs in the West Indies; in Jamaica bark from this species is used for rope.

Datisca cannabina (Cretan "hemp"). Asia Minor to India. Plant, about 7 ft high. Fiber from bast in stalk, somewhat similar to hemp. Natives use it for cordage.

Debregeasia hypoleuca. Southern Himalayan region. Large shrub. Fiber from bark used for cordage by hill tribes.

Dirca palustris (leatherwood). North America. Shrub. Fibrous bark very strong. Used by American Indians for cordage.

Dombeya buettner and *D. cannabina.* Madagascar and East Africa. Shrub or small tree. Fibrous bark used by natives for cordage.

Epilobium angustifolium and *E. hirsutum* (willow herb). Europe and North America. Shrub. Fibers from under bark in stalk, used as substitute for jute, especially in Germany.

Eupatorium cannabinum (agrimony "hemp" and water "hemp"). Europe. Plant. Fiber from bast of stalk. Used for cordage and fabrics.

Euphorbia gregaria and *E. gumifera.* South Africa. Shrub. Bast fiber from stalks and twigs. Fiber removed by retting. Natives use it for cordage, occasionally for textiles.

Ficus benghalensis and *F. nekbudu* (banyan fiber and other native names). Ceylon, southern Asia, Africa, and South America. Tree.

Bark stripped off and fiber removed by beating and washing. Natives use fiber for cordage.

Fremontia california (mountain leatherwood). North America. Shrub. Fibrous bark used for cordage by American Indians.

Girardinia palmata (syn. *heterophylla*) (pha-pat, hypetye, and various other native names). Burma, India, East Pakistan, Indochina, and Malaya. Plant, 6 to 10 ft. Leaves, stems, and stalk covered with hairs that irritate skin of workers handling plants. Fiber, which is said to have moderately good strength, is obtained from stalks either by stripping bark with fiber adhering to it and washing or scraping until fiber is clean or by stripping bark with fiber adhering to it from stalk, drying it, and after drying freeing fiber by pounding with a wooden mallet. Fiber is then boiled with lye made from wood ashes and afterward washed until clean. Fiber used for cordage and for fabrics, which in some localities are called "bangra."

Grewia occidentalis (Kaffir "hemp"). South Africa. Plant. Fiber removed from stalk by retting, is strong and light colored. Natives use it for cordage and clothing fabrics. *G. oppositifolia.* Asia. Similar to *G. occidentalis.*

Helicteres isora (screw plant in Australia; puteran and various other vernacular names in Indonesia). Tropical Asia and Australia and Indonesia. Plant 6 to 12 ft. Bast fiber from stalk obtained by retting; is light brown to silver color. Used for twines. *H. viscida.* Indonesia. Plant, 4 to 8 ft. Fiber has uses similar to those from *H. isora.*

Hibiscua sabdariffa (roselle, rosella, roselle "hemp," and Java "jute"). India, East Pakistan, southeast Asia, Ceylon, Indonesia, Philippine Islands, and West Indies. Has been grown on a small experimental scale in the United States.

Plant has general appearance similar to that of kenaf (*H. cannabinus*); stalks and leaves of roselle are dark green to reddish, flowers are creamy white to yellow. Roselle is a perennial and in favorable climate will produce 2 crops annually. It is, however, grown as an annual in most areas as the roots generally do not withstand continued cutting of stalks, and, in many of the areas where it is grown, the growing season is not continuous; growing roselle on a continuous basis would either place land on a nonproductive status during part of the year or result in destruction of roselle plants.

Indonesia (Central and East Java) is the most important producer of roselle fiber. Cultivation of the fiber was established during the 1920's and 1930's as a result of a subsidized government program to provide fiber for sugar sacks. Before World War II, annual production is said to have been as high as 3000 short tons. Postwar annual production ranges between 500 and 1000 short tons, the decrease in production being due in a large measure to the need for food crops and, beginning with 1952, to decreased price of jute fiber. The entire crop is used by a mill erected in central Java during the 1930's, which manufactures sacking fabrics and sacks. Quantity of fiber produced in areas other than Indonesia is small; principal uses are for sacking fabrics and for twines.

Best results are secured on moderately rich, friable, well-drained soil located in tropical or subtropical areas free of strong winds and with ample rainfall, about 10 in. per month during the growing season. Seeds are sowed very thickly. Weeding must be done until young plants become established and begin to shade the ground, usually for a period of 4 to 6 weeks after plants appear above ground.

Plants are ready for cutting when in full flower, usually about 110 to 130 days after planting, depending upon growing conditions in the area. In Indonesia, plant is grown as an annual and only 1 crop a year is harvested as the area in Java where it is grown is subject to a 5-month dry season from May to October. In most areas, including Indonesia, fiber is removed from the stalk by retting, then stripping or beating to free fiber, and washing in a manner similar to that used for jute. In Ceylon, bark with fiber adhering to it is stripped from the stalks in the field immediately after they are cut. These strips are then retted; after the ret is complete the fiber is freed from the bark and shive by washing. This procedure requires less retting time and less expenditure of labor than if the whole stalk is retted. In some areas in the West Indies, mechanical decortication is used to a very limited extent to remove fiber; considerable experimental work is being done in the United States as well as in other countries to improve mechanical decorticators. Annual yield of fiber ranges from 600 to 2000 lb per acre, with the average ranging between 800 to 1200 lb in most areas.

Carefully prepared roselle fiber is creamy to silvery white, lustrous, and with moderately good strength. Comparison of the breaking strength, as well as other selected physical factors, of roselle with that of kenaf, urena, and jute is shown in Table 21 in the section on kenaf. Length of fiber strands is 3 to 5 ft. Mendiola reported that length of ultimate fibers ranged from 0.05 to 0.13 in. and averaged 0.07 in. and that diameter ranged from 10 to 32 μ, with an average of 20 μ.

Other species of the genus *Hibiscus* from which fiber is reported to be obtained are listed below. Fiber from these plants has general

Tree. Bast tissue in inner bark is stripped from trunk, dried, and cut into strips. Used for cordage and is fairly strong when dry. Presently used in many parts of Europe, Asia, and Japan. Used by American Indians in ancient times.

Touchardia latifolia (olona). Hawaiian Islands. Plant, to 12 ft. Fiber from stalks. Used by natives for rope and fishing twine; in ancient times fiber was so highly prized that it was used as currency for payment of taxes.

Triumfetta cordifolia (punga, a native name used in equatorial Africa to designate fiber from several plants). West Africa and French Equatorial Africa. Plant, 3 to 7 ft high. Fiber obtained from under bark of stalks and twigs by retting. Used for twine by natives. Has been tested as possible jute substitute; results indicate that it might be usable to some extent if large enough quantity of uniformly high quality fiber were available at low cost. About 100 species of *Triumfetta* have been classified. Those from which fiber is reported to be obtained follow; fiber and uses are similar to fiber from *T. cordifolia: T. pentandra* (syn. *neglecta*), tropical Africa; *T. semitriloba* (punga), tropical Africa and America and West Indies; *T. Bartramia*, tropical America; *T. rhomboidea* (denje and nzonogwe in Africa), tropical Africa and most tropical areas throughout the world.

Vigna sinensis (yawa). Nigeria. Vine. Fiber separated by crushing stalk by hand and peeling fiber in form of ribbons; appearance of ribbons similar to that of raffia. Ultimate fibers said to be long with well-defined lumens. Fiber used by natives for ropes and twines, especially for fish nets. Beans used for human food. This vine is cultivated in many parts of Africa, the Mediterranean area of Europe, southern Asia in Indonesia, in the Philippines, and in the Americas for the beans for human food, as a forage crop, and also as a green manure crop. In East Africa, it is called "kunde" and in India "lubia." In southern United States it is known as "cowpeas" and as "black-eyed peas."

Villebrunea integrifolia (risa, mesakhi, and sometimes called ban or rhea, being confused with ramie). India, East Pakistan, Burma, and Malaya. Plant. Fiber used for twines. *V. rubescens* (nangsi and various vernacular names). Indonesia. Shrub or small tree. Fiber similar to that from *V. integrifolia.*

Wisteria floribunda. Asia, Japan, Europe, America. Vine cultivated principally for flowers. In some areas fibrous bark is used for cordage.

BOTANICAL ORDERS AND FAMILIES OF BAST FIBERS

Table 22 classifies the bast fibers discussed in this chapter by botanical order and family. For convenience, the list is arranged alphabetically by order and subalphabetically by family, genus, and species.

TABLE 22. Botanical Orders and Families of Bast Fibers

Order	*Family*	*Genus and Species*
Asterales	Compositae	*Eupatorium cannabinum*
Gentianales	Apocynaceae	*Apocynum cannabinum* and *A. venetum*
		Chonemorpha macrophylla
	Asclepiadeceae	*Asclepias syriaca, A. fruticosa,* and *A. incarnata*
		Calotropis gigantea
		Cryptoslegia grandiflora
		Marsdenia tenacissima
Geraniales	Euphorbiaceae	*Euphorbia gregaria* and *E. gumifera*
	Linnaceae	*Linum angustifolium* and *L. usitatissimum*
Laminales	Labiatae	*Phlomis lychinitis*
Loasales	Datiscaceae	*Datisca cannabina*
Malvales	Malvaceae	*Abutilon angulatum, A. bedfordianum, A. incanum, A. indicum, A. graveolens, A. longicuspe, A. muticum, A. persicum* (syn. *polyandrum*), and *A. theophrasti* (syn. *avicennae*)
		Adansonia digitata
		Hibiscus abelmoschus, H. cannabinus, H. esculentus, H. ferox, H. ficulneus (syn. *strictus*), *H. furcatus, H. heterophyllus, H. kitaibelifolius, H. lasciocarpus, H. lunarifolius, H. moscheutus, H. mutabilis, H. quinquelobus, H. radiatus, H. rosa-sinensis, H. rostellatus, H. sabdariffa, H. tiliaceus,* and *H. vitifolius*
		Lavatera arborea and *L. maritima*
		Malachra capitata and *M. radiata*
		Pavonia velutina (syn. *malocophylla*), *P. Schimperiana* (syn. *tomentosa*), and *P. urens*
		Paritium elatus (syn. *Hibiscus elatus*)
		Plagianthus betulinus and *P. pulchellus*
		Pseudabutilon spicatum
		Sida acuta, S. cordifolia (syn. *mollis*), *S. micrantha, S. rhombifolia* (syn. *carpinfolia* and *latifolia*), and *S. ulmifolia*
		Sphaeralcea umbellata
		Thespesia macrophylla (syn. *lampas*) and *T. populnea*
		Urena lobata and *U. sinuata*

TABLE 22. BOTANICAL ORDERS AND FAMILIES OF BAST FIBERS (*Continued*)

Order	*Family*	*Genus and Species*
Malvales (Cont.)	Moraceae	*Artocarpus elastica* *Broussonetia papyrifera* *Cannabis sativa* *Ficus benghalensis* and *F. nekbudu*
	Sterculiaceae	*Abroma augusta* *Commersonia fraseri* and *C. eschinata* *Dombeya buetnner* and *D. cannabina* *Fremontia california* *Helicteres isora* and *H. viscida* *Sterculia acerifolia, S. diversifolia, S. lurida*, and *S. villosa*
	Tilliaceae	*Cephalonema polyandrum* *Corchorus acutangulus* (syn. *fuscus*), *C. aestuans, C. capsularis, C. hirsutus, C. olitorius*, and *C. siliquosus* *Grewia occidentalis* and *G. oppositifolia* *Honckenya ficifolia* *Sparmannia africana* *Tilia americana, T. europaea*, and *T. japonica* *Triumfetta cordifolia, T. pentandra* (syn. *neglecta*), *T. semitriloba, T. bartramia*, and *T. rhomboidea*
	Urticaceae	*Boehmeria cylindrica, B. nivea*, and *B. tenacissima* *Debregeasia hypoleuca* *Girardinia palmata* *Laportea gigas* *Maoutia puya* *Pouzolzia hypoleuca* and *P. viminea* *Sarcochlamys pulcherrima* *Touchardia latifolia* *Urtica dioica, U. urens*, and *U. pilulifera* *Villebrunea integrifolia* and *V. rubescens*
Myrtales	Onagraceae	*Epilobium angustifolium* and *E. hirsutum*
	Lecythidaceae	*Couratari tauari*
Polygalales	Polygalaceae	*Securidacea longipendunculata*
Rosales	Leguminoseae	*Acacia leucophloea* *Bauhinia racemosa* and *B. vahli* *Brachystegia spicaeformis* and *B. tamarindoides* *Crotalaria juncea* (syn. *tenuifolia*) *Cytisus scoparius* *Pueraria thunbergiana* and *P. phaseoloides* *Sesbania exaltata* *Lonchocarpus sericeus* *Sparticum junceum* *Vigna sinenses* *Wisteria floribunda*

TABLE 22. Botanical Orders and Families of Bast Fibers (*Continued*)

Order	*Family*	*Genus and Species*
Sapindales	Anacardiaceae	*Rhus typhina*
Thymelaeales	Thymelaeaceae	*Aquilaria agallocha* and *A. malaccensis* *Daphnopsis guacacoa* and *D. occidentalis* *Dirca palustri* *Lagetta lintearia*

Authorities for Classifications

Bailey, L. H., *Standard Cyclopedia of Horticulture,* The Macmillan Co., New York (1935).

Bailey, L. H., and Bailey, Ethel Zoe, *Hortus Second,* The Macmillan Co., New York (1941).

Hooker, Joseph D., director, and Jackson, B. Daydon, editor, *Index Kewensis,* and Supplements I through X, Clarendon Press, Oxford (1895 and supplements through 1940).

Hutchinson, J., *The Families of Flowering Plants,* The Macmillan Co., London (1926).

Pool, Raymond J., *Flowers and Flowering Plants,* McGraw-Hill Book Co., New York (1941).

Royal Horticultural Society of London and Royal Botanical Gardens *Index Londonensis,* and supplements, Clarendon Press, Oxford (1929 and subsequent supplements).

Van Wijk, Gerth H. L., *A Dictionary of Plant Names,* Dutch Society of Scientists at Haarlem, The Hague (1911).

BIBLIOGRAPHY

Note: Names of fibers to which reference especially relates are given after reference.

Adriano, Fiori, "Boschi e Plante lignose del Eritrea," Supplement to *L'Agricultura Colomale* (12), Firenze, Italy (1911). *Zada buack.*

Ahmed, Rashid, "The First Complete Jute Year, 1948–49," Directorate of Jute Prices, Government of East Bengal, Narayanganj, Dacca, East Pakistan (1949). *Jute.*

Allison, R. V., "Long Florida Days Spur Growth of Fiber Plant, Kenaf," *Florida Grower,* Tallahassee (1951). *Kenaf.*

Berendt, Karl Herman, "El Ramio," *Aldana Rivas,* Yucatan (1871). *Ramie.*

Blau, Gerda, et al., "World Fiber Survey," Food and Agriculture Organization, United Nations, Washington (1947). *Jute, flax, hemp.*

Bretschneider, E., "Botanicum Sinicum," Part II, *J. China Branch Roy. Asiatic Society,* Kelly and Walsh, Shanghai, etc. (1892). *Jute, flax, ramie, hemp.*

British Board of Trade, "Jute," *Working Party Repts.,* H.M. Stationery Office, London (1948). *Jute.*

British Intelligence Objectives Subcommittee, "Report of the Linen Industry in Germany," *Final Report* 1218 (22 and 31), H.M. Stationery Office, London (1946). *Flax.*

Brown, Lewis Dean, "Belgian Congo Fibers," *World Trade in Commodities,* **VI,** Part 19 (10), Office of International Trade, U. S. Department of Commerce, Washington (1948). *Urena and punga.*

Brown, William H., "Philippine Fiber Plants" *Bull.* 19, Philippine Dept. Agr. and Natural Resources, Manila (1919). *Various fibers.*

Brown, William H., *Useful Plants of the Philippines,* Vols. 1, 2, and 3, Department of Agriculture and Commerce, Republic of the Philippines, Manila (1941–43). *Various fibers.*

Bruna, Tommaso, and Passavalli, Luigi Puecher, *Corso Practico di Canapitoltura,* Consorzio Nazionale Canapa, Arti, Grafiche, s.p.a., Bologna, Italy (1952). *Hemp.*

Bryan, William Alanson, *Natural History of Hawaii,* The Hawaiian Gazette Co., Honolulu (1915). *Olona.*

Burkill, I. H., *A Dictionary of the Economic Products of the Malay Peninsula,* Government of the Straits Settlements and Federated Malay States, Crown Agents for the Colonies, London (1935). *Various fibers.*

Butowsky, A., *The Means of Improving the Management of Hemp Cultivation,* translated by Peter Von Schmidt, Minister of the Treasury, St. Petersburg, Russia (1842). *Hemp.*

Carreri, Loris, "La Ginestra," Federazione Nazionale de Consori per la Difesa della Canapicoltura, Rome (1937). *Spartium junceum.*

Carter, Gipson L., and Horton, Paul M., "Ramie: A Critical Survey of the Facts Concerning Growing and Utilization of the Fiber-Bearing Plant *Urtica nivea,*" *Univ. Studies* 26, Louisiana State University Press, Baton Rouge (1936). *Ramie.*

Carter, Herbert A., *Ramie,* Technical Book Publishing Co., London (1910). *Ramie.*

Castagno, E., and Pham-Gia-Tu, "Étude des textiles du nord de l'Indochine," translated by Henry D. Barker (U.S.D.A.), *Archives de l'Institute des Recherches Agronomiques de l'Indochine* (1950).

Chaudhuri, Nibaran Chandra, *Jute and Substitutes,* W. Newman and Co., Calcutta (1933). *Jute.*

China Handbook, 1932–1943, Chinese Ministry of Information, The Macmillan Co., New York (1943). *Jute, ramie, hemp.*

Chittenden, A. E., and Coomber, H. E., "Tingo Fiber from Nyasaland," *Colonial Plant and Animal Products,* **1** (2), H.M. Stationery Office, London (1950). *Tingo.*

Commonwealth Economic Committee, "Industrial Fibres," Intelligence Branch, H.M. Stationery Office, London (1951). *Jute, flax, hemp, sunn.*

Consulate General of Pakistan, "1952 with Pakistan Jute," Consulate of Pakistan, New York (1953). *Jute.*

Coss, Harold T., and Taylor, James L., "Ramie Today," Ga. Inst. of Tech., State Engineering Expt. Sta., Atlanta, **X** (14), Circular (Aug. 1948). *Ramie.*

Cross, C. F., Bevan, E. J., and King, C. M., *Report on Indian Fibres and Fibrous Substances,* E. & F. Spon, London (1887). *Jute, ramie, hemp, kenaf, sunn.*

Cruz, Eugenio E., "Ramie Culture in the Philippines," Ministry of Agriculture and Natural Resources, Manila (1949). *Ramie.*

DAVENPORT, PHILIP M., "Miscellaneous Fibers Cuba," *World Trade in Commodities,* **VI,** Part 19 (22), Office of International Trade, U. S. Department of Commerce, Washington (1948). *Kenaf, ramie, majagua.*

DEWEY, LYSTER H., "Ramie, A Fiber-Yielding Plant," U. S. Dept. Agr., *Bull.* 110, Washington (1949). *Ramie.*

DIAMOND, JAY G., "Hemp, Greece," *World Trade in Commodities,* **VI,** Part 19 (21), Office of International Trade, U. S. Department of Commerce, Washington (1948). *Hemp.*

DODGE, C. R., Reports on "Fiber Investigations," Nos. 1, 3–10, U. S. Dept. Agr. *Yearbook,* Washington (1890–98). *Various fibers.*

DODGE, C. R., "Report on Cultivation of Ramie in the United States," U. S. Dept. Agr., Washington (1895). *Ramie.*

East Bengal, Government of, *Monthly Summary of Jute Statistics,* Nos. 55 and 60, Directorate of Jute Prices, Department of Commerce, Labour, and Industry, Narayanganj, Dacca, East Pakistan (1952 and 1953, respectively). *Jute.*

Empire Marketing Board, "Indian (Sunn or Sann) Hemp," Imperial Institute, H.M. Stationery Office, London (1930). *Sunn.*

FERGUSON, A. M., and J., *All About Aloe and Ramie Fibers,* Colombo Observer Press, Colombo, Ceylon (1890). *Ramie.*

FEUELL, A. J., and JARMAN, C. G., "Pavonia Urens Fibre from Uganda," *Colonial Plant and Animal Products,* **II** (4), H.M. Stationery Office, London (1952). *Pavonia urens.*

FILLMAN, GWENDOLYN R., "The Hard and Bast Fiber Textile Industry of Japan," East Asian Inst., Columbia University, New York (unpub.) (1953).

Food and Agricultural Organization of the United Nations, *Monthly Bulletin of Agricultural Economics and Statistics,* **I** (1), Rome (1952). *Various fibers.*

Food and Agricultural Organization of United Nations, *Yearbook of Food and Agricultural Statistics,* **V,** Part 1, Rome (1952). *Various fibers.*

GARCES, M., "El Ramio," Costa Rican Ministry of Agriculture, San Jose (1895). *Ramie.*

GILES, HERBERT A., *Chinese-English Dictionary,* Kelly and Walsh, Shanghai, etc. (1912). *Jute, flax, ramie, hemp.*

GILLEN, J. FRANK, and HAYLES, J. ORLO, "Ramie or China Grass," Stanford University, Palo Alto (1923). *Ramie.*

GOULDING, ERNEST, "Textile Fibres of Vegetable Origin," *Bull. Imp. Inst.,* **35** (1), H.M. Stationery Office, London (1937). *Various fibers.*

GRANGER, W. B., "History, Culture, Processing and Marketing of Ramie in Florida," State Dept. Agr., Tallahassee (1948). *Ramie.*

Gunny Trades Association, "Report of the Committee, 1 April 1950—31 March 1951," Calcutta (1951). *Jute.*

HANAUSEK, T. F., "The Microscopy of Technical Products," translated by Andrew L. Winton, assisted by Kate Barber Winton, John Wiley & Sons, New York (1907). *Various fibers.*

HAYAT, M. ASLAM, "The Golden Fibre," Publications and Foreign Publicity Dept., Government of Pakistan, Karachi (1948 and 1950). *Jute.*

HENRY, IVES, "Plantes à Fibres," Librairie Armand Colin, Paris (1924). *Ramie.*

HEYNE, K., *De Nuttige Planten van Indonesië,* Vols. I and II, N. V. Uitgeveriz, W. van Hoeve, Bandung, Indonesia (1950). *Various fibers.*

Höhnel, F. X., "Die Mikroskopie der technisch verwendeten Faserstoffe," A. Hartleben, Leipzig (1905). *Various fibers.*

India, Government of, "Fibers and Silk," Dept. Revenue and Agr., Simla (1877). *Ramie.*

Indian Jute Mills Association, *Monthly Summary of Jute and Gunny Statistics,* Nos. 89 and 95, Indian Jute Mills Association, Calcutta (1952 and 1953, respectively). *Jute.*

Irish Linen Guild, "Irish Linen," Belfast (1945). *Flax.*

Ispahani, M. M., Ltd., "Report on Pakistan Jute," Dacca, East Pakistan (1950). *Jute.*

Jute Annual, Yearbook, and Directory, British Continental Press, London (1931–50). *Jute.*

Kaempfer, Engelbrecht, "Amoenitation Exoticarum," Henry Wilhelm Meyer, Holland (1712). *Ramie.*

Kirby, R. H., "*Abroma Augusta* Fibre from Uganda," *Bull. Imp. Inst.,* **46** (2–4), H.M. Stationery Office, London (1948). *Abroma.*

Kirby, R. H., "Jute and Its Substitutes," Imperial Institute, H.M. Stationery Office, London (1948). *Various fibers.*

Lecomte, H., *Textiles vegeteaux, leur examin microchimique, Encyclopedia Scientifique des Aide-Mémoire,* Gauthier-Villars et Fils, Paris (1892). *Various fibers.*

Lecomte, M. H., *Flore generale l'Indo Chine,* Masson et cie, Paris (1907–12). *Cuban "jute" or punjia (Urena sinuata).*

Lefranc, Émile, "Ramie, Origin, Value, Advantages and Extraction Processes," Renaissance Louisianaise, New Orleans (1869). *Ramie.*

Lefranc, Émile, "Culture and Manufacture of Ramie and Jute in the United States," U. S. Dept. Agr., Washington (1873). *Jute, ramie.*

Leggett, William F., *The Story of Linen,* Chemical Publishing Co., New York (1945). *Flax.*

Lindsay, H. A. F., et al., "Commercial Plant Fibres of the British Empire," Imperial Institute, H.M. Stationery Office, London (1936). *Various fibers.*

Lokotsch, Karl, "Etymologisches Wörterbuch, der Europaischen Wörter Orientalischen Ursprungs," Carl Winter's *Universitatsbuchhandlung,* Heidelberg (1927). *Various fibers.*

Luniak, Bruno, *Die Unterscheidung der Textilfasern,* Leeman, Zurich (1949). *Jute, flax, ramie, hemp, sunn, kenaf, others.*

Luniak, Bruno, *Ramie Kulter,* Leeman, Zurich (1949). *Ramie.*

Meadows, Barkley, "Trends in Consumption of Fibers in the U. S., 1892–1948," U. S. Dept. Agr., Washington (1950). *Jute, flax, hemp.*

Mendiola, N. B., "A Study of Philippine Bast Fibers," *Philippine Agriculture and Forestry,* **6**, Manila (1917). *Various fibers.*

Mexican Ministeria de Fomento, Colonizacion e Industria, "Documentos Relativos al Cultivo y Beneficio del Ramio en Diversa Paises," Mexico City (1886). *Ramie.*

Moore, Alfred S., *Linen,* Sir Isaac Pitman Sons, London (1913). *Flax.*

Müller, Hugo, *Die Pflanzenfaser unter ihre Aufbereitung für die Technik,* F. Vieweg und Sohn, Braunschweig, Germany (1876). *Various fibers.*

Neller, J. R., "Culture, Fertilizer Requirements and Fiber Yields of Ramie in the Florida Everglades," Univ. of Florida, Agr. Expt. Sta. *Bull.* 412, Gainesville (1945). *Ramie.*

NELSON, ELTON G., "Progress of Kenaf," *Jute and Gunny Rev.* (March–April 1953).

Pakistan, Government of, "Pakistan Jute Survey" (unofficial), Department of Commercial Intelligence, Karachi (1950). *Jute.*

Philippines, Republic of the, "Amendment of Fiber Inspection Administrative Order No. 4 (Revised) to Include Ramie (*Boehmeria nivea*) and Establish Standard Grades for Such Fiber under Its Regulations," Dept. Agr. and Natural Resources, Manila (1945). *Ramie.*

PHILIPPS, JAMES CECIL, *On the Cultivation of Ramie,* M. C. DeSouza, Kingston, Jamaica (1884). *Ramie.*

PORTER, HORACE G., and COOPER, MAURICE R., "Statistics on Jute and Jute Manufactures," U. S. Dept. Agr., Washington (1945). *Jute.*

PRINGLE, A. V., *Theory of Flax Spinning,* H. R. Carter Publication, Belfast (1949). *Flax.*

PYNAPPEL, J., *Maleisch-Nederdiutsch Woordenboek, Verschiedens Faserpflanzen,* Haarlem, Amsterdam (1863). *Ramie.*

RABECHAULT, H., *La Ramie—Études morphologique et taxonomique en vue de la sélection,* J. Desseaux, Editeur, Paris (1951). *Ramie.*

RAFFLES, SIR THOMAS STAMFORD, *History of Java,* John Murray, London (1817). *Ramie.*

RECORD, SAMUEL J., and HESS, ROBERT W., *Timbers of the New World,* Yale University Press, New Haven (1943). *Couratari tauari.*

ROBINSON, BRITTAIN B., "Flax Fiber Production," U. S. Dept. Agr., *Farmers' Bull.* 1728, Washington (1934). *Flax.*

ROBINSON, BRITTAIN B., "Ramie Fiber Production," U. S. Dept. Agr., *Circ.* 585, Washington (1940). *Ramie.*

ROBINSON, BRITTAIN B., and SCHOFFSTALL, CHARLES W., "Italian Hemp Industry," P.B. Rept. 15595, U. S. Dept. Commerce, Washington (1948). *Hemp.*

ROBINSON, BRITTAIN B., ET AL., "Status of the Fiber Plant Industry in Latin America," Pan American Union, Washington (1947). *Jute, flax, ramie, hemp, kenaf, others.*

ROEZL, BENITO, "Ramie Plant, Its Propagation, Culture and Cleaning Process," Renaissance Louisianaise, New Orleans (1868). *Ramie.*

ROYLE, J. FORBES, *Fibrous Plants of India,* Smith, Elder and Co., Cornhill, England (1855). *Jute, flax, ramie, hemp, sunn, kenaf, others.*

RUMPF, GEORG EBERHARD, *Herbarium Amboinese,* Amsterdam (1741–50). *Ramie.*

ST. HILAIRE, AUGUSTO DE, *Flora Brasiliae Meridionales,* A. Belin, Paris (1825). *Juta paulista* (*Hibiscus kitai belifolius*).

SALANT, NATHAN B., "Hemp, Italy," *World Trade in Commodities,* **VI,** Part 19 (21), Office of International Trade, U. S. Dept. Commerce, Washington (1948). *Hemp.*

SCHIEFER, HERBERT F., "Machines and Methods for Testing Cordage Fibers," RP1611, Natl. Bur. Standards, U. S. Dept. Commerce (1944). *Jute, hemp, kenaf, others.*

SCHOFFSTALL, CHARLES W., "Burlap," War Changes in Industry *Rept.* 26, U. S. Tariff Comm., Washington (1947). *Jute.*

SEMLER, HENRICH, "Plantas Textis," Brazilian Ministry of Agriculture, Rio de Janeiro (1913). *All fibers.*

SHIH KING, **IV**, Part I, *The Chinese Classics,* translated by James Legge, Lane, Crawford & Company, Hongkong (1871). *Ramie.*

SLAUGHT, S. H., "Development and Encouragement of Ramie," U. S. Congress, Senate Com. on Manufacturers, *Rept.* 6460, Washington (1907). *All fibers.*

Soil Science Society of Florida, "Symposium III: Production of Long Vegetable Fibers in Florida," *Proc. Eighth Annual Meeting,* April 1947, Belle Glade (1947). *Ramie.*

STRABO, *Geography,* translated by Horace L. Jones, G. P. Putnam's Sons, London (1917). *Various fibers.*

Supreme Commander for the Allied Powers, "Crop Statistics for Japan, 1878–1946," Natural Resources *Sec. Rept.* 108, Tokyo (1948). *Jute, flax, ramie, hemp.*

TAYLOR, JAMES L., "Processing of Domestic Flax for Textile Use," Ga. Inst. of Tech., State Engineering Expt. Sta., Atlanta (1946). *Flax.*

Textile Foundation, "Flax and Its Products," Washington (1942). *Flax.*

TURNER, A. J., "Bast and Leaf Fibres," *J. Textile Inst.,* **42** (8), Manchester, Eng. (Aug. 1951). *Flax, hemp.*

TURNER, A. J., "Structure of Long Vegetable Fibers," *J. Textile Inst.,* Manchester, Eng. (Oct. 1949). *Jute, flax.*

United States Departments of Commerce and Agriculture, and Univ. of Florida, Everglades Expt. Sta., "Ramie Production in Florida," Washington (1948). *Ramie.*

United States Works Progress Administration, "Flax in Oregon," Portland, Ore. (1936). *Flax.*

VAN DEN ABEELE, MARCEL, and VANDENPUT, RENÉ, "Plantes textiles," Centre d'Information et de Documentation du Congo Belge et du Ruanda-Urundi, Ministère des Colonies, Brussels (1952). *Various fibers.*

VAN HALL, C. J. J., and VAN DE KOPPEL, C., *De Landbouw in de Indische Archipel,* Vol. III, N. V. Uitgeverij, W. van Hoeve, Bandung, Indonesia (1950). *Various fibers.*

VAN WOERDEN, C. L. L. H., "Report on Wild Fiber Plants Found on Java," Kebun Raya, Indonesia, Bogor, Indonesia. Unpublished. *Various fibers.*

VÉTILLART, MARCEL, *Études sur les fibres végétales textiles employées dans l'industrie,* Firman, Didot et cie., Paris (1876). *Various fibers.*

VOLIN, LAZAR, "A Survey of Soviet Russian Agriculture," U. S. Dept. Agr., Washington (1951). *Flax, hemp.*

WALKER, JOE E., "Kenaf: Producing It for Fiber and for Seed," U. S. Dept. Agr. and Cuban Ministry of Agr. (1951). *Kenaf.*

WALLY-VAN VREESWIJK, A. C., "De Culture, Winning en Verwerking van de Ramievezel in Japan," Ministerie van Welvaart van de Republiek der Verenigde Staten van Indonesië, Djakarta, Indonesia (1948). *Ramie.*

WATT, SIR GEORGE, *Commercial Plants of India,* John Murray, London (1908). *Various fibers.*

WEINDLING, LUDWIG, *Long Vegetable Fibers,* Columbia University Press, New York (1947). *Jute, flax, ramie, hemp, sunn.*

WHITFORD, A. C., "Textile Fibers Used in Eastern Aboriginal North America," American Museum of Natural History, New York (1945). *Various fibers.*

WIESNER, JULIUS, "Die Rohstoffe des Pflanzenreichs," Engelmann, Leipzig (1873). *Various fibers.*

CHAPTER VIII

THE LEAF FIBERS

Bernice Montgomery

Leaf fibers are obtained from the leaves of monocotyledonous plants. The fibers occur in bundles, i.e., aggregates, of individual cells, with the ends overlapping so as to produce continuous filaments throughout the length of the leaf. The position of the fibers in the leaf is not uniform. For most of the plants included in the group, however, the fiber is located in greatest quantity near the outer, i.e., under, surface of the leaf, which in cross-section is frequently concave. Toward the upper or inside surface of the leaf the fibers become fewer and the proportion of cellular tissue increases. The leaves are generally characterized by being rather thick and fleshy, frequently with hard surfaces. The last point applies especially to those genera whose native habitat has a rather arid climate, the leaves serving to store moisture for the plants.

The fibers are held in place by the cellular tissue of the leaf and by gummy and waxy substances. These substances also serve to hold the fibers to each other within the bundles. The function of leaf fibers is to give strength and rigidity to the leaf and to give support to the water-conducting vessels. In one notable instance, the *Musa* genus, the fibers also serve to support the portion of the leaf which protects the true stem of the plant, the fibers occurring in the petioles of the leaves, the petioles being sheathlike in form and folded around each other and the true stem.

Leaf fibers are often termed "hard" fibers because they are generally harder, stiffer, and coarser in texture than those in the bast fiber group, which were utilized for textile purposes on a large scale before the leaf fibers were "discovered." This distinction, however, does not hold true for all fibers of each group. Pineapple fiber, for example, is softer and finer than many of the fibers belonging to the bast fiber group. Because their functions are more or less mechanical, leaf fibers are also sometimes called "structural" fibers.

Leaf fibers are utilized commercially as the full-length bundles. These bundles, after removal from the leaf, are termed "strands," or in the fiber trade simply fiber. Their principal use is for various types of cordage and twines, though the fibers are also used in the manufacture of woven fabrics.

Most of the plants from which leaf fibers are obtained are closely related. The most important from a commercial standpoint come from plants of the Order Iridales. These include abacá, sisal, and henequen, which account for more than 80 per cent of all commercial leaf fiber production. A table (38) showing botanical orders and families of leaf fibers is given at the end of this chapter.

In contrast with the bast fiber group, there are comparatively few genera in the leaf fiber group from which fiber is utilized even to a moderate extent. Like the bast fiber group, however, a number of the leaf fiber genera are awaiting more efficient cultivation and processing methods that their full potentialities may be realized.

Relative importance of each of the leaf fibers on the basis of world production is given in Table 1.

TABLE 1. RELATIVE IMPORTANCE OF LEAF FIBERS ON BASIS OF WORLD PRODUCTION

(Thousands of short tons)

Fiber	*1951*	*1950*	*Average 1934–38*
Sisal	390	343	250
Abacá	157	119	222
Henequen	105	128	122
Cantala	3	2	23
Palma (Palma istle)	15	17	15
Fique (*Furcraea macrophylla*)	40	40	12
Phormium	18	18	7
Caroa	10	10	1
Letona	4	3	3
Mauritius	2	2	1
Cabuya (*Furcraea andina*)	1	1	1
Other leaf fibers	neg.	neg.	neg.

neg. Negligible, or not available.

MUSA FIBERS

Plants of the genus *Musa,* of which there are a large number of species, are among the world's most useful plants. They furnish an important proportion of the world's supply of cordage fibers as well as fibers for coarse and some fine fabrics; the fruits are important in the diet of the people of many countries; in some countries the flowering bud of the plant is eaten as a vegetable; the juice of the plant is used as a dyestuff by the people of some countries; and the leaves are used as lining for cooking vessels, as serving dishes, as wrapping for foods and other articles sold in shops, for polishing floors, and as both rain and sun umbrellas.

The plants are perennials belonging to the Family Musaceae and include the largest of the herbaceous plants. The name of the genus, and of the family, was derived from that of Antonio Musa, a physician to Octavius Augustus, first Emperor of Rome, 63–14 B.C.

The most widely known species from which fiber is obtained is *M. textilis,* more widely known as "abacá." By far the most widely known *Musa* species, however, is *M. sapientum,* the fruit of which is the commercial banana. Similar fruits are common to all plants of this genus and their known use is of great antiquity. They have varying degrees of edibility. Fruits from some are inedible; some, as the fruit from *M. sapientum,* are edible in the raw state when ripened; others must be cooked to become edible. This last group is often called "plantains," though the plants are not related to plants of the genus *Plantago,* commonly termed plantain, of the Plantaginaceae family.

Abacá

Nomenclature. The world's most widely sought-after cordage fiber is obtained from plants of the genus *Musa,* species *textilis,* of which there are a large number of varieties. The term "abacá," its Philippine name, is now generally used to designate this fiber, though in the past it was more usually known as "Manila hemp," because hemp (*Cannabis sativa*) fiber was the cordage fiber used in greatest quantity in the Western Hemisphere when abacá was introduced there from its native habitat, the Philippines.

Because fiber is obtained from a large number of species of the genus *Musa,* some confusion attended the identification and naming of the species yielding abacá fiber. The first term used in the Western Hemisphere to designate plants now known as *Musa textilis* was *Musa mindanensis,* by Rumph in 1690. Don Luis Nee in a memoire, "Anales de Ciencias" published in Spain in 1801, was the first person to designate the plant as *Musa textilis.* This memoire was translated into English and published in the British *Annals of Botany,* Volume I, shortly after its publication in Spain. Following this publication, the designation *Musa textilis* came into general use, though in 1820 Colla gave the species the name of *Musa sylvestris;* in 1825 Perrottet, *Musa*

Samar, and the Visayan Islands. During the early 1900's, abacá plantings were established in Davao Province in southern Mindanao. Labor was scarce, and, as plantations expanded in Davao, Japanese workers were brought into the area. Later, Japanese capital was invested in plantations in the area. These plantations were largely operated on a small tenant basis, the tenant leasing the land, usually for 15 years, and returning a part of the crop as rent. In 1915, Davao production was about 3½ per cent of the total; by 1940, Davao accounted for more than half the total and has continued to be the most important source of exports, especially for the medium grades; most of the high-quality, fine fiber comes from the Bicol area. Of the 1940 production in Davao, Japanese-owned and -operated plantations produced about two-thirds.

The exceedingly strong position which Philippine abacá held in the market for cordage fiber was somewhat affected during the period following 1910 when, as a result of variations in quality of abacá, manufacturers of binder twine began to use henequen and sisal. Both World Wars had adverse effects on abacá production in the Philippines. The inflation which developed during World War I culminated in a serious national financial crisis in 1920. As a result, planting of abacá was discouraged in favor of coconuts and other crops. During the late 1920's production increased but declined again during the depression years of the 1930's. War preparations in the late 1930's again stimulated production, but conditions existing during the following World War II disrupted production seriously. Plantations were untended, and disease and jungle growth destroyed many plants. The heavy demand for and short supply of cordage fiber following the war led to wasteful overharvesting. Urgent need for food crops retarded rehabilitation of abacá. Redistribution of land and determination of legal ownership of plantations owned by the Japanese during the pre-World War II period also contributed to delay in rehabilitation. The Philippine Government has undertaken a program to correct the situation, but, because of the many ramifications, successful solution of the problem may require several years.

Production on the island of Sumatra in Indonesia was disrupted during World War II, when lack of care and disease destroyed many plantings, and has been rehabilitated slowly because of economic and political conditions following the war. Production in North Borneo is less than that during the late 1930's, lack of care and disease having destroyed a large part of the plantings during World War II. Plans have been announced, by private enterprise, to increase production from this area.

Production in Central American countries from the plantings made during the 1930's and 1940's increased rapidly in response to war demands and postwar shortage of fibers. In 1947, production was 36.5 million pounds; [3] overharvesting as a result of urgent war needs and the appearance of disease resulted in decreased production after 1947.

Ecuador is presently producing only a very small quantity of fiber, about 15 tons annually, though the quality of the soil and climatic conditions prevailing in the so-called "garua" (drizzle) belt are said to be favorable for increasing production to a much higher level. Very small quantities are also produced in Brazil and the Belgian Congo.

Table 2 gives production data by countries for 1951, 1950, 1949, and the average for 1934–38.

TABLE 2. Production of Abacá by Countries

(Thousands of short tons)

Country	*1951*	*1950*	*1949*	*1948*	*Average 1934–38*
Philippines	138	105	93	140	201
British North Borneo	1	1	1	1	1
Indonesia	7	3	1	2	20
Costa Rica	2	2	5	7	negligible
Guatemala	4	4	4	5	negligible
Honduras	2	1	3	4	negligible
Panama	3	3	3	4	negligible
Total	157	119	110	163	222

Sources: "Yearbook of Food and Agricultural Statistics," V, Part 1, "Production." "Monthly Bulletin of Agricultural Economics and Statistics," I (1), Food and Agriculture Organization of the United Nations, Rome (1952). 1950 and 1951 figures for the Philippines and figures for Indonesia were computed on the basis of trade statistics and unofficial government estimates.

Utilization. The principal use of abacá fiber is for cordage. A small proportion of total production is used for hat braids, woven stiffening materials, and paddings. Waste is utilized by the paper industry.

Almost all of the world production of abacá is exported from the producing countries to other countries for manufacture, only a small

[3] "World Study of Hard Fibers and Hard Fiber Products," Part I, Franklin F. Kidd, assisted by Ann Q. O'Connell and Gayle D. Dean, U. S. Dept. Commerce, Washington (1949).

quantity being retained in the producing countries for manufacture into goods for domestic use or export. Pre-World War II, the principal importing countries were the United States, the United Kingdom, and Japan, which together took about three-fourths of the total. The postwar import pattern reflects not only the economic and currency as well as the abacá production conditions prevailing during this period but also the impact of the increasing production of sisal fiber. In 1938, for example, sisal represented about 40 per cent of total imports of leaf fiber into the United Kingdom; in 1950, sisal represented 85 per cent of the total leaf fiber imports.[3a] Abacá fiber produced by the Philippines goes to more than 25 countries; that from Central America goes to the United States. A large part of the production from Indonesia also goes to the United States.

Table 3 shows data for imports, by principal importing countries, for 1951, 1950, 1949, 1948, and the average for 1935–38.

TABLE 3. IMPORTS OF ABACÁ BY PRINCIPAL IMPORTING COUNTRIES

(Thousands of short tons)

Country	*1951*	*1950*	*1949*	*1948*	*Average 1935–38*
United States	91	61	48	62	43
United Kingdom	23	12	6	11	41
Japan	19	17	16	20	63
France	8	4	4	1	6
Germany (Bizone 1948 and 1949, Federal Republic 1950 and 1951)	4	2	3	3	6
Netherlands	2	3	2	2	4
Canada	6	3	3	3	4
Spain	*	*	*	*	3
Belgium	*	2	1	3	3
Australia	*	*	*	*	3
Norway	2	2	1	4	2
Denmark	3	3	3	3	*
Other countries	7	12	7	9	15
Total	165	121	94	121	193

* Less than 500 short tons.

Source: "Yearbook of Food and Agricultural Statistics," **VI,** Part 2, "Trade," Food and Agriculture Organization of the United Nations, Rome (1952).

In the United States, the chief use of abacá is for ropes and cables for the navy and merchant marine, oil-well drilling, fishing, and other

[3a] *Industrial Fibres,* Commonwealth Econ. Com., H.M. Stationery Office, London (1951 and 1952).

industrial uses. It has been estimated that abacá fiber is used for about 80 per cent of all rope manufactured in this country. Because of urgent war needs and the shortage of supply, with consequent high prices, abacá has not been used for wrapping twines, except in very negligible quantities, since the late 1930's. In the early 1900's, abacá was widely used in the United States for binder twine but was gradually displaced by henequen and sisal fibers which were lower priced and, for a time, of a more stable quality than abacá.

Cultivation. The plants give most satisfactory results on well-drained, friable, moderately rich loam at elevations of less than 1500 ft. Best results have been obtained in areas where rainfall averages 100 to 110 in. annually and is evenly distributed throughout the year, with an average relative humidity of 80 to 90 per cent. Temperatures should average about 80 to 85° F., not falling below 70° F. The area should be free of high winds as the shallow root structure of the plant allows it to fall easily under pressure from wind. One of the reasons for the increasing production from the Davao area in the Philippines during the past 30 years is its freedom from the typhoons which strike fairly often in the more northerly areas where abacá is grown. Windbreaks are often planted around fields in these areas.

Propagation may be made by seeds, by rhizomes sent out by mature roots, or from pieces of mature rootstock. The last named is preferred. Seeds seldom breed true and are used principally for experimental work in developing new or improving old varieties. Rhizomes, which are termed "suckers," are used to a considerable extent in the Philippines when pieces of rootstock are not available. A longer time is required for plants grown from suckers to become established than those grown from pieces of rootstock. Rootstock pieces are usually referred to as "seed," "bits," or "seed pieces." To form this "seed," rootstock from mature plants is cut into pieces, about 5 to 6 in. in diameter at the top, care being taken to have at least 2 or 3 buds on each piece.

Methods of cultivation in the Philippines vary widely, depending on the degree of mechanization available. Since a large part of the crop is produced on small holdings, comparatively little mechanization is practiced. The method used in many areas is to clear the land by cutting all jungle growth and trees during the driest season of the year and then burning over the land, thereby destroying brush and small growth. Tree trunks remain on the land, preventing, to some extent, growth of weeds until abacá plants develop sufficiently to shade the land. By that time the tree trunks will have rotted and shade from the abacá will largely prevent growth of weeds. A more modern method is to undercut the jungle growth by hand or with the aid of machinery, plant the abacá rootstock, then fell all trees. The resulting debris prevents, to a large extent, the growth of weeds until the abacá develops sufficiently to shade ground. Another method, coming into wider use, is to clear the land completely by cutting and burning and then removing remaining debris, preferably with the aid of machinery. After planting, the land is cultivated at regular intervals to prevent recurrence of jungle growth until abacá plants shade the ground. This method is also generally followed when an old planting is to be replaced. After plants begin to shade the ground, cultivation and weeding are done usually twice a year. If the mat becomes overcrowded, stalks are thinned and roots pruned.

After land is cleared, holes are dug, of the proper size and sufficiently deep to permit covering the piece of rootstock to a depth of 2 to 4 inches. Distance between holes is 8 to 10 feet, depending upon the variety being planted. In areas where land clearing is incomplete, spacings between holes are necessarily irregular. Planting is done when the rains begin after the dry season. A cover crop is usually planted just before or after planting abacá. Formerly sweet potatoes were the most usual cover crop; beginning with the 1930's, legumes, frequently cowpeas or broad beans, have been planted. Sometimes abacá is planted with coconuts, and several crops of abacá are obtained until coconuts come into bearing, when abacá is removed. Upland rice is also used as a cover crop.

Fertilization depends upon composition of soil, local custom, and amount of fertilizer available which the farmer can afford. For a long time, the custom was to grow abacá without fertilization until the soil was exhausted, then to clear and plant new land. This practice began to decline during the 1930's, with improved knowledge of cultivation and increase of the practice of dividing the land into smaller areas for farming by individual growers.

Methods of land preparation, planting, and cultivation used in Indonesia and British North Borneo are similar to those used in the Philippines. Methods used in Central America are also generally similar but are highly mechanized. Amount of cultivation and use of fertilizer are more extensive than is general in the Far East. Methods used in Ecuador and other countries generally follow methods used in the Philippines.

There are a number of diseases and insect pests which cause injury to the plants. The most serious diseases in the Philippines and other Far Eastern areas are bunchy top, mosaic, and vascular wilt. Drought or excessive moisture, inadequate fertilization, and lack of care all provide conditions for the increase of these diseases. The Philippine Government has undertaken a program of eradication. A part of the cure for the diseases is to remove all plantings in affected areas. The high prices being paid for abacá fiber, however, have resulted in many growers showing reluctance to remove plants from which any fiber might be obtained. In Central America, tipover, a disease which affects the roots of the plants, has caused the most serious trouble. The insect pest which appears over the widest area, both in the Far East and Central America, is the banana borer, *Cosmopolites sordidus*.

Harvesting. The stalk is ready for harvesting when the blossom appears; if it is not cut at this time the fiber is generally coarser and not as strong; after fruit appears, the stalk begins to deteriorate. The entire stalk is cut down, close to the ground. In the Philippines, the leaf blades at the top of the stalk are generally cut after the stalk is felled; in Central America, these are cut before the stalk is felled, with a banana knife called a "pulla."

Depending upon variety, skill, and adequacy of cultivation and growing conditions, the parent rootstock, in 18 to 24 months, will have become established and sent out rhizomes which in turn begin to send up stalks, 2 to 3 of which will be ready for harvesting for fiber. After the initial harvesting, two to four stalks may generally be harvested from each mat every 4 to 6 months; in Central America, the cycle is usually four times a year. The first stalks harvested do not have as many or as large sheaths as those from older plants and, in consequence, yield less fiber. By the end of the fourth or fifth year, quantity of fiber from stalks is greater, the yield under favorable circumstances being as high as 4000 lb or more per acre. The planting reaches its peak yield by the sixth year and usually continues at this level until about the eighth year, when yield begins to decline. Generally, plants are replaced after 10 yr; in some areas it has been found economical to replant after 6 yr.

Average yield in the Philippines during the 1930's period ranged from 1000 to 2000 lb per acre; postwar average annual yield has ranged from 1000 to 1500 lb per acre. High prices, which encourage overharvesting, often termed "butchering," and typhoons, which blow over a large number of plants from which fiber must then be extracted, cause wide fluctuations in average annual yields; the yield increases during periods of overharvesting and typhoon damage and then decreases during subsequent years until plants can develop mature stalks or be replaced. Average yield per acre in Central America approximates 1500 lb per acre. Yield has been affected by war demand for fiber which resulted in overharvesting, by the fact that many of the plantings are young and only beginning to come into the stage of heaviest production, and by serious inroads of disease and insects in some areas.

Fiber Removal. In the Philippines, the most widely used and oldest method of removing fiber from the leaf sheaths consists of two basic operations: (1) separating the fibrous outer layer from each leaf sheath, this outer layer being termed a "tuxy" and the operation "tuxying"; and (2) removing pulpy material, thus freeing the fiber strands, generally termed simply fiber, from the tuxy, the operation being termed "stripping" or "cleaning." Both operations must be performed as soon as possible after the stalk is felled.

The tuxying operation is usually done in the field. The workman inserts the point of a knife between the outer and middle layers of the leaf sheath, freeing an end of the outer layer 1 to 3 in. wide. This strip or tuxy is then pulled off the entire length of the sheath. Each leaf sheath furnishes 2 to 3 tuxies. When all tuxies are removed from a leaf sheath it is removed from the stalk and allowed to remain on the field for organic fertilizer. Usually another workman picks up the tuxies and carries them to the place where the stripping or cleaning operation is to be performed.

The sheaths, on the basis of color and quality of fiber, are usually classified into four groups, which are, from outer to inner: babá, segunda babá, middle, and ubud. One study [4] showed the proportion of tuxies from each of these groups in relation to total weight of tuxies to be: babá 13 to 15 per cent, segunda babá 16 to 18 per cent, middle 27 per cent and ubud 42 per cent; proportion in relation to total weight of stalk was babá 2 per cent, segunda babá 2½ to 3 per cent, middle 4 to 4½ per cent, and ubud 6 per cent. In the Bicol area, the tuxies are kept separated by groups during the stripping operation. This facilitates grading and accounts in a large measure for the fact that most of the higher and finer quality of abacá comes from this area. In some parts of this area, only three groupings are used: babá, segunda babá, and inner, which includes the middle and ubud.

The stripping or cleaning operation to free the fiber from the pulpy material remaining on its surface is accomplished in two ways: (1) "hand stripping" and "spindle stripping." The operation must be

[4] "Aspects of Abacá Production in the Philippines Today," M. M. Saleeby, *Cord Age,* New York (Dec. 1928).

done immediately after tuxying, otherwise the pulpy material hardens and the resulting fiber can never be properly cleaned.

Hand stripping consists of scraping pulpy material from the fiber by pulling the tuxy, by hand, between a knife with a serrated edge, which is counterweighted, and a block of wood. The workman usually scrapes, that is, strips the root end of the tuxy first, then reverses the tuxy and strips the remaining length. The mechanism is primitive, but the world's finest quality of abacá fiber is produced with it. The quality of the knife, especially the number and evenness of the serrations, and the amount of pressure it exerts on the tuxy determine to a large extent the quality of the fiber. The greater the number of serrations and the heavier the pressure, the cleaner and finer the fiber; but, obviously, waste will be greater and the work harder. Consequently the price of the fiber is often the determining factor for the quality of fiber produced. Low prices, and especially smaller price differentials between grades, mean a decrease in incentive to produce fine-quality fiber. Production per man of a 2-man team averages 15 to 20 lb of fiber per day, the quantity varying with the fineness and cleanness of the fiber produced. From 30 to 40 per cent of the total abacá fiber produced in the Philippines is hand stripped, the method being used extensively in the Bicol area, Leyte, and Samar.

Spindle stripping is done with a small, American-invented machine, called a "hagotan." The machine has a motor-driven, revolving, cone-shaped spindle just in front of the frame holding the scraping knife. The tuxy is inserted under the blade of the knife and one end, usually the butt end, is wound around the spindle to hold the tuxy in place. As the spindle revolves, the full length of the tuxy is automatically wrapped around it, thereby being drawn under the knife, and the fiber is scraped clean. The tuxy is then reversed and the butt end drawn under the knife after the tip end has been wound around the spindle. Usually 5 or 6 men work as a team in the operation of one machine. Production averages 50 to 70 lb per man per day. There is also a smaller model, requiring fewer men and giving a somewhat lower production of fiber.

Immediately after stripping, the fiber is hung in the sun to dry. If cleaning has been properly done, sunlight will not discolor the fiber; if pulpy material remains on fiber, sunlight will turn this a brownish color. Fiber must be dried promptly or it loses luster and tensile strength. From 6 to 20 hr are required for the fiber to dry, depending upon the quality of the stripping operation and, of course, atmospheric conditions; the cleaner the fiber, the more quickly it dries. Some growers have drying sheds for use in case of rain; most of the smaller growers do not have this facility.

Abacá fiber is also cleaned in the Philippines by means of a decorticator. Small raspadors, similar to the machine invented by a Franciscan friar for cleaning sansevieria fiber, have been in use for many years. A larger, American-designed version of this machine was introduced during the 1920's. These machines decorticate individual leaf sheaths. During the 1930's, a large, stationary machine, German designed, utilizing the basic principle of the raspador, was successfully used for abacá. For this machine, the abacá stalks are cut into lengths of not less than 4 nor more than 6 ft, then fed horizontally through a crusher and squeeze rolls, which flatten and spread them out for the action of the scraping blades, sometimes called beaters. The operation of the machine then proceeds as described in Chapter VII, under the section "Ramie." This type of machine was first successfully used for abacá in Indonesia in Sumatra; later one of the machines was installed in British North Borneo. During the late 1930's two were installed in the Philippines, one of which is still in operation. A mechanical drier is operated in conjunction with these machines. A narrow-gauge railroad is generally used to transport cut stalks from field to decorticator.

Central American abacá is cleaned by machine decorticators of the large, stationary type, similar to the machines used in Indonesia, British North Borneo, and the Philippines. Mechanical driers are used. Mules are used to transport cut stalks, which are termed "junks," from field to decorticator.

Cleaning in Ecuador and other countries is principally by hand, generally following the methods used in the Philippines.

Percentage of dry fiber, in relation to weight of freshly cut stalk, obtained by the various methods of fiber removal varies widely. Hand stripping results from 1½ to 2½ per cent; spindle stripping from about 2 to 3 per cent; decorticating from about 2½ to 3½ per cent. Approximately 1 lb of fiber is obtained, on the average, from each stalk, depending upon the variety, growing conditions, and maturity of stalk.

Marketing and Grading. In the Philippines, in areas other than Davao, fiber for export is produced principally by small growers. These people usually sell their fiber to a middleman who in turn sells to an export firm; fiber may be graded and baled for export at the middleman's warehouse, if he owns one, or at a warehouse designated by the export firm. In Davao, following a pattern introduced during the 1930's, growers generally bring their fiber to privately owned central warehouses, equipped with baling presses, where fiber is graded, baled, and sold to the highest bidder at regularly scheduled public auctions.

All grading of fiber for export is done by government inspectors, under a system begun in 1915 in answer to complaints that much of the Philippine abacá was not of uniform quality. The system has expanded and improved and is currently considered to rank among the most reliable fiber-grading systems of the world. The fiber after grading is pressed into export bales weighing 278.3 lb each.

There are three sets of official Philippine grading standards:[5] (1) hand- or spindle-stripped fiber especially prepared for tagal braid and other fine textile uses; (2) hand- or spindle-stripped fiber especially prepared for cordage; and (3) decorticated fiber.

Grades for tagal braid and related uses are based primarily on fineness and luster of fiber, cleanness, color, and strength. Length of fiber in any one hank within a bale must average not less than 1½ meters. Grades are listed in Table 4.

TABLE 4. GRADES OF PHILIPPINE ABACÁ FOR TAGAL BRAIDS AND RELATED USES

Letter Designation	*Name of Grade*
TA	Tagal Extra Prime
TB	Tagal Prime
TC	Tagal Superior
TD	Tagal Good
TE	Tagal Fair

Grades of hand- and spindle-stripped fiber prepared especially for cordage are based primarily on cleanness, color, and tensile strength. Length designations for fiber classes in these groups are: Long, 2 meters and above; Normal, 1 meter to 2 meters; Short, 60 cm to 1 meter; and Very Short or Tow, under 60 cm. Grades AB, CD, E, F, I, J1, J2, L1, L2, and DL are usually Normal to Long length; other grades, above residual, usually vary from Short to Normal. There are five classes of cleaning. Consideration is given to the fact that some varieties produce coarser fibers than others. The classes of clean-

[5] "Fiber Inspection Administrative Order No. 4" (Revised), December 1, 1939, Republic of the Philippines, Dept. Agr. and Natural Resources, Manila (1940).

ing and the grade designations are given in Table 5. This group of grades constitutes the bulk of export fiber. Grades I and J1 are generally in greatest demand and supply and are customarily used as a basis for quoting prices.

TABLE 5. GRADE DESIGNATIONS FOR HAND- AND SPINDLE-STRIPPED PHILIPPINE ABACÁ FIBER PREPARED ESPECIALLY FOR CORDAGE

Cleaning and Letter Designation	*Name of Grade*
Excellent cleaning	
AB	Superior Current
CD	Good Current
E	Midway
F	25% over Fair Current
S2	Streaky Two
S3	Streaky Three
Good cleaning	
I	Fair Current
J1	Superior Seconds No. 1
G	Soft Seconds
H	Soft Brown
Fair cleaning	
J2	Superior Seconds No. 2
K	Medium Seconds
M1	Medium Brown
Coarse cleaning	
L1	Coarse
L2	Coarse Seconds
M2	Coarse Brown
Very coarse cleaning	
DL	Daet Coarse
DM	Daet Coarse Brown
Residual grades	
Y1	Damaged One
Y2	Damaged Two
Y3	Damaged Three
Y4	Damaged Four
01	Strings One
02	Strings Two
03	Strings Three
T1	Tow One
T2	Tow Two
T3	Tow Three
Waste grade	
W	Waste

Grade designations for decorticated fiber are shown in Table 6. An initial, as approved by the Manager of the Fiber Inspection Service,

TABLE 6. GRADE DESIGNATIONS FOR DECORTICATED PHILIPPINE ABACÁ

Letter Designation	*Name of Grade*
AD-1	Abacá Decorticated Superior
AD-2	Abacá Decorticated Good
AD-3	Abacá Decorticated Fair
AD-4	Abacá Decorticated Strips
AD-Y	Abacá Decorticated Damaged
AD-O	Abacá Decorticated Strings
AD-T	Abacá Decorticated Tow

designating the decorticating machine used, may be inserted after the letter designation and before numeral denoting grade. The following initials have been approved: C for Corona, P for Prieto, and R for Raspador. Length varies from a minimum of 60 to 120 cm, being governed principally by lengths into which stalk is cut for decortication.

Central American abacá is graded by official standards promulgated by the United States Government. Grades are based primarily on color, with consideration also being given to strength, cleaning, and length. Minimum length of line fiber is 30 in.; fibers shorter than this length are classified as Tow. The grades established by the United States Reconstruction Finance Corporation on 1 July 1946 were, in a descending order: Superior, Good, Streaky, Brown, Tow, and Flume Waste. On 17 December 1948, a new grade, Clear, was designated to appear between Superior and Good; and on 7 February 1949, the grade Clear was designated to take the place of Superior and Good. Present grades are: Clear, Streaky, Brown, Tow, and Flume Waste. Principal grades produced are Clear, Streaky, and Tow. Prior to 1 January 1949, fiber was pressed into bales weighing 275 lb each; beginning on that date, standard bale weight has been 300 pounds.

Indonesia and British North Borneo have not as yet adopted official grading standards, the designations prevailing with large growers being those used principally in trade. The most frequently used are: Excellent, Good, Fair, and Fair X.

Characteristics. The commercial fiber is utilized in the form of fiber strands. These fiber strands, generally termed fiber, are made up of bundles of individual fibers. Individual fibers are held together and to each other by the natural gums of the plant. The length of the fiber strands, that is, commercial fiber, depends not only upon the length of the sheath but also on the method used for removing fiber from the sheath. If fiber is removed from the full length of the sheaths, as in hand or machine stripping, fiber strands from the middle sheaths may run as long as 15 ft or more; average length ranges from 3 to 9 ft. Length of decorticated fiber strands depends upon length to which stalk was cut before fiber was removed.

The fiber, when properly cleaned and dried, has a naturally high luster. Color ranges from an almost pure white through ivory, cream, ochre, light brown, to dark browns, reds, purples, and approximately black, depending upon the position of the leaf sheath in stalk, and upon variety. Average spectral reflectance values for 10 grades of Philippine abacá in terms of percentage relative to standard white magnesium oxide at wave length of 500 mμ, as determined by Becker,[6] are shown in Table 7. The 500 mμ wave length is the one used by the United States Navy in computing "Becker values" for color of abacá rope.[7]

TABLE 7. AVERAGE SPECTRAL REFLECTANCE VALUES FOR 10 GRADES OF PHILIPPINE ABACÁ FIBER

Grade of Fiber	*Reflectance in Percentage at 500 mμ*
AB	59.3
CD	54.9
E	49.9
F	46.5
S2	45.4
S3	33.5
I	42.5
J1	40.0
G	31.3
H	21.5

Abacá has excellent strength, satisfactory elongation and flexing qualities, and an unusually high resistance to the effects of microorganisms found in salt water. Breaking length and strength and percentage of elongation of Philippine abacá cordage fiber strands for six selected samples are shown in Table 8.

[6] "Spectral Reflectance of the Philippine Islands Government Standards for Abacá Fiber," Genevieve Becker, Natl. Bur. Standards RP628, U. S. Dept. Commerce, Washington (1933).

[7] "Evaluation of Manila Rope Fiber for Color," Genevieve Becker and William D. Appel, Natl. Bur. Standards RP627, U. S. Dept. Commerce, Washington (1933).

TABLE 8. Breaking Length and Strength and Percentage of Elongation of Philippine Abacá Cordage Fiber

(Basis 15-in. bundle of fibers weighing 5 grains)

Sample	Grade	Breaking Length of Dry Bundle (1000 ft)	Condition of Fiber					
			Dry		Wet		Dry after Soaking in Salt Water for 28 Days	
			Breaking Strength (pounds)	Elongation (per cent)	Breaking Strength (pounds)	Elongation (per cent)	Breaking Strength (pounds)	Elongation (per cent)
1	E	158	90	2.1	74	2.4	83	2.8
2	J2	180	103	2.8	96	4.0	58	3.1
3	I	166	95	3.9	62	n.s.	72	2.9
4	E	142	81	1.9	57	n.s.	67	2.3
5	F	138	79	2.8	66	n.s.	78	3.0
6	J1	133	76	3.3	59	n.s.	70	2.9

n.s. Not stated.
Source: "Machines and Methods for Testing Cordage Fibers," Herbert F. Schiefer, Natl. Bur. Standards RP1611, U. S. Dept. Commerce, Washington (1944).

Table 9 gives average breaking strength in grams per gram meter for various grades of Philippine abacá.

From Table 9, it is obvious that position of sheath in the stalk has an important bearing on fiber strength. Fiber from outer and older sheaths, which is classed, because of color and boldness, in the lower grades of each cleaning group, is generally stronger than that from middle or inner sheaths. Berkley et al.[8] found that strength, as well as other properties, also varies with the position of the fiber in the length of the sheath, the fiber nearer the base of the sheath being stronger than that near the tip. In this same study, Berkley et al. also found that samples of prewar Philippine abacá fiber were about 16 per cent stronger than samples of Central American fiber produced during World War II. Samples collected from postwar production, both in the Philippines and Central America, varied widely in strength and other properties. The postwar Philippine abacá, though somewhat superior in general, had decreased to approximately the same strength as that shown by the Central American fiber. It was sug-

[8] "Study of the Quality of Abacá Fiber," Earl E. Berkley, Lyle E. Hessler, Edna B. Burneston, and Chester F. Chew, U. S. Dept. Agr., Washington (1949).

TABLE 9. Average Breaking Strength per Gram Meter for Various Grades of Philippine Abacá

Grade		Breaking Strength (grams)
Excellent cleaning		
AB	Superior Current	49.096
CD	Good Current	51.317
E	Midway	50.240
F	25% over Fair Current	52.415
S2	Streaky Two	52.861
S3	Streaky Three	52.873
Good cleaning		
I	Fair Current	46.315
J1	Superior Seconds No. 1	45.553
G	Soft Seconds	47.057
H	Soft Brown	47.029
Fair cleaning		
J2	Superior Seconds No. 2	not given
K	Medium Seconds	41.012
M1	Medium Brown	Averaged with M2—40.350
Coarse cleaning		
L1	Coarse	Averaged with L2—35.912
L2	Coarse Seconds	Averaged with L1—35.912
M2	Coarse Brown	Averaged with M1—40.350
Very coarse cleaning		
DL	Daet Coarse	33.875
DM	Daet Coarse Brown	30.472

Source: Republic of the Philippines, Dept. Agr. and Natural Resources, Manila, undated.

gested by the authors that the lower strength values of the postwar Philippine fiber may have resulted from the practice of overharvesting.

A comparison of the breaking strength of abacá (origin of fiber not stated) with that of other principal leaf fibers used for cordage is given in Table 10. The data are based on studies made by six authorities.

Abacá is generally considered to be quite buoyant, an important characteristic for marine cordage. The results of one study are given in Table 11.

Individual fibers may be separated from the fiber strands by boiling in an alkali solution. These resulting individual fibers are smooth and even, fairly uniform in diameter, and lustrous. Longitudinal shape is approximately cylindrical; cross-section is irregularly oval to polygonal with rounded corners. Ends of the fiber are usually pointed. The lumen in cross-section is rounded, large, and well de-

TABLE 10. Comparison of Breaking Strength of Abacá with that of Other Principal Leaf Fibers

Abacá = 100

Authority	*Abacá*	*Sisal*	*Henequen*	*Phormium*	*Sansevieria*	*Cantala*
Heim	100	74	n.s.	64	n.s.	n.s.
Braga	100	145	99	46	n.s.	n.s.
Botkin	100	69	n.s.	n.s.	n.s.	n.s.
Dewey	100	65	48	54	n.s.	28
Schiefer	100	78	56	n.s.	80	n.s.
U. S. Dept. Agr.	100	75	79	n.s.	67	n.s.

n.s. Not stated.

Sources

Heim, F., and Roehrich, O., "Methode Nouvelle d'Appreciation de la Valeur Technologique des Fibres Textiles et Filasses Determination de la Souplesse," *Bulletin de L'Agence Générale des Colonies,* Paris (1920).

Braga, Okiro de Senna e Wollner, Wittus Christiano, "Contribuicao ao Conhecimento dos Texteis Nacionais," *Boletim do Instituto de Experimentacao Agricola,* Rio de Janeiro (1944).

Botkin, C. W., and Shires, L. B., "Tensile Strength of Yucca Fibers," *Tech. Bull.* 316, N. M. Coll. Agr. and Mechanic Arts, State Coll. (1944).

Dewey, L. H., and Goodloe, Marie, "The Strength of Textile Fibers," Bur. Plant Industry *Circ.* 128, U. S. Dept. Agr. (1913).

Schiefer, Herbert F., "Machines and Methods for Testing Cordage Fibers," Natl. Bur. Standards RP1611, U. S. Dept. Commerce, Washington (1944).

U. S. Dept. Agr., unpublished data.

TABLE 11. Buoyancy of Philippine Abacá Fiber

(6-in. lengths of fiber, not oiled)

Grade of Fiber	Size of Bundle					
	100 Fiber Strands in Bundle			Bundles of Equal Weight		
	Weight of Bundle (grams)	Time to Sink		Weight of Bundle (grams)	Time to Sink	
		Minutes	Seconds		Minutes	Seconds
F	0.46	20	0	1.50	30	0
G	1.32	6	0	1.50	11	0
L1	2.43	4	0	1.50	6	0

Source: "Absorption of Water by Sisal and Manila on Immersion; Increase of Weight and Girth," *Bull. Imp. Inst.*, H.M. Stationery Office, London (1932).

fined. See Fig. 2. Cell walls, in relation to size of area of cross-section, are thin. Table 12 gives data on length and diameter of individual fibers from studies made by five authorities.

TABLE 12. MEASUREMENTS OF INDIVIDUAL ABACÁ FIBERS

	Length (inches)			Diameter (microns)		
Authority	*Min.*	*Max.*	*Mean*	*Min.*	*Max.*	*Mean*
Espino and Esguerra	0.10	0.33	n.s.	14	35	n.s.
Höhnel	0.11	0.47	n.s.	16	32	n.s.
Lecomte	0.12	0.47	0.24	16	32	24
Luniak	0.08	0.47	0.20	10	50	25
Vétillart	0.12	0.47	0.24	16	32	24

n.s. Not stated.

Sources

Espino, R. B., and Esguerra, Felix, "Comparative Study of Fiber Produced by Six Varieties of Abacá When Grown in Los Baños," *Philippine Agriculturist, 12* (3 and 4), Manila (1923).

Höhnel, F. X., *Die Mikroskopie der technisch verwendeten Faserstoffe*, A. Hartleben, Leipzig (1905).

Lecomte, H., "Textiles Vegeteaux leur Examin Microchimique," *Encyclopedia Scientifique des Aide-Memoire*, Gauthier-Villars et Fils, Paris (1892).

Luniak, Bruno, *Die Unterscheidung der Textilfasern*, Leemann, Zurich (1949).

Vétillart, M., *Études sur les Fibres Végétales Textiles Employée dans l'Industrie*, Firmin, Didot et cie., Paris (1876).

The fiber bundles often show the presence of a series of stegmata, that is, thick, strongly silicified plates. These are flat, tabular cells occurring in certain ferns and other plants and contain a mass of silica in contact with their inner cell wall. In abacá, these stegmata in longitudinal view (Fig. 3) appear quadrilateral and solid, with a round bright spot in the center of each; the edges are serrated; their length is about 30 μ. They may be most easily observed after the fiber bundles have been macerated in a chromic acid solution. After fiber has been extracted with nitric acid, then ignited and dilute acid has been added to the ash, the stegmata (Fig. 4) will appear in the form of a string of pearls, frequently in long chains with sausage-like links.

Abacá fiber has a high percentage of cellulose with a relatively large proportion of lignin. The chemical components of the fiber, as determined by two studies, are given in Table 13.

Aniline sulfate gives a yellow color; iodine and sulfuric acid give a golden-yellow to green color; caustic soda gives a faint yellow tinge and causes a slight distension; and ammoniacal copper gives a blue color and causes considerable swelling of the fiber.

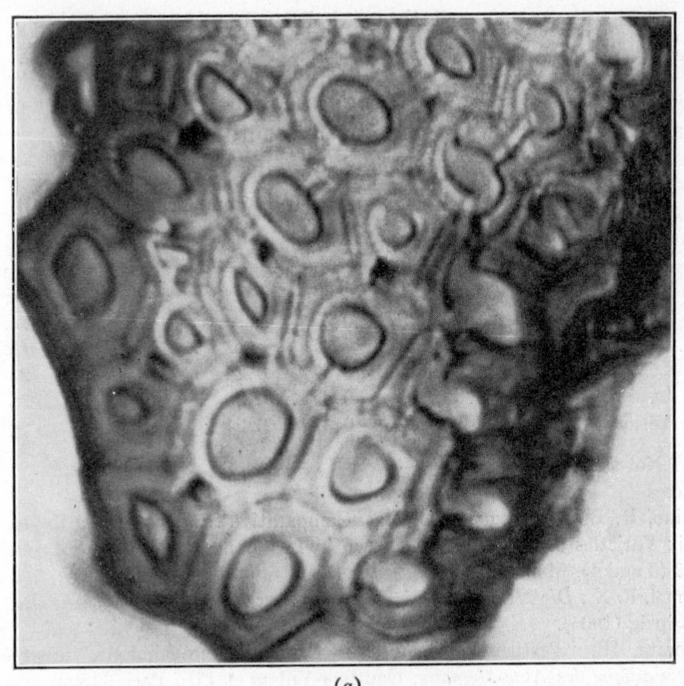

(*a*)

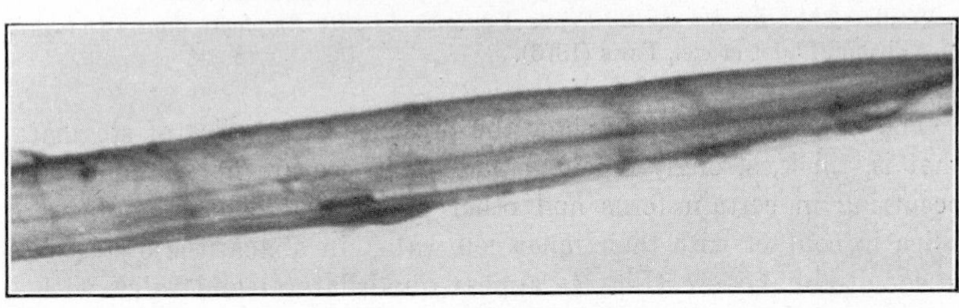

(*b*)

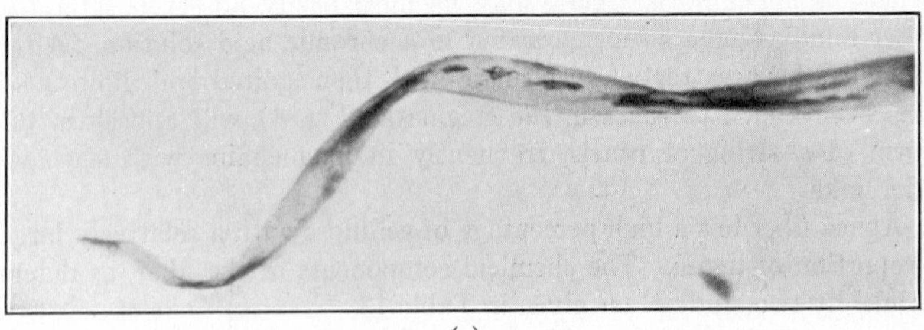

(*c*)

Fig. 2. Abacá fiber. *a*, Cross-section (×800); *b*, longitudinal section (×800); *c*, end of fiber (×500).

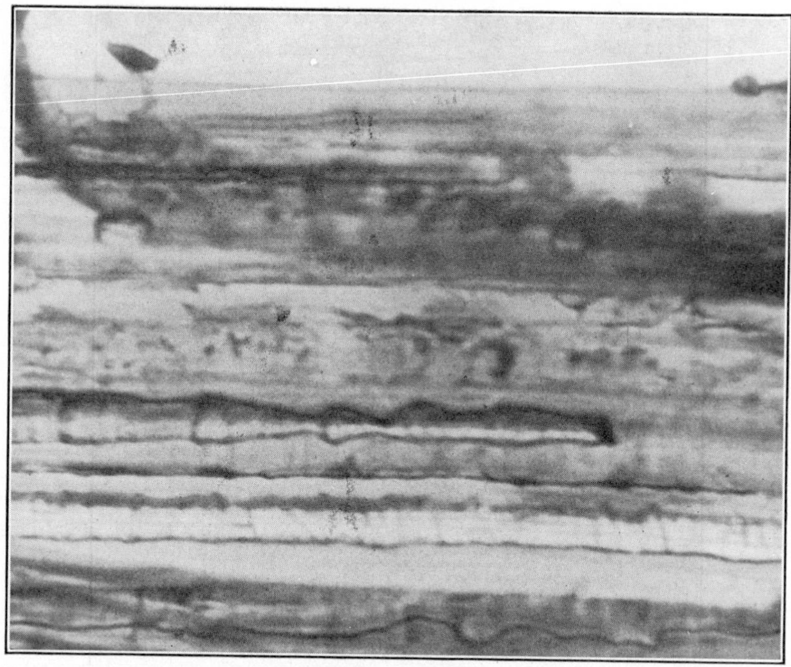

FIG. 3. Longitudinal view (×500) of abacá fiber, showing stegmata. (*Courtesy George Moro.*)

TABLE 13. CHEMICAL COMPONENTS OF ABACÁ FIBER IN PER CENT

(Methods of analyses used in studies were not uniform)

	Study by	
Component	*Müller*	*Turner*
Moisture	11.85	10.00
Ash	1.02	..
Aqueous extract	0.97	1.40
Fat and wax	0.63	0.20
Lignin	..	5.10
Cellulose	64.72	63.20
Hemicelluloses	..	19.60
Pectin	..	0.50
Incrusting and pectic matter	21.83	..
Total	101.02	100.00

Sources

Müller, Hugo, *Die Pflanzenfaser und ihre Aufbereitung für die Technik*, F. Vieweg und Sohn, Braunschweig, Germany (1876).

Turner, A. J., "The Structure of Long Vegetable Fibers," *J. Textile Inst.*, **40** (10), Manchester, England (1949).

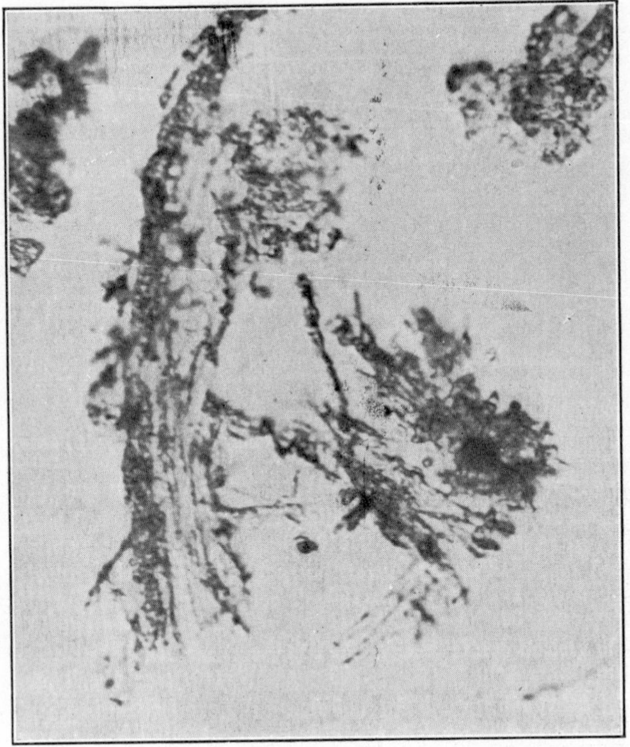

Fig. 4. Ash of abacá fiber (×500), showing form of stegmata more clearly. (*Courtesy George Moro.*)

Canton

This plant of the *Musa* species grows in the Philippines and is held by some authorities to be a natural hybrid between *M. sapientum* and *M. textilis* and by others to be a hybrid between *M. textilis* and various wild species of *Musa*. In appearance, canton plants are generally similar to those of *M. textilis* (see Abacá). The leaf blades of the canton plant, however, are not as pointed as those of *M. textilis*, though not as rounded as those of *M. sapientum*, and the characteristic dark line usually found on the underside of the leaf blade of *M. textilis* does not usually appear on the leaf blades of canton. There are four recognized varieties of canton.

The fiber is generally weaker than abacá, with strength deteriorating as the fiber ages. Distinguishing canton fiber from abacá is difficult. Various authorities hold that canton fiber has a musty smell; breaks with less snap than abacá, with ends fraying; has a lower cellulose content; and, when burned, leaves less and a whiter ash than abacá.

Quantity of canton produced and exported is small. The Philippine Government has a separate grading system for canton fiber prepared for cordage uses; any mixture of canton with abacá will result in all the fiber being classified as canton. The grades for canton include also fiber from amokid and fibers, except pacol, from plants of unknown origin of the *Musa* species. Amokid is the Bicol dialect word for mountain abacá, which grows in a wild state in this area. Official grades of canton are: Can-1, Canton One; Can-2, Canton Two; Can-3, Canton Three; and Can-X, Canton X.

Pacol

Pacol fiber is obtained from plants of the *Musa* species which produce fiber that is much weaker and softer than abacá or canton fibers. Pacol is easily recognized because of these characteristics. The amount produced is negligible. Philippine Government grading standards for pacol prepared for cordage purposes are: Pcl-1, Pacol One; Pcl-2, Pacol Two; and Pcl-X, Pacol X.

Other Musa Fibers

Nomenclature, Appearance, and Fiber Preparation. Fiber from plants of the genus *Musa*, other than abacá, canton, and pacol, does not have any generally recognized name, except perhaps the term "banana fiber." The principal species from which fiber is known to be obtained are listed below. There are other species from which fiber is obtained in areas where they occur in a wild state.

Musa paradisiaca.	Occurs principally in the Far East but is now also to be found in the Western Hemisphere.
Musa ensete *Musa livingstonia* *Musa ulugurensis*	Occur principally in East Africa but have been transported to other parts of the world.
Musa cavendishii.	Occurs in both Eastern and Western Hemispheres.
Musa fehi.	Occurs in Polynesia, notably Tahiti, from where it was brought to Hawaiian Islands.
Musa sapientum.	Occurs in both Eastern and Western Hemisphere; is sometimes termed the true edible banana.

The use of fiber from these plants for textile purposes by the natives of the areas where they grow predates written history. Some species or varieties occur in a wild state in all the moist, tropical areas of the world, but, because the plants have not been cultivated on a large scale for fiber use, little is known about the fiber or its products, outside the individual areas where it grows and is processed.

Plants are similar in general appearance and growing habits to those of *M. textilis* (see under Abacá); leaf blades are more rounded at the tip and usually tougher than those of *M. textilis;* fruit is larger and, from most species, edible.

Harvesting and fiber removal are done by methods similar to those used in the Philippines for hand-stripping abacá. In many areas, the stripping operation is done entirely by hand, without use of the primitive mechanism utilized in the Philippines, by scraping away the pulp from the fiber strands, either with a knife held against a block of wood or with a piece of bamboo or hard wood, as in some areas iron is believed to stain the fiber. As in abacá, the outer sheaths produce the coarsest fiber, those from inner sheaths, the finest. Generally, if fiber is to be used for fabrics, fiber strips from each leaf sheath are kept separated into three groups, in relation to their position in the stalk. In some areas the leaf sheaths are split lengthwise into narrow strips and the resulting strands dried and used without removing pulpy material.

After removal, fiber strands, usually termed simply fiber, are washed in clean, cold water to remove any shreds of pulp remaining on them and are dried in the shade, as, until fiber is completely clean, sunlight causes it to darken in color. The plant juices contain a watery latex, which turns dark brown upon exposure to sunlight and which is utilized as a textile dye in many areas. In Hawaii and Tahiti, the designs on tapa cloth are made with this fluid and in India it is used to dye fabrics a dark khaki color.

Data on yield of fiber varies widely. One study [9] reports that in Java yield of dry fiber is 0.9 per cent of weight of freshly cut stalk and in the Philippines 2.0 to 2.5 per cent. This would mean that about 4 oz to approximately 1 lb of fiber is obtained per stalk.

If the fiber is to be made into fabric, it is usually soaked, scraped, and washed several times more to remove, as completely as possible, waxes, pectins, and gums remaining on it after it was freed from the fiber strips. In some areas, fiber is boiled in a mild solution of lye, made from wood ashes, or other form of alkali. After fiber has been

[9] Kervegant, D., "Le Bannier," *Société d'Editions Geographiques Maritimes et Coloniales,* Paris (1935).

thoroughly cleaned, sunlight will not affect it, though it is more frequently dried in the shade.

Spinning is a twisting or knotting operation. In twisting, which is done by hand, the number of fibers used depends, of course, upon the fineness of the fiber, the degree to which the fiber strands have been separated into individual fibers, and the kind of product being made. Ends of fibers are sometimes moistened as they are twisted into the yarn. The coarser yarns are made from single fiber strands, the ends being knotted together. In some areas, the ends of the finer strands are also knotted, with almost invisible knots, and the resulting yarn is used for weaving. If the yarn is to be woven into a soft and highly lustrous fabric, it is pounded, before weaving, with a wooden paddle to soften it further and to increase its luster.

Weaving is done on a simple hand- or foot-operated loom. Fabrics made range from coarse ones used for sacking to fine ones used for clothing and household purposes. If yarn has been carefully prepared and well pounded, the resulting fabrics will resemble silk in softness and luster. Native names for the fabrics, obviously, vary. One used in many areas in Southeast Asia is "ban"; another, used in the Ryukyu Islands is "bashofu." In Argentina, the fabric has been termed "batista de banano." In the Philippines, a considerable quantity of fabric is made by the natives for their own use. Fiber from *M. textilis* as well as fiber from other species is used. One medium-fine, crisp fabric is termed 'sinnamay." A finer fabric, the yarns well pounded, is called "pinolpok" in the Tagalog dialect and "pinolpog" in the Visayan dialect. The finest fabric is termed "jusi" (given the Spanish pronunciation, "hoosee"). This fabric is usually so fine and lustrous that many definitions of it state that it is all or part silk and silk is sometimes used. Basically, however, the word "jusi," in the Philippines, means a gauzy fabric; true "jusi," it is said, is made from the fiber of plants of the genus *Musa*. Another Philippine name for fabric from musa fiber is "agna." In Indonesia and Malaya, twines made from the fiber are termed "tali pisang."

Characteristics. Obviously, few data exist concerning this fiber. It is considered to be strong, though not as strong as fiber from cultivated plants of the *M. textilis*. *M. paradisiaca* generally is thought to yield the largest amount of fiber and to be nearest *M. textilis* in strength, with *M. ensete, livingstonia,* and *cavendishii* next in order. Fiber from *M. sapientum* generally is reputed to have the lowest strength, especially when taken from plants which have borne fruit. Musa fiber is naturally lustrous; almost white or very light colored, depending upon species and variety, position in stalks, and care of preparation; and has a high resistance to the effects of moisture. It apparently takes native dyes readily.

Microscopically, individual fibers from the *Musa* spp. exhibit many of the same general characteristics (see under Abacá). Figure 5 shows cross-section and longitudinal views of fiber from *M. sapientum.*

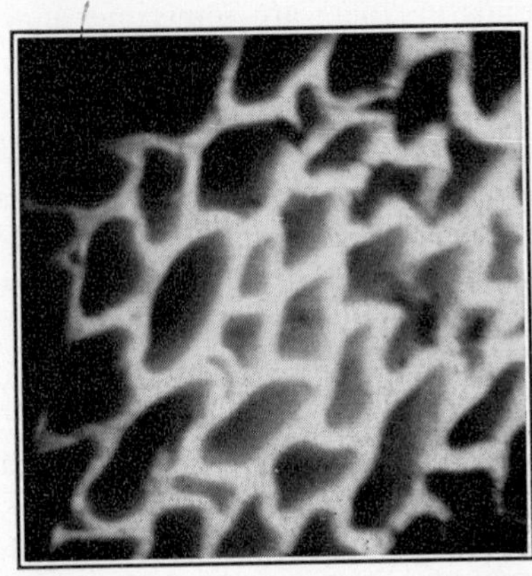

Fig. 5. Longitudinal and cross-sections of *Musa sapientum,* ×500. (*Courtesy von Bergen.*)

Table 14 gives data on measurements of individual fibers from three *Musa* species other than *M. textilis.*

TABLE 14. Measurements of Individual Fibers of Three *Musa* Species

		Length (inches)			Diameter (microns)		
Authority	*Species*	*Min.*	*Max.*	*Mean*	*Min.*	*Max.*	*Mean*
Saito	*M. sapientum*	0.11	0.25	0.12 to 0.22	18	31	not given
Vétillart	*M. paradisiaca*	not given		0.20	20	40	28
Anon.	*M. ensete*	0.02	0.20	0.09 to 0.10	7	26	18

Sources

Saito, K., "Anatomische Studien ueber wichtige Faserpflanzen Japan mit besonder Beruecksichtigung der Bastzellen," *J. Coll. Sciences,* Imperial University, **15** (3), Tokyo (1901).

Vétillart, M., *Études sur les Fibres Végétales Textiles Employées dans l'Industries,* Firmin, Didot et cie., Paris (1876).

Anon., "Fibers in East Africa," *Irish and International Fiber and Fabrics J.,* **7**, (11) (1941).

The fiber has a high percentage of cellulose. Apparently no data exist for purified fiber. Data from one study [10] show almost 80 per

[10] *Report on Indian Fibers and Fibrous Substances,* C. F. Cross, E. J. Bevan, and C. M. King, E. & F. N. Spon, London (1887).

cent cellulose on a dry basis, for *M. paradisiaca* fiber, which apparently had been hand cleaned in the usual manner.

AGAVE FIBERS

The *Agave* genus, a member of the Amaryllidaceae family, is native to Mexico and other parts of the Caribbean area. Plants were taken from there to Europe, Africa, and the Far East by the Spanish and Portuguese, where they naturalized rapidly, especially in the high arid regions around the shores of the Mediterranean and in parts of the Indo-Pakistan subcontinent. The plants were first classified by Clusius in 1575 as *aloes* but were recognized as a separate species by Linnaeus in 1748, who gave the genus the name *Agave*, apparently from the Greek adjective "agavos," meaning high born. The confusion of the *Agave* genus with the *Aloe* genus, however, has persisted into modern times. Considerable confusion has also occurred in the identification and classification of the various species of the *Agave* genus; more than 75 have now been classified.

The earliest European record of the economic value of the *Agave* spp. occurs in Chanca's account of his observations of the new world during the second voyage of Columbus in 1493–94.[11] Gomara's *Historia Generale de los Indios*, published in Spain in 1554, gives a further description of the plants and their uses under the native names of "metl" and "maguey" or tree of wonders. Subsequent historical records describe in more detail the utilization of the fiber from the plants for textiles, uses of the plants as a vegetable and for medicinal purposes, uses of juices from the plants as beverages and also, from some species, as soap.

Agaves are characterized by fleshy, rigid, hard-surfaced, lanceolate leaves growing directly out from the central stalk to form a dense rosette. The stalk, sometimes termed the trunk, in some species is very short, in others it rises to a height of 10 ft. The leaves of the various species range in length from a few inches to several feet; in most species the edges of the leaves are equipped with sharp spines or thorns. Agaves flower from 4 to 15 or 20 years after planting. A central flower stalk is sent up to a height usually two or three times greater than the height of the plant, and dense clusters of flowers are

[11] "The Letter of Dr. Diego Alvarez Chanca, dated 1494, related to the Second Voyage of Columbus to America," trans. by A. M. Fernandez de Ybarra, Smithsonian Miscellaneous Collection, **III,** Part 4, Smithsonian Institution, Washington (1907).

borne on branches growing out from this stalk. The long time required for the plants to flower gave rise to one of their common names, "century plant." After flowering is completed, the old plant dies. As the flowers begin to wither, buds appear in the axils of the flower stems. These develop into small plants with characteristic leaves and are known as "bulbils." When their leaves are a few inches long, the bulbils become detached from the plant and fall to the ground where they take root. New plants also grow from rhizomes sent out by the root system of the parent plant.

The plants generally grow best in warm, rather arid regions. Some species thrive on well-drained rocky soil; others, especially the cultivated species, give better results on moderately rich, well-drained soil.

The leaves contain numerous lengthwise fibers which serve to support the cellular tissue and vascular system of the leaf. These fibers are more numerous on the under sides and edges of the leaf. They are relatively strong and flexible and constitute the agave fibers of commerce.

Sisal

Nomenclature and History. Sisal fiber is obtained from the plant *Agave sisalana,* of which there are several varieties. For a long time, *A. sisalana* was classified as *A. rigida,* then as a variety of this species. The classification *A. sisalana* is now considered to be correct.

There are two schools of thought concerning the origin of the plant *A. sisalana.* One of these holds that the native habitat of the plant is Yucatan, where it is known as "yaxci." The other maintains that the species developed from some plants of what is now classed as *Agave fourcroydes,* which were planted in Florida in the United States in 1833, where they naturalized and mutated. These plants were sent to Florida by Dr. Henry Perrine during the period when he was United States Consul at Campeche in Yucatan, Mexico. The first recorded description of the derivation of the word "sisal" appears in a report made by Perrine to the 25th U. S. Congress,[12] in which he tells of having named the naturalized plants growing in Florida "sisal," stating that he derived this word from the word "sosquil," the Spanish-Mexican "generic name for fibers from henequen."

The plants continued to grow in Florida, spreading to some of the nearby areas, with comparatively little attention being given to cultivating them for commercial fiber production until 1888, when cultiva-

[12] Perrine, Henry, "Tropical Plants," 25th U. S. Congress, 2d Session, House of Representatives Rept. No. 564, Washington (1838).

tion was begun on a small scale in the Bahamas. In 1893, upon the recommendation of Dr. Richard Hindorf, the Deutsche Ostafrikarische Gesellschaft imported 1000 plants from Florida to East Africa. Only 62 plants survived the shipment. These were planted in Kikogwe in Tanganyika, where they thrived; by 1898 the number of plants had increased to 63,000. In 1900 the Amboni Estates, also of Tanganyika, imported some plants from the Bahamas. Commercial plantings in Tanganyika were soon well established. Post-World War I, plantings were established in Kenya and in Uganda. During the 1920's, plantations were also established in Portuguese East Africa (Mozambique) and Portuguese West Africa (Angola). Plantings were also established during this period in Madagascar and the Comoro Islands. Other areas in Africa, notably Eritrea, the Belgian Congo, French Equatorial Africa, French West Africa, North and South Rhodesia, and the Union of South Africa also began growing sisal, chiefly on a small scale.

Cultivation of sisal was begun in Indonesia on the islands of Java and of Sumatra in 1913 from plants imported from East Africa. Production increased rapidly. The fiber was carefully and efficiently prepared, and Indonesian sisal came to be considered more desirable than that grown in other areas. The Philippines also began the cultivation of sisal on a small scale. Small plantings were established on Formosa during the 1920's.

Plantations for producing sisal on a commercial scale were established in Haiti during the 1920's. During World War I, strong demand and high prices for fibers encouraged cutting and sale of wild sisal and aroused interest in the possibility of growing the fiber on a commercial basis. Great care was used in the preparation of Haitian sisal and it came to be considered on a par with the quality of Indonesian sisal. Sisal was first cultivated in Brazil on a commercial scale in 1939. Venezuela began cultivation of sisal in 1938.

Appearance of the Plant. Sisal plants have short thick stems or trunks, about 15 in. in diameter and rising to 3 ft when the plant is mature. Mature leaves are grayish to dark green, 4 to 6 ft long, about 3 in. wide at the base and 4 to 7 in. in breadth at the widest part, gradually tapering to a sharp point, and are without spines along the edges. In cross-section, they are concave, sometimes termed "horseshoe," for most of their length, flattening near the base where they are from 1¼ to 1¾ in. thick.

Flowers appear from 4 to 8 yr after planting and are borne in clusters at the ends of branches growing out from a central flower stalk which is approximately 20 ft in height. Their color is greenish-white; they are about 2½ in. long and have an unpleasant odor. Seeds, when produced, are small. *A. sisalana*, like other agaves, produces bulbils, the number per plant varying from 2000 to 4000.

World Production. Sisal is now the world's most important leaf fiber, constituting more than half the total commercial production of

FIG. 6. Sisal plants, British East Africa. Leaves are being harvested. A portion of a flower stalk may be observed in upper right-hand corner of picture. (*Courtesy Mohegan Fiber Equipment Corp., New York.*)

all leaf textile fibers. Production has been stimulated by heavy demand for fibers, by decreased production of abacá, and by economic conditions affecting foreign exchange. Since most of the sisal fiber production is in "soft"-currency countries and since more countries have "soft"-currency credits than "hard"-currency credits, purchase of sisal has been facilitated; most of the abacá production comes from "hard"-currency countries.

Earliest commercial production of sisal was in the Bahamas, which exported 150 tons in 1892. Export from German East Africa, now Tanganyika, began in 1900, when 7½ tons were shipped. Production from this area had risen to 40 million lb per year by 1913 and continued to increase until World War I, when the rate of production decreased. In 1919, however, production again started to increase. Present production from the Tanganyika, Kenya, and Uganda area in East Africa makes up more than half total world production of sisal. Production from other areas in Africa has also been maintained at a high level.

Production in Indonesia was sharply curtailed by conditions prevailing during World War II. Postwar, the pressing need for food crops and general economic and political conditions have retarded the recovery of the industry; current production is approximately 15 per cent of prewar levels.

Sisal production in Brazil was first increased to a level sufficient to satisfy domestic needs; strong demand for fiber post-World War II has resulted in further production increases. Production in Haiti has been maintained at the high level attained during World War II in response to strong demand for leaf fibers.

Table 15 gives data on sisal production by countries for 1951, 1950, 1949, 1948, and average 1934–38.

TABLE 15. PRODUCTION OF SISAL FIBER BY COUNTRIES

(Thousands of short tons)

Country	*1951*	*1950*	*1949*	*1948*	*Average 1934–38*
Haiti	35	36	34	33	7
Brazil	64	55	33	29	0
Venezuela	5	3	2	3	0
Formosa	1	1	1	3	1
Indonesia	10	5	2	4	67
Angola	26	24	21	19	7
Eritrea	1	1	1	1	1
French Equatorial Africa	2	2	2	1	2
French West Africa	2	2	1	2	4
Kenya	46	45	41	39	33
Madagascar and the Comoro Islands	4	3	4	4	3
Mozambique	21	21	21	19	23
South Rhodesia	1	1	1	1	1
Tanganyika	163	136	141	135	99
Uganda	1	1	1	2	1
Other countries, including the Bahamas, Nyasaland, North Rhodesia, and Belgian Congo	8	7	5	2	1
Total	390	343	311	297	250

Sources: "Yearbook of Food and Agricultural Statistics," **V**, Part I, "Production." "Monthly Bulletin of Agricultural Economics and Statistics," **I** (1), Food and Agricultural Organization of the United Nations, Rome (1952). Figures for Indonesia and certain other countries were obtained from trade statistics and unofficial government estimates.

Utilization. Sisal is used principally for ropes and twines for agricultural, marine, tying and wrapping, and general industrial purposes. For a time, sisal was not considered desirable for marine cordage, many users believing that it was weak and would deteriorate rapidly after immersion in salt water. Tests made during the 1920's, the necessity for using large quantities of sisal during World War II when the supply of abacá was disrupted, and the increasing availability of sisal have served to overcome the prejudices against it.

Data for imports of sisal and other agave fibers by countries are given in Table 16. Separate data are not available for sisal imports.

TABLE 16. IMPORTS OF SISAL AND OTHER AGAVE FIBERS BY COUNTRY OF ORIGINAL DESTINATION

(Thousands of short tons)

Country	*1951*	*1950*	*1949*	*1948*	*Average 1935–38*
Belgium	6	13	4	1	19
Czechoslovakia	*	*	*	2	19
Denmark	8	9	6	9	7
France	46	34	49	19	35
Germany (Bizone 1948 and 1949, Federal Republic 1950 and 1951)	28	39	24	6	52
Italy	1	2	2	1	2
Netherlands	11	12	11	8	26
Portugal	3	4	6	4	2
Spain	1	2	†	3	5
Sweden	*	4	1	1	9
United Kingdom	78	72	63	81	33
Yugoslavia	†	0	0	0	4
Canada	46	30	21	41	25
United States	195	179	151	136	140
Argentina	7	*	*	6	3
Japan	3	11	25	11	11
Australia	15	10	10	6	5
New Zealand	3	1	†	1	1
All other countries	22	24	29	11	15
Total	473	446	402	347	413

* Not available. † Less than 500 tons.

Source: "Yearbook of Food and Agricultural Statistics," VI, Part 2, "Trade," Food and Agricultural Organization of the United Nations, Rome (1952).

The data in the table include sisal, henequen, cantala, letona, and tula istle [*A. lophantha* (syn., *lecheguilla*)]. Sisal, however, represents the larger proportion of the figures in the table. Exports of sisal by the producing countries for the same periods as those shown in the table, in short tons, were; 1951—397,000; 1950—315,000; 1949—296,000; 1948—261,000; and average 1935–38—253,000.

In the United States, sisal is used chiefly for binder and baler twines, alternating with henequen in relation to price and supply of leaf fibers, and for ropes, depending upon supply and prices of abacá, and for tying and wrapping twines, again depending upon world supply and prices of leaf fibers. Imports of sisal fiber into the United States for the years 1951, 1950, 1949, and average 1934–38 are shown in Table 17 by country of origin.

TABLE 17. UNITED STATES IMPORTS OF SISAL FIBER BY COUNTRY OF ORIGIN

(Thousands of short tons)

Country of Origin	*1951*	*1950*	*1949*	*Average 1934–38*
Haiti	33	33	32	6
Brazil	44	29	7	0
British East Africa	36	17	41	17
Portuguese East Africa	7	3	11	[a]
Portuguese West Africa	1	1	2	0
Indonesia	3	[a]	[a]	32
Other countries	9	1	2	3
Total	133	84	95	58

[a] Less than 500 short tons. Included in total.

Note: Published U. S. import data for sisal are combined with those for henequen; above data is calculated on the basis of import figures by countries. Figures for Brazil may have a small quantity of caroa included; those for other countries, a small quantity of fibers other than sisal.

Source: Data published by U. S. Department of Commerce, Washington.

Cultivation. Sisal grows best in a warm, moist climate, on moderately rich, well-drained soil; it can also be grown, though with a smaller yield, in a climate with a dry season for a part of the year and on somewhat rocky soil. Propagation is by means of the bulbils or the rhizomes sent out by mature plants. These are usually planted in nurseries, and 1 year to 18 months later they are transplanted to the field. Planting is done just before or at the beginning of the rainy season. The distance between plants in the field is usually 4 to 8 ft, and between the rows 10 to 12 ft, depending upon variety and local custom. Double-row planting is used in some areas. Methods of cultivation vary, depending upon type of soil and local custom. Fertilization depends upon type of soil and amount and type of fertilizer available. The amount of mechanization used in an area for cultivating operations is related to the cost of labor in the area. Cultivation and weeding, on well-kept plantations, are usually done every 3 or 4 months during the first 2 years, when plants are small; as plants become larger, cultivation and weeding are done once or twice a year. Cover crops are frequently planted between rows. There are apparently few diseases and insects that damage sisal; so far these have responded to control and eradication measures.

Harvesting. Harvesting is accomplished by cutting the outer leaves, which have attained their full length, close to the stalk by hand with a knife. If not cut when they have attained their maximum size, leaves begin to deteriorate. After cutting, leaves are hauled to the plant, usually by narrow-gauge railroad or tractor-drawn wagon trains since most sisal is produced on large plantations.

In British East Africa and in Indonesia, plants are ready for the first cutting during the fourth or fifth year after planting. In Haiti, cutting begins at the age of 3 yr. Approximately 70 leaves may be obtained from the first cutting; thereafter, about 25 leaves are usually obtained annually. Life of the plant for fiber production averages about 7 to 8 yr. During this period, the plant will produce from 250 to 300 leaves. If the plant sends up a flower stalk during its useful life as a fiber plant, the stalk is cut to prevent flowering and deterioration of plant.

Leaves weigh from 2 to 2½ lb each, approximately 80 to 85 per cent of which is moisture. Average dry fiber yield is 3 to 4 per cent of the weight of the freshly cut leaf. Average yield of fiber per acre varies with area—700 to 800 lb in British East Africa [13] to 1500 lb in Haiti.[14] Yield in Indonesia ranges from 800 to 1200 lb per acre.

Fiber Removal. The success of sisal as a commercial fiber has resulted, in a large measure, from the fact that the fiber is successfully machine decorticated. In the early 1900's, small raspador-type machines were used. These were gradually improved, and during the 1930's the large stationary machine, patented in Germany, offered possibilities of even greater efficiency. This machine, or similar ones that have also been adapted for the decortication of ramie and abacá,[15]

[13] Calculated from data in "Industrial Fibres," Commonwealth Econ. Com., H.M. Stationery Office, London (1951 and 1952).

[14] "Status of Fiber Plant Industry in Latin America," Brittain B. Robinson et al., Pan American Union, Washington (1947).

[15] See Chapter VII, section on Ramie, for brief description of principle of operation.

has been responsible, to a great extent, for the high quality attained by Indonesian and Haitian sisal. The machines are widely used in the areas producing the largest volume of fiber. They crush the leaf, scrape cellular tissue from the fiber, then wash the fiber to remove any pieces of pulp remaining on fiber after scraping.

Some areas still utilize small, hand-fed Raspador-type machines. Fiber, after decortication, is washed, and sometimes pounded and then rewashed, by hand to remove pulp remaining on it after decortication. In some areas, where fiber is grown for local use, decortication is done entirely by hand. Other areas use water retting, similar to the method used for flax and jute, to remove fiber.

After decortication and washing operations are completed, the fiber is dried, either with mechanical driers or in the sun. In some areas, especially British East Africa, fiber is next brushed or burnished to remove knots and rough ends and to soften and bring out luster. The operations of fiber removal and washing and drying must be done promptly after leaves are cut, otherwise gums in leaf harden, causing pulp to adhere to fiber and making it impossible to clean fiber properly.

If the fiber is intended for export, it is graded and baled. Weight of bales varies by areas. Approximate bale weights used in some areas are: Indonesia, most bales are 700 lb or more, though some 450-lb bales are used; in Haiti, 570 lb; in Kenya, 230 lb; in Tanganyika, 450 lb; and in Portuguese Africa, 560 lb.

Grading. Grade designations for sisal vary by areas. Table 18 lists those most widely used. The grades have been arranged in *approximate* comparison; exact comparison obviously is *not* possible because of variation in specifications. Interpretation of the specifications also varies.

Characteristics. Commercial sisal fiber is utilized in the form of strands. These strands, which run the length of the leaf, are made up of a large number of small, individual fibers which are held together by the natural gums of the plant. Length of strands varies in relation to length of leaf and efficiency of decortication; average length of good-quality fiber ranges from 40 to 50 in. or longer; average diameter of strand is 0.08 to 0.15 in.[16] Fiber strands, generally termed simply fiber, are white and lustrous when properly cleaned.

Sisal has very good strength and elongation properties and good resistance to the effects of microorganisms found in salt water. Table

[16] "Sisal," S. G. Barker, *Bull.* 64, Empire Marketing Board, H.M. Stationery Office, London (1933).

TABLE 18. GRADE DESIGNATIONS OF SISAL FIBER BY AREAS

(Arrangement of grades only *approximately* comparable)

	Indonesia						
Haiti	*H.V.A.*	*Various Growers*	*Other Growers*	*Kenya*	*Mozambique*	*Philippines*	*Brazil*
Line							
A	X	A	A	△1	Extra	SR-1	1
X	Y	B	B	A	Selected	SR-2	3
B	..	..	..	..	..	..	..
Y	Z	C	C	◇2	Ord. 1st	SR-3	5
S	..	..	..	[3L]	Ord. 2d	..	7
..	..	..	..	③	..	SR-Y	9
Peasant	..	..	..	UG	..	SR-O	..
Tow							
T	XX	D	D	SCWF	Selected	SR-T	Busha-1
T3	..	..	..	..	Short Type 1	..	Busha-2
T4	..	..	..	..	Short Type 2	..	..

Sources and specifications

Haiti. Haitian Executive Order No. 262, dated 8 April 1943, promulgated in *Le Moniteur* 12 April 1943, official export standards.

A 36 in. min. length, white or light in color.
X 36 in. min. length, white or greyish white, some few yellow or brown stains.
B 24 to 36 in. long, white or light color.
Y 24 to 36 in. long, white or greyish white, some few yellow or brown stains.
S 24 in. min. length, greyish white, slightly pulpy.
Peasant Fiber produced by small growers and processed by hand or with the aid of small hand-fed machines.
T Tow, white.
T3 Tow, pale cream.
T4 Tow, deeper cream.

Indonesia. No official standards. Growers set up own grades: the three systems in general use are given below.

H.V.A. Estates (Handelsveereniging Amsterdam, whose plantations are reputed to produce more than half the total Indonesian sisal production).
X 105 cm min. length, white.
Y 75 to 105 cm long, white.
Z 50 to 75 cm long, white.
XX Inferior quality.

Various growers
A 105 cm min. length, white.
B 75 to 105 cm long, white.
C 50 to 75 cm long, white.
D Tow.

Other growers
A 90 cm min. length, white.
B 60 to 90 cm long, white.
C 50 to 60 cm long, white.
D Tow.

Kenya. The Kenya Sisal Board established these grades and bale marks in January 1950. They apply generally to all sisal exported from British East Africa.

△1 3 ft min. length, avg. 3 ft 6 in.; creamy white to cream, free of defective decortication: properly brushed: free of tow, bunchy ends, knots and harshness.

TABLE 18. GRADE DESIGNATIONS OF SISAL FIBER BY AREAS (*Continued*)

A Same as △1 except color yellowish, sunburned, slightly spotted or discolored.

◇2 2 ft 6 in. min. length, otherwise same as △1.

[3L] 3 ft min. length: consists of fiber that does not conform to △1, A, and ◇2: minor defects in color and cleaning permitted but fiber must be free of barky or undecorticated fiber and knots.

③ 2 ft min. length; otherwise same as [3L].

UG 2 ft min. length: otherwise is fiber that does not conform to foregoing grades with respect to length, color, and cleaning.

SCWF 18 in. min., 24 in. max., length: otherwise same as ③.

Mozambique. Established by the Portuguese Government for export fiber: *Portaria* **3** (896), 30 November 1939 and 7 August 1940. A 3 per cent tolerance is permitted for all grades.

Extra 90 cm min. length; good white, ivory, or light-yellow color; clean, dry and of high breaking strain.

Selected 70 cm min. length: otherwise same as Extra.

Ordinary 1st 70 cm min. length; white, ivory, or light-yellow.

Ordinary 2d Any length (except tow); spotted colors.

Tow—Selected Good ivory or cream color, clean, dry, and with high breaking strength.

Tow—Short Type 1 Not as white as good ivory and with lower breaking strain than Tow Selected.

Tow—Short Type 2 Below Tow Type 1 in quality.

Philippines. Republic of the Philippines, Dept. Agr. and Natural Resources, *Fiber Inspection Administrative Order* 4 (Revised), dated 1 December 1939. Grades apply to retted and decorticated sisal, whether washed or not in sea or fresh water. Length designations are: Long, 1 meter and above: Normal, 60 cm to 1 meter; Short, 40 to 60 cm; and Tow, under 40 cm.

SR-1 Cleaning good, properly and carefully carried out, practically no scales on fiber; color dull white; strength high.

SR-2 Cleaning fair; not so thoroughly carried out as for SR-1; many scales and some bark present; color dingy white; strength normal.

SR-3 Usually retted fiber, decorticated fiber rarely, if ever, falling in this grade; cleaning poor, fiber not washed or washed and dried insufficiently, scales abundant and considerable bark present; color light brown; strength low.

SR-Y Below preceding grades.

SR-O Strings. Consists of strings and twisted or knotted strands.

SR-T Tow. Consists of very short or tangled fiber.

Brazil. Brazilian Government, Ministerio da Agricultura, Decree No. 14,269, 15 December 1943. Color is predominant basis for grading; there are no length specifications. Only odd numbers are used for grade designations.

Tipo 1 Cream white; normal strength; free of impurities or processing defects.

Tipo 3 Cream white; strong; free of impurities and tangled fibers.

Tipo 5 Cream; normal strength; free of impurities.

Tipo 7 Yellowish, greenish or gray; coarse; normal strength.

Tipo 9 Coarser but otherwise similar to Tipo 7.

Busha 1 Tow, short and tangled fibers.

Busha 2 Below Busha 1.

19 gives breaking length and strength and percentage of elongation at rupture for nine samples of sisal fiber.

TABLE 19. BREAKING LENGTH AND STRENGTH AND PERCENTAGE OF ELONGATION OF SISAL FIBER

(Basis 15-in. bundle weighing 5 grains)

Sample Number	Breaking Length of Dry Bundle (1000 ft)	Condition of Fiber					
		Dry		Wet		Dry after Soaking in Salt Water for 28 Days	
		Breaking Strength (pounds)	Elongation (per cent)	Breaking Strength (pounds)	Elongation (per cent)	Breaking Strength (pounds)	Elongation (per cent)
7	119	68	2.6	62	2.9	75	3.4
8	119	68	2.7	63	4.0	74	3.8
9	126	72	2.5	56	3.0	79	2.6
10	149	85	3.0	69	2.7	73	3.6
11	117	67	3.3	60	3.8	57	2.8
12	100	57	2.6	59	2.6	61	3.2
13	116	66	3.3	51	4.4	65	3.6
14	135	77	3.4	65	3.6	65	3.1
15	100	57	2.9	55	n.s.	56	2.6

n.s. Not stated.
Source: "Machines and Methods for Testing Cordage Fibers," H. F. Schiefer, Natl. Bur. Standards RP1611, U. S. Dept. Commerce (1944).

Table 20 gives comparative data on strength of ropes made from sisal, abacá, and phormium after different periods of immersion in sea water.

TABLE 20. PERCENTAGE DECREASE IN AVERAGE STRENGTH OF SISAL, ABACÁ, AND PHORMIUM ROPES AFTER DIFFERENT PERIODS OF IMMERSION IN SEA WATER

Period of Immersion (months)	*Sisal Rope*			*Abacá Rope*			*Phormium Rope*
	African No. 1 Brushed	*African No. 2 Unbrushed*	*Java*	S3	K	M1	*Fair*
2	21.3	25.2	24.3	8.1	17.7	11.2	15.2
4	51.6	54.6	58.9	50.4	53.9	53.6	54.9
6	58.2	63.8	70.5	65.1	62.5	64.7	66.2
9	66.3	73.7	79.3	73.3	74.5	72.6	71.4

Source: "Percentage Decrease in Average Strength of Sisal, Manila Hemp (*sic*), New Zealand Hemp (*sic*) (Phormium) Ropes after Different Periods of Immersion," *Bull., Imp. Inst.*, **30** (2), London (July 1932).

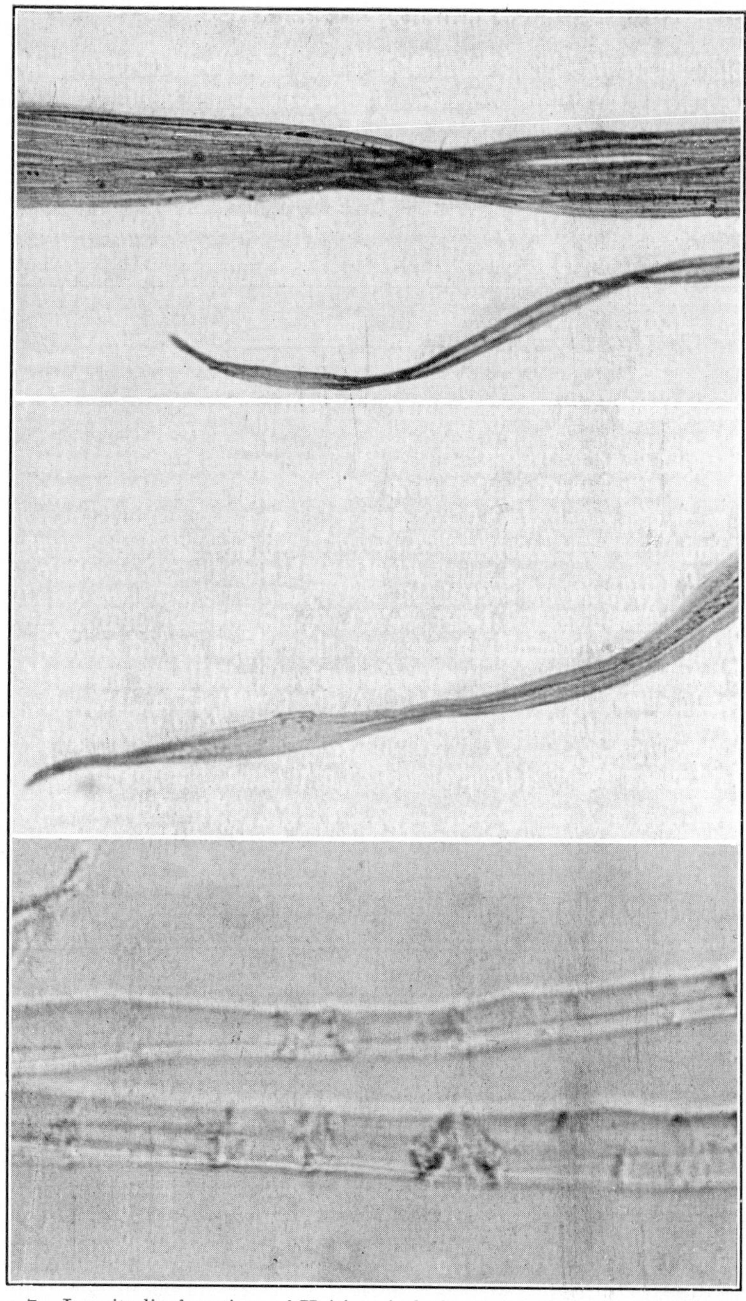

Fig. 7. Longitudinal sections of Haitian sisal, showing surface characteristics and end of fiber at ×250 (upper photo) and at ×800 (middle and lower photos). (*Courtesy George Moro.*)

A comparison of the strength of sisal with that of other leaf fibers is given in Table 10, page 382. According to the results of these studies, sisal ranks second among the principal leaf fibers, being exceeded only by abacá.

Initial moisture absorption by sisal is rapid and in consequence sisal rope sinks rapidly. One study [17] found, however, that upon prolonged immersion total moisture absorption by ropes made from sisal was approximately the same as that absorbed by those made from abacá.

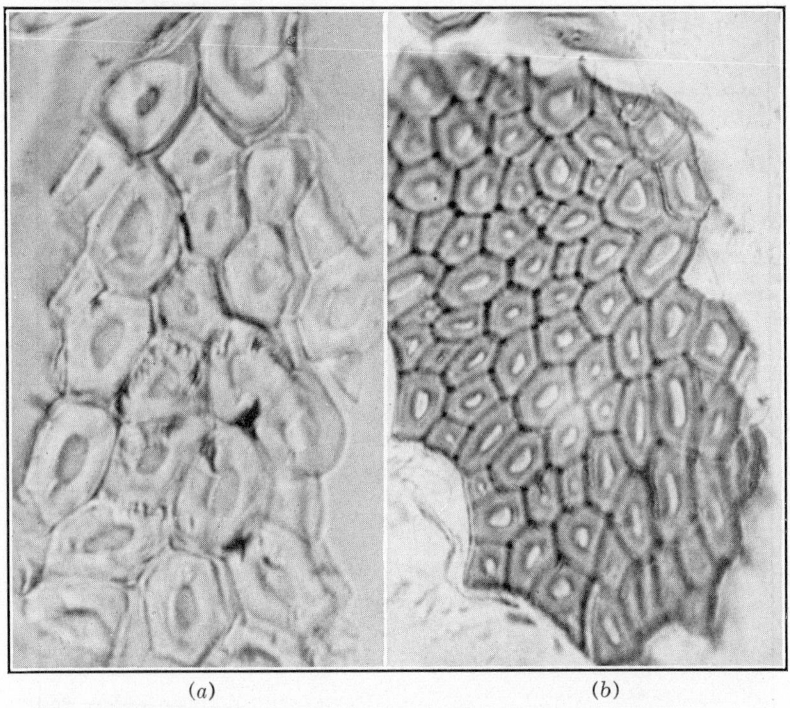

(*a*) (*b*)

FIG. 8. Cross-sections of Haitian sisal, *a*, ×800, and *b*, ×500. (*Courtesy George Moro.*)

Individual fibers are usually somewhat stiff in texture. Their longitudinal shape (Fig. 7) is approximately cylindrical with characteristic broadening toward the middle. Ends are generally blunt and thick, sometimes pointed, occasionally forked. Cross-section of the cell is

[17] "Absorption of Water by Sisal and Manila on Immersion: Increase of Weight and Girth," *Bull. Imp. Inst.*, London (July 1932).

polygonal (Fig. 8). Lumen is well defined and varies in size, though it is usually fairly large; cross-section is irregularly oval to rounded polygonal. The cell wall is usually thick but varies in relation to size of lumen. Short, thick-walled fiber cells are present in large numbers. These have narrow lumina and distinct surface pores. Table 21 gives data on measurements of individual fibers as determined by four studies.

TABLE 21. MEASUREMENTS OF INDIVIDUAL SISAL FIBERS

	Length (inches)			*Breadth (microns)*		
Authority	*Min.*	*Max.*	*Mean*	*Min.*	*Max.*	*Mean*
Höhnel	0.20	0.60	n.s.	16	32	n.s.
Luniak	0.03	0.30	0.10 to 0.18	7	47	24
Turner	0.04	0.20	n.s.	n.s.	n.s.	24
Wiesner	0.09	0.17	n.s.	n.s.	n.s.	n.s.

n.s. Not stated.

Sources

Höhnel, F. X., *Die Mikroskopie der technisch verwendeten Faserstoffe*, A. Hartleben, Leipzig (1905).

Luniak, Bruno, *Die Unterscheidung der Textilfasern*, Leemann, Zurich (1949).

Turner, A. J., "The Structure of Long Vegetable Fibers," *J. Textile Inst.*, **40**, (10), Manchester, England (1949).

Wiesner, J. v., and Baar, H., *Beiträge zur Kenntnis der Anatomie des Agave Blattes*, Engelmann, Wien (1914).

Interlaced with the individual cells are occasional spiral vessels and parenchymatous cells containing single calcium oxalate crystals which are often as long as 0.19 in. They usually occur in a longitudinal series and taper off at the ends, resembling a thick needle in form, and have a quadrilateral cross-section.

Sisal fiber has a high percentage of cellulose and a relatively high proportion of lignin. Table 22 gives two analyses of chemical composition of fiber.

Iodine and sulfuric acid give a yellow color when applied to the fiber. The ash obtained from the ignition of fiber shows the presence of glistening crystals of calcium carbonate, which are derived from the crystals of calcium oxalate found in the parenchymatous cells interlaced with the fiber cells.

Henequen

Nomenclature and History. Henequen fiber is obtained from leaves of the *Agave fourcroydes*. The plant is a native of Mexico, where the fibers have been used for textiles since prehistoric times. The name

TABLE 22. CHEMICAL COMPOSITION OF SISAL

(Methods of analysis used in studies were not uniform)

Component	*Matthews*	*Turner*
Moisture	11.5%	10.0%
Ash	1.0	..
Lignin	14.5	9.9
Cellulose	72.0	65.8
Hemicellulose	..	12.0
Pectin	..	0.8
Alcohol-benzene soluble	1.0	..
Water solubles	..	1.2
Fat and wax	..	0.3
Total	100.0%	100.0%

Sources

Matthews Textile Fibers (ed. by Mauersberger), 5th Ed., John Wiley & Sons, N. Y. (1947).

Turner, A. J., "The Structure of Long Vegetable Fibers," *J. Textile Inst.*, **40** (10), Manchester, England (1949).

"henequen" is the Spanish spelling of a Carib word used since ancient times to designate fiber from the plant. There are four recognized varieties of *A. fourcroydes;* originally these were classified as separate species. They include: *ixtli, longifolia, minima,* and *rigida.* Some authorities hold that two other species of *Agave* which are cultivated for fiber, *A. sisalana* and *A. cantala,* are strains of *A. fourcroydes* that have undergone mutation as a result of climatic and petrological factors and that if plants of these species are brought to their native habitat in Mexico, they will shortly assume the characteristics of *A. fourcroydes.*

Appearance of the Plant. *Agave fourcroydes* has a stalk or trunk which sometimes reaches a height of 6 ft; when the plant is cultivated, the stalk grows to approximately 3 ft. Leaves are 4 to 7 ft long and about 4 in. wide and 1½ in. thick at the base, and 4 to 6 in. in breadth at widest part, tapering to a thorny point; the edges have sharp barbs; the color is greyish-green. They grow directly out from the stalk in the dense rosette form characteristic of agaves. In cross-section, the leaves are flat at the base, becoming somewhat concave along the length. The flower stalk rises to a height of 20 ft; flowers are greenish-white, about 3 in. across, and have an unpleasant odor.

World Production. Henequen ranks third in world production of textile leaf fibers, being exceeded only by sisal and abacá; during the post-World War II period, until 1951, henequen ranked second. The largest quantity is produced in Mexico, with most of the production in the State of Yucatan. Until about 1910, when sisal began to appear in the market on a commercial basis, Mexico had a virtual monoply on production of commercial agave fiber. Cuba, where the plant was introduced during the nineteenth century, produces about 10 to 15 per cent of total supply, having reached this level of production during the 1920's. Henequen is Cuba's chief fiber crop, the Province of Matanzas being the principal producing area. Small quantities of henequen are grown in Jamaica and other areas of the West Indies and in Costa Rica, Guatemala, and Honduras.

Subsequent to the appearance of sisal on the market, demand for henequen has varied in relation to price and to total supply of leaf fiber in relation to demand. Sisal is generally preferred, but price and supply influence the consumption pattern and, in consequence, the production pattern of henequen. A major factor affecting price of henequen is the higher labor cost that generally prevails in henequen-producing areas in comparison with labor cost in sisal-producing areas.

Table 23 shows production of henequen by countries for 1951, 1950, 1949, and average for 1934–38.

TABLE 23. PRODUCTION OF HENEQUEN BY COUNTRIES

(Thousands of short tons)

Country	*1951*	*1950*	*1949*	*Average 1934–38*
Mexico	85	108	135	106
Cuba	19	18	14	13
Other countries	1	2	2	3
Total	105	128	151	122

Sources: "Yearbook of Food and Agricultural Statistics," V, Part 1, "Production." "Monthly Bulletin of Agricultural Economics and Statistics," I (1), Food and Agricultural Organization of United Nations, Rome (1952).

Utilization. Formerly the principal use of henequen was for binder twine. As the use of the combine increased, demand for binder twine decreased. The appearance and increasing use of the automatic hay baler, however, with a consequent need for twine, approximately compensated for the decrease in binder twine demand. Other uses for henequen are for ropes and tying and wrapping twines; in the countries where it is grown fiber is also used for coarse fabrics for bags, hammocks, and similar items, and for shoe soles.

Since the 1880's, most of the henequen exported by Mexico has been sent to the United States. Pre-World War II, about 20 per cent went to European countries. Postwar, the problems of foreign exchange and increased production of sisal have influenced the export pattern of henequen. In 1947, the last year for which detailed figures are available, only a few tons were exported to Europe.[18] A similar export pattern has also prevailed for Cuba, since exports of fiber were begun in 1920. Cuban Government regulations control export of henequen fiber by means of a permit system, domestic cordage manufacturers having priority.

In the United States, henequen is used for binder and baler twines and for tying and wrapping twines. It is also used for ropes, the extent depending upon the supply and prices of abacá and sisal. Table 24 shows imports by countries for 1951, 1950, 1949, and average 1934–38.

TABLE 24. United States Imports of Henequen by Countries

(Thousands of short tons)

Country	*1951*	*1950*	*1949*	*Average 1934–38*
Mexico	46	77	34	65
Cuba	10	9	12	5
Honduras	0	0	[a]	[a]
Total	56	86	46	70

[a] Less than 500 tons, included in total.
Source: U. S. Dept. Commerce, Washington.

Cultivation. Henequen is propagated and cultivated in a manner similar to sisal. Soil on which henequen is grown is generally more rocky and climate more arid than that in areas where sisal is grown. There are various diseases and insects which attack henequen plants. One of the most serious, which has attacked plants in both Mexico and Cuba, is a disease known as "Mancha Negra" or henequen leaf spot disease, which causes the entire loss of many leaves and stains and weakens the fiber in others.[19]

Harvesting, Fiber Removal, and Marketing. Leaves are cut in the same manner as those of sisal. First harvesting of henequen leaves may generally be done when the plant is 3 or 4 yr old and in many

[18] "World Study of Hard Fibers and Hard Fiber Products," Part I, Franklin F. Kidd, assisted by Ann Q. O'Connell, and Gayle D. Dean, U. S. Dept. Commerce, Washington (1949).

[19] "Status of Fiber Plant Industry in Latin America," Brittain B. Robinson et al., Pan American Union, Washington (1947).

areas may continue until plant is 15 or 16 yr old. Cutting cycle varies, 3, 4, 6, and 9 months, and yearly being used by various growers. Average total annual harvest of leaves is 25. Yield of fiber varies but usually averages about 3 to 4 per cent of weight of freshly cut leaves. Average annual yield of fiber per acre ranges from 700 to 1200 lb.

Decorticating machinery is used for fiber removal. Earliest machines used were of the small raspador type.[20] During the latter part of the nineteenth century and early 1900's, improved and larger versions of the raspador began to be used. The large stationary machines, which were developed during the 1930's and 1940's, are now used in some areas. The best quality of fiber is washed, dried, and brushed. Fiber is generally dried in the sun. Quality of cleaning of fiber varies somewhat in relation to the market and labor costs. For example, if prices are low and/or labor costs high, marginal spines may not be removed from the leaves before decortication. These remain in the tow, lowering its quality.

All sales of fiber in Mexico are handled by a state government cooperative, Asociacion de Henequeneros de Yucatan, which also concerns itself with the production of fiber, compilation of statistics on production, and related matters. Henequen growers operated independently until 1912. In that year, the Comision Reguladora del Mercado de Henequen was established by the State of Yucatan; in 1915 formation of producers' associations was authorized; in 1918 the functions of the Comision were more definitely fixed; for the period 1919 to 1925, there was no organization; in 1925 Henequeneros de Yucatan, a cooperative, was organized; this last organization was replaced in 1938 by the present one.

If the fiber is intended for export, it is baled after drying and grading. Size of bales in Mexico is 400 lb; in Cuba 500 lb.

Grading. Grading of Mexican henequen is controlled by the Asociacion de Henequeneros de Yucatan and the State of Yucatan. In Cuba, growers established grading. Table 25 lists grade designations used for henequen on an *approximately* comparable basis; variations in specifications preclude exact comparisons.

Characteristics. Henequen, like other textile leaf fibers, is utilized in the form of fiber strands, which are composed of bundles of individual fibers held together by the natural gums of the plant, the strands running the length of the leaf. Average length of fiber strands

[20] See Chapter VII, section on Ramie, for description of raspador and other decorticating machines.

TABLE 25. Grade Designations of Henequen

(Arrangement of grades only *approximately* comparable)

Mexico[a]					Cuba[b]		
Grade	*Length*	*Color*	*Cleaning*	*Percentage of Impurities Permitted*	*Grade*	*Length*	*Color*
AA	1 m or more	White	Brushed or washed	2	A	3 ft or more	White
A	1 m or more	White	Clean	2	..	..	..
B	75 cm to 1 m	White	Clean	3	B	Less than 3 ft	White
B-1	75 cm to 1 m	White	n.s.	3 or more	..	and also 3 ft or more	White with some spotting
C	60 cm to 75 cm	White	Clean	3	C	All other line fiber	..
M	75 cm or more	Streaky or dark	Clean	3	..	..	..
M-1	60 cm or more	n.s.	n.s.	5	..	..	..
Tow	..	..	..	..	..	..	..

n.s. Not specified.

[a] "La Producion de Fibras Duras en Mexico, Mesa, Manual and Villanueva, Rogelio," *Monographia Industriales del Banco de Mexico*, Mexico City (1948).

[b] Grades generally prevailing among growers.

is 4 to 5 ft; the diameter of the strand is finer, generally, than that of sisal fiber strands. When properly prepared, the fiber strands are white, lustrous, and with fairly good strength and elongation, and with fair resistance to the effects of microorganisms found in salt water. A comparison of the strength of henequen with that of other leaf fibers used for cordage is given in Table 10, page 382. Table 26 gives data

TABLE 26. Breaking Length and Strength and Percentage of Elongation of Henequen Fiber

(Basis 15-in. bundle weighing 5 grains)

Sample Number	Breaking Length of Dry Bundle (1000 ft)	Condition of Fiber					
		Dry		Wet		Dry after Soaking in Salt Water for 28 Days	
		Breaking Strength (pounds)	Elongation (per cent)	Breaking Strength (pounds)	Elongation (per cent)	Breaking Strength (pounds)	Elongation (per cent)
16	86	49	4.9	41	6.0	52	6.3
17	86	49	4.4	43	5.4	51	5.4

Source: "Machines and Methods for Testing Cordage Fibers," Herbert F. Schiefer, Natl. Bur. Standards RP1611, U. S. Dept. Commerce, Washington (1944).

on breaking length and strength and percentage of elongation at rupture, of henequen.

Shape and measurements of individual henequen fibers are similar to those for individual sisal fibers. Chemical properties are also similar.

Cantala

Cantala fiber is obtained from *Agave cantala,* which grows in the Philippine Islands, Indonesia, India, and other parts of the Far East. This plant is a native of Mexico. It was introduced into the Philippines by the Spanish in 1783,[21] where it is also known by the name of "maguey." The date of its introduction into Indonesia and India is not known. It was sufficiently well established by 1804 that Roxburgh thought it native to India.

In appearance, the plant is generally similar to henequen.

The fiber is cultivated on a commercial scale in Indonesia and the Philippines. Table 27 shows production by these two principal producing countries.

TABLE 27. Production of Commercial Cantala Fiber

(Thousands of short tons)

Country	*1951*	*1950*	*1949*	*1948*	*Average 1934–38*
Indonesia	1	*	*	1	5
Philippines	2	1	2	2	18
Total	3	2	3	3	23

* Less than 500 tons.

Sources: "Monthly Bulletin of Agricultural and Economic Statistics," **I** (1), Food and Agriculture Organization of United Nations, Rome (1952), and trade statistics and unofficial government estimates.

United States imports in 1949 were 444 short tons, all from the Philippines, and, in 1950, none.

Cantala is used for the same purposes as sisal and henequen, though being somewhat softer it is more often used for woven fabrics by the natives of the countries where the plant grows. In the United States, the small quantity imported is used principally for tying and wrapping twines.

[21] "The Cultivation of Maguey (*sic*) in the Philippine Islands," H. T. Edwards, *Farmers' Bull.* 13, Dept. Interior, Manila (1906).

Cultivation and harvesting methods are generally similar to those used for sisal and henequen, varying in relation to local custom and degree of mechanization available. Yield of fiber in Indonesia is approximately the same as that for sisal; in the Philippines, yield is about 700 to 800 lb per acre.

Mechanical decortication is used in Indonesia, and the fiber, known as Java cantala, is prepared with the same care given to sisal. The same grading system is used. Cantala, because of the greater length and finer diameter of the fiber strands, usually commands a premium over Indonesian sisal of the same grade.

In the Philippines water retting as well as mechanical decortication is used to extract the fiber. Salt (sea) water is often used for retting. Steps in this process are: (1) remove marginal spines, (2) beat, crush, or split leaf, (3) ret in salt water until fiber is easily freed, (4) wash thoroughly in fresh water, and (5) dry in the sun. Philippines cantala, or "maguey," is generally not as strong as Java cantala because of differences in methods of fiber removal. Grades are, in a descending order,[22] MR-1, MR-2, MR-3, MR-Y (Damaged), MR-O (Strings), and MR-T (Tow), cleaning and color being primary factors in grading. Length designations are: Long, 1 meter and above; Normal, 60 cm to 1 meter; Short, 40 to 60 cm; Very Short (Tow), under 40 cm.

Fiber characteristics of cantala, including long length and fine diameter of fiber strands, are similar to those of henequen. Chemical composition is also similar.

Letona

Letona fiber is obtained from the *Agave letonae* plant. The fiber is sometimes termed Salvadorian "henequen," since it grows chiefly in the country of El Salvador.

The stalk, i.e., trunk, of the plant is 3 to 4 ft in height. Mature leaves are medium green and glaucous, 4 to 6 ft long, 3 to 5 in. wide, and about 1½ to 2 in. thick, with dull brown spines along the edges. The flower stalk is 15 to 30 feet tall.

The plant is cultivated for fiber on a commercial scale in El Salvador, especially in the eastern section of the country. A small quantity is also reported under cultivation in Guatemala. Annual production in El Salvador averages from 3000 to 4000 short tons; annual production in Guatemala is 1000 short tons or less.

[22] Republic of the Philippines, Dept. Agr. and Natural Resources, "Fiber Inspection Administrative Order No. 4" (Revised), dated 1 December 1939, Manila (1940).

About three-fourths of total production of letona in El Salvador is used by a bag factory for manufacture into coffee bags. The balance is used by the handicraft industry in the manufacture of cordage, hammocks, and similar items, and in one factory for the manufacture of sandals. From 10 to 25 per cent of the total production is exported, principally to the United States. Imports into the United States in 1949 were 900 short tons, in 1950, 500 short tons, and in 1951, 460 short tons.

The plant thrives in a rather rocky, well-drained soil and in a somewhat arid climate. Propagation is generally by means of rhizomes. Cultivation and weeding are hand operations and are generally similar to those used for sisal and henequen. Letona is affected by the same diseases and insects that attack henequen.

Harvesting begins from 3 to 4 years after planting. The plant produces usable fiber for about 15 years. Leaves are harvested, that is, cut, by hand, from two to four times a year. The number of leaves harvested from each plant per year ranges from 25 to 40. Annual yield of fiber per acre averages about 650 lb. Fiber is removed from the leaves by means of machine decorticators and, on the smaller plantings, by means of hand scraping. After decortication, the fiber is washed thoroughly and dried in the sun. Grading of fiber is generally done by agreement between grower and buyer and involves length, color, texture, and cleanness.

The fiber strands of letona, when properly prepared, are creamy white, lustrous, and 3 to 5 ft in length. General characteristics are similar to those of henequen.

Other Agave Fibers

There are several other plants of the *Agave* genus from which textile fiber is obtained, principally for domestic use in the country where grown, the chief exception being the ixtle fibers. These agaves are listed below together with their common names, if any, and native habitat. Fiber from some of these is better known in the United States for its uses as brush fiber, and the plants are, therefore, discussed more completely in Chapter IX, section on Brush Fibers.

Agave amaniensis (Blue "sisal"): Origin is obscure. First reported in 1933 at agricultural research station at Amani in East Africa, under cultivation with plants of *A. lespinassei*. Leaves are greyish blue-green, 4 to 6 feet in length and 4 to 6 inches in width with margins strongly incurved. Leaves from plant are ready for cutting for fiber 6 to 12 months sooner than those from plants of *A. sisalana*. Fiber of

A. amaniensis is reported to be finer, softer and of greater strength than that from *A. sisalana*. Chief drawback to cultivation on a commercial scale was incurving margins of leaves which prevented efficient machine decortication. A new variety has, however, been developed in Indonesia which has much flatter leaves and is being cultivated there.

Agave cocui (dispopo). Venezuela.

Agave decípiens (false "sisal"). Native or intensively naturalized to Florida (U. S.). Closely related to *A. tequilana* and *A. zapupe.*

Agave deweyana (zapupe larga). Mexico.

Agave falcata (guapilla). Mexico. See Chapter IX for more complete description.

Agave heterocantha (syn. *funkiana*) (Jaumave ixtle). See Chapter IX for more complete description.

Agave lespinassei. Africa.

Agave lophantha (syn. *lechuguilla*) (tula ixtle). Mexico. See Chapter IX for more complete description.

Agave lurida. Maguey, Mexico. Plant cultivated and fiber prepared in a manner similar to methods used for henequen. Fiber is shorter and somewhat stiffer than henequen. Plant has also, in the past, been variously classified as *A. mexicana* and as *A. americana.* United States imports very small quantity; in 1950, 16 short tons.

Agave palmeri (Chino bermejo, mano largo). United States.

Agave pes mulae (pata de mula, pie de mula). Mexico.

Agave pseudotequilana. Mexico.

Agave striata (espadinin). Mexico.

Agave tequilana. Mexico.

Agave zapupe. Mexico.

FURCRAEA FIBERS

Plants of the genus *Furcraea,* of the Amaryllidaceae family, are closely related to those of the *Agave* genus. The *Furcraea* genus was named by Etienne Pierre Ventenat, a French botanist, in 1793, reportedly after a contemporary, François de Fourcroy, a French chemist. For a time, the genus was designated as *Fourcroya.* The plants are indigenous to the Western Hemisphere, in tropical South America, Mexico and the West Indies from where they were taken to other parts of the world. They are generally similar in appearance to those of the *Agave* genus and like plants of the *Agave* genus were, and occasionally still are, confused with plants of the *Aloe* genus.

Mauritius Fiber

Mauritius fiber is obtained from leaves of the *Furcraea gigantea* plant, which is cultivated on the Island of Mauritius. The plant, a native of Brazil, is said to have been brought to Mauritius from that country about 1790 and to East Africa, Ceylon, and St. Helena during the latter part of the nineteenth century; fiber industry is reported to have started in Mauritius about 1875. Various native names for the plant in Mauritius are "aloes vert," "aloes creole," and "aloes malgaches."

The stalk of the plant is very short. Leaves are about 8 ft long and 8 in. wide at the widest part, tapering to a thorny point, with a few marginal spines, some varieties having no spines. The color is a greyish-green. The flower stalk, which appears when the plant is 8 to 10 yr old, is about 25 ft tall; flowers are about 1½ in. long.

Annual production on the Island of Mauritius ranges from 1000 to 2000 short tons, of which only a small portion is exported. Principal use of the fiber is for the manufacture of bagging and other coarse textiles. Production in Brazil and other areas where the plant grows is very small.

Cultivation in Mauritius is principally on large plantations, and methods used are similar to those used for henequen. Leaves are ready for first harvesting 3 to 4 yr after planting, almost all the leaves on the plant being ready for cutting at the same time. Average number of leaves per plant is 25 to 30. From 18 to 36 months are required between harvests. Life of the plants is 8 to 10 yr.

Fiber yield is about 1½ to 2½ per cent of the weight of freshly cut leaves. Annual yield per acre averages about 700 to 1000 lb.

Fiber is machine decorticated in most areas. In some areas it is hand decorticated; leaves are frequently retted for 1 or 2 days before decortication, sometimes in a soapy solution. Unless carefully done, retting may result in stained fiber. After decortication, the fiber is washed and dried. After drying, it may be brushed to soften and add luster. Grades in Mauritius, as established by Mauritius Hemp Producers Syndicate,[23] are as follows: Extra Prime (sometimes termed Superior), 5 ft plus, white, very soft, free of bark and black spots, thoroughly brushed, free of dust and cuttings; Prime, 4 ft, white to light cream, soft, bark and black spots rare, well brushed, practically free of dust and cuttings; Very Good, 4 ft, cream to yellowish, rather

[23] "Rapport du President pour l'Année 1942," *La Revue Agricole,* **22** (6), Mauritius (1943).

soft, minor quantity of bark and black spots, fair brushing, contains some dust and cuttings; Good, 3½ ft, yellow to reddish, rather hard, contains bark and black spots, brushing is somewhat defective, contains dust and cuttings; Fair, 2½ ft, defective color, hard, contains bark and black spots, brushing mostly defective, contains dust and cuttings; Common, all fiber below Fair, except raw fiber and tow. In Brazil, grades established by Decree No. 14269, 15 December 1943, are: Tipo 1, 3, 5, 7, and 9, and approximate those established for sisal.

Fiber strands are 4 to 7 ft long, and, when properly cleaned, are creamy white with fair luster. Strength is generally considered to be below that of sisal and henequen. Fiber has fair resistance to the effects of fresh water but is reported to have poor resistance to those of salt water.

Measurements of individual cells vary. Data cited in the fifth edition of *Matthews Textile Fibers* (1947) are: length, 0.05 to 0.15 in., and diameter, 15 to 24 μ. Data shown by Luniak [24] are: length, 0.04 to 0.24 in., and diameter, 14 to 42 μ, with a mean of 21 μ. Longitudinal shape of the cell is approximately cylindrical; cross-sectional shape is polygonal. Lumen is very large, and its cross-section is polygonal. Cell wall is relatively thin. Fiber has a large percentage of cellulose and a relatively high percentage of lignin. It has a fairly good affinity for dyestuffs.

Other Furcraea Fibers

There are a number of other species of the genus *Furcraea,* from which fiber is obtained. These are listed below, together with their common names, if any, principal areas of production, and brief comment. Cabuya, once thought to be a name applying only to one species, is now generally held to be also the native name of fiber from various species of the *Furcraea* genus.

Furcraea andina (cabuya). Ecuador. Principally in wild state. Leaves from a few inches to about 4½ ft long, with marginal spines. May be harvested from the time plant is 3 to 4 yr old; from 100 to 1000 leaves may be produced during the life of the plant. Flower stalk appears when the plant is 10 to 20 yr old; after flowering, plant dies. Leaves are cut by hand and spines cut from edges. Fiber is removed by hand or with the aid of small decorticating machines. Total production of fiber averages about 1.25 million lb annually. Principal uses are for bagging fabrics for rice, coffee, cacao, and cotton baling, and threads and cordage. Exports of fiber pre-World War II

[24] Luniak, Bruno, *Die Unterscheidung der Textilfasern,* Leemann, Zurich (1949).

went principally to Great Britain, averaging slightly more than 100,000 lb annually; during the war exports went chiefly to the United States and Argentina; postwar exports are small.[25]

Furcraea cabuya (cabuya blanca, cabuya blancho, cabuya sinlakina). Central America. Approximately similar to *F. andina,* except without spines.

Furcraea cubensis (syn. *hexapetala*). Haiti and other Caribbean islands. Cultivated and wild states. Fiber said to be softer, finer, and more flexible than henequen. Production small.

Furcraea geminispera (cocuiza). Cultivated in Venezuela. Native habitat unknown. Similar to *F. humboltiana.*

Furcreae humboltiana (cocuiza, sometimes incorrectly called fique). Venezuela. Wild state. Production varies from 1 to 2 million lb annually. Principal uses, bagging fabrics and hammocks and other household articles.[25]

Furcraea macrophylla (fique, also sometimes termed cabuya). Colombia. Both cultivated and wild states. Production varies from 25 to 80 million lb annually, depending largely upon demand. Principal uses are for bagging fabrics for coffee; other uses are cordage, hammocks, and related items. All fiber is manufactured in Colombia, chiefly for domestic uses; a small amount is exported in the form of bagging fabrics, principally to Venezuela. Plant has short stalk, about 12 in. high. Leaves are green, smooth on top and rough on under surface, about 5 to 6 ft long and 3 to 6 in. wide at the base. Some varieties have marginal spines; these are said to have longer leaves and better quality fiber than varieties without spines. Varieties with spines are ready for first harvesting 3 to 4 yr after planting; life is from 10 to 20 yr. Fiber yield is from 3 to 4 per cent of weight of freshly cut leaves; yield may be as high as 8 per cent. Grows wild on semiarid hillsides but when it is cultivated, higher production is obtained from plantings on flat, fertile land. Yield on plantations averages 1000 lb of fiber per acre. Harvesting is done by hand. Fiber removal is done both by hand and with mechanical decorticators. In the hand operation, leaves are first split into narrow strips. These are then drawn through a primitive scraping device called a "carrizo." Amount of fiber a worker can produce in a day is limited not only by the primitive character of the equipment but also by the fact that the juice from the leaves is caustic and can be injurious to the worker's hands. Mechanical decorticators used are, for the most part, of the

[25] "Status of Fiber Plant Industry in Latin America," Brittain B. Robinson et al., Pan American Union, Washington (1947).

small raspador type. After decortication fiber is dried in the sun.

Furcraea pubescens. Habitat thought to be Mexico. Approximately similar to *F. andina.*

Furcraea selloa. Colombia (South America).

Furcraea tuberosa. Cuba, Haiti, and Lesser Antilles.

PHORMIUM

Nomenclature and History. Phormium fiber, often termed New Zealand "flax" or "hemp," is obtained from *Phormium tenax,* a member of the Liliaceae family. The plant is indigenous to New Zealand, where the natives had, for time unknown, used the fiber for fabrics, cordage, and baskets. Knowledge of the plant was given to the western world by Captain Cook, who observed it in New Zealand on his first voyage to the Antipodes in 1771. Some of the native fabrics were so fine that they were mistaken for linen woven from flax fiber, hence the name New Zealand "flax." "Phormium" is derived from a Greek word meaning basket, one of the first uses of the fiber observed by Captain Cook and his men.

The plant was introduced into southern Ireland in 1798, where it grows luxuriantly, primarily as an ornamental plant. Subsequently, it was introduced into parts of Europe, St. Helena, the Azores, Australia, the Union of South Africa, and Japan. During the 1930's, cultivation of the plant was begun in Chile, Argentina and Brazil. From the standpoint of commercial fiber production, it has been planted only experimentally in the U. S.; plants are grown principally in gardens as ornaments.

Appearance of the Plant. The plant consists of 8 to 12 or more shoots emanating from a central rootstock, each bearing 5 or more leaves arranged in fanlike form. The leaves are swordshaped, flat on top, and curved on the under side, near the base, becoming almost flat on both sides and rather limplike near the tip. They are characterized by a pronounced middle rib or keel on the under side. Length generally ranges from 3 to 9 ft; width is 2 in. at the base, tapering to a point. Color is dark green with the outer surface smooth and hard; margins and keel on many varieties are a bright or brownish-red color. The flower stalk, which rises from the center of the plant, is 12 to 15 ft high; flowers are borne in bunches, are usually yellow, and about 1½ in. long. Seeds are numerous, flat, shiny, and black.

World Production. Production in New Zealand during the early 1900's averaged 40 to 50 million lb annually. Total world production during the period 1935–38 averaged 15 million lb annually, of which

study [28] indicates that average yield is 8000 to 11,000 lb per acre on a 3- to 4-yr harvesting cycle, which is about 2000 to 3000 lb per acre on an annual basis; in Chile, average annual yield per acre is said to be about 2000 lb.

TABLE 28. GRADE DESIGNATIONS FOR PHORMIUM

(Arrangement of grades only *approximately* comparable)

New Zealand	*St. Helena*	*Chile*
A—Superior	Prime	A or I
B—Fine	Tiger	..
..	J. D. & Co.	B or II
C—Good Fair	..	..
..	..	C or III
DD—High Point Fair	..	..
..	..	D or IV
D—Fair	..	..
E—Common	..	..
F—Rejected	..	..
Tow 1st	Tow 1	..
Tow 2nd	Tow 2	..
Tow 3rd	..	..
Stripper slips—1st	..	..
Stripper slips—2nd	..	..

Sources

New Zealand. E. H. Atkinson, "*Phormium tenax*—The New Zealand Fiber Industry," N. Z. Dept. Agr., *Bull.* 95, Wellington (1922); and British Ministry of Supply, "Control of Hemp Order," dated 1 September 1939, *Statutory Rules and Orders, 1939,* No. 1004. Grades are based on scoring, with 25 points each, for stripping, scutching, color, and strength. Points for each grade are: A—Superior, 90 to 100; B—Fine, 80 to 89; C—Good Fair, 70 to 79; DD—High Point Fair, 65 to 69; D—Fair, 60 to 64; E—Common, 50 to 59; F—Rejected, under 50. Tow is waste fiber from scutching; stripper slips are waste fiber produced during stripping, that is, fiber removal from leaf.

St. Helena. British Ministry of Supply, "Control of Hemp Order," dated 1 September 1939, *Statutory Rules and Orders, 1939,* No. 1004.

Chile. No official standard. Fiber grading as used by principal producer, Sociedad Agricola e Industrial Formio Chileno, is system in general use. It is based on system of grading leaves as follows: A or I, leaf length 1.20 meters or longer; B or II, 1.00 to 1.20 meters; C or III, 0.75 to 1.00 meters; and D or IV, 0.50 to 0.75 meters.

Grades. Official grades of phormium are in use in New Zealand and also in St. Helena, having been established in New Zealand as early as 1901. Table 28 gives grade designations in general use for

[28] "Status of the Fiber Plant Industry in Latin America," Brittain B. Robinson et al., Pan American Union, Washington (1947).

phormium in New Zealand, St. Helena, and Chile. Comparison of grades from each area is obviously *approximate* as specifications vary. In Argentina and the Azores, only two grades are used: "hemp" and "tow."

Characteristics. Commercial phormium fiber is used in the form of fiber strands which are composed of bundles of individual fibers, the bundles running the length of the leaf. The average length of fiber strands ranges from 3 to 7 ft. Fiber strands, when carefully prepared, are creamy white, sometimes with a reddish-yellow tinge, and quite flexible. They have fair strength, good luster, and a good resistance to the effects of microorganisms found in salt water. Table 10, page 382, gives a comparison of the strengths of phormium and of other hard fibers. Table 20, page 402, shows percentage losses of strength of phormium, sisal, and abacá after immersion in sea water.

Individual fibers are approximately cylindrical in longitudinal shape, with pointed ends and a generally smooth surface with occasional wavelike irregularities in the cell wall. In cross-section, the shape is approximately circular with uniformly thick cell walls. The lumen is relatively small, circular in cross-section, and disappears in a point near the end of the cell. Table 29 gives measurements of individual fibers obtained by six authorities.

TABLE 29. MEASUREMENTS OF INDIVIDUAL PHORMIUM FIBERS

	Length (inches)			*Breadth (microns)*		
Authority	*Min.*	*Max.*	*Mean*	*Min.*	*Max.*	*Mean*
Hanausek	n.s.	n.s.	n.s.	10	18	16
Lecomte	0.07	0.20	0.12	10	17	14
Luniak	0.08	0.59	0.24	5	25	14
Turner	0.10	0.59	n.s.	10	20	n.s.
Vétillart	0.20	0.59	0.31 to 0.39	10	20	16
Wiesner	0.11	0.22	n.s.	8	19	14

n.s. Not stated.

Sources

Hanausek, T. F., *The Microscopy of Technical Products*, translated by Andrew L. Winton, assisted by Kate Barber Winton, John Wiley & Sons, New York (1907).

Lecomte, H., "Textiles vegeteaux, leur examen microchimique," *Encyclopedia Scientifique des aide-memoire*, Gauthier-Villars et Fils, Paris (1892).

Luniak, Bruno, *Die Unterscheidung der Textilfasern*, Leemann, Zurich (1949).

Turner, A. J., "The Structure of Long Vegetable Fibers," *J. Textile Inst.*, **40** (10), Manchester, England (1949).

Vétillart, M., *Études sur les fibres végètales textiles employées dans l'industries*, Firmin, Didot et cie., Paris (1876).

Wiesner, Julius, *Die Rohstoffe des Pflanzenreiches*, Engelmann, Leipzig (1873).

"Thin-walled fibers with broad lumen (q', Fig. 9) [and] also porous elongated parenchyma cells (f' p', Fig. 9) are sometimes found accompanying thick-walled forms. These are from the . . . fibrovascular bundles which lie inside the zone in which are distributed the

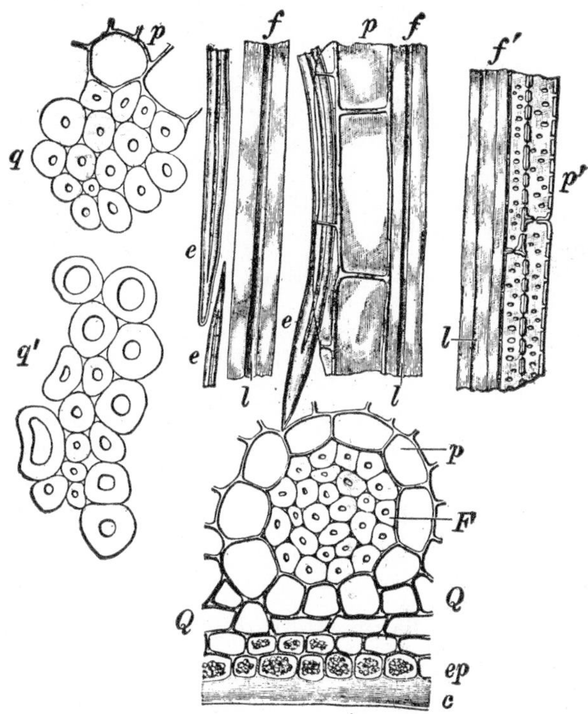

Fig. 9. New Zealand flax. *f*, Sclerenchymatous bundles; *f'*, vascular fibers; *e*, fiber ends; *p'*, porous elements of vascular bundles; *q*, cross-section of bast fibers; *q'*, cross-section of vascular bundles; *Q*, cross-section of bast fiber bundle with accompanying elements; *ep*, epidermis; *c*, cuticles; *F*, bundle proper; *p*, parenchyma; *l*, lumen. (*Hanausek.*)

isolated . . . fiber bundles. Since vessels occur only in connection with these fibers, it is evident that they are seldom found in the commercial product." [29]

Chemically the fiber has a moderately high percentage of cellulose with a relatively high percentage of lignin. Table 30 gives results of two analyses of chemical components of the fiber.

[29] *The Microscopy of Technical Products*, T. F. Hanausek, translated by Andrew L. Winton, assisted by Kate Barber Winton, John Wiley & Sons, New York (1907).

TABLE 30. Chemical Components of Phormium Fiber

(Methods of analyses used in studies were not uniform)

	Study by	
Component	*Church (per cent)*	*Turner (per cent)*
Moisture	11.61	10.00
Ash	0.63	..
Water solubles	21.99	2.20
Fat and wax	1.08	0.70
Pectin	1.69	0.70
Lignin	..	11.20
Cellulose	63.00	45.10
Hemicellulose	..	30.10
Total	100.00	100.00

Sources

Church, as cited in *Matthews Textile Fibers*, 5th Ed., John Wiley & Sons (1947).

Turner, A. J., "Structure of Long Vegetable Fibers," *J. Textile Inst.*, **40** (10), Manchester, England (1949).

Iodine and sulfuric acid on the fiber give an intense yellow color; aniline sulfate a pale yellow; chloriodide of zinc, a yellowish brown; and ammoniacal solution of fuchsine, a red. With Schweitzer's reagent, fibers are rapidly separated into their elements, but they do not dissolve.

SANSEVIERIA FIBER

Sansevieria fiber is obtained from the leaves of a genus of plants belonging to the *Liliaceae* family, *Sansevieria*, named after Raimond de Sangro, Prince of Sanseviero, born in Naples in 1710. The genus is indigenous to tropical Africa and India, though now it is to be found growing wild or cultivated in most tropical or subtropical areas of the world. Most of the cultivation is for ornamental purposes. In Yucatan, Mexico, commercial fiber is obtained from plants growing both in a wild and in a cultivated state; about 20 to 40 tons are exported to the United States annually. In the United States, experimental work has been done on growing some species for fiber on a commercial scale. Plants of the *Sansevieria* genus like those of the *Agave* and the *Furcraea* genera have sometimes been incorrectly classified as members of the *Aloe* genus.

Principal uses are cordage, fish-net twines, and coarse fabrics for bagging. In Africa, natives use the "ife" fiber (*S. cylindrica*) extensively for fish nets, especially for salt-water fishing. In India, the Circars used the fiber for bowstrings, hence the name "bowstring 'hemp,'" said to have been given the fiber by Roxburgh.

There are several species which are utilized for fiber in various areas of the world. A list of these is given in Table 31 together with common names.

TABLE 31. Principal Sansevieria Species from Which Fiber Is Obtained

Genus and Species	*Common Name*
Sansevieria cylindrica (syn., *sulcata*)	Ife
Sansevieria eherenbergii	Somaliland bowstring "hemp"
Sansevieria kirkii	Pangane
Sansevieria metallica	African bowstring "hemp"
Sansevieria roxburghiana	Bowstring "hemp"
Sansevieria thyrsiflora (syn., *guineensis*)	Guinea bowstring "hemp" or konje
Sansevieria zeylanica	Bowstring "hemp"

Plants of the *Sansevieria* genus send up stiff, pointed leaves from the base at the root or from rhizomes sent out by the parent root. Leaves vary by species from terete (cylindrical) to acuminate (sword-like) shape. Surface of the leaves is hard and smooth. Color varies by species, ranging from a dark to a light green, some species and varieties being variegated with bands of cream color. The number of leaves per plant varies by species, generally ranging from 8 to 15. Height also varies; range is from 1 to 8 ft. Flower stalk rises from the center of the plant about 1 ft above the leaf height. Flowers are small, greenish-white, in some species creamy white tinged with pink, and are often borne in dense racemes.

Plants grow best on a well-drained, moderately rich soil. Cultivation is much the same as that given to sisal. Leaves are cut by hand; two crops may be harvested each year. Yield of fiber per acre, when the plants are well cultivated, is said to average as high as 2000 lb annually. Fiber is removed from the leaves by hand scraping, by water retting and hand scraping, or, when grown commercially, on machines similar to those used for sisal.

Fiber strands are 1½ to 6 ft long, creamy white, quite soft and lustrous, and have good strength, elongation, and very good resistance to the effects of microorganisms found in salt water. A comparison of the strength of sansevieria fiber with that of other leaf fibers is shown in Table 10, page 382. Schiefer[30] found that for a 15-in. bundle

[30] "Machines and Methods for Testing Cordage Fibers," H. F. Schiefer, Natl. Bur. Standards RP1611, U. S. Dept. Commerce, Washington (1944).

of fiber weighing 5 grains, average of 4 samples, dry breaking length was 141,000 ft and dry breaking strength 68 lb; elongation of dry fiber at rupture averaged 4.0 per cent.

Individual fibers are approximately cylindrical in longitudinal shape, with rounded ends. In cross-section, their shape is polygonal. The lumen is very large, oval to polygonal in cross-section; cell walls are correspondingly thin. One study[31] reports length of individual fiber ranging from 0.04 to 0.28 in., with mean at 0.16 in.; breadth 13 to 40 μ, mean at 24.

Chemically, sansevieria has a fairly high percentage of cellulose and a relatively high percentage of lignin. Table 32 gives data for chemical composition of two species of *Sansevieria*.

TABLE 32. CHEMICAL COMPOSITION OF *Sansevieria* FIBER

Component	*S. metallica* (*per cent*)	*S. zeylanica* (*per cent*)
Moisture	9.4	9.2
Ash	0.7	0.6
Cellulose	75.2	76.1
Lignin	12.6	11.8
Water soluble	2.1	2.3
Total	100.0	100.0

CAROA

Caroa fiber is obtained from leaves of the plant *Neoglazovia variegata,* of the Bromeliaceae family, which is indigenous to the American tropics. It grows most abundantly in Brazil where it has been utilized for textile fibers by the natives for an unknown length of time.

Caroa grows wild over large areas in northeast Brazil, in the states of Pernambuco, Paraiba, Clara, Rio Grande do Norte and Bahia. Although produced commercially to a small extent in Pernambuco and Ceará, this fiber has not been cultivated, since it grows wild so extensively as to provide more than sufficient fiber for Brazil's requirements. Fiber is obtained from the leaves . . . which may grow as long as 12 feet. Caroa leaves yield from 12 to 14 per cent of fiber. . . . The fiber, i.e., fiber strands, is stronger than jute, and finer than sisal and abacá. It is light in weight, lustrous and white in color when well prepared, but may shrink when wet. . . . It grows well on dry land not suited for other agricultural crops.

It is used in the manufacture of cord, rope, twine, paper, rayon, burlap in mixture with other fibers, cheap shoe soles, and cloth. During World War II, when linen imports from Europe were shut off, caroa was used extensively in

[31] *Die Unterscheidung der Textilfasern,* Bruno Luniak, Leemann, Zurich (1949).

61,000 ft and from *Y. macrocarpa,* 128,000 ft; dry breaking strength of *Y. elata* was 35 lb and of *Y. macrocarpa,* 73 lb. Individual fiber measurements from three studies are given in Table 37.

TABLE 37. MEASUREMENTS OF INDIVIDUAL FIBERS OF *Yucca* SPP.

	Length (inches)			*Breadth (microns)*		
Authority	*Min.*	*Max.*	*Mean*	*Min.*	*Max.*	*Mean*
Camin						
Y. aloifolia	0.05	0.20	n.s.	7	14	n.s.
Y. angustifolia	0.06	0.19	n.s.	11	14	n.s.
Y. filamentosa	0.03	0.09	n.s.	9	24	n.s.
Y. gloriosa	0.05	0.15	n.s.	11	26	n.s.
Y. karlsruhensis	0.03	0.10	n.s.	11	19	n.s.
Luniak—*Yucca* spp.	0.02	0.24	0.08	4	26	12
Vétillart—*Yucca* spp.	0.02	0.24	0.14 to 0.16	10	20	n.s.

n.s. Not stated.

Sources

Camin, E., "Beiträge zur Anatomie der Yucca und zur Kenntnis ihrer Aufbereitungs-möglichkeiten," *Faserforschung,* **13** (4), (1938).

Luniak, Bruno, *Die Unterscheidung der Textilfasern,* Leemann, Zurich (1949).

Vétillart, M., *Études sur les fibres végétales textiles employées dans l'industries,* Firmin, Didot et cie., Paris (1876).

Nolina spp. Liliaceae family. Beargrass, jirica, sacahuista. Mexico, United States (New Mexico, Arizona, and California).

Hesperaloe funifera. Liliaceae family. Mexico and United States (New Mexico and Texas). Source of zamandoque fiber, which is also sometimes termed Tampico fiber. Plant somewhat similar to *Yucca funifera* and was at one time so classified. Stemless leaves are medium green, 3 to 4 ft long, and about 1 in. wide. Principal use of fiber is for brushes. See further discussion in Chapter IX.

Palmaceae. There are several members of this family from which leaf fiber is obtained for textile usage. These include: *Acrocomia sclerocarpa, Acrocomia armentalis* (syn., *crispa*), *Attalea funifer, Bactris setosa, Borassus flabellifera, Caryota urens, Dictyosperma fibrosum, Elaeis guineensis, Leopoldinia piassaba, Raphia gaertneri, Raphia pedunculata,* and *Raphia vinifera.* Fibers from the leaves of these palms are used by the natives in the areas where the palms grow for cordage, fishing nets, and coarse fabrics. For commercial purposes, however, the fiber from most of these genera and species is best known in the United States for its use in brushes; hence the plants are described in more detail in Chapter IX, section on Brush Fibers. Fiber is also obtained from the leaves of the *Vonitra* spp., which are found principally in Madagascar.

Aloe spp. Liliaceae family. Fiber is apparently present in some degree in the fibrovascular structure of leaves of plants of the *Aloe* spp., but so far as is known this fiber is not utilized. The plants are important because of the juice extracted from the leaves, which has wide use for medicinal and industrial purposes. It has not been clearly determined which species of *Aloe* contains fiber in significant amounts. Formerly this was believed to be *A. perfoliata*. In recent years, however, many *Aloe* plants originally classified as *A. perfoliata* have been reclassified as other species of the *Aloe* genus. Some authorities have indicated their belief that *A. vera* contains a significant amount of fiber. The term Indian "aloe" fiber is fiber from plants of the *Agave* spp., especially those species that were growing in India prior to the nineteenth century; Bombay "aloe" fiber is fiber from *Agave cantala*. Agave fiber was misnamed by Western botanists of the eighteenth and early nineteenth centuries who classified as *Aloes* the *Agaves* they found growing in India. Similar confusion occurred in early classifications of plants of the *Furcraea* and *Sansevieria* genera.

Canna orientalis. Cannaceae family. Wild plant found in many warm, moist regions. Widely cultivated as ornamental plant. Fiber from stalk, formed by petioles of leaves, has been tested in India and Australia as possible jute substitute. Tests indicated canna fiber of lower strength and spinning quality than jute; one report indicated strength of canna fiber was better than that of sunn fiber (quality and origin of sunn not stated).

BOTANICAL ORDERS AND FAMILIES OF LEAF FIBERS

Table 38 gives the botanical nomenclature of the leaf fiber plants discussed in this chapter. For convenience, the list is arranged alphabetically by order and subalphabetically by family, genus, and species.

TABLE 38. BOTANICAL ORDERS AND FAMILIES OF LEAF FIBERS

Order	*Family*	*Genus and Species*
Iridales	Amaryllidaceae	*Agave amaniensis, A. cantala, A. cocui, A. deweyana, A. falcata, A. fourcroydes, A. heterocantha* (syn. *funkiana*), *A. lespinassei, A. letonae, A. lophantha* (syn. *lechuguilla*), *A. lurida, A. palmeri, A. pesmulae, A. pseudo tequilana, A. sisalana, A. tequilana,* and *A. zapupe* *Furcraea andina, F. cabuya, F. cubensis* (syn. *hexapetala*), *F. gigantea, F. geminispera, F. humboldtiana, F. macrophylla, F. pubescens, F. selloa, F. tuberosa*
	Bromeliaceae	*Aechme magdalenae* *Ananas comosus* (syn. *sativa*) *Bromelia argentina, B. fastuosa, B. karatas, B. pinguin, B. sagenaria, B. serra,* and *B. silvestris* *Neoglazovia variegata*
	Cannaceae	*Canna orientalis*
	Musaceae	*Musa cavendishii, M. ensete, M. fehi, M. livingstonia, M. paradisiacha, M. sapientum, M. textilis,* and *M. ulugurensis*
Liliales	Liliaceae	*Aloe spp.* *Hesperaloe funifera* *Phormium tenax* *Samuela carenosana* *Sansevieria cylindrica, S. eherenbergii, S. kirkii, S. metallica, S. roxburghiana, S. thyrsiflora* (syn. *guineensis*), and *S. zeylanica* *Yucca* spp.
Palmales	Palmaceae	*Acrocomia sclerocarpa, A. armentalis* (syn. *crispa*) *Attalea funifera* *Bactris setosa* *Borassus flabellifera* *Caryota urens* *Dictyosperma fibrosum* *Elaeis guineensis* *Leopoldinia piassaba* *Raphia gaertneri, R. pedunculata, R. vinifera* *Vonitra* spp.

Authorities for classifications

Bailey, L. H., *Standard Cyclopedia of Horticulture,* The Macmillan Co., New York (1935).

Bailey, L. H., and Bailey, Ethel Zoe, *Hortus Second,* The Macmillan Co., New York (1941).

Hooker, Joseph D., director, and Jackson, B. Daydon, editor, *Index Kewensis,* and Supplements I through X, Clarendon Press, Oxford (1895 and supplements through 1940).

Hutchinson, J., *The Families of Flowering Plants,* The Macmillan Co., London (1926).

Pool, Raymond J., *Flowers and Flowering Plants,* McGraw-Hill Book Co., New York (1941).

Royal Horticultural Society of London and Royal Botanical Gardens, *Index Londonensis,* and supplements, Clarendon Press, Oxford (1929 and subsequent supplements).

Van Wijk, Gerth H. L., *A Dictionary of Plant Names,* Dutch Society of Scientists at Haarlem, The Hague (1911).

BIBLIOGRAPHY

Note: Names of fibers to which reference especially relates are given after reference.

ATKINSON, E. H., "*Phormium tenax*—The New Zealand Fiber Industry," *Bull.* 95, New Zealand Dept. Agr., Wellington (1922). *Phormium.*

BARKER, S. G., "Sisal," Empire Marketing Board, *Bull.* 64, H.M. Stationery Office, London (1933). *Sisal.*

BECKER, GENEVIEVE, and APPEL, WILLIAM D., "Evaluation of Manila Rope Fiber for Color," Natl. Bur. Standards RP627, U. S. Dept. Commerce, Washington (1933). *Abacá.*

BELL, D. W., ET AL., "Report to the President of the United States by the Economic Survey Mission to the Philippines," U. S. Dept. of State, Washington (1950). *Abacá.*

BERKLEY, EARL E., HESSLER, LYLE E., BURNESTON, EDNA B., and CHEW, CHESTER F., "A Study of the Quality of Abacá Fiber," U. S. Dept. Agr., Washington (1949). *Abacá.*

BLANCO, P., Fr. Manual, "Flora de Filipinas," D. Candido Lopez, St. Thomas, P. I. (1837). *Abacá.*

BLAU, GERDA, ET AL., "World Fiber Survey," Food and Agriculture Organization, United Nations, Washington (1947). *Various fibers.*

BROWN, WILLIAM H., "Useful Plants of the Philippines," Vols. 1, 2, and 3. Dept. Agr. and Commerce, Republic of the Philippines, Manila (1941–1943). *Various fibers.*

BURKILL, I. H., "A Dictionary of the Economic Products of the Malay Peninsula," Government of the Straits Settlements and Federated Malay States, Crown Agents for the Colonies, London (1935). *Various fibers.*

CAMIN, E., "Beiträge zur Anatomie der Yucca und zur Kenntnis ihrer Aufbereitungs-möglichkeiten," *Faserforschung,* **13** (4), (1938). *Various fibers.*

Commonwealth Economic Committee, "Industrial Fibres," H.M. Stationery Office, London (1951 and 1952). *Various fibers.*

COPELAND, E. B., "Nomenclature of Abacá Plant," *Philippine J. Sci.,* **33** (2), Manila (June 1927). *Abacá.*

CORREA, M. PIO, "Fibras Textes e Cellulose," Ministerio da Agricultura, Industria, e Commercio, Rio de Janeiro (1919). *Caroa.*

CROSS, C. F., BEVAN, E. J., and KING, C. M., *Report on Indian Fibers and Fibrous Substances,* E. & F. N. Spon, London (1887). *Various fibers.*

DAVIS, ROSELAND J., "World Study of Hard Fibers and Hard Fiber Products," Part II, U. S. Dept. Commerce, Washington (1951). *Various fibers.*

DEWEY, LYSTER H., "Sisal and Henequen Plants Yielding Fiber for Binder Twine," U. S. Dept. Agr. Circ. 186: 1–12, Washington (1931). *Sisal and henequen.*

DODGE, C. R., "Report of the Secretary of Agriculture, 1892," U. S. Dept. Agr., Washington (1893). *Various fibers.*

DODGE, C. R., "Report of Fiber Investigations," Nos. 1, 3–10, U. S. Dept. Agr., Washington (1890–98). *Various fibers.*

DODGE, C. R., "Useful Fiber Plants of the World," U. S. Dept. Agr., Washington (1897). *Various fibers.*

EDWARDS, H. T., "Abacá (Manila Hemp)," *Farmers' Bull.* 12, Philippine Commonwealth, Dept. Interior, Manila (1904). *Abacá.*

EDWARDS, H. T., "The Cultivation of Maguey in the Philippine Islands," *Farmers' Bull.* 13, Philippine Commonwealth, Dept. Interior, Manila (1906). *Cantala.*

EDWARDS, H. T., "The Introduction of Abacá (Manila Hemp) into the Western

Hemisphere," *Ann. Rept. of the Smithsonian Institution for Year ending* June 30, 1945, Washington (1946). *Abacá.*

EDWARDS, H. T., "Production of Henequen Fiber in Yucatan and Campeche," *Bull.* 1278, U. S. Dept. Agr., Washington (1924). *Henequen.*

ESPINO, R. B., and ESGUERRA, FELIX, "Comparative Study of Fiber Produced by Six Varieties of Abacá When Grown in Los Baños," *Philippine Agriculturist,* **12** (3 and 4), Manila (1923). *Abacá.*

ETTIGHOFFER, P. C., *Sisal Das Blonde Gold Afrikas,* Ce. Bertelsmann Gütersloh, Berlin (1943). *Sisal.*

Food and Agricultural Organization of the United Nations, "Monthly Bulletin of Agricultural Economics and Statistics," **I** (1), Rome (1952). *Various fibers.*

Food and Agricultural Organization of United Nations, "Yearbook of Food and Agricultural Statistics, **V,** Part 1, "Production," and **VI,** Part 1, "Trade," Rome (1952). *Various fibers.*

GILMORE, JOHN W., "Preliminary Report on Commercial Fiber of the Philippines," Philippine Commonwealth, Bur. Agr., Manila (1903). *Pineapple fiber.*

GOULDING, ERNEST, "Textile Fibres of Vegetable Origin," *Bull. Imp. Inst.,* **35** (1), H.M. Stationery Office, London (1937). *Various fibers.*

HANAUSEK, T. F. (translated by Andrew L. Winton, assisted by Kate Barber Winton), *The Microscopy of Technical Products,* John Wiley & Sons, New York (1907). *Various fibers.*

HEYNE, K., *De Nuttige Planten van Indonesië,* Vols. I and II, N. V. Uitgeveriz, W. van Hoeve, Bandung, Indonesia (1950). *Various fibers.*

HÖHNEL, F. X., *Die Mikroskopie der technisch verwendeten Faserstoffe,* A. Hartleben, Leipzig (1905). *Various fibers.*

Imperial Institute, *Bulletin,* "Absorption of Water by Sisal and Manila on Immersion; Increase of Weight and Girth," H.M. Stationery Office, London (1932). *Various fibers.*

Imperial Institute, *Bulletin,* "Empire Crown Sisal," Empire Marketing Board, H.M. Stationery Office, London (Oct. 1928). *Sisal.*

Imperial Institute, *Bulletin,* "Percentage Decrease in Average Strength of Sisal, Manila Hemp, New Zealand Hemp (Phormium) Ropes after Different Periods of Immersion," **30** (2), London (July 1932). *Various fibers.*

Imperial Chemistries Industries, Ltd., "Textile Fibers under the Microscope," London (1942). *Various fibers.*

KERVEGANT, D., "Le Bannier," Société d'Editions Geographiques Maritimes et Coloniales, Paris (1935). *Musa.*

Kew Bulletins, "Bulletin of Miscellaneous Information, Royal Botanic Gardens, Kew, H.M. Stationery Office, London, 1890, 1892, 1893, 1894, 1908, 1915, 1933, and 1934. *Various fibers.*

KIDD, FRANKLIN F., assisted by O'CONNELL, ANN Q., and DEAN, GAYLE D., "World Study of Hard Fibers and Hard Fiber Products," Part I, U. S. Dept. Commerce, Washington (1949). *Various fibers.*

LECOMTE, H., "Textiles végéteaux leur examen microchimique," *Encyclopedia scientifique des aide-memoire,* Gauthier-Villars et Fils, Paris (1892). *Various fibers.*

LINDSAY, H. A. F., ET AL., "Commercial Plant Fibres of the British Empire," Imperial Inst., H.M. Stationery Office, London (1936). *Various fibers.*

LUNIAK, BRUNO, *Die Unterscheidung der Textilfasern,* Leemann, Zurich (1949). *Various fibers.*

MCKELVEY, SUSAN DELANO, "Yuccas of the Southwest U. S.," Arnold Arboretum, Boston (1938). *Yucca.*

MEADOWS, BARKLEY, "Trends in the Consumption of Fibers in the U. S., 1892–1948," U. S. Dept. Agr., Washington (1950). *Various fibers.*

MÜLLER, HUGO, *Die Pflanzenfaser und ihre Aufbereitung für die Technik,* F. Vieweg und Sohn, Braunschweig, Germany (1876). *Various fibers.*

MULLER, THEODORE, "Industrial Fiber Plants of the Philippines," *Bull.* 49, Philippine Commonwealth, Bur. Educ., Manila (1913). *Various fibers.*

PERRINE, HENRY, "Tropical Plants," 25th U. S. Congress, 2d Session, House of Representatives, Rept. No. 564, Washington (1838). *Sisal.*

Republic of the Philippines, "The Abacá Industry of the Philippines," Dept. Commerce and Industry, Manila (1950). *Abacá.*

ROBINSON, BRITTAIN B., "Status of the Fiber Plant Industry in Latin America," Pan American Union, Washington (1947). *Various fibers.*

ROYLE, J. FORBES, *Fibrous Plants of India,* Smith, Elder and Co., Cornhill, England (1855). *Various fibers.*

SAITO, K., "Anatomische Studien über wichtige Faserpflanzen Japan mit besonder Beruecksichtigung der Bastzellen," *J. Coll. Sciences,* **15** (3), Imperial University, Tokyo (1901). *Musa.*

SALEEBY, M. M., "Aspects of Abacá Production in the Philippines Today," *Cord Age,* New York (Dec. 1928). *Abacá.*

SCHIEFER, HERBERT F., "Machines and Methods for Testing Cordage Fibers," Natl. Bur. Standards RP1611, U. S. Dept. Commerce, Washington (1944). *Various fibers.*

STANDLEY, P. C., "Trees and Shrubs of Mexico," Contributions from U. S. Natl. Herbarium, **23,** U. S. Natl. Museum, Washington (1920–26). *Various fibers.*

TRELEASE, WILLIAM, "Agave in the West Indies," *Mem. Natl. Acad. Sci.,* **XI,** Washington (1913). *Agaves.*

TRELEASE, WILLIAM, "New Species of Agave from the Republic of Salvador," *J. Wash. Acad. Sci.,* **15** (17), Washington (1925). *Letona.*

TURNER, A. J., "The Structure of Long Vegetable Fibers," *J. Textile Inst.,* **40** (10), Manchester, England (1949). *Various fibers.*

United States Department of Agriculture, "The Jute and Hard Fibers Situation," Washington (1951). *Various fibers.*

VAN HALL, C. J. J., and VAN DE KOPPEL, C., *De Landbouw in de Indische Archipel,* Vol. III, N. V. Uitgeverij, W. van Hoeve, Bandung, Indonesia (1950). *Various fibers.*

VAN WOERDEN, C. L. L. H., "Report on Wild Fiber Plants found on Java," Kebun Raya, Indonesia, Bogor, Indonesia. Unpublished. *Various fibers.*

VÉTILLART, M., *Études sur les fibres végétales textiles employées dans l'industrie,* Firmin, Didot et cie., Paris (1876). *Various fibers.*

WATTS, SIR GEORGE, *The Commercial Products of India,* John Murray, London (1908). *Various fibers.*

WEINDLING, LUDWIG, *Long Vegetable Fibers,* Columbia University Press, New York (1947). *Various fibers.*

WIESNER, JULIUS, *Die Rohstoffe des Pflanzenresiches,* Engelmann, Leipzig (1873). *Various fibers.*

WIESNER, J. V., and BAAR, H., *Beiträge zur Kenntnis der Anatomie des Agave Blattes,* Engelmann, Wien (1914). *Sisal.*

WIGGLESWORTH, ALFRED, "Hard Fibers," *Proc. Empire Textile Conf.,* The Textile Institute, Manchester, England (1924). *Various fibers.*

WIGGLESWORTH, ALFRED, "The Hard Fiber Industry," *Roy. Soc. Arts,* London (1931). *Various fibers.*

CHAPTER IX

MISCELLANEOUS PLANT FIBERS

A. C. WHITFORD

SEED FIBERS

Seed fibers are used mainly in the manufacture of life belts, buoys, for stuffing pillows and mattresses, and for other similar purposes. The Bombaceae family contains the greatest number of genera of seed-fiber-bearing plants, including *Bombax* (tree cotton), *Ceiba* (kapok), *Ochroma* (tree cotton, red), and *Chorisia* (tree cotton). Other plant families producing seed fibers are the *Cochlospermaceae* (another tree cotton), *Apocynaceae, Typhaceae* (cattail floss), and *Asclepidaceae* (milkweed floss). Other practical seed-fiber plants may be discovered as investigation proceeds, such as certain of the Compositae (thistles and dandelion). Most of these fibers have not as yet been spun economically into usable textile yarns owing to some such factor as unsatisfactory strength, smoothness, or elasticity.

Coir (*Cocos nucifera*)

Coir fiber is obtained from the husk surrounding the nut, that is, the fruit, of the coconut plant.

Ceylon is the home and center for the preparation of coir fiber and yarn from which cordage and coarse cloths and bristles for brushes are made. Galle, on the southwest part of the island and the chief seat for native manufacture, turns out a fiber that is considered superior to the mill product. The coconut husks are thrown into a bamboo enclosure which the natives have built in the sea. After softening in water, they are pounded with a stone to remove the woody portions, after which the fibers are hackled with a steel comb, and dried.

When the fiber is prepared by machinery the process is different. The husks are purchased by the bullock cartload at a very low price or even for the cart hire. They are quartered and put in large water tanks and weighted with a network of iron rails. After 5 days the husks are removed and run through a machine composed of two corrugated iron rollers known as a "breaker," which crushes them and prepares them for the next machine, called the "drum."

The drums are in pairs, a coarse one for the first treatment and a finer one for the second. They are circular iron wheels, 3 ft in diameter, which revolve at high speed. They have rims about 14 in. wide,

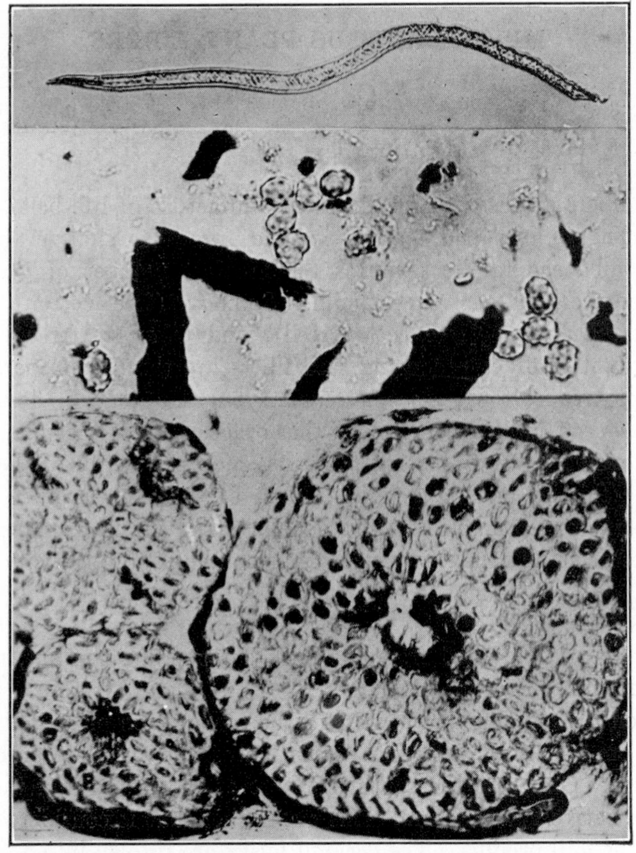

Fig. 1. Coir fiber (*Cocos nucifera*). *Top,* single cell showing spiral structure (×115); *middle,* siliceous remains in ash (×500); *bottom,* cross-section of fiber bundle with hollow center (×230). (*Textile Fiber Atlas.*)

studded with spikes. The husks are held against the revolving drums and the spikes tear out the woody part, leaving the long, coarse fibers separate. The torn and broken fiber that falls from the drum spikes is fanned, then dried by being spread out in the sun; it is subsequently cleaned and then baled as mattress fiber. The longer and stronger fibers are washed, cleaned, and dried, and then taken to a room where they are further hackled by women, who comb them through long rows of steel spikes that are fixed to tables. It is estimated that 1000 coconut husks will produce 70 to 80 lb of bristle fiber and about 300 lb of mattress fiber and yarn.

The fibers are now made into hanks about a foot long and as thick as a man's forearm. They are bound together, put into a hydraulic press, and baled for shipment as fiber for making brushes.

For brush-making purposes the coir (coconut) fiber is selected and sorted as to color and length and put up into bundles 2 in. in diameter, which are tied with fiber. According to the solidity and length of the fiber selected, the bundles are sold as grades 1-Tie for the short, 2-Tie for the medium, and 3-Tie for the long. The bundles, ranging in length between 5 and 12 in., are solid only in the middle portion, each end being tapered. In Europe sizable quantities of this fiber are used in making brushes. The United States uses a very small amount of coir fiber for this purpose. One well-known use for the fiber is for door mats.

The longer fibers are spun into yarns for fish nets and marine cordage. In 1949, and also in 1950, the United States imported 6 million lb of this yarn, principally from India. In the South Seas it is employed in the manufacture of oakum for caulking boats.

Individual fibers are from 0.01 to 0.04 in. in length and from 12 to 24 μ in diameter; the ratio of the length to the thickness is only 35. The cell wall is thick but rather irregularly so; in consequence the lumen has an irregularly indented outline. The points terminate abruptly and are not sharp, and there appear to be a large number of pore canals penetrating the cell wall. On the surface the fiber bundles are occasionally covered with small lens-shaped silicified stegmata, about 15 μ in diameter. These stegmata fuse together on ignition, giving a blister on the ash. If the fiber is boiled with nitric acid previous to its ignition, the stegmata then appear in the ash like yeast cells hanging together in the form of round, siliceous skeletons.

Coir gives the following microchemical reactions: with iodine and sulfuric acid, golden yellow; with aniline sulfate, intense yellow; Schweitzer's reagent does not attack the fiber. These reactions indicate a lignified fiber. According to Schlesinger, coir contains 20.6 per cent of hygroscopic moisture.

Tree Cotton (Malvaceae, *Bombax*)

Besides the cotton derived from the ordinary species of the cotton plant (*Gossypium*), described elsewhere, there is a very similar seed hair or fiber obtained from a plant known as the cotton tree, belonging to the Bombaceae family. The fiber is known as vegetable down or bombax cotton. It grows almost exclusively in tropical countries. Its fiber is soft, but rather weak as compared with ordinary cotton; it is quite lustrous, and it ranges from white to yellowish-brown. The fibers have a length of ¼ to 1¼ in. and a diameter of 20 to 45 μ. Owing to its weakness and lack of elasticity, bombax cotton is not used by itself as a textile fiber. It is occasionally mixed with ordinary cotton and spun into yarn, but it is principally used as a wadding and upholstery material.

In its physical appearance, bombax cotton differs from commercial cotton. It does not possess any convolutions, and it shows irregular thickenings of the cell wall; the fiber usually consists of one cell, though occasionally it has been found to have two. Unlike cotton, the fiber does not grow directly from the seed, but originates at the inner side of the seed capsule.

There are several varieties of plants from which bombax cotton may be obtained. In Brazil it is secured from the *Bombax septenatum* and *B. ceiba,* and the product is known as paina limpa or ceiba cotton. It is also produced in the West Indies and other parts of tropical America.

All the varieties of bombax cotton are very similar in appearance and properties, and it is practically impossible to discriminate between them with any degree of certainty. In *B. ceiba,* the fiber has a length of 0.4 to 0.59 in., whereas in *B. septenatum* the fiber length is ¾ to 1⅛ in., the longest and strongest variety of bombax cotton. *B. malabarica* of south Asia and Africa has fibers from ⅜ to ¾ in. in length, and is known in India as simal cotton or red "silk-cotton."

Other species of *Bombax* plants are *B. cumanensis* of Venezuela, a product known as "lana del tambor" or "lana vegetale"; *B. pubescens* and *B. villosum* come from Brazil; *B. carolinum* from South America; *B. rhodognaphalon* from West Africa, the fiber of which is known as "wild kapok" and is used largely for the stuffing of pillows and mattresses.

Microscopically bombax cotton fiber is seen to consist of a single cell, possessing a cylindrical shape, being rather thick at the base and tapering gradually to the point. The base of the fiber is frequently swollen and exhibits a lacelike structure (Fig. 2). The cell wall is usually very thin, occupying not more than one-tenth the cross-sectional area of the fiber, although the cuticle is well developed. In cross-section the fiber is circular and not flat as that of cotton. It ranges from 20 to 40 μ. The inner canal is partly filled with a dried protoplasmic material.

Bombax cotton differs in chemical constitution from ordinary cotton since it contains a certain amount of lignin. Consequently, it produces a yellow coloration when treated with aniline sulfate or with iodine and sulfuric acid. By these tests it may be distinguished readily from true cotton. Owing to the presence of lignin, the fibers also swell

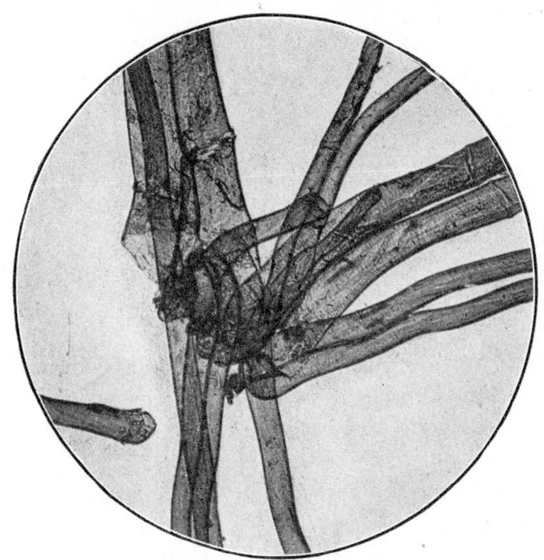

Fig. 2. Bombax cotton. (*Herzog.*)

slightly when treated with Schweitzer's reagent. The fiber from *Bombax ceiba* is distinguished by its decidedly yellowish color.

None of the bombax cottons are pure white but range from pale yellow to brown. The paina limpa is the lightest in color.

Indian Kapok. This is the floss secured from the seeds of *Bombax malabarica,* a large tree indigenous to India, which has been used for many years as a source of floss for stuffing pillows. This kapok was for a time under some disfavor because it was adulterated with the seed fiber from a mildweed, *Calotropis procera.* The government took steps to prevent adulteration, so pure Indian kapok is now available.

Buoyancy, freedom from waterlogging, weight-bearing capacity, and resilience are the principal physical properties required in a material used as kapok. In 1919 the Imperial Institute of London undertook a series of tests to determine the comparative merits of Java (ceiba) kapok and Indian bombax floss. Their findings indicate that in all respects, except resilience, the bombax floss is as satisfactory as the ceiba, and in resilience there is a slight balance in favor of the Javanese material. The bombax floss is slightly more brownish-yellow than the ceiba floss, but in all other respects is very similar. Table 1 gives the principal measurements of both bombax and ceiba floss.

TABLE 1. LENGTH, DIAMETER, AND SPECIFIC GRAVITY OF JAVA AND INDIAN KAPOK

Details	*Java Kapok*	*Indian Kapok*
Length of fiber	0.6 to 1.1 in.	0.7 to 1.1 in.
Diameter of fiber	15 to 25 μ	15 to 35 μ
Specific gravity at 30° C.	0.0388	0.0554

Indian kapok loses 10 per cent of its buoyancy after being in water for 30 days, but, after drying, it fully regains its buoyancy and resilience. Indian kapok and Java kapok are very similar in chemical composition in that they both contain from 61 to 64 per cent cellulose, the balance being composed of lignin and other miscellaneous materials.

Java Kapok (*Ceiba petandra*)

These seed fibers are very similar to the bombax cottons discussed above. It is stated that in the compressed condition kapok in water can support up to 36 times its weight. It has an advantage over cork in that it dries quickly.

Kapok is obtained from southeast Asia and Indonesia. It is very extensively used as an upholstery material. On account of its great buoyancy, freedom from waterlogging, and low specific gravity, it has been employed to a large extent in the manufacture of life buoys and belts, waistcoats, seat covers, and other appliances used for life saving at sea. Java kapok is usually specified in United States Navy requirements.

A life jacket tested in aqueous alcohol (sp. gr. 0.928) contained 1 lb 8.7 oz of kapok, and, since the average floating power of compressed kapok fiber in this medium is equal to fifteen times its weight, the jacket, when submerged, exerts a lifting power of 23 lb. When placed in water and partly submerged by a weight of 19.8 lb, the jacket still supported an extra load of 2.8 lb after 72 hr; after 100 hr it still required an addition of 2.2 lb to submerge it, and after 192 hr the weight required was 1.98 lb.

Uncompressed Java kapok will carry 20 to 30 times its own weight in water, whereas Indian kapok will carry only 10 to 15 times its own weight. Java kapok loses its buoyancy very slowly by immersion in water. A 30-day immersion test showed that it lost only 10 per cent.

Kapok has also been used in surgery as a substitute for absorbent cotton.

Kapok is soft, very brittle and so inelastic that it cracks easily when subjected to spinning, because of the tension and twisting required. It is very resilient; a mattress 3 by 6½ ft requires only 17 to 20 lb of kapok, against 26 to 29 lb of horsehair, 33 to 35 lb of seaweed, or 30 to 60 lb of straw. Furthermore, it will not retain moisture, which is very important for bedding used in moist climates. Kapok mattresses are also very sanitary and quite vermin-proof.

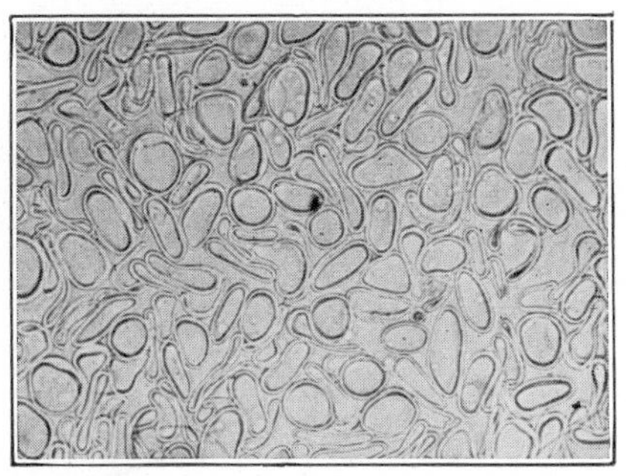

Fig. 3. Cross-sections of kapok fibers. Note thin walls. (×250.) (*Bailey, Jr.*)

In the preparation of kapok, the bolls (or capsules) are picked from the tree by the natives and broken open with mallets. The seed and its fiber are removed and dried in the sun. This is done inside a wire netting in order to prevent the fiber from blowing away. The fiber is separated from the seed by hand. The seed with the fiber is thrown into a basket and stirred with a short stick. The heavy seeds drop to the bottom, and the fiber is removed from the top. This is a slow and expensive process.

Attempts have been made to invent a machine for removing the fiber, but without success, owing to its brittle nature and smooth character. There has been much adulteration of kapok fiber by mixing it with low-grade cotton and cotton waste. The fiber is packed in square bales at a pressure of 150 to 450 lb per in. The bales are covered with jute cloth and fastened with iron bands. Owing to the importance of kapok cultivation in Java, the planters on that island have tried to protect their trade by marking the product "Java kapok," and stamping each bale to indicate the quality, as a guarantee against adulteration.

Exporters state that the United States requires highest grades only; medium grades go to Europe and the lowest to Australia.

The Soerabaya Handelsbereeniging recognizes the following broad descriptions: Good Clean Prime Madura; Good Clean Prime Porrong; Good Clean Prime East Java; Fair Average Quality of the Crop. Another classification is as follows: Fancy grade, with a maximum of 1½ per cent of seeds and dirt; a good marketable quality, with a maximum

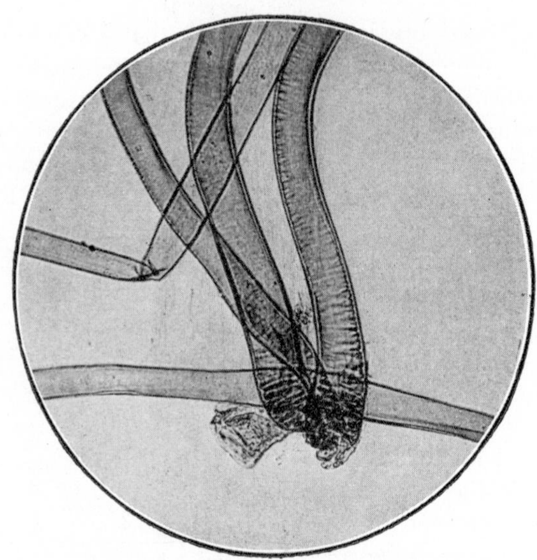

Fig. 4. Root portion of kapok fiber. (*Herzog.*)

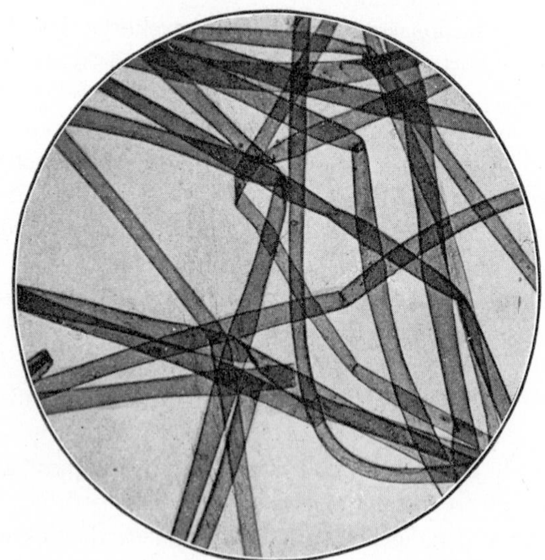

Fig. 5. Kapok fiber. (*Herzog.*)

of 5 per cent of seeds and dirt; lowest quality, with a maximum of 6 per cent of seeds and dirt.

Kapok fiber has a length of 0.3 to 1.25 in., an average of 0.7 in., and a diameter of 30 to 36 μ. It has a beautiful silky luster, is yellowish-brown, and is very light weight. The fiber is generally circular or oval in cross-section (Fig. 3), with a wide lumen and consequently a very thin wall. The resistance of the thin wall to natural conditions is fairly high, but it offers little resistance to the wear and tear of working into yarn. The cross-sections also show some flattened fibers, which are unripe or dead. When examined microscopically kapok is seen to have a tapering cylindrical form. The fiber consists of a single cell with a bulbous base (Fig. 4) and resembles a smooth, transparent, structureless rod, frequently doubled over on itself (Fig. 5).

Like the bombax cottons, kapok contains lignocellulose, and hence gives yellowish-brown coloration with iodine and sulfuric acid. Table 2 shows partial analyses of kapok from different sources.

TABLE 2. Analysis of Different Kapok Samples

Elements	*Lagos Kapok (per cent)*	*Java Kapok (per cent)*	*Seychelleo Kapok (per cent)*
Moisture	9.9	10.9	10.00
Ash	2.8	1.3	2.08
Cellulose	50.3	63.6	61.30

Table 3 is a comparative analysis of cotton and kapok, which shows the chemical differences.[1]

TABLE 3. Cotton and Kapok Compared

Components	*Kapok (per cent)*	*Cotton (per cent)*
Cellulose (approximately)	64	95
Lignin	13	None
Pentosans	23	5
Total	100	100

It was formerly assumed that the impermeability of kapok to water is due to the presence of oils, waxes, and resins in the wall of the fiber. It has been shown that this is not so. The amounts of such constituents vary considerably in different samples, but the variations do not show

[1] Streicher, Lathar, *Kapok and Akon* (1914).

any correlation with the resistance of the fiber to water. The resistance is not appreciably affected by the removal of these substances.

Three laboratory tests are recommended for the rapid determination of quality. The first is an observation as to the degree of lignification of the fiber, by the phloroglucinol test. The best samples do not give any reaction with phloroglucinol, but the lower qualities show a reddish-brown or even a magenta-red coloration, typical of lignocelluloses. The second test consists in the microscopical measurement of the

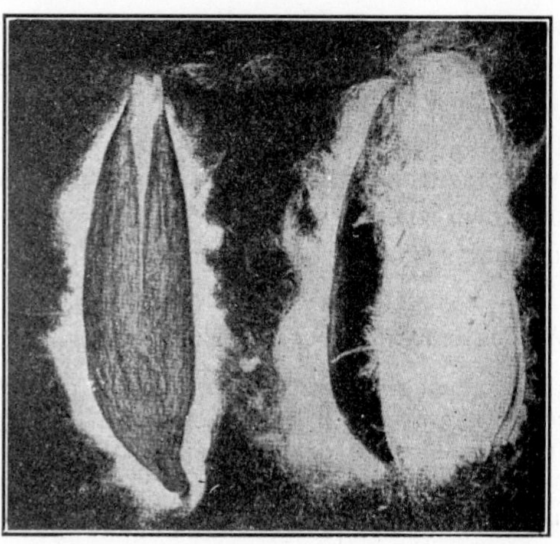

FIG. 6. Seed capsules of kapok.

diameters of the fibers; the more uniform the diameter, the higher the quality of the material. The third test is carried out by floating the fiber on the surface of aqueous alcohol (sp. gr. 0.928) and determining the relative rates of wetting and sinking of the different samples.

Owing to the flammability of kapok, many fire insurance companies have refused to take risks on establishments in which this material is used; others have accepted the risks only at high premiums. The kapok seed yields about 25 per cent of oil, which is used in the manufacture of soap. The pomace, from which the oil has been pressed, is used for fertilizing and for feeding cattle.

Balsa Fiber (*Ochroma pyramidale*)

Fibers from this plant, grown in the West Indies, have a length of 0.2 to 0.59 in., and are thicker (6 to 7 μ) in the middle than at the ends. The cell wall is much thicker than that of bombax cotton, and the fibers are also more lignified. The walls are especially thick at the base and apex, and show the presence of granular matter. The fiber is dark brown. Vegetable down occurs in trade as *édrédon végétale* or *pattes de lièvre,* and it originates mostly in Guadeloupe and Martinique. The typical fibers show a deep yellow color under the microscope or are nearly colorless, flattened, often much folded, with indistinct outline and finely striated surface. The typical fibers have a diameter of 25 to 50 μ. The *ouate végétale* of the French trade is a mixture of fibers of *Bombax, Ochroma,* and *Chorisia.* It is chiefly used for the stuffing of mattresses and cushions.

Kumbi (galgal) (*Cochlospermum gossypium*)

This fiber, grown in India, furnishes fair qualities of vegetable down (Fig. 7). It is used for stuffing cushions.

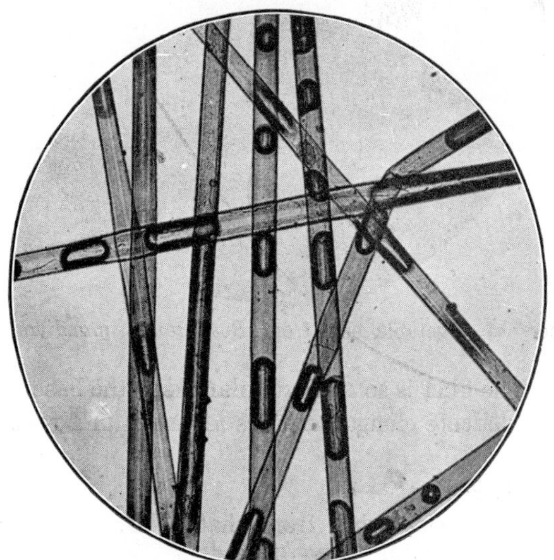

FIG. 7. Fibers of *Cochlospermum gossypium* showing air cells in lumen. (*Herzog.*)

Chorisia speciosa

This fiber is reputed to be excellent for winter mattresses and pillows. The tree is known in Brazil as *arvore de paina.* According to Spon, the plant yields a fiber of which textiles are made that are so much like spun silk in their luster, fineness, and pliability as to be scarcely distinguishable from it.

Beaumontia grandiflora

These fibers (Fig. 8) are probably the best variety of vegetable silk, as the fiber is not only very lustrous but also is pure white. Furthermore, it possesses great tensile strength, and the fibers are easily separated from the seeds. The fibers are from 1.18 to 1.77 in. in length and from 20 to 50 μ in diameter. The cell wall is thin, being about 3.9 μ

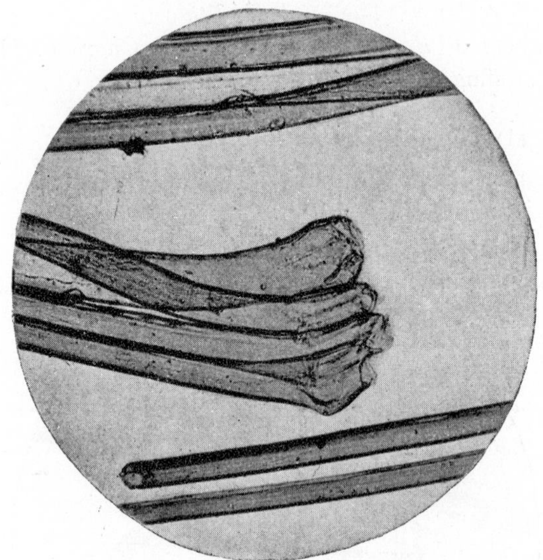

FIG. 8. Fibers of vegetable silk from *Beaumontia grandiflora*. (*Herzog.*)

in thickness. The fiber is somewhat enlarged at the base, and the walls are pierced by delicate elongated pores arranged in a row.

Strophanthus spp.

This fiber differs somewhat from that of *B. grandiflora*. At the base pores occur in the cell walls. This fiber is also not easily removed from the seeds and has a reddish-yellow color.

Milkweeds (*Asclepias*)

These plants afford a seed fiber which is often called "vegetable silk" but is more properly called milkweed floss. Many attempts have been made to use this material as a textile fiber for spinning and weaving, but they have all failed owing to the texture and brittleness of the fibers. In 1941 a new approach to the utilization of this material was developed in Chicago. Boris Berkman conceived and worked out a patent for the cleaning of the material in a gin and then processing the material as a substitute for kapok and other raw materials, which were then scarce. In 1943 a plant was in commercial production.

The genus *Asclepias* contains some 80 distinct species, of which approximately 45 are indigenous to America. There are two, however, which produce the best and most abundant floss—*Asclepias syriaca* and *A. incarnata*. The former is the common milkweed and the latter

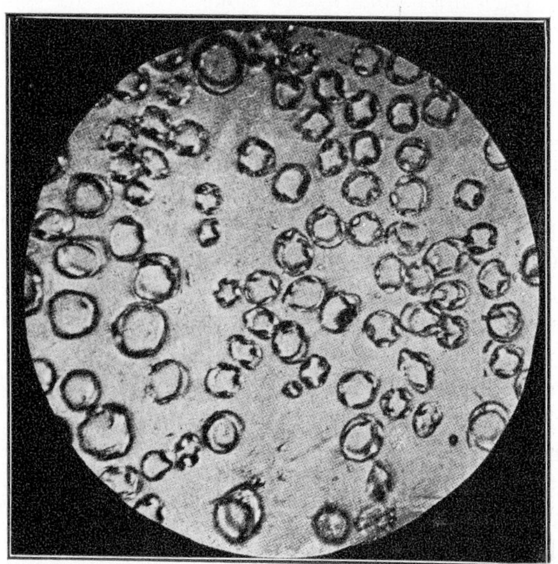

FIG. 9. Cross-sections of *Asclepias* vegetable silk (milkweed).

is the butterfly weed. They are distributed well throughout the United States and grow on practically all types of soil.

These plants may be cultivated or gathered in the wild state. If cultivated, they are perennials and need little attention. The only special care required is to "cure" the seeds before they are planted. They need a considerable length of time to rest before they will germinate. In order to increase germination they may be treated with various stimulants such as ether and carbon tetrachloride. They may be treated by the freezing method, which consists in keeping the seeds in a refrigerator at a subfreezing temperature for some days before sowing. If the seeds are planted in the spring the pods are harvested in October. They are allowed to cure until their moisture content is approximately 30 per cent. They are then ginned to remove the seed, and the floss is further treated and then marketed.

The chief physical quality of this floss is its high degree of luster and softness. When examined under the microscope, the fiber exhibits thickened ridges in the cell wall, which serves to distinguish it from bombax cotton. These ridges or longitudinal thickenings occur from two to five times in each fiber—in some cases very distinct, in others scarcely noticeable. Owing to these ridges, the fibers appear to have indistinct longitudinal striations, thus distinguishing them from other seed hairs. Each fiber consists of a single cell, usually somewhat distended at the base. It has a yellowish white color; it ranges in length from 3/8 to 1 1/8 in. and in diameter from 20 to 50 μ.

Physically, milkweed floss has a high degree of insulative value. The State of Maryland, Department of Health, gave the following figures as a result of tests. A sample had 30 times its weight attached to it and was immersed in hydrant water. It floated for 41 days. Another sample with 33 times its weight attached floated for 44 days. The second sample was then dried and immersed again with the same weight attached to it and it floated for 30 days.

Chemically, milkweed floss is slightly lignified and contains approximately 60 per cent cellulose and from 0.33 to 0.4 per cent extractable oils and waxes. With phloroglucinol, the floss gives a deep red coloration, showing the presence of considerable lignin. The material, when properly processed, finds use in the manufacture of life buoys and belts, waistcoats, and other life saving equipment at sea as well as for padding of pillows and mattresses. Owing to the presence of air spaces between the fibers, when packed, and the entrapped air in the fiber itself, it provides an insulating material of a high order. Furthermore, when the hairs are dewaxed according to the Berkman patent they may be cemented together by an adhesive solution and carded into a felt-like texture.

Calitropis Floss ("Akund")

This is the seed fiber of the *Calitropis* member of the Asclepidaceae family—*C. gigantea* and *C. procera*. These plants are indigenous to southern Asia and Africa, but they have been transported to South America and the Caribbean islands, where they are cultivated. The floss is harvested and recovered by a primitive hand method, as no machinery has been perfected.

The fibers of *Calotropis gigantea* consist of thin-walled colorless cells showing pitted markings at the base; they are 3/4 to 1 1/8 in. in length and 12 to 42 μ in diameter; the cell wall is 1.4 to 4.2 μ in thickness. At the base, the fiber is somewhat enlarged and flattened, though this formation is not so perceptible as in the case of *Beaumontia grandiflora*. It is yellower than the *Asclepias* floss.

Cattail Fibers (Typhaceae)

Cattail fibers are obtained from two common species of the genus *Typha, T. latifolia* and *T. augustifolia*. It is with these two species that the Handicraft Division of the Burgess Battery Co. did experimental work. In 1943 they erected a plant capable of handling some 50,000 spikes per day, producing 1200 lb of finished floss.

The heads of the cattail are gathered when the floss is mature and the seeds are ripe. Harvesting consists in cutting the spikes; one man can gather between 2000 and 7000 per day, depending upon stand, condition of the ground, and other factors. The gathering season in the North is from August through February. After the spikes are gathered, they are dried by a combination of sun and forced air until approximately 70 per cent of the moisture is removed. The next operation is to feed the dry and partly decomposed spikes into a hammer mill, provided with an exhaust fan, which blows the fuzz, stems, leaves, pollen, and other trash into a settling chamber. From this chamber the fibers with the attached seeds are blown through numerous baffle boards, which serve to detach many of the seeds from the seed hairs. The material is discharged through a long spout into another settling chamber, which consists of mosquito netting and a cement floor. From this settling chamber the fluff is transferred to the baling press, where it is compressed into 50-lb bales ready for storage or shipment.

The fibers are of a dull gray color and are soft and fine. Their average length is 3/8 to 1 in. and their diameter approximately 15 μ. Under the microscope each bundle of fibers appears like a parachute, i.e., there is a central fiber to which other fibers are attached; when the seed is dry and the wind catches it, the side fibers or ribs open out like a parachute. Each fiber is more or less round in cross-section, although some fibers are irregular in shape. This is due to being gathered when immature, which tends to collapse the fibers. (See Figs. 10 and 11.)

The physical properties show the fiber to be a good insulating material, both for heat and sound. It has a very high buoyancy. The fibers themselves have a weight of a fraction of a pound per cubic foot.

A series of tests demonstrate that the fibers possess good sustaining power. One pound of material packed at a density of 3 lb per cu ft

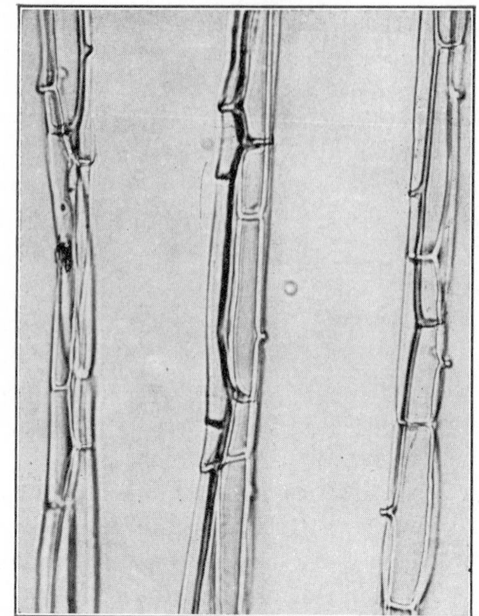

FIG. 10. Typha fiber. Longitudinal view. (×500.) (*Krauss.*)

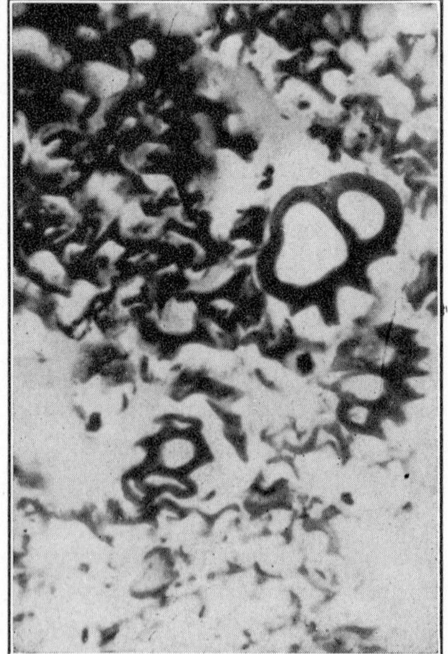

FIG. 11. Dyed typha fiber, cross-section. (×500.) (*Krauss.*)

submerged in fresh water showed the average buoyancy per cubic foot in Table 4, which compares favorably with kapok. The fibers seem to be highly cutinized [2] as can be seen from Table 5.

TABLE 4. AVERAGE BUOYANCY OF CATTAIL FIBER

After 48 hr	52.25 lb
After 96 hr	48.55 lb
After 144 hr	44.25 lb
After 192 hr	42.00 lb

TABLE 5. CHEMICAL ANALYSIS OF CATTAIL FIBER

Components	*Per Cent*
Ether extract (fat and cutin)	3.85
Ash	0.46
Lignin	19.16
Cellulose and hemicellulose, by difference	76.53
Total	100.00

The percentage of lignin is undoubtedly the cause of the brittleness of the fibers. Typha is sold as Grade 1 and Grade 2. Grade 1 is a mixture by weight of 40 per cent seed and 60 per cent fiber. Grade 2 contains 20 per cent less seed. The principal uses are in the manufacture of buoyant materials, in heat insulation, and in the acoustic trade.

Other Seed Fibers

Other plant fibers which have received attention are the fibers growing on certain cacti belonging to the genus *Cereus*. These fibers are reddish-brown, have a rather harsh feel, and are brittle. They average 1 in. in length and under the microscope appear nearly round in cross-section, although many seem to have become flattened and have an irregular shape. The fibers are often folded over upon themselves. They are best suited for padding and for heat insulation.

Pulu fiber can also be classed under the general name of "vegetable down." It is the hair obtained from the stems of tree ferns, more especially *Cibotium glaucum* of the Hawaiian Islands. The fibers are lustrous golden-brown, very soft, and not especially strong. They have

[2] Cutinize, to change into cutin, which is a waxy substance combined with cellulose forming cutocelluloses, which are nearly impervious to water. Cutin differs from ordinary cellulose in staining yellow instead of blue when treated with sulfuric acid and iodine.

a length of about 2 in. and are composed of a series of very flat cells, pressed together in a ribbonlike form (Fig. 12).

The fiber is only employed as an upholstery material and is never spun. Similar fibers are also obtained from *Cibotium barometz, C. menziesii,* and *C. chamissoi; menziesii* produces the best fiber.

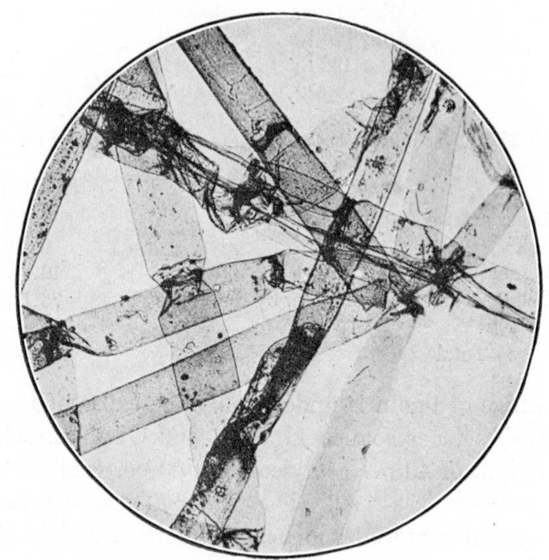

FIG. 12. Pulu fiber from *Cibotium glaucum.* (*Herzog.*)

PLANT BRUSH FIBERS

The brush fibers are in a class by themselves, as they possess different properties than are required of fibers for other uses. They must be stiff but not brittle and must possess a high degree of flexibility. A number of fibers are used for this purpose, most of which belong to the Palmaceae (palms), although some belong to the *Agave* and *Yucca* groups. The principal ones only will be discussed here.

Piassava or Bass

This fiber is derived from several palms as follows (see Fig. 13).

Bahia bass, a member of the piassava group of hard bast fibers, is obtained from the palm *Attalia funifera.* It grows wild and profusely in the low swamp lands and in the sandy soil of the regions to the south of Bahia, in northern Brazil, and also extends into parts of Venezuela. It is customarily called Bahia fiber in the brush trade, although it is also known as piassava, piassaba, and piacaba.

The adult palm has feathery, pulpy leaves, and the trunk with leaves can attain a height of 30 to 35 ft. Fiber is removed from the leaf stalks by water retting and is pounded to remove pithy, scaly growth. It is then dried. The combing and cleaning follow, preparatory to baling of the fiber for export. With very little if any selection, the thick coarse fibers, along with the short or fine, are baled together in a crude, long bale. A small portion of the fiber is cut to length, sorted for stiffness and thickness, then baled for export, in bales averaging 112 lb each. For local consumption the natives use the finer fibers to make cordage products.

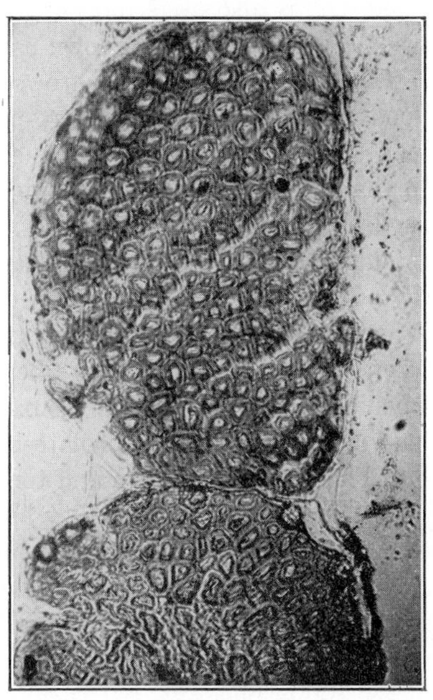

FIG. 13. Cross-section of *piassava*. (×230.) (*Krauss*.)

The fiber is strong, hard, smooth, of an impermeable texture, and ranges in color from a light brown to a deep brown-red. In texture it can vary from the coarse butt end, $3/16$ in. in diameter, to the fine hair-like tip, and runs from 3 to 20 ft in length. The length of the cells ranges from 0.011 to 0.035 in. Even when moistened the fiber retains its elasticity.

Before the crudely baled, unsorted fiber can be further processed for brush or broom making, all of it is subjected to a very careful hand selection, sorting out the extra fine, fine, medium fine, and other grades down to the extra coarse butts. Each grade has a particular use in the making of a fine brush or coarse, heavy-duty, industrial broom. Then the fiber is cut to the length desired, oiled, combed, and mixed on special machines, and the resultant product is of uniform color, stiffness and quality. To do this all the shortest fibers, woolly bark, pith, and other wastes must be removed. The uniform dressed fiber is a rich brownish-red, enhanced by the use of oil, which also serves to prevent drying out and further improves its later use in brushes.

Because of its desirable texture, color, and stiffness, Bahia fiber is easily blended with other fibers, and its use in mixing is practically unlimited, since it contains no strawlike material. It is exported from Brazil in quantities ranging from 2000 tons to over 5000 tons annually, making it one of the most important South American fibers. Its use in the brush industry covers a wide range, from excellent clothes brushes to the heavy-duty, durable industrial sweeper brushes.

Para piassava is obtained from the palm *Leopoldinia piassaba.* The palm grows in northern Brazil adjoining the Bahia piassaba area, i.e., the valleys of the Amazon River and its tributaries. The fiber is customarily known as "monkey bass," although the name of "Para piassava" is also used and possibly comes from the fact that the port of export was formerly known as Para.

The palm plant usually grows on sandy soils which are subject to floods; it resembles, in many respects, the Bahia piassava. The pulpy leaves are 8 to 15 ft long, and the fiber is obtained in a manner similar to that used to secure Bahia piassava. Usually the older leaves are used for industrial fiber purposes.

The fiber, when cleaned and scraped, measures from 2 to 6 and 7 ft in length. It is used locally to make ropes, baskets, and twine. Whereas Bahia piassaba is impermeable and retains its elasticity even when wet, the monkey bass fiber is smoother and loses its elasticity when moistened. There is a similarity in color, although the monkey bass is more of a rich chocolate-brown; the fiber ranges from a coarse butt end to a hairlike tip and tends to be brittle.

Brittleness and permeability handicap the monkey bass in competition with the Bahia fiber in the brush fiber market.

African piassava comes from the palm *Raphia vinifera,* which grows in the valleys along the Atlantic Coast of central Africa between the equator and 10° N. latitude. It is obtained in much the same manner as the Bahia piassava, but is carefully graded. The grades are named after the port from which the fiber is shipped and, although all are more or less similar, each has its distinguishing characteristics. The principal grades are as follows:

Sherbro	Monrovia	Cape Palma	Prime Sherbro
Sulimah	Grand Bassa	Opobo	Sinoe
Cape Mount	Rivercess	Calabar	

Calabar or flexible bass, as it is sometimes called, is the most desirable. In comparison of weight to bulk it is the heaviest of all grades and is also the coarsest in texture. The fiber is hard-surfaced, oval in cross-section, has a core, is uniformly dark brown, and ranges in length from 2 to 5 ft. It contains a small proportion of straw fibers. Owing to the small output (under 200 tons per yr), this grade is mostly used in blends. It is so flexible that it can be blended with more brittle fibers and is used in stapled or drawn work. Taken by itself, Calabar makes the highest quality fiber broom. It is often blended with Bahia for such heavy-duty work as railroad track brooms and rotary street sweepers.

Opobo piassava is in general the same as Calabar but is slightly shorter in length. Sherbro is probably the most important grade, as it can be obtained in large quantities. It is lighter and less uniform in color than Calabar; is also rougher, rounder, less flexible, and lighter in weight, but is not brittle. It is tough, fairly uniform in size of strands, and contains less straw than other grades, except Calabar. Prime Sherbro is a slightly different grade shipped from the same port. It is a smoother, darker, flatter fiber than Sherbro and is very uniform in color. Its average length is under 4 ft, and the size of the fiber ranges from fine to the coarseness of Calabar. It is easily sorted and produces a very high-class finished product .

Sulimah piassaba is about the same as regular Sherbro, although shipped from a different port, but may be a little less regular in quality.

Cape Mount is a stiffer stock than either of the above two and reaches as much as 6 ft in length. It is more brittle, less uniform in texture, and not as tough as Sherbro. In color it is about the same as Sherbro, and contains more straw.

Grand Bassa and *Monrovia* are the least uniform of all the grades. They run in length up to 5 ft; each bundle contains very light yellow strawlike strands and stiff, coarse black fibers as hard and tough as Calabar.

Cape Palma is the softest and shortest grade, attaining a length of 3 to 4 ft. It is a round, pithy, uniform, light brown fiber and is lighter in ratio of weight to bulk than any of the other grades.

Palmyra and Bassine (*Borassus flabellifera*)

These are obtained from the palm which has a fanlike leaf and is indigenous to Ceylon and the eastern coast of India and Burma. The leaf stalks are beaten to loosen the fiber from the woody pulp, which is then scraped off and the fibers dried in the sun. Palmyra is the cinnamon-brown fiber obtained from the leaf stalk, which is not dressed, graded, or prepared. It is tied in bundles 3 or 4 in. in diameter, roughly butted at one end, and packed in heavily compressed bundles for shipping.

For convenience in the brush industry Palmyra is sorted into three different lengths designated by different shippers as short, medium, and long, #1, #2, #3, A, B, C, or similar designations. The lengths range from 9 to 12 in. for the short, 12 to 14 in. for the medium, and 14 to 16 in. for the long, with perhaps a few bundles as much as 18 in. (The lengths are the overall lengths and not lengths to which sizes can be cut solid.) Palmyra fiber from the various districts varies slightly in color and stiffness. The principal districts from which palmyra is shipped are Malabar, Tuticorin, and Coconada. The fiber from each district bears the name of that district.

Bassine is palmyra fiber which has been selected for stiffness and has been dyed, dressed, and cut to specific sizes. There are three principal qualities in which bassine is prepared:

Prima Cuta, the stiff outside fiber from the leaf stem.

Segundas, the soft fiber obtained from the inside of the leaf stem.

Ungraded, unsorted palmyra, dyed and dressed, but obtained from the entire leaf stem.

Different shippers have different marks for various grades, such as Vavasseur's HV for the stiff, G for the soft, and XLA for the ungraded.

Kittool Fiber (*Caryota urens*)

This fiber is obtained from the petioles and the older broad sheath bases of the palm "kittul," as it is called by the natives. It is widely distributed throughout the hotter parts of India, the Malay Peninsula, and Indonesia. The fiber varies greatly in texture, from very fine hairlike strands to heavy coarse strands about ⅛ in. in diameter. It is used very widely by the natives, in the regions where it grows, in the fabrication of fish lines, nets, and mats. The natural color of the fiber is brownish black and when oil-dyed, as used in the brush trade, has a very glossy black appearance. The individual fiber strands are very tough and are made into large cables or hawsers for tying up ocean steamers. It is imported as packed by the natives, tied in bundles 3 or 4 in. in diameter and ranging in length from 6½ to 28 in. It is largely used in the manufacture of scrubbing, horse, and brewery brushes and the like. It is much more expensive than other fibers adapted to the same uses.

Palmetto (*Sabal palmetto*)

This plant is known also as the cabbage palm because of the shape of the edible heart contained therein. It is a member of the palm family growing wild throughout the coastal regions of the United States Atlantic seaboard, from the Carolinas through Florida; it is also found in the Bahamas, Cuba, and Mexico. The Sabal palmetto is known to the Seminole Indians by the name of "tah-lah-kul-kee."

Aside from the broomcorn produced in the middle western United States, it is the only brush fiber produced commercially in this country.

The palm, having a trunk 15 to 35 ft in height, is fan shaped, and the fiber is obtained from the base, or "boots," surrounding the terminal bud. In time, with the growing of the upper part of the trunk, the lower part of the trunk becomes smooth and turns brownish.

For the manufacture of brushes the boots, averaging about 3 ft in length, are obtained by cutting the palm at the base and opening the trunk. By cutting the boot away from the palm, the plant will continue to live and develop. The coarser and tougher fibers are obtained from the well-developed pulpy leaves. The boots are cut and brought into a mill, where they are thoroughly steamed to soften the hard pulpy mass surrounding the fiber within the boot. By a hackling and combing operation the fiber is separated from the pulp and pithy material, and then is oiled. A seasoning operation follows, and the resultant fiber, almost cylindrical in shape, of a rich, reddish-brown color, measures from 500 to 1000 μ in diameter and from 8 to 25 in. in length. It is very resistant to the deteriorating action of water, and is highly elastic and durable.

For local purposes the leaves are used for making mats and baskets. For brush-fiber purposes the fiber is commonly known under the name of "palmetto" fiber. After a thorough mixing and blending it is a uniform reddish-brown durable product, used in the manufacture of good-quality clothes brushes.

Palma (*Samuela carnerosa*)

Palma is a valuable fiber originating in Mexico and used extensively in the cordage and brush fiber business. It is also known as ixtle de palma and palma zamandoque. This plant grows extensively throughout the states of Zacatecas, San Luis Potosí, Coahuila, and Nuevo León, where it is abundant in the central plains of the Sierra Madre, ranging from 4000 to 9000 ft in altitude. The trunk is usually 5 to 15 ft tall, on the top of which grows a symmetrically shaped rosette of leaves very similar in appearance to the ixtle de lechuguilla (tula ixtle) leaves, although of a darker green color. They are also longer than tula ixtle, ranging from 2 to 4 ft in length and from ½ to 3 in. in width. The leaves used for fiber purposes are those taken from the central cogollo; they range from 15 to 30 in. in length.

The species is remarkably hardy and endures severe heat as well as frosts. If allowed to bloom, the plants have clusters of beautiful creamy white, large, bell-shaped flowers, which are highly prized as food.

Since the plant is so tall, the clean fibers require a long-handled "arrancador," or stick with an iron ring at one end, to remove the central cogollo, the same as with the tula ixtle. The tula ixtle plants customarily grow close together, but the palma plants form huge forests in some regions and are spaced far apart.

The cleaning of the palma fiber differs from that of the tula ixtle in that the palma fiber is very tough and requires a preboiling operation. The leaves from the central cogollo are collected in the fields, then brought to a little town. Here the leaves are carefully placed in a crudely made tank. They are covered with some dried palma leaves, weighted down with stones, and the tank filled with water. A slow fire is maintained under the tank for about 3 hr, after which the contents are allowed to remain from 8 to 10 hr.

The water is then drained, and the boiled, dark-colored, brownish leaves are removed and allowed to dry for several hours in the sun. The scraping operation is similar to that applied to tula ixtle. After the fiber is scraped it is tied into loose bundles and spread in the sun to dry.

Attempts to clean this fiber by a mechanical process have failed, owing to the inability of machines to handle the shorter length fibers and also to the variable pressure required in the scraping operation.

The fiber varies considerably in quality, according to the region from which it comes, as well as the care taken in the boiling and scraping processes. For cordage purposes the undesirable red runners and sticks are not removed, but their removal is very essential for brush fibers. This red runner is the tough outside edge of each leaf. Laboratory tests conducted at the University of Mexico show that palma fiber by weight has the ability to absorb 95.7 per cent oil and has a stretch of 10 per cent. The breaking point per gram is equal to 7.7 kilos. The number of fibrils per fiber diameter is 59, with each cell 2.42 μ in length.

Common palma, used for cordage purposes, is very seldom selected, and all grades and lengths without selection are packed in the bales. A large portion of the palma for cordage purposes, amounting to somewhat more than a million kilos per month, is consumed within Mexico. The remaining portion, or probably half a million kilos, is exported.

Specially selected palma is produced in a small region and state around San Luis Potosí. Because of the requirements of the brush fiber business, this palma is selected for color and cleanliness, as well as for packing. But the production of this high-quality material is small and varies between two and six carloads monthly.

Production of palma fiber will vary considerably, depending entirely upon the demand for the fiber, the prices paid to the cleaners, and the fact that other more profitable fibers growing in the same region will attract the scraper. The scraper may find it more profitable to collect the rubber plant guayule or the candelilla wax plant than to scrape the palma fiber.

Export of the commodity is government controlled; because of the World War II demand for this fiber, its price on the American market rose from 4½¢ per lb shortly before the war to 8½¢ per lb. For specially selected palma, used in the brush trade, a premium is paid.

Yucca Pita (*Yucca treculeana*)

This fiber is known commercially as "palma pita" or "pita." It is fairly limited in its region of growth and is found in the warm climates and sandy soil around Cuatro Cienegas and Monclova, Coahuila, in northern Mexico. In color and length of leaves it is similar to the palma plant. The fiber extracted from the central cogollo is very dark colored and differs from the palma fiber in that it is thinner, of harsher texture, and contains no "sticks" or red runners.

Used by both the cordage and brush fiber industries, it usually bears a trade name representing the producer's initials. Pita palma fiber is produced only in response to orders, which usually average about 180 tons per month.

Zamandoque (*Hesperaloe funifera*)

This is a fiber produced in Mexico during World War I but not now being exploited. It grows wild in the warmer climates of the states of San Luis Potosí, Nuevo León, and Coahuila. Its leaves are exceptionally long, measuring from 4 to 6 ft. The fiber, which is dark brown, is collected from the outer leaves only and ranges from 40 to 60 in. in length.

Tula Ixtle

The name "ixtle" is supposed to have been derived from the early Mexican Indian tribe of Nahuatlans, whose word "ixtli" means a plant giving fiber. Today the word "ixtle" (pronounced issel) is commonly used to denote fibers known as Tampico fiber, tula and lechuguilla, all derived from the genus *Agave*. Tula ixtle is derived from the leaves of *Agave lophantha* var. *poselgaeri,* formerly known as *Agave lechuguilla.*

Lechuguilla, which literally means "little lettuce," was at an early date included in the *agaves.* To the early Indians it meant the source of food, clothing, drink, and sustenance. Inasmuch as the larger proportion of exportations of this fiber is made through the port of Tampico, on the eastern seaboard, it is named Tampico fiber.

The tula ixtle plant thrives mostly in the north central plateau of Mexico. The plant also grows farther south in the states of Hidalgo, Querétaro, and Oaxaca (toward the Central American border), but in this section it has not been commercially produced. The plant grows also in the southwestern part of Texas and in New Mexico and Arizona. From a commercial point of view, all of the fiber obtained grows in the five important producing states of Nuevo León, Coahuila, San Luis Potosí, Zacatecas, and Tamaulipas, included in a region stretching from San Luis Potosí on the south to the Rio Grande Valley on the north, close to the eastern plateau of Mexico. To the east it stretches as far as the city of Victoria, Tamaulipas, and to the west it extends as far as the city of Torreón, Coahuila. The larger portion of this region lies in the temperate zone and ranges in altitude from 3000 to 6000 ft.

The tula ixtle grows wild throughout this region, which is a semidesert, the plant finding sustenance in the rocky, limestone-rich soil. Aside from numerous cacti and yucca plants and a few mesquite, this entire arid region has very little vegetation. Rains seldom occur, and, when they do, they come usually in torrential downpours.

The quality of the fiber obtained from this hardy plant varies considerably in response to dry or rainy seasons and to types of soil—rocky, mountainous soil, and loose loam soil.

For commercial purposes the fiber is extracted only from the central spike, called cogollo, which contains anywhere from 6 to 15 individual leaves and which is the new and tender part of the plant. Under favorable conditions ordinarily the first crop of fiber leaves can be harvested when the plant is approximately 6 to 10 yr of age, and when the central part contains leaves which range from 6 to 20 in. in length. The outside leaves are seldom cut or used for fiber-scraping purposes because this fiber lacks life and the leaf itself is very difficult to scrape because of its dryness. In normal times the plant produces one full-grown cogollo a year, and in a rainy season it will produce even two cogollos annually.

The color of the entire plant varies from light to dark green, the young center part being usually somewhat lighter. The plant grows in a symmetrical shape, and the leaves on the outside of the central heart vary in length from 10 to 20 in. The leaf itself does not grow straight but usually curves outward at the center and throughout its width. Along the edges are small thorns as much as ½ in. in length. If allowed to continue growing, the leaves on the outside of the central heart gradually separate from it and begin to fall lower and lower, as new leaves grow in their place. These outside secondary and tertiary leaves eventually wither and die. In the drier seasons the butt end of the leaves, those within the central trunk of the plant, become tougher to a point where they grow a coarse, woody end, sometimes as much as 2 in. in length; these are called "needles."

If the center heart, or cogollo, is left uncut it grows into a stalk some 4 or 5 ft in height, producing a large cluster of cream-white flowers. Once the plant has flowered, it dies. The central stalk becomes a hard, woody stick, which is used by the Mexicans in building roofs for their huts.

The scraping and collecting of the fiber are controlled by a government-subsidized organization, with its respective cooperative societies covering the various ixtle-producing regions. The ixtle cleaner, or scraper, called a tallador, gathers and scrapes the fiber.

The first step in producing the fiber is the making of the rudimentary implements used in the gathering and scraping of the fiber. The Indian tallador makes an ixtle fiber netting from home-made rope in the form of a basket, called a "huajaca," which is used for collecting the cut ixtle cogollos. The "arrancador," which is used to remove the central heart of the plant, is made from a wooden stick, or limb, 3 to 6 ft long, with an iron ring fastened to one end. The basket ordinarily holds from 44 to 66 lb of the cogollos and requires 1 to 2 hr to fill.

Once his basket is filled, the tallador begins on the most difficult part, the removal of the fiber from the leaf.

Some operators remove the red spiny growth along the edges of the leaves before beginning the scraping operation; others remove it while scraping. A basketful of the cogollos yields, when scraped, from 4.4 to 6.6 lb of greenish, moist fiber. The average cogollo weighs about ¼ lb, and if the scraper continues his daily operation it will mean that in the course of 8 to 9 hr he will scrape and clean from 13 to 18 lb of fiber.

Inasmuch as the average fiber content of the leaf is only 6 to 8 per cent by weight, it would mean an unnecessary transportation problem if the cogollos were first cut in the fields, and then later scraped at some distant point. For this reason the tallador solves the problem by scraping the leaves in the field.

In some regions the ixtle plant grows alongside various types of yuccas, which produce other types of fiber and plants producing candelilla wax and rubber. The ixtle tallador may choose that plant which is easiest for him to handle and which will give him the greatest income.

Each ixtle tallador gathers the fiber after a week's work and takes it to the nearest central collection station, where he receives either cash or merchandise for his product. These collection stations, usually situated in some small town or on some little ranch, are the centers where the crudely scraped ixtle is collected, purchased, selected, and sorted for length and color, tied into bundles, and baled for export.

The ixtle tallador finds considerable use for the fiber. He usually makes his own ropes for tethering cattle, his small fiber bag for carrying his personal goods, sacks and bags, fancy adornments, rugs, homemade brushes, and saddle blankets.

The ixtle fiber is not at all uniform in its quality. It varies in color from creamish to a green and in length from 7 to 20 in. Also it varies from a stiff, hard, round tapered fiber to a fine, soft fiber. Laboratory experiments at the University of Mexico show an average weight of 0.25 gram, and an extension of 5 per cent for the fiber. Its percentage of water by weight, when dry, is 10.9 per cent, and its ability to absorb oil is 40 per cent. The number of cells per fiber diameter is 160, with a length of 93 μ.

At present, all grades of ixtle fiber exported by the government-subsidized organization are graded according to length and color. Mexico No. 1 is 12 in. and up, good color, and from any of the ixtle-producing regions. Mexico No. 2 is 9 to 12 in. long of the same quality. Mexico No. 3 (also called San or Coa) is a poor quality, mostly short and stained. In addition there are several marks representing excellent quality or very poor quality, but the production is very small and comes only from very limited regions. Approximately 15 to 20 per cent of the ixtle fiber is consumed within Mexico for cordage purposes; the remainder is exported. The production of this fiber varies considerably according to prices paid to the ixtle scraper, the demand in foreign markets, and supplies on hand. The production figure varies anywhere from 10,000 to 18,000 tons annually. By far the larger portion of this fiber consumed outside of Mexico is used for brush-making and sells at a price ranging from 7½ to 9¢ per lb, for the baled crude fiber placed at the United States borders.

Ixtle de Jaumave (*Agave heterocantha*)

This fiber, similar in many respects to the tula ixtle, is obtained from *Agave heterocantha,* formerly known as *Agave funkiana.* The fiber is obtained from plants which grow in a very limited area, the small town of Jaumave, Tamaulipas. The leaves of the plant are similar to those of the tula ixtle plant but are straighter and longer, ranging from 20 to 40 in. in length. The fiber is extracted and cleaned in the same manner as tula ixtle. The fiber is lighter in color and much softer and thinner. Because it is found in a very limited region, it is much more uniform in its quality. It is graded and sold according to length and color. Laboratory experiments at the University of Mexico show a fiber longer in average length than the ixtle, of the same extension, with a percentage of water, by weight, of 9.7 per cent, and an ability to absorb oil, by weight, of 39.7 per cent. The number of cells per fiber diameter is 112, and the cell length is 104 μ.

Jaumave fiber is produced at the rate of 80 to 130 tons per month, and practically all is exported for use in making brushes. Some ixtle fiber is very similar in all characteristics to jaumave. Prices paid for jaumave fiber are a little higher than those paid for ixtle fiber.

Guapilla (*Agave falcata*)

This fiber is known either as guapilla or huapilla. It grows throughout the states of Nuevo León, Coahuila, Tamaulipas, San Luis Potosí, and Zacatecas, in the north central section of Mexico. The leaves from which the fiber is extracted are very long, sometimes as much as 40 in., very narrow, not exceeding 3/8 in. in cross-section, and triangular in shape.

The guapilla fiber ranges in length from 20 to 30 in., is dark brown, quite brittle, light in weight, hard, and contains no sticks. It is obtained from the small central heart, although the outer leaves are also used. A laboratory test at the University of Mexico reported its average weight at 4.4 oz, with an extension of 5 per cent and a breaking point per gram-meter of 8.68 grams. This fiber could easily serve as a substitute for palma or pita fibers, but it is not being commercially produced.

Zacaton or Rice Root (*Epicampes macroura*)

This brush fiber comes from the roots of a grass. Its region of growth extends into the southern part of Mexico and into Guatemala, although only in certain portions of the higher altitudes of Mexico is the fiber produced commercially. A similar bunchgrass known as Venetian grass, or Italian rice root, comes from *Andropogon gryllas.*

Growing in large bunches, the plant has blades from 20 to 50 in. long, which are of no commercial use. The roots, which are used for fiber purposes, are crinkly, canary yellow or yellowish brown, tough and undulated, and very brittle when dry. Each bundle selected for stiffness and color contains fibers ranging from 8 to 18 in. in length, butted at one end.

Where the rice root is produced, it grows wild, around the base of dormant volcanoes, although some attempts have been made to cultivate it in the state of Veracruz. This region is 7000 ft and more in altitude and is known as the cold country. The strong winds, over a period of time, have carried a fine, siltlike sand from the lowlands and deposited it among the fissures and crevices caused by the volcanic lava.

To remove the rice root plant and to obtain the useful root fibers, the native employs a crude, homemade, V-shaped tree limb, one end of which is placed under the ground directly beneath the head of the plant. Carefully and forcefully, with pressure exerted on the other end of the implement, he extricates the plant. The blades of grass, growing above ground, are removed and the root is placed in a basket.

The roots are carefully washed to remove the excess soil and are then rubbed over some rough object to remove the tough outer bark. They are then dried in the sun and taken to a collection station, where they are subjected to burning sulfur fumes for several hours. Again the roots are washed and selected according to length and quality and are given another sulfur fume treatment to improve the color. The bundles are removed, classified, selected for quality and grade, and packed in bales weighing 112 lb each. The washed, crude fiber is used locally for making crude scrub brushes.

Rice root from different regions is of varying qualities, and customarily each grade or mark bears the producer's name. Within each grade there are the usual percentages of qualities ranging from Supreme and Superior down to the Extra, Fine, Medium, and Ordinary. Most shipments are made through the port of Veracruz, on the Atlantic seaboard of Mexico.

Miscellaneous Brush Fibers

Mexico produces several fibers which are useful in making brushes and brooms but are produced in such small quantities as to be of little importance. Among these is a type of plant growing in the northern part of Mexico known as jirica, or *Nolina microcarpa*. Another is a genus of palm growing in the tropical climates of the central part of

Mexico, *Raphia vinifera*. It is principally used in the building of huts and homes; some brooms are made from the thinner stalks.

Broomcorn, *Holcus sorphum*, used for brooms and whisks, grows through the central part of the United States plains and to some extent in Mexico.

In addition, there is a type of fiber obtained from woody stems such as rattan (*Calamus* sp.), split bamboo (*Bambusa* sp.), and others coming from the Orient, including the Chinese palm fiber from southern China, *Trachycarpus excelsa*.

OTHER PLANT FIBERS

Spanish Moss (*Tillandsia usneoides*)

Spanish moss is not a true moss but belongs to the same family of plants as the pineapple (Bromeliaceae). A true epiphyte (air plant), it grows on either dead or live trees and on telephone poles and wires.

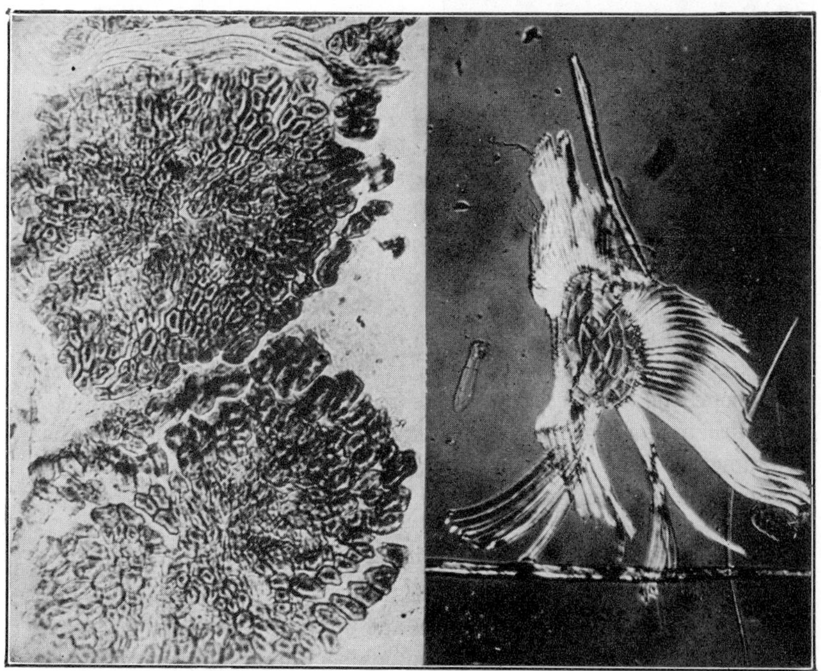

FIG. 14. Spanish moss (*Tillandsia usneoides*). *Right,* scale from outer surface of fibers in polarized light (×85); *left,* cross-section of fiber bundles (×230). (*Textile Fiber Atlas.*)

It is distributed from the Dismal Swamp of Virginia south and westward to Florida, Louisiana, and Texas. Other species grow south into Mexico and Central America.

It is commonly prepared by collecting it into heaps, which are wetted by throwing water on them. It is left this way for 2 or 3 months and turned over, so that the center of the pile will be on the outside. It is then again soaked with water and left for 2 to 4 weeks. It is occasionally examined to see that it does not ferment too rapidly and thus weaken the fiber. When the gray outer covering slips easily, it is spread out to dry, after which it is run through a sort of gin. It is then raked back and forth over a latticework floor to free the black fiber from bark and other foreign matter, after which it is sorted and baled for market. (See Fig. 14.)

Fig. 15. Redwood bark (*Sequoia sempervirens*) showing phloem parenchyma and cell structure. (*Inst. of Paper Chemistry.*)

Spanish moss is used principally for stuffing mattresses and upholstered furniture and as stuffing for cushions and upholstery for automobiles, railway cars, and airplanes. It is a black fiber, very retentive of its high resiliency, and is very curly when properly prepared Under the microscope the cross-section shows it to be composed of polygonal cells with a much greater diameter in one direction than the other. The lumen is large and open It is lignified and thus has a harsh feel. It is not readily bleached or dyed.

Redwood Bark Fiber (*Sequoia sempervirens*)

This comes from the bark of the California redwood tree. The bark of the redwood is a complex tissue made up of at least four cell types: the sieve cells, phloem parenchyma, phloem fiber (better known as redwood bark fiber), and phloem ray parenchyma, in addition to cork cells.

The redwood bark fibers make up about 25 to 35 per cent of the bark by weight. They are arranged in tangential, uniseriate rows (marked

A in Fig. 15) which occur rather regularly. It is impossible to determine with accuracy the frequency of formation of these fibers in the older section of the bark, because of the formation of bark periderm and the sloughing off of the outer dead bark. There is some indication that approximately one row is formed each year, particularly during the early years. It seems more probable, however, that the number

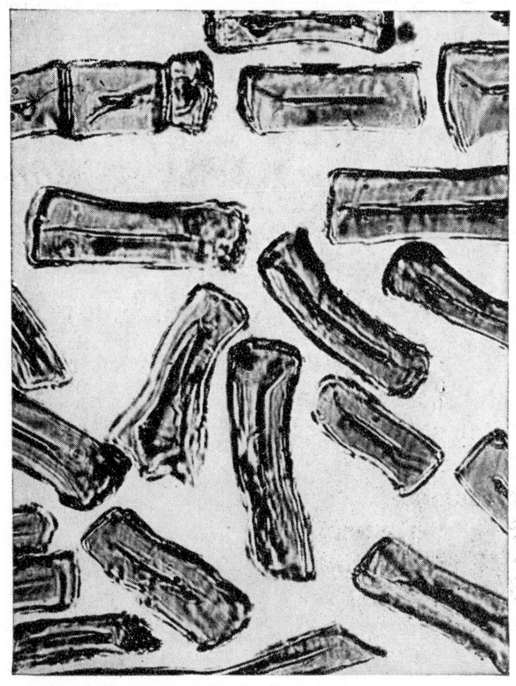

Fig. 16. Cross-section of redwood bark fiber. (×500.) (*Textile Fiber Atlas.*)

of rows and dimensions of the fibers are dependent upon environmental factors.

The fibers are recovered from the peeled bark by running the bark strips through a mill of the type of a hammer mill to loosen the bundles from the other cells and amorphous material. The macerated bark is then passed through a textile cleaning operation, which separates the fibers from waste material. The fibrous material produced commercially is sold either as insulation (this consists of fiber filaments or strands 1 in. or more in length with some adhering shorter cells and binder) or is distributed as a textile fiber (which is made up of cleaned fiber filaments approximately ⅜ in. long, each filament consisting of a number of ultimate fibers). The average length of the ultimate bark fiber is approximately 0.23 to 0.27 in., although its length may range from 0.1 to 0.39 in. The average tangential diameter of 150 fibers measured was 46 μ, and the average radial diameter 18 μ.

The cross-section is of peculiar rectangular shape, as shown in Fig. 16 at $\times$500. The surface character is shown in Fig. 17, at $\times$500. It is a most unusual vegetable fiber in that, as it loses its natural moisture,

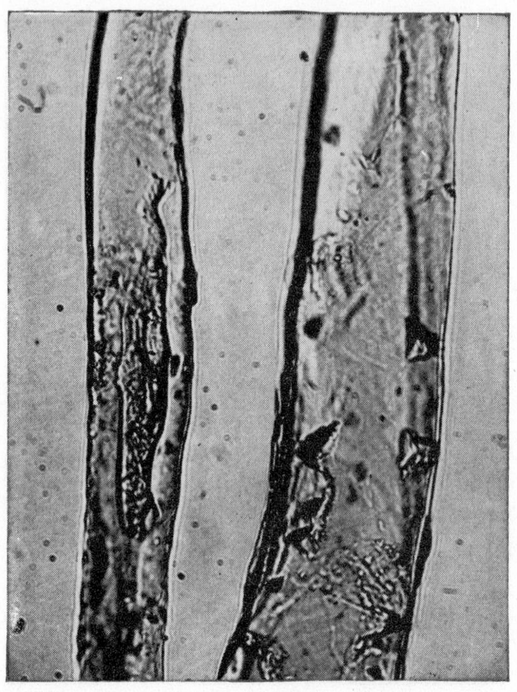

FIG. 17. Surface character of redwood bark fiber. ($\times$500.) (*Textile Fiber Atlas.*)

it curls into a corkscrew shape. This curled fiber felts very readily.

The ultimate fiber itself is largely cellulose and lignin. In the crude insulation fiber and even in the purified textile fiber, there is present a large amount of phenolic acid compounds of unidentified structure. This product is reddish brown and is found throughout the dead bark. A small amount of hot-water-soluble pectin is also present. A typical chemical analysis of the insulation fiber has been made by the Institute of Paper Chemistry, shown in Table 6.

The material called "lignin" in the Table 6 analysis is made up of both the true lignin and the phenolic acid, which appears as lignin in the analysis. The latter may be closely related to lignin, although

TABLE 6. Chemical Analysis of Redwood Bark Fiber

Items Present	*Per Cent Extractive-Free*
Ash	0.3
Pentosans	7.7
"Lignin"	37.9
Cellulose	* 53.8

* Contains some pentosans.

it differs fundamentally in having carboxyl groups but no methoxyl groups.

Since textile redwood bark fiber is mixed quite often with wool, its dye affinity is of considerable importance. Redwood bark fiber in its natural state has the shade of a 2 per cent dyeing of amido naphthol brown 3G A (general). It can be bleached to the shade of a Manila envelope, which is necessary for lighter and bright shades. It is best done by boiling off with soda ash, bleaching with peroxide, followed by a reduction with Blankit I.

Generally speaking, many acid colors, chrome colors, direct, basic, and acetate colors have affinity for redwood fiber. All acid colors dye redwood fiber readily and show certain fastness to washing and can be dyed from a neutral bath. Neutral dyeing acid colors give the best results on this fiber, when dyed in an acid bath.

It is not feasible to dye chrome colors on wool and redwood fiber in the same bath, as the affinity of all chrome dyes is greater for wool than for redwood fiber, especially in the top chrome procedure. Ordinarily it is best to dye the two fibers separately and then mix, if a uniform shade is desired. Two-tone effects can be obtained easily, because of their different dyestuff affinity. The monochrome method gives better results than the top chrome process.

For dark colors, such as browns, blues, and blacks, it is better to use the fiber unbleached. The self color of redwood bark fiber gives good browns. A monochrome mordant and a chrome brown dye give the same depth on wool and redwood fiber. The fastness of most chrome colors on redwood bark fibers seems to be sufficient for all practical purposes, although it is not as good as on wool.

In addition to the use of the fiber for insulation, the cleaned textile fiber is used as a blending agent with other textile fibers, such as wool, cotton, and the like. Mixtures with wool have been used for blankets, overcoating, and other textile purposes, whereas mixtures with cotton have been made into mattresses, decorative pillows, comforters, etc. The textile fiber is also used in some grades of hat felt.

PAPER FIBERS AND YARNS

Edward Robert Chatterton

History and Development

Paper cords were first produced from finished paper, it is claimed by Emil Claviez, who in 1895–97 took out patents for producing yarn from paper strips and for a spindle for twisting them. This yarn, known as Xylolin, was first produced in Saxony (Germany) and later in Austria. Other systems, known as the Kellner-Tueck and the Kron systems, were later introduced.

Undoubtedly this research was started to find suitable substitutes for cotton, jute, and wool, which were not always available or economical in those countries. The minimum working limit in spinning is obtained with fibers 0.11 to 0.19 in. in length, and, as this is the maximum length in papermaking, it may be seen that, by converting shorter fibers into paper and the paper into yarns, economy would result.

During World War I, the development of paper yarns and paper fabrics reached tremendous proportions in Germany, Austria, England, and France. Because of necessity, cartridge belts, sandbags, backing for rugs and carpets, and many similar items were made of the paper yarns. In carpets especially this practice was continued, because of the natural body of the yarn, whereas other yarns had to be sized, an extra operation and cost.

In the United States, paper yarns received their first attention from the furniture and basket trades. Paper was also folded into narrow strips and woven partly by machinery and partly by hand to make webbing for paneling in backs of chairs and davenports. Twisted yarns were also woven by hand and machine into baby carriages, ferneries, and porch furniture. Glue sizings and paint kept these items in condition for outside use. Gradually paper fibers were used for numerous other items because the raw material, paper, was made here, and reduced the necessity for large inventories of foreign-grown fibers.

Types of Fibers

The first and main consideration of the manufactured product is, of course, the raw material. Then there is the question of twisting paper into yarn, and to do it economically and in quantities to meet commercial demands. The great paper industry of the United States owes its modern development to an insect, the wasp. A German named

permits longer life without molding or rotting. A familiar use is woven paper fabric as a covering for car seats.

BIBLIOGRAPHY

1. "Paper," *Doubleday's Encyclopedia,* Vol. 8, Doubleday Doran & Co., New York (1938).
2. *The Paper Salesman's Study Course,* Walden Sons & Mott, New York (1938).
3. Del Mar, W. A., *Electric Cables,* McGraw-Hill Book Co., New York (1924).
4. *Paper and Twine J.* (March 1937).
5. TAPPI Section, *Paper Trade J.,* **127** (5), (July 29, 1948).

CHAPTER X

WOOL: HISTORY, GRADES, AND STATISTICS [1]

WERNER VON BERGEN

The woolly, hairlike covering of the sheep constitutes one of the most important and most typical of the textile fibers that are obtained from the skin tissues of different animals. The hairy coverings of a large number of animals are employed to a greater or less extent as raw materials for the manufacture of different textile products. Those of the various species of sheep make up the great bulk of these fibers which possess any considerable technical importance.

The wool-bearing animals belong to the order Ruminantia, which includes those animals that chew their cud. The principal members are sheep, goats, and camels. The sheep belong to a number of species of the class Ovidae, which vary considerably in physical appearance and geographical distribution, as well as in the character of the wool produced. Under the term "wool" are included commercially the hairs of the Angora goat, Cashmere goat, camel, alpaca, llama, and vicuña.

DEVELOPMENT OF BREEDS OF SHEEP

Sheep is one of man's oldest helpmates, and it was probably one of the first animals to be domesticated. According to Burns and Moody [2], very little is known concerning the remote ancestors of sheep; undoubtedly, they are intimately related to the urial and moufflon types of wild sheep.

Primitive sheep were covered only with hair, and wool was merely a soft light down next to the skin. The Scotch blackfaced sheep and the Navajo sheep are some of the present breeds most closely related to this type.

In the earliest pastoral industry one finds that Abraham, the patriarch of the Old Testament, thrived and prospered through the value of his great flocks and herds.

[1] Adapted, by permission, from the *American Wool Handbook,* 2d Ed., Textile Book Publishers, copyright 1948 [21].

From central Asia, the cradle of civilization, sheep were introduced gradually into new localities, until today they are found over the entire globe. Sheep, probably of the fine type, had been introduced into Spain by the Phoenicians hundreds of years before the Christian Era. There is little doubt that a number of different types of finer "wool" sheep from Asia, Africa, Greece, and Italy were brought into Spain and the various blood lines fused into the famous Spanish merino sheep, the ancestor of the finest wool-bearing sheep of today.

Spanish Merino Sheep

The development of merino sheep husbandry in Spain is the saga of sheep breeding. Its main development took place between A.D. 1400 and 1700. Although sheep breeding and improvement had been known at an earlier date, it did not reach its fullest development until the appearance of the merino in Spain.

In the period from 1500 to 1700 great flocks of traveling and stationary sheep comprised the prevailing type husbanded in Spain. The migratory sheep numbered about 10,000,000 and made up about half this population. In contrast to the stationary flocks, which remained in the same district for the entire year, the migratory sheep started north about the middle of April with their lambs, which had been born the previous November. Along the way, they were sheared and the wool prepared for the market in the shortest possible time. The flocks reached the mountain pastures in about 6 weeks and remained there until the end of September, and then returned to the south. Thus, these hardy sheep traveled twice each year over a trail 400 miles long. Is it any wonder that the Spanish merino and its descendants furnish the foundation upon which our western sheep industry is built? The annual trek of their ancestors is duplicated today in many sections of our West, where the sheep travel from 100 to 300 miles between their winter and summer ranges. The Spanish sheep industry worked out a system of management for these migratory sheep which was, and still is, a model of efficiency for the conduct of a flock.

The exportation of merino sheep was guarded against with great care. No one being allowed to take a live merino out of the Kingdom under the penalty of death, it was, therefore, very difficult to obtain any specimens. European royalty, most of which was related to the Spanish King, often asked as a gift some of the hoofed bearers of the golden fleece. Others did not trouble to ask, but smuggled sheep out through Portugal. Through this exportation of the Spanish merino in the second half of the eighteenth century, the foundation of the great wool-raising industry was laid all over the world.

European Merino Sheep

Spain, however, was not the only country with a sheep industry. From the tenth century on, Spain had a rival in England, and by the thirteenth century England was the greatest wool-producing country in the world, although the wool was of a much coarser type than the Spanish. By the opening of the nineteenth century, there were about 13,000,000 sheep in England. The merino sheep was introduced into England about the year 1791. The climate of the country was not compatible with the requirements of the breed, and in consequence, the quality of the wool could not be preserved, although much advantage was gained by crossing the merino with native breeds. France, Germany, and Austria also produced some wools of fine quality, but only after the introduction of the Spanish merino did the sheep industry in the various countries make considerable headway.

In Germany, the year 1765 marks the date when the Elector of Saxony, a cousin of the King of Spain, was able to obtain a gift of 300 sheep from the Royal Escorial flocks. These selected Spanish merinos, under the excellent care of a Saxon shepherd, developed the finest fleeces the world had ever seen up to that time. Maria Theresa was responsible for the importation of Spanish merino into Austro-Hungary in 1771. They were established on a government farm in Hungary.

France made its debut in the wool-growing business in 1786, when Louis XVI bought a flock of 380 sheep from the King of Spain, which he established on the Rambouillet estate, an experimental government farm. These sheep did so well that in 1799 another flock of 237 sheep was obtained. During the reign of Napoleon it was said that approximately 20,000 merinos were brought into the country and distributed throughout France. In developing the Rambouillet type, the French put special value on the development of the mutton quality. The blood of the Rambouillet flock has been kept pure since the first introduction of Spanish merino into France. The Rambouillet breed is of special interest to the United States, because it was this breed which since 1893 has spread rapidly throughout the country as the best breeding type.

Another important sheep country is Russia, where the first merino sheep were introduced in 1802 by a Frenchman. They were brought to the southern part of Russia. Later a great many American and Australian merinos have been used to improve the Russian flocks.

Australian Merino Sheep

When Australia was first settled, little thought was given to its natural herbiage, and most writers described it as insufficient to nourish animals in any numbers. Not a single sheep was living in Australia up to 1788. Brought to Australia by Governor Phillip from the Cape of Good Hope in that year, the first sheep were of Bengal or Dutch origin, had hairy fleeces and fat tails, and were designed for food and not for wool production.

Fig. 1. Australian merino ram of New South Wales. (*Courtesy J. F. Wilson, Univ. of Calif.*)

In 1789 the first Spanish merino sheep reached Australia, also from the Cape Colony, through Captain Waterhouse, who had been authorized to obtain them. An army officer, Captain MacArthur, was the first man in the colony to cultivate land. Among the original livestock on his farm were some sheep from India, a rather coarse and hairy type used for mutton. The captain noticed very quickly the great improvement in the natural fleece covering of these sheep when kept under Australian conditions. In 1797 he obtained some Spanish merinos from South Africa. The result obtained with this sheep convinced MacArthur that Australia had a great future as a sheep- and wool-raising district. It was through his influence that the Australian merino and its grade of wool became famous throughout the world.

In the following quarter of a century numerous flocks were established in Australia and Tasmania, and the noted breeding flocks of later years were firmly established. In 1840, half the area of New South Wales was occupied by sheep stations and was well on its way to become one of the greatest wool-breeding districts of the country. Tasmania also became famous as a stud sheep-breeding country and today produces the well-known superfine wool, which is without peer in the Antipode. Today, Australia has well over 100,000,000 head of sheep. The wool produced in the 1944–45 season consisted of 76 per cent merino and 24 per cent crossbred type and amounted to one-quarter of the world's wool production.

South African Merino Sheep

The Dutch Government in 1724 was in possession of the Cape Colony and was the first to import a few merino sheep. This undertaking did not meet with much success. After the Colonies were ceded to Great Britain, the merino received an extensive trial in South Africa. In the most favored district around Port Elizabeth, Durban, and part of the Transvaal, the flock established, thrived, and produced a good commercial quality of wool. Since about 1920 some excellent flocks and breeding stocks have been established through importation from Australia, and in wool production South Africa compares favorably with other countries.

In the 5-yr period 1941–45, its sheep population amounted to 38,000,000 head, which produced approximately 6 per cent of the world wool production. The bulk of the wool is of the fine merino type.

South American Merino Sheep

The early livestock husbandry in Argentina was confined exclusively to cattle raising. The first sheep of Spanish blood were introduced from Peru in 1587. The first merino to come direct from Spain to Argentina was brought to what is now Uruguay in 1794. That is the same year when the first merino was brought to Australia, but the Uruguayan sheep were not as fortunate as the Australian. They were soon lost without any appreciable effect on the sheep population of the country. In the latter part of the eighteenth century various lots of merinos were smuggled out of Spain by traders and taken to Buenos Aires. These sheep were badly neglected, and their descendants were miserable and undersized. They did not produce good mutton or good wool. However, in later years the sheep of Argentina and Uruguay have been much improved, so that today they produce a good quality of wool.

The sheep population in Argentina in the 5-yr period 1941–45 was 52 million head, and the production of grease wool amounted to 500 million lb. In Uruguay, the sheep population for the same period was 20 million head and the production of grease wool amounted to 144 million lb. In both countries the percentage of merino wool is approximately 10 per cent.

Development of American Sheep in the United States

Sheep were not known to the native American Indians. The wool used by the colonists came from animals of imported stock. The first sheep were introduced into Virginia in 1608, into Massachusetts about 1630, and are reported to have been introduced into the other colonies soon after they were founded. It is not definitely known just what was the breed of these first animals. The English unimproved sheep seem to have been the most generally brought over. Premiums were offered for the first full-blooded merino that was introduced into the Colonies, which was as early as 1785.

The first two sheep of the merino type arrived in 1793 in Cambridge, Mass., and the owner, in his ignorance of their value, simply ate them. The first full-blooded merino ram actually used for breeding purposes was brought from Spain by Messrs. du Pont de Nemours and Delessert in 1801. The next groups to come were those brought in by Robert Livingston and David Humphreys in 1802. Both men were convinced that this breed of sheep might be introduced with great benefit to our country.

William Jarvis, American Consul to Portugal in 1809, seized the opportunity offered by the then current convulsions in Spain and by the lifting of the American embargo to ship some 4000 sheep to the United States. The shipments were begun in 1810, with other large importations following in 1811. Approximately 25,000 merino sheep had been secured in this period. The animals were distributed over nearly every state.

The acquisition of such a number of pure-blooded merinos laid the basis for substantial production of fine wool. As a result of governmental assistance and the formation of agricultural societies, the animals spread westward with great rapidity, reaching Ohio and Kentucky.

Attempts to improve the quality of the wool were not limited to the merino. During the early years of the century some of the long-wooled varieties, such as Leicester, were also introduced, and spread through New Jersey, Pennsylvania, and New York. Between 1810 and 1814 the number of sheep is estimated to have increased from 7,000,000 to 10,000,000 head. During the depression from 1815 to 1820, which was especially disastrous to the production of fine fabrics, the merino breed encountered a setback.

With the beginning of the new decade, a general improvement set in, and another fine-wool mania started, not in Spanish merino, but in the

German Saxony merino. This animal produced an even finer quality of wool than the Spanish merino and, therefore, could be sold for higher prices. Introduction in volume began in 1824 and ended in 1826, during which period 3300 sheep were brought in. This Saxony merino did not spread so rapidly over the country, and on account of its small numbers its influence was not as great as that of the Spanish merino had been. Still, the Saxony merino made a valuable contribution to the improvement of American wool.

The best flocks of the Spanish and Saxony merino sheep were concentrated in Washington County, N. Y., Vermont in general, West Virginia, and around Steubenville, Ohio. In 1830 the amount of wool produced was enough to supply the needs of all woolen mills of that time. Wool growing developed rapidly in western Massachusetts, Vermont, and New York in the 1830's.

The first accurate figures available relative to the number of sheep are those for 1840, when the Census reported 19,000,000 head. The greatest center of sheep production was Vermont. The Vermont sheep were notable for the heavy weight of fleece they produced. During the forties, there was a rapid shifting of the sheep industry from the East to the West. By 1850 the center of the wool production was in Ohio, which had become the leading sheep-raising state in the Union. The sheep farmers remaining in the East reduced their flocks and turned their attention to the production of mutton and wool.

During the decade of 1850 to 1860, the westward movement continued; but where the land was level and was easily cultivated the sheep industry was not able to compete with wheat, corn, cattle, and hogs. Consequently, sheep raising as a pioneer industry rapidly passed across the level prairies to the Far West. Sheep have persisted, however, to the present day on the rough or uneven lands of eastern Ohio and southern Michigan.

The first development of the industry in the Far West was in Texas and New Mexico and northward. The sheep industry of New Mexico had been in existence since an early date. As early as 1700, sheep were driven from New Mexico to California. In the expansion of the western industry, New Mexico was drawn upon for much of the foundation stock, which has been gradually improved by the introduction of merino blood. By 1860 there were many sheep in Texas and California.

The Navajo sheep in New Mexico are traced back to descendants of the unimproved Churro long-wool breed of Spain. These sheep were probably the companions of the Spanish explorer Coronado, who landed in Mexico in 1504. The sheep were his fresh meat supply on his way through the Rio Grande country and up into the present state of New Mexico.

The origin of the present type of Navajo sheep is shrouded in mystery. During the Navajo revolt in 1860 the sheep were almost entirely exterminated. The War Department later gave a contract to a New Mexican citizen to replace these sheep, but where he obtained the replacement was not definitely known.

Fig. 2. American champion A type merino ram. (*Courtesy U. S. Department of Agriculture.*)

After 1870 there was a rapid expansion in the Far West, where free grazing could be obtained throughout the year. This western expansion of the sheep industry continued until most of the range country was overcrowded. The maximum number of range sheep seems to have been reached in the year 1884; that year marks the high point of the industry for the United States as a whole, when the number of sheep reported was 50,627,000, exclusive of lambs.

Fig. 3. American B type merino ewe. (*Courtesy U. S. Department of Agriculture.*)

By 1900 sheep raising in the East was largely confined to areas where, because of much rough land or soil conditions, most of the farm land was only usable for pasture, as in southwestern Michigan and parts of Iowa. Since then the sheep industry has been subject to severe competition throughout the country. In the East, dairying had continued to make inroads upon the sheep industry, and in those sections of the West where dry farming was important, cattle had replaced sheep to a considerable extent.

From the early 1880's on, the range operators realized that it was profitable to fatten sheep for the market. This practice was encouraged greatly by the development of great packing centers in the upper

Mississippi Valley. The Far West was shipping sheep to these packing centers. It soon became evident that it was profitable to give some of these animals "a better finish" before they were slaughtered. The increased demand for mutton caused the wool growers to develop sheep which yielded good mutton as well as good wool.

The development of the United States sheep industry since its peak year 1884 is best illustrated by Fig. 4 and Table 1. The industry recovered from the 1923 low, reaching a new peak in 1942, but thereafter declined steadily to reach a new low in 1950.

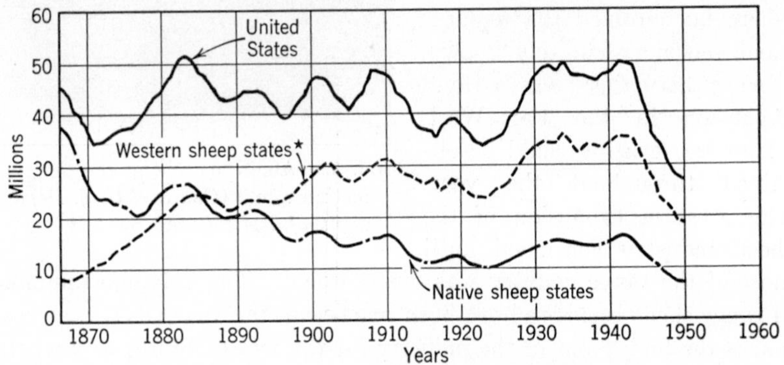

* Includes 11 western states.

FIG. 4. Stock sheep and lambs, Number on farms Jan. 1, 1867, to 1950. (*Source: U. S. Department of Agriculture.*)

Wool Production

Total production of wool in the United States, both shorn and pulled, was 455 million lb in 1942. Of this quantity, 388 million lb was shorn wool and 67 million lb was pulled wool. In 1950 the total was 247 million lb, and of this quantity 212 million lb was shorn and 35 million lb was pulled. The 1942 production of shorn wool was the largest on record, and the 1950 production was the lowest on record.

The number of sheep shorn in 1950 is estimated at 27,064,000 head, with the weight of wool per sheep shorn averaging 8 lb. In 1949 sheep shorn numbered 27,651,000 head, and the average weight of wool per sheep was 8.11 lb. The production of 1950 was estimated at 218,-239,000 lb.

The average local market price of shorn wool in 1949 was $1.52 per lb clean, compared with $1.14 per lb clean in 1942. The cash income from wool in 1949 was $107 million compared with $155 million in 1942.

TABLE 1. SHEEP AND LAMBS: NUMBER AND VALUE ON FARMS, UNITED STATES, JAN. 1, 1900–52

[U. S. Agricultural Marketing Service.]

Year	Stock Sheep			Feeder Sheep, Number (Thousands)	All Sheep, Number (Thousands)	Year	Stock Sheep			Feeder Sheep, Number (Thousands)	All Sheep, Number (Thousands)
	Number (Thousands)	Farm Value					Number (Thousands)	Farm Value			
		Per Head (Dollars)	Total (1000 dollars)					Per Head (Dollars)	Total (1000 dollars)		
1900 *	*39,938*	..	..	..	..	1926	35,719	10.53	376,134	4,644	40,363
1900	45,065	2.97	134,046	3,040	48,105	1927	38,067	9.79	372,784	4,348	42,415
1901	46,126	2.96	136,335	2,975	49,101	1928	40,689	10.36	421,582	4,569	45,258
1902	46,196	2.62	121,904	3,040	49,236	1929	43,481	10.71	465,609	4,900	48,381
1903	44,436	2.62	116,548	3,100	47,536	*1930* *	*41,780*	..	..	..	..
1904	41,908	2.55	106,961	3,550	45,458	1930	45,577	9.00	410,290	5,988	51,565
1905	40,410	2.77	111,962	3,415	43,825	1931	47,720	5.40	257,742	5,513	53,233
1906	41,965	3.51	147,352	3,560	45,525	1932	47,682	3.44	164,246	6,220	53,902
1907	43,460	3.81	165,371	3,800	47,260	1933	47,303	2.91	137,671	5,751	53,054
1908	45,095	3.87	174,650	3,100	48,195	1934	48,244	3.77	181,718	5,259	53,503
1909	47,098	3.42	161,192	3,695	50,793	*1935* *	*48,358*	..	..	..	..
1910 *	*39,644*	..	..	..	..	1935	46,139	4.33	199,705	5,669	51,808
1910	46,939	4.06	190,673	3,300	50,239	1936	45,386	6.35	287,985	5,701	51,087
1911	46,055	3.83	176,431	4,500	50,555	1937	45,422	6.02	273,610	5,597	51,019
1912	42,972	3.42	147,118	4,925	47,897	1938	45,119	6.13	276,671	6,091	51,210
1913	40,544	3.87	156,949	4,108	44,652	1939	45,710	5.75	262,643	5,885	51,595
1914	38,059	3.91	148,745	5,030	43,089	*1940* *	*40,129*	..	..	..	..
1915	36,263	4.39	159,146	4,250	40,513	1940	46,558	6.35	295,763	5,841	52,399
1916	36,260	5.10	184,856	3,750	40,010	1941	47,804	6.78	323,996	6,479	54,283
1917	35,246	7.06	248,917	3,640	38,886	1942	49,807	8.67	426,584	6,775	55,979
1918	36,704	11.76	431,679	2,960	39,664	1943	48,796	9.69	472,792	6,979	55,775
1919	38,360	11.49	440,730	3,515	41,875	1944	45,777	8.70	398,101	5,941	51,718
1920 *	*35,034*	..	..	..	..	1945	46,520	6.38	252,705	6,911	46,520
1920	37,328	10.59	395,235	3,415	40,743	1946	42,436	7.48	266,280	6,837	42,436
1921	35,426	6.34	224,454	4,053	39,479	1947	37,818	8.41	270,171	5,693	37,818
1922	33,365	4.79	159,839	3,557	36,922	1948	34,827	9.69	295,971	4,788	35,332
1923	32,597	7.50	244,452	4,206	36,803	1949	26,940	..	..	4,003	30,943
1924	32,859	7.94	260,819	4,280	37,139	1950	26,182	..	..	3,644	29,826
1925 *	*35,590*	..	..	..	..	1951	27,253	..	..	3,382	30,635
1925	34,469	9.63	331,971	4,074	38,543	1952	27,841	..	..	3,884	31,725

* Italic figures are from the Census. Census dates were June 1, 1900; Apr. 15, 1910; Jan. 1, 1920 and 1925; Apr. 1, 1930; Jan. 1, 1935; Apr. 1, 1940. 1900, 1910, 1930, and 1940 exclude spring-born lambs. Figures for 1949–52 are from "Wool Situation," U. S. Bur. Agr. Econ., Tables 1 and 2, p. 20 (Jan. 1952).

Production of pulled wool in 1942 was exceeded in only one other year—1932. Under normal conditions the record slaughter of sheep and lambs in 1942 would have resulted in a production of pulled wool much larger than in any other year. Demand for shearling skins for the production of aviators' equipment, however, resulted in the diversion of many skins which normally would have been pulled.

Number of Breeds

Hart [11] states that it is impossible to give an absolutely correct list of the original breeds of sheep. In the early stages of civilization, sheep were taken from one country to another by nomads and exchanged for other commodities. Different climatic conditions and changed circumstances again produced fresh types. No other animal in existence is as adaptable as the sheep to local conditions, and no other animal is so readily influenced by environment. Under these circumstances it is impossible to trace sheep back to the original breeds, and even the best authorities can give us only a vague idea of the different sheep existing when that animal was first partially domesticated by primitive civilization.

Some of the ancient breeds have become quite extinct without leaving any trace of relationship behind them, whereas others have undergone such changes during the past century that the original type is now unrecognizable. These numerous changed types are confined chiefly to eastern Europe and are now recognized as distinct breeds with a separate classification. It is estimated that about 20 of the ancient breeds can still be found in Asia and northern Africa, but the original types have undoubtedly undergone considerable change.

As the domestic sheep is cultivated in every country of the world, numerous varieties are produced in the various countries. Today, there are several hundred different types, which vary considerably in appearance and in the character of the wool they produce. The main causes of the numerous varieties are: different conditions of soil, climate, pasturage, crossbreeding, and changing demand on the part of the wool manufacturers.

Classification of Breeds

Figure 5 shows the general pedigree of the domestic sheep and its development into the various types. Practically all fleece wools can be classified into the five general types: fine wool, medium wool, long wool, crossbred wool, and carpet or mixed wool. The breed of the sheep influences the character of the wool grown and governs to a large extent the diameter and the lengths of the fibers. Other points, such as strength, luster, waviness, color, and shrinkage, vary considerably according to breed. In the diagram are listed only the breeds that played a more or less important part in the development of the American sheep husbandry. In addition to them are the breeds that supply the domestic market with the additional raw material needed.

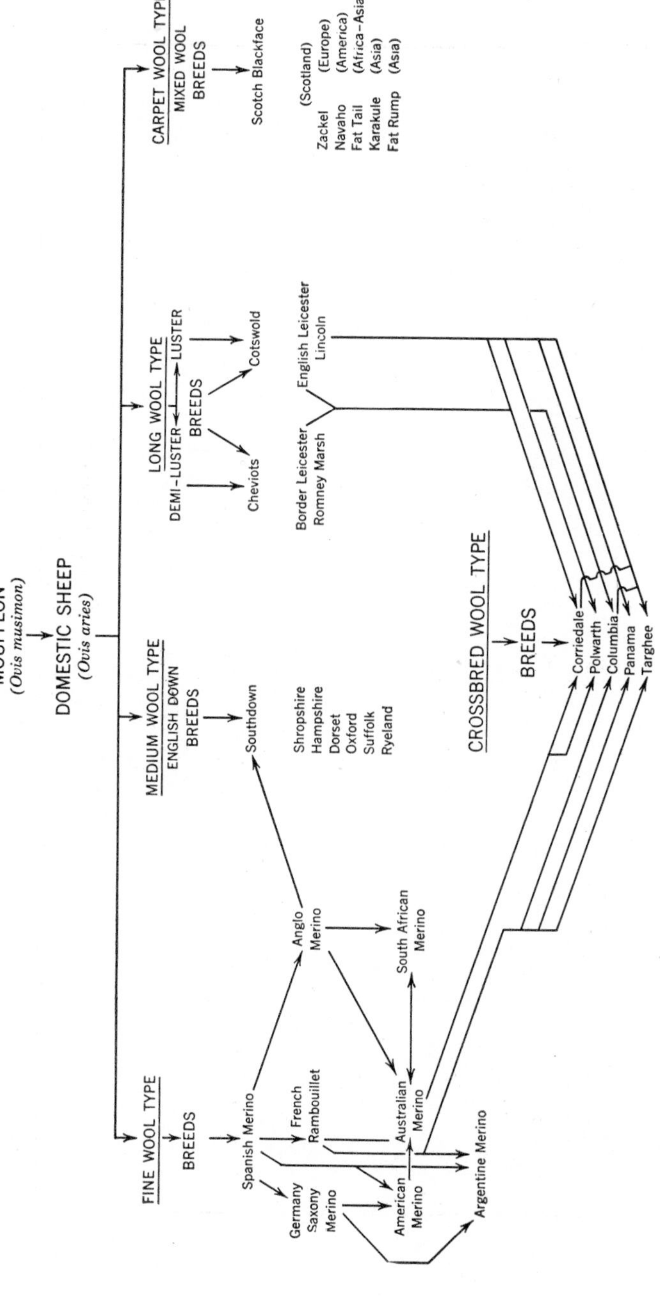

FIG. 5. General pedigree of domestic sheep. (*Courtesy R. H. Burns.*)

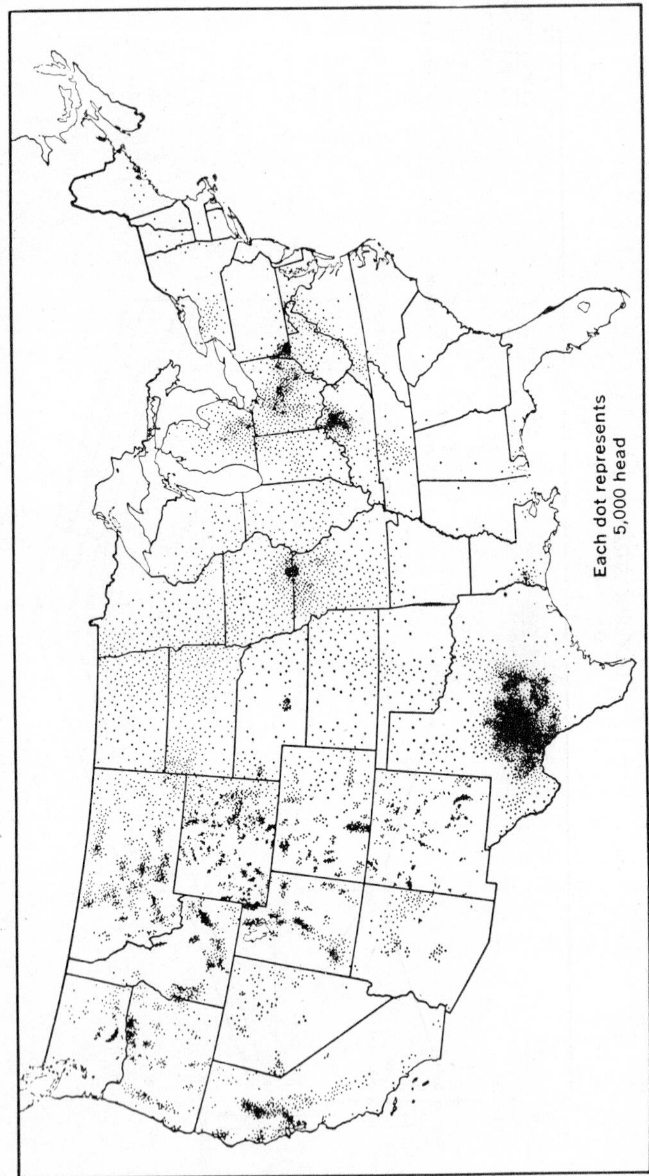

FIG. 6. Sheep and lambs over 6 months old. On April 1, 1940 there were 8,448,000 sheep in Texas, more than in Wyoming, Montana and Ohio combined. United States total number on farms and ranches, 40,129,000. (*U. S. Census Bur.*)

There are approximately 30 breeds of improved sheep that have been brought to fixed types as adapted to the needs of their native countries. Of these breeds, 13 are well established in the United States and a number of others are gaining in popularity. According to Spencer, the United States Census enumerations of 1930 include 18 breeds of sheep in the tabulations of pure-bred livestock (see Table 2). In the area

TABLE 2. BREEDS PREVALENT IN UNITED STATES

Merino	Oxford	Romney Marsh
Rambouillet	Suffolk	Black-faced Highland
Southdown	Columbia	Tunis
Hampshire	Corriedale	Karakul
Shropshire	Cotswold	Ryeland
Dorset	Leicester	Romeldale
Cheviot	Lincoln	

covered by Ohio, West Virginia, and Pennsylvania all of these 18 breeds are represented.

Types of Sheep

The term "type" as applied to sheep is used in various ways. In the diagram giving the general pedigree of the domestic sheep the five types classify the breeds according to the type of wool they grow. The two main fiber characteristics on which the classification is based are fineness and length. The breed of the sheep influences the character of its wool. It governs to a large extent the length and diameter of the fibers, and also other physical properties, making up the "quality of the wool fiber," such as strength, elasticity, shrinkage, color, luster, and waviness.

In the same way as the breed influences the character of the wool it must be borne in mind that the quality of the meat is affected just as much. Therefore, the sheep are also divided into the "mutton type" and the "wool type." Breeds developed primarily for lamb and mutton are grouped under the mutton type, and those developed especially for wool belong under the wool type. Whereas the improvement of the fleeces of sheep by selection and breeding has been practiced for centuries, the development of the mutton breeds was started less than 200 yr ago. A few breeds are "dual" types, developed for both mutton and wool.

In Table 3 Henning [13] applies the two classifications to the most important breeds found in the United States.

Definitions. In order to understand the various terms used to describe fineness and length of a wool type from a manufacturing angle,

TABLE 3. Classification of Types of Breeds

Main Types	*Sub-Types*	*Breeds*
Mutton Type	Medium Wools	1. Shropshire
		2. Hampshire
		3. Dorset Horn
		4. Southdown
		5. Cheviot
		6. Oxford Down
		7. Suffolk
		8. Tunis
		9. Corriedale
		10. Ryeland
		11. Columbia
		12. Panama
		13. Romeldale
Mutton Type	Long Wools	14. Lincoln
		15. Cotswold
		16. Leicester
		17. Romney Marsh
		18. Black-faced Highland
Wool Type	Fine Wools	19. Merino
		Class A
		Class B
		Class C
		20. Rambouillet
		Class B
		Class C
		21. Tasmanian Merino
		22. Australian Merino

it is necessary to explain their background. Wool as a commodity of commerce is extremely complex, varies widely in its characteristics, and is one of the most difficult to classify and grade for the benefit of the trade. Although the variation in wool occurs somewhat in correlation with the types and breeds of sheep, wide variations exist within the breeds. Fleeces having the same fineness often vary greatly in fiber strength, spinning properties, length, and their contents of grease and dirt. Soil, climate, and feed all have a far-reaching influence on the character of wool.

In some sections of the western range where grass is sparse and sandstorms are frequent, fleeces of merino or Rambouillet sheep may shrink as much as 65 to 75 per cent or more, owing to grease and dirt, when scoured or cleaned preparatory to manufacture. Fleeces from sheep of these same breeds grown on excellent blue grass pastures where sandstorms are rare, if ever, will shrink only 50 to 60 per cent.

yield by the scoured value. In the above example it would be 0.40 (yield) × $2.00 (scoured value), which equals $0.80, grease price.

Within the last 30 yr the average fleece weight for all United States wool has increased from 6.8 lb in 1910 to 8 lb in 1940, whereas the average shrinkage for the same period has fluctuated not more than 3 per cent, namely, between 59 and 62 per cent. For the last 7 yr the shrinkage was 61 per cent, indicating that the changes from year to year are very small, and in no instance was there more than 1 per cent between successive years. This average figure for the whole country is not of much value to the wool buyer or the farmer, because of the tremendous variation between wools from the various states and ranges. Of far more value to them is a knowledge of the various shrinkages of each state or, even better, of the various sections in each state, and also the relationship which exists in the shrinkage between the various grades.

FIG. 8. American champion C type Rambouillet ewe. (*Courtesy Univ. of Wyoming.*)

Table 5 shows the main United States wools, their shrinkage and fleece weight for the 5-yr period 1937–41. It has to be remembered that these figures include all the wools—fine, medium, and coarse—in each state.

Different Types of Wool

In describing the five types of wool—fine, medium, long, crossbred, and carpet—in general terms it must be remembered that each type groups together numerous breeds carrying fleeces which differ widely in some of the properties making up the "quality" of the wool. Under each wool type, some of the characteristic breeds are briefly described.

Fine Wool Type. Only the merino breeds produce fleeces which can be classified under this type. The principal merino families of today are the Spanish, Rambouillet (or French), Saxony, Silesian, Australian, American, South American, and South African.

American Merino. The varied experiences the merino has had to go through have steadily molded this breed into types best suited to a great variety of conditions. Within the merino breed the skin folds on the animal show wide variation. Some individuals are covered almost entirely over the body and neck with these folds, whereas some have only a moderate development, and others are almost free of them. This made it advisable to recognize and establish three different body types for show ring purposes, depending upon the extent of development of the folds. A, B, and C types were thus set up, the A type embracing those individuals most heavily folded, the C type the smoothest ones. While the A type merino undoubtedly served a useful purpose in years gone by in increasing the fleece weights of the breed, its usefulness is apparently at an end here and is rapidly disappearing. Even the B type is fast losing its popularity. The density of fleece on the heavily folded types has been bred into the present C type, and it has been found that the smooth sheep are more practical for the grower.

American merino rams range in weight from 140 to 225 lb, and ewes from 80 to 150 lb. The Rambouillet is much larger, having a better mutton form. The rams range from 200 to 275 lb and ewes from 130 to 170 lb. Rams of both breeds usually have spiral horns and the ewes have none.

There is not much difference in size of the American merino breeds and the Australian and Argentinian breeds, as seen from Table 6. The

TABLE 6. Fine Wool Type Breeds [16]

Country	Breed	Body Weight (pounds)		Weight per Fleece (pounds)		Grade	Length (inches)	Shrinkage in Ewe Fleeces (per cent)
		Ram	Ewe	Ram	Ewe			
Australia	Fine wool merino	130 to 170	80 to 100	14 to 20	6 to 10	64's to 90's	2¼ to 4	40 to 50
	Medium wool merino	150 to 200	100 to 140	18 to 28	8 to 14	60's to 70's	3 to 4	45 to 55
	Strong wool merino	200 to 260	140 to 180	22 to 34	15 to 18	56's to 64's	3 to 5	50 to 58
United States of America	A type merino	140 to 175	85 to 135	20 to 30	13 to 20	64's to 80's	1½ to 2	58 to 70
	B type merino	140 to 185	90 to 140	20 to 30	13 to 20			
	C type merino	150 to 225	90 to 150	15 to 25	10 to 18	64's to 80's	2½ to 3½	
	Rambouillet	200 to 275	130 to 170	15 to 25	10 to 18	58's to 70's	1½ to 3½	55 to 65
Argentina	A type merino	132 to 165	88 to 120	25 to 35	9 to 22		1¾ to 2	65
	B type merino	155 to 175	110 to 132	22 to 31	9 to 18	60's to 64's	2 to 2¾	60
	C type merino	155 to 200	120 to 145	18 to 27	9 to 15		2¾ to 3¾	55
France	Rambouillet 1927	185	100	26	13	64's to 70's	2½ to 3½	

table showing the main characteristics of fine wool type breeds and also the other tables covering medium wool, long wool, and crossbred breeds refer to major animals of pure breeding, 2 to 4 yr old, in excellent condition, and in 12-month fleece. No attempt has been made to include in the data those rare individuals attaining very unusual size or producing extraordinarily heavy fleeces; Table 6 indicates the normal weight ranges to be expected under conditions set forth above. A breed of sheep may attain a certain average size and produce a certain average fleece weight in one part of a country, whereas the same breed grown in another section or in another country may be lighter or heavier and may produce more wool or less, depending on its adaptability to feed, climate, and other local conditions. Furthermore there are strains or families within each breed possessing the propensity for size or the lack of it and for heavier or lighter fleece weights; and finally, some of the breeds whose fleece weights may seem low have such light-shrinking wool that the clean fiber content may make them fully comparable to others whose fleece weights seem high. Table 6 was carefully edited by various authorities [16].

In searching for the information given in this table, the need for more definite facts on this subject was evident. The value of such tables was recognized by the National Association of Wool Manufacturers [3], which published a similar table for its reference book.

Characteristics of Merino Wools

Merino wools are the most valuable wools produced in the world. Approximately 32 per cent of the world's production in 1950 came under the merino classification. Of this, 66 per cent was produced in Australia.

The merino wools are noted for their softness, fineness, strength, and elasticity and are especially desired for their superior spinning and felting properties. For spinning the finest woolen and worsted yarns, merino wools are an absolute necessity. Flannels and knit goods of high quality, suiting and dress goods of fine texture, face-finished fabrics such as broadcloths, billiard cloths, doeskins, meltons, and various uniform cloths are dependent on merino stock. No other wool would give the required appearance, handle, finish, and character which distinguishes each of these fabrics, and in many cases no other wool could be spun to the required fine yarn sizes.

Saxony, Silesian, Spanish, and French merino wools are all grown in Continental Europe, and the great bulk is manufactured into textiles in the countries where the wool is grown. Very little of this wool ever enters the open market, and none is imported by the United States. These European merino wools are noted for their fineness; the major portion of them are worked on the woolen system. The length of fiber is usually under 2.5 in.

Australian Merino Wools. The wools sold in the 1944–45 season consisted of 76 per cent merino and 24 per cent crossbred. The bulk of the merino wool is a bold well-grown 64's of medium spinning quality, showing good length of staple, and reflecting breeding characteristics of constitution, backed by ideal climatic and pasture conditions. In Australia also, finer counts, up to 100's, are to be found in certain markets, whereas in other centers strong merino or 60's may be had, showing good length of staple and body.

In the crossbred section, some fine types are displayed, from choicest style three-eighths blood to braid. Approximately 93 per cent of Australian wool sold at auction is greasy, the balance, 7 per cent, being scoured. Also 95 per cent of the total represents wool from grown sheep, 5 per cent being lamb's wool.

The figures grouped in Table 7 show the number of 300-lb bales of shorn wool available for the past three seasons in the Australian selling centers.

TABLE 7. Bales of Wool Sold and Appraised at the Various Australian Centers [6]

Center	*1945–46*	*1946–47*	*1947–48*	*1948–49*	*1949–50*
Sydney and Newcastle	1,155,211	1,090,281	1,079,182	1,149,201	1,378,560
Melbourne, Albury, Ballarat	395,585	567,654	588,172	644,222	704,066
Geelong	172,173	233,454	254,888	265,189	291,001
Brisbane	591,415	469,033	478,680	484,045	521,726
Adelaide	228,397	276,762	330,579	331,286	357,323
Perth	267,544	267,467	295,790	316,768	292,804
Tasmania	52,381	51,321	52,421	53,520	52,460
Total bales	2,862,706	2,955,972	3,079,712	3,244,231	3,597,940

Source: Dalgety's *Ann. Wool Rev.* (1949–50), p. 17.

Table 8 gives an analysis in percentages of the main grades for each state for the two seasons 1940–41 and 1947–48.

The percentage figures of merino and crossbred wool of the four seasons 1946–47, 1949–50, for each state, are as follows [6]:

In the state of Queensland 99 per cent merino is the recorded figure of wool production, the general character of the staple being fine spinning quality. New South Wales registers 79 per cent merino and 21 per cent crossbred, the merino on the average being of medium to medium fine in spinning quality. Western Australia sells 92 per cent

TABLE 8. Percentage of Greasy Wool in Each Quality Appraised or Sold at Auction by States

Name of Wool	*1940–41*	*1947–48*
Queensland		
64's and up	77	65
60–64's	22	33
58's and below	1	2
New South Wales		
64's and up	71	44
60–64's	20	37
58's and below	9	19
Victoria		
64's and up	34	21
60–64's	34	25
58's and below	32	54
South Australia		
64's and up	11	7
60–64's	75	63
58's and below	14	30
Western Australia		
64's and up	45	21
60–64's	46	62
58's and below	9	17
Tasmania		
64's and up	20	14
60–64's	34	19
58's and below	46	67

Source: *Wool Digest* (March 29, 1949) [23].

merino and 8 per cent crossbred, the spinning quality being medium on the average of the former type.

South Australia shows 89 per cent and 11 per cent respectively for merino and crossbred; the merino is a type outstanding in the Commonwealth, since the spinning quality on the average is medium to strong. Victoria produces 42 per cent merino, which varies from extra superior types to average dusty top-making sorts, and 58 per cent crossbred qualities from the choicest style half-bloods, Corriedales, Polwarths, Leicesters, and Lincolns to average dusty top-making descriptions. Tasmania records only 24 per cent merino and 76 per cent crossbred wools. The bulk of these offerings is superior in style from superfine 100's to 36's, and temperate climatic conditions reflect well-grown wools for color, style, character, handle, and condition.

Cape Merino Wools. They are grown in the following four South African states: Cape Province (48 per cent), Orange Free State (34 per cent), Transvaal (12 per cent), and Natal (5 per cent). The main concentration and shipping points are East London, Durban, Port Elizabeth, and Capetown.

Some wools are shorn after about 6 or 9 months of growth; hence the staple is short and can only be classed as "clothing" wool. About 60 per cent of a 12-month clip has a length of 2 to 2½ in. The analysis of the 1948–49 clip showed that 89 per cent of the wool is classified as 64's–70's; 1 per cent crossbred; 5 per cent coarse mixed wool; 5 per cent karakul [6]. Although the South African clip is finer than some of the Australian wool, it lacks the staple found in the Australian product. Cape and Orange Free State wools vary in shrinkage from 50 to 60 per cent. The area around Port Elizabeth is noted for its "snow white capes."

Transvaal wool shrinks between 48 and 53 per cent, whereas some of the Natal wool shrinks less than 40 per cent. The wool is keenly sought, especially for its suitability in the manufacture of woolen-spun uniform cloths, such as flannels, meltons, and kerseys. Generally excellent felting wools, some Cape wools are said to be inelastic and some nonfelting.

South American Merino Wools. The chief wool-producing areas of South America are Argentina, which produced three-fifths (60 per cent in 1949) of the South American wools; Uruguay, which grew about one-fifth (22 per cent in 1949); and Chile, Brazil, Peru, and Falkland Islands, which yielded the remainder.

Buenos Aires, Montevideo, and Punta Arenas are stations for the collection and dispatch of the wool to the manufacturing countries. Most of the Argentine clip is collected at Buenos Aires, the wools grown in Uruguay and southern Brazil are gathered at Montevideo, and wools from Patagonia and Tierra Del Fuego are shipped from Punta Arenas, the Chilean port on the Straits of Magellan. South American wools often are known by the initials of the ports of shipment; the Buenos Aires wools are classed as "B.A.," Montevideo wools as "M.V.," and the Punta Arenas wools are known as "Punta wools" or "P.A."

Argentine Merino Wools. The percentage of merino wool in the Argentine wool clip is about 15 per cent. According to Link [15], of the 17 main breeds, amounting to 153,960 sheep in 1936, the merinos were represented by 17,809 Argentine merinos and 5018 Australian merinos. See Table 9.

Argentina may be divided into three parts: the Andes area of the north, the Pampas area and the Parana River basin, and Patagonia in the south. Crossbred wools are reared on sheep in the valleys where

TABLE 9. Argentine Wool Production

Type of Wool	*Per Cent*
Merino	15
Fine crossbred (Cruza fina)	36
Medium crossbred (Cruza mediana)	17
Coarse crossbred (Cruza gruesa)	30
Carpet wool (Criolla y Mestiza)	2

Source: Link, P., *Produccion Lanera de las Americas* (1948).

good pastures allow dual purpose sheep. Merino sheep are kept on the high grounds of the Andes and in the Patagonia regions.

The finest merino wools of South America come from Patagonia and are known by the names of the states—Chubut, Buenos Aires, Rio Negro, Neuquen, Santa Cruz, La Pampa, Entre Rios. The Chubut wool quality is about 64's–70's but the wool is rather dry, resembling somewhat Brisbane wools. The wool is excellent for French spinning. The shrinkage varies between 66 and 68 per cent. A serious defect of the wool grown from the Argentine merino is the presence of "kemp."

Uruguay Merino Wools. As in Argentina, only a small percentage of the Montevideo wools is of the merino type—10 per cent; the largest percentage is crossbred wool of the finer grades 50's and up—70 per cent. For further grade and quality classification see Tables 10 and 11.

TABLE 10. Grade Classification of South American Wools

Argentina and Uruguay	*English Equivalent*	*United States Equivalent*	
Superior	80's	80's	
Bueno to superior	70's	70's	Fine
Bueno to corriente	64's	64's	
Corriente	60's	62's	½ Blood
Primera cruza	58's	58's to 60's	
1	56's	56	⅜ Blood
1 to 2	50's to 56's	..	
2	50's	..	¼ Blood
2 to 3	48's to 50's	..	
3	48's	..	
3 to 4	46's to 48's	..	Low ¼ Blood
4	46's	..	
4 to 5	44's	..	Common
5	40's to 44's	..	
5 to 6	40's	..	
6	36's	..	Braid
6 to 7	32's	..	

Source: Pablo Link [15].

TABLE 11. Classes of South American Wools

Supras	Super	Well skirted, attractive wool of good quality.
Primeras	First quality	Sound, clean, well grown.
Segundas	Inferior	Less attractive wool, burry and faulty.

United States Wools

The American wools are divided into two classes: domestic and territory wools. But neither of these terms is generally applied to Texas and California wools, which are separately designated. See Table 12.

TABLE 12. Leading Sheep and Wool States as of January 1, 1950 [3]

Leading Wool States			*Leading Sheep States*		
State	*Wool (thousand pounds)*	*Shorn (per cent)*	*State*	*Sheep (thousands)*	*Total (per cent)*
Texas	51,480	23.90	Texas	6,638	24.50
Wyoming	17,120	7.94	Wyoming	1,901	7.01
California	14,936	6.93	California	1,652	6.10
Montana	12,662	5.88	Montana	1,623	5.99
New Mexico	11,309	5.25	New Mexico	1,343	4.95
Colorado	11,090	5.15	Utah	1,326	4.89
Utah	10,856	5.04	Colorado	1,198	4.42
Idaho	9,400	4.36	Missouri	1,054	3.89
Oregon	8,366	3.88	Idaho	990	3.65
Ohio	7,896	3.66	Ohio	930	3.43
Shorn wool	155,115	71.99	Number of sheep	18,655	68.83
Total U. S.	215,422	100.00	Total U. S.	27,099	100.00

Domestic Wools. In general, all domestic wools are those grown in the United States, as contrasted with foreign wools. In the domestic woolen trade the term "domestic" is applied to wools grown east of the Rocky Mountains and Texas, exclusive of the western (range) portions of the Dakotas, Nebraska, and Kansas. Most of these wools are known in the trade as fleece wools. As the states in which they are grown are classified as farm states, in government statistics the term "farm-grown wools" is applied. That term also includes the wool grown in the Willamette Valley of western Oregon and in parts of western Washington, as it is essentially farm grown.

The principal states growing domestic merino wools are Ohio, Pennsylvania, West Virginia, New York, Michigan, Vermont, and Indiana. The most important section is the Ohio River Valley; it comprises Ohio, southwestern Pennsylvania, and the eastern part of West Virginia.

These wools compare favorably with any in the world and are equal to the fine Australian wools. They are unusually sound and strong and are the most valuable American wools. The domestic wools are, as a rule, almost free from burrs and dirt. Special attention is given to breeding, the sheep being housed and given every possible attention. The length of domestic merino wools ranges from 2 to 5 in. Merino wools from the Ohio Valley that are 3 in. and over are known as "delaine" wools. They are obtained by careful selection in breeding, combined with excellent feeding.

Territory Wools. Territory wools, also known as western or range wools, are those grown in the states of Montana, Wyoming, Idaho, Nevada, Utah, Arizona, New Mexico, and Colorado, also the western portions of the Dakotas, Nebraska, and Kansas. Territory includes most of the wools produced in Washington and Oregon but does not include wools of Texas and California. The name "territory" dates back to the time when the regions west of the Missouri River, previous to their admittance to statehood, were called the territories.

The name "territory" is not strictly adhered to, as many of the territory wools are called by the name of their state, when sold in bulk lots. The production of Texas and California wool is included in government compilations under the term "range wools."

The sheep roaming in these western states seldom receive any housing or protection from winter storms and blizzards, and they are rarely furnished with fodder. Tenacious burrs abounding in the greater part of the ranges become entangled in the fleeces. The soil in most of the western ranges is sandy and alkaline. The nature of the soil, sickness due to insufficient nourishment at various times, and exposure may weaken the wool in the fleeces of these sheep. Therefore, at their best, the territory wools are seldom equal to similar domestic wools. Most of these territory wools range from 1½ to 3 in. in length. Owing to the excessive exposure to the elements, the wool generally feels quite harsh. The wool varies slightly in its characteristics from one state to another, and an expert wool buyer seldom errs, when judging the fleece, as to the state in which the wool was grown. However, the wools grade into one another almost imperceptibly. Montana, Wyoming, and Idaho produce the best of the territory wools. They are of about equal value and are usually grouped together in the market quotation for wool in the trade papers. Wyoming wools are noted for their whiteness when scoured, and are especially sought for the production of knitting yarns.

Texas and California Wools. These two wools, though grown far apart, are usually grouped together. Quite a high percentage of the sheep are sheared twice a year. According to the season shorn, the fleeces are known as "spring" or "fall" Texas or California; or, based on the number of months on the sheep's back, they are designated as 6-month, 8-month, and 12-month wools.

Texas produces over 23 per cent of the total wool clip in the United States, and 95 per cent is 64's or finer. Texas is probably the only state in the Union where 80's wools are produced. Especially in the last few years some Texas ranches produced wool which compares favorably with the best Ohio wools or even some of the Australian wools. The only setback is that they do not have the length. The custom of shearing twice a year is reflected in the unevenness in lengths of most of the Texas wools. The length varies from half an inch to 1½ in. for 6- and 8-month wools, and from 2 to 3½ in. for 12-month wools. Many of them are deficient in color.

California Wools. According to Wilson [22], the California clip as a whole is predominantly a fine wool clip. Parts of northern California produce some of the best wools in the United States, whereas the wool from the central and southern parts of California is short and defective.

TABLE 13. UNITED STATES AVERAGE WOOL PRODUCTION, OF SHORN, PULLED, AND CLEAN WOOL, 1936–40, IN MILLIONS OF POUNDS

Items	*Fine*	*½-Blood*	*⅜-Blood*	*¼-Blood*	*Low*	*All Grades*
Production, grease basis:						
Shorn:						
Farming region	12	8	35	32	4	91
Range region	183	51	34	11	3	282
Total shorn	195	59	69	43	7	373
Pulled	17	7	24	14	3	65
Total shorn and pulled	212	66	93	57	10	438
Production, scoured basis:						
Shorn:						
Farming region	4.6	3.5	18.6	18.2	2.3	47.2
Range region	62.2	20.4	14.6	5.3	1.6	104.1
Total shorn	66.8	23.9	33.2	23.5	3.9	151.3
Pulled	10.2	4.9	18.5	11.5	2.5	47.6
Total shorn and pulled	77.0	28.8	51.7	35.0	6.4	198.9

Generally, California wools do not command the prices brought by Texas and territory wools, because most of them are liable to contain more injurious vegetable matter than wools of the territory states.

The Tariff Commission [20], in surveying the wartime supply situation, has made a study of United States production of shorn and pulled wools, by grades, their estimated clean scoured yields, and production on the scoured basis. This study covers the 5-yr period, when conditions of production were approximately normal. (See Table 13.)

Shorn and Pulled Wools Produced. Table 14 shows the United States production of shorn and pulled wools as estimated by the U. S.

TABLE 14. RAW WOOL: UNITED STATES PRODUCTION, 1931–50, IN MILLIONS OF POUNDS

Year	*Shorn*	*Pulled*	*Total*	*Year*	*Shorn*	*Pulled*	*Total*
1931	376.3	66.1	442.4	1941	387.5	65.8	453.3
1932	351.0	67.1	418.1	1942	388.3	66.7	455.0
1933	374.2	64.2	438.4	1943	378.8	65.2	444.0
1934	368.9	60.5	429.4	1944	338.3	73.5	411.8
1935	361.5	66.0	427.5	1945	307.9	70.5	378.4
1936	353.2	66.2	419.4	1946	280.5	61.3	341.8
1937	356.1	66.2	422.3	1947	252.8	56.6	309.4
1938	359.9	64.5	424.4	1948	233.9	46.6	280.5
1939	361.7	64.5	426.2	1949	217.0	36.4	253.4
1940	372.0	62.0	434.0	1950	212.0	35.0	247.0
Av. 1931–40	363.5	64.7	428.2	1951	225.5	24.9	250.4
Av. 1936–40	360.6	64.7	425.3	Av. 1941–50	299.7	57.8	357.5
				Av. 1946–50	239.2	47.2	286.4

Source: Estimates of U. S. Department of Agriculture.

Department of Agriculture for the 20-yr period 1931–50. In the five years prior to World War II, 1936–40, when conditions of production were approximately normal, the shorn wools averaged 373 million lb and pulled wools 65 million lb per year. However, in the five years following World War II, 1946–50, the average production for shorn wool dropped to 239 million lb and for pulled wool dropped to 47 million lb.

The percentages of production of farm- and range-shorn wools and of all pulled wools by grades are shown in Table 15. The yield of each type grown is shown in this table and is used to give quantitative figures for clean scoured wool produced. In 1936–40, the average annual production of farm-shorn wools was 91 million lb, as compared with 282 million lb of range wools. Because of relatively high scoured yields, averaging 51 per cent, the farm-grown wools had a scoured

TABLE 15. Percentage Distribution of Raw and Clean Scoured Wools, 1936–40

[Source: U. S. Tariff Commission, compiled from trade data.]

Item	Fine	Half-Blood	Three-Eighths Blood	Quarter-Blood	Low	All Grades
	Production					
Production, by grades:						
Shorn: * Farming region	13	9	38	35	5	100
Range region	65	18	12	4	1	100
Average, shorn wools	52	16	18	12	2	100
Pulled	26	11	37	21	5	100
Average: Shorn and pulled grease	49	15	21	13	2	100
Shorn and pulled scoured	39	14	26	18	3	100
	Clean Scoured Yields					
Average clean scoured yields:						
Shorn: * Farming region	38	44	53	57	58	51
Range region	34	40	43	48	54	37
Average, all shorn †	34	40	48	55	56	40 to 41
Pulled	60	70	77	82	84	73
Average, shorn and pulled	36	44	56	61	64	45 to 46

* As shorn, i.e., grease basis. † To the nearest unit percentage.

weight of 47,200,000 lb; the range wools, with an average scoured yield of 31 per cent, had a scoured weight of 104,100,000 lb. Thus, although the weight of the range wools, as shown, was three times that of the farm wools, on the scoured basis the volume of the range wools was only about 2¼ times as great as that of the farm wools. The 65,000,000 lb of pulled wools, with an average yield of 73 per cent, had a scoured weight of 47,600,000 lb. The total annual production of 438,000,000 lb of shorn and pulled wools, with an average yield of about 45.5 per cent, had a scoured weight of 198,900,000 lb.

Percentage Production of Farm and Range Wools

As between the farming and the range regions, the distribution of shorn wools, by grades, exhibits striking differences. Fine wools constitute only about 13 per cent of all farm wools, whereas they amount to 65 per cent of the range wools. In the farming region, fine-wooled sheep are generally the remnants of flocks of such sheep that predominated in certain areas years ago. The few that are left occupy the rougher grazing areas, where it is difficult to raise enough harvested foods for mutton types of sheep, or where the limited production of such crops can be fed more profitably to other livestock. Elsewhere in the farming states, mutton breeds or types have largely displaced merinos. Merino types predominate in the range region because of the herding instinct, i.e., the desire of the flock to stay together. This trait is highly necessary in sheep kept on the rough unfenced ranges commonly found in the Far West, where losses from straying would otherwise be prohibitively high. Of equal importance is the capacity of the merino to thrive under adverse conditions.

About 9 per cent of the wools shorn in the farming region is half-blood, as compared with 18 per cent in the range region. In some of the more favorable range areas, particularly when lush summer feed is available for the production of fat market lambs, the larger crossbred ewes, which produce half-blood wool, are preferred to fine wool ewes. In the farming states, where conditions of production favor larger sheep and more emphasis on market lambs, most sheep raisers make a clean break from merinos and use chiefly medium wool types of ewes. It is for this reason that three-eighths blood and quarter-blood wools predominate in the farming region. In the range region comparatively few areas have sufficiently good grazing during about half of the year to support medium wool crossbred ewes without too costly use of concentrates. Partly for this reason, three-eighths blood and quarter-blood wools form only 12 and 4 per cent, respectively, of the range-shorn wools. The percentage of quarter-blood wools is small chiefly because the crossbred ewes that grow it have been bred too far away from the merino to be well adapted to the western range country. Low quarter-blood and coarser wools constitute only about 1 per cent of the range production, the type of sheep that produces them not being adapted to range conditions. The few such sheep in the range region are kept chiefly for the production of crossbred range breeding stock.

Comparative Clean Scoured Yields of Farm and Range Wools

Fine wools in the farming region have an average clean scoured yield of 38 per cent, as compared with 34 per cent in the range region, where the clip is much heavier with earthy matter. About 15 yr ago the difference was somewhat larger, but a rapid increase in the number of sheep (almost entirely fine wools) in Texas and a rapid growth in the use of fenced ranges (which result in cleaner fleeces) has raised the average scoured yield in Texas by several points and has raised the average for range-grown fine wools by about 1 per cent. (See Table 15.) There is also a 4 per cent difference (44 compared with 40) in the yields of farm- and range-grown half-bloods. In three-eighths bloods, however, there is a greater difference, the yield being 53 per cent for the farming and 43 for the range region. The respective yields of quarter-bloods in the two regions are 57 and 48 per cent. The wide differences shown by these two grades result largely from the fact that most of the crossbred range sheep spend about 8 months of the year on dusty, sparsely vegetated desert and semi-desert grazing land, where their relatively loose fleeces become so burdened with silt and sand as to partly offset their natural tendency toward a high clean yield. In the farming regions, most of the sheep graze on well-grassed pastures.

The difference between scoured yields of low quarter-blood and coarser wools is much less; these yields are 58 per cent for the farm and 54 per cent for the range wools. Coarse wool sheep in the range region usually are not grazed on dusty range lands for long periods; therefore their fleeces carry much less foreign matter than those of finer wool range stock.

Yield of Pulled Wools

Before sheep pelts are treated to loosen the fibers, they are washed and usually well brushed. A large part of the foreign matter present in the wool is thus removed before pulling takes place. As a result, the estimated clean scoured yield ranges from an average of 60 per cent for fine to 84 per cent for low quarter-blood and coarser.

The clean scoured production of each grade is also shown as a percentage of the total. Because of differences in yields of the various grades, there is a striking difference between the relationship of the grades in the grease and of the grades on the scoured basis. Fine wools amount to 49 per cent of the total production in the grease, but to only about 39 per cent on the scoured basis. There is little change for half-bloods, but three-eighths bloods amount to 21 per cent of the total in the grease and to 26 per cent on the scoured basis. Quarter-bloods amount to 13 and 17.6 per cent and low wools to 2 and 3.2 per cent, respectively, on the two bases.

Medium Wool Breeds

By far the largest percentage of this wool type is produced by breeds that originated in Great Britain. The following breeds are included in the medium wool class: Southdown, Shropshire, Hampshire, Oxford, Suffolk, Dorset, Cheviot, Ryeland, and Tunis. The first five are collectively referred to as "down" breeds, because of the nature of the country in which they were developed—ranges of hills or "downs" in southern England. The "down" breeds have all been bred primarily for mutton, with special emphasis upon some useful character considered necessary for the style of farming and the markets of the various counties or "shires," from which most of the breeds take their names.

FIG. 9. First prize Hampshire ram. (*Courtesy U. S. Department of Agriculture.*)

The face and leg color of all down breeds is some shade of brown or black, and the fleece occupies a middle position between the length and coarseness of the long wools and the extreme fineness and density of the fine wools. Although there are breed variations in fineness, length, and density, the fleece is always close and dry enough to furnish excellent protection.

FIG. 10. Champion Cheviot ram. (*Courtesy U. S. Department of Agriculture.*)

Most of the down sheep are today found all over the world, because they can be fattened for the meat market better than any other sheep. Southdown and Shropshire rams are sold to Australia, New Zealand, Argentina, Chile, Peru, West Indies, United States, Canada, Kenya, Scandinavia, Japan, and China. In the United States over 50 per cent of all breeds are down sheep.

Dorset Horns. The Dorset is of the medium wool type but is not a down breed. Both rams and ewes have horns, and the faces and legs are white. It is the only common medium wool breed in the United

States that has horns. The native home of the Dorset horn is in the counties of Dorset and Somerset in south central England.

Cheviots. The Cheviot possesses the characteristics of hill or mountain breeds; it is very active and alert, which indicates that it is well adapted to grazing over rough and rugged country. It is a native of the Cheviot hills, which form about 30 miles of the border country between England and Scotland. The wool is noted for its use in tweeds.

Characteristics of Medium Wools

The fleece of medium wool occupies a middle position between the high fineness and density of the merino fleece and the length and coarseness of the long wools. There is no clear-cut borderline between fine and medium wools. The main criterion for the classification is the fineness of the fibers, which ranges from low quarter- to half-blood, respectively, from 46's to 60's.

The fibers may range in length from 2 to 5 in.; generally they are of good combing length. The fleeces are considerably lighter than merino fleeces, and because of their openness they contain less sand and are less greasy. In scouring, the shrinkage ranges between 40 and 60 per cent, depending on the grade and the origin of the wool.

TABLE 16. United States Medium Wool Type Breeds [16]

Breed	Body Weight (pounds)		Wool Weight per Fleece (pounds)		Grade	Length (inches)	Shrinkage (per cent)
	Ram	Ewe	Ram	Ewe			
Southdown	140 to 180	90 to 140	5 to 8	4 to 7	56's to 60's	2	45 to 56
Shropshire	150 to 225	120 to 170	6 to 10	5 to 9	48's to 56's	2½ to 3	
Hampshire	170 to 275	135 to 200	5 to 9	4 to 8	48's to 56's	2½	
Suffolk	225 to 300	165 to 225	6 to 9	5 to 7	48's to 56's	2 to 2¾	38 to 50
Oxford	250 to 325	180 to 250	12 to 15	10 to 12	46's to 50's	3 to 4	
Dorset Horn	150 to 225	125 to 150	6 to 9	4 to 7	48's to 56's	2½ to 3	
Cheviot	150 to 200	115 to 150	7 to 10	6 to 8	48's to 56's	4	35

TABLE 17. Relationship Between Grade, Shrinkage, and Length

Grades	*Shrinkage, Domestic (per cent)*	*Shrinkage, Territory (per cent)*	*Approximate Length (inches)*
Fine	62	66	1½ to 3
Half-blood	56	60	
Three-eighths blood	47	57	2 to 4
Quarter-blood	43	52	3 to 5
Low	42	46	3½ to 6

The relationships between grade, shrinkage and length are given in Tables 16 and 17.

As the ability to felt decreases with the increase in the diameter of the fibers, the medium wools (especially the down wools) are very suitable for hosiery and knit goods, whether machine or hand knitted. The standard wool grade for hand-knitting yarn is 52's–54's. The medium wools are also extensively used for ladies' wear fabrics, such as suitings, coatings, and fine tweeds and for men's medium worsted suitings, serges, flannels, overcoatings, and blankets.

Long Wool Breeds

The long wool breeds—Lincoln, Cotswold, Leicester, and Romney Marsh—bred chiefly for mutton, are the largest sheep of all breeds. All of them are large-framed, square-bodied sheep, with very broad backs. Their fleeces are open or loose, as compared with the fine wools and medium wools, and are coarser and very long. As their size indicates, the breeds of this class have been developed for level lands, where feed can be obtained without much travel. With proper attention they will thrive upon lands that are too low and wet for the breeds of the medium wool class (though the keeping of any sheep on marshy ground is not advised). The long wool sheep have been found to thrive in regions of excessive rainfall because the long wool carries the water off the body.

FIG. 11. Champion Lincoln ram. (*Courtesy U. S. Department of Agriculture.*)

Lincolns. This breed, the largest of all sheep, originated in Lincolnshire, the low country on the east coast of England. The face and legs are white with the exception of the hoofs and the skin at the lip and nostrils.

The wool covers the body in broad locks with the characteristic curl on the outer end. It forms a tuft on the forehead, but does not extend over the top of the head above the eyes. The Lincoln leads the mutton breeds in length of wool. In the United States its distribution is limited to Oregon and to the mountain states, where over 80 per cent of all Lincolns are bred. The breed is very popular in Argentina, Australia, New Zealand, and Canada.

Cotswolds. The typical Cotswold is a big-bodied, rather tall sheep of stylish appearance. Its native home is the Cotswold Hills of Gloucester, England. The Cotswold sheep resembles the English Leicester. The face, ears, and legs are white, or white mixed with a little brown. The wool extends up over the poll and hangs in ringlets of various lengths over the face. All over the body the wool hangs in wavy ringlets 10 to 14 in. long; these do not show in the same way on any other breed with the exception of the Angora goat. One fleece will shear from 10 to 14 lb. The shrinkage is low on account of lack of excess of grease, and the quality is coarse, usually grading "braid." The Cotswolds are most popular in Oregon and the mountain states.

FIG. 12. Romney ram of New Zealand. (*Courtesy J. F. Wilson, Univ. of Calif.*)

Leicesters. The breed commonly known as Leicester is divided into English-Leicester and Border-Leicester. The English-Leicester is well covered with wool at the crown of the head, similar to the Cotswold, whereas the head of the Border-Leicester is bare of wool. In the United States and in Canada breeders have mixed Cotswolds and Leicesters.

Romney. The Romney, which originated in the plain of southeastern England, is popular in Oregon, Washington, and California and is widely distributed in South America, Australia, and New Zealand. Wool is not as long nor as lustrous as Cotswold or Lincoln, but is denser and finer, grading low quarter-blood to quarter-blood. Rams range in weight from 225 to 250 lb and ewes from 175 to 200 lb. Shrinkage is 20 to 35 per cent.

Characteristics of Long Wools

In the pedigree diagram of the domestic sheep (Fig. 5), two classes of breeds are listed as yielding long wools, namely, the breeds growing demi-luster wools and the breeds yielding luster wools. The breeds growing demi-luster wools originated from various crosses of luster and down sheep and of luster and English mountain sheep. Because of this foundation the fineness of the demi-luster wools overlaps that of the medium wools. The fineness range is from 44's or common to

50's or quarter-blood; the lengths range from 6 to 9 in. The wool is of a lustrous nature and is manufactured into plain cloths, tweeds, serges, overcoatings, blankets, and felts.

The true long wools are the luster wools derived from the Lincoln, Leicester, and Cotswold sheep (see Table 18). The standard is set by

TABLE 18. CHARACTERISTICS OF LONG WOOL TYPE BREEDS [16]

Country	Breed	Body Weight (pounds)		Wool Weight per Fleece (pounds)		Grade	Length (inches)	Shrinkage (per cent)
		Ram	Ewe	Ram	Ewe			
United States of America	Lincoln	300 to 350	200 to 250	16 to 22	12 to 16	36's to 46's	8 to 12	20 to 35
	Cotswold	250 to 275	200 to 250	14 to 20	10 to 12	36's to 40's	10 to 14	
	Leicester (English)	225 to 250	175 to 200	10 to 15	9 to 12	40's to 48's	6 to 8	
New Zealand	Romney	225 to 250	150 to 190	22 to 26	10 to 12	44's to 50's	5 to 6	25 to 30

the Lincoln wool, which has a world-wide reputation on account of its length of staple and beautiful luster. The luster wools are the coarsest wools grown, ranging in fiber diameter from below 36's or braid to 44's or common. They also hold the length record with 32 in. staple of yearling Lincoln ewes. Normally, the wool grows from 8 to 15 in. Whereas the wool of the Lincoln and Leicester forms broad locks, that of the Cotswold forms curly locks, resembling mohair. All long wools are light shrinking, losing from 20 to 35 per cent in weight through scouring. The luster wools are manufactured into braids, buntings, shoe laces, linings, lustrous worsted fabrics, and pulp felts.

Crossbred Wool Breeds

The crossbred breeds produce medium fine wool and are, therefore, often classified with the medium wool breeds. The breeds representing these groups were developed in the last 50 yr, by crossing merino or Rambouillet with long wool sheep. The following main breeds were developed by crossbreeding: the Corriedale, Columbia, Panama, Romeldale, Polwarth, and Targhee.

Corriedales. The Corriedale, which is the oldest of this class of sheep, has been developed in New Zealand since 1880. Lincoln rams were crossed with merino ewes; and after close culling toward the desired type, the half-breeds were mated. The type is practically intermediate between the Lincoln and the merino, being smaller and less heavily fleshed than the Lincoln and larger and more heavily fleshed than the merino. The fleece possesses much of the fineness and softness found in the merino, but with much greater lengths than occur in the same grades with other fleeces.

This breed is most valuable where sheep are bred equally for lambs and wool under range conditions. The face, ears, and legs are white, and other breed characteristics are quite similar to the two amalgamated parental breeds. The fleece obtains a length of 3 to 4 in.; it weighs from 10 to 12 lb. The quality grades are quarter-, three-eighths, and half-blood, and shrinkage is less than in most other wools of similar quality. The breed is increasing in popularity in the western ranges and is most common in Wyoming, California, and Oregon.

FIG. 13. Champion Corriedale ram. (*Courtesy Univ. of Wyoming.*)

Columbias. The Columbia is a crossbreed of Lincoln rams and Rambouillet ewes developed by the Division of Animal Husbandry, United States Department of Agriculture. The development work was begun in 1912 at Laramie, Wyoming, and since 1917 has been continued at the United States Sheep Experiment Station, Dubois, Idaho. The purpose of this work was to develop a crossbred sheep that would be suitable to western range conditions and breed true to type.

The Columbia is a large, vigorous, and heavy-boned animal with rather long legs. Ewes average about 135 lb and rams up to 275 lb under normal range conditions. Columbia ewes are very prolific. They consistently yield long-stapled fleeces of three-eighths or quarter-blood quality. During a 3-yr period the fleece weights of mature Columbia ewes, under strict range conditions, averaged 11.27 lb. For the same period 75.74 per cent of the ewes each produced and weaned one lamb annually. These lambs averaged 78.02 lb in weight at weaning time.

Panama. The Panama is similar to the Columbia breed. It was started in 1912 by James Laidlaw of Muldoon, Idaho. In this case, Rambouillet rams were bred to Lincoln ewes.

Romeldale. This breed was developed by the Spencer Ranch Co. of Cranmore, California, by mating Romney rams with Rambouillet ewes. Through careful selection of the crossbreeds in all these cases a type of sheep has been introduced which is about halfway between the two parental breeds.

Polwarth. The Polwarth originated in 1880 in Victoria and Tasmania. Pure Australasian merino was mated with a pure Lincoln. In Australia they are known as "comeback" sheep. The Polwarth produces even quality, high-yielding wool, about 58's grade and 4 to 6 in. long. The breed is considered valuable for their country by Argentine breeders.

FIG. 14. Columbia ewe. (*Courtesy U. S. Sheep Experimental Station, Dubois, Idaho.*)

Targhee. Development of the Targhee breed of sheep resulted directly from experimental work in the United States Bureau of Animal Industry. This fixed breed is the product of the selective breeding of crossbred strains of sheep best adapted to the intermountain range region, through the interbreeding of hybrids from breeds having both desirable and undesirable characteristics for the production of lamb meat and wool. According to Spencer [17] the foundation stock of the Targhee breed is as follows: 66.3 per cent Rambouillet, 8.7 per cent merino and 25 per cent Lincoln, so that the Targhee is three-quarters fine wool blood and one-quarter coarse wool blood. The Targhee are adapted to range that is intermediate in availability of forage.

Characteristics of Crossbred Wools

In regard to fineness, crossbred wools belong to the medium type, but they have the added value of being 1 to 3 in. longer, and the amount of wool produced per sheep is from 75 to 100 per cent higher than that of the down breeds. Table 19 shows the comparison of the wool produced by the crossbred breeds and two down breeds in Australia.

In addition, Table 20 shows that because of the longer staple of the crossbred wools the yield on noils in combing is only half of that of the down wool, which increases their value still further.

New Zealand is the largest mutton-producing country in the world and therefore the greatest supplier of crossbred wools. Of the more than 350 million lb of wool produced annually in New Zealand, only 3 per cent is derived from merino sheep. The 1949–50 clip amounted to

TABLE 19. Characteristics of Crossbred Wool Type Breeds [16]

Country	Breed	Body Weight (pounds)		Wool Weight per Fleece (pounds)		Grade	Length (inches)	Shrinkage (per cent)
		Ram	Ewe	Ram	Ewe			
United States of America	Corriedale	150 to 250	125 to 145	15 to 19	10 to 12	50's to 60's	3 to 4	45 to 56
	Columbia	175 to 275	135 to 155	15 to 20	10 to 12	50's to 56's	3½	50
	Panama	200 to 275	145 to 160	16	10 to 12	50's to 58's	3 to 3½	45 to 50
	Romeldale	175 to 225	115 to 150	12 to 17	8 to 11	58's to 60's	3½ to 4	40 to 45
	Targhee	200	130	. .	11	58's to 60's	3	45
	Thribble Cross	200	150	15	10	56's to 58's	3	45
Australia	Corriedale	175 to 275	130 to 160	17 to 26	10 to 14	48's to 56's	4 to 7	35 to 40
	Polwarth	125 to 175	110 to 125	12 to 18	8 to 10	56's to 64's	4 to 6	30 to 35
New Zealand	Corriedale	175 to 250	125 to 150	18 to 24	10 to 14	50's to 58's	4 to 6	30 to 40

TABLE 20. Comparison of Australian Crossbred and Down Wools [12]

Breeds	*Length (inches)*	*Weight of Fleece (pounds)*	*Grade*	*Yield (per cent)*	*Noil Yield (per cent)*
Polwarth	5½	8 to 9	56's to 64's	60 to 66	4 to 6
Corriedale	5½	10	50's to 56's	64 to 68	5 to 7
Southdown	2½	3 to 4	54's to 56's	60 to 65	12
Shropshire	3½	6	50's to 56's	60 to 65	12

370 million lb, of which approximately 14 per cent was slipe or pulled wool [14]. The main breeds of sheep in New Zealand, as recorded by Hind [14] are shown in Table 21.

TABLE 21. Breeds of Sheep in New Zealand

Type	*Percentage*	*Type*	*Percentage*
Crossbred *	75.00	Merino	3.25
Romney	10.50	Luster	0.75
Southdown	6.25	Shropshire and Ryeland	0.25
Corriedale	4.00		

* Mostly Romney blood.

Other important producers of crossbred wools for the world market are Argentina, Uruguay, Brazil, and Chile.

Some of these wools, especially the ones collected at Punta Arenas, on the southern tip of South America, are noted in the hosiery trade for their good color and springiness, which is accompanied by a full and lofty handle. The crossbred wool is used mainly in the knitting trade, but it is also very suitable for all types of worsted fabrics, for ladies' as well as men's wear, such as serges and tweeds. It is also very desirable in the manufacture of a medium class of felts.

In 1950 approximately 50 per cent of the total world production consisted of crossbred wool.

Carpet or Mixed Wools

Carpet wools are produced by sheep which live under primitive conditions in all parts of the world. A large proportion of the carpet wool comes from the Asiatic countries, and the preponderance of the sheep from which these wools come are of the fat-tailed and broad-tailed varieties, although some carpet wool is produced by sheep of the thin-tailed varieties.

The merino sheep has left its imprint on nearly all the European countries, North and South America, Australia, and South Africa. In Asia it has made but little progress, for here the prevailing sheep is quite a different animal carrying a distinct type of fleece.

As the urial sheep migrated across arid deserts in the summer and through barren wastes in the winters, such features as fat tail, broad tail, fat rumps, long legs, and big horns were developed. Fat-tailed sheep are found in desert regions, where they have to live on little food during certain periods, and are able to survive on the store of fat carried in their tails.

Fat-rumped sheep grow two lumps of fat, one on each buttock; but they have very short tails, which in some cases do not exceed 3 in. in length. These animals often weigh 200 lb each and have from 30 to 40 lb of fat. Long-legged sheep live on the lowlands. Their length of leg enables them to cross marshy ground with speed and ease.

The wool grown by these sheep is composed of a mixture, a long hairy outer coat protecting the finer undercoat of true wool, which keeps the animal warm. This type of fleece protects the sheep against low temperatures, high winds, and extremes in moisture ranging from extreme dryness to excessive rain and fog.

Representative of the Asiatic breeds [5] producing carpet wools are the Somali, fat-rumped, Hirrik, and Sikkim-Bera breeds, for which the following descriptions are given:

Fat-Rumped. This breed and its several sub-breeds or local breeds are an "Asiatic" type which ranges from the Black Sea and confines of Europe, throughout central Asia, and through the greater part of

China and Siberia. Enormous flocks are kept by nomad Kirghiz, Kalmuks, and Mongols. In Siberia they are largely bred by Russians. In China the fat-rumped sheep appears to be almost the indigenous domesticated breed of sheep. Some flocks include 10,000 to as many as 15,000 head. In many districts, the breed is not pure but has been crossed with sheep of other kinds, so there is great variation in the amount of fat on the rump and in the length of tail. The Tatarian breed, which extends from the Kirghiz Steppes to southern Siberia, is a typical representative of the groups. The urial is thought to be the original ancestor of the fat-tailed and fat-rumped groups (Fig. 15).

Fig. 15. Arabian fat-tailed sheep: Iraki or Hirrik. (*Courtesy Calif. Wool Growers Assoc.*)

Hirrik or Iraki. This breed is not only one of the best producing carpet wools but is also a good representative of the Arabian sheep family. The breed is hornless and belongs to the fat-tailed group with the tail rather flat and oval in shape. The coarse wool is quite long and white and extends over the top of the skull. The head, ears, and legs are brown, with some exceptions that are black or mottled in color. Rams average 4½ lb and ewes 3 lb of wool per year. Thousands of this type of sheep supply the Syrian and Palestine mutton markets.

Sikkim-Bera Breed (India). This breed is a native of Sikkim Province. It thrives well from sea level to an altitude of 18,000 ft. A ram has an average height of 2 ft 6 in. and an average length of 3 ft 6 in. from base of horns to root of tail. The wool is very coarse and ashy. Annual shearing is from 2 to 4 lb. When left to natural grazing, 60 to 70 lb of meat is obtained from a ram. Ewes measure slightly less and give less wool.

In addition to these Asiatic breeds, there are a number of European breeds producing carpet types of wool. The best known belong to the British mountain sheep such as the Scotch blackface and Welsh mountain.

Scotch Blackface [7]. The Scotch blackface is a well-known mountain sheep of Scotland. This breed extends from the Grampians to Pentland Firth; to Hebrides, Shetlands and Orkneys; and to the heathery moors of Yorkshire and Lancashire (England). These sheep are wild, extremely hardy, and impatient of restraint; the ewes make good mothers. This breed is medium-sized; it matures quickly and responds quickly to a favorable habitat. Crossed with Border-Leicester, these sheep produce excellent market lambs. Their wool is long, strong, durable, and elastic; it is much used in carpet making. They have a fine carriage. The Scotch blackface is horned, has a bare face, a long hairy mottled black and white fleece, and bare legs. Shrinkage is 30 per cent.

FIG. 16. Scotch blackface mountain sheep. (*Courtesy Eavenson & Levering Co.*)

Welsh Mountain. The Welsh mountain sheep is a small active animal, which has a fleece of rather poor wool seldom exceeding 2 lb in weight. The small carcass of this animal is very solid and forms a notable type of mutton. These sheep have tan-colored faces, which are taken as an indication of their hardy constitutions. They are good climbers that cannot be restricted by walls and fences. The rams have horns, but the ewes are hornless. Several attempts have been made to improve the breed by Southdown influence, but they have not proved very successful, although Wiltshire rams make a suitable cross. These sheep have to be sheared early in the summer as they tend to shed their fleeces in the warmer weather. Certain flocks of black Welsh mountain sheep are maintained to supply wool for the Welsh flannel trade.

The Navajo Sheep [10]. In the United States the only sheep producing carpet wools are the Navajo sheep. The sheep is quite small. The rams of the flocks supervised by the United States Department of Agriculture weigh between 135 and 170 lb and the ewes between 80 and 130 lb. The ram fleeces range in weight from 7 to 10 lb and the ewe fleeces from 4 to 8 lb, yielding from 55 to 70 per cent clean wool. The fleeces are composed of an undercoat of true wool fibers from 3 to 4 in. long and an outer coat of long wool fibers from 4 to 6 in. long. The weight percentage of the undercoat ranges from 60 to 80 per cent. In common with other unimproved wools, the fleeces contain small percentages of kemp and other medullated fibers.

The nearly 65,000 Navajo Indians make their home in a reservation area of about 16 million acres in northeastern Arizona, northwestern New Mexico, and southern Utah, and their main occupation is sheep raising. The number of mature sheep and goats on the reservation is about 420,000 head. Approximately 400,000 lb of wool, or about 18 per cent of the total annual production on the reservation, is woven by the women into blankets and rugs. In 1939 not more than 5 per cent of the wool produced on the reservation was of the Navajo type.

Fig. 17. Navajo sheep. Ewe from Fort Wingate, N. M. (*Courtesy U. S. Department of Agriculture.*)

Characteristics of Carpet Wools

The carpet wool fleeces are composed of a mixture of long, hairy fibers forming the outer coat and a fine undercoat of true wool. These two types of fibers make up the main part of the carpet wool fleece, but a third type of fiber, the so-called kemp, also occurs in varying amounts. This is a brittle, opaque fiber, which is easily identified. All degrees of variation among these three types of fibers are found, and when these wools are analyzed macroscopically, several subtypes of fibers have been distinguished under each type.

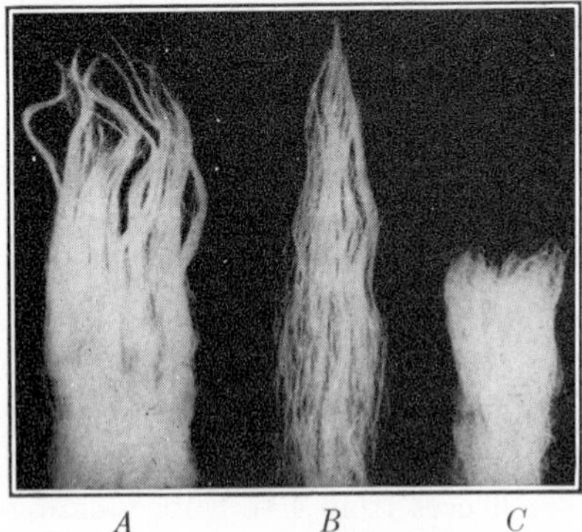

Fig. 18. A lock of Navajo wool *A;* separated to show long, coarse outercoat fibers *B;* and undercoat fibers *C.* (*Courtesy U. S. Department of Agriculture.*)

Burns, Johnston and Chen [1] describe the various fiber types as follows:

Carpet Fiber Types. Chinese and other carpet wools of mixed wool type consist of different varieties of fiber such as true wool (fine undercoat), kemps (usually lying loose in the fleece), heterotypical fibers (hair and intermediate fibers), and colored fibers.

True wool refers to those fibers that make up the fine undercoat of the mixed wool sheep. Those fibers are oval in cross-section, have a solid cortical mass making up the shaft of the fiber, show no medullation, and are usually quite fine. Even in fleeces of coarse appearance these true wool fibers of the undercoat may be of 64's to 70's spinning quality.

Kemps, which lie loose in the fleece, are easily distinguished from the longer coarse medullated fibers, which are not normally shed.

Heterotypical Fibers. Heterotypical fibers, as the name implies, are neither wool nor kemp. Originally the name was applied to those fibers which within the same fiber shaft showed the characteristics of wool fibers, kemps, and hairs. Later, as the kemps were subdivided, the name came to be applied to those fibers which showed the fiber shaft characteristics of both wool and hair in the same fiber, particularly in respect of medullation and nonmedullation. The structure of heterotypical fibers may vary considerably from the proximal to the distal end.

Colored fibers range from pale yellow to black in the true wool; in the kemps, from black to red or fawn and on to yellow or buff. A great amount of variation in color exists, even in the same fiber.

Analysis of Carpet Wools

It has already been pointed out that carpet wools are of the mixed wool type and consist of a mixture of true wool, hair, including heterotypical fibers, and kemp.

Chen in trying to find the ideal carpet wool type made a study of five samples of Chinese wools and compared them with Vicanere and Aleppo wools, which were considered by mill men to be the ideal types of carpet wool. A sample of Romney Marsh wool was also included in the study, as this type of improved wool is similar to the carpet types and is often used for this purpose.

Description of Samples. 1. True Sining wool is a type of Tibetan wool which is considered the best of all Chinese carpet wools. It is rarely obtainable in its pure type today.

2. Mixed Sining wool is a mixture of true Sining and Kansu wool.

3. Lanchow wool comes from the province of Kansu. It is often blended with Tibetan wools.

4. Szechwan (Szechuen) wools come from the province after which they are named and are classed with Tibetan wools.

5. Woosung (Woozie) wools come from the neighborhood of Shanghai and are short in staple and suitable only for filling wools in carpet making. They are known in the trade as one of the poorest carpet wools.

6. Vicanere wool is produced in north central India and is of the finest carpet wools. It is exceptionally lively and lofty.

7. Aleppo wool is grown in Syria, Asia Minor, and is considered one

TABLE 22. PERCENTAGES OF EACH FIBER TYPE IN CARPET WOOLS, DETERMINED BY COUNTING AND WEIGHING

Wool Types	Types of Fibers							
	True Wool		Heterotype		Kemp		Colored	
	By Count	By Weight	By Count	By Weight	By Count	By Weight	By Count	By Weight
Romney	100.00	100.00	....	.....	....	.....	....	....
Lanchow	91.03	74.49	5.89	13.18	3.08	12.33	0.00	0.00
True Sining	88.65	42.84	9.14	46.19	0.12	0.23	2.09	10.74
Szechwan	87.12	57.65	5.80	27.85	7.08	14.50	0.00	0.00
Mixed Sining	84.66	61.51	3.93	16.42	11.35	22.02	0.06	0.05
Woosung	83.72	55.56	0.00	0.00	16.27	44.37	0.01	0.07
Aleppo	74.69	43.82	18.87	52.30	2.86	3.15	3.58	0.73
Vicanere	59.22	23.23	40.67	76.67	0.11	0.14	0.00	0.00

TABLE 23. FIBER THICKNESS AND LENGTH OF CARPET WOOLS

Wool Types	True Wool Fiber		Heterotypical Fiber		Kemp *	
	Thickness (microns)	Length Stretched (inches)	Thickness (microns)	Length Stretched (inches)	Thickness (microns)	Length Stretched (inches)
Romney	32	8.7	....	...	....	...
Aleppo	24	5.5	41	8.8	39.6	2.0
Szechwan	20.6	4.8	33.3	8.5	25.8	2.7
Lanchow	19.6	4.3	21.1	4.1	27.5	2.0
True Sining	17.5	4.4	36.3	8.5	....	...
Mixed Sining	17.4	3.2	32.4	7.8	28.4	2.4
Vicanere	17.4	2.9	25.7	4.7	....	...
Woosung	16.3	2.8	....	...	29.9	1.3

* Kemp thickness is arithmetic average of three parts of fiber.

of the better class carpet wools. It has good length and is well known for its color, strength, and resilience.

8. New Zealand Romney wool is an improved type of wool similar in type to carpet wools but more uniform. It is included in this study to represent a type of improved wool suitable for use in carpet manufacture. It is similar to the South American wools grown mainly by Lincolns, which are now furnishing a large part of the carpet wool imports to the United States.

Chen established the main characteristics of these various samples, and his results are tabulated in Tables 22 and 23.

Burns, Johnston, and Chen [1] have found certain definite relationships between objective tests in the laboratory and subjective tests by dealers and mills, and these relationships have been incorporated in a tentative guide of wool type for carpet wool producers (see below).

Tentative Guide of Wool Type for Carpet Wool Producers

1. An ideal carpet wool should contain at least 15 per cent by count or 35 per cent by weight of heterotypical fibers. These fibers should have an average thickness of at least 30 μ, and the fiber sizes should not vary more than 15 per cent. The average length of these fibers should be at least 4 in. for normal growth (12 months), and the variability of the fiber length should be less than 20 per cent.

2. An ideal carpet wool should contain not more than 2 per cent by count or 4 per cent by weight of kemp fibers. The dimensional characteristics of the kemp fibers are not so important. The important thing is to eliminate kemp from the fleeces, and this can be done, according to the experimental work carried out by Bryant (1933) working with Scotch blackface sheep.

3. An ideal carpet wool should contain not more than 85 per cent by count or 65 per cent by weight of true wool fibers. These fibers should have an average thickness not exceeding 25.4 μ, and their variation in fiber thickness should not exceed 25 per cent. They should have an average length of at least 4 in. for normal growth (12 months), and the variation in fiber length should not exceed 25 per cent.

The principal geographical sources of carpet wools for the American market are British East India; Near East, including Iran, Armenia, Turkey, Iraq, Syria, Arabia; the North African countries; the British Isles; and South America. Each of these geographical areas raises several different breeds of sheep suitable for carpet wool purposes; thus in any one area the quality characteristics of these wools and their values for carpet use vary greatly.

The method of grading and marketing carpet wools differs in each geographical area. In general there are two main classifications—shorn wool and pulled wool, and these are further divided into greasy wools and scoured wools. The shorn wools are graded into different classes depending upon the country involved, such as fleece, second clip, lambs' wool, pieces and matchings, locks, tufts, brokes, crutchings, cotts, and britch; and into color classifications of white, fawn, gray, mixed lots, etc.

Table 24, worked out by Alexander Smith & Sons Carpet Co., gives some fiber characteristics observed in wools from the geographical areas.

TABLE 24. PRINCIPAL CARPET WOOL CHARACTERISTICS

	*Average Fineness * (microns)*	*Coeff. of Variation (per cent)*	*Kemp (per cent by weight)*
New Zealand	30.0 to 40.0	20 to 30	1 to 4
China	20.0 to 30.0	30 to 75	1 to 10
British East India	25.0 to 40.0	25 to 50	1 to 30
Near East	25.0 to 35.0	30 to 45	1 to 8
North Africa	25.0 to 35.0	25 to 45	1 to 6
British Isles	30.0 to 40.0	25 to 50	1 to 15
South America	30.0 to 40.0	15 to 50	1 to 3

* Including true wool fibers, heterotypical fibers, and kemp fibers.

In general the wools from South America and the British Isles and New Zealand are the coarsest and longest of carpet wools. As can be seen from the variability of fiber diameter shown in Table 24, the chief characteristic of carpet wool types is a wide distribution of fiber diameter within fleeces and lots, with the greatest variability in the China types and the lowest in New Zealand and some South American breeds.

Of the 4 billion pounds of wool produced in 1950, approximately 800 million lb or 25 per cent were carpet wools.

Uses of Carpet Wools

As the name indicates, carpet wools are principally used in the manufacture of carpets and rugs. Wools from different geographical areas have certain definite quality characteristics used in floor covering. In general, wools from the East India region furnish characteristics of loftiness and coverage to the pile yarn and resist crushing and matting and show high relative wear value. Some New Zealand types have the highest resistance to abrasive wear, but other types are smooth and contribute to shedding or fluffing. China wools are excellent spinning wools but show relatively lower abrasive wear resistance than other types. Some types of South American wools furnish high luster but contribute to a thin yarn and shedding or fluffing. The whiteness of South American and New Zealand types makes them especially desirable for very light colors.

At times when wools of the other classes are high in price, cloth manufacturers turn to the better carpet wools for relief; but these wools do not give the same results as those they replace. Some of the better grades of carpet wools are mixed with other wools in the manufacture of coarse fabrics, such as the cheaper grades of cloakings, overcoatings, coarse tweeds, and cheviots. Some grades are also used for felt boots, horse blankets, coarse upholstery goods, robes, paper makers' felts, and wadding for gun cartridges. A large source of supply for carpet wools, other than those produced by unimproved native sheep, are the skirtings, britch, badly cotted fleeces, tags, and pieces from coarse domestic and crossbred wools. Carpet wools are comparatively coarse and are usually graded as coarse, medium, and good.

Table 25 contains most of the important varieties of carpet wools, the country of production, and character and usual grade of the wool. Many of the wools included in Table 25 come on the market as pulled, skin, or tanner's wool.

TABLE 25. Main Carpet Wools

[Source: Alexander Smith & Sons Carpet Co.]

Grades	*Length (inches)*	*Yield (per cent)*	*Descriptions*
Afghanistan			
Afghanistan	1 to 7	65 to 75	Long, white, coarse, kempy.
Arabia			
Arabian	1 to 8	65 to 75	Long, lofty, soft, medium.
Argentina			
B.A. 5/6's Fleece	1 to 13	68 to 75	Long, silky, coarse. 12 mo growth.
B.A. 5/6's Nov. 2d Clip	1 to 8	60 to 70	Coarse, silky. 6 to 8 mo growth.
B.A. 5/6's Mar. 2d Clip	1 to 5	67 to 72	Coarse, silky. 4 to 6 mo growth.
Cordova Fleece	1 to 13	52 to 60	Long, coarse, kempy. 12 mo fleece.
Cordova 2d Clip	1 to 6	48 to 55	Coarse, kempy. 6 to 9 mo growth.
Criolla	1 to 8	48 to 55	Long, medium, coarse.
British Isles			
Haslock	1 to 14	75 to 85	Coarse blackface type. Pulled wool.
Scotch Blackface	1 to 15	65 to 75	28 to 32. Very coarse with kemp and gray.
English Wethers	1 to 13	65 to 75	36 to 40. Crossbred. Lustrous, long.
Radnor	1 to 10	65 to 75	36 to 40. Welsh mountain. Lustrous, long.
Scotch Cross	1 to 13	65 to 75	36 to 40. Crossbred. Lustrous, long.
Irish Kerry	1 to 12	60 to 75	28 to 32. Medium length. Coarse, kempy.
Welsh Mountain	1 to 10	60 to 75	28 to 32. Welsh mountain. Medium length. Soft but springy, staple, kempy.
Cape South Africa			
Cabretta	1 to 4	75 to 85	Hybrid fiber; part goat. Low grade kempy.
Kempy Cape	1 to 4	75 to 85	Practically all kemps. Short.
China			
China Northern Fleece	1 to 6	40 to 45	Medium fine, kempy.
China Open Ball	1 to 4	60 to 65	Very fine, but kempy. Combed or pulled from sheep.
China Hinning	1 to 8	55 to 60	Long combing length. Medium coarse, kempy.
China Chinchow	1 to 5	45 to 50	Average length. Coarse, kempy carpet type.
China Koolung	1 to 5	45 to 50	Average length. Coarse, kempy carpet type.
China Hailar-Manchurian	1 to 8	45 to 50	Average length. Very kempy, coarse wool.
China Urga-Mongolian	1 to 8	50 to 55	Average length. Quite kempy, coarse wool.
China Uliassutai	1 to 7	50 to 55	Average length. Medium amount kempy.
Shantung	1 to 6	45 to 50	Southern wools not as kempy as northern.

TABLE 25. Main Carpet Wools (*Continued*)

Grades	Length (inches)	Yield (per cent)	Descriptions
China—*Continued*			
Szechwan	1 to 8	55 to 60	As above. More yellow, long.
Woosung	1 to 4	45 to 50	As above. Very yellow, soft, fine, few kemps.
Shanghai Skin	1 to 4	55 to 60	As above. Shorter, lime-pulled.
China Lambs	1 to 4	45 to 50	Very fine.
Cyprus			
Cyprus	1 to 14	50 to 55	Long, coarse carpet.
Egypt			
Egyptian	1 to 8	65 to 85	Medium length, coarse.
France			
Mazamet	1 to 4	75 to 90	Blend of various pulled, medium coarse wools.
India			
Bhatinda	1 to 7	65 to 85	Medium length, resilient, lofty.
Bewar	1 to 4	70 to 85	As above.
Bibruck	1 to 4	65 to 85	As above.
Fasilka	1 to 9	70 to 85	As above.
Harnai	1 to 5	75 to 85	As above.
Marwar	1 to 4	65 to 85	Very kempy, straight.
Peshawar	1 to 6	65 to 85	Medium length, lofty, resilient; some kemp.
Vicanere	1 to 7	70 to 85	Medium length, lofty wool.
Iraq			
Awassi	1 to 10	65 to 85	Medium fine, lofty. Of the better carpet type.
Karadi	1 to 14	70 to 90	Coarse, long combing.
Morocco			
Morocco	1 to 10	45 to 65	Medium length, medium fine, very lofty.
New Zealand			
New Zealand Fleece	1 to 12	65 to 75	36's to 40's. Medium, lustrous.
New Zealand Crutchings	1 to 8	70 to 70	36's to 40's. Short wool.
Iran			
Persian	1 to 8	65 to 85	Good carpet types. Good length. lofty, resilient.
Baghdad	1 to 8	65 to 85	Good carpet types. Good length, lofty, resilient.
Persian Gulf	1 to 8	65 to 85	Good carpet types. Good length, lofty, resilient.
Portugal			
Churra	1 to 14	35 to 80	Very long, coarse, yellow with red hair.
Oporto	1 to 14	35 to 80	Very long, coarse, yellow with red hair.
Russia			
Donskoi	......	65 to 85	Medium length and fineness, white wool.
Georgian Section			
Nouka	......	65 to 85	As above.
Spain			
Spanish Pyrenees Fine	1 to 10	40 to 55	Medium length, medium fineness, good, resilient
Spanish Pyrenees Medium	1 to 12	45 to 60	Long, slightly coarse, strong wool.
Spanish Pyrenees Coarse	1 to 14	50 to 65	Very long, very coarse.
Syria			
Aleppo	1 to 14	55 to 90	Long combing length, very resilient.
Damascus	1 to 12	55 to 90	Long combing length, very resilient.
Syrian	1 to 12	55 to 90	Long combing length, very resilient.
Turkey			
Anatolian	1 to 12	40 to 60	Long, medium fine wool.
Smyrna	1 to 12	40 to 60	Long, medium fine wool.
Kassapbatchi	......	40 to 60	Long, medium fine skin wool.
Tibet			
Tibet	1 to 10	55 to 70	Soft.
Uruguay			
Montevideo	......	60 to 75	36's to 40's. Lustrous, long, strong.
Central Europe			
Zackel	1 to 14	50 to 90	Long, very hairy and coarse wool.

SHEEP AND WOOL STATISTICS [3]

TABLE 26. NUMBER OF SHEEP IN THE WORLD BY CONTINENTS, AND IN SPECIFIED COUNTRIES *

(In thousands)

Area	Average 1936–40	Average 1941–45	1948	1949	1950	1951 [p]	1952 [p]
World—Estimated Total[1]	746,800 [r]	758,700 [r]	718,700 [r]	733,200 [r]	749,100	778,500	808,300
North America—Estimated Total[1]	59,700 [r]	60,800	42,300 [r]	38,500 [r]	37,400	38,900	40,300
United States	51,404	52,517	34,337 [r]	30,943 [r]	29,826	30,635	31,725
Mexico	4,809 [e]	4,632	NA	5,100	5,100	5,750	6,000
Canada	2,651	2,710	1,587	1,322	1,259	1,268	1,302
Europe—Estimated Total[1]	123,600 [r]	113,100	109,200 [r]	115,300 [r]	117,300	118,400	120,700
United Kingdom	26,112	20,881	18,164	19,493 [r]	20,430	19,984	21,000
Spain	20,000 [e]	23,509 †	NA	24,921	NA	NA	26,200
Rumania[2]	10,176 †	NA	NA	NA	NA	NA	NA
Yugoslavia	9,796	NA	NA	NA	NA	NA	NA
France [a]	9,648	7,162	7,406	7,510 [r]	7,480	7,510	7,562
Italy	9,350 [e]	8,400	9,190	10,100 [r]	10,376	10,300	9,500
Bulgaria[3]	8,746	8,782	NA	NA	NA	NA	NA
Greece	8,304 †	NA	7,056	6,631 [r]	6,337	6,793	7,650
Portugal	3,948	3,800	NA	NA	NA	5,000	NA
Poland	1,941	NA	1,406	1,621	NA	NA	NA
Eire	3,706	2,681	2,058	2,183	2,385	2,616	2,700
Germany—Western	1,889 †	2,327 †	2,352	2,492	2,020	1,642	1,662
Norway	1,742	1,715	1,629	1,736	1,812	1,929	2,000
Albania	1,576 †	NA	NA	NA	NA	NA	NA
Hungary	1,490	1,207	590 [a]	650	NA	NA	NA
Finland	1,007	833	999	1,067	1,207 [r]	1,250	1,250
Soviet Union	66,000 [e]	NA	64,800	74,000	78,000	86,000	93,000
Asia—Estimated Total[1]	152,600	145,300	150,500	149,000	150,300	153,600	161,100
India	41,000 [e]	38,000 [e]	NA	NA	38,900	38,900	42,400
China[4]	26,000	22,000	NA	NA	NA	NA	NA
Turkey	21,656	23,641	24,496	25,840 [r]	23,033 [r]	23,083	25,000
Iran	14,497	13,854	13,200	11,100	13,572	14,672	NA
Iraq	7,090 †	6,719 †	NA	7,077	7,490 [r]	9,000	10,000
Syria	2,060 †	2,539 †	3,176	2,843	2,443	2,707	3,200
Indonesia	1,614 †	NA	NA	NA	1,740 [r]	NA	NA
South America—Estimated Total[1]	100,900	113,700	119,200 [r]	114,000 [r]	115,900 [r]	120,800	125,700
Argentina	44,900 †	52,288 †	50,000	45,000	47,000	50,500	51,500
Uruguay	17,931 [e]	20,289 [e]	22,600 [r]	23,000 [r]	23,000 [r]	23,409	26,000
Peru	14,900 [e]	16,200	17,288	NA	NA	18,200	18,500
Brazil	11,438 †	11,346	NA	NA	NA	14,251	NA
Chile	5,855 †	6,057 †	6,328	6,000	6,000	6,200	6,300
Bolivia	2,608 [e]	3,987 †	NA	4,195	NA	NA	NA
Colombia	916	1,240	1,013	1,061	1,198 [r]	1,339	1,500
Ecuador	NA	1,400 †	1,802	NA	NA	NA	NA

TABLE 26. NUMBER OF SHEEP IN THE WORLD BY CONTINENTS, AND IN SPECIFIED COUNTRIES * (*Continued*)

(In thousands)

Area	Average 1936–40	Average 1941–45	1948	1949	1950	1951 [p]	1952 [p]
Africa—Estimated Total [1]	100,000	105,600 [r]	97,600 [r]	99,900 [r]	103,400 [r]	110,900	113,500
Union of South Africa	39,899	37,888	32,612	31,908	31,361 [r]	32,000	NA
French Morocco [5]	9,976	12,172	7,423	8,474	9,149	10,375	11,500
French West Africa and Togo	8,674 †	8,260	9,100	NA	NA	NA	NA
Algeria [5]	6,180	6,071	3,105	3,839	4,531	6,000	6,100
Kenya	3,274 †	3,148	3,300	NA	NA	NA	NA
Tunisia [5]	3,026	3,250	1,752	1,587	1,894	2,390	NA
South West Africa	2,972 †	3,534 [e]	NA	2,628	NA	NA	NA
Anglo-Egyptian Sudan	2,500 †	NA	NA	NA	NA	NA	NA
Tanganyika	1,780	2,001	2,316	2,153	NA	2,379	NA
Egypt	1,771 †	1,600 [r]	1,800 [r]	1,760 [r]	1,729 [r]	1,730	1,760
Basutoland	1,443	1,545 [e]	NA	1,558 [r]	NA	NA	NA
Oceania—Estimated Total [1]	144,000	153,200	135,100	141,600	146,800	149,900	154,000
Australia	112,571	120,209	102,559	108,735	112,891	115,607	118,000
New Zealand	31,352	32,976 †	32,483	32,845	33,857 [r]	34,300	36,000

* For each country the date of estimate is usually consistent from year to year, but as between countries the periods of estimate vary within the 12 months from October of the preceding year to September of the year noted.

[p] Preliminary.

[r] Revised.

[a] Official statistics; may be an underestimate of actual number.

[e] Figures available only for single year.

† Figures available only for 2–4 years.

[1] Estimated totals for the world and by continents include estimates for countries not specified in the table and for specified countries for which official data are not available.

[2] Present territory; excludes Southern Dobrudja.

[3] Includes Southern Dobrudja beginning 1944.

[4] Includes China Proper (22 provinces), Manchuria, Jehol, and Sinkiang (Turkestan).

[5] Data include only number taxed.

NA. Not available.

Data for years 1944–47 were published in the 1948 *Bulletin*, Vol. LXXVIII, pages 112–115.

Source: Office of Foreign Agricultural Relations, United States Department of Agriculture.

TABLE 27. WOOL PRODUCTION IN THE WORLD BY CONTINENTS AND IN SPECIFIED COUNTRIES

(In millions of pounds, greasy basis)

Area	Average 1936–40	Average 1946–50	1947	1948	1949	1950	1951 [p]	1952 [p]
World—Estimated Total [a]	3,930	3,900	3,720	3,760	3,870 [r]	4,000	4,000	4,070
North America—Estimated Total [1]	452	309	335	302 [r]	271 [r]	271 [r]	275	285
United States	425	285	309	278 [r]	249 [r]	248 [r]	250	260
Canada	16	12	14	12	10	10 [r]	9	9
Europe—Estimated Total [1]	480	427	398	425 [r]	445 [r]	468 [r]	479	483
United Kingdom	110	81	72	75	83 [r]	89 [r]	88	90
Spain	70	83	77	88	82	90 [r]	90	90
Rumania [2]	41	30	NA	NA	NA	NA	NA	NA
France [3]	37	31	29	29	34	35	40	40
Yugoslavia	35	NA	NA	NA	NA	NA	NA	NA
Germany (Western)	32	17	25	17 [r]	19 [r]	17 [r]	17	17
Italy	30	30	27	30 [r]	35	35 [r]	36	35
Bulgaria [4]	29	26	26	27	27	27	28	NA
Greece	19	17	19	18	17	17	17	19
Eire	17	13	13	12	12	14 [r]	14	15
Portugal	16	18	18	18	17	21 [r]	22	22
Hungary	13	5	4	5	6	6 [r]	NA	NA
Poland [2]	7	5	NA	NA	NA	NA	NA	NA
Norway	6	6	6	6	7	7	8	8
Netherlands	3	5	5	5	6	7	7	7
Finland	3	3	2	3 [r]	4 [r]	4 [r]	4	5
Soviet Union [6]	310	304	286	305	315	325	335	370
Asia—Estimated Total [1]	344	356	342	368 [r]	344 [r]	359 [r]	370	382
China [5]	88	75	75	75	75	75	75	75
India and Pakistan	73	52	81	53 [r]	46 [r]	51 [r]	52	58
Turkey	68	71	71	76	71	67	73	75
Iran	36	30	30	30	25	33	34	35
Iraq	22	27	24	33	27	29	30	32
Afghanistan	15	16	15	17	17	18	18	18
Syria	11	12	13	12	10	13 [r]	15	16
South America—Estimated Total [1]	639	735	752	685 [r]	713 [r]	728 [r]	750	742
Argentina	411	450	475	419	420	420 [r]	430	420
Uruguay	126	163	159	144 [r]	163 [r]	181 [r]	187	188
Brazil	36	46	43	45	49	47	52	52
Chile	33	42	42	42	46	44 [r]	44	45
Peru	19	18	16	17	19	19	21	21

TABLE 27. WOOL PRODUCTION IN THE WORLD BY CONTINENTS AND IN SPECIFIED COUNTRIES (*Continued*)

(In millions of pounds, greasy basis)

Area	Average 1936–40	Average 1946–50	1947	1948	1949	1950	1951 [p]	1952 [p]
Africa—Estimated Total [1]	337	282	268	279 [r]	283 [r]	305 [r]	307	311
Union of South Africa	252	216	205	219	218	228 [r]	224	220
French Morocco	35	27	25	28	30	33	35	40
Algeria	23	16	14	12	16 [r]	20 [r]	23	24
Tunisia	12	10	11	8	8	11	12	13
Egypt	8	7	6	8	6	8	7	7
Oceania—Estimated Total [1]	1,366	1,422	1,335	1,398 [r]	1,499 [r]	1,532 [r]	1,484	1,490
Australia	1,052	1,050	973	1,031 [r]	1,109 [r]	1,160 [r]	1,110	1,100
New Zealand	314	372	362	367	390	372	374	390

[a] Rounded to tens of millions. Includes wool produced mostly in the spring in the Northern Hemisphere and that produced in the season beginning July 1 or October 1 of the same calendar year in the Southern Hemisphere.

[r] Revised. [p] Preliminary.

[1] Estimated totals for the world and by continents include estimates for countries not specified in the table and for specified countries for which official data are not available.

[2] Based on present boundaries.

[3] Data for years 1945 and 1946 not comparable with prewar and 1947.

[4] Includes Southern Dobrudja beginning 1944.

[5] Includes China proper (22 provinces), Manchuria, Jehol, and Sinkiang (Turkestan).

[6] Based upon number of sheep and average fleece weight of 4.7 lb per head.

NA. Not available.

Comparable data for 1944–46 were published in the 1949 *Bulletin*, Vol. LXXIX, pages 120–122.

Source: United States Department of Agriculture: 1943–46 "Wool Statistics" (CS-37-1949), 1946–52; "Foreign Crops and Markets."

TABLE 28. Total World Consumption of Virgin Wool [8]

(Million pounds, clean basis)

	1934–38 Average	1946	1947	1948	1949	Annual Rate 1950 *
United Kingdom	435	393	443	494	502	548
United States	330	738	698	693	500	628
France	232	214	256	256	231	250
Germany	180	30	40	47	91	120
Japan	108	19	9	5	8	25
Belgium	60	65	75	61	59	75
Italy	57	80	130	136	125	120
Spain	35	37	36	33	30	33
Poland	35	20	29	34	39	40
Czechoslovakia	24	14	34	20	15	17
Canada	20	41	42	35	30	26
Austria	13	4	8	12	13	15
Switzerland	12	18	20	18	15	15
Sweden	11	23	26	33	29	30
Netherlands	10	32	39	39	40	36
Portugal	10	13	14	13	10	10
Turkey	20	39	40	40	40	40
U.S.S.R.	180	140	155	170	195	200
Australia	35	66	70	80	75	70
New Zealand	4	8	7	7	8	8
South Africa	1	6	7	9	11	12
Argentina	36	56	72	80	87	85
Uruguay	3	7	8	8	10	10
Other Europe	89	59	68	66	70	75
Other Africa	12	20	21	22	21	22
Other America	31	53	51	46	44	45
Other Asia	75	70	73	73	70	70
Total	2058	2265	2471	2530	2368	2625

* Estimated on basis of first six months of the year.

Source: Commonwealth Economic Committee and International Wool Textile Organization.

Fig. 19. Wool production of the world from 1921 to 1950. (*Courtesy U. S. Department of Agriculture* [18].)

TABLE 29. Ten Leading Countries in World Wool Production

(Grease basis [19]; millions of pounds)

Country	*1934–38 Average*	*Per Cent*	*1944–48 Average*	*Per Cent*	*1950*	*Per Cent*
Australia	995	26.8	975	25.6	1150	28.8
United States	425	11.5	348	9.2	254	6.4
Argentina	370	10.0	482	12.6	440	11.0
New Zealand	299	8.1	368	9.7	390	9.8
British South Africa	239	6.4	219	5.8	220	5.5
Russia (U.S.S.R.)	210	5.7	260	6.8	325	8.1
Uruguay	118	3.2	152	4.0	165	4.1
United Kingdom	108	2.9	88	2.3	85	2.1
India/Pakistan	85	2.3	82	2.2	85	2.1
China	78	2.1	81	2.2	75	1.9
Total	2928	79.0	3055	80.3	3189	79.7
Estimated world total	3710	100	3802	100	4000	100

TABLE 30. DETAILS OF WOOL PRODUCTION IN UNITED STATES, 1930–50 [9]

Year	Sheep and Lambs Shorn (Thousands)	Weight per Fleece (Pounds)	Shorn Wool Production (1000 pounds)	Price per Pound (Cents)	Cash Receipts (1000 dollars)	Total Pulled Wool Production (1000 pounds)	Apparel Wool				Carpet Wool, Imports for Consumption [2] (1000 pounds)
							Total Production (1000 pounds)	Exports, Domestic [1] (1000 pounds)	Imports for Consumption [2] (1000 pounds)	Total New Supply [3] (1000 pounds)	
1930	44,549	7.90	352,129	19.5	68,739	61,900	414,029	162	70,135 [4]	484,002	90,621 [4]
1931	46,832	8.04	376,301	13.6	51,039	66,100	442,401	274	42,915	485,042	113,795
1932	45,207	7.76	350,996	8.6	30,202	67,100	418,096	179	13,522	431,439	39,195
1933	46,005	8.13	374,152	20.6	77,065	64,200	438,352	19	59,341	497,674	114,468
1934	46,421	7.95	368,860	21.9	80,709	60,500	429,360	119	29,258	458,499	79,084
1935	44,991	8.04	361,531	19.3	69,613	66,000	427,531	20	41,984 [5]	469,495	158,477
1936	44,663	7.91	353,211	26.9	94,915	66,200	419,411	16	110,712	530,107	143,276
1937	44,284	8.04	356,078	32.0	113,807	66,200	422,278	68	150,160	572,370	172,091
1938	44,889	8.02	359,925	19.1	68,917	64,500	424,425	1,343	30,812	453,894	71,908
1939	45,195	8.00	361,689	22.3	80,683	64,500	426,189	179	98,194	524,204	144,875
1940	46,313	8.03	372,014	28.4	105,539	62,000	434,014	456	222,983	656,541	134,691
1941	47,722	8.12	387,520	35.5	137,754	65,800	453,320	38	613,566 [5]	1,066,848 [5]	203,249
1942	49,287	7.88	388,297	40.1	155,728	66,700	454,997	111	782,647 [5]	1,237,533 [5]	72,017
1943	47,892	7.91	378,843	41.7	157,825	65,200	444,043	27,924	642,887 [5]	1,059,006 [5]	33,489
1944	43,165	7.84	338,318	42.4	143,513	73,500	411,818	7,476	581,848 [5]	986,190 [5]	34,775
1945	38,763	7.94	307,949	41.9	129,122	70,500	378,449	28,797	725,237 [5]	1,074,889 [5]	79,521
1946	34,718	8.08	280,487	42.3	118,639	61,300	341,787	16,008	924,015 [5]	1,249,794 [5]	125,807
1947	31,241	8.09	252,798	42.0	106,052	56,600	309,398	12,720	528,171	924,849 [5]	112,120
1948	29,060	8.05	233,924	48.8	114,072	46,600	280,524	1,154	596,466	875,836	160,634
1949	26,975	8.04	216,873	49.4	107,137	35,600	252,473	15,775	. .	584,662	. .
1950 [6]	27,150	8.11	220,135	57.3	126,171	32,400	252,535	6,796	550,801	796,540	165,755

[1] Includes hair of the Angora goat, alpaca, and other like animals.

[2] General imports less re-exports, 1930–33, inclusive. Apparel wool for all years includes the item "not finer than 40's" both free and dutiable. Carpet wool includes only Donskoi, Smyrna, East Indian, Chinese, and similar wool without merino or English blood.

[3] Production, minus exports, plus imports; stocks not taken into consideration.

[4] For the years 1930–35 the item "not finer than 40's" has been deducted from carpet wool totals reported by the Department of Commerce and added to apparel wool, thus making entire series comparable.

[5] Does not include 222,222,220 pounds in 1942; 275,476,308 pounds in 1943; 2,725,929 pounds in 1944; 5,372,698 pounds in 1945, and 14,840 pounds in 1946, imported free of duty as an act of international courtesy. Wool so imported consisted almost entirely of wool stored in this country for the British Government, and later re-exported. This wool was not available to domestic mills.

[6] Preliminary.

Source: Bureau of Agricultural Economics. Imports and exports from Foreign Commerce and Navigation of the United States and other official reports of the Department of Commerce. Data for 1909–29 in Agricultural Statistics, 1942, table 556.

TABLE 31. Annual Mill Consumption of Apparel and Carpet Class Shorn and Pulled Wool of the Sheep

(Aggregate in millions of pounds)

Year	Total		Apparel Class		Carpet Class	
	Scoured Basis	Greasy Shorn Basis	Scoured Basis	Greasy Shorn Basis	Scoured Basis	Greasy Shorn Basis
1926	342.7	644.6	254.7	524.1	88.0	120.5
1927	354.1	681.8	258.7	551.1	95.4	130.7
1928	333.2	650.0	232.4	511.9	100.8	138.1
1929	368.1	712.1	253.2	554.7	114.9	157.4
1930	263.2	533.5	200.7	447.9	62.5	85.6
1931	311.0	648.4	237.7	545.2	73.3	103.2
1932	230.1	498.4	188.5	439.8	41.6	58.6
1933	317.1	673.0	245.5	572.2	71.6	100.8
1934	229.7	470.1	167.6	381.4	62.1	88.7
1935	417.5	890.1	319.0	748.4	98.5	141.7
1936	406.1	818.9	299.8	656.4	106.3	152.5
1937	380.8	732.2	274.2	579.5	106.6	152.7
1938	284.5	607.0	219.6	514.0	64.9	93.0
1939	396.5	822.8	293.1	673.8	103.4	149.0
1940	407.9	820.9	310.0	683.3	97.9	137.6
1941 *	648.0	1213.6	509.0	1011.8	139.0	201.8
1942	603.6	1161.7	560.5	1101.6	43.1	60.1
1943	636.2	1179.1	603.3	1134.3	32.9	44.8
1944	622.8	1117.4	577.0	1055.9	45.8	61.5
1945	645.1	1134.3	589.2	1057.9	55.9	76.4
1946 *	748.1	1302.4	620.2	1122.5	127.9	179.9
1947	698.2	1263.6	525.9	1021.2	172.3	242.4
1948	693.1	NA	485.2	NA	207.9	NA
1949	500.4	NA	339.0	NA	161.4	NA
1950	624.8 [r]	NA	436.9	NA	197.9	NA
1951	478.7	NA	377.0	NA	101.7	NA

[r] Revised.

* Revised annual consumption totals for which no monthly revisions were published differ from the above data as follows (*in millions of pounds, scoured basis*): 1941—514.4; 1946—609.6.

NA. Not available.

Comparable annual data for 1918–25 were published in the 1949 *Bulletin*, Vol. LXXIX, page 85.

Source: Bureau of the Census.

1926–34—Supplements to March and September 1935, *Monthly Reports on Wool Consumption.*

1935–37—*Raw Wool Consumption Report* for the reporting year 1938.

1938–44—*Monthly Raw Wool Consumption Reports.*

1945–51—*Facts for Industry*, Series M15H, "Wool Manufactures."

TABLE 32. WOOL TEXTILE MACHINERY IN PRINCIPAL MANUFACTURING COUNTRIES OF THE WORLD [3]

Country	Year	Looms	Spindles			Combs
			Woolen	*Worsted*	*Total*	
Argentina	1936	2,800	85	65	150	60
Australia	1947	5,031	NA	NA	386	293
Austria	1947	3,300	105	81	186	63
Belgium	1947	12,660 [b]	352	443	795	737
Canada	1947	3,909 [g]	171	119	290	56
Czechoslovakia	1938	7,400	NA	NA	857	100
Denmark	1937	400	85	15	100	Na
Eire	1947	882 [a]	38 [a]	32 [a]	70 [a]	15[a]
France	1947	47,000	889	1918	2807	3010
Germany and Austria	1938	96,313	2426	3211	5637	3553
Hungary	1937	2,100	71	32	103	28
Italy	1947	21,000 [c]	780	675	1455	1217
Japan	1937	29,421	121	1128	1249	1355
Netherlands	1947	8,230	225	81	306	NA
New Zealand	1947	655 [h]	45	25	70	50
Norway	1937	1,444	85	8	93	12
Poland	1937	13,700	325	474	799	458
Soviet Union	1934	11,917	259	175	434	199
South Africa	1947	NA	NA	NA	NA	NA
Spain	1947	9,087 [d]	245	251	496	657
Sweden	1935	3,900	NA	NA	277	NA
Switzerland	1937	3,600	60	150	210	160
United Kingdom	1947	78,802 [e]	3311	2309	5620	2616
United States	1947	38,572 [f]	1574	1909	3483	2656

NA. Not available.

[a] 1948.

[b] 200 automatic, 12,460 nonautomatic.

[c] 500 automatic, 20,500 nonautomatic.

[d] 260 wide automatic, 6572 wide nonautomatic; 2255 narrow nonautomatic.

[e] 61,171 wide, 11,822 narrow, 5809 nonwool.

[f] 28,703 wide automatic, 6509 wide nonautomatic, 3360 narrow nonautomatic.

[g] 1484 wide automatic, 6 narrow automatic, 1721 wide nonautomatic, 697 narrow nonautomatic.

[h] 42 automatic, 613 nonautomatic.

Source: Commonwealth Economic Committee (Supplement to July 1949 issue of "Wool Intelligence"), *Bull. Wool Manufacturers* (1949).

BIBLIOGRAPHY

1. Burns, R., Johnston, A., and Chen, J., *J. Textile Inst.* **XXXI,** T37–T38 (1940).
2. Burns, R., and Moody, E. L., *J. Heredity,* **26** (1935).
3. *Bull. Natl. Assoc. Wool Mfrs.,* LXXXI, pp. 2–32 (1951).
4. Bureau of Agricultural Economics, Bureau of the Census.
5. California Wool Growers Assoc., *California Wool Grower* (Sept. 1939, 1940, 1941).
6. Dalgety's *Ann. Wool Rev.* (1949–1950).
7. Eavenson and Levering Co., *Wool,* **43** (1951).
8. *Foreign Agr. Circ.,* Office of Foreign Agr. Relations U. S. Dept. Agr. (Jan. 1, 1951).
9. Goe, J. A., U. S. Dept. Agr., Wool Div., personal correspondence.
10. Grandstaff, J. O., U. S. Dept. Agr. *Bull.* 790 (1942) and personal correspondence (1951).
11. Hart, H., *Wool,* Philadelphia Textile School (1924).
12. Hawkesworth, A., *Australian Sheep and Wool,* 6th ed. (1930), Wm. Brooks & Co. Ltd.
13. Henning, W. L., and Connell, W. B., *Circ.* 146, Pa. State Coll. (1934).
14. Hind, John R., *Woolen and Worsted Raw Materials,* **83** (1934).
15. Link, P., *Razas Ovinas,* **14** (1937).
16. Personal correspondence with U. S. Dept. Agr., D. A. Spencer, R. Burns of Univ. of Wyoming, and J. F. Wilson of Univ. of California.
17. Spencer, D. A., and Stoehr, J. A., U. S. Dept. Agr., Animal Husbandry Division, *Bull.* 42, "Columbia Sheep" (Oct. 1941), and *Bull.* 43, "Targhee Sheep" (Oct. 1941).
18. U. S. Dept. Agr., Livestock Marketing Service *Bull.* 13 (May 1943).
19. U. S. Dept. Agr., Office of Foreign Agricultural Relations (Jan. 1951).
20. U. S. Tariff Comm. on United States Wools (March 10, 1942).
21. von Bergen, W., and Mauersberger, H. R., *American Wool Handbook,* 2d ed. (1948).
22. Wilson, J. F., Calif. Agr. Extension Service *Circ.* 106 (1937).
23. *Wool Digest,* International Wool Secretariat (Mar. 29, 1949).

CHAPTER XI

WOOL: MICROSCOPIC AND PHYSICAL PROPERTIES [1]

WERNER VON BERGEN

Wool is an animal fiber forming the protective covering of sheep. As a product of the skin or cuticle of the vertebrate animals, it is similar in origin and general composition to the various other skin tissues found in animals, such as horn, nails, and hoofs. Wool is an organized structure, growing from the root situated in the dermis or middle layer of the skin. The purpose of the hair covering is to keep the body temperature of the animal normal. The wool fibers are poor conductors of heat and, therefore, prevent abnormal temperature changes in the body. At the same time, the air between the fibers is uniform in temperature, which adds to the protection against sudden changes. The fleece works as a sense organ because of its contact with the nervous system of the skin.

GROWTH OF THE WOOL FIBRE

REGINALD J. BRAY [2] [9]

The development and growth of the wool fibre would appear at first sight to be of direct interest only to those studying the problems of wool production. It must however be remembered that the properties of the mature fibre, including those which are important in textile manufacture, are the result of the complex processes which take place in the wool follicle. Some understanding of how the fibre grows and of the biological structures associated with its growth is therefore desirable even for the general student of wool textiles.

A useful approach to the study of the follicle structure is to follow its stage-by-stage development in the skin of the sheep (Figs. 1–5). Most of the wool follicles which produce the mature fleece are already present before the birth of the lamb. Follicles first begin to appear when the unborn lamb, or foetus, is two months old—birth takes place at about five months. The skin of the lamb is built up of minute cells and consists of two main parts: first an "under skin" or dermis and overlying this an "outer skin" or epidermis (Fig. 1). These two parts of the skin retain their indentity throughout the growth of the animal.

[1] This chapter is taken in part from *American Wool Handbook,* 2nd ed., Textile Book Publishers, New York (1948).

[2] Scientific liaison officer, International Wool Secretariat, London.

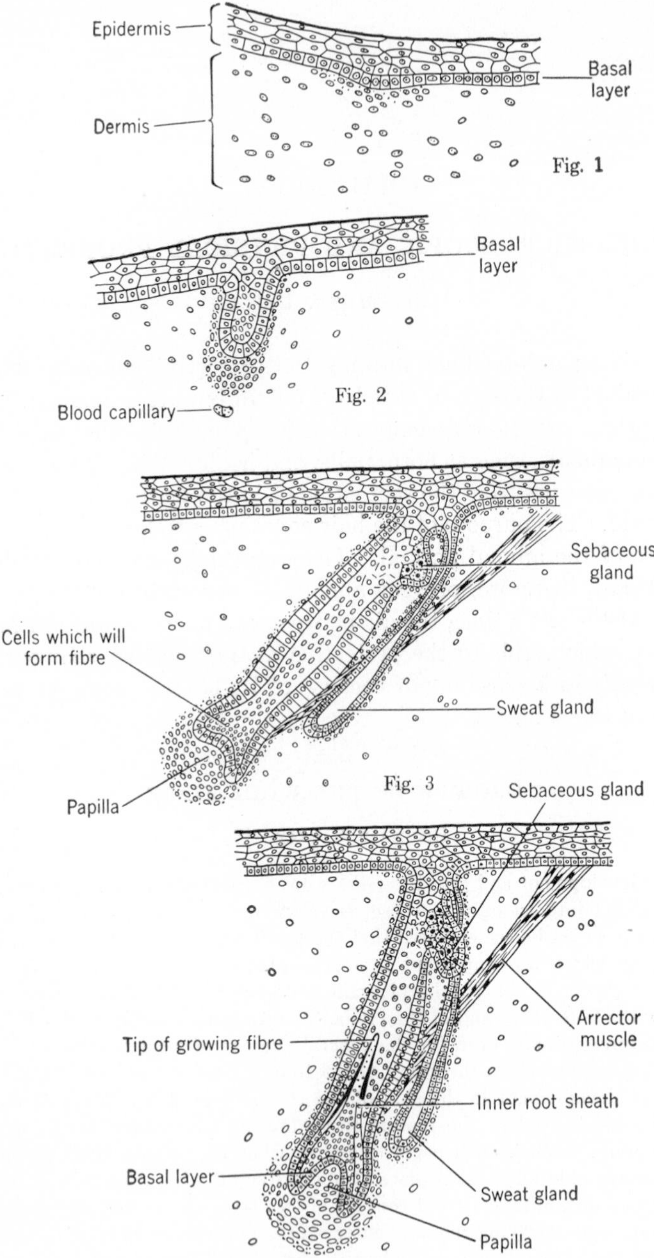

FIGS. 1 through 4. Stages in the development of a wool follicle in the skin of the unborn lamb. Vertical sections of skin magnified about ×100. (*After Wildman* [66], *from* [91].)

The epidermis is formed by the constant growing and dividing of a very active layer of cells, called the "basal layer" (Fig. 1). There is continuous wear on the outermost layer of the epidermis and this is replaced by cells derived from the basal layer. *This basal layer is also important because it plays a large part in the formation of the wool follicle.*

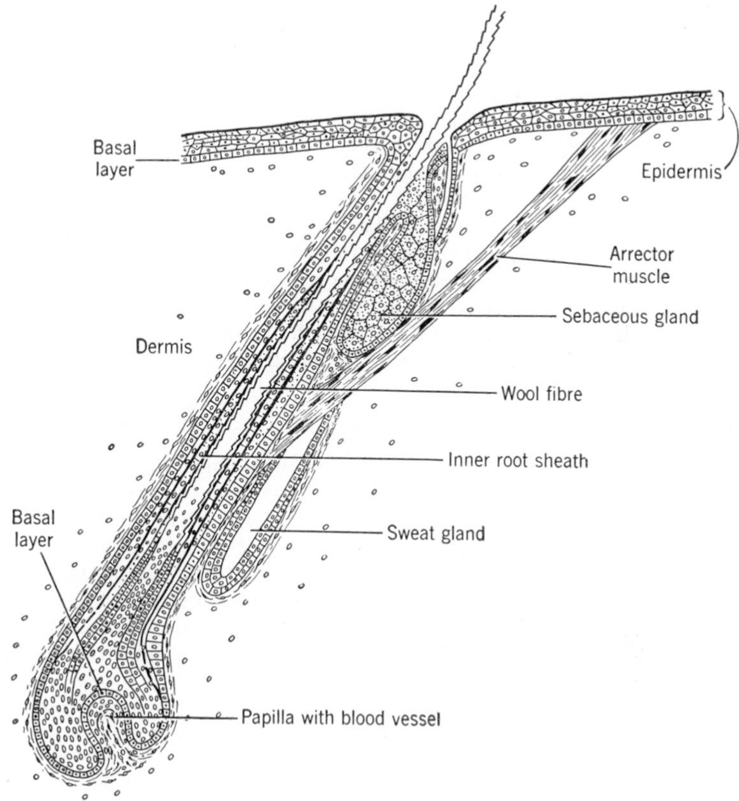

Fig. 5. Longitudinal section of a completely developed wool follicle (primary, non-medullated) magnified about ×100. (*After Wildman* [66], *from* [9].)

At certain positions in the skin the basal layer thickens and begins to grow down into the dermis to form a sort of plug of cell tissue (Fig. 2). This plug will ultimately form the wool follicle with its accessory structures. As the plug grows downwards two outgrowths appear from it, usually on the same side (Fig. 3). These are the rudiments of (*a*) a bi-lobed wax or sebaceous gland and (*b*) a thin sac-like or slightly coiled sweat gland (sometimes called a sudoriferous gland). The lower end of the plug gradually becomes bulbous; the base of the bulb then becomes turned in and grows upwards to form a dome-like structure of actively dividing cells, called the papilla, which is well supplied with small blood vessels (Fig. 4). It will be noted that the basal layer is continuous over the dome of the papilla and in this region its cells are very actively dividing. The cells thus divided off gradually elongate and form both the wool fibre itself (i.e., the fibre cuticle and cortex) and also, close round the young fibre, an inner root sheath (Fig. 5). This latter structure is complex, consisting of three layers, the innermost of which has scales pointing towards the base of the follicle, i.e., in the opposite direction to those of the fibre cuticle which they surround.

The tip of the growing fibre together with its inner root sheath is pushed upwards through the follicle plug by the pressure of new cells being formed continuously from the dome of the papilla. Meanwhile the cells of the sebaceous gland multiply and extend into the neck of the follicle. Here they break down leaving a cavity or passage which is reached by the tip of the young growing fibre. The fibre tip becomes slightly bent over at the top and then breaks through the skin surface.

One other structure of interest associated with the fibre is the arrector muscle. This is attached at its lower end to the follicle sheath and at the upper end to the basal layer. It is inserted on the same side of the follicle as the sweat and sebaceous glands. This is the muscle which, when contracted in man and many other animals causes the hair to stand on end. In the sheep it is inserted too high up the follicle to serve this purpose effectively and the sheep does not erect its fibres.

The Mature Non-Medullated Wool Follicle

Figure 5 is a vertical section of a mature wool follicle containing a non-medullated wool fibre. The figure is idealised in some respects because most wool follicles are not so straight as the one illustrated. It is important to notice that the papilla is usually directed towards one side of the follicle so that the follicle has the shape of a golf-club. Further, the "shaft" of the follicle and fibre is usually curved in two planes, i.e., in the form of a short spiral possessing two waves in a longitudinal direction. It is possible that this orientation of the papilla and the shape of the follicle are connected with the formation of crimp (or waviness) in the fibre.

The sebaceous gland normally has two lobes separated from one another in the horizontal plane in such a way that only one lobe is seen in a vertical section (as in Fig. 5). Both lobes are visible in a horizontal section through the skin such as Fig. 8. The two lobes may be further subdivided in some cases.

The sweat gland has in most sheep breeds the shape of a thin elongated bag although in the merino it may be coiled at the lower end. It opens *into the neck of the follicle* just above the sebaceous gland. In this respect the structure of the wool follicle is different from that of the human hair follicle, in which the sweat glands open directly to the surface of the skin and appear to have no definite association with the hair follicle. In the sheep the sweat gland lies between the two main lobes of the sebaceous gland (see Figs. 5 and 8). The sebaceous gland of the sheep secretes a complex mixture of esters, formed by various combinations between the alcohols cholesterol, β-cholestanol, agnosterol and lanosterol and some thirty different fatty acids. This mixture is collectively known as wool grease. The sweat gland secretes potash salts of various fatty acids together with small quantities of sulphate, phosphate and nitrogenous materials (collectively known as suint). All these products spread over the surface of the wool fibre and have economic importance. The sebaceous and sweat glands are not always present (see below).

The Development of the Medulla

It is possible to distinguish three main types of fibre in the sheep's fleece—true wool fibres, hairy fibres and kemps. Hairy fibres and kemps differ from true wool fibres in both possessing a hollow canal up the centre of the fibre, known as the medulla.

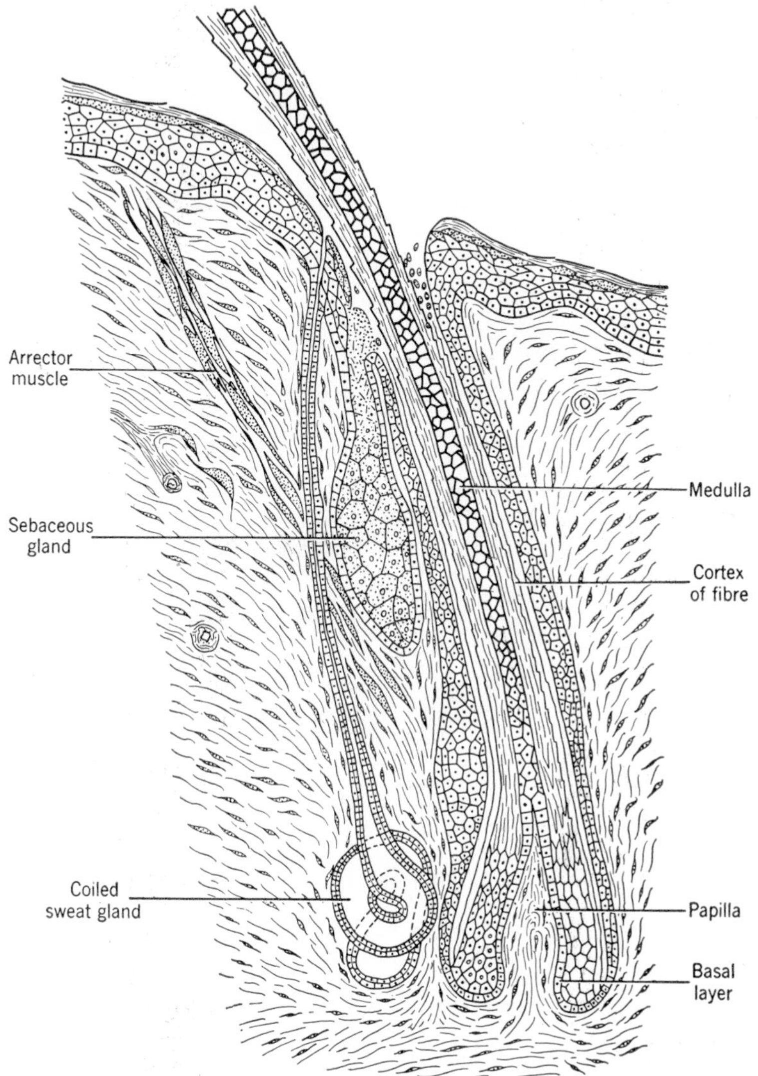

Fig. 6. Longitudinal section, magnified ×100, of a wool follicle in a merino lamb, showing a growing medullated fibre. Note formation of the medulla from the basal layer. (*After Duerden and Ritchie, from* [9].)

The development of the medulla is essentially the same in hairy fibres and kemps. In true wool fibres the basal layer is continuous over the papilla (see Fig. 5) and gives rise to the cells of the cortex and cuticle only. In medullated fibres, however, the individual cells of the basal layer at the apex of the dome of the papilla pass upwards into the centre of the growing fibre and form the

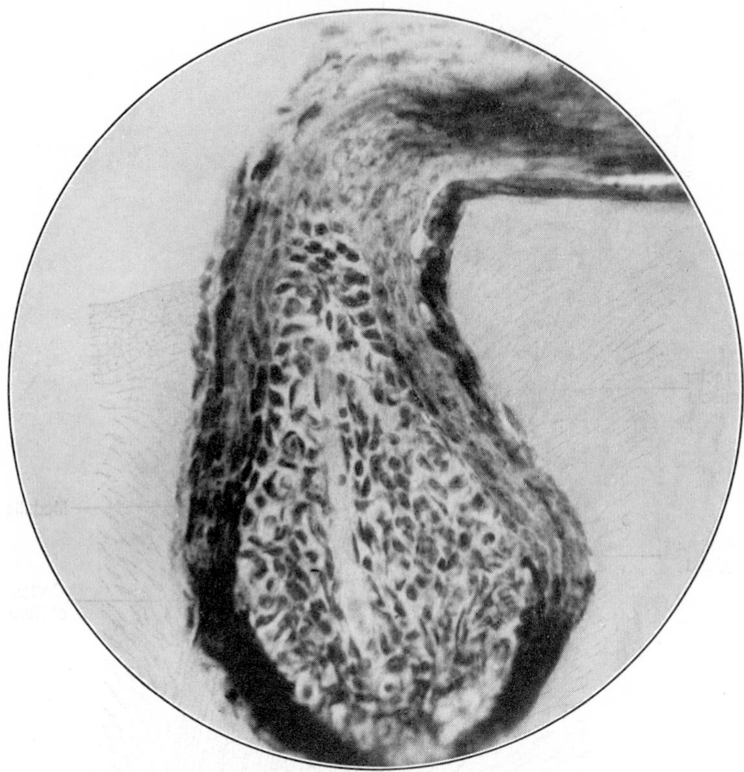

Fig. 7. Photograph of a vertical section (stained) of the papilla of a medullated wool fibre magnified about ×50. The dome of the papilla consists of a mass of dark stained cells produced from the basal layer, from which the medulla is formed. The fibre is bent sharply to the right. The blood capillary of the papilla is also visible. (*After Wildman and Burns, from* [9].)

medulla. (See Figs. 6 and 7.) The cells of the medulla may break down completely during the keratinisation of the rest of the fibre so as to leave a completely hollow canal. In very coarse hairy fibres and kemps the medullary cells become replaced by a hollow network (see Fig. 6) which may be airfilled.

The Arrangement of Follicles in the Skin

The follicles lie at an acute angle to the skin surface and usually have a common direction of slope. In many breeds of sheep it has been observed that the earliest growing follicles in the unborn lamb tend to be arranged in groups of three. This arrangement follows that in the growth of the early follicles in many other mammals (e.g., the cat). Such a grouping is known as a "trio." The follicles forming the trio are known as "primary follicles" and characteristically have *all* the accessory structures present with each follicle, i.e., sebaceous gland, sweat gland, and arrector muscle. The accessory structures are all developed round the underside of the primary follicle (i.e., the side of the follicle lying furthest from the skin surface). In a horizontal section of a trio the accessory structures therefore all lie on the same side of the primary follicles (see Fig. 8).

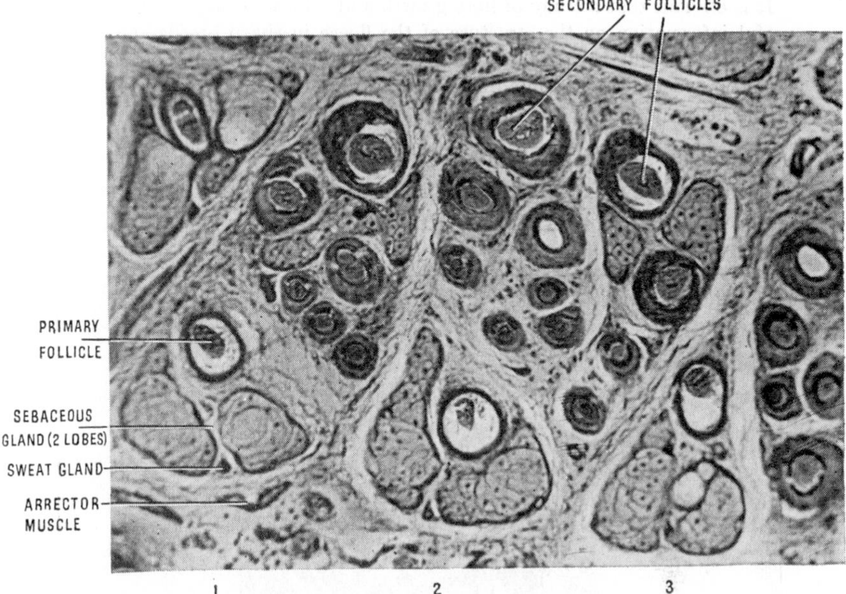

FIG. 8. Horizontal section magnified ×150 of the skin of a Romney lamb showing a follicle bundle with its trio of primary follicles (1, 2, 3), accessory structures, and associated secondary follicles. (*After Wildman and Burns, from* [9].)

Later, new follicles appear associated with the primary follicles; they develop only on the upper side of the primaries, i.e., on the opposite side from that containing the accessory structures of the primary follicles. These later growing follicles are known as "secondary follicles" (see Fig. 8). The secondary follicles also differ from the primaries in having an incomplete set of accessory structures, the sweat gland and usually the arrector muscle being absent; the sebaceous gland is generally present but is smaller in size than that of the primary follicle.

In the mature skin the primaries and the associated secondary follicles are further grouped into "follicle bundles" which are separated from adjacent bundles by bands of connective tissue. A follicle bundle may contain either a trio (i.e., three primary follicles) with their associated secondary follicles, or only two, or one primary and associated secondaries (i.e., the trio is incomplete). A horizontal section through a follicle bundle at the appropriate level will thus show the sebaceous glands of the primary follicles bounding one edge of the bundle whilst bounding the opposite edge will be the secondary follicles (see Fig. 8).

In the merino it is not possible to discern a grouping of the early follicles into trios and therefore it is hardly possible to determine a primary follicle by its position in a follicle bundle. Primary follicles have therefore been defined in the merino (Carter [11]), on the basis of their other characteristics noted above, i.e., the possession of a sweat gland and an arrector muscle in addition to a bi-lobed sebaceous gland. The other follicles are termed secondary.

It is obvious that a study of fibre growth and follicle arrangement can furnish useful information on the structure of the fleece in sheep breeds and its yield of wool. The number and arrangement of the sebaceous and sweat glands are important factors in determining the proportion of yolk (i.e., grease plus suint) in the fleece.

Fleece Density. Wool hairs grow in groups of 5 to 10. The groups are so arranged in a mature skin that they form horizontal lines, see Figs. 8 and 10. The arrangement is governed by a definite law. As

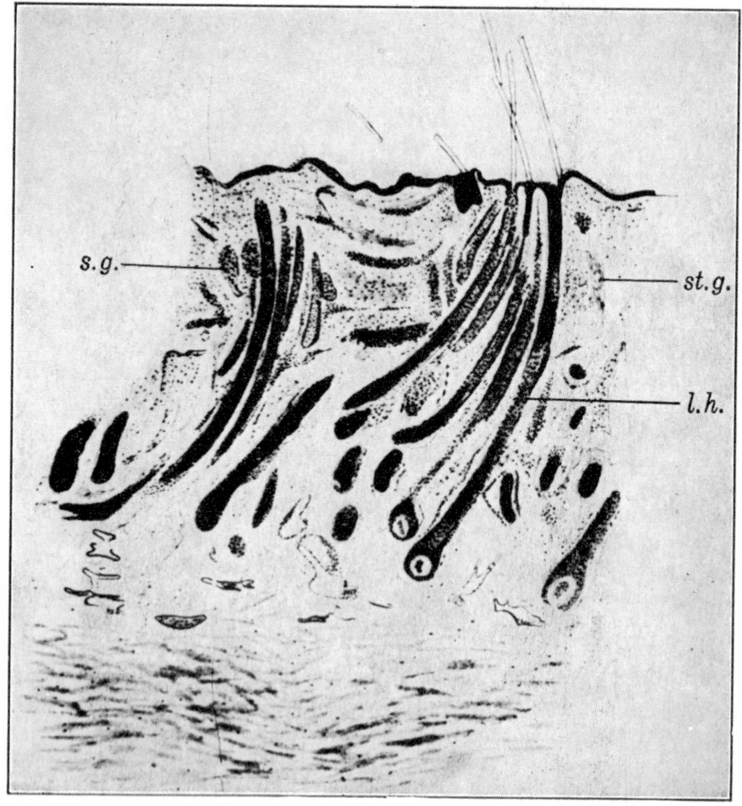

FIG. 9 Vertical cut through skin of Hampshire sheep. *s.g.*, sebaceous gland; *st.g.*, suint gland; *l.h.*, lead hair. (*Spoettel and Taenzer* [56].)

stated above, in each group a leading or primary hair is present and is recognized by its possession of a sweat gland and an arrector muscle. This main hair differs in no way from the others in size or structure, as proved by studies of Spoettel and Taenzer [56] (Figs. 9 and 10). The density of the hair over the entire body of a sheep varies according to the breed as well as in each individual fleece. Fleece density is one

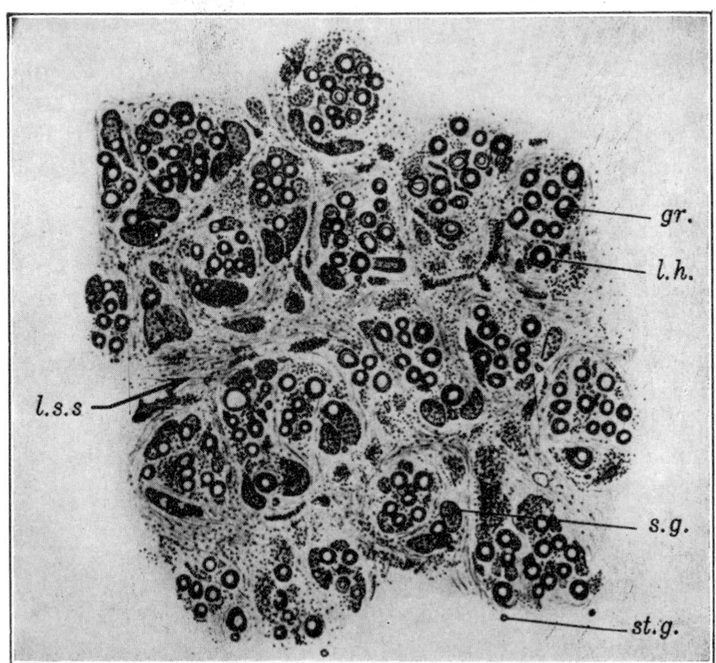

FIG. 10. Horizontal cut through skin of Hampshire sheep. *s.g.*, sebaceous gland; *gr.*, group; *l.h.*, lead hair; *l.s.s.*, lengths skin seams; *st.g.*, suint glands. (*Spoettel and Taenzer.*)

of the primary factors in wool production, as it has a direct relationship to the amount of wool obtained.

Considerable variation of fleece density is found in the different breeds, and no classification can be made because certain breeds overlap others. Burns [10] found that the number of fibers may vary in the different parts of the body from 10,000 to 22,000 per sq in. of skin.

In Burns' [10] review of the published work on fleece density, various research workers gave the data on the number of fibers per square inch of skin shown in Table 1.

Assuming that a sheep has a skin measuring 12 sq ft and that the fiber has grown fairly uniform on the skin of different parts of the

TABLE 1. Fleece Densities by Breeds

Breeds	*Number of Fibers per Sq In. of Skin*
Hampshire	8,000 to 25,000
Hampshire Rambouillet (crossbred)	12,000 to 34,000
Rambouillet	17,000 to 56,000
American Rambouillet rams (four animals)	33,000
Australian Merino rams (two animals)	61,000
American Merino, type B	16,000 to 23,000
Tasmanian Merino	27,000 to 40,000
South African Merino	35,000 to 60,000

body, the total number of fibers grown on the sheep may be calculated. The Hampshire has from 16 million to 43 million fibers; the Hampshire Rambouillet has 21 million to 59 million fibers; the Rambouillet has 29 million to 97 million fibers; and the Australian merino grows up to 120 million fibers.

There is a considerable drain on the body of the sheep when nourishing from 16 million to 100 million or more fibers, all growing uniformly at the rate of about ½ in. per month. Spoettel and Taenzer [56] estimated the number of fibers over the whole carcass of the merino lamb as 20 million and a full-grown merino 126 million fibers.

Change of Hair. The ancestor of the domestic sheep lost its entire body covering each spring. The covering of the wild sheep is very different from that of domesticated sheep. It consists of two distinct coats—the outer of long fibers and the inner of short fibers. The long fibers are medullated, brittle, and very coarse; the short fibers are elastic, fine, and wavy. This woolly undercoat, through the aid of very careful breeding and in the course of evolution, has developed considerably, and it now represents the main covering of domestic sheep. The wool of domestic sheep grows continuously, and, if not shorn or if protected or prevented from breaking off at the tip, it may attain a length several times its annual growth.

The annual shedding or molting process still occurs in certain breeds yielding mixed wool, such as wild sheep, like the Rocky Mountain sheep, and hair-carrying animals, such as goats and camels, yielding fibers closely related to wool.

Wool, Hair, and Kemp. Wild sheep carry two distinct coats, the outer of which consists of long fibers that are classified as hair; if they are especially coarse, brittle, and strongly medullated, they are known as kemp. The under coat consists of fine, crimpy fibers called wool. Unfortunately, up to the present time breeding has not entirely banished the coarse fiber, for it is still evident in all breeds of sheep except the merino, where it has disappeared. In medium and long wool type breeds, the kemp and hairy fibers are noticeable on the head, legs, and britch, though the proportion in the numerous breeds varies considerably. In the mixed wools, such as Scotch blackface, Welsh wool, or carpet wools in general, the entire fleece is a mixture of all three fibers.

The under coat consists of fine, crimpy fibers, whereas the outer coat is formed by long, coarse, wavy hairs. Both coats are intermingled with short, coarse kemp fibers. By careful examination fibers will even be found which have the characteristics of both wool and hair. That is, they may have certain parts that are perfectly fine and that possess all the characteristics of true wool and other parts that present very hairy characteristics. They are known as heterotype fibers. The hair portion is, as a rule, strongly medullated and is generally found at the tip of the fiber. In other fibers the base may be medullated and the distal portion fine, or the tip and the base may be medullated and the central portion perfectly fine.

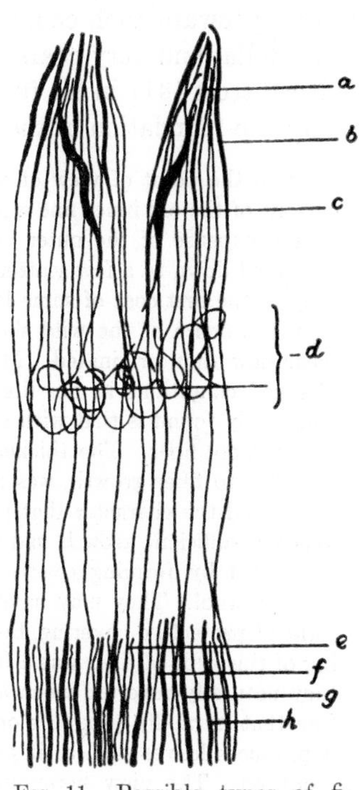

FIG. 11. Possible types of fibers present in a wool staple. *a*, heterotype fiber thickened at tip (*a*) and base (*g*); *b*, heterotype fiber thickened only at tip; *c*, kemp fiber; *d*, cotted zone; *e*, true wool fiber; *f*, developing fiber; *h*, developing medullated fiber which may result in a heterotype of the *a* or *b* class or in *c*, the kemp fiber. (*Northcroft.*)

Northcroft [41] found the following type of fibers in adult staples of New Zealand wools.

1. *True Wool.* (*a*) Fibers running throughout the length of the staple. (*b*) Fibers at the base of the staple and running only for a short distance. (*c*) Fibers which have been shed and appear anywhere in the staple. These may sometimes be much longer than *a*, and lower ends are frequently found at the same level in the staple and so form a distinct zone—the cotted zone. This necessarily varies considerably in degree of cotting, and can become a dense tangled mat.

2. *Heterotype Fibers.* (*a*) Growing fibers running throughout the length of the staple. (*b*) Shed heterotypes, which as a rule are found

toward the ends of the staple, the proximal end being found in the cotted zone.

3. *Kemp.* Fibers shed from the follicle. They are short, wavy, tapering toward each end, dead white or opaque, with a large amount of medulla, and very coarse and brittle (Fig. 11).

Northcroft [41] in his further study of New Zealand wool fibers explains the foundation of the various fiber types as follows:

> From the point of view of evolution, the true wool fiber is clearly the component of the old inner fine wool coat of the wild sheep. It has been developed at the expense of the outer or kemp coat, which has, in the domestic sheep, dwindled down to a few scattered fibers in the adult and is strongly represented only in the first coat of some lambs.
>
> In the fleece of the wild sheep there are no heterotype fibers, and it is not clear how they originated. May it not be that they are a result of suddenly changed conditions in the life of the individual? The heterotype fiber most commonly found is that with a thickened tip and with a great part of the fiber a pure-wool fiber. The thickened part is, of course, the part that was sudden stimulus to fiber growth, was responded to by a production of fibers many of which had the character that preponderated in the coat of the ancestral forms. When a sufficient growth had taken place many of the follicles that had thus responded by forming coarse fibers resumed their more modern function of forming wool. They may have formed kemp because that constituted the best form of protective covering, but it is more likely that it was because the forming of this type of fiber was a function older in time and therefore one to which they naturally reverted when a sudden call was made upon them. If a wattle tree that normally produces only phyllodes in the adult condition is cut back it produces leaves such as it produced in its first year, or such as its ancestors produced. The view here put forward as to the origin of thickened tip is rendered the more probable, seeing that it is more common in rigorous climates. Further, where tip and base are both thickened, it may be that adverse conditions have occurred twice in the year.
>
> From the foregoing it is evident that there is no distinct dividing line between true wool and true hair fibers, a fact which was already recognized by Luccock in 1805.

Histology of Wool Fiber. The minute structure and external shape of the wool fibers were established by the classic researches of Nathusius [40] in 1864, in Germany. In the United States the classic work in establishing the physical properties of American wools was done by W. McMurtrie [35], Professor of Chemistry at the University of Illinois, 1880–86. McMurtrie's work was provided for by an Act of Congress (approved June 16, 1880) for the examination of wools and other animal fibers by the Department of Agriculture, under the following terms:

> For testing, by scientific examination, the tensile strength, felting capacity, and other peculiarities of the different wools and other animal fibers on exhibi-

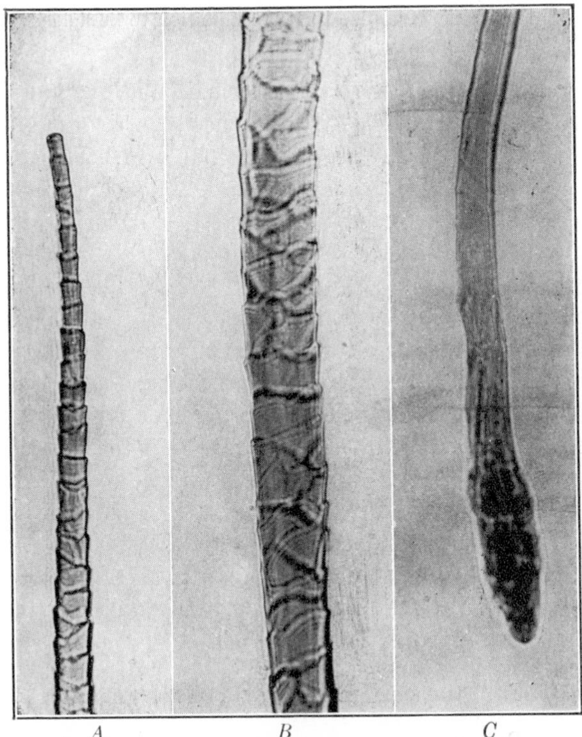

FIG. 12. Parts of a merino wool fiber. *A*, tip; *B*, stem; *C*, root. (×500.) (*von Bergen.*)

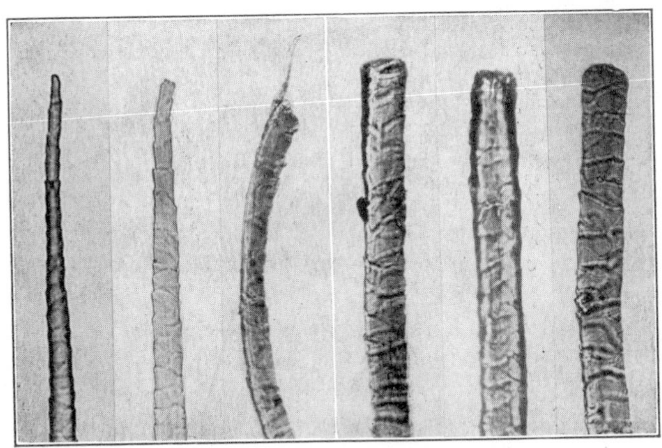

FIG. 13. *Left*, tips of lamb's wool. *Right*, tips of shorn wool. (×250.) (*American Wool Handbook.*)

tion at the International Sheep and Wool Exhibition to be held in Philadelphia in 1880, four thousand dollars.

Very little had been added to this information until about 1941 when Hock, Ramsay, and Harris [26] made new contributions concerning the fine details of the structure of the wool fiber. This was greatly aided by the invention of the electron microscope and the use of the new technique of phase contrast microscopy as developed by Zernike.

A growing fiber consists of a root and shaft; the root is the living part situated beneath the surface of the skin. The root is fixed at the base of the shaft, and, when the hair is pulled out, part of the hair follicle having a scallion-like form comes with it. See Fig. 12*C*. The shaft is cylindrical and tapers to a point at its free end. Once cut the hair grows with the cut end. The tapering ends are characteristic of lambs' wool, whereas the cut ends indicate that the animal has been previously shorn. See Fig. 12 and Fig. 13. Since the cells of the root are alive and growing, whereas the cells of the shaft are dead, there exist profound physical and chemical differences between these two parts of the fiber. Several of these differences can be revealed by microchemical color tests. The differences established between the root and shaft are given in Table 2.

TABLE 2. DIFFERENCES BETWEEN ROOT AND SHAFT OF WOOL

Root	*Shaft*
Soft and easily crushed.	Tough and horny.
Cells roundish.	Cells elongated.
Positive test for nucleic acid.	Negative test for nucleic acid.
Nuclei stained with hematoxylin.	Nuclei unstained with hematoxylin.
Cytoplasm granular in appearance.	Cells distinctly fibrous.
Not birefringent.	Birefringent.
Positive test for sulfhydryl groups.	Negative test for sulfhydryl groups.
No Allwoerden reaction with chlorine water.	Many large Allwoerden "sacs."

Increase in fiber length is brought about by the proliferation of new cells in the root and the subsequent emergence of these cells into the shaft. The dead cellular units composing the shaft form three distinct regions: a thin outer covering, the epidermis or cuticle; a middle region, the cortex; and an inner central core, the medulla. The medulla is usually absent from fine wools and hairs. McMurtrie's [35] diagram (Fig. 14) showing these three possible cell layers is still one of the best illustrations, even though made around 1880.

Epidermis or Cuticle. The outside or surface of the fiber is made up of flat irregular horny cells or scales. They overlap like the shingles of a roof with the free end projecting outward and pointing toward the tip of the hair, causing the surface of the fiber to present a "serrated" appearance.

Depending on the diameter of the fiber, the number of scales necessary to cover the circumference of the fiber varies considerably. The average height of the scales is approximately 28 μ and the average

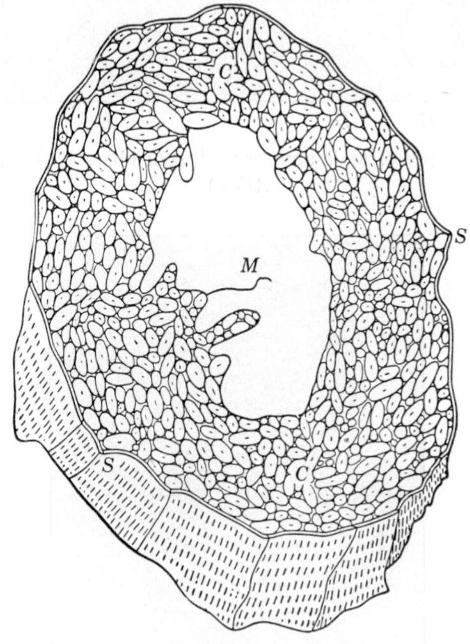

Fig. 14. Cross-section diagram showing structure of wool fiber. *M*, medulla or marrow; *C*, cortical cells; *S*, scales or epidermis. (*McMurtrie*.)

width approximately 36 μ. The thickness varies between 0.5 and 1 μ. The scales form a pattern on the surface of the fiber the complexity of which varies not only from fiber to fiber but also upon one fiber. The scale patterns can be separated into the following types:

a. Coronal. Each scale forms a complete ring around the fiber, the top of one scale overlapping the bottom of the next like a column of flowerpots set into one another (see Fig. 15*A* and *B*). Coronal scaling is characteristic of very fine fibers up to 20 μ, particularly those present in merino wools.

b. Coronal-reticulate. The scale pattern is in the form of a network, but the scales tend to be grouped in bands around the fiber. These bands often run diagonally across the fiber (see Fig. 15*C*). This type

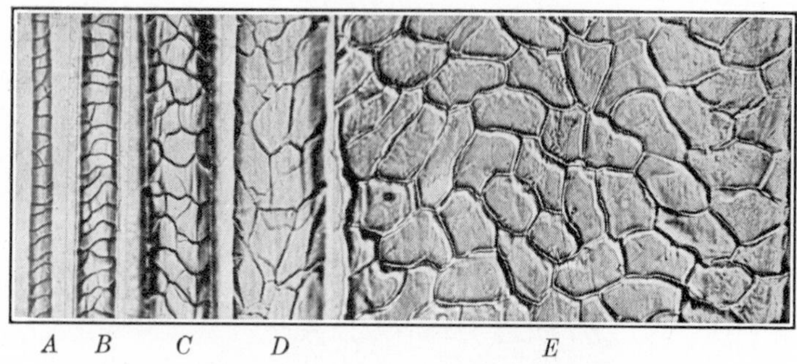

Fig. 15 Various types of scale structure of wool fibers (×250). (*Textile Fiber Atlas.*)

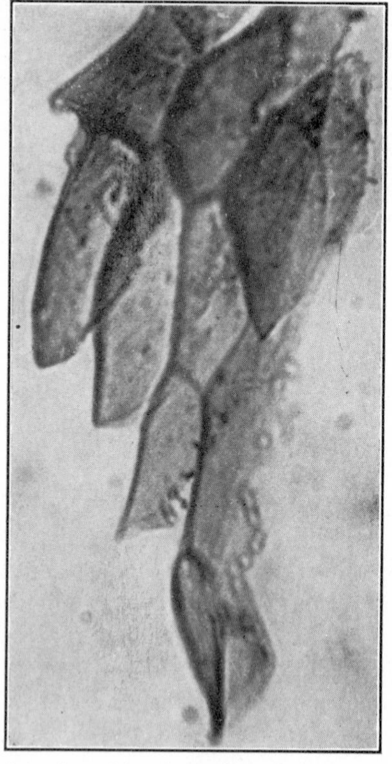

Fig. 16. Group of scales released by the action of pepsin on reduced and methylated fibers. (×1420.) (*Hock, Ramsay, and Harris.*)

of scaling is often found in the luster and Down wools, also in some kemp fibers. The pattern represents a transition from the coronal type of scaling to the completely reticulate type in which grouping of the cells in bands round the fiber is absent.

c. Reticulate and polyhedral structure. As the name implies, the scales form over the surface of the fiber an irregular network having many faces, sides, and aspects. The individual scales overlap at the sides as well as at the upper and lower edges (see Fig. 16). Figure 15*E* shows a typical polyhedral type resembling a honeycomb. These patterns are only present in coarse fibers of the hair and kemp types.

The visible scale height is an important characteristic for differentiation between wool and related hair fibers, such as mohair and camel

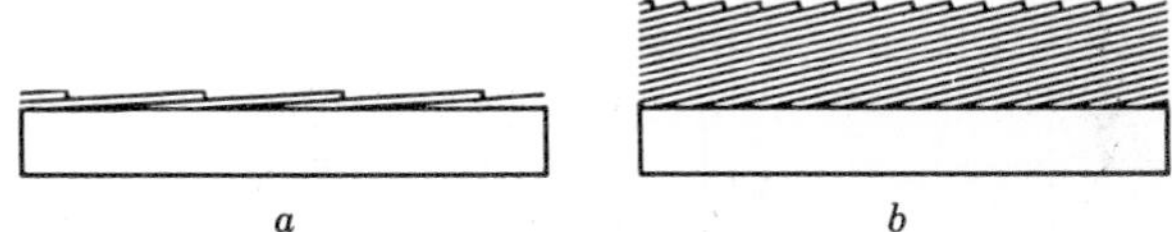

FIG. 17. Diagrams of scale patterns. (*Rudall.*)

hair. In fine wools these visible scale lengths are 8 to 10 μ. In coarse wool the scale length may increase to 18 μ. This decreases the overlapping of the scales and gives the entire fiber a smoother appearance. As the free edges of the scales fit over each joining scale very closely, coarse wool is usually more hairlike and lustrous in texture. The number of scales per 100 μ (or $\frac{1}{253}$ in.), when counted along the edge of the fibers, averages 8 with a range from 4 to 12 for fine and medium wools.

The thickness of the epidermis varies considerably with different animal fibers. Whereas in wool the thickness is between 0.5 and 1 μ or about equal to the thickness of one individual scale, in human hair (3 μ) and in some fur fibers (kolinsky fur 7 μ) the peripheral layer is greatly thickened. Rudall [44], by observing the swelling of fiber sections in sodium hypochloride solution, came to the conclusion that the thickness of the epidermis is a function of the length of the cuticle cell and the degree of overlap of these cells.

In fibers such as wool, the scale cells are arranged as in Fig. 17*a*. Thus, the thickness of the epidermis is from one to two times the thickness of the individual cell. In fibers such as guard hairs (distal region) of ermines and martens the epidermis is of the type shown in Fig. 17*b*.

In the kolinsky fur fiber where the epidermis measured 7 μ by swelling with sodium hypochloride, the layer separated clearly into at least 18 layers of flattened platelike cells. (Figs. 18 and 19.)

Hock demonstrated excellently that the epidermis scales surround the main layer of the wool fiber in a tubelike fashion. In following microscopically the changes which chemically altered wool undergoes in pepsin, he found that the scales remained attached to each other in the form of tubes. (Fig. 20.)

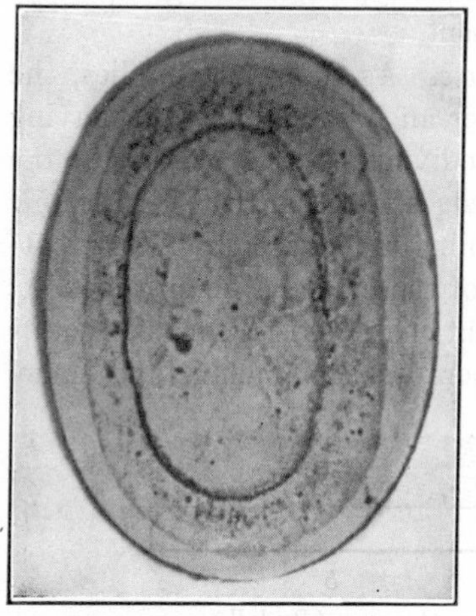

Fig. 18. Cross-section of guard hair from a kolinsky fur pelt. Maximum thickness of epidermis about 7 μ. (×750.) (*Rudall.*)

When the Feulgen test for nucleic acid was applied to untreated wool fibers, the scale cells of the shaft gave a negative test.

The cuticle as revealed by the optical microscope was regarded until recently simply as a sheath of flattened overlapping cells closely covering the cortex.

The application of electron microscopy to the study of the hair fibers has led to considerable advances in our knowledge of their histology. In particular the studies of the cuticle with the electron microscope have led to the view that the cuticle is a more elaborate structure of several more or less distinct

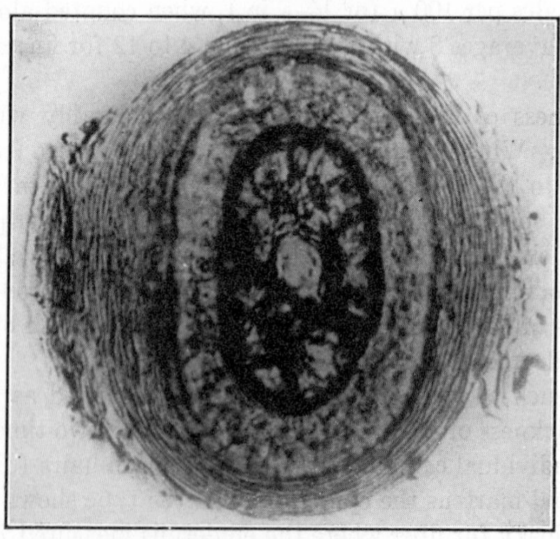

Fig. 19. Cross-section of guard hair from a kolinsky fur pelt swollen with sodium hypochlorite. Epidermis separated into a series of flattened platelike cells. (×500.) (*Rudall.*)

compounds. The first papers were published in 1943 by Zahn [68] in Germany and Hock and McMurdie [25] in the United States. A very detailed investigation was made by Mercer and Rees [36] in 1946 and by Mercer, Rees, and Farrant [37] (1947) in Australia. Studies have also been made by Gorter and Houwink [19] (1948) in Holland, Lindberg, Philip, and Gralen [32] (1948) in Sweden, and Swerdlow and Seeman [58] (1948) in the United States.

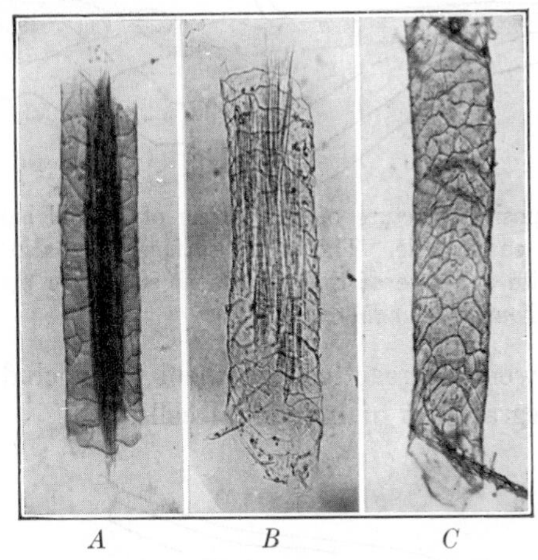

FIG. 20. Reduced and methylated wool fibers treated with solutions of pepsin. *A*, *B*, and *C* show three stages in the removal of cortical cells from the fibers. *A* and *B* unstained; *C* stained with Orange II. (×350.) (*Hock, Ramsay, and Harris.*)

In 1949 Lindberg, Mercer, Philip, and Gralen [32] summarized their work and postulated that the structure of the cuticle cell is of the type represented by Figs. 21 and 22. Proceeding from the outside of the fiber inward, the following three layers have been described: (*a*) a very thin epicuticular membrane covering the whole of the surface and thus forming the external surface of the fiber, (*b*) an exocuticle layer, and (*c*) an endocuticle. The intermediate layer, the exocuticle, was first pointed out by Mercer and Rees who refer to it as K_1. The endocuticle consists of the flattened scale remnant which is the usual result of tryptic digestion, and is often referred to as the "cuticle" (meaning the whole cuticle). The relation of these three layers is shown diagrammatically in Fig. 21. It is not known whether the other side (inward) of the scale cells is similarly elaborate, but there is no evidence as yet for this. Cementing material may be assumed to be between all the layers mentioned and the cortex.

The evidence of epicuticle is not challenged. But Zahn [68] does not believe that this fine membrane covers the whole surface forming a tubelike covering of the entire fiber. Zahn and Mueller's evidence,

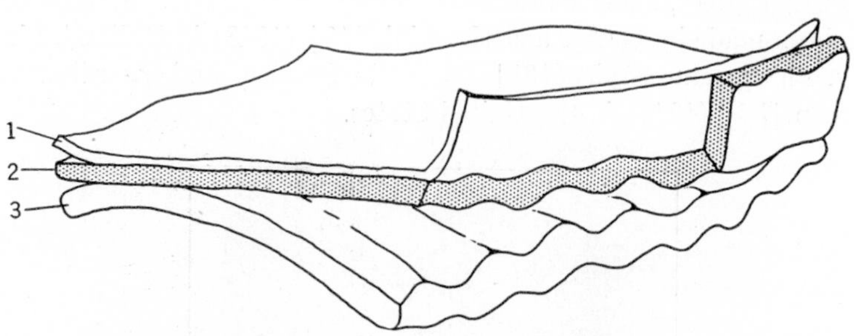

FIG. 21. The composite structure of the cuticle of animal hair. 1, Epicuticle; 2, exocuticle; 3, endocuticle. The under surface may also be complex, but there is no definite evidence of this; a cement substance probably covers the lower surface. (*Courtesy Lindberg.*)

studying the Allwoerden reaction, led them to conclude that the epicuticle is an integral part of individual cells.

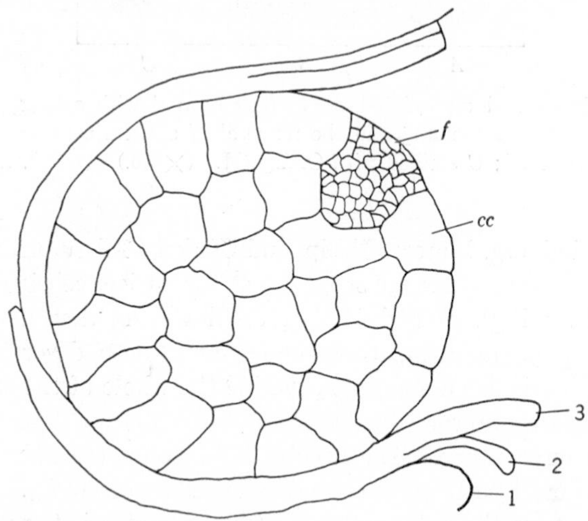

FIG. 22. Cross-section of nonmedullated wool fiber—purely diagrammatic to show relative positions of the components of the cuticle (cf. Fig. 21), the cortical cells (*cc*), and fibrillae (*f*) of the cortex. (*Courtesy Lindberg.*)

The epicuticle as seen in the electron microscope appears as a thin uniformly thick (about 100 A) film. Its most remarkable property is its chemical stability. Lindberg and Philip describe the various methods for isolating the various layers of the cuticle as well as of the cortex.

Mechanically removed scales, according to Hock and McMurdie, appear structureless (see Fig. 23).

X-ray data by Astbury and Street [3] show that the X-ray spectrum of the cuticle, especially in the stretch condition, differs from that of

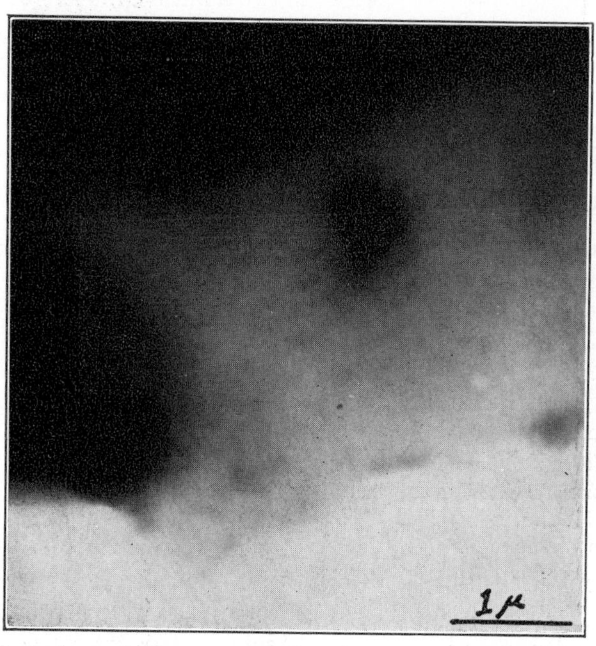

Fig. 23. Part of a scale from a wool fiber showing lack of fibrillate structure. (Electron micrograph, ×16,500.) (*Hock and McMurdie.*)

the whole fiber and suggests a more or less random orientation in the cuticle.

Cortical Layer. The cortex is found below the protective epidermis scales. It constitutes the principal body of the wool fiber and is made up of long, slightly flattened and more or less twisted, spindle-shaped cells. The average cells range from 80 to 110 μ in length, 2 to 5 μ in width, and 1.2 to 2.6 μ in thickness. Cortical cells liberated from the fibers by chemical agents show fibrillated ends; the cells are in most cases prominently striated. Hock has shown by microdissection that the striated appearance of the cortical cells is due to the presence of many fibrils, which can be separated with microneedles. When wool fibers are mounted in water, these longitudinal striations are clearly visible through the epidermis. Near the center of each cell is a nucleus, which has a granular structure. Between crossed nicols, the fibrillar part of the cortical cells appears birefringent, whereas the nucleus does not (Figs. 24 and 25).

Nuclei are not easily observed in untreated cross-sections but are clearly visible after they have been properly stained or swollen. Hotte claims that in human hair there are two additional layers between the scale and the cortex—the cuticle, a very thin membranous layer, and next to it an inner or intermediate layer of a soft, plastic material, approximately the same thickness as the scale layer. Hotte states that the intermediate layer is more or less interlinked with the cortex of the hair, so its exact thickness cannot be determined.

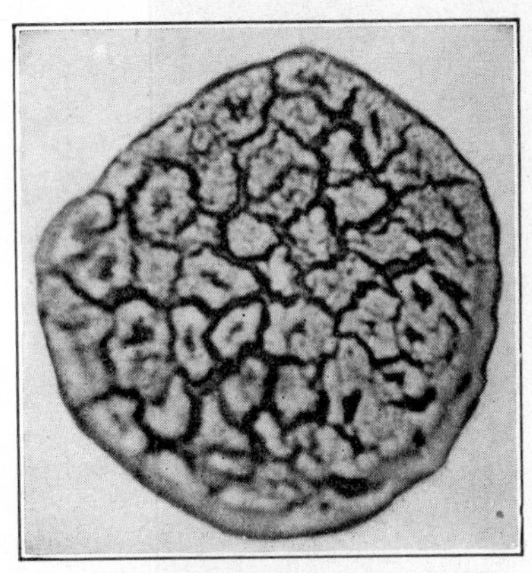

Fig. 24. Cross-section of a wool fiber after several weeks in a solution of pepsin followed by swelling with 9 per cent sodium carbonate. The photomicrograph shows the outline of the individual cortical cells and their nuclei. (×1500.) (*Hock, Ramsay, and Harris.*)

Reumuth [43] produced further evidence in favor of the existence of an intermediate layer between the epidermis and the cortex revealed by the microscopic examination of bleached wool damaged by bacteria. Lehmann [31] agrees with Reumuth. He isolated a membrane which he called the "subcutis" representing about 5 per cent of the total wool substance. Lehmann obtained the membrane by heating hair and wool fibers in a formaldehyde solution at 130° C. for several hours. Alexander separated a similar membrane by treating wool in a 1.6 per cent aqueous solution of peracetic acid for 25 hr at room temperature, followed by an ammonia wash. The one soluble membrane left represents between 7 and 10 per cent of the wool substance.

Gralen, Lagermalm, and Philip in studying the Alexander membrane came to the conclusion that the isolated membrane of Alexander and Erland [1] consisted of parts of the cuticle and the outer cells of the cortex. Zahn and Hasselmann succeeded in mechanically isolating smooth bands from horsehair which they localized beneath the scale cover. By reason of the double refraction and their fibrillary structure they regarded them as a covering zone of the cortical layer. They

According to their arrangement, medullas are classified in four groups: (*a*) the fragmental, (*b*) the interrupted, (*c*) the continuous, and (*d*) the discontinuous. In true wool only the first three are found (Fig. 28). The discontinuous medulla is characteristic of fur fibers such as rabbit hair.

The presence of medullated fibers in any wool is detrimental to quality from the standpoint of the manufacturer. They are defective because of their hair character—straight, coarse, and lustrous. The spinning properties are lower, and in piece-dyed fabrics they produce a "tippy" effect by dyeing a lighter shade. The medulla is in no way necessary for the growth of the fiber; its main function is to increase the protective properties of the fiber by adding internal air spaces.

Further experiments were made by Rudall [44] on New Zealand Romney lamb's wool to study the causes of medullar production. The result of his experiments proved conclusively that the medulla-producing effect often found after shearing is due to exposure and not to the mechanical effect of shearing. In Table 3 are given the results of

TABLE 3. VARIATION IN NUMBER OF MEDULLATED FIBERS DUE TO EXPOSURE

Animals	*No. of Follicles*	*Continuous Medulla* (1)	*Discontinuous Medulla* (½)	*No Medulla* (0)	*Total Medulla as a Per Cent*
Unshorn side	104	0	9	95	4.5
Shorn side	104	10	26	68	22
Unshorn side	104	5	66	33	35.6
Shorn side	102	47	26	29	59
Unshorn side	101	21	15	65	28
Shorn side	98	58	20	20	69.5
Unshorn side	103	0	11	92	5
Shorn side	104	60	24	20	69

some of the tests, showing the medulla-producing activity in follicles from the shorn and unshorn sides of differentially shorn lambs. A well-marked increase in the number of follicles producing a continuous medulla is shown in each case.

Kemp Hair. Kemp fibers are mainly present in mixed wools such as carpet wools. Their presence is always a sign of poor breeding. They are easily recognized with the naked eye. They are normally short, wavy, and tapering toward each end, are of a dead-white or opaque color, and very coarse and brittle. They shed naturally from the skin after several months of growth and are found mostly in the upper part of the staple. They are especially present in fleeces of lambs which are born with comparatively few medullated fibers, but which after birth develop an outer coat of medullated, coarse kemp fibers. Microscopically these kemp fibers are strongly medullated, smooth, and tapering at each end. The medulla usually starts a short distance above the hair bulb and at its greatest diameter may form 90 per cent or more of the fiber. Toward the tips, the medulla com-

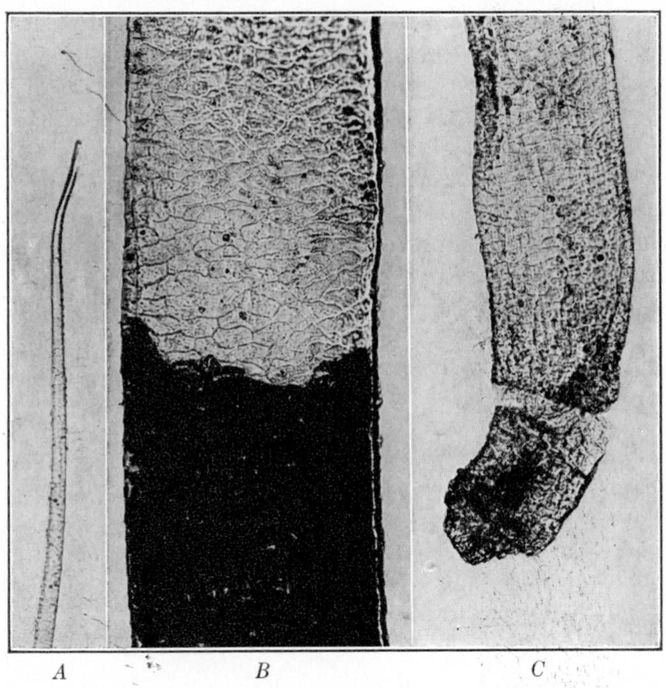

Fig. 29. Parts of a kemp fiber: *A*, tip; *B*, stem; *C*, root. (×250.) (*von Bergen.*)

mences to taper again to a point; it then becomes interrupted, and finally disappears, leaving the tip entirely free (Fig. 29). The kemp cross-section is generally ribbonlike, as seen in the photomicrograph (Fig. 30).

X-Ray Analysis. The technique of X-ray analysis has found an important place in disclosing the submicroscopic structure of the wool fiber. The work of Astbury is outstanding in this field.

Hair and wool protein (keratin) has a large capacity to stretch and great elasticity which distinguishes it sharply from silk fibroin. Unstretched human hair, wool, fur, and also horn, nails and spines, and whalebone all give the same X-ray photograph, but when stretched they give another kind of pattern. Mammalian hairs differ in this respect from fibers of cellulose and natural silk. When cellulose or natural silk is stretched the X-ray photograph remains unchanged, except for orientation effects, whereas the mammalian hairs show long-range reversible elasticity; when released in water they recover their original length exactly.

X-rays show that the wool fiber is built up of crystals which are far too small to be seen with the aid of a visible light. They exist in certain shapes and sizes and lie in certain directions in the fibers. As far as is known keratin exists in three forms. The X-ray shows definite existence of two of these: the unstretched form (α-keratin, Fig. 31) built from folded polypeptide chains and the stretched form (β-keratin, Fig. 32) built from the same chains pulled out straight. The third is the "supercontracted" form, assumed after the fiber has been stretched and treated with heat and moisture for a short time. If it is allowed to contract, it will contract to a shorter length than the α-form. The X-ray pattern does not reveal any new definite repeating pattern for this form.

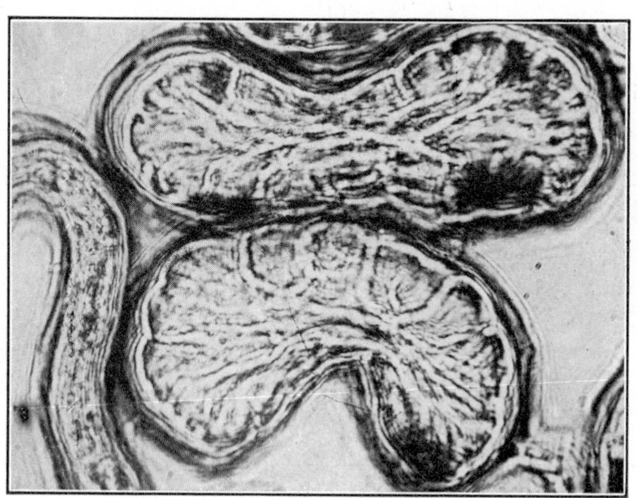

Fig. 30. Cross-sections of kemp fibers. (×500.) (*von Bergen.*)

Cotswold wool gives the best keratin diagrams obtainable in wool, and many chemical and physicochemical data are known about it. For two reasons it has been much studied by X-rays. The two X-ray photographs show the characteristic molecular pattern of an unstretched and stretched wool fiber. From this pattern Astbury together with Speakman interpreted the molecular structure of the wool fiber as shown in Fig. 1 of Chap. 12. In Fig. 32 of Cotswold wool, stretched 90 per cent of its initial length, there is a remarkable contrast to Fig. 31 of unstretched fiber. So long as hot water is avoided, the intramolecular transformation from α- to β-keratin and back again, with corresponding changes in the X-ray photographs, may be repeated as often as desired.

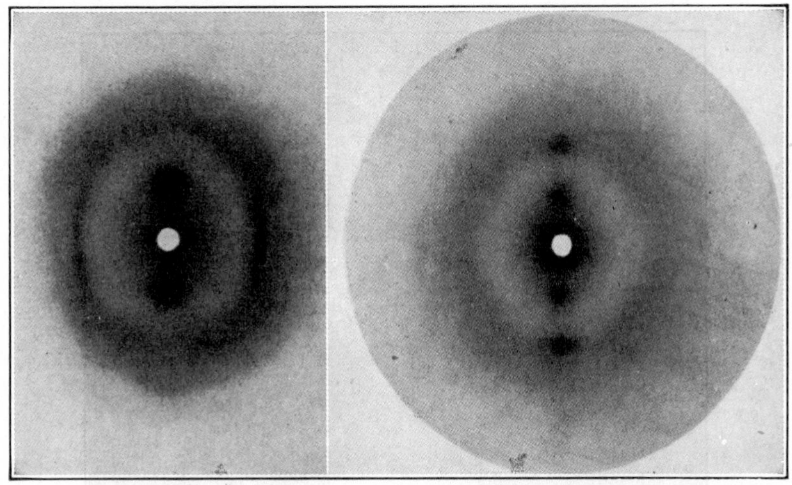

(*Left*) Fig. 31. Unstretched Cotswold wool, showing α-keratin. (*Astbury.*)
(*Right*) Fig. 32. Stretched 90% Cotswold wool, showing β-keratin. (*Astbury.*)

Astbury and his co-workers have already elucidated much unknown detail of the nature and structure of wool and its response to many manufacturing processes, and his work has been further enlarged by Wrinch, Neurath, Pauling, and Niemann.

Physical Properties

In estimating the value and suitability of wools, several characteristics are implied in the quality. First and foremost of these is fiber diameter or fineness. The length, the amount of impurities or shrinkage value, strength, color, luster, and vegetable matter content are also significant. In all these properties the wool fiber varies within wide limits, depending on the breed and geographic location of the sheep and the part of the fleece from which the wool is derived.

Conversion of fibers into yarns and goods brings out additional physical characteristics, such as the contour, crimp, elasticity, resilience, rigidity, felting quality, specific gravity, moisture content, electric properties, and warmth (heat conductivity).

Fineness. The average fineness of the wool fiber is its dominant dimensional characteristic, greatly affecting its manufacturing value. The fineness is judged in the trade mainly by visual inspection. In routine commercial practice wool is graded by men of long experience in the industry, who, by merely handling and observing the material, assign its proper grade. Such an estimate has possibilities of error, based principally upon mental and physical qualities of the individual. Other factors on which a grade is assigned are, for example, length, color, and luster of the hairs. Through experience, it was found that the grade assigned in a weak light is too high and in the direct sun it is too low. For more than a century and a half the replacing of the manual sorting by a scientific system of measurements has been felt necessary.

The U. S. Department of Agriculture promulgated the Official United States Standards for Wool and Top in July 1926 [60]. These standards gave the scientist the foundation upon which to base an accurate method of measurement.

The most astonishing results were found by Winston [67], who found that for a range of selected British tops (the same tops were used in making up the U. S. master set) the progressive scale of fineness, from 48's to 80's quality, is *in geometric progression.* A similar relationship was found in the French, German, and Italian standard tops, proving that the fundamental basis underlying wool sorting is the same in all countries.

Since the wool fiber is of microscopic structure, the fineness is expressed on the basis of microscopical measurements, either as the width or diameter of the fiber, depending on the measuring method used.

In judging the diameter of the wool fiber with the eye, the average person is under the impression that the individual fibers are very uniform in their fineness. As a matter of fact, the diameter of wool fibers varies greatly, even in the same fleece; it may range from 10 to 70 μ. The least variation is found in the merino wool staples, which normally range from 10 to 30 μ, whereas a staple of carpet wool usually consists of fibers ranging from 10 to 70 μ and more. In addition, kemp fibers are present, the diameter of which ranges from 70 to 200 μ.

The dispersion range existing in commercial samples of four main types is illustrated in Tables 4 and 5.

Further variations within the whole length of the individual fiber are caused by physiological changes in the organs of the animals due

TABLE 4. FINENESS DISPERSION RANGE OF WOOL FIBERS

Range, μ	Fine Wool		Medium Wool		Coarse or Long Wool	Carpet or Mixed Wool
	Super Merino	Merino	Fine	Coarse		
10 to 20	88	41	22	6	2	15
20 to 30	12	57	64	39	18	35
30 to 40	..	2	14	41	27	26
40 to 50	..	..	..	13	40	8
50 to 60	..	..	..	1	10	6
60 to 70	..	..	..	..	3	2
Over 70 (kemp)	..	..	..	..	..	8
Average microns	17	21	24	32	40	36
Grades	90's	70's	62's	48's	36's	..

TABLE 5. FINENESS MEASUREMENTS ON SIX MARKET GRADES

[Educational Set, U. S. Department of Agriculture, Nov. 1942]

	Fine	*½ Blood*	*⅜ Blood*	*¼ Blood*	*Low ¼ Blood*	*Common and Braid*
No. of fibers	600	800	1200	1200	1600	1600
Per cent of fibers from:						
10 to 20 μ	31.2	17.8	9.7	7.1	4.3	0.8
20 to 30 μ	61.8	67.6	51.7	36.1	34.8	20.7
30 to 40 μ	6.8	14.1	27.7	43.3	40.6	43.7
40 to 50 μ	0.2	0.5	10.8	12.7	18.1	31.9
50 to 60 μ	....	....	0.1	0.8	1.8	2.7
60 to 70 μ	....	....	....	....	0.4	0.2
Average microns	22.8	24.9	29.12	31.43	33.05	36.71
Coeff. of variation, %	23.2	21.3	26.7	25.1	25.4	20.7
A.S.T.M. grade	64/62's	60's	56/50's	50/48's	46's	40's

NOTE: The samples in this new arrangement comprise bulk types and were selected to present a general average of the grade rather than the lower edge, as in the standard forms. Microscopically the fine and ⅜ blood samples are on the lower edge, whereas the other four are perfect selections.

to nutrition, gestation, weaning, or sickness. For instance, good feeding produces a larger and coarser fleece, whereas malnutrition produces a smaller and finer fleece; in the same way lactation and the suckling of lambs reduce appreciably the fiber fineness, the fleece density, and the wool production. The tips of the staples, covering the back and side of the animal, are changed through atmospheric influences, such as sun and rain.

Fiber Contour. The shape of the cross-section varies greatly. Some cross-sections are nearly circular. As a rule they are irregular and have a varying degree of ovality or ellipticity. The most common method of expressing the ellipticity is by the ratio of the major to the minor axis as the contour figure. Barker [4] has claimed that in two wools of the same fineness the more circular wool spins better. According to trade opinion the spinning properties of wool can be divided into three groups:

Group No. 1, very good spinning, with contour figure below 1.2.
Group No. 2, medium spinning, with contour figure 1.2 to 1.22.
Group No. 3, fair spinning, with contour figure above 1.22.

Crimp. Wool fibers grow in a more or less wavy form and with a certain amount of twist. Crimp is probably a direct consequence of the formation of the fiber itself within the follicle. Equality of crimp is associated with uniformity, and, therefore, a sign of good quality. Crimps occur in the form of "waves" or "curls." They range from flat waves through normal waves to highly bent waves. The number of waves in different wools is more or less an indication of fineness. Generally, the more crimps per inch, the finer the fiber, a condition that often strongly influences the wool buyer and the wool sorter in their judgment of the fineness. It is, therefore, of great interest to the practical wool man to know how far the agreement is of value to him.

Bosman made a study of the relationship between the fiber fineness and crimping on South African wools. Observations were carried out on 1000 samples produced in different areas of the Union. Out of 1000 samples only 28 per cent showed a perfect agreement between the standards of crimps and those of fiber fineness. The rest, or 72 per cent, did not conform, 36 per cent being finer and 36 per cent being coarser than the crimps indicated. Of the 36 per cent that was coarser than the crimps indicated, 17 per cent was coarser by one quality number, 12 per cent was coarser by two quality numbers, and 6 per cent was coarser by more than two quality numbers. Therefore, if a wool man bases wool quality on crimping, he can form a correct estimate in only 28 per cent of the cases. This makes crimps alone an unreliable guide to fiber fineness for the South African clip as a whole. This is even more the case where individual samples are concerned.

American wools do not differ from the above findings for South African wools. McMurtrie [35] established these facts many years ago.

In the U. S. Standard Grades of Raw Wool, issued by the Department of Agriculture, the relationship of the crimps and the grade of wool was found as shown in Table 6.

TABLE 6. Grade and Crimps in Wool

Grades	Number of Crimps per Inch	Grades	Number of Crimps per Inch
Very fine	22 to 30	¼ blood	5 to 8
Fine	14 to 22	Low quarter	2 to 5
½ blood	10 to 14	Common	0 to 2
⅜ blood	8 to 10	Braid	0 to 1

In making up these standard grades, it is very difficult to select individual staples for this purpose by visual inspection only. Microscopical measurement is necessary to establish the correct grade. The greatest deviation from the rule is observed in wools with highly or over-bent waves and in wools with adverse or flat waves. In wools with a high amount of grease, the crimps are more numerous in contrast to dry wool, which looks coarser.

U. S. Government Wool and Top Grade Specifications. The present microscopical grade specifications for wool and tops, as promulgated by the United States Department of Agriculture, are given in Table 7.

TABLE 7. United States Official Standards for Grades of Wool

	Grades							
	80's	70's	64's	62's *	60's	58's	56's	50's
Fineness range								
Average diameter, μ								
Minimum	18.1	19.6	21.1	22.6	24.1	25.6	27.1	29.1
Maximum	19.5	21.0	22.5	24.0	25.5	27.0	29.0	31.5
Fineness distribution								
Fiber diameter, μ								
10 to 20, per cent, minimum	60	50	36	27	18	16	9	4
10 to 25, per cent, minimum	92	84	..	..	..	..	..	..
10 to 30, per cent, minimum	..	..	94	88	83	74	64	45
25.1 to 30, per cent, maximum	8	..	..	..	..	..	..	..
25.1 to 40, per cent, maximum	..	16	..	..	..	..	..	..
30.1 to 40, per cent, maximum	..	2	6	12	17	..	..	..
30.1 to 50, per cent, maximum	..	..	..	..	..	26	36	55
40.1 to 50, per cent, maximum	..	..	..	..	..	2	5	10
30.1 and over, per cent, maximum	0.25 (0.5) †							
40.1 and over, per cent, maximum	..	0.25 (0.5) †	0.333 (1.) †	0.50 (1.) †	0.50 (1.) †	..	..	..
50.1 and over, per cent, maximum	..	..	..	..	..	0.75 (1.5) †	1. (2.) †	1.25 (2.5) †
Fibers required for test								
Minimum number of fibers required for test per sample	400	400	600	600	800	800	1200	1200

* A grade officially promulgated for wool top only.

† Numbers in parentheses represent maximum percentage of fibers of that range permissible in substandard grades.

Up to 1951 there were no officially accepted specifications for the grades from 48's to 36's. Tentative specifications are published by the American Society for Testing Materials and are based on microscopical measurements made by the Wool Section of the U. S. Department of Agriculture. The results of these measurements are given in Table 8.

TABLE 8. MICROSCOPIC MEASUREMENTS OF U. S. STANDARD TOP SAMPLES

[*U. S. Department of Agriculture*]

Types	*48's*	*46's*	*44's*	*40's*	*36's*
Number of fibers	3500	3000	3800	2600	2700
Percentage of fibers from					
10 to 20 μ	4.5	3.8	2.9	1.3	1.6
20 to 30	33.9	28.4	23.9	17.0	13.1
30 to 40	44.4	46.3	43.2	44.3	36.8
40 to 50	15.7	18.9	24.4	31.7	36.7
50 to 60	1.23	2.5	4.8	4.9	10.1
60 to 70	0.12	0.13	0.8	0.8	1.6
Over 70	....	....	....	0.1	0.2
Average microns	32.5	33.7	35.7	37.5	39.7
Coefficient of variation in %	24.3	23.7	24.3	20.8	23.4

Length. The length of the fiber plays an important part as a quality factor, as "combing" and "clothing" wools are classified according to their length. Generally speaking, "clothing wool" is understood to be wool with an average staple length below 2 in., whereas "combing wools" commonly range from 2½ to 7 in. Since the wool fiber is not a straight fiber but exhibits crimps and curls, the measurement of the proper fiber length is complicated by its waviness. So far there is no satisfactory method for the direct determination of the fiber length. Depending upon the number of crimps, the stretched length may be 1.2 up to 1.9 times the natural length.

The length of the wool fibers varies in large limits not only in different breeds but also on the same animal. The average length variation of the main breeds is illustrated by Table 9.

These figures show that the greatest length is associated with the coarser fiber and the shortest wools are among the merino. In the marketing of wool, the term length refers to the staple or group length, which is the average length from the base of the staple up to the longest fibers forming the tip of the staple. In each group of fibers there are short, medium, and long fibers, because the wool does not grow uniformly long out of the skin. The uneven growth is partly responsible for the variation in the length of fibers of semi-manufactured products, such as wool tops. This original length difference is

TABLE 9

Wool Type	*Breeds*	*Length Variation (in inches)*
Fine	American Merino	1½ to 3
	Rambouillet (U. S. A.)	2½ to 3½
	Australian Merino	3 to 5
Medium	English Down	2 to 4
	Corriedale	3 to 7
Coarse	Romney	5 to 6
	Leicester English	6 to 8
	Cotswold	10 to 14

considerably accentuated by fiber breakage in manufacturing, especially carding.

This is illustrated by the length curves of four wool tops in Fig. 33, whereas in the example given by Schadow [45] the coefficient of variation is less than 15 per cent after 5 months' growth, in tops the average is over 30 per cent.

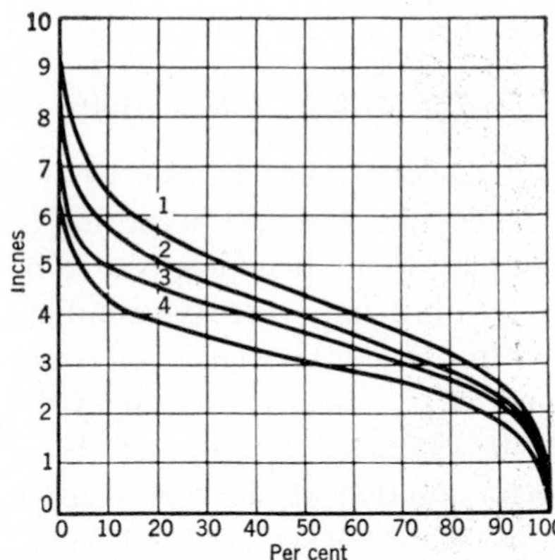

Fig. 33. Length curves of tops. 1, 48's top at 5.1 in. ± 1.6 in.; 2, ± 50's top at 4.1 in. ± 1.4 in.; 3, 56's top at 3.7 in. ± 1.1 in.; 4, 62's top at 3.1 in. ± 1.0 in. (*American Wool Handbook.*)

Breaking and Tensile Strength. McMurtrie was probably one of the first to estimate the breaking load of wool. Hill [24] concluded that the breaking strength of wool is more nearly proportionate to the diameter of the fiber than to the square of the diameter. Hardy [20] stated that the tensile strength of wool decreased with an increase in relative humidity from 40 to 80 per cent and showed the tendency to increase thereafter to saturation.

Kronacher [30] (1924) found a high correlation between fineness and breaking strength and gave standards of breaking strength for the various fineness groups. Barker and Hedges [5] (1927) found a decrease of approximately 0.57 per cent in the breaking strength of yarns for each 1 per cent rise in relative humidity. Cunliffe [15] (1933) published photographs of fibers under stress, which showed clearly the diminution of fiber diameter during stretching.

An extensive series of experiments on the elastic properties of wool was commenced by Speakman [47] (1924, 1926 to 1931) using English Cotswold wool. The whole literature reflects the difficulty in obtaining average strength figures for any type of wool or hair fibers based on single-fiber tests.

By breaking a large number of fibers, in the form of bundles, a much clearer insight can be obtained into the relationship between fineness and strength. In a study on South African merino wools conducted by Bosman, Waterston, and Van Wyk [8] using the bundle method, 100 fibers per sample, the following was established:

> Within the same staple, the coarse fibers were 52 per cent stronger per fiber than the fine fibers; there was a significant correlation of 0.9508 between fiber

TABLE 10. Strength of Foreign Wool Tops

Official U. S. Top Standards, Box #134, Effective January 1, 1935

Bundle Test: Conditions: 65% R. H. at 72° F.

Grade	Fineness (microns)	Approx. No. of Fibers	Breaking Strength		Tensile Strength	
			Bundle (kg)	Single Fiber (grams)	Kg/cm^2	Coefficient of Variation (per cent)
80's	19.5	2990	14.3	4.78	1597	1.7
70's	20.8	2630	13.8	5.25	1546	1.0
64's	21.9	2380	14.0	5.88	1564	2.3
60's	23.5	2060	14.7	7.14	1649	1.2
58's	24.8	1850	15.6	8.43	1743	1.2
56's	26.9	1570	16.2	10.32	1816	1.6
50's	30.4	1230	17.0	13.82	1903	1.3
48's	33.0	1050	16.8	16.00	1877	2.0
46's	34.8	940	17.1	18.19	1904	2.5
44's	36.6	850	17.3	20.35	1929	1.3
40's	38.3	780	18.4	23.59	2053	1.4
36's	39.3	740	19.0	25.68	2124	2.0

Bundle length:
2 in. for grades 80's, 70's, 64's, 60's, 58's, 56's.
3 in. for grades 50's, 48's, 46's, 44's, 40's, 36's.

Average bundle size: 2 in., 0.06 gram.
3 in., 0.09 gram.

Coefficient of correlation:
Fineness: breaking strength, +0.990.
Fineness: tensile strength, +0.966.

diameter and breaking strength and a significant negative correlation of 0.4822 between the fiber diameter and tensile strength. The average breaking strength per fiber was 1 to 11 grams (mean 5.50 grams) and the tensile strength 600–1600 kg/sq cm (average 1243). With different samples, the correlation between fiber fineness and breaking strength was significant, that between fiber fineness and tensile strength insignificant. The regression coefficient of the breaking load on fiber fineness was 0.445, indicating that, on an average, every increase of one micron in fiber diameter was associated with an increase of 0.445 gram in the breaking strength.

Kronacher [30] reported a regression coefficient of 0.5819. Research conducted by Forstmann Woolen Co. has produced results (Tables 10 to 12) which show that the wool fiber possesses considerably greater strength than it had hitherto been credited with. Tables 10 and 11

TABLE 11. Strength of Domestic Wool Tops

Official U. S. Top Standards, Effective January 1, 1940

Bundle Test: Conditions: 65% R. H. at 72° F.

Grade	Fineness (microns)	Approx. No. of Fibers	Breaking Strength		Tensile Strength	
			Bundle (kg)	Single Fiber (grams)	Kg/cm^2	Coefficient of Variation (per cent)
80's	19.5	3000	13.7	4.57	1526	1.6
70's	20.0	2840	13.7	4.82	1537	1.6
64's	21.8	2350	13.3	5.66	1499	3.9
62's	23.5	2060	13.2	6.41	1477	3.8
60's	24.7	1820	13.3	7.31	1490	2.2
58's	25.8	1680	13.5	8.04	1510	1.3
56's	27.7	1450	14.7	10.14	1649	1.2
50's	30.2	1260	14.4	11.43	1614	2.7

Bundle length: 2 in. Average bundle size: 0.06 gram.

Coefficient of correlation:
Breaking strength, 0.9887.
Tensile strength, 0.6195.

show the average breaking and tensile strength as measured on the official U. S. standard tops as well as breaking and tensile strengths of important hair fibers (Table 12).

The breaking strength results are the average of 10 tests, performed on bundles of equal weight in relation to the bundle length for each of

TABLE 12. BREAKING STRENGTH OF VARIOUS HAIR FIBERS

Bundle Test: Conditions: 65% R. H. at 72° F.

Type	Fineness (microns)	Approx. No. of Fibers	Breaking Strength		Tensile Strength	
			Bundle (kg.)	Single Fiber (grams)	Kg/cm²	Coefficient of Variation (per cent)
Human hair: Female, 14 yr (light brown) *	58.6	330	21.9	66.36	2439	2.3
Female, 38 yr (dark brown) *	84.8	160	21.4	133.75	2388	2.6
Horsehair: Female, tail, 9 yr (blueronde) *	260.0	17	15.1	888.24	1681	5.7
Female, tail, 15 yr (chestnut) *	181.0	35	17.1	488.57	1914	5.5
Mixed, mane, Argentine (dirty white) *	129.0	70	16.1	230.00	1799	3.1
Cow hair: Mixed, tail (dirty white) *	187.0	30	18.1	603.33	2023	3.8
Mohair: super kid top	25.4	1800	19.1	10.61	2154	2.4
36's top	28.7	1360	20.0	14.70	2231	1.1
22's top *	36.4	870	18.6	21.38	2138	2.5
Cashmere top *	15.0	5000	12.7	2.54	1444	3.3
Camel's hair: Fine top *	20.7	2750	15.4	5.60	1790	3.2
Coarse top	26.6	1570	16.3	10.38	1808	3.2
Alpaca: White top *	27.0	1640	17.1	10.43	1820	0.7
Brown top	27.0	1540	15.4	10.00	1747	2.6
Black top	27.0	1590	15.3	9.62	1682	3.4

Bundle length:
3 in. for: Argentine Horsehair, kid mohair, 36's mohair, 22's mohair, alpaca white, brown, black
2 in. for: Human hair, female 14 yr, female 38 yr, horsehair tail, 9 yr, tail 15 yr, cow hair, camel's hair, fine, coarse.
1 in. for: Cashmere.

Correlation coefficient of fibers marked *
Fineness: breaking strength, 0.980.
Fineness: tensile strength, 0.076.

Average bundle size:
1 in., 0.03 gram.
2 in., 0.06 gram.
3 in., 0.09 gram.

the wool grades analyzed (30 mg per in. of fiber length). In view of the low variations in the individual test results, 10 tests were deemed adequate. In consequence, the number of fibers per bundle varies with the diameter of the fibers.

The converted results obtained for the breaking strength of the individual fibers for the foreign and domestic wools indicate that direct relationship exists between the fiber diameter and fiber breaking strength. This is in agreement with the findings of Bosman and associates. However, a higher correlation was found on the tests performed on fibers in top form than in the results obtained by Bosman which were derived from wool in staple (fleece) form. This is understandable in view of the greater uniformity and degree of mixing obtained in commercial top samples. Each top standard represents a cross-section or composite average of wools obtained from a variety of clips of diverse origin. A significant correlation of 0.990 between fiber diameter and breaking strength was found for the entire set of foreign wool samples, as compared with a correlation of 0.992 for the grades 80's to 50's inclusive. For the domestic wools, a correlation of 0.989 between fineness and breaking strength for the grades between 80's and 50's was observed.

A significant difference is evident in the correlation between fiber diameter and tensile strength for foreign and domestic wools. Comparison between the correlation coefficient of domestic and foreign fine wools (fineness range between 80's and 50's) reveals a significant plus correlation for the foreign wools of 0.957 and a significant plus correlation of 0.620 for the equivalent domestic grades. A further characteristic of the results obtained on the foreign and domestic wools showed that the tensile strength distribution fell into three definite groups, which more or less coincide with the three main wool types—fine, medium, and coarse. This factor is even more pronounced in the domestic wool samples. There is no correlation between fiber diameter and tensile strength in the fine grades, 58's and up, whereas there is a definite upward trend in the medium (crossbred) types, 56's to 50's. The regression coefficient of the breaking load on fiber fineness for domestic wool is 0.549 gram, indicating that, on an average, every increase of 1 μ in fiber diameter is associated with an increase of 0.549 gram in the breaking strength.

In the wet state, wool loses from 10 to 25 per cent of its strength. In Table 13 are shown the relationships between the dry and wet strength of 1940 standard tops.

TABLE 13. WET AND DRY TENSILE STRENGTH OF WOOL IN KG/CM^2

Top Grades	*Dry*	*Wet*	*Loss % of Dry*	*Top Grades*	*Dry*	*Wet*	*Loss % of Dry*
80's	1525	1197	21.5	50's	1614	1321	18.1
70's	1537	1199	22.0	48's	1877	1544	17.8
64's	1499	1212	18.3	46's	1904	1641	13.9
62's	1477	1244	15.8	44's	1929	1633	15.4
60's	1490	1269	14.8	40's	2053	1751	14.8
58's	1510	1300	13.9	36's	2124	1835	13.7
56's	1649	1300	21.1				

The strength data on the specialty hair and the other animal fibers reveal that each type of fiber seems to have its definite strength level, with the human hair the strongest. By using the human hair as 100 per cent, the various fibers are rated in regard to tensile strength in the following order in Table 14.

TABLE 14. STRENGTH RELATIONSHIP FOR VARIOUS ANIMAL FIBERS

Type of Fiber	*Tensile Strength* (per cent)	*Type of Fiber*	*Tensile Strength* (per cent)
Human hair	100	Camel's hair	75
Mohair	90	Alpaca	72
Long wools	80	Medium wools	70
Horsehair	75	Merino	62

Elasticity. If a wool fiber is slowly elongated without rupture, a definite extension will result. When the load is subsequently released the fiber makes an immediate partial recovery, leaving a residual extension, resulting in a "temporary set," which the fiber slowly loses if given time.

Speakman [48] has demonstrated that wool fibers can be elongated 30 per cent without permanent deformation or weakening if the duration of the strain is short.

Figure 34 according to Harris and Sookne [21] shows the behavior of a typical wet wool fiber during two successive stress-strain determinations. The fiber was allowed to relax for approximately 24 hr between the first and second extensions. It is noteworthy that the entire stress-strain cycle is reproducible. The 30 per cent index is the energy required to elongate a fiber 30 per cent after a treatment divided by the similar energy requirement prior to the treatment, which in the above case amounts to 0.99.

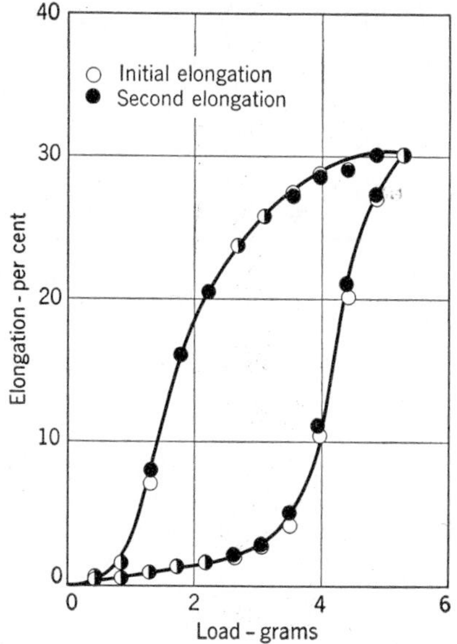

FIG. 34. Typical untreated wool fiber during the two stress-strain cycles, separated by 24 hr. (30 per cent index equals 0.99.) (*Harris and Sookne.*)

A very extensive study on the stress-strain properties of dry single wool fibers was made at the Textile Research Institute of Princeton

(International Wool Project). The study included two fine wools, an Australian merino, a domestic merino (Rambouillet), and two medium crossbred wools: a New Zealand and a domestic.

When a wool fiber is extended at a constant rate, a curve similar to Fig. 35 is obtained. Medium and fine wools from different sources follow the same general type of curve with some modification due to fiber history and testing conditions. The major features of the shape and size of the curve can be described by the parameters shown.

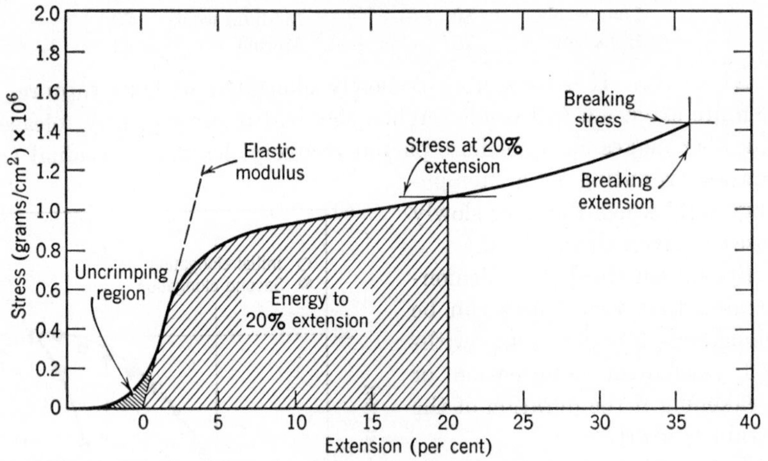

Fig. 35. A typical stress-strain curve for a wool fiber, 70° F., 65 per cent R.H. (*Textile Research Inst., Princeton.*)

Table 15 lists the results of a series of measurements on single wool fibers from the four wools, giving pertinent characteristics of the samples. One-inch sections of fibers approximating the staple length were extracted from the top and tested at 70° F. and 65 per cent R.H., using a rate of extension of ½ in. per min. Cross-sectional areas were determined by the vibroscope technique, using an average density of 1.305 gm/cm³.

Compressibility. The most comprehensive study on the elastic behavior of wool (South African) in bulk was made by Van Wyk [62]. In studying the relationship which exists between pressure and volume and the effect of the mass of the wool sample, he found that the following facts played a major role:

There is a marked reduction in resistance to compression with the absorption of water. There is normally no correlation between resistance to compression and fiber fineness. But there is a highly sig-

TABLE 15. STRESS-STRAIN DATA FOR FOUR TYPES OF WOOLS

	Australian Fine	*Domestic Fine*	*New Zealand Medium*	*Domestic Medium*
Diameter, microns	19.2	21.4	26.7	25.7
Standard deviation	2.7	2.6	4.2	3.4
Fibers	144	288	240	432
Breaking extension, per cent *				
Median	33.9	35.0	35.8	36.1
Mean	32.7	32.8	33.6	33.9
Standard deviation	8.0	9.6	9.2	9.0
Fibers	143	288	240	432
Elastic modulus, gm/cm^2	30.8×10^6	29.0×10^6	35.1×10^6	31.0×10^6
Standard deviation	5.2×10^6	4.3×10^6	6.2×10^6	5.1×10^6
Fibers	141	288	239	432
Stress at 20 per cent extension, gm/cm^2	1.047×10^6	1.058×10^6	1.198×10^6	1.090×10^6
Standard deviation	0.059×10^6	0.056×10^6	8.4×10^6	0.072×10^6
Fibers	132	255	215	399
Energy to 20 per cent extension, $gm\text{-}cm/cm^3$	16.84×10^4	17.42×10^4	19.52×10^4	17.88×10^4
Standard deviation	1.2×10^4	1.0×10^4	1.7×10^4	1.3×10^4
Fibers	132	255	214	399
Breaking stress, gm/cm^2	1.34×10^6	1.37×10^6	1.55×10^6	1.44×10^6
Standard deviation	0.22×10^6	0.24×10^6	0.30×10^6	0.26×10^6
Fibers	143	288	240	432

* Breaking extension has a badly skewed distribution.
Source: Textile Research Institute (International Wool Project).

nificant positive correlation coefficient of +0.433 between the resistance to compression and the number of crimps per inch for wools whose fineness and crimp agree with Duerden's standard.

The resistance to compression increases with the quality number. One of the best illustrations for this is the difference in the amount of fine wools and mohair fibers which can be compressed in a bag. Approximately twice the amount of straight mohair fibers can be compressed in the same space as wool.

Fiber length has no influence down to staple lengths of approximately 1 in. There is no correlation between the resistance to compression of a sample and the surface friction or the tensile strength of the fibers.

Resilience. Resilience is the springiness of a fiber mass, or the ability of a fiber to come back to its original volume after being compressed. This property is especially predominant in wool. It is by reason of this quality that wool fabrics hold their shape, drape gracefully, and do not wrinkle easily. This property is desired to a high degree in carpet wools. There is no accurate way of measuring this property as yet.

Rigidity. The rigidity of the wool fiber is the property which determines its resistance to the insertion of twist, and is, therefore, of great interest in spinning. The rigidity depends to a marked degree on the amount of water combined with the wool; actually, the rigidity of dry wool fibers is about fifteen times greater than that of wool fibers saturated with water. For this reason all modern spinning rooms are equipped with humidifying systems to keep the humidity of the spinning room as high as possible. Normally from 70 to 80 per cent humidity keeps the moisture in wool between a 15 and 18 per cent regain.

Felting. This is one of the most important characteristics of wool, lacking in many other textile materials, and of a purely physical nature. To make felting possible a fiber must possess a surface scale structure, ease of deformation, and the power of recovery from deformation. Under the influence of pressure, heat, and moisture the wool fiber tends to migrate in the direction of its root end, owing to its scale structure.

The best survey of the mechanism of felting is given in *Wool Science Review*, 1949. Monge [39] in 1790 observed that, as a result of the greater friction in the tip-to-root (antiscale) than in the root-to-tip (with scale) direction, wool fibers travel rootward when rubbed, and he attributed to this behavior the ability to felt. It is now generally accepted that the prime causative factor in felting is fiber travel produced by the differential frictional effect, which is a ratchet effect due to the projecting scale structure of the cuticle cells of the fiber.

Fiber travel can be caused, in a mass of fibers, in two ways: first, by rubbing, and second, by putting the mass through a series of deformation-recovery cycles. When a fiber is deformed while in frictional contact with other fibers it will tend to move in a direction of less friction, and move again in the course of recovery. The power of recovery from deformation-elasticity thus plays an important part in determining the felting power of a material. The elasticity of animal fibers varies considerably with the *p*H and temperature, and changes in these factors therefore affect the rate and maximum extent of felting, as Speakman [49] and others have shown.

Two *p*H ranges with which wool fibers felt the best are: an alkaline range between *p*H 9 and 11, or around *p*H 10, and an acid range around *p*H 2. The best belting temperature is around 100° F. The best alkaline medium is soap, whereas sulfuric acid is the best fulling agent to be used in the low *p*H range. In regard to the movement of the fibers which lead to the complex entanglement existing in the felt, Arnold [2] advanced his "earthworm theory."

The pressure of the fulling rolls brings about the closest possible contact between the fibers, whereby the scales find the necessary resistance on each other. The frictional movement forces the hair in the direction of its root end, either wholly or partly, causing a stretching. Because of its elasticity, the moist fiber tends to counteract this elongation. This occurs in the direction of the root, and, because the fiber is held in position firmly by the scales, a steady forward movement results. When pressure is released the stretched fibers contract and cause shrinkage by drawing other fibers together, forming a close and compact mass.

Martin [33] found that the rootward ends of the fibers play a very critical part in the process. An antishrink treatment applied to the rootward ends of the fiber made the material unfeltable, whereas a similar treatment of the tip ends had no such effect. The interlacing and interlooping of the wool fiber with others can best be described by saying that each "operative fiber" acts like a needle and thread, and, to get the best felting property, the fiber should consist of rigid rootward ends and soft flexible "tails."

Animal fibers are relatively uniform in rigidity over their length; the felting power of a wool material therefore depends on the balance existing between the flexibility needed in the tip portion and the penetrating power required in the root. Fibers which are too rigid cannot give a very close packing (mohair). Fibers which are too soft (cashmere) cannot penetrate into a compact structure with their rootward ends. The tip-softening technique is utilized on rabbit fur for felt hat manufacture, in a treatment known as "carroting." The reagent (usually nitric acid and hydrogen peroxide) is applied to the pelt by brushing and is thus restricted to the fiber tips.

The felting of wool is also aided by its crimp, which increases the amount of interfiber contact. Whereas the untreated hair and rabbit fur fibers are straight, the carroted portions coil up on immersion in hot water [7]. As stated above, the ability to felt depends primarily on the differential frictional effect, but its extent is influenced by other factors, mainly the fiber rigidity and elasticity. All three factors vary in magnitude with external conditions, such as moisture content, *p*H, and the temperature of the felting medium. Further, their relative importance is not the same under all circumstances; the changes in elasticity will have little effect on the rate of felting in a case where fiber travel can be caused by simple rubbing rather than a deformation (e.g., the felting up of loosely knitted socks in a laundering machine). The part played by fiber characteristics such as crimp and fiber length and factors such as fulling agents, type of felting machine, yarn and fabric structure, has been extensively studied, but the results obtained are in most cases valid only over a very narrow field.

The condition and the action of the various working parts in a rotary fulling mill were analyzed by von Bergen [64]. This study illustrates the number of variables involved in one type of felting machine. Therefore it is not surprising that accurate predictions of the felting behavior of various wools and hair fibers under any circumstances is hardly possible.

Luster. Wools vary in luster considerably. Certain wools are naturally lustrous. This luster cannot be noted in a single hair, but only in locks and accumulated quantities. Luster varies with origin and breed of animal and with climate. The trade differentiates between *silver* luster, *silk* luster, and *glass* luster. The silver luster is especially prominent in the finest and strongly crimped merino wools, where it is often characterized as a mild luster. The silk luster is present in the long staple and long waved wools, represented by the English wools, and designated as "luster wools." The Lincoln and Leicester wools are especially valued for this reason.

The highest, the glass luster, always points to the straight, smooth hairs which are especially apparent in goat hair, such as mohair. The glassy hairs on sheep are found on the head, neck, tail root, and lower part of the legs. This variation in luster of different wools is of great value in the manufacture of certain types of materials, because it influences the beauty and vividness of color and appearance of goods. The luster of wools can be altered through changes in the physical structure. Epidermis cells may have lost their smoothness, and the rough surface makes an unfavorable reflection surface. Such wools are known as dull wools. The rough surface is caused by atmospheric influences or mildew, whereby the scales are partly destroyed or dissolved.

Color. Wool from most domesticated breeds of sheep is nearly always white, though it may occur in the natural colors of gray, brown, or black. The degree of whiteness may vary considerably. Of the domestic wools, the Wyoming wools are known for their whiteness, whereas many Texas wools are more ivory in shade. Australian wools are generally pure white. South American wools, such as Montevideo wools, and some of the Buenos Aires wools may range from a light ivory to dirty ivory shade. In some instances the whole fleece is colored, whereas in others the color may be limited to the head and leg parts. For example, the English Down sheep are recognized by the chocolate-brown or black hairs covering part of the head and legs. The largest amount of colored wools is produced by the primitive breeds growing carpet wool types.

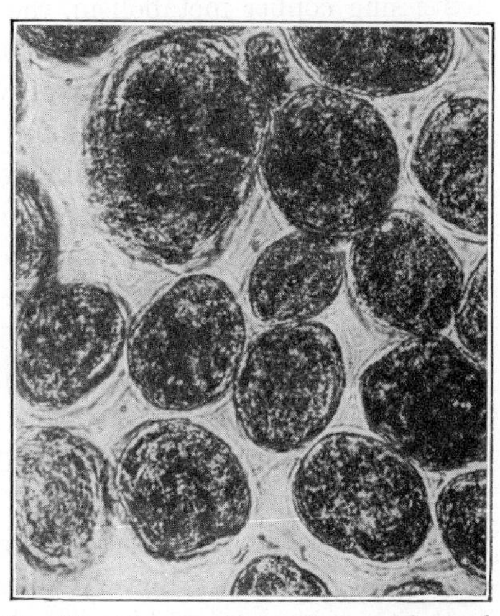

Fig. 36. Cross-section of natural wool showing presence of color pigment. (×500.) (*American Wool Handbook.*)

Beyond the difference in color, there is not any noticeable difference in structure or properties between black wool and white wool. Climate seems to have no influence on the occurrence of black wool, and it is as likely to occur in one breed as in another. The amount of black wool appearing in the American domestic breed is about 3 to 5 per cent of the total clip.

The color is produced by pigments, which are distributed mainly through the cortical and medullary cells. There are two forms present: diffuse or nongranular; and granular, which predominates. The epidermis cells are free from coloring matter. The photomicrograph in Fig. 36 illustrates these facts.

The color of the pigments seems to be influenced by the presence of certain metals. Goss [18] in California found that adding 200 ppm of molybdenum salts to the diet of a sheep carrying natural black wool caused the black pigmentation to disappear. The white color persisted for as long as the molybdenum supplement was administered. By feeding alternately a normal ration and then a normal ration plus excessive molybdenum, a black-and-white banded fleece was produced. By adding to the normal ration plus excessive molybdenum so much copper that molybdenum could not completely function in depressing copper metabolism, the color changed to black.

Specific Gravity. Wool is one of the lightest natural textile fibers. The density or specific gravity of wool is one of its fundamental characteristics, which seems to be more or less constant in all varieties and conditions of the fiber. Specific gravity of wool, as recorded in the literature, varies according to the liquid used in its determination. According to King [29], the specific gravity as found in benzene seems to be the correct value, established as 1.304. Van Wyk and Nel [63] determined the specific gravity of 54 samples of South African merino wool. The mean value was 1.3052 at 25° C., water at 4° C., with a standard deviation of ± 0.0035 and a coefficient of variability of ± 0.27 per cent. No correlation was found between specific gravity and fiber fineness.

No appreciable differences are found in medulla-free wools, whether merino or crossbred. Lower values are obtained in medullated wools as the tendency toward kempy nature increases. This is undoubtedly due to the incomplete removal of the air present in the medulla.

Moisture Content. Wool is more hygroscopic than any other fiber. However, the amount of moisture varies considerably according to the humidity and temperature of the atmosphere.

The condition of the material also has an effect upon its moisture content. The presence of more or less hygroscopic wool fats, oils, acids, and alkalies, the degree of looseness or compactness during manufacturing, and the changes the fiber undergoes in processes such as scouring, dyeing, steaming, and drying are all factors which may influence the moisture content. The effect of the length of time during which atmospheric humidity acts upon the fibers is important. The change of the moisture content depends greatly upon the nature of its surface accessibility. For instance, wool spread out in thin layers is influenced far more easily than compressed or baled wool, especially that stored in large piles in closed warehouses.

Aside from the area of surface exposure, the rate with which the fiber takes up moisture or relinquishes it depends chiefly upon the time of exposure to a particular humidity. Generally speaking, up to a certain point, the rate of moisture desorption exceeds the rate of adsorption until a state of equilibrium is reached. For practical purposes this state is reached in 4 to 5 hr.

The changes occurring in the regain of wool by exposure to atmospheres of different humidity at a constant temperature are recorded in Table 16, compiled by the English Wool Industries Research Association.

TABLE 16. Average Moisture Regain of Wool in Various Forms

Various Forms	R. H. of Atmosphere (Per Cent) at 72° F.						
	43.3	55.4	62.3	74.6	81.5	86.2	90.0
	Regain (Per Cent) Mean Values						
Scoured wool	12.08	14.22	15.51	16.55	17.86	19.61	21.17
Card ball	12.13	14.35	15.52	17.02	18.73	20.86	22.65
Backwashed ball	11.92	14.19	15.29	16.86	18.52	20.58	22.38
Noils	11.66	13.59	14.93	15.79	17.17	18.89	20.43
Tops	11.77	13.94	15.07	16.56	18.12	20.15	21.92
Yarns	12.22	14.36	15.36	16.86	18.50	20.31	21.97

The moisture content of wool in the grease is considerably lower than that established for scoured wool. Sommer reports the figures shown in Table 17.

TABLE 17. Moisture Content of Grease Wool in Percentage of Dry Weight

Relative Humidity (per cent)	*Moisture Regain* (per cent)
30	6.0 to 8.5
40	7.2 to 9.7
50	8.5 to 11.0
60	9.6 to 12.2
70	11.0 to 13.0
100	39.0 to 48.0

A study in the variation in the content of the hygroscopic moisture in worsted yarns has been made by Hartshorne [22]. This study led to the establishment of a standard for conditioning wool in the United States.

The complexity of the behavior of the wool toward moisture has been clarified considerably by Speakman, Stott, and Cooper. Speakman was the first to show that a marked hysteresis exists in the moisture content of wool between adsorption and desorption conditions. In dealing with six different types of wool, Speakman [50] found them remarkably similar in adsorptive power; the affinity for water appears to increase slightly as the wool becomes coarser. In view of the alternations in the adsorption and desorption experienced by wool in everyday processing, it is important to know the range of humidity over which wool must be dried in order to pass from the state of taking up water to the state of giving off water, when the regain is below saturation. In their latest study, using Australian 70's merino wool, Speakman and Cooper [54] obtained the data represented in graphical form in Fig. 37. The temperature maintained throughout these tests was 25° C. (77° F.).

As shown in Fig. 37, the short-range desorption experiments define the course of drying from adsorption to desorption conditions for wools at different initial regains. The range of humidity over which wool must be dried in order to pass from adsorption to limiting desorption conditions seems to be independent of regain and is about 18 per cent.

In regard to the influence the temperature of drying has on the affinity of wool for water, Speakman and Stott [55] reached the following conclusions: (1) When wool is dried from regains below saturation, its adsorptive power decreases with increasing temperature of drying. The reduction is produced by partial as well as complete drying, but not by drying from saturation, nor by heating wool at a low temperature. (2) A normal affinity for water may be restored to wool, which has been dried at a high temperature, by allowing it to reach saturation with water vapor. On the other hand, the reduced adsorptive power of the wool heated over water at a high temperature is irreversible. The results of their studies are shown in Fig. 38.

Speakman [51] found that wool will attain a state of moisture equilibrium at diverse amounts of moisture retention depending on whether the material approached equilibrium by taking up or giving off moisture to the surrounding atmosphere. For example, a 64's wool top taken out of a conditioning oven bone dry and exposed to a standard atmosphere of 65 per cent R.H. at 72° F. absorbed 13.9 per cent of moisture, whereas the same top, upon being thoroughly wet, desorbed water until it came to equilibrium at a moisture content of 15.7 per cent, based on the dry weight of the wool.

Gillam [17] made an investigation on the rate of increase of regain of samples of tops toward the equilibrium value. He found that fine

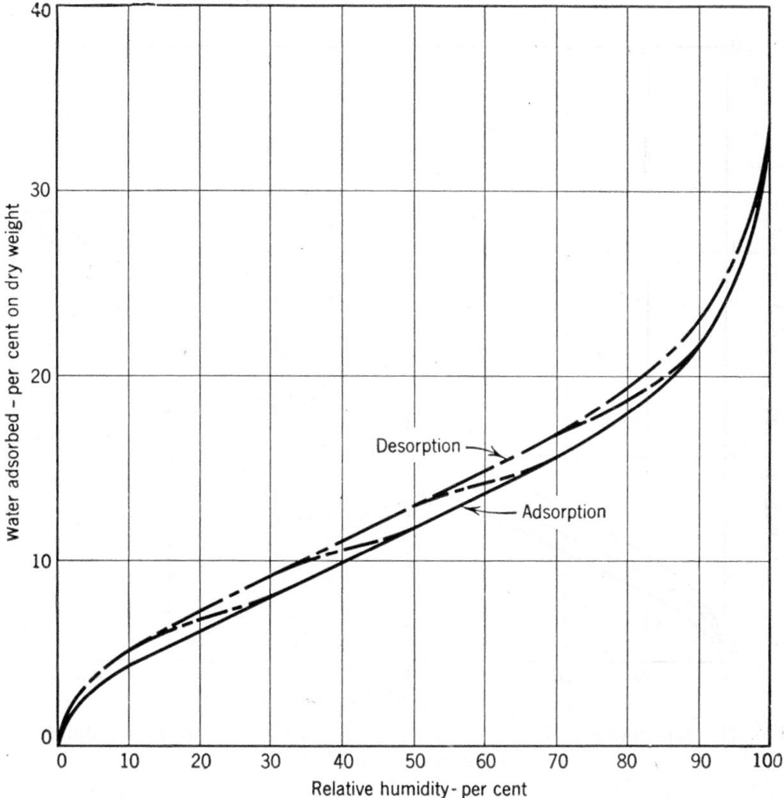

Fig. 37. Adsorption and desorption curves for wool. (*Speakman and Cooper.*)

wools (64's) react more rapidly than coarse wools (46's). He also found that the presence of oils generally lowers the rate of change; that carbonizing and acid dyeing lower the rate of change whereas soap and wool grease increase it. Also, the level of the equilibrium values are influenced by the various chemicals present. Oil increases the level, whereas dyed samples lower the value. Similar studies conducted by Story [57] indicate that the *p*H value plays an important part. Studies conducted at the Textile Research Institute (International Wool Project [59] indicate that wools having a *p*H of 4 and lower have a moisture absorption capacity 1 to 2 per cent lower than when the same wool is in an alkaline condition, *p*H 9.

Interesting results were obtained by Wiegerink [65] in the determination of the amount of moisture retained by the various fibers when brought to equilibrium at temperatures ranging between 100° F.

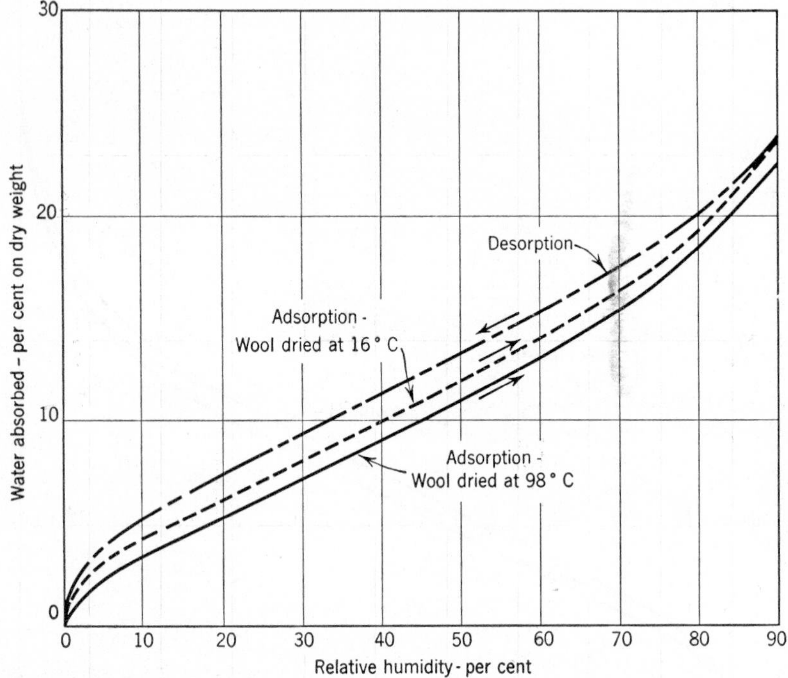

Fig. 38. Adsorption and desorption curves for wool dried at 16° C. and 98° C. (*Speakman and Stott.*)

(37.8° C.) and 302° F. (150° C.), with various humidities at each temperature to characterize the moisture content—relative humidity relationship. This information provides a basis for determining the limiting moisture content for textile fibers, which may be approached in any specified industrial drying process under definite atmospheric conditions.

The results of the study on clothing wools as reported by Wiegerink are given in the form of graphs showing moisture content against R.H. (see Fig. 39). These curves indicate the limits in moisture content which may be expected in wool fibers, if the atmosphere in contact with the fiber during drying is maintained at any desired temperature and relative humidity. The desorption curve for the given temperature is to be used if the fiber is initially wet, and the adsorption curve is to be used if the fiber is initially dry. Weigerink emphasizes that the curves apply, of course, only to the samples examined. The two wools tested

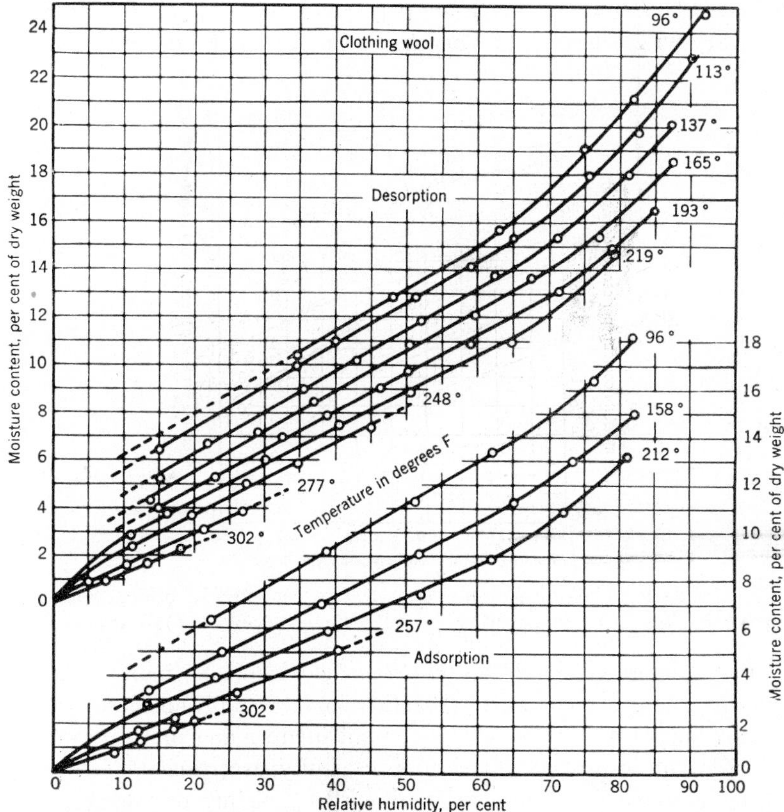

FIG. 39. Moisture content against relative humidity at various temperatures of clothing wools. (*Wiegerink.*)

were in the form of yarns which were extracted with alcohol and ether and rinsed with warm water.

A study of these data revealed that if the logarithm of the moisture contents of any fixed relative humidity is plotted against the reciprocals of the corresponding absolute temperatures ($1/T$), straight-line relations are obtained, the slopes of which change between 200° and 220° F. Above 30 per cent relative humidity the slope of the linear relation changes very little with increasing humidity in the range between

100° to 200° F. Below 30 per cent relative humidity the slope increases appreciably with decreasing humidity. Above 200° F. the slopes change for all relative humidity with decreasing humidity up to 50 per cent (see Fig. 40).

The hygroscopic quality of wool is of considerable importance in commerce because the weight of any given lot of wool in any form will vary within large limits according to climatic conditions.

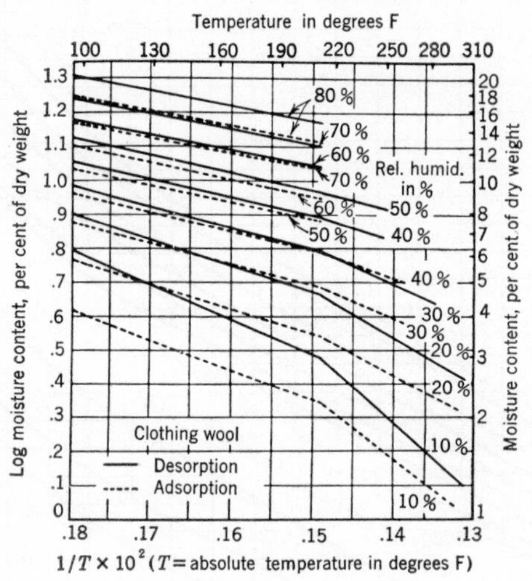

FIG. 40. Logarithm of the equilibrium moisture content of clothing wool yarn in relation to the reciprocal of the absolute temperature ($1/T$). (*Wiegerink.*)

In the commercial relations between wool dealers, manufacturers, and government agencies, this has led to the establishment of conditioning houses where the actual amount of fiber and moisture in any given lot of wool, top, or yarn is carefully ascertained. The true weight is based on a standard per cent of moisture or "regain." In Europe, this practice has been long established, whereas in this country its development is newer. Table 18 shows the specifications in use in the United States.

TABLE 18. AMERICAN MOISTURE REGAINS

Form or Condition	*Regain Per Cent*
Scoured wool	13.63
Top: Dry-combed (French)	15.00
Oil-combed (Bradford)	15.00
Woolen yarns	13.00
Worsted yarns: Oil-spun (Bradford)	13.00
Dry-spun (French)	15.00

The U. S. Treasury Department [61] specifies 12 per cent moisture content for scoured wool to be used for calculating the clean net weight of grease wool. Table 19 shows the specifications for moisture regains in use in Europe.

TABLE 19. EUROPEAN MOISTURE REGAINS

Form or Condition	*Regain Per Cent*
Scoured wools	17.00
Top in oil (Bradford)	19.00
Top (French)	18.25
Bradford and French worsted yarns	18.25
French noils	16.00
Noils (Lister and Noble)	16.00
Carbonized and scoured noils	17.00
Shoddy	17.00
Woolen yarns	17.00
Cloth, worsted or woolen	16.00

Heat of Absorption. Meredith [38] states than when textile fibers absorb moisture they evolve heat. This produces a thermostatic action in clothing; for example, Cassie [12] calculated that in passing from a room at 18° C. and 45 per cent R.H. into an outside atmosphere at 50° C. and 95 per cent R.H., a man's woolen jacket weighing 1 kg will produce 100,000 calories, i.e., as much heat as normal body metabolism will produce in 1 hr.

From the theoretical and practical point of view we are interested in the heat of absorption (w), which is defined as the heat evolved when 1 gram of water is absorbed into a large mass of fiber. This quantity can be calculated from two absorption isotherms at different temperatures, but the accuracy is not high. It is better obtained by measuring experimentally the heat of wetting (W), which is the heat evolved per gram of fiber when completely wetted. The relation between these two quantities is:

$$W_a = \int_a^{a'} w \cdot da$$

where a = initial moisture regain;
a' = saturation moisture regain.

Figure 41 shows the relationship between heat of wetting and moisture regain for several fibers where it will be seen that wool evolves more heat than any of the other fibers, that evolved by nylon being the smallest.

In interpreting this graph (Fig. 41) the above formula must be kept in mind; the value given at each per cent regain is that amount of heat evolved in taking the fiber from the designated regain to saturation.

The advantage of wool in keeping a person warm by such a mechanism is apparent.

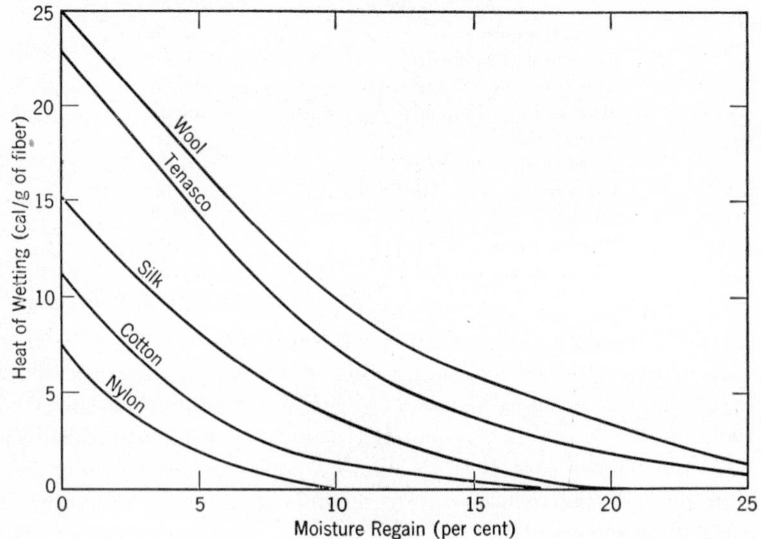

FIG. 41. Heat of wetting *vs.* percentage of moisture regain. (*From Meredith, "Properties Depending on Amorphous Regions," p. 199 in J. M. Preston,* Fibre Science, *1949 Textile Inst.*)

The process of water absorption by wool was considered by Hedges [23] to fall into three stages with no sharp line of demarcation between them: first, water entering the wool (up to 5 per cent) is absorbed at the large surface presented by the capillary structure and is accompanied by a large heat of absorption; second, during the second stage of the absorption, i.e., when the true absorption is complete, there is a filling up of the pores (5–25 per cent regain). The third stage (25–33 per cent regain) is an osmotic absorption, and the heat of absorption becomes very small as saturation is approached. Speakman [52] confirms the above mechanism.

Cassie, in a debate with Rose [13] on natural vs. man-made fibers, cites the importance of heat of moisture. It is known that the relative humidity of air indoors is less (particularly in winter) than air outdoors. The relative humidity indoors is 40–50 per cent; outdoors

90–100 per cent in the summer months. The philosophy is that clothing worn indoors at low R.H. will have a low regain. When taken outside it will absorb water vapor from the air; the greater the access of fibers to the air, the more rapid the pickup of water vapor. Absorption and condensation of water vapor is accompanied by a large evolution of heat, which is thus available to counteract air temperature decrease in going from indoors to outdoors. The amount of heat is a significant practical amount. For example, if indoor conditions are 65° F. and 45 per cent R.H. with outdoor conditions of 40° F. and 95 per cent R.H., corresponding wool regains are 10 per cent and 27 per cent. Thus when a person proceeds outdoors his wool clothing ultimately absorbs 15 per cent of its weight of water from the atmosphere. A man's greatcoat weighs roughly 5 lb; it will thus absorb as much as ¾ lb or ⅔ of a pint of water on going from indoors to outdoors in winter. The heat evolved is that required to evaporate this amount of water by boiling; or as much heat as the average man's body loses in 3 to 4 hr when he is awake. The wool thus takes water vapor from the air and uses it to generate heat, which in turn opposes a drop in air temperature. The heat is not liberated rapidly but as it is required, thus opposing temperature change for several hours' duration. Ultimately, of course, the fibers become conditioned to the outside air, but by then the body is prepared for the temperature change, and any feeling of chill is greatly reduced. Wool is the outstanding fiber in offering this protection.

Thermal Qualities. There has been a wide divergence of opinion regarding the warmth of wool as compared with cotton, silk, and rayon fibers and fabrics. Throughout the literature on the thermal properties of textiles, there is a general lack of data, and great discrepancies in the results. In some instances, the thermal characteristics of wool are expressed in units of heat conductivity. The two main factors which influence the conductivity of textiles are texture and apparent density. The influences of the two factors are recorded in Tables 20 and 21, taken from McAdams [34].

TABLE 20. Influence of Temperature on Thermal Conductivity of Wool

Apparent Density at Room Temperature	*B.T.U.*	*Temperature*
lb per cu ft	$ft^2 \times hr \times °F. \times ft$	°F.
8.5	0.022	32
8.5	0.027	100
8.5	0.033	200

TABLE 21. Influence of Density on Thermal Conductivity of Wool

Apparent Density at Room Temperature	*B.T.U.*	*Temperature*
lb per cu ft	ft^2 × hr × °F. × ft	°F.
6.9	0.021	86
8.5	0.027	100
20.6	0.030	86

Baxter and Cassie [6] have measured the heat transmitted through successive layers of carded wool, shown in Table 22. The wool was

TABLE 22. Total Insulating Value of Carded Wool

Laps	*Apparent Density at Room Temperature* (pounds per cubic foot)	*Thickness* (load 0.07 lb per sq in.)	*Oz per Yd*	*T.I.V.*
1 lap	0.075	0.36 in.	10.6	68
2 laps	0.115	0.52 in.	16.6	79
4 laps	0.200	0.80 in.	28.9	82

supported by a piece of burlap. Here the warmth of the cloth is determined by its overall insulating value, and the results are termed total insulating value (T.I.V.).

As a further example Schiefer [46] of the National Bureau of Standards states:

> The analysis of many thermal transmission measurements indicates that the kind of fiber has no effect on the thermal insulation of fabrics. The small effect which might be due to the kind of fiber is either too small to measure or is masked by other factors which have a much greater effect. As far as the measurable properties of blankets are concerned, the only property which is definitely related to the kind of fiber used is the compressional resilience. The compressional resilience of blankets is related linearly to the wool content of wool-cotton blankets. The relationship has not yet been established for other fiber mixture, except that we know that viscose rayon lowers the resilience more than cotton, and that acetate seems to lower it less. Since a definite relationship exists between the thickness and thermal insulation of fabrics it follows that if any factor affects the thickness it would likewise affect the thermal insulation. A blanket containing all wool and having a high compressional resilience probably will retain its original thickness more nearly during use than a blanket made from cotton or viscose rayon. It therefore might be expected to retain its original thermal insulation more nearly than cotton or rayon blanket.

The Forstmann Woolen Company has done considerable research on the thermal properties of fabrics. Figure 42 shows the variation of warmth with fabric thickness, as determined by their work. Warmth, or thermal insulating value, is defined as the ratio of the difference between the heat losses of the unclothed body and of the clothed body to that of the unclothed body, or:

$$\text{Warmth} = \frac{\text{Heat loss of unclothed body} - \text{Heat loss of clothed body}}{\text{Heat loss of unclothed body}}$$

In this figure 100 per cent warmth would correspond to no heat loss through the fabric. It is seen that a fabric 0.020 in. thick will give 29

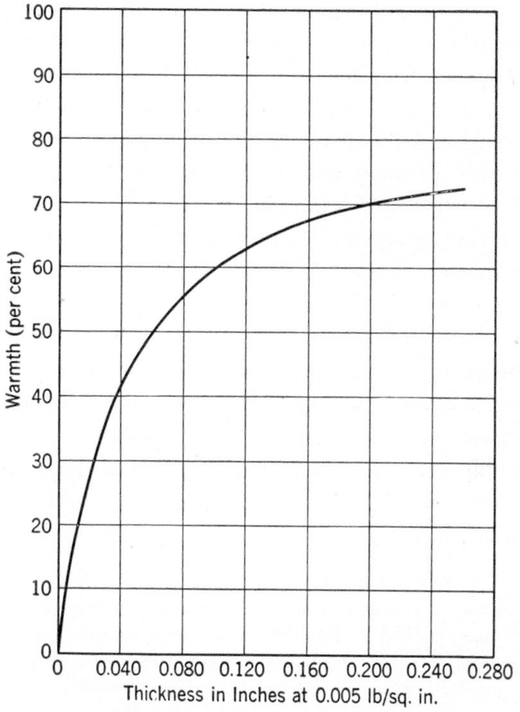

FIG. 42. Variations of warmth with thickness at 12 mph wind speed (evaporation losses not included). (*Forstmann Woolen Co.*)

per cent warmth, whereas the thickest coating, 0.250 in. thick, will give 72 per cent warmth.

It should be noted that a fabric twice the thickness of another fabric does not give twice the warmth; for example, a fabric 0.200 in. thick gives 70 per cent warmth whereas one 0.100 in. thick gives 60 per cent warmth. In fact, any increase of thickness above 0.250 in. provides practically no increase in warmth. It has been estimated that a total of 12 in. would be required to reach 100 per cent warmth. Since this curve is valid for all apparel fabrics it is evident that under ordinary conditions the warmth of a fabric is not affected by the weight and construction of fibers used in the fabric, e.g., a cotton flannel is just as warm as a wool worsted if they are of the same thickness. This predominance of thickness over all other fabric variables in determining warmth has also been reported by Rees, Baxter, Cassie, Sommers and other workers.

Although the warmth curve was obtained with a wind velocity of 12 miles per hour, the same general relationship between thickness and warmth holds for other wind speeds. At higher wind speeds the warmth will be greater since the heat loss from the unclothed body increases more rapidly than that from the clothed body. This increase in heat loss with increasing wind speeds is due primarily to the decrease in the effective thickness of the static air layer above the fabric. Rees states the thickness of this layer is 0.32 in. in still air.

The relationship of thickness and warmth discussed above holds for all normal climatic conditions. However, there are additional factors which are necessary for maintaining the comfort and health of the body. There must be sufficient ventilation through the clothing to permit the escape of the perspiration evaporated from the skin. When the amount of perspiration is greatly increased by severe exercise, the skin becomes wet, i.e., the perspiration is sensible. Under such conditions the clothing becomes moist by absorption of the perspiration.

Hock, Sookne, and Harris [27] in a study on the thermal property of moist fabrics state:

> Practical experience has demonstrated that moist fabrics in contact with the body produce an unpleasant sensation commonly referred to as a "chilling effect" or a "clammy feel." The degree of the sensation varies with different fibers and fabrics; thus, on the basis of general experience, the merits of wool fabrics over similar cotton fabrics have long been recognized. This is one of the reasons, for example, for the preference given to woolen underwear and other garments for use in cold climates under conditions where physical labor causes considerable perspiration. It also accounts for the approval usually expressed for woolen bathing suits.

The chilling effect or clamminess produced by moist fabrics in contact with the body was evaluated by measurement of the drop in temperature that ensues when the moist fabrics are placed on an artificial skin surface, and by tests to measure the extent of contact between the fabrics and the surface. (See Fig. 43.)

Fabrics of various fiber composition and construction gave an excellent correlation in these tests. The extent of contact between the fabrics and the skin appears to be the significant factor. Tests show that those fabrics making the poorest contact cause the least chilling.

The results of these experiments show clearly the progressive improvement of the fabrics with respect to chilling as their wool content is increased, and also the superiority of certain types of construction which minimize the extent of contact of the fabrics with the skin. From this point of view the desirability of wool fibers, which are highly crimped and possess long-range elasticity, is apparent. These properties permit a type of fabric construction which minimizes the extent of contact with the skin. In contrast, cotton exhibits considerable plasticity when wet and is less desirable from the same point of view. However, the results show that special types of construction, especially those which produce a napped or fuzzy surface, reduce appreciably the contact which even wet cotton fabrics make and thereby lessen the chilling effect.

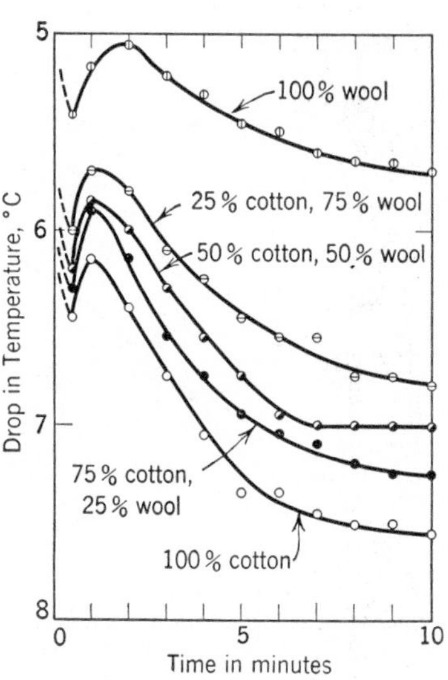

Fig. 43. Thermal conductivity of various wet fabrics. Relation between temperature drop and length of contact. (*Hock, Sookne, and Harris.*)

Another factor which plays an important part in this whole question of warmth of textiles is the hygroscopic property of the material. This was already touched upon under the heading of heat of absorption. Cassie [12] already in 1940 showed that hygroscopic textiles can give a large measure of protection against sudden temperature changes at the skin. A temperature change in the surrounding atmosphere begins to be propagated through textiles as if they had no hygroscopic property; but, once the initial temperature is attained, the rate of change of textile temperature becomes very slow.

Figure 44 shows a curve obtained experimentally for wool: air with a constant water vapor pressure and at 15° C. (59° F.) was blown through a cylinder of wool until the wool was fully conditioned. The temperature of the air entering the wool was then raised to 31° C.

(87.8° F.), and curve *B* shows the rise in temperature with time at the center of the cylinder. Rapid establishment of an initial temperature of 22.5° C. is clearly shown, and this is followed by the slow change to 31° C. If the wool was nonhygroscopic, its temperature would have increased according to curve *C*. The ratio of the times required to reach, say, 27° C. by following curves *B* and *C* is roughly 20 : 1.

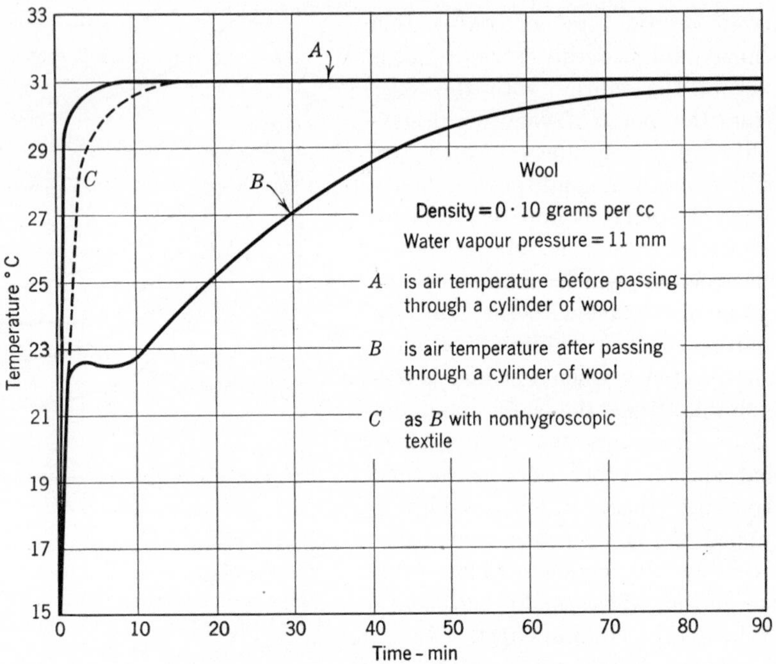

Fig. 44. Thermal transmission of wool fabric. (*Cassie.*)

Theory and experiment thus agree that hygroscopic textiles prevent sudden temperature changes from reaching the skin. The degree of protection increases as the standard deviation increases, and this factor is proportional to the rate of increase or regain with relative humidity: Roughly, hence, the greater the regain of a textile, the greater its protective power, provided, of course, that the absorbed water does not give surface wetting of the fibers. Animal fibers are superior to others in this respect; they absorb more water than other textiles without losing their physical properties; in particular they show no surface wetting. They have long been recognized as supreme in avoiding sudden temperature changes at the skin, and there can be little doubt that this is due in a large measure to their high regains.

TABLE 1. VARIATION IN PERCENTAGE OF FOREIGN IMPURITIES IN WOOLS

Type of Wool	*Grease and Suint*	*Sand and Dirt*	*Vegetable Matter*	*Moisture*	*Wool Fiber*
Fine	20 to 50	5 to 40	0.5 to 2	8 to 12	20 to 50
Medium crossbred	15 to 30	5 to 20	1 to 5	8 to 12	40 to 60
Long wool	5 to 15	5 to 10	0 to 2	8 to 12	60 to 80
Carpet wool	5 to 15	5 to 20	0.5 to 2	8 to 12	60 to 80
Hairs	2 to 10	5 to 20	0 to 1	8 to 12	60 to 80

tained from wool. However, the fatty secretion in wool is, strictly speaking, a wax rather than a fat, since it contains no glycerin in combination with the fatty acids. Yet, wool wax in many of its chemical and physical properties differs from other waxes. Many of its constituent alcohols and acids are not only unusual and complex but also are not found in other waxes. Although wool wax cannot be used, therefore, as a substitute for other waxes, it has almost unlimited actual and potential uses of its own.

The purified form of wool wax, known as lanolin, is especially valuable because of its unique similarity to the compounds exuded by the glands of the human skin. As an emollient lanolin is unsurpassed.

Lanolin is, for the most part, a complex mixture of complicated organic compounds known as steroid esters the chemical nature of which is not yet fully understood. The Botany Worsted Mills' research laboratory has reported that the alcoholic portion of lanolin, which can be obtained by splitting the esters, comprises about 40 per cent by weight of the total, whereas the fatty acid portion from the same ester splitting constitutes the balance of about 60 per cent. About 14 to 16 per cent of the total weight of the lanolin consists of cholesterol, $C_{27}H_{45}OH$. Of this, 1 to 2 per cent is present in the free state, the remainder occurring as an ester. Analytical and physical data for wool wax are given in Table 2.

The principal esters found in lanolin may be divided into three classes: the sterols, including cholesterol, metacholesterol, and isocholesterol; the triterpene alcohols, agnosterol and lanasterol; and normal aliphatic wax alcohols such as cetyl and ceryl alcohols. These alcoholic substances exist both in the free state and chemically combined in the form of esters of numerous fatty acids, 32 of which have thus far been identified. Each class of alcohols comprises about one-third of the total unsaponifiable matter or alcohols of the wax.

Owing to the recognition of their effect on human metabolism, the importance of the sterols, including cholesterol, ergosterol or provitamin D_2, the sex hormones, digitalis glucosides, and the saponins,

TABLE 2. ANALYTICAL AND PHYSICAL DATA FOR WOOL WAX

Characteristic	*Wool Wax*
Ash content, per cent	0.4–0.11
Acid value, per cent	0.4–2.0
Iodine value (Wijs)	19.8–30.0
Saponification value	97
Hydrocarbons, per cent	Nil
Unsaponifiable matter, per cent	50
Free cholesterol, per cent	3.0–4.5
Combined cholesterol, per cent	15.3
Melting point, °C.	37–38
Specific gravity, 15.5° C.	0.944–0.947
Refractive index, 40° C.	1.480

Source: D. T. C. Gillespie, Report T.3, Commonwealth of Australia, Council for Scientific and Industrial Research Information Service (Feb., 1946).

has increased. Consequently, the importance of wool wax has also become greater, since, although cholesterol, the best known of the sterols, occurs in most animal fats, nowhere has it been found in such large quantities as in wool wax. One of the best descriptions including chemical compositions is given by Lower [75].

There is a definite correlation between wool quality and grease content, that is, the finer the wool, the higher is the grease content. This relationship can be seen in Table 3.

TABLE 3. CORRELATION BETWEEN QUALITY OF WOOL AND GREASE CONTENT

Quality	*Wool Fat (per cent)*
Fine (70's)	17.4
½ Blood (60's)	12.7
(58's)	10.5
⅜ Blood (56's)	9.8
¼ Blood (48's)	8.6

Source: F. P. Veitch and L. C. Benedict, "Wool Scouring Waste Liquors, Composition and Disposal," *Trans. Am. Inst. Chem. Eng.*, pp. 3–22 (June 1925), [140].

As shown in Table 1, the percentage of yolk varies widely in fleeces of various breeds of sheep and even in sheep of the same breed. Not only does the percentage of yolk vary, but also the composition of the wool wax as can be seen from Marston's [81] analytical data on wool fats from Australian merino given in Table 4.

Lifschuetz [71] was the first to show that the amount of the wax and the composition of the wax vary even within the individual staple.

TABLE 4. VARIATION IN WOOL FATS FROM AUSTRALIAN MERINO WOOL

Fat in Wool Sample (per cent)	*Saponification Value*	*Iodine Value*	*Unsaponifiable Matter (per cent)*	*Free Cholesterol (per cent)*	*Total Cholesterol (per cent)*
10 to 20	92 to 107	16.5 to 19	21 to 27	3.5 to 7.0	7.5 to 16.0

The composition of the wax obtained from the tippy portion of the staple was very different from that of the wool wax taken as a whole (Table 5). The surface fat contains a much larger proportion of

TABLE 5. VARIATION OF WOOL GREASE FROM ROOT AND TIP PARTS

	South American Crossbred Wool		*Montevideo Merino Wool*		*Australian Merino Wool*	
	Roots	*Tips*	*Roots*	*Tips*	*Roots*	*Tips*
Fat content, per cent	9.20	4.30	22.60	19.50	24.27	14.21
Acid number of fat extracted	15.68	25.70	2.24	14.56	Almost neutral	17.92
Acid number after saponification	28.00	50.40	11.76	27.44	7.28	28.00
Free cholesterol	Traces	..	Traces	Traces	Large amount	Traces
Free isocholesterol	Large amount	..	Large amount	Traces	Large amount	Traces
Free oxycholesterol	..	Large amount	..	Large amount	Traces	Large amount

fatty acids and soaps; it also contains oxycholesterol in place of the isocholesterol present in fat near the roots. He suggested that the changes are brought about by hydrolysis and oxidation under the influences of moisture, light, and air.

Recovery of Wool Grease. The recovery of grease from the scouring liquors may be accomplished in various ways (*Wool Science Review*, Sept. 1950, p. 43).

1. The acid cracking or the Magna process, in which the waste liquors are treated with a slight excess of sulfuric acid. The grease and soap fatty acids are collected and the grease separated by hot pressing.

2. The hypochlorite process. This process involves the pretreatment of the scouring liquor with calcium hypochlorites prior to the cracking with sulfuric acid. This additional treatment is claimed to destroy the natural emulsion stabilizers of a protein character. By this method it is claimed that recovery up to 75 per cent may be realized. The

actual proportion of grease recovered by acid cracking rarely rises above 50 per cent of that originally present in the liquors.

3. The centrifugal method. The two best known processes are the Duhamell and the American Chemical Paint (A.C.P.), in which the scouring liquors are centrifuged in continuous-sludge, discharge-type centrifuges. The recovery of grease is about 40 per cent.

4. The aeration process. This uses the principle of separating the grease by concentrating it into a froth. The liquors are subjected to a series of fine air streams, whereby the grease rises as a froth to the surface of the liquor. The froth is washed and eventually recovered free from dirt and water by heating in a low-pressure autoclave. Recovery is between 45–50 per cent.

5. The solvent extraction method. This method for cleansing raw wool has been in use on a batch basis since the early 1900's, especially at the Arlington Mills, U.S.A. More recently, continuous extraction processes have been worked out in various countries. In the United States the Smith Drum & Company has developed a machine for the continuous degreasing of wool by treating the wool in mat form. After processing the solvent is recovered and reused. The dirt which is removed during the processing is delivered from the machine as a dry dirt, and the wool grease is also recovered. The main advantage of solvent extraction is the high return of grease attained of over 90 per cent. But further purification methods are necessary which reduce the overall yield to about 65 per cent.

From the various recovery methods of wool grease it is clear that a wide variety of grades of wool grease appear on the market. They may be classified under the following headings:

Crude grease—acid cracked. In England it is known as Yorkshire Brown Grease and on the Continent as degras or suintine. This is a grease directly recovered at the scouring plants by the acid cracking process. Its free acidity varies from 13–20 per cent.

The centrifugal neutral wool greases: There are two types, one with moisture of 15–32 per cent and one moisture free. They have a free acidity of 1.5 to 4 per cent. A typical analysis is given in Table 6.

Lanolin can be prepared from any of the above greases by decolorizing by adsorption, followed by bleaching with peroxide. See Table 6.

Lanolin B.P. and U.S.P. or Adeps Lanae anhydrosus represent lanolin which satisfies the rigid specification of the pharmacopoeia. Usually a melting range of about 36–42° C. and an acid value less than 0.5 per cent are specified, together with limits on the iodine value, and saponification value.

TABLE 6. Grease and Lanolin Obtained by A.C.P. Process

Crude Hydrous Grease	
Color	Light to dark tan
Odor	Slight to putrid
Moisture and volatile matter, per cent	15 to 32 (Xylol solvent method)
Ash content on dry grease, per cent	0.62 to 1.02
Free fatty acid (as oleic), per cent	0.26 to 2.0
Na_2CO_3, per cent	0.1 to 0.2
Soap (as sodium oleate), per cent	0.95 to 1.75
Refined Lanolin	
Color	A.S.T.M. Union Colorimeter 2.5 Bleached and filtered 4 to 4.5 Unbleached and unfiltered
Odor	Clean and agreeable
Melting point, °C.	38 to 42
Free fatty acid, per cent	0.025 to 0.03
Moisture, per cent	0.025 to 0.05
Ash, per cent	Less than 0.05
Saponification value	73 to 90
Iodine value	18 to 36

Wool Grease Statistics. Wool grease statistics indicate the increase of the yield of wool grease in the United States since 1935 as shown in Table 7.

TABLE 7. United States Production and Importation of Wool Grease

(Thousands of pounds)

Year	*Domestic*	*Imported*	*Total*
1935–1939	7,321	4,902	12,223
1940–1944	14,176	1,144	15,320
1945	17,522	1,290	18,812
1946	19,959	1,439	21,398
1947	22,190	139	22,329
1948	18,874	290	19,164
1949	9,023	8,427	17,450

Source: *Bull. Wool Mfrs.* (1949).

The use of wool grease is increasing especially in the engineering, leather, and pharmaceutical trades. Many new outlets are sought. One of the most complete lists of its uses is given by Gillespie in a report entitled "Wool Wax," a review of its properties, recovery, and utilization, Melbourne, February 1946, p. 61.

The total world wool production of wool grease is of the order of 440 million lb. Based on current wool production, it is calculated that the practicable recovery may be in the neighborhood of 160 million lb. However, only a small proportion of this amount is actually produced today. The only definite figures available are for the United States.

Suint. Suint represents the water-soluble portion of the extraneous material present in the fleece, which is derived from the perspiration of the sheep. It consists chiefly of the potassium salts of the various fatty acids, together with small quantities of sulfate, phosphate, and nitrogenous materials. The amount of suint in wools appears to be variable from fleece to fleece even in the same environment, a result to be expected when one considers the origin of suint. Hill [57] has found that under similar conditions the Hampshire breed has 5 per cent suint, Leicester breed has 12 per cent, and range Rambouillet has 13 per cent suint.

The variability of the amount of wax in the wool of various breeds of sheep is accompanied by a similar variation in the amount of suint, which ranges from 2 to 15 per cent. As the amount of wax increases, the amount of suint also increases. Wright determined the amount of suint in New Zealand wools as shown in Table 8.

TABLE 8. SUINT IN NEW ZEALAND WOOLS

	Greasy Wool (per cent)
¾ Bred	12.72
½ Bred	10.30
Greasy Leicester	7.81
Lincoln	2.26

The suint in slipe wool is very low as is to be expected, the suint being removed during treatment of the skin. Veitch and Benedict [140], working on domestic, South American, Cape, Australian, and New Zealand wools ranging from 70's quality and lower, found that the suint content of greasy wool was independent of wool quality, the average content being 15.2 per cent.

Hill [57] has determined the regains of all constituents of the fleece, and in the wool from the shoulder of a Leicester fleece at 55 per cent humidity and 70° F. his average value for four samples of suint is 23 per cent. He suggests that the regain of suint is 2½ times that of pure wool under similar conditions.

The yield of potash salts recovered from wool suint is variable, owing to the different character and proportion of the suint in different lots of fleece wools. Stirm [132] gives the following figures: 11,000 lb of raw wool gave 335 lb of raw potash salts having the composition given in Table 9.

TABLE 9. Per Cent Composition of Raw Potash Salts

Potassium carbonate	78.5	Sodium sulfate	4.6
Potassium chloride	5.7	Insoluble matter	5.0
Potassium sulfate	2.8	Organic matter	3.0

Ash. Besides the mineral matter existing in the soluble suint, there is a small amount of mineral matter which appears to be an essential constituent of the fiber itself. It is left as an ash when scoured wool is ignited. It amounts to about 0.5 per cent and consists of the alkaline sulfates, the majority being soluble in water. Bowman [30] shows a typical composition of the ash of Lincoln wool in Table 10.

TABLE 10. Per Cent Composition of the Ash of Lincoln Wools

Potassium oxide	31.1	Silica	5.8
Sodium oxide	8.2	Sulfuric anhydride	20.5
Calcium oxide	16.9	Carbonic acid	4.2
Aluminum oxide, Ferric oxide	12.3	Phosphoric acid	Trace
		Chlorine	Trace

Chemical Constitution of Wool

Nature of the Protein. The wool fiber is composed of animal tissues and is classed as a protein called keratin. Proteins are very complicated chemical compounds, and keratin is no exception. Wool fiber has been found to consist of five chemical elements—carbon, hydrogen, oxygen, nitrogen, and sulfur. Sulfur is distinctly characteristic of wool and all hair fibers. As its constituents are not rigidly constant in their proportion, no definite chemical formula can be assigned to wool. Its chemical composition is as shown in Table 11.

TABLE 11. Chemical Composition of Wool

Elements	*Per Cent*
Carbon	50
Oxygen	22 to 25
Nitrogen	16 to 17
Hydrogen	7
Sulfur	3 to 4

The wool fiber as a whole does not appear as a homogeneous chemical compound but is composed of several chemically distinct substances, a fact substantiated by research by Geiger [47], who states as follows:

Analytical studies on the cuticle and whole wool show that, although both contain the same amino acids, the proportions of these in the two materials differ. The presence of larger amounts of sulfur presumably means that the protein scale contains more sulfur cross-links between its peptide chains than do the more digestible proteins of the cortex. Nevertheless, even when the sulfur cross-links have been broken, the material is not digested by enzymes. Moreover, the scale material was found to be more stable toward alkali than wool that had been reduced and alkylated in the same way, since the alkali-solubility of the scale material was found to be only 42 per cent and that of the treated wool 85 per cent.

Two possible explanations might be advanced at this time to account for the difference in behavior of the cuticle and the cortex of wool. Speakman [117] and also Rudall [109] have suggested that, since the cortex of wool fibers is attacked more rapidly by sodium sulfide than are the scales, cross-links, other than those involving sulfur, may be present. This hypothesis is given support by the results of the present work, although direct proof of the existence and nature of such cross-links is still lacking. An alternative explanation might be sought in the recent demonstration by Hock and McMurdie [58] with the electron microscope that the cuticle and cortex differ widely in physical organization.

TABLE 12. Composition of Untreated Wool and Wool Scales

Constituents	Untreated Wool	Wool Scales	
		Analytical Value	Corrected Value *
Sulfur	3.50	4.83	5.42
Cystine	12.2	† 18.1	† 20.3
Nitrogen	16.67	13.53	15.17
Arginine	8.6	4.3	4.8
Tyrosine	6.1	3.0	3.3
Serine	9.5	9.9	11.2
Ethyl groups	0.0	4.0	...
Ash	0.2	4.1	...
Lipid	...	2.7	...

* Corrected for the presence of ethyl groups and bound lipid.
† Calculated from the sulfur content.

Keratin is of amphoteric nature, exhibiting acid as well as basic properties, predominantly basic, however. Through hydrolysis it decomposes into various amino acids, as Harris [52] shows in Table 13.

TABLE 13. Amino Acid Composition of Wool

Amino Acids	*Percentage Present in Wool*	*Grams of Residue per 100 Grams of Wool*	*Grams of Side-Chain per 100 Grams of Wool*
Clycine	6.5	4.94	0.09
Alanine	4.4	3.52	0.74
Serine	9.41	7.80	2.76
Proline	6.75	5.69	2.46
Valine	4.72	3.99	1.73
Threonine	6.76	5.74	2.59
Cystine	* 12.72	10.83	4.89
Leucine isomers	11.3	9.75	4.92
Aspartic acid	7.27	6.28	3.22
Lysine	3.3	2.89	1.63
Glutamic acid	15.27	13.40	7.58
Methionine	0.71	0.62	0.36
Histidine	0.7	0.62	0.37
Hydroxylysine	0.21	0.19	0.11
Phenylalanine	3.75	3.34	2.07
Arginine	10.4	9.33	5.97
Tyrosine	5.8	5.23	3.43
Tryptophane	0.7	0.64	0.45
Total	110.67	94.80	45.37
Ammonia N	1.18	−0.30	−0.30
Total, corrected for ammonia N		94.50	45.07

* Based on 3.55 per cent total sulfur, subtracting methionine sulfur.

Astbury [12] states that the detailed structure of the proteins is still largely unknown, or as Taylor [136] expresses it:

> The X-ray evidence in the field of the proteins is most definite in the case of the fibrous proteins. With the silk protein, fibroin, and the hair protein, keratin, precise knowledge is available concerning certain details, while in others there is much that is still indefinite.

Harris, Mizell, and Fourt [55] in 1942 summarized information on the molecular structure of wool and the factors responsible for its mechanical properties. Proteins are polycondensation products in which the different amino acids are linked together to form the polypeptide chain, shown in the following scheme:

$$-\mathrm{HN}-\underset{\substack{|\\ \mathrm{R}}}{\mathrm{CH}}-\mathrm{CO}-\mathrm{HN}-\overset{\substack{\mathrm{R}\\ |}}{\mathrm{CH}}-\mathrm{CO}-\mathrm{HN}-\underset{\substack{|\\ \mathrm{R}}}{\mathrm{CH}}-\mathrm{CO}-\mathrm{HN}-\overset{\substack{\mathrm{R}\\ |}}{\mathrm{CH}}-\mathrm{CO}$$

The mechanical properties of such chains can be considered, in general, to depend on the following four factors:

1. They exhibit great flexibility. This enables the protein molecule to assume a great number of possible configurations which could be either of the folded or spiral type. The importance of this molecular flexibility was first recognized by Astbury and Woods [18], who in their earlier work on wool preferred a rather specific type of fold for the molecules of the fiber in the unstretched state, which they referred to as the α-keratin configuration. The long-range extensibility of wool was ascribed to the opening of these folds into the more nearly straight-chain configuration known as the β-keratin form. The original α-keratin configuration has been shown to be untenable by Neurath [96], and a new type of fold has now been proposed by Astbury and Bell [14]. Such structures have been suggested on the basis of the X-ray data and should accordingly be found principally in the "crystalline" regions of the fiber. Since these regions account for only a relatively small proportion of the total wool fiber as indicated by the X-ray diffraction patterns, it appears that one may assume a more or less random type of folding in the "amorphous" regions which make up the bulk of the fiber. That a variety of configurations can exist is readily demonstrated by the construction of molecular scale models of polypeptide chains.

2. They possess a large number of the highly polar peptide linkages which give rise to inter- and intramolecular hydrogen bonding.

3. They contain relatively large side chains (R groups in the polypeptide chain) which prevent close packing of the protein molecules and thus decrease the extent to which hydrogen bonding can occur. In wool nearly all of the constituent amino acids are of the type having large side chains, as shown by the data in Table 13. From these data it can be estimated that close to 50 per cent of the weight of wool is in the side chains. They exhibit association forces other than those contributed by hydrogen bonds, namely, the presence of covalent disulfide cross-links between the molecular chains.

4. Cystine (as first suggested by Astbury and Street [17]) is responsible for a considerable amount of covalent cross-linking in the fiber, and later chemical evidence has been offered which supports the

original conclusion. Wool may thus be considered a network of polypeptide chains linked together by the disulfide groups of the amino

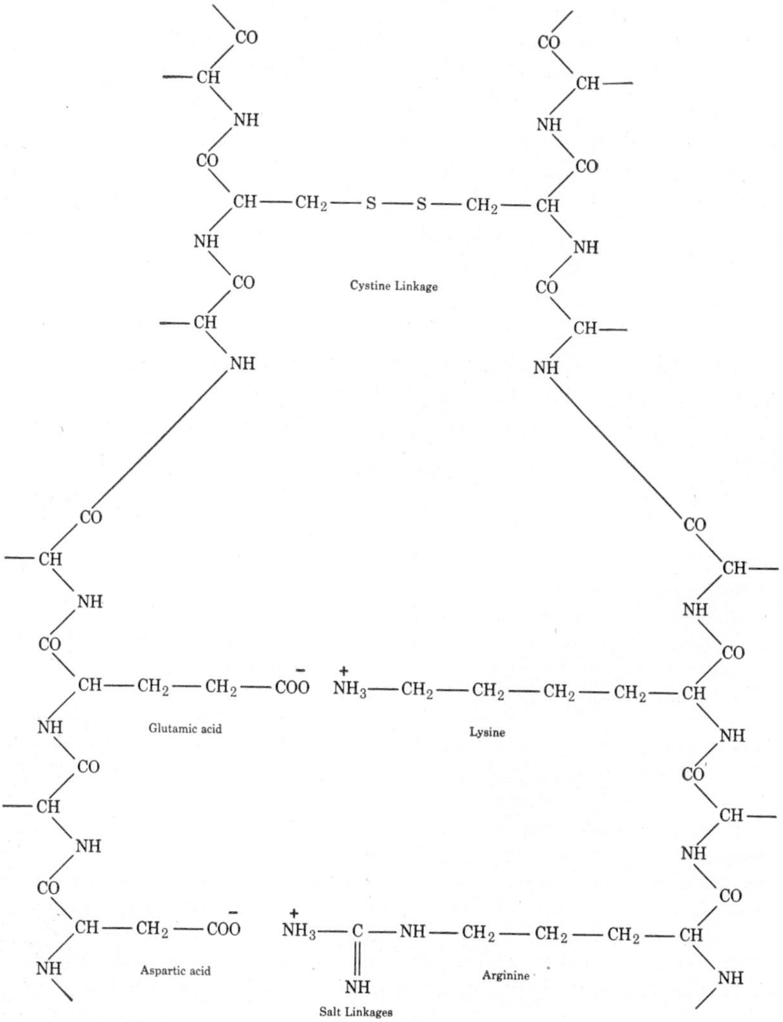

CH—CH$_2$—S—S—CH$_2$—CH

Cystine Linkage

CH—CH$_2$—CH$_2$—$\bar{\text{COO}}$ $\overset{+}{\text{N}}$H$_3$—CH$_2$—CH$_2$—CH$_2$—CH$_2$—CH

Glutamic acid Lysine

CH—CH$_2$—$\bar{\text{COO}}$ $\overset{+}{\text{N}}$H$_3$—C(=NH)—NH—CH$_2$—CH$_2$—CH$_2$—CH

Aspartic acid Arginine

Salt Linkages

Fig. 1. Structural formula of wool. (*Astbury and Speakman.*)

acid, cystine. Such a concept suggests that the role of cystine in wool is important, and indeed it has been shown that many of the chemical, physical, and biological properties of wool protein are dependent on the presence of these cross-links.

Structural Formula. Astbury [16] and Speakman [120] suggest that the structure of the wool fiber, reduced to its simplest terms, consists of long peptide chains bridged by cystine and salt linkages as shown in its structural formula, Fig. 1.

This structural arrangement accounts for much of the chemical stability of the wool molecules which make up the fiber. However, it has been found that any reagent which will alter the state of this disulfide group in the cystine linkage will alter or destroy the physical structure of the fiber as a whole. In general, these groups are susceptible to attack by oxidizing and reducing agents, light, and alkalies. Strong oxidation may result in practically no change in the outward appearance of the wool, yet the incipient damage may be so great as to render the wool nearly worthless. This knowledge is utilized in the control of practical bleaching and chlorination. From the standpoint of dyeing and carbonizing, researches have further increased knowledge of the amphoteric nature, i.e., the acid and basic properties, of the wool fiber. Lundgren [77] in reporting the present status of investigations on the chemical composition and structure of wool states as follows:

> Wool consists essentially of protein, and, as illustrated in Table 14, only slight variation in amino acid content is found among different wools. On the other hand, significant differences in composition are found among the proteins from a single fiber. A primary objective of current chemical research on wool is the elucidation of the composition and structure of these various fiber proteins, which are in separate morphological units. Present work indicates that the protein substance of the spindle cells and the intercementing materials are relatively easily solubilized, provided the disulfide stabilizing bonds are severed by treatment with either oxidizing or reducing agents [7, 73, 85, 86]. Alexander reports that as much as 90 per cent of whole substance is solubilized when it is first oxidized with peracetic acid and then treated with dilute ammonia. The insoluble part is principally membranous material.
>
> The solubilized matter is separable into three portions distinguishable with respect to composition and molecular size. These portions have the following molecular weights: 70,000, 13,000, and less than 4500. Since the average amino acid residue weight in wool protein is close to 115, it follows that the number of amino acids present in the three proteins are respectively about 608, 112, and 39, if we assume that each of the molecules is comprised of a single chain. It is possible that each consists of two or several associated or chemically linked chains.
>
> The composition of the epicuticle is still uncertain. The chief difficulty is the isolation of the material in quantity sufficient for detailed analysis [69, 70]. It appears that the epicuticle contains glucosamine. The proportion of glucosamine is not known; presumably it is linked chemically to a protein matrix.
>
> Significant progress is being made towards the understanding of the process of generation of the wool fiber within the follicle [40, 84].
>
> Present research is also concerned with the sequence of amino acids in the protein chains. Towards this end detailed studies have been reported on the

TABLE 14. COMPARISON OF AMINO ACID CONTENTS OF WOOLS OF DIFFERENT ORIGIN

(Grams from 100 grams of dry protein)

	New Zealand Medium (WC-2 60's)		*Domestic Medium (WC-5)*		*Australian Fine (WC-3)*		*Domestic Fine (WC-4)*	
Amino Acid	*Average*	*Duplicate Runs*	*Average*	*Duplicate Runs*	*Average*	*Duplicate Runs*	*Average*	*Duplicate Runs*
Alanine	3.80	(3.75–3.84)	3.85	(3.36–4.09)	3.73	(3.32–4.02)	3.73	(3.43–4.03)
Arginine	9.18	(9.10–9.25)	9.23	(9.15–9.31)	9.03	(8.95–9.10)	9.09	(9.01–9.17)
Aspartic acid	6.41	(6.11–6.89)	6.60	(6.58–6.61)	6.29	(6.18–6.39)	6.23	(6.05–6.40)
Cystine	11.3	(10.8–11.8)	10.9	(10.8–11.1)	11.0	(10.8–11.3)	10.8	(10.4–11.1)
Glutamic acid	13.5	(13.3–14.3)	13.2	(13.0–13.4)	12.8	(12.7–12.8)	12.6	(12.5–12.7)
Glycine	5.27	(5.17–5.37)	5.26	(5.15–5.37)	5.26	(5.21–5.33)	5.56	(5.45–5.66)
Histidine	0.94	(0.93–0.95)	0.96	(0.93–0.99)	1.02	(1.01–1.02)	1.00	(0.99–1.01)
Hydroxylysine								
Isoleucine	3.87	(3.79–3.95)	3.88	(3.84–3.92)	3.79	(3.75–3.85)	3.72	(3.71–3.74)
Leucine	7.55	(7.43–7.67)	7.98	(7.82–8.14)	7.64	(7.49–7.80)	7.74	(7.73–7.75)
Lysine	3.03	(2.96–3.10)	3.10	(3.04–3.16)	3.15	(3.15–3.15)	3.11	(3.09–3.13)
Methionine	0.52	(0.49–0.54)	0.56	(0.55–0.57)	0.55	(0.55–0.55)	0.54	(0.52–0.55)
Phenylalanine	3.28	(3.26–3.30)	3.50	(3.48–3.51)	3.40	(3.36–3.44)	3.42	(3.36–3.48)
Proline	6.46	(6.32–6.60)	6.34	(6.15–6.53)	6.46	(6.40–6.49)	6.34	(6.21–6.47)
Serine	7.52	(7.44–7.60)	7.08	(6.94–7.26)	7.15	(6.92–7.33)	7.23	(7.00–7.48)
Threonine	6.73	(6.44–7.02)	6.62	(6.48–6.76)	6.58	(6.46–6.70)	6.53	(6.45–6.60)
Tryptophan								
Tyrosine	4.10	(4.01–4.18)	4.08	(3.95–4.12)	4.10	(4.06–4.14)	4.28	(4.17–4.40)
Valine	5.68	(5.53–5.82)	6.02	(6.00–6.03)	5.78	(5.67–5.89)	5.82	(5.70–5.94)

With the exception of cystine, the analyses were made by microbiological methods by Neva Snell of the Western Regional Research Laboratory. Cystine analyses were made by Hiroshi Fujikawa and Thomas Lubisich of the same laboratory, using Vassel's method (*J. Biol. Chem.* **151,** 643–645, 1943) and represent cystine + cysteine.

The samples were scoured by extracting successively with benzene, ethyl alcohol, and water.

composition of simple peptides isolated from wool following hydrolysis by acids, alkalies, and enzymes [29, 35, 36, 37, 90]. Use is made of the newer methods of partition chromatography, particularly paper chromatography. The identification of simple peptides establishes the amino acid groupings present in the original protein chains. Although the results so far indicate extreme complexity, it is significant that no particular order in arrangement of the amino acids is observed; neither is there an alternation of polar and nonpolar amino acid residues along the chains as postulated by Astbury in order to account for his model of the alpha folding of the chains.

Much of the continuing research on the mechanism of dye uptake and on the interaction of wool with water, detergents, acids, bases, finishing and modifying agents is centered around study of reactivities of specific sites on the protein molecules [4, 6, 10, 66, 72, 79, 83, 131, 135, 141]. Each amino acid residue in a protein contributes a peptide group and a side-chain group towards the total reactivity of the protein. The peptide groups contribute to the protein interactions by virtue of their ability to form hydrogen bonds. Hydrogen bonds can form whenever an active hydrogen atom is in juxtaposition with an electronegative acceptor atom, usually oxygen or nitrogen. The side-chain groups carry several types of reactive groups, including those which can undergo hydrogen bonding. Two important classes of reactive side-chain groups are acid groups, contributed by the acidic amino acids (glutamic acid and aspartic acid) and the basic groups, contributed by the basic amino acids (arginine, lysine, and histidine).

The presence of these groups in wool provides for its ability to interact with basic or acidic substances. Additional reactive groups in wool are the phenolic hydroxyl (contributed by tyrosine) and the alcoholic hydroxyl (contributed by serine and threonine residues).

Besides the ability of the protein chains to interact with other molecules, they have the power of mutually interacting to form the networks which characterize each morphological unit. The details of these structures are far from established. Because each structure contributes to the chemical and physical behavior of the fiber as a whole, much attention is being given towards developing an understanding of the nature and extent of network stabilization, especially as influenced by the surrounding chemical and physical environment [9, 34, 42, 64, 78, 89, 102, 107]. The chief bonds responsible for stabilization of wool structure are the cystine disulfide bonds and the hydrogen bonds.

The regular folding of the chains in the crystalline portion of unstretched wool has long been recognized. It now appears that regular folding is a fundamental property of all polypeptide chains. Recent work on synthetic polypeptides indicates that folding and unfolding occur in these materials and the process is similar to that observed in the natural polypeptides. It is of interest to mention that solubilized wool protein has been regenerated to fibers which exhibit the characteristic alpha fold. Moreover, these fibers, like wool, undergo unfolding upon stretching [7, 9, 51].

Another characteristic of wool fibers involving folding of the chains is the tendency to supercontract when exposed to extreme conditions which favor severance of stabilizing disulfide and hydrogen bonds [2, 43, 128]. Wool contracts to as much as 30 to 40 per cent of its initial length. The contraction is attributed to the complete randomization of the chains to more compact coiled configuration. Since contraction can occur without involvement of the crystalline areas, it appears that the chains in the amorphous wool, like the chains in the crystalline regions, are folded in their natural state.

Current interest in the precise nature of the folding in proteins has been stimulated by several recently proposed models which attempt especially to account for information derived from X-ray and electron diffraction and from infrared spectra [8, 12, 20, 95, 100, 137]. None of the models so far has answered all requirements. Undoubtedly the real situation is more complex than present analysis permits. The ultimate aim of chemical investigations of wool is the precise knowledge of the contribution of each unit of structure to the observed chemical, physicochemical, and mechanical behavior. Undoubtedly the properties of wool in some instances will be directly traceable to the ultimate molecular structure; in other cases fiber properties will be found to be correlated more closely with disposition and properties of the larger units. It is anticipated that knowledge of this sort, when more adequate, will provide the basis for improved mechanical processing. Moreover, such knowledge should and does provide background for development of new and improved chemical treatments designed to overcome certain limitations of wool as a textile fiber [1, 3, 5, 44, 62, 74].

Presence of Nitrogen. The presence of nitrogen in wool becomes evident by simply burning a small sample of the fiber. The characteristic empyreumatic odor of nitrogenous animal matter is then observed. Heating wool in a small combustion test tube shows that ammonia, which can be tested for, is among the gaseous products evolved.

Presence of Sulfur. The sulfur in wool is present in the form of the amino acid, cystine, which occurs naturally to a greater or lesser extent in almost all protein foods and is an essential factor in body growth. The possible significance of sulfur in the sheep diet, and its influence on the composition and properties of wool, was first pointed out by King [67] and has been investigated by various workers. Sulfur is essential to the formation of wool substance, and a deficiency will result in an abnormal fleece.

Marston and Robertson [82], arguing from their conclusion that wool keratin has a constant percentage of sulfur, anticipated no alteration in chemical composition as a result of an enriched cystine diet, but an increase in the total fleece weight, proportionate to the extra amount of sulfur utilized by the animal for wool production.

Experimental verification of improved quality and weight of fleece through cystine feeding, especially in the form of wool hydrolysate, is reported by the Division of Animal Nutrition, Adelaide. Beadles, Braman, and Mitchell [28] find that in rats an increased hair growth results from a cystine-rich diet. On the other hand, the evidence advanced by Barritt and King [26] that the sulfur content in wool keratin is far from constant (shown in Table 15) has been further strengthened by their investigations with Pickard [103] on Angora rabbit wool.

TABLE 15. Sulfur Content of Various Wools

Type of Wool	*Per Cent Sulfur on Dry Weight*	*Type of Wool*	*Per Cent Sulfur on Dry Weight*
Cape Merino Kaffrarian	4.00	Turkey mohair (fine)	3.36
Welsh Mountain	3.97	Devon lamb	3.34
Blackface (fine)	3.82	Fine Ripon	3.34
Australian Merino 100's	3.76	Blackface (coarse)	3.33
Peruvian (1924)	3.75	Blackface (kempy)	3.24
South African Merino	3.67	New Zealand crossbred	3.22
Australian stud ram	3.56	Lincoln (white)	3.10
New Zealand 50's	3.47	Turkey mohair (coarse)	3.03

Harris and Smith [56] found similar large variations in the sulfur content of fur fibers and the various specialty hair fibers. Their results are reported in Table 16, in which all samples were solvent cleaned and comprise the average of three tests.

TABLE 16. SULFUR AND NITROGEN CONTENT OF VARIOUS ANIMAL FIBERS

[Dry weight.]

Class	*Type*	*Sulfur Per Cent*	*Nitrogen Per Cent*
Fur fibers	Raccoon	5.78	15.55
	Muskrat	4.68	15.95
	Russian rabbit	3.84	15.87
Specialty hairs	Alpaca	4.17	16.30
	Vicuña	4.10	16.26
	Turkey mohair	3.58	16.40
	Texas mohair	2.92	16.51
	Camel's hair	3.41	16.48
	Cashmere	3.39	16.42
Wools	Domestic wool	3.50	16.41
	Cordova carpet	3.32	16.29
	Egyptian carpet fawn	3.25	16.10

Effect of Sunlight. The photochemical decomposition in "weathering" takes place on the back of the animal, which is exposed to light.

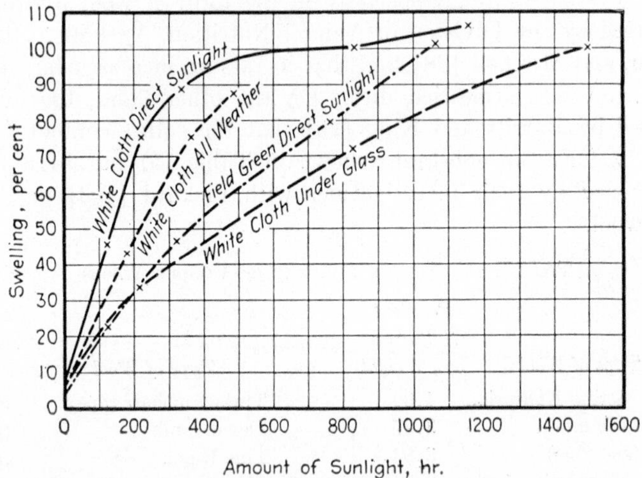

FIG. 2. Curves showing the relation between the amount of sunlight, exposure time and swelling with 0.1 N NaOH on wool, taken out of exposed woolen cloth. (*von Bergen.*)

It results in a yellowish-brown discoloration accompanied by a harsh feel in the upper tips of the staples on the back and the flanks of the animal. This is caused by the formation of sulfuric acid from the sulfur present in the wool. The exposed fibers become brittle and weak and also become sensitive to alkalies, which in the case of caustic soda causes a strong swelling effect, i.e., curling of hairs. Von Bergen [143] found that the extent of the swelling is, up to a certain limit, in direct proportion to the length of exposure to sunlight.

The relation between the amount of sunlight and the swelling with 0.1 *N* NaOH is shown by the curves in Fig. 2. The damage done to raw wool, while still on the back of the sheep, is proved by the data given in Table 17.

TABLE 17. Effects of Sunlight on Raw Wool

Origin	Place on Animal	End of Staple		
		Width, Unswollen, μ	Width, Swollen, μ	Swelling, Per Cent
Australian wool	back	23.08	44.46	92.63
	belly	27.27	29.88	9.6
Virginia wool	back	35.06	45.23	29.00
	belly	42.08	44.37	5.44
Württemberg wool	back	33.49	43.42	29.65
	flanks	33.00	35.8	8.5
	belly	27.7	29.3	5.8
Swiss mountain wool	back	28.57	50.69	77.4

The photochemical decomposition of wool has been further investigated by Smith and Harris [113]. The deterioration, as evidenced by the decrease in cystine content and the increase in alkali-solubility, ammonia nitrogen, and sulfate sulfur, is accelerated by acids and decelerated by alkalies. The extent to which wool is degraded during irradiation is directly proportional to the decrease in cystine content and to the increase in alkali-solubility. The sulfur content of untreated and acid-treated wool decreased during irradiation. The data suggest that a portion of the sulfur in wool is converted to hydrogen sulfide, some of which is subsequently oxidized to sulfuric acid.

McMahon and Speakman [80] further illustrated the extent of light damage in fleece wool as recognized by von Bergen [143] by measuring the sulfur contents of tip, middle, and root sections of New Zealand Romney wool (Table 18). The staples were taken from a single ani-

TABLE 18. Effect of Sunlight on Sulfur Content

Part of Staple	Sulfur Content (per cent on dry weight)		
	Britch (uncovered)	Neck (uncovered)	Side (covered)
Tip	2.78	2.83	3.27
Middle	3.26	3.18	3.23
Root	3.45	3.55	3.53

mal, part of whose fleece had been fitted with a fabric cover, so that the britch and neck wools were freely exposed to light during the whole period of growth, whereas the side wool was protected by the cover.

Thus, about 14 per cent of the total sulfur in the tip wool is lost when the fibers are exposed to light during growth or, if it is assumed that the sulfur is lost as hydrogen sulfide, about 28 per cent of the disulfide bonds in the exposed tip section of the wool is hydrolyzed under the influence of light.

The titration curves of root and tip wool, taken from staples selected from the side and shoulder of a New Zealand Romney fleece, have been determined with a view to interpreting the decomposition undergone by wool fibers on exposure to sunlight during growth. Since the acid titration curves of intact (root) and exposed (tip) wools are practically identical, there can be no doubt that the main peptide chains of animal fibers are not hydrolyzed under the influence of sunlight and air. The disulfide bonds, on the other hand, are severely attacked, undergoing changes similar to the main reaction taking place in caustic soda solution. Aldehyde and sulfhydryl groups are developed, the latter being responsible for the increased affinity of exposed (tip) wool for alkali as well as the change in affinity for wool dyes. The root of locks of wool dyes to a different shade from that of the tip with many acid, chrome, and vat dyes.

Rowe, Speakman, and collaborators [108] found that the reducing groups, namely, aldehyde (—CHO) and mercaptan (—SH), present in the tip prevent the full development of shade of many chrome dyes which depend on oxidation as well as formation of the chrome complex to give the true shade. Exposed wool swells more than unexposed wool in the dye liquor, since there are fewer cross-linkages to tie the polypeptide chains together. Consequently, if the dye particles are relatively large they can penetrate the "exposed" wool more readily than they can diffuse into the normal wool. This means that the fast-to-milling acid dyes, such as the Coomassie, Polar, or Sulphonine brands, color exposed wool a heavier shade in the same bath.

On the other hand, the so-called molecularly dispersed or level-dyeing acid colors, such as Azo-Geranine 2GS or Xylene Light Yellow 2G, give weaker shades on "exposed" wool than on the normal wool, since the swollen pores of the exposed wool cannot retain the discrete particles of dyes so tenaciously. By adding sulfuric acid to the dye bath, the level-dyeing acid dyes are aggregated to larger particles so that equal depths of shade are obtained on exposed and unexposed wool or tips and roots of the fibers. In an extensive study of this problem made in 1946 by the New York section of the American Association of Textile Chemists and Colorists it was found that tippiness can be minimized and even eliminated by the careful selection of the dyes and by the use of certain leveling agents ["The Tippy Dyeing of Wool and Its Control," *Am. Dyestuff Reptr.*, **54,** 486–506 (Nov. 1947)].

Kertess [65], Sommer [115], and Cunliffe [38] studied the deterioration of woolen fabrics during exposure to light as evidenced by decrease in strength and by the Pauly test. Exposed wool cloth becomes more acid, wets out more rapidly, deteriorates more during wet processing, and fulls more slowly than unexposed cloth.

Action of Heat. When wool is heated in dry air at 212° to 220° F. (100 to 105° C.) over a long period it loses its moisture and the fiber becomes harsh and loses strength. If returned to moist air, it rapidly reabsorbs moisture and regains more or less its softness and strength. If 212° F. is exceeded for any length of time the wool will decompose, will acquire a yellow color, and ammonia and hydrogen sulfide will evolve.

Studies made by Raynes [106] show that H_2S and NH_3 are evolved even at 212° F. when the heating is prolonged over 48 hr. The studies made by Stirm and Rouette [133] show the effect of temperature, time, humidity, and *p*H value on the decomposition of wool. The amounts of NH_3 and H_2S evolved by the process were taken as a measure of the decomposition. The amounts of NH_3 and H_2S increased rapidly when the temperature rose over 100° C. and when the humidity increased. When the wool was treated with alkali more NH_3 and H_2S evolved, showing increased decomposition.

Wiegerink [147] determined the effects of drying under selected conditions of temperature and atmospheric humidity on certain properties of worsted yarns and found that for clothing and carpet wools the effect of heat is less than the effect of humidity. This is particularly true of carpet wool, which shows the greatest deterioration at a high humidity. Carpet wool is less resistant to heat and humidity than clothing wool.

Wool when burned gives off a characteristic odor, similar to that of burning hair or feathers, due chiefly to the presence of nitrogen in the compound. When removed from the flame, wool will stop burning and each single fiber exhibits a black knob or charred globule on its end. Wool is, therefore, fire resistant. The vapor coming off during the burning process has an alkaline reaction, turning moist red litmus paper blue.

Action of Cold. The influence of a low temperature on wool has become of importance since the introduction of the frosted wool process. The wool is treated at temperatures from 40 to 60° F. below zero. The wool is still pliable, only vegetable and fatty matter being frozen, enabling it to be separated from the wool by mechanical action. Low temperatures have no chemical effect on the fiber.

Water and Steam. Water and steam, respectively moisture and heat, are the basis of many finishing processes. When wool is exposed to water, cold or hot, and steam, with or without tension, the behavior of the wool substance shows important peculiarities. As a plastic substance, similar to horn, it will change its shape and its affinity toward dyes. Wool is insoluble in water under ordinary conditions. Boiled for 2 hr in distilled water, the wool loses approximately a quarter of one per cent of its weight. Humfield, Elmquist, and Kettering [61] reported a 29 per cent decrease in strength of a serge fabric through 12 hr boiling in water. In cold and warm water the fiber swells or increases in size approximately 10 per cent (chemically damaged wool may swell 20 per cent or more), but, on drying, the fiber returns to its former diameter. With water under pressure at temperatures above 250° F., wool dissolves. In dyeing processes the boiling time influences the breaking strength.

Steam (212° F.) when applied for a short time has no damaging effect, but extended periods of application attacks the wool to a point where it loses all its strength. Elliott [39] reports a wool fabric losing 5 per cent of its average dry breaking strength after 25 hr in the dry heat of an autoclave at 100° C. but 75 per cent after the same treatment in moist heat; at 120° C. the corresponding losses were 16 per cent and 100 per cent. Browning of wool has been described by Fort [45] as progressive with duration of steaming and is greater at 100° C. than that brought about by boiling water or dry heat. A wool steamed at 99° to 100° C. for 3, 6, 12, 24, 36, 48, and 60 hr was observed by Scheurer [110] to lose 18, 23, 28, 40, 50, 64, and 74 per cent of its original strength.

Walde, Barr, and Edgar [146] showed that the degradation of wool by steam increases with an increase in time or pressure. The mechanical failure is more rapid than loss of weight, nitrogen, or sulfur, indicating a breakdown of fibrous structure preceding the formation of soluble degradation products, as shown in Tables 19 and 20.

Humfield, Elmquist, and Kettering [61] reported that three intermittent steamings of half an hour each at 100° C. of serge fabrics produced 9.3 per cent loss in strength index; four steamings increased the loss to 14 per cent. In autoclaving the same fabric dry and wet for half an hour at 15 lb steam pressure, the loss in the strength index was 4.6 per cent for the dry and 31.2 per cent for the wet, which indicates that the effect of dry heat is less damaging than wet steam.

Plastic Properties. In regard to the plastic properties, the following principles govern the behavior of wool: *First,* if wool in the dry state is deformed by imposing some strain, for example in the process of spinning, the fiber will tend to recover its original form when the hu-

TABLE 19. EFFECT OF STEAM AT VARIOUS PRESSURES ON WOOL FABRIC

[Time, one hour.]

Steam Pressure (lb per sq in.)	Temperature (°C.)	Residual Keratin				
		Weight (per cent of wool)	Nitrogen (per cent of wool)	Sulfur (per cent of wool)	Breaking Strength of Wet Warp (lb per in.)	Elongation at Breaking Load (per cent)
0	100.0	99.4	16.44	3.88	13	50
10	115.2	99.0	16.44	3.74	11	55
15	121.0	99.1	16.25	3.75	8	40
20	126.0	98.9	16.36	3.75	2	49
30	134.5	98.7	16.13	3.68	<1	..
40	141.5	93.9	15.72	3.33	<1	..

TABLE 20. Effect of Steaming Time on Wool Fabric

[Steam Pressure 10 lb, Temperature 115.2° C.]

Time (hours)	Residual Keratin				
	Weight (per cent of wool)	Nitrogen (per cent of wool)	Sulfur (per cent of wool)	Breaking Strength of Wet Warp (lb per in.)	Elongation at Breaking Load (per cent)
0	100.0	16.49	3.99	15	56
1	99.0	16.44	3.74	11	55
3	99.1	16.39	3.76	7	42
5	98.6	15.80	3.69	2	47

midity is increased. This may be brought about by wetting out or exposing to a moist atmosphere like steaming. *Second,* wool loses its rigidity almost completely, i.e., becomes plastic, in boiling water. *Third,* the behavior of the wool under the influence of moisture and heat is greatly affected by time and temperature. The plasticity of wool increases rapidly with a rise of temperature and may be so great that stretched fibers, after steaming, for example, are no longer able to return to their original length when released in cold water. In other words, they take a "permanent set."

This is the basis of finishing processes such as "crabbing" and "blowing." The conditions for the realization of a permanent set were determined by Speakman [122], and a discovery was made that the "set" imposed at any one temperature is permanent only to water at a lower temperature than that at which it was imposed. This discovery has far-reaching consequences in connection with wool finishing processes, particularly London shrinking, tentering, and the production of crepe effects in wool goods. Woods [148] found that the temporary set developed in fibers when stretched and steamed is not due to the intercellular material but is a property possessed by the cortical cells as units. A direct relationship exists between the extension of steam-set fibers and the extension of the cortical cells, as shown in Table 21, where all fibers were measured in water and the normal length of wet cells was 109 μ.

The elongated cells recover only partially when they are boiled in water, and the permanent set remaining is of the same order as that

TABLE 21. Lengths of Cotswold Wool Cells from Fibers Set in Steam at Various Extensions

Extension of Fibers (per cent)	*No. of Cells*	*Mean Length* (μ)	*Standard Deviation* (μ)	*Extension of Cells (per cent)*
10.0	224	114	25.4	5
15.0	202	118	25.4	8
19.5	130	121	26.4	11
20.0	246	120	26.4	10
30.5	203	131.5	27.0	21
40.0	216	144.5	27.7	33
53.0	203	155	30.4	42

which the fibers would have shown. Permanent set is thus also a property of the cells themselves.

Cotswold wool fibers which have been relaxed in dilute caustic soda can also be disintegrated into cells which recover during the process to rather less than the normal length. These relaxed cells can be supercontracted still further by boiling water. In this way cells of about half the normal length can be obtained; their crystalline part shows itself in the β form, just as does that of highly supercontracted fibers.

By the combined action of lateral pressure and steam the cells from normal fibers may be compounded into coherent transparent sheets which are elastic in cold water for extensions up to about 50 per cent and are extensible in steam or caustic soda by twice this amount. These sheets can be relaxed, set, and supercontracted in the same way as fibers, and their tensile strength in water is about 25 per cent of that of fibers. This suggests that the coherence developed during the steam treatment is similar to the development of permanent set in a stretched fiber.

Isoelectric and Isoionic Points. On the significance of these two points Harris [54] gives the following explanation:

> It has generally been assumed that the isoelectric point of wool represents the point of maximum stability of the fiber. Although the isoelectric points of some proteins appear to be close to the points of maximum stability, they are not necessarily the same. Actually, it is possible for the stability region of a protein to be far from the isoelectric point. Whether the point of maximum stability will be at or near the isoelectric point will depend upon the reactivity of specific linkages in the molecules. For example, assume that a protein containing disulfide linkages from the amino acid cystine has an isoelectric point in the alkaline region as a consequence of a high content of either lysine or arginine. In view of the known instability of disulfides in even weakly alkaline solutions, it is very unlikely that the point of maximum stability of such a substance would be located near its isoelectric point.

The concept of the isoelectric and isoionic points can be utilized in practical wool processing. Since the isoionic point involves only the acidic and basic properties of the fiber, it should be considered in studying such wool processes as are related to these properties. Dyeing with soluble dyes, felting, and removal of ash constituents from the fiber are processes that probably fall within this category. In addition, the swelling and tensile properties of wet fibers are a function of the state of their acidic and basic groups.

The isoelectric point, on the other hand, is concerned primarily with the total net surface charge and must only be considered in relation to processes involving either the removal or deposition of materials on the surface of the fiber. In other words, it would play an important part in such processes as scouring and finishing. Scouring is facilitated when the charge on a fiber and the charge on the material being removed from the fiber are the same and therefore tend to repel each other. For example, dirt particles and particles of most inert substances carry negative charges. Obviously then, such macroscopic particles are best removed from fibers which also have a large net negative charge. Similarly, the deposition of certain finishing materials on fibers or fabrics is best accomplished when the charges on the fibers and material to be deposited are of opposite sign. Although the dyeing problem is undoubtedly more complicated, it is probable that dyeing with colloidal dyes is related to the isoelectric point.

In acetate buffers, the isoelectric point of wool scales and cortical cells was found to be at *p*H 4.5. Samples of ground or powdered wool show an isoelectric point at *p*H 4.2. The isoionic point of commencement of combination of the wool fiber with acid, according to Speakman [127], is around *p*H 4.8 and *p*H 5.0, which is in close agreement with Elöd's figure [41] of *p*H 5.0. Harris [54] states that in the absence of salt the *p*H at zero combination is in the range 4.7 to 5.1. Wool does not combine with any significant amount of alkali below *p*H 10 and for general purposes may be regarded as possessing an isoionic range from *p*H 5 to 10.

Acid and Basic Nature. In its chemical reactions wool exhibits the characteristics of both an acid and a base. The reason for this amphoteric nature lies in its composition—it contains various amino acids.

The titration curve reflects best the acidic and basic characteristic of the wool fiber and affords a proof of the real existence of salt linkages within the fiber. The best known studies were made by Speakman and Stott [126], McMahon and Speakman [80], and Steinhardt, Fugitt, and Harris [129]. In analyzing the curves as shown in Figs. 3 and 4 Steinhardt and Harris [130] and collaborators came to the following conclusions:

The maximum acid-binding capacity of hydrochloric acid at 0° C., independent of ionic strength, is 0.82 millimole per gram; the maximum base-binding capacity of potassium hydroxide is greater than 0.78 millimole. With salt absent, no appreciable binding of acid or base

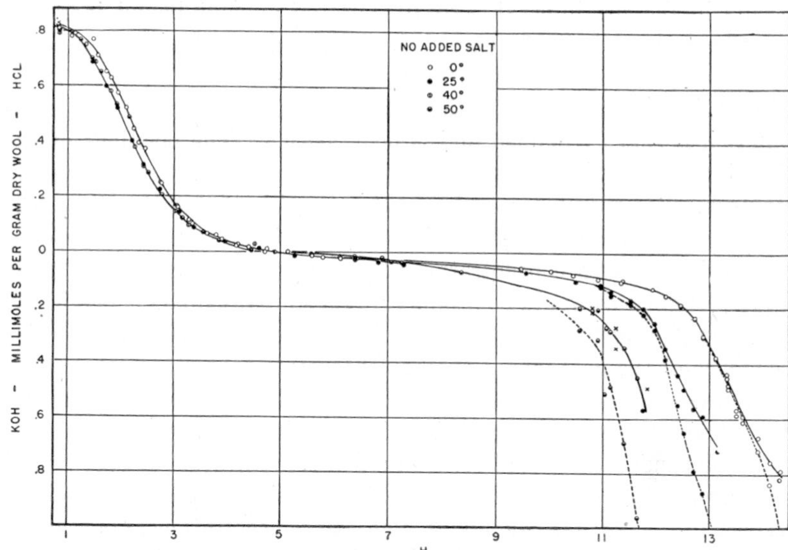

FIG. 3. Combination of wool with hydrochloric acid and with potassium hydroxide as a function of pH and temperature, in the absence of salt. (*Steinhardt, Fugitt, and Harris.*)

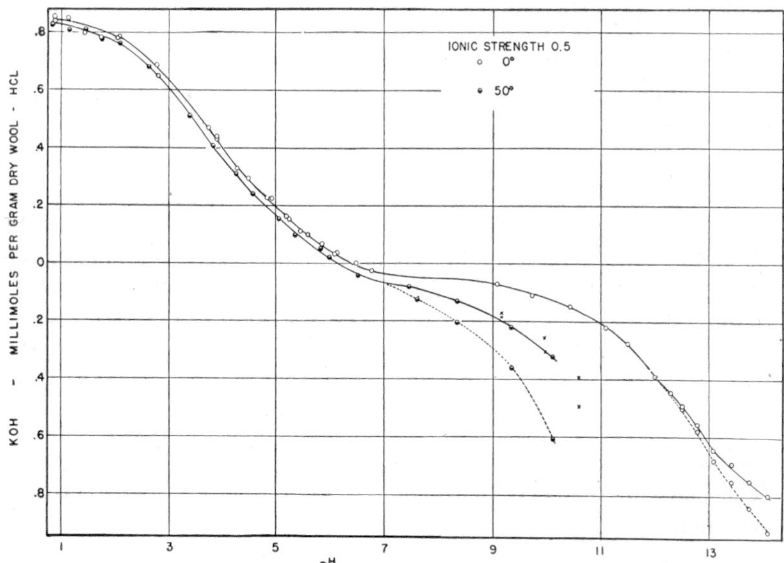

FIG. 4. Combination of wool with hydrochloric acid and with potassium hydroxide as a function of pH and temperature, at 0.5 M ionic strength. (*Steinhardt, Fugitt, and Harris.*)

occurs in the pH interval 5 to 10, but the amount bound increases sharply as these limits are exceeded. When salt is present, the amount of acid or base bound changes with pH more gradually and there is no wide region in which combination fails to occur; the point of zero combination is sharply defined and is near pH 6.4. The positions of the titration curves with respect to the pH axis are different at every ionic strength. The differences are larger than can be attributed to the effect of salts on the dissociation of acids; thus, in dilute solutions an n-fold change in the total concentration of chloride ions produces a change almost as great as would be produced by a similar n-fold change in the concentration of hydrogen ions. This approach to stoichiometric dependence of the acid bound on the concentration of anions as well as of hydrogen ions accounts for the greater steepness of the titration curve when the source of both ions is the acid alone.

The dependence of acid bound on anion concentration or base bound on concentration of cations shows that the positions of the curves with respect to the pH axis should, at high salt concentrations, approach a limit which should correspond to the titration curve of the same protein in the dissolved state. This is further supported by the fact that the data for wool agree very closely at high salt concentrations with those for a similar but soluble protein, egg albumin.

The analysis of the composition of the titration curve in terms of the constituent diacidic and dibasic amino acids of wool leads to the conclusion that the binding of acid and base by wool occurs at the free carboxyl, imidazole, amino, and guanidino groups, but that no combination of base with the tyrosine hydroxyl group takes place in the pH range of this investigation.

The data in Fig. 3 support the assumption made in accounting for previously reported titration measurements at 0° C. that the carboxyl and amino groups of wool in the uncombined state are completely ionized. Thus, changes in the pH coordinates of the titration curves brought about by changes in temperature are small in the pH range in which acid is combined, which indicates that combination with acid is equivalent to back-titration of the carboxyl groups, but are large in the pH range in which base is combined, which indicates that combination with base is equivalent to back-titration of amino groups.

The heats of dissociation calculated for the two kinds of groups, approximately 2500 and 14,000 calories, are in good agreement with values for these groups in comparable compounds and in soluble proteins. The value obtained in the acid range also agrees with the results of calorimetric measurements on the combination of acid with wool.

Approximately equal parts of the total heat changes in the acid range are associated with the dissociation of hydrogen ions and chloride ions from the fiber. An appreciable part of the total heat effect may be ascribed to a heat of transfer of the ions between the two phases of the heterogeneous titration system.

Effect of Acids. The titration curve of wool shows that the action of acid begins at *p*H 5 and in the case of hydrochloric acid is completed at *p*H 1. In hydrochloric acid solutions wool combines stoichiometrically not only with the hydrogen ions of the acid but with the chloride ions as well. Hence, the specific affinities for wool of the anions of different strong acids vary considerably and therefore the positions of the titration curves of wool with respect to the *p*H axis vary by correspondingly large amounts, according to the acid used. This has been well established by Speakman and Stott [125] and Steinhardt, Fugitt, and Harris [129].

The titration curves of strong acids (Fig. 5) are S-shaped and form a coherent family, near neighbors following a fairly parallel course. If the position of each curve is characterized by the *p*H value at which half the maximum amount of acid (about 0.4 millimole per gram) is taken up, there is a difference of 2 *p*H units between the curves shown at the extremes of the series.

The anion-wool associations for strong acids are fully reversible, and the wool in combining with acid suffers no permanent alteration until amounts which approach 0.8 millimole per gram are combined. The curves for the acids of lower affinity are characterized by flattening in the neighborhood of 0.83 to 0.84 millimole per gram combined. This fairly well marked "maximum" corresponds closely to the primary amino content of the fibers. With acids of higher affinity, however, the curves show a definite increase in the slope, which represents a second step of acid combination. The amounts of acid bound at low *p*H in some of the acids are far in excess of 0.8 millimole per gram of wool. This increase in the acid-binding capacity is due to hydrolytic decomposition.

With hydrochloric acid, even with high concentrations, negligible amounts of ammonia at 0° C. are found, whereas with acids of higher affinity ammonia is liberated more rapidly and the acid-binding capacity increases in direct relation to the amount of ammonia liberated. With some acids this increase amounts to over 0.3 millimole per gram of wool. However, where the hydrolysis of the peptide bonds leads to the formation of some insoluble decomposition products a real increase in acid-binding power is observed.

In Table 22 are assembled the calculated anion affinity constant $1/K_{A'}$ of 33 strong acids at three different temperatures as established by Steinhardt, Fugitt, and Harris [129]. The data show a fairly consistent relationship between the affinity and the molecular weights of strong organic acids.

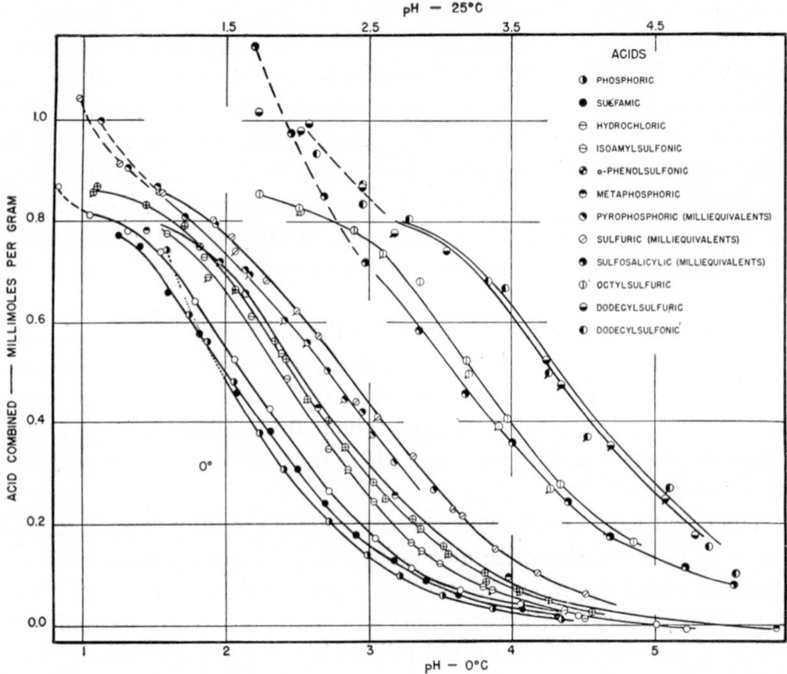

FIG. 5. Combination of wool protein with 12 different strong acids at 0° or 25° C. (*Steinhardt, Fugitt, and Harris.*) *Note:* The *p*H scale at the bottom of the figure applies to the data obtained at 0° C. The scale at the top of the figure refers to the data obtained at 25° C.

Of special interest are the following observations: The lowest affinity is shown by phosphoric acid and refers to the dihydrogen phosphate ion. The data for phosphoric acid are congruent with the other curves only for amounts combined of less than 0.45 millimole per gram, because the first step in the dissociation is not complete in the range of *p*H below 2. The presence of appreciable amounts of unionized acid results in the combination of additional amounts of acid in the undissociated form.

Hydrochloric acid titration curves with proteins are clearly affected by the specific affinity of the chloride ion for the protein and must not

TABLE 22. Calculation of Anion Affinity Constants ($1/K_{A'}$) at Three Different Temperatures

	Molecular Weight	pH of Half-Maximum Combination	$-\log K_A'$
	0° C.		
Phosphoric	98.0	2.155	0.115
Sulfamic	97.1	2.22	0.20
Hydrochloric	36.5	2.32	0.43
Ethylsulfuric	126.1	2.33	0.44
Hydrobromic	80.9	2.47	0.69
Nitric	63.0	2.58	0.89
Isoamylsulfonic	152.2	2.58	0.89
Benzenesulfonic	158.2	2.63	1.00
p-Toluenesulfonic	172.2	2.66	1.035
o-Phenolsulfonic	174.2	2.66	1.035
o-Xylene-*p*-sulfonic	186.2	2.71	1.12
Metaphosphoric *	$(80.0)_{3n}$	2.72	* (1.14)
Trichloroacetic	163.4	2.73	1.16
o-Nitrobenzenesulfonic	203.2	2.86	1.39
Pyrophosphoric †	178.0	2.94	1.53
4-Nitrochlorobenzene-2-sulfonic	237.6	3.07	1.76
Sulfuric †	98.1	3.08	1.78
2,5-Dichlorobenzenesulfonic	227.1	3.13	1.87
2,4-Dinitrobenzenesulfonic	248.2	3.17	1.94
Naphthalene-β-sulfonic	208.2	3.24	2.06
2,4,6-Trinitroresorcinol	245.1	3.64	2.73
Picric	229.1	3.86	3.08
Flavianic †‡	314.2	4.24	3.67
	25° C.		
Hydrochloric	36.5	2.16	0.265
Naphthalene-β-sulfonic	208.2	3.03	1.82
Octylsulfuric	210.3	3.47	2.56
Sulfosalicylic	218.1	3.34	2.34
Picric	229.1	3.52	2.64
Dodecylsulfuric	266.4	4.02	3.42
Flavianic †	314.2	4.07	3.495
Dodecylsulfonic ‡	250.4	4.08	3.51
Orange II ‖	328.3	‡ 4.63	‡ 4.28
	50° C.		
Hydrochloric	36.5	2.17	0.28
Naphthalene-β-sulfonic	208.2	2.95	1.68
Sulfuric †	98.1	§ 2.97	1.71
Diphenylsulfonic	234.3	3.16	2.04
p-Hydroxyazobenzene-*p*′-sulfonic	278.3	3.24	2.18
Anthraquinone-β-sulfonic	288.3	3.40	2.44
p-Diphenylbenzenesulfonic	310.4	3.70	2.93
iso-Propylnaphthalenesulfonic	250.3	3.74	2.99
Dodecylsulfonic	250.4	3.96	3.33
Orange II	328.3	4.17	3.64

* The affinity indicated is minimal, for reasons explained in the text.

† The data given refer to combination with the divalent anion, but K_A' is expressed, for purposes of comparison, as if the anion were monovalent.

‡ The affinity given is minimal because equilibrium may not have been attained.

§ Extrapolated from the lower (normal) portion of the titration curve. The actual midpoint pH was 2.92.

‖ The midpoint pH of the curve obtained with Orange II at 25° C. has been reevaluated by applying a correction for ash to these data. Both values of $-\log K_A'$ are based on the reevaluated midpoint.

be regarded as representing a limiting case governed by the hydrogen-ion dissociation equilibrium of the carboxyl groups alone.

Sulfuric and pyrophosphoric acid are dibasic and the amounts combined are therefore plotted as milliequivalents per gram, instead of millimoles per gram. The curves of both indicate that their doubly charged anions have relatively high affinities, considering their molecular weights.

The curve obtained with metaphosphoric acid is not strictly comparable with those obtained with other acids because of the presence of chloride, divalent monohydrogen trimetaphosphate, and trivalent metaphosphate ions. Its position is probably determined prodominantly by the affinity of the divalent ion (or its dimer), since the concentration of this acid ion increases almost proportionally to the increase in hydrogen ion, as is the case when curves are obtained with strong acids in the absence of salt.

Among the data given for 25° C. are measurements made with a third divalent anion sulfosalicylate, commonly used as a protein precipitant. The affinity, as would be expected, is high but not so high as that of two other protein precipitants of higher molecular weight, picric and flavianic acids. As in the case of flavianic acid, amounts far in excess of 0.8 milliequivalent per gram are bound at low *p*H values. The anion present in this region of *p*H is the monovalent ion, and a plateau near 0.8 millimole rather than 0.8 milliequivalent would presumably be found.

Octylsulfuric, dodecylsulfonic, and dodecylsulfuric acids are strong aliphatic acids of high molecular weight. The affinities of the two larger molecules are among the highest so far measured. Orange II, a dyestuff acid, shows the highest affinity of all acids. At 50° C. the wool decomposes rapidly in the more concentrated solutions of this dye.

With sulfuric acid the data at 50° C. are much like those obtained at 0° C. when the amounts combined are less than 0.3 milliequivalent per gram; beyond this point the increase in the amounts combined as the *p*H decreases is smaller than at the lower temperature. This anomaly may be attributed to the formation of the more acid solutions of the low-affinity bisulfate ion, a process which is enhanced by high temperature (the second dissociation constant of sulfuric acid decreases as the temperature is raised). Thus, at *p*H values below 3 there is considerably more bisulfate ion at 50° C. than at 25° C. This effect of high temperatures in effectually diminishing the affinity of sulfuric acid is of importance in dyeing, where not only high temperature but the presence of sulfate in addition to sulfuric acid favors the formation of bisulfate ion.

Weak Acids. The titration curves obtained with eight organic acids by Steinhardt, Fugitt, and Harris [129] are compared in Fig. 6 with the curve of hydrochloric acid. This graphic comparison brings out

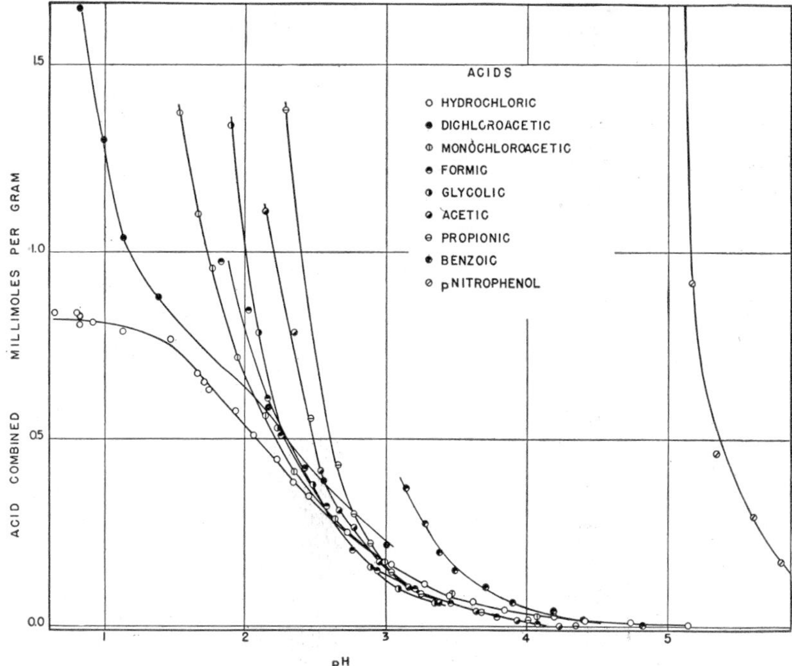

Fig. 6. Combination of purified wool with a number of weak acids at 0° C. The curve for hydrochloric acid is given for comparison. (*Steinhardt, Fugitt, and Harris.*)

clearly the principal difference between the behavior of strong and weak acids with respect to wool. Over a wide range of low concentrations, many of the acids are combined by wool at a given *p*H to about the extent that it combines with hydrochloric acid. The presence of undissociated acid at these concentrations is without appreciable effect. At higher concentrations, however, the amounts of weak acids which are combined increase more sharply than the amounts combined of hydrochloric acid, and, unlike hydrochloric acid, give no indication of approaching a saturation value at about 0.8 millimole per gram. Indeed, determinations have been made of amounts combined which are far beyond the upper limits of Fig. 6 (up to 4 millimoles per gram).

Most of the acids shown in Fig. 6 are organic acids of relatively low molecular weight and would be expected, if totally dissociated, to give titration curves of wool similar to the curve obtained with hydrochloric acid. If attention is confined to the lower portion of the curves obtained with acids of molecular weights below 80, it appears that this expectation is well founded. Marked departures from the curve for hydrochloric acid appear only at concentrations at which the amounts of undissociated acid become greater than about 0.01 mole. The increased uptake of weak acids which appears at high concentrations is a rough measure of the amounts of undissociated acid that have combined with the wool, possibly by solvating it in competition with water. In Table 23 are shown data for monochloroacetic acid, which has been chosen as an example because the lower part of the curve of this acid coincides most closely with that for hydrochloric acid.

TABLE 23. Combination of Undissociated Monochloroacetic Acid with Wool at 0° C.

pH	*Acid Combined* * *(mmoles/g)*	*HCl Combined at Same pH* *(mmoles/g)*	*Difference* *(mmoles/g)*	*Total Acid* *(mmoles/liter)*	*Undissociated Acid* † *(mmoles/liter)*	*Excess Combination Divided by Concentration of Undissociated Acid*
1.36	2.08	0.79	1.29	0.971	0.937	1.4
1.52	1.39	0.77	0.62	0.477	0.455	1.4
1.66	1.12	0.71	0.41	0.282	0.265	1.5
1.76	0.97	0.66	0.31	0.184	0.070	1.8
1.95	0.73	0.59	0.14	0.0874	0.0769	1.8
2.15	0.580	0.504	0.076	0.0398	0.0332	2.3
2.35	0.431	0.403	0.028	0.0172	0.0132	2.1

* No corrections have been applied for the error in calculating the uptake of acid which is introduced by the absorption of water by the fibers.

† The values in this column are derived from the total acid present by utilizing Wright's value of the dissociation constant [146] and applying the law of mass action. Since the proportion ionized is small, except in the more dilute solutions, little error is introduced by the neglect of activity coefficients.

In Table 24 are summarized the relative affinities of undissociated acids for wool as calculated by the method shown in Table 23. Approximate values for a few cyclic compounds not represented in Fig. 6 are also included. The range of the affinities of the undissociated acid for wool, as shown in Table 24, is approximately 300 to 1.

Speakman and Stott [127] stated that the far greater extent to which the weak acids combine with wool at low *p*H than hydrochloric acid is closely related to the greater swelling and higher heat of reaction. In concentrated hydrochloric acid at a *p*H of 0.6 the wool

TABLE 24. AFFINITIES OF UNDISSOCIATED ACIDS FOR WOOL PROTEIN AT 0° C.

Acids	*Partition Quotient*	*Acids*	*Partition Quotient*
Propionic	0.3	Benzoic	11
Acetic	0.4	*p*-Nitrophenol	20
Glycolic	0.6	2,4-Dinitrophenol	50
Formic	0.7	2,6-Dinitrophenol	60
Monochloroacetic	1.8	2,6-Dichloro-4-nitrophenol	100
Dichloroacetic	2	2,4,6-Trichlorophenol	100

fibers swell about 3 per cent, in monochloroacetic acid at the same *p*H 18 per cent, and in 98 per cent formic acid approximately 50 per cent.

Effect of Alkalies. One of the most characteristic chemical properties of wool is the ease with which it is degraded in alkaline solutions. A 5 per cent solution of caustic soda at boiling temperature completely dissolves wool in a few minutes. Investigations by Harris and Crowder [52] and Speakman [118] have shown that such degradation is closely associated with the lability toward alkalies of the disulfide groups in the cystine of the wool. It was found that, although the atomic ratio of nitrogen to sulfur in wool is about 10 to 1, these elements are removed from wool in the ratio of about 1 to 1 by the action of an alkali during the first stages of its attack. If wool protein were simply being dissolved, there should be 10 atoms of nitrogen in the solution for every atom of sulfur, but the analysis showed that the sulfur was present in a much greater proportion. About 40 per cent of the sulfur content of the wool is lost during an alkaline treatment which dissolves only about 9 per cent of the wool, but thereafter the sulfur is removed in proportion to the wool dissolved. For example, treatment of wool yarn with a solution of caustic soda which is one-fourth normal (1 per cent by weight) reduces the sulfur content of the wool from its original value of 3.16 per cent to 1.85 per cent in 20 min at 50° C. The same result is obtained in 4 hr by the use of 0.065 caustic soda at 65° C. Further research by Harris [53] brought forth similar results. (See Tables 25 and 26.)

The study of the course of the alkali degradation reveals that during the early stages a rapid splitting off of a portion of the sulfur occurs, closely approaching 50 per cent of the original amount of sulfur. For each sulfur atom lost a molecule of cystine is destroyed and, according to Horn, Jones, and Ringel [60], a more stable sulfur, containing amino acid and having the formula $(HOOC—CH(NH_2)—CH_2)_2S$, is formed. Mizell and Harris [94] have found more than 25 per cent of the residual

TABLE 25. Continued Action of 0.05 *N* Sodium Hydroxide at 65° C. on Wool

Time of Treatment	Loss in Weight	Alkali-Treated Wool	
		Sulfur Content	Cystine Content, by Sullivan Method
	Per Cent	*Per Cent*	*Per Cent*
Minutes:			
0	0.00	3.72	13.40
15	2.27	2.91	6.91
30	3.52	2.56	4.85
45	4.67	2.35	5.13
Hours:			
2	6.40	2.24	4.41
4	9.38	2.13	3.70
8	15.21	2.03	2.64
46 *	61.50	2.28	2.65

* The samples became gelatinous and part of the residual wool was lost during washing. The accuracy of these values is questionable.

noncystine of sulfur left in alkali-treated wool as lanthionine. No significant amounts of sulfhydryl groups are in the treated wools. The mechanism of this reaction as advanced by Nicolet and Shinn [97] involves a rupture between sulfur and carbon to yield dehydroalamine and a —CH_2—S—SH residue. An atom of sulfur is then eliminated from the latter and the sulfhydryl group thus formed reacts with dehydroalamine to form lanthionine.

The injurious effect of alkaline solutions is of wide practical importance in view of the numerous alkali treatments which wool undergoes in being converted from raw stock to the finished fabric, in addition to the alkaline laundering which wool fabrics may receive in use. Hence, soaps and scouring and fulling agents in general should be free from appreciable amounts of caustic alkalies. The weaker alkaline salts, such as the carbonates and soaps, are not so destructive in their action, and when employed at moderate temperatures they are not regarded as deleterious and are largely used in scouring and fulling.

Barmore [22], in studying the effect of temperature of wool and *p*H concentration of the scouring bath, found that for a bath of the same temperature the tensile strength of wool is decreased by immersion in baths of *p*H values greater than 4.8, although the amount is practically

TABLE 26. EFFECT ON WOOL OF TREATMENT WITH ALKALI BY THE FLOW METHOD

Sample	Cystine		Total Sulfur *	Alkali Solubility	Serine
	Found	Calculated			
0.1 N NaOH flow for 600 hr at 0° C.					
	Per Cent	*Per Cent*	*Per Cent*	*Per Cent*	*Per Cent*
Untreated	11.3	...	3.50	10.5	9.5
Treated	4.4	3.1	2.40	5.0	9.4
Treated $C_6H_5CH_2Cl$	4.2	...	....	...	...
0.1 N NaOH flow for 8 hr at 50° C.					
Untreated	12.5	...	3.50	...	...
Treated	2.7	1.1	1.98	...	...
Treated $C_6H_5CH_2Cl$	2.5	...	....	...	...

* Calculated on the basis that each atom of sulphur lost by the wool represents the destruction of one molecule of cystine.

zero until the pH value becomes greater than 7.0. The loss in tensile strength from this pH value upward slowly increases, the rate of loss becoming greater until the last 50 to 75 per cent of tensile strength disappears within an increase of one in pH value. He found further that for scouring raw wool the temperature of 50° C. is best, the pH value of the solution may range from 9.5 to 11.0, and the scouring time should not exceed 10 min. Under such conditions no damage occurs in the wool. Barmore's findings check with practical experience in large-scale scouring.

Data obtained by Harris [53] show that breaking strength tests do not indicate alkali damage, since the strength of wool yarn may actually increase as the result of alkali treatment, due to the matting of the fibers, although the yarn may be harsh and practically dissolved. Reflectance and compression resilience tests give more consistent measurements, but they fail to detect damage until it has become too apparent and serious.

The action of concentrated solutions of caustic alkalies on wool is a rather peculiar one. Studies of Speakman [118] and Barr and Edgar

[23] show that wool fibers are disintegrated by dilute NaOH solutions, the rapidity increasing with increased concentration of NaOH up to 15 per cent; beyond this point the strength of the yarn increases until 38 per cent of NaOH in solution is used. Investigation of the action of caustic solutions on individual wool fibers under carefully controlled conditions showed that (*a*) the elastic properties of single wool fibers are completely unaffected after immersion in 38 per cent NaOH solution for 5 min at 19° C.; (*b*) the immunity of the fibers is due to the low partial pressure of H_2O vapor in equilibrium with 38 per cent NaOH solution and to the formation of the complex hydrate $2NaOH \cdot 7H_2O$ with correspondingly low OH-ion concentration; (*c*) the 30 per cent increase in the strength of wool yarn after immersion in 38 per cent NaOH solution is due to the surface gelatinization of the fibers which binds them firmly together in the dried yarn.

Soda ash, potash, and ammonia are not as destructive to wool, but their use must be kept below certain concentration, depending on the temperature and time of the treatment; otherwise they have a yellowing and tendering effect. For example, soda solution used in raw wool scouring should be limited to 3 grams per liter or approximately 0.5 oz per gal at 130° F. and a *p*H of 11 with a total treatment time of 10 min. In piece scouring, at a working temperature of 70° F. (20° C.) the concentration may reach 3 per cent or approximately 4 oz per gal at the start of the process. Ammonia is a weak base, so if used in concentrated solution it causes disintegration even at low temperatures; but it may be used safely in a weak solution of 1 gram per liter for stripping purposes. Wiegerink [147] reports that wool treated with 0.1 per cent of carbonate solutions retains from 0.5 to 1 per cent more moisture than similar untreated wool.

The alkalies having the least effect on wool, perhaps, are ammonium carbonate and borax. Sodium phosphate is also a mild alkali which may be used in connection with wool without fear of injury. Whenever woolen goods are treated with alkaline solutions of whatever character, great care should be taken to give the material subsequently a most thorough washing in order to remove the last trace of alkali, as otherwise after drying and storing alkali spots may form, resulting in a weakening of the fiber and a discoloration of the goods. Also, if subsequently dyed, the pieces may exhibit streaks or spots due to the action of alkaline residues. Treatments of wool with oxidizing agents prior to an alkali treatment will increase the damaging effect of the alkali.

Effects of Salts. Neutral metallic salts are not very reactive, as wool does not absorb them appreciably from their solutions. Neutral salts, such as common salts, Glauber salt, potassium chloride, and magnesium sulfate, are hardly absorbed even in boiling solutions. Lime and magnesium salts, present in hard water, may cause a yellowing effect on the prolonged boiling or in "crabbing" and "blowing." Glauber salt or sodium sulfate when used as a stripping agent for acid colors will give wool a harsh feel, as it has a dissolving action on the fiber substance in concentration of 5 per cent or more. In the presence of acids this harshening effect is far less pronounced.

Certain salts are used with wool for the purpose of giving increased weight to the fabric. Magnesium chloride is the most used loading agent on account of its possessing great hygroscopic properties. Magnesium sulfate and zinc chloride are used in a similar manner. According to Siefert [111], when wool is treated with concentrated calcium or barium thiocyanate solutions and then steamed, a considerable fiber contraction takes place. This reaction may be used to produce crepe effects in fabrics. Similar effects result from the use of concentrated solutions of zinc chloride or sulfate, calcium chloride, or stannous chloride.

Studies were made by Hambraeus and Steele [50] on the effect of lithium bromide solutions on the structure of keratin fibers. The conclusions from this work may be summarized as follows:

1. Solutions of lithium bromide are able to penetrate and swell all the ordered regions of α-keratin fibers which contribute to the normal X-ray diagram. The driving force for this effect is the action of the hydrated lithium ion in reducing the strength of salt bridges and breaking intermolecular hydrogen bonds. There is no evidence that intramolecular hydrogen bonds are broken at room temperature.

2. Lithium bromide solutions at a concentration of $7M$, which contain 6 water molecules per lithium ion, are most effective in reducing the resistance to extension of wool and hair. At higher concentrations two effects tend to increase the resistance to extension of the swollen fiber. One is that the limit of radial swelling has been reached, and the second is that the partially hydrated lithium ions clustering on the polar polypeptide restore interchain forces through physical interference or by cross-links which are essentially chains of the partially hydrated ions.

With salts of heavy metals, in particular those of aluminum, iron, chromium, copper, and tin, wool is very reactive; the salts include the sulfates, chlorides, nitrates, and acetates. When wool is boiled in solutions with these salts they combine with the wool to form water-insoluble compounds. This is the reason why metal stains, such as iron and copper, are so common in wool processing.

With salts which are acid in reaction and are capable of being easily dissociated in the presence of acids, such as alum, potassium bichromate, and sodium bichromate, the wool fiber possesses considerable attraction when boiled in their solutions. The mordanting of wool with various metallic salts is based on this reaction as a previous preparation or an aftertreatment in dyeing of mordant colors such as with chrome dyes. The metallic salt chiefly employed for the developing of mordant colors is sodium bichromate. If wool is boiled in a 0.2 per cent solution of sodium bichromate, the wool takes a considerable portion of the chromium compound, which imparts a yellow color to the wool. The primary action is the absorption of chromic acid from the solution, to form a compound in which the wool substance acts as a base, combining with about 10 per cent of chromic acid. The compound formed is stable in water. In the presence of acids and certain organic compounds such as tartar, the action of the chrome compound is promoted and accelerated.

Action of Oxidizing Agents. Wool is quite sensitive to oxidizing agents. Strong solutions of hydrogen peroxide, potassium permanganate, and potassium bichromate damage wool more or less, depending on the temperature, the concentration, and the *p*H. According to Harris and Smith [56] the oxidizing agents attack the disulfide groups of the cystine, resulting in a lower strength, weight loss, increase in the solubility in alkaline solutions, and reduction of the wool sulfur content. Stoves [134] found that hydrolysis of the cystine linkage and subsequent oxidation give rise to sulfonic acids. The main use of oxidizing agents is in bleaching.

The most common oxidizing agent for bleaching wool is hydrogen peroxide, which gives the best permanent white. In strong solutions the wool is easily damaged by overbleaching or oxidation. Smith and Harris [114] found that the extent to which wool is oxidized depends on the concentration, temperature, and *p*H of the hydrogen peroxide solution and the duration of the treatment. The data obtained by them clearly indicated critical values for the concentration, temperature, and *p*H of the hydrogen peroxide solutions but not for the duration of the treatment. The critical concentration of hydrogen peroxide is 4-volume at 50° C. for a 3-hour treatment. Increasing the concentration above this point causes both the cystine and nitrogen content to decrease sharply. With a 2-volume hydrogen peroxide solution the critical temperature is 50° C. for a 3-hour treatment. When wool was treated with 2-volume hydrogen peroxide solutions differing in *p*H for 3 hr at 50° C., it was found that the *p*H had no appreciable effect below a *p*H of 7. Between *p*H 7 and 10 the damage steadily increased. Above *p*H 10 the alkali concentration is sufficiently high to dissolve portions of the oxidized wool. In the presence of small amounts of metal such as copper and iron the damage through overoxidation may be greatly increased.

Dilute solutions of potassium permanganate may also be employed for the bleaching of wool. When steeped in such solutions the wool acquires a dark brown color by reason of the precipitation of a hydrate of manganese in the fiber. Subsequent treatment with a solution of sodium bisulfate is necessary to remove the manganese compound, leaving the wool white. Barr and Edgar [25] made a special study on the degradation of wool by potassium permanganate.

Spontaneous combustion of wool is due primarily to processes of auto-oxidation. In the presence of air and light the water content exercises a catalytic action on the fat or oil of the wool, and the fatty acids which are produced promote oxidation, according to Lucchini [76].

Action of Reducing Agents. Reducing agents attack, as the oxidizing agents do, the keratin molecule on its weakest link, the disulfide groups, forming sulfhydryl groups. The splitting of the disulfide groups according to Speakman [119] is corrected with the removal of the internal stresses present in the wool fiber. The maximum *p*H values to produce these effects are at *p*H 4 and *p*H 10. A *p*H 4 concentrated solution of bisulfites and metabisulfites destroys the disulfide group because of the swelling effect characteristic of weak acids; and at *p*H values of 10 and higher the reducing agents act because the alkali hydrolizes the disulfide groups, forming sulfhydryl and sulfur acid groups. The sulfur acid groups are then reduced through the reducing agent to sulfhydryl groups. Some alkali salts with reducing anion (Na_2S, sodium thioglycolate) dissolve wool already in weak alkaline solution and at low temperatures, as found by Goddard and Michaelis [49].

Modified Wool. According to Speakman [128], when reduced wool is treated in solution with divalent metal ions (Ca, Ba, Zn, Cu, Ni) it is brought back into a more stable form by the formation of new cross-linkages between the sulfur atoms of the type S—X—S (X = divalent metal). Speakman's work [127] was the first step to confirm the prediction that, if wool's weak cross-links, the disulfide or cystine bonds, could be broken down and built up again in chemically stable form, the defects of wool would be eliminated or largely reduced and its desirable properties retained. The metal-treated-reduced wool has a higher stability toward steam and alkali.

Harris [48] and his collaborators went a step farther toward this goal with their chemically modified wool by breaking down the disulfide linkages with soluble organic sulfur compounds, known as mercaptans, and reconstituting the reduced wool with alkyl dihalides. The best results were obtained by using thioglycolic acid (0.2 *M*) at a *p*H 4.5 as reducing agent and subsequent alkylation of the reduced product with trimethylene dibromide. The reaction with the dihalides results in the formation of new cross links in which sulfur atoms of the cystine are connected by short hydrocarbon chains. The reaction appears to affect only the disulfide groups of the cystine in wool and may be represented by the following equations:

$$\underset{\text{Wool}}{W\text{—}S\text{—}S\text{—}W} + \underset{\text{Thioglycolic acid}}{2HS\text{—}CH\text{—}COOH} = \underset{\text{Reduced wool}}{2W\text{—}SH} + \underset{\text{Dithioglycolic acid}}{(S\text{—}CH_2\text{—}COOH)_2} \quad (1)$$

$$\underset{\text{Reduced wool}}{2W\text{—}SH} + \underset{\text{Trimethylene dibromide}}{(CH_2)_3Br_2} = \underset{\text{Modified wool}}{W\text{—}S\text{—}(CH_2)_3 - S\text{—}W} + \underset{\text{Hydrobromic acid}}{2HBr} \quad (2)$$

The analysis showed that the modified wool contained 6.5 per cent of cystine; the mode linkage of approximately half of the sulfur atoms had been altered, since untreated wool contained 12.4 per cent of cystine.

The change in the physical and chemical properties of modified wool yarn produced on a laboratory scale is given in Table 27.

TABLE 27. Properties of Modified Wool in Yarn Form

Type of Wool	*30 Per Cent Index*	*Breaking Strength of Yarns (grams)*	*Alkali Solubility (per cent)*	*Moisture Content (per cent)*
Untreated	0.99	1310	10.5	16.0
Reduced	0.65	1170	50.0	....
Modified	0.90	1460	5.3	16.0

In addition, tests have shown that modified wool seems to be not only more resistant to alkalies but also to attack by moths, enzymes, and bacteria. It is more resistant to shrinking in laundering, with a "feel" only slightly harsher than that of untreated wool. Its affinity toward acid and chrome dyes is increased. The above 2-step process involving reduction with thioglycolic acid and subsequent alkylation, although yielding wool of good stability, is laborious and expensive. Brown and

Harris [31] have developed a new single-step procedure involving the use of sulfoxylates as reducing agents in the presence of cross-linking agents.

Action of Halogens. Treatment of wool with chlorine, bromine, or iodine leads to absorption and chemical change. The size and type of the chemical change depends essentially on the presence of water. Depending on the conditions of the chlorine solution, the wool fiber undergoes rather remarkable transformations, leading to a considerable alteration in its physical and chemical properties. It may become harsh and yellow, acquire a high luster, lose its felting ability, and at the same time show an increased rate of dyeing. These three properties of chlorinated wool lead to the commercial application of halogenation for the purpose of lustering of oriental rugs, in the manufacting of non-felting yarn for socks, underwear, and sweaters, and in the printing of woolen fabrics to increase their dye affinity.

According to Vom Hove [142], in the reaction of dry Cl, Br, and I in the gaseous state or in nonaqueous inert solvents upon completely dry wool, only a slight chemical reaction takes place with the wool protein (substitution). Halogens with normal moisture content are adsorbed by dry wool, with haloamine formation. Furthermore, some substitution and a small amount of oxidation of wool protein take place. In aqueous solution a very rapid consumption of Cl and Br by the wool takes place, where the halogens go through the hypoacid and haloamine stage and effect a hydrolytic splitting of the wool protein by oxidation and haloamine decomposition, with formation of the corresponding halo-H acids. The resulting peptones, polypeptides, and reactive amino groups immediately enter into a chloramine or bromamine formation. From the haloamines, HCl and HBr are formed, which effect new hydrolytic splitting. At the same time active halogen penetrates to the interior of the fiber, where it forms halogen-H acid with water, which oxidizes the fiber. A substitution of the halogens in the tyrosine of the wool protein takes place also. The resulting halogen-H acids give cause to a Donnan membrane equilibrium and the blistering of the fiber surface known as Allwörd's reaction. The blisters or swellings arise on the surface of the fibers in sacs. Hock, Ramsay, and Harris [59] have shown that these sacs arise solely from the scales, and their formation is associated with the reaction of the chlorine with disulfide groups of the cystine in the scales. In cases where the cystine content is low on account of the degradation through sunlight or alkali the sacs do not form.

With iodine the oxidation at the fiber surface is considerably slower than with the other halogens, so that iodine penetrates almost exclusively by adsorption from the solution to the interior of the fiber, where it slowly forms HI. The amounts of halogen substituted in the tyrosine of the wool protein increase with rising initial concentration of the halogen solutions in the ratio of simple multiple proportions to a maximum value which is six times that of the smallest halogen content found. The increased dyeing capacity of halogenated wool is due to the destruction of the outer fiber layer, thus exposing the interior of the fiber to the dyes. The destruction of wool effected by the oxidizing action of the halogens increases with rising halogen concentration.

Nonfelting Wool. Processes for reducing the felting properties of wool have become very important because of the increased demand for woolen underwear and socks which will not shrink when washed. It is essential to remember that there are two types of shrinkages in woolen fabrics, namely, the relaxation shrinkage which occurs in steaming, pressing, and sponging, and the shrinkage due to felting in washing. The relaxation shrinkage arises from the relaxation of the fibers which were stretched when they were processed into yarns and fabrics. Yarns and fabrics are held taut during spinning and weaving, and fabrics are stretched in both length and width during the final stages of finishing. This stretch has to be removed by shrinking the fabric before making it up into garments. In the process known as London shrinking, stretched, wet wool fabrics are allowed to relax and are dried after all the stretched fibers have had an opportunity to return to their normal lengths.

Fabrics made from nonfelting wool tend to show the same amount of relaxation shrinkage as similar fabrics made from normal wool. On the other hand, whereas normal garment fabrics will rapidly contract in size in washing with warm soap solutions, garments made of nonfelting wool will retain more or less their original size.

As described under Felting, Chapter XI, elasticity and the frictional effect of scale surface are responsible for the felting shrinkage of the wool fiber. Therefore, either the elasticity of the wool fiber or the directional frictional effect of its surface must be destroyed to prevent its felting. Since the elasticity of the fiber is the most valuable property, all methods of reducing the felting properties of wool aim at destroying or altering the frictional properties of the fiber surface. It is known that any chemical reagent which attacks and rounds off the free edges of the epidermis scales diminishes the felting properties of woolen fabrics. With the newest methods the scale structure is preserved but, according to Speakman and Goodings [123], the layer under the scales is converted into a degraded protein capable of swelling under the action of acids and alkalies. Because the scales rest on this insecure foundation they no longer exert a directional effect on the frictional properties.

Of all the chemical reagents which attack the scales of wool, chlorine is the most powerful and, therefore, it was first used to produce an unshrinkable finish on hosiery, undergarments, shirts, pants, and vests which are frequently washed. The process most widely adopted was wet chlorination, which consists in treating the fabric or fashioned garments with acidified solutions of either sodium hypochlorite or bleaching powder. This process is difficult to control because chlorine has a great affinity for wet wool and skill is needed to see that every part of a large batch of fabric or garments absorbs the same amount of chlorine. Trotman [138] found that when using bleaching powder and hydrochloric acid it is rarely safe to use a solution containing more than 0.6 gram of available chlorine per liter. But if hypochlorous acid is employed much greater concentration, up to 2 grams per liter, is comparatively safe.

Meunier and Latreille [87] in France (1923) were possibly the first to see that the fundamental obstacle to the easy control of the wet chlorination process was caused by the water. Wool fibers absorb and hold water, which provides a vehicle through which acids and salts can penetrate into the interior of the fibers. This explains why the action of chlorine water on the wool fiber can be so profound. The chlorine is not restricted to the surface of the fibers, but it penetrates through the water to the interior of the fibers. Furthermore, the attack of the wet chlorine on the wool is so vigorous that the fibers on the outside of the yarns of the fabric may absorb all the chlorine and prevent its reaching the fibers in the interior of the yarns. Meunier and Latreille attempted to overcome these difficulties by exposing the air-dry wool to chlorine gas. Their process does not appear to have made much headway commercially, probably because even air-dry wool contains so much water that it reacts with chlorine gas too rapidly to enable the process to be controlled. The next step forward was made by King and Galley [68] at the Wool Industries Research Association in 1933. Before subjecting the wool to the action of chlorine gas, they reduced its regain to 10 per cent. At the same time, in order to assist the penetration of the gas throughout the wool, they put the wool in a closed vessel from which they pumped most of the air before admitting the chlorine gas. A great deal of work has since been necessary to get the process under strict control, but for possibly the first time wool had been made nonfelting solely by causing a slight disorganization of the surface of all the fibers. The success of this method undoubtedly stimulated the search for other methods, which are summarized in Table 28.

TABLE 28. Chronological List of Patents on Nonfelting Wool

Inventors	*Chemicals Used*	*Year Issued*	*Patent Number*
Trotman	Hypochlorous acid	1925	U. S. 1,522,555
Jackson, E. L.	Tertiary-butyl hypochlorite and methyl alcohol in an inert solvent	1929	U. S. 2,132,342
Reichart, J. S., and Peakes, R. W.	Tertiary-butyl hypochlorite in an inert solvent	1930	U. S. 2,132,345
Smith and Ruby	Sodium hypochlorite and alkali	1930	U. S. 1,781,415
Feibelmann, R.	*p*-Toluene sulfondichloramide and HCl	1932	U. S. 1,892,548
King and Galley (Wool, T. R. Assoc.)	Dry chlorine or bromine gas at low pressures	1933	E. 417,719
Irvinebank Dyeworks	"N.S." process—wet contact process	1935	. .
Hall, A. T.	Sulfuryl chloride in an inert solvent	1935	U. S. 2,107,703
Phillips and Middlebrook	Papain in a sodium bisulfite solution	1938	E. 513,919
Wiegand	Sodium hypochlorite + H_2SO_4 + amines	1938	U. S. 2,144,824
Solvay Process Co.	Nitrosyl chloride	1939	U. S. 2,213,399
Freney and Lipson	Caustic soda and potash in methylated spirits	1939	
Hall, Wood and Tootal Broadhurst Lee Co., Ltd.	Inorganic and organic bases in mixtures of alcohols and inert solvents	1939	E. 538,396 E. 538,428
Parker, Farrington, Stubbs, Speakman, and Bleachers' Assoc., Ltd.	Inorganic sulfides in mixtures of alcohols	1940	E. 539,057
Clayton and Edwards	"Negafel"—chlorine in aqueous solutions containing formic acid	1940	E. 537,671
American Cyanamid Co.	Alkylated methylol-melamine	1943	U. S. 2,329,622
Higgins, Middlebrook, Phillips	Dry chlorination followed by a papain treatment	1943	B. P. 546,915

Frishman, Hornstein, Smith, and Harris [46] found that the *p*H of solutions containing active chlorine used in nonfelting wool is of great importance in determining the type and extent of modification the wool undergoes. The oxidation solutions decrease with increasing *p*H, and the extent of modification of the fiber is found to be an inverse function of *p*H. Their data indicate that the treatment of wool with solutions of active chlorine can be most advantageously performed in the region of *p*H 8 to 9.

Chlorine water, chlorine gas, the organic hypochlorites, sulfuryl chloride, and nitrosyl chloride all act by causing oxidation of the disulfide sulfur, thereby disorganizing the surface layers of the wool. Probably the bisulfite used in the enzyme method also reacts on this disulfide sulfur, but in addition the enzyme brings about the breakdown of the polypeptide chains. Instead of producing disorganization by oxidation, the methods involving the use of alkalies produce disorganization by hydrolysis and disruption of the disulfide linkage and also possibly of the polypeptide chains.

The application of synthetic resins is a new trend. The modification that the fibers undergo by the incorporation of the water-soluble methylol-melamine-type resin appears to be of a purely physical nature. With the fibers thoroughly penetrated the formation of the resin in the process of polymerization will take place within the cortical cells as well as on the surface of the epidermis cells. The outside film probably reduces the frictional forces of the scales, whereas the resin within the fiber affects its elastic properties.

From the number of patents granted it is obvious that a great deal of experimental work has been done and that the methods now available to produce nonshrinkable wool are bewildering in their variety. (See Table 28.) Some of these processes are, of course, in a more advanced state of development than others. In England, according to Phillips [101], the dry chlorination process, the "N.S." process, the sulfuryl chloride process, and the Negafel process have already set a new standard of unshrinkability, and, with improved wet processes, have led to big economies in the wool required by the British armed forces. In the United States the development was retarded by unfortunate experiences with some processes and the negative reaction of the general public.

This has considerably changed, mainly due to the research done under the auspices of the United States Army Quartermaster Research Division. Early in 1944 the Army began to include in its specifications a nonfelting treatment for cushion sole socks, and developed a simplified modification of a wet chlorination process. By the end of 1944, the Army was purchasing 7 million pairs of fully washable cushion sole socks per month, whereas in 1943 it had been buying none. Shrinkage of untreated socks amounted to 22 per cent after only 12 days' average wear. After treatment, shrinkage was reduced to only 5 per cent after 46 days' average wear. The effected savings were estimated at $1.5 million per month on shrink-resistant socks alone.

By the end of the war in 1945, the Quartermaster Corps extended its research in this field to include the application of wet chlorination and several other processes including resin treatments to flannel shirting, blankets, and woolen underwear with the aim of supplying troops in the future with washable woolen equipment. This resulted in the issuing of two specifications in 1950 for shrink-resistant wool fabrics, viz., for a 10½-oz flannel shirting, specification number MIL-C-2184, and a 16-oz wool shirting, MIL-C-10752.

Since that time millions of yards have already been treated. Both of these fabrics are treated with the shrink-resistant process applied in the piece. Some manufacturers do it by wet chlorination, and others prefer the application of resin.

In the men's hose trade the largest percentage of wool socks are sold as shrink resistant, respectively washable. Most of the wool in these socks is subjected to one of several wet chlorination processes. Most of the research work done is summarized in publications by the Office of the Quartermaster General: *Textile Series Rept.* 46, Aug. 1947; *Textile Series Rept.* 53, Sept. 1948 (Louis I. Weiner); and *Textile Series Rept.* 55, May 1949 [99].

Action of Formaldehyde. Formaldehyde may be used for two purposes: (1) as a protective agent against the chemical action of alkalies and (2) for sterilization. Kann [63] found that if sheep wool or any animal hair is treated with a solution of formaldehyde for some time, cold or hot, or by the vapors of formaldehyde and then dried without rinsing, the fiber has become much less liable to attacks by hot solutions of alkalies such as soda and caustic soda. This protective action is also effective against the damaging influence of steam and of boiling water of neutral reaction. Barr and Edgar [24] reported a protective action even against acid. In their experiments they immersed the wool 1 hr in 50 volumes of 1 per cent formaldehyde at 70° C. and dried the samples in air without rinsing. No difference was found in the analysis of treated (formaldehyde-wool) and untreated wool. In its behavior against a 10-hr treatment in diluted alkali at 40° C., the formaldehyde-wool had a measurable wet strength at 0.2 N caustic soda, a concentration four times that beyond which the untreated fabric failed. When wool is treated with a 4 per cent solution of formaldehyde in addition to the resistance toward alkalies, it shows a decreased dye affinity and also a loss of its felting properties.

ence on the fiber, prevented or notably retarded the development of mildew. The only definite indication which can be given regarding the effect of the molecular weight of the dye is that certain electronegative groups (particularly halogens, NO_2 and CO_2H) seem to exert a retarding action on the development of molds; this action occurs with all classes of dyes, but it becomes apparent only when there is an accumulation of such groups in the molecule. The preponderant factor in the development of mildew is the presence or absence on the wool of degradation products of the fiber proteins. All treatments which remove these products remove the possibility of development of molds; such treatments are equally effective whether carried out before, during, or after dyeing. The most important and simplest of these treatments is chroming; the efficiency of the chrome dyes is due not to their constitution but to the fact that treatment with chromium removes the protein degradation products which are always present on the wool. This confirms the findings of Burgess [33].

Protection is obtained also by aftertreatment with copper sulfate, chromium fluoride, or formaldehyde of certain direct dyes; but in these cases the action is due to the bactericidal power of the chemicals rather than to removal of the degradation products of the proteins, so that the protective action is much weaker than with chroming. Where the bacteria damage occurs before dyeing the damage will appear as light spots after dyeing. In indigo-dyed goods reduction of the dye takes place, resulting in its destruction.

Insect Moths and Carpet Beetle Damage

Woolen and worsted fabrics are readily eaten by larvae of clothes moths and carpet beetles. There are two distinct types of moths which cause the annual loss of some $100,000,000 to consumers alone for damages and expenditures for their control. The two differ mostly in the type of cocoon in which they pass their dormant stage and have been named accordingly, i.e., webbing moth (*Tineola bisselliella*) and case-bearing moth (*Tinea pellionella*).

The carpet beetle larvae, sometimes called "buffalo moths," are known as "dermestid pests," because they belong to the Dermestidae family. There are four of these, the common carpet beetle (*Anthrenus scrophulariae*), the furniture carpet beetle (*A. vorax*), the varied carpet beetle (*A. verbasci*), and the black carpet beetle (*Attagenus piceus*).

The mothproofing of woolen and worsteds has gained in importance because of the discovery of effective chemical compounds and simpler application. Fabrics treated with "mothicides" and "dermesticides" are rendered resistant to the attacks of both the moth and the beetle. It is frequently asserted that a fabric treated with a "mothicide" may not be protected against dermestids. But Back [19] found that fabrics resistant to carpet beetles were also protected against clothes moth larvae.

Innumerable substances have been suggested from time to time for preventing damage to wool by moth larvae. However, since most of these are of only temporary effectiveness, if not totally ineffective, very few have found use in industry. The ideal mothproofing agent should provide permanent protection, that is, its effectiveness should not be altered by frequent washings or dry cleanings, nor should it deteriorate with time or exposure to light or varying climatic conditions.

Mothproofing agents may be applied to wool in three general ways:

1. By adding substances to the wool which (*a*) makes it unpalatable to the larvae, or (*b*) are poisonous to the larvae;

2. By storing the wool in a closed container with a volatile substance whose vapor makes the atmosphere inimical to moth life;

3. By spraying the wool and its storage place periodically with a liquid insecticide.

Methods 2 and 3, although useful in many cases, must be regarded as temporary measures. The first method provides either temporary or permanent protection for the useful life of the article, depending upon the substance which is added to the wool.

For permanent mothproofing, woolen manufacturers have found the following types of commercial compounds applicable: Eulan CN (pentachloro-dihydroxy-triphenyl methane sulfonic acid); Mitin FF (a halogen-substituted acylamino sulfonic acid, U. S. Patent 2,311,-062). Both of these products are in a sense colorless organic dyes under quantitative exhaustion from a hot bath. The treatment is best performed with the dye process.

Organic fluorides such as Amuno were found to give measurable protection which is retained after repeated dry cleanings and washings.

Various inorganic fluorides such as sodium fluoride and sodium acid fluorides are quite effective, but their weakness is that their efficiency is destroyed with washing.

The volatile substances most used are paradichlorobenzene and naphthalene. They are considered very ineffective for the simple reason that moths and beetles have become quite immune to these products.

For households, the various insecticidal sprays have found great use. These materials consist essentially of powerful insecticides, e.g., pyrethrum, dissolved in a volatile solvent such as "white spirit." They are only temporary, and the sprays have to be applied at frequent intervals.

The use of DDT sprays has become quite widespread. The National Institute of Cleaning and Dyeing reported recently the successful application of Erustomoth, a mixture of DDT and an absorbent powder for the mothproofing of wool garments. The treatment of the garments is combined with the extracting process after dry cleaning.

Reprocessed and Reworked Wool

The world's wool supply is insufficient to meet all industrial requirements. The demand for cheap grades of wearing apparel leads the manufacturers of such goods to use various waste products, recovered fibers (reprocessed and reworked wool), and vegetable and various rayon fibers. The importance of the various additional raw materials used in the woolen and worsted industry of the United States is apparent from Table 30.

TABLE 30. VARIOUS FIBERS CONSUMED BY WOOL INDUSTRY *

(millions of pounds)

	1939	*1948*	*1949*	*1950*
Shorn and pulled wool	297	401	308	363
Other wool of sheep	63	106	109	126
Mohair	19	10	15	19
Other specialty hair	7	6	7	9
Recovered fibers †				
Reprocessed	98	61	66	70
Reused		17	14	16
Rayon	11	23	25	36
Cotton	9	26	19	22
All others	13	11	19	17
Total	517	661	582	678

* Includes material consumed in the worsted and woolen system.
† Mainly wool.
Source: U. S. Bureau of the Census.

Most reprocessed fibers are produced by the woolen mills themselves, whereas a large percentage of the reused wools are bought by shoddy manufacturers who may operate independent enterprises. In turn, the recovered fibers are then sold to woolen mills. Table 30 shows that in 1939 the American mills consumed 98 million lb of these fibers, which is approximately one-fifth of the total wool consumption. This figure has dropped to about one-seventh of the total wool fibers consumed. Recovered fibers are almost entirely employed in the lower grades of woolen goods, and practically none enters worsted goods. The sources of recovered fibers are clippings, new and old woolen and worsted rags, and other wastes made in the manufacture of garments. During and after the war the use of cotton and rayon fibers has steadily increased. In "all others" are included the newest synthetic fibers, mainly nylon.

Labeling. Since July 15, 1941, the Wool Products Labeling Act of 1939, which was approved on October 14, 1940, by Congress, has been effective. On May 25, 1941, the Federal Trade Commission issued 35 rules and regulations to guide the textile and apparel trades in properly labeling their products under this Wool Products Labeling Act. In this act, the manufacturers as well as the retailers are required to label their product not only as far as wool and other fibers are concerned but also to state the amount of reprocessed and reused wool present. The definitions as laid down in the act for wool, reprocessed and reused wool, are as follows:

The term "wool" means the fiber from the fleece of the sheep or lamb or hair of the Angora or Cashmere goat (and may include the so-called specialty fibers from the hair of the camel, alpaca, llama, and vicuña) which has never been reclaimed from any woven or felted wool product.

The term "reprocessed wool" means the fiber resulting when wool has been woven or felted into a wool product which, without ever having been utilized in any way by the ultimate consumer, subsequently has been made into a fibrous state.

The term "reused wool" means the resulting fiber when wool or reprocessed wool has been spun, woven, knitted or felted into a wool product which, after having been used in any way by the ultimate consumer, subsequently has been made into a fibrous state.

In addition to the above three classifications of wool (mentioned in the rules) the Federal Trade Commission recognizes a further classification known as virgin or new wool, which is defined as "wool which has never been used or reclaimed or reworked or reprocessed or reused from any spun, woven, knitted, felted, or manufactured or used product."

Through the reconverting process of bringing a finished fabric back into a fibrous state involving rigorous mechanical treatment such as garnetting and picking, the wool fibers are severely damaged. The protective scales are torn away and the fibrous cortical layer is splintered and broken. The five fibers in Fig. 7 show the various degrees of

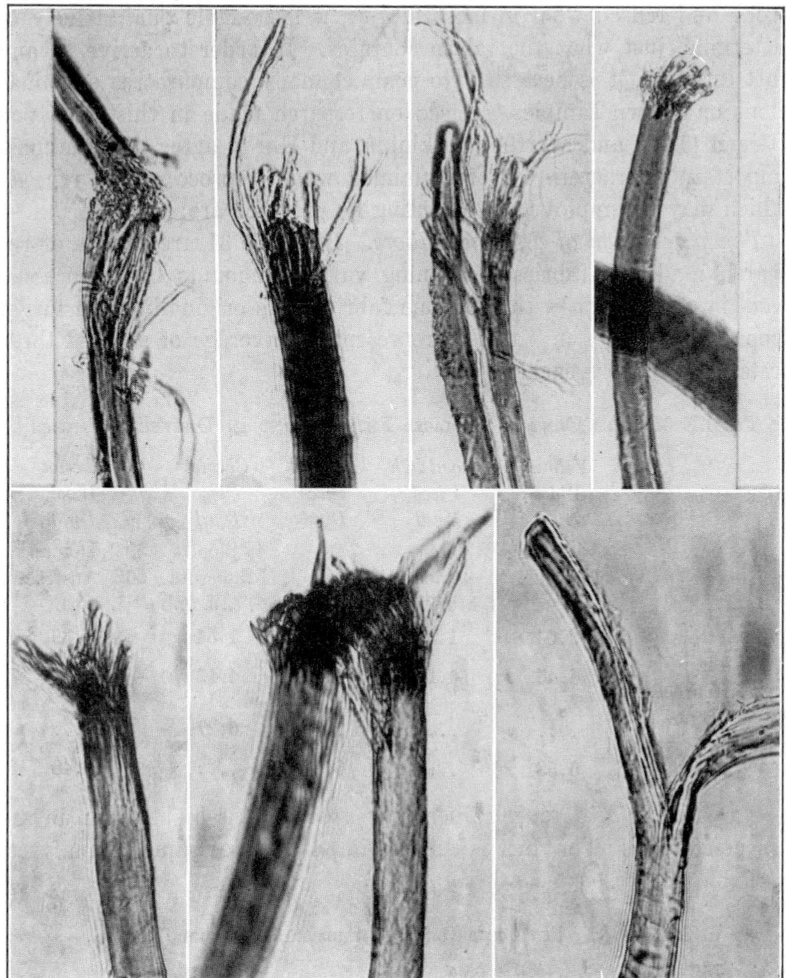

FIG. 7. Damaged wool fibers found in reprocessed and reused wool. (*Courtesy American Wool Handbook.*)

such damage. If, in addition to this treatment, a fabric has received considerable wear before reduction to the fibrous state, the percentage of damaged fibers is still higher.

The examination of fabrics made from reprccessed wool, reused wool, or mixtures of both with wool is one of the most difficult problems for the textile microscopist. It requires a high degree of accuracy coupled with long experience.

Despite certain difficulties in recognizing virgin wool, reprocessed wool, and reused wool in most fabrics, it is possible qualitatively to determine just what the fabric contains. In order to arrive at any just estimate, it is necessary to conduct many comparative examinations on known samples. Based on research made in this field, von Bergen [145], and Matthews, Skinkle, and Hardy agree that the most important characteristics of reclaimed wool (reprocessed or reused) which may be employed in detecting its presence are:

The percentage of damaged fibers. In Table 31 are results of research made on fabrics containing various amounts of reprocessed wool in comparison with the same fabric made originally from virgin wool. The figures in Table 31 represent the average of at least three tests of 600 fibers each.

TABLE 31. Per Cent of Damaged Fibers Found in Different Fabrics

	Velour Wool Dyed	*Broadcloth Piece Dyed*	*Flannel Piece Dyed*	*Cheviot Piece Dyed*	*Cheviot Wool Dyed*
	½ Blood Missouri	64's Penn Delaine 6 Mo. Texas	70's Ohio Delaine	⅜ Blood Minnesota S. A. Lamb	50% Domestic 50% Australian Lambs
100% Virgin	2.04	1.27	1.79	1.54	1.39
50% Virgin 50% Reprocessed	4.45	4.15	4.91	4.12	....
30% Virgin 70% Reprocessed	....	....	....	6.27	....
100% Reprocessed	6.58	....	6.90	....	6.46

The number of damaged fibers in reused wool is higher than in reprocessed wool. This fact is substantiated by three samples analyzed in Table 32.

TABLE 32. Per Cent Damaged Fibers in Various Blends

75% Wool 25% Reused Wool	65% Wool 35% Reused Wool	65% Wool 35% Reused Wool
4.1	6.1	5.83

According to these figures, 35 per cent reused wool has approximately the same amount of damaged fibers as blends containing 100 per cent reprocessed wool.

The presence of fibers other than wool. Today much reclaimed wool is recovered from fabrics containing various amounts of cotton, rayon, and silk. The presence of various percentages of cotton or, especially, of rayon fibers of different sizes, in their dull and lustrous forms, indicates reworked wool. In establishing the proper percentage of these different fibers present, the microscopical count of a fine cross-section is preferable, but the chemical analysis should be used in addition. (See Fig 8.)

Fibers of many colors. Variety in color of the fibers is also characteristic of reclaimed wool, as most reclaimed fibers are made up of

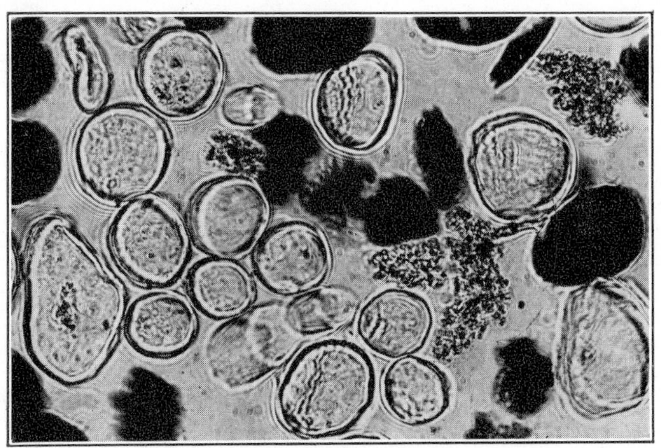

FIG. 8. Cross-section of a shoddy yarn containing wool, rayon, and cotton. (×500.) (*Courtesy American Wool Handbook.*)

various colored wools. Though many of these fibers are redyed, covering up their original shade, the original color of the individual fibers is revealed through the medium of fine cross-sections.

BIBLIOGRAPHY

1. ALEXANDER, P., *J. Soc. Dyers Colourists,* **66,** 349–357 (1950).
2. ALEXANDER, P., *Ann. N. Y. Acad. Sci.,* **53,** 653–673 (1951); *Research,* **2,** 246–247 (1949); *Melliand Textilber.,* **31,** 550–555 (1950).
3. ALEXANDER, P., BAILEY, J. L., and CARTER, D., *Textile Research J.,* **20,** 385–399 (1950).
4. ALEXANDER, P., and CHARMAN, D. A., *Textile Research J.,* **20,** 761–770 (1950).
5. ALEXANDER, P., CARTER, D., and EARLAND, C., *J. Soc. Dyers Colourists,* **66,** 579–583 (1950).
6. ALEXANDER, P., CARTER, D., EARLAND, C., and FORD, O. E., *Biochem. J.,* **48,** 629–637 (1950).
7. ALEXANDER, P., and EARLAND, C., *Textile Research J.,* **20,** 298–300 (1950).
8. AMBROSE, E. J., and ELLIOTT, A., *Proc. Roy. Soc.* (*London*) *A,* **208,** 75–90 (1951).

9. ALEXANDER, P., HUDSON, R. F., and FOX, M., *Biochem. J.*, **46**, 27–32 (1950).
10. ALEXANDER, P., and KITCHENER, J. A., *Textile Research J.*, **20**, 203–214 (1950).
11. ARMAND, L., *Tiba*, **12**, 675–679, 751–755, 831–835, 917–923 (1934); **13**, 23–27 (1935).
12. ASTBURY, W. T., *Nature*, **164**, 439–440 (1949).
13. ASTBURY, W. T., *Trans. Faraday Soc.*, **36**, 871–880 (Sept. 1940).
14. ASTBURY, W. T., and BELL, F. O., *Nature*, **147**, 696 (1941).
15. ASTBURY, W. T., and DAWSON, J. A. T., *J. Soc. Dyers Colourists*, **54**, 6 (1938).
16. ASTBURY, W. T., *J. Soc. Dyers Colourists*, Jubilee Issue, 24 (1934); *J. Textile Inst.*, **27**, P282–297 (1936).
17. ASTBURY, W. T., and STREET, A., *Trans. Roy. Soc. (London) A.*, **230**, 75–101 (1931).
18. ASTBURY, W. T., and WOODS, H. J., *J. Textile Inst.*, **23**, T17–34 (1932).
19. BACK, E. A., U. S. Dept. Agr. *Leaflet* 150 (1938); *Leaflet* 145 (1940); *Textile World* (Feb. 1938).
20. BAMFORD, C. H., HANBY, W. E., and HAPPEY, F., *Proc. Roy. Soc. (London) A*, **205**, 30 (1951); *Nature*, **164**, 138–139, 751–752 (1949); **166**, 829–830 (1950).
21. BANCROFT, W. D., *J. Phys. Chem.*, **26**, 736–772 (1922).
22. BARMORE, G. M., Rensselaer Polytech. Inst. *Bull.* 35 (Feb. 1932).
23. BARR, M., and EDGAR R., *Proc. Iowa Acad. Sci.*, **41**, 170 (1934).
24. BARR, M., and EDGAR R., *Textile Research*, **7**, 175 (Feb. 1937).
25. BARR, M., and EDGAR R., *Textile Research*, **11**, 429–437 (Aug. 1941).
26. BARRITT, J., and KING, A. T., *J. Textile Inst.*, **17**, T386 (1926); **20**, T151 (1929).
27. BARRITT, J., and PICKARD, J. N., *Biochem. J.*, **24**, 1061–1065 (1930).
28. BEADLES, J. R., BRAMAN, W. W., and MITCHELL, H. H., *J. Biol. Chem.*, **88**, 623–627 (1930).
29. BLACKBURN, S., *Chem. and Ind.*, 614–615 (1950); *Nature*, **165**, 316–317 (1950); *Biochem. J.*, **47**, 443–451 (1950).
30. BOWMAN, F. H., *Structure of Wool Fiber*, Macmillan, London (1885, rewritten 1908).
31. BROWN, A. E., and HARRIS, M., *Ind. and Eng. Chem.*, **40**, 316 (Feb. 1948).
32. BROWN, A. E., HORNSTEIN, L. R., and HARRIS, M., *Textile Research J.*, **21**, 222 (April 1951).
33. BURGESS, R., *J. Soc. Dyers Colourists*, **47**, 96–99 (1931); *J. Textile Inst.*, **21**, T441–452 (1930); **19**, T315–322 (1928); **20**, T333–372 (1929); **25**, T391–400 (1934).
34. CARTER, E. G. H., MIDDLEBROOK, W. K., and PHILLIPS, H., *J. Soc. Dyers Colourists*, **62**, 203 (1946).
35. CONSDEN, R., *J. Textile Inst.*, **40**, 814 (1949).
36. CONSDEN, R., GORDON, A. H., and MARTIN, A. J. P., *Biochem. J.*, **44**, 548–550 (1949).
37. CONSDEN, R., and GORDON, A. H., *Biochem. J.*, **46**, 8–20 (1950).
38. CUNLIFFE, P. W., *J. Textile Inst.*, **27**, T25–36 (1936).
39. ELLIOTT, M., Thesis, Iowa State College (1928).
40. ELLIS, W. J., GILLESPIE, J. M., and LINDLEY, H., *Nature*, **165**, 545–548 (1950).
41. ELÖD, E., *Trans. Faraday Soc.*, **29**, 327 (1933); *Z. physik Chem.*, **137A**, 142 (1928).
42. ELÖD, E., and ZAHN, H., *Melliand Textilber.*, **28**, 291–294 (1947).
43. ELÖD, E., and ZAHN, H., *Melliand Textilber.*, **30**, 17 (1949).

44. Farnworth, A. J., Neish, W. J. P., and Speakman, J. B., *J. Soc. Dyers Colourists,* **65,** 447–453 (1949).
45. Fort, M., *J. Soc. Dyers Colourists,* **32,** 184–187 (1916).
46. Frishman, D., Hornstein, L., Smith, A. L., and Harris, M., *Ind. and Eng. Chem.,* **40,** 2280 (December 1948).
47. Geiger, W. B., *Textile Research,* **14,** 82–85 (March 1944).
48. Geiger, W. B., Patterson, W. I., Mizell, L. R., and Harris, M., *J. Research, Natl. Bur. Standards,* **27,** 459–468, RP1433 (Nov. 1941).
49. Goddard, D. R., and Michaelis, L., *J. Biol. Chem.,* **106,** 605–614 (Sept. 1934); **112,** 351 (1935).
50. Hambraeus, E., and Steele, R., "Communication No. T 08 of the International Congress of Sciences Applied to the Textile Industry, Ghent, 1951."
51. Happey, F., and Wormell, R. L., *J. Textile Inst.,* **40,** T855–869 (1949).
52. Harris, M., and Crowder, J. A., *J. Research, Natl. Bur. Standards,* **16,** 475–480, RP885 (May 1936).
53. Harris, M., *J. Research, Natl. Bur. Standards,* **15,** 63–71, RP810 (1935).
54. Harris, M., *J. Research, Natl. Bur. Standards,* **8,** 779–786, RP451 (June 1932).
55. Harris, M., Mizell, L. R., and Fourt, L., *J. Research, Natl. Bur. Standards,* **29,** 73–86, RP1486 (July 1942).
56. Harris, M., and Smith, A. L., *J. Research, Natl. Bur. Standards,* **18,** 623–628, RP998 (May 1937).
57. Hill, J. A., Univ. of Wyoming Agr. Expt. Sta. *Bull.* 132 (June 1922).
58. Hock, C. W., and McMurdie, H. F., *J. Research, Natl. Bur. Standards,* **31,** 229, RP1561 (1943).
59. Hock, C. W., Ramsay, R. C., and Harris, M., *J. Research, Natl. Bur. Standards,* **27,** 181, RP1412 (1941).
60. Horn, M. J., Jones, D. B., and Ringel, S. J., *J. Biol. Chem.,* **139,** 138–141 (1941).
61. Humfield, H., Elmquist, R., and Kettering, J. H., U. S. Dept. Agr. *Tech. Bull.* 588 (Sept. 1936).
62. Jones, H. W., and Lundgren, H. P., *Textile Research J.,* **21,** 620–634 (1951).
63. Kann, A., U. S. Patent 787,923 (April 25, 1905).
64. Katz, S. M., and Tobolsky, A. V., *Textile Research J.,* **20,** 87–94 (1950).
65. Kertess, A., Färberztg., **30,** 137–141 (1919).
66. King, G., *J. Soc. Dyers Colourists,* **66,** 27–34 (1950).
67. King, A. T., *J. Textile Inst.,* **25,** 33–42 (1934).
68. King, A. T., and Galley, R. A. E., *Wool Ind. Research Assoc.* English Patent 417,719 (1933).
69. Lagermalm, G. (private communication from H. P. Lundgren).
70. Lagermalm, G., and Philip, B., *Textile Research J.,* **20,** 668–670 (1950).
71. Lifschuetz, J., *Hoppe-Seyler's Z. physiol. Chemie,* **141,** 146 (1924).
72. Lindberg, J., *Textile Research J.,* **20,** 381–384 (1950).
73. Lindberg, J., Mercer, E. H., Philip, B., and Gralen, N., *Textile Research J.,* **19,** 673 (1949).
74. Lipson, M., and Speakman, J. B., *J. Soc. Dyers Colourists,* **65,** 390–401 (1949).
75. Lower, E. S., *Chemical Composition of Various Wax Alcohols,* Croda Ltd. (June 1946).
76. Lucchini, V., *Boll. chim.-farm.,* **54,** 673–680; *Chem. Zentr.,* **87,** I, 1102 (1916).
77. Lundgren, H. P. (private communication—present status of investigations on the chemical composition and structure of wool, Nov. 1951).

78. Lundgren, H. P., Abstracts of papers, 119th meeting of Am. Chem. Soc., 15-P (April 1951).
79. McLaren, A. D., and Rowen, J. W., *J. Polym. Sci.,* **7,** 289–324 (1951).
80. McMahon, P. R. and Speakman, J. B., *Trans. Faraday Soc.,* **33,** 844–849 (July 1937).
81. Marston, H. R., *Sci. Ind. Res. Council (Australia) Bull.* 38, Melbourne, Green (Govt. Printer), 36 pp. (1928).
82. Marston, H. R., and Robertson, T. B., *Sci. Ind. Research Council (Australia) Bull.* 39, 5–51 (1928).
83. Mellon, E., Korn, A. H., and Hoover, S. R., *J. Am. Chem. Soc.,* **71,** 2761–2764 (1949).
84. Mercer, E. H., *Biochem. Biophys. Acta,* **3,** 161–169 (1949); *J. Textile Inst.,* **40,** T640–649 (1949).
85. Mercer, E. H., *Nature,* **163,** 18–19 (1948).
86. Mercer, E. H., and Olafsson, B., *J. Polym. Sci.,* **6,** 261–269 (1951).
87. Meunier, L., and Latreille, H., *Chemie et Industrie,* **10,** 636–642 (1923).
88. Meyer, K. H., *Melliand Textilber.,* **7,** 605–693 (1926).
89. Middlebrook, W. R., and Phillips, H., *Biochem. J.,* **41,** 218–223 (1947).
90. Middlebrook, W. R., *Nature,* **164,** 501–502 (1949).
91. Millson, H. E., *Am. Dyestuff Reptr.,* **32,** 502–512 (1943).
92. Millson, H. E., and Turl, L. H., "Studies on Wool Dyeing," *Am. Dyestuff Reptr.,* P647 (Oct. 2, 1950).
93. Millson, H. E., Royer, G. L., Wisseman, M. E., and Stearn, E. I., *Am. Dyestuff Reptr.,* **28,** 632 (1939); **29,** 697 (1940); **32,** 285 (1943).
94. Mizell, L. R., and Harris, M., *J. Research, Natl. Bur. Standards,* **30,** 47–53, RP1516 (Jan. 1943).
95. Mizushima, S., Simanouti, T., Tsuboi, M., and Kate, E., *Nature,* **164,** 918–919 (1949).
96. Neurath, H., *J. Phys. Chem.,* **44,** 296 (1940).
97. Nicolet, B. H., and Shinn, L. A., *J. Biol. Chem.,* **139,** 687 (1941).
98. Olafsson, B., *J. Soc. Dyers Colourists,* **67,** 57–66 (1951).
99. Office of the Quartermaster General; *Textile Series Rept.* 46 (Aug. 1947); 53 (Sept. 1948) (Louis I. Weiner); 55 (May 1949).
100. Pauling, L., and Corey, R. B., *Proc. Nat. Acad. Sci.,* **37,** 205–211, 235–240, 251–256, 272–281, 282–285 (1951).
101. Phillips, H., *J. Soc. Dyers Colourists,* **58,** 245–253 (Dec. 1942).
102. Phillips, H., "Fibrous Proteins," proceedings of a symposium held at Leeds, Soc. Dyers Colourists, **39** (1946).
103. Pickard, J. N., and Barritt, J., *Biochem. J.,* **24,** 1061–1065 (1930).
104. Porai-Koschitz, A. E., *Trans. Leningrad Chem. Tech. Inst.* (U.S.S.R.), **1,** 157–171 (1934).
105. Prindle, B., *Textile Research,* **5** (12) (Oct. 1935); and **6** (1) (Nov. 1935).
106. Raynes, J. L., *J. Textile Inst.,* **18,** T46–47 (1927).
107. Reese, C. E., and Eyring, H., *Textile Research J.,* **20,** 743–753 (1950).
108. Rowe, F. M., Race, E., Speakman, J. B., and Vickerstaff, T., *J. Soc. Dyers Colourists,* **54,** 141–171, 421–422 (April 1938).
109. Rudall, K. M., *Proc. Leeds Phil. Lit. Soc.,* Sci. Sect. IV, Pt. 1, **13** (July 1941).
110. Scheurer, C., *Bull. Soc. Ind. Mulhouse,* **87,** 129–135 (1921).
111. Siefert, Z., *Angew. Chem.,* **69,** 86 (1899).

112. SMITH, A. L., and HARRIS, M., *J. Research, Natl. Bur. Standards,* **19,** 81–87, RP1012 (1937).
113. SMITH, A. L., and HARRIS, M., *J. Research, Natl. Bur. Standards,* **17,** 97–100, RP904 (1936).
114. SMITH, A. L., and HARRIS, M., *J. Research, Natl. Bur. Standards,* **16,** 301–307, RP875 (April 1936).
115. SOMMER, H., *Z. ges. Textil-Ind.,* **30,** 465–468, 482–483 (1919); *Chem. Zentr.,* II, 1417 (1927).
116. SPEAKMAN, J. B., *J. Textile Sci.,* **3,** 91 (1930).
117. SPEAKMAN, J. B., *J. Soc. Chem. Ind.,* **50,** T1 (1931).
118. SPEAKMAN, J. B., *J. Soc. Chem. Ind.,* **48,** T321–324 (1929).
119. SPEAKMAN, J. B., English patents 453,700 and 453,701 (1935).
120. SPEAKMAN, J. B., *J. Textile Inst.,* **27,** P231–248 (1936).
121. SPEAKMAN, J. B., *J. Soc. Dyers Colourists,* **52,** 121–135 (1936).
122. SPEAKMAN, J. B., Univ. of Leeds, Clothworkers' Dept. *Rept.* (Dec. 1931).
123. SPEAKMAN, J. B., and GOODINGS, A. C., *J. Textile Inst.,* **17,** T607–614 (1926).
124. SPEAKMAN, J. B., and PEILL, P. L. D., *J. Textile Inst.,* **34,** T70–76 (Sept. 1943).
125. SPEAKMAN, J. B., and STOTT, E., *J. Soc. Dyers Colourists,* **50,** 341 (1934).
126. SPEAKMAN, J. B., and STOTT, E., *Trans. Faraday Soc.,* **30,** 539–548 (1934).
127. SPEAKMAN, J. B., and STOTT, E., *Trans. Faraday Soc.,* **31,** 1425–1432 (1935).
128. SPEAKMAN, J. B., and WHEWELL, C. S., *J. Soc. Dyers Colourists,* **52,** 380 (1936).
129. STEINHARDT, J., FUGITT, C. H., and HARRIS, M., *J. Research, Natl. Bur. Standards,* **30,** 123–128, RP1523 (Feb. 1943); **29,** 201–216, RP1453 (Feb. 1942).
130. STEINHARDT, J., and HARRIS, M., *J. Research, Natl. Bur. Standards,* **24,** 335, RP1286 (1940).
131. STEINHARDT, J., and ZAISER, E. M., *J. Biol. Chem.,* **183,** 789–802 (1950).
132. STIRM, K., *Die Gespinstfasern,* 143.
133. STIRM, K., and ROUETTE, P. L., *Melliand Textiber.,* **16,** 4–6 (1935).
134. STOVES, J. L., *Trans. Faraday Soc.,* **38,** 501–506 (1942).
135. SWANSTON, K., and PALMER, R. C., *J. Soc. Dyers Colourists,* **66,** 632–638 (1950).
136. TAYLOR, H. S., *Proc. Am. Phil. Soc.,* **85,** 1–12 (1941–42).
137. TAYLOR, H. S., *Proc. Am. Phil. Soc.,* **85,** 1 (Nov. 1941).
138. TROTMAN, S. R., *J. Soc. Chem. Ind.,* **41,** T219–224 (1922).
139. TROTMAN, S. R., and SUTTON, R. W., *J. Soc. Dyers Colourists,* **41,** 121–127 (1925).
140. VEITCH, F. P., and BENEDICT, L. C., *Trans. Am. Inst. Chem. Engrs.* (adv. copy), 3–22 (June 1925).
141. VICKERSTAFF, T., *The Physical Chemistry of Dyeing,* New York Interscience Press (1950).
142. VOM HOVE, H., *Angew. Chem.,* **47,** 756–762 (1934).
143. VON BERGEN, W., *Am. Soc. Testing Materials,* **35,** Part II (1935).
144. VON BERGEN, W., *Melliand,* I, 1084–1093 (1929); *Melliand Textilber.,* **6,** 745–751 (Oct. 1925); *Melliand,* II, 9–15, 186–192 (1930).
145. VON BERGEN, W., *Textile Fiber Atlas,* 16 (1942).
146. WALDE, E. C., BARR, M., and EDGAR, R., *Textile Research,* **6** (5), 235–240 (March 1936).
147. WIEGERINK, J. G., *Textile Research,* **10,** 493 (Oct. 1940).
148. WOODS, H. J., *Proc. Roy. Soc. (London) A,* **237,** 76–96 (May 1938).
149. ZAHN, H., *Kolloid Z.,* **113,** 157–159 (1949); *Textil-Praxis,* **5,** 315 (1950).

CHAPTER XIII

SPECIALTY HAIR FIBERS [1]

WERNER VON BERGEN

Besides the fiber obtained from the various types of sheep, large quantities of animal fibers not strictly classified as wool but known as specialty hair fibers are used in the manufacture of clothing. They are used in conjunction with wool to produce special effects or to give additional beauty, color, softness, or luster. These fibers are obtained from related species such as goats, camels, cows, horses, and fur-bearing animals. The chart below shows the various animals yielding these specialty fibers.

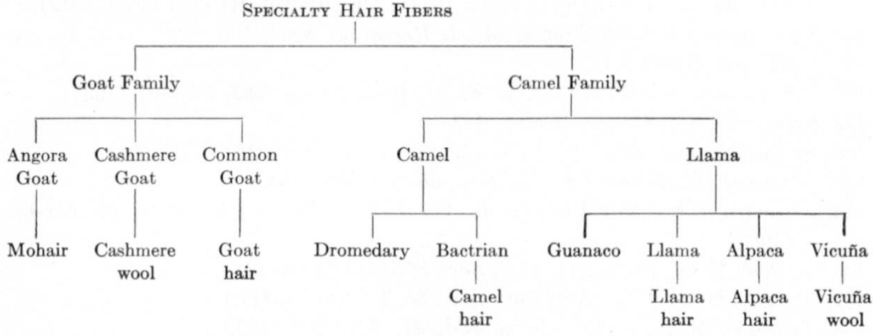

Mohair

Mohair is the main specialty hair fiber and forms the long lustrous coat or covering of the Angora goat, which originated in Asia Minor. The goat owes its name to the province of Angora in Turkey, where it has been cultivated for thousands of years. Today three countries—Turkey, the Union of South Africa, and the United States—breed this goat on a commercial basis for the quality of its hair.

World Production of Mohair. Table 1 shows that the United States is the largest producer of mohair. It is also the largest consumer. In the ten years 1930–39 prior to World War II, the annual importation

[1] Adapted, by permission, from the *American Wool Handbook,* 2d ed., Textile Book Publishers, copyright 1948 [19].

averaged 554,000 lb and, in the war years 1940–46, the importations averaged 785,000 lb. After the war, production started to decline like domestic wool production from a high of 22 million lb in 1945 to a low of less than 15 million lb in 1949.

TABLE 1. Head of Goats and Mohair Production in Principal Countries
[In millions.]

Years	United States		Union of South Africa		Turkey		Total	
	Head	Pounds	Head	Pounds	Head	Pounds	Head	Pounds
1932	4.201	16.9	1.511	6.4	3.315	7.9	9.027	31.2
1933	4.092	16.5	1.339	15.7	3.081	7.0	8.512	39.2
1934	3.916	16.2	0.944	6.5	2.637	7.7	7.497	30.4
1935	3.565	15.7	0.742	10.6	2.743	12.1	7.050	38.4
1936	3.715	16.1	0.700	6.3	3.193	13.9	7.608	36.3
1937	3.774	16.5	0.700	4.6	3.700	12.0	8.174	33.1
1938	3.918	16.8	0.700	5.1	3.200	16.3	7.818	38.2
Averages	3.883	16.4	0.948	7.9	3.124	11.0	7.955	35.3
Per cent	48.9	46.5	11.8	22.4	39.3	31.1	100.0	100.0

Source: U. S. Dept. Agr. and Natl. Assoc. Wool Mfrs.

Development of the Mohair Industry. Up to the early part of the nineteenth century the breeding of mohair goats was limited to Turkey [15]. Many attempts were made to establish Angora goats in Europe, but these attempts were not successful. The rapid growth of manufacturing in Europe in the first half of the nineteenth century created a demand for mohair far in excess of what the Turks were able to meet. By 1860, efforts were directed to the production of mohair in South Africa by grading up the herds of common goats with imported sires. The first importation of Angora goats into South Africa took place in 1838. Up to 1880, about 3000 Angora goats had been imported, and the industry had become firmly established [16, 18, 24].

United States Mohair. It is now over three-quarters of a century since the first importation of Angora goats into the United States. A short time after the annexation of Texas by the Union during the administration of President Polk; the Sultan of Turkey requested Polk to recommend someone to experiment in the production of cotton in Turkey. James B. Davis of Columbia, S. C., was recommended, and he received the appointment. When Davis returned to the United States in 1849, he brought with him nine choice goats, seven does and two bucks. Ten years later just before the outbreak of the Civil War there were many fair-sized herds of Angoras in the South and Southwest. Smaller herds were also maintained in the North and West. Soon after the close of the war the growing of Angora goats spread into the West, principally into Texas and California. As the natural con-

TABLE 2. UNITED STATES MOHAIR PRODUCTION IN POUNDS, 1900–49

[Source: U. S. Department of Agriculture]

Year	*Weight of Mohair (thousand pounds)*	*Year*	*Weight of Mohair (thousand pounds)*
1949	14,633	1934	16,180
1948	16,591	1933	16,540
1947	18,476	1932	16,940
1946	19,329	1931	19,380
1945	22,038	1930	17,580
1944	20,467	1925	11,150
1943	20,156	1924	9,857
1942	20,730	1923	9,067
1941	21,780	1922	8,488
1940	21,140	1921	9,362
1939	18,790	1920	8,474
1938	16,830	1915	6,540
1937	16,530	1910	5,920
1936	16,120	1900	961
1935	15,720		

TABLE 3. UNITED STATES MOHAIR PRODUCTION BY STATES, 1946–48

[Source: U. S. Department of Agriculture]

	Thousands of Goats Clipped			*Average per Goat (pounds)*			*Total Mohair (thousands of pounds)*		
States	*1946*	*1947*	*1948*	*1946*	*1947*	*1948*	*1946*	*1947*	*1948*
Texas	3580	3445	3100	5.0	5.1	5.1	17,880	17,407	15,810
New Mexico	103	72	46	5.0	5.1	5.3	516	368	243
Arizona	105	72	45	4.0	3.2	3.1	420	232	138
Oregon	58	57	50	3.5	3.8	4.1	203	217	205
Missouri	67	61	56	2.9	2.9	2.3	194	177	129
Utah	10	4	3	4.4	3.0	3.2	44	12	10
California	20	18	16	3.6	3.5	3.5	72	63	56
Total	3943	3729	3316	4.9	5.0	5.0	19,329	18,476	16,591

ditions in those regions proved to be best suited to Angoras, the greatest development of the Angora goat industry has taken place in that part of the country, particularly in Texas and to a considerable extent in New Mexico, Arizona, California, Oregon, and, of late, Utah. The greatest concentration of Angoras in this country is on the Edwards Plateau of western Texas.

Improvement of Angora Goats. Angora goats in the United States have been developed through a long period of selective breeding. This has been accomplished by the use of imported stock and by crossing the improved Angora bucks on a foundation of common does.

Since 1900 a registry system has been established for Angora goats by the American Angora Goat Breeders' Association, Rock Springs, Texas. This system was initiated by means of official inspection of pure-bred and high-grade American Angoras and by admitting to the official register only such animals as measured up to the standard of excellence required by the association. As a rule, range herds of goats are composed of select high-grade does that are mated with pure-bred bucks purchased from breeders who specialize in the production of superior registered animals.

Characteristics of Improved Angoras. Mature bucks usually weigh about 130 to 135 lb; 18-month-old bucks, 75 to 80 lb; mature wethers, 90 to 140 lb; mature does about 75 lb; and 18-month-old does around 65 lb. Both bucks and does have horns. The ears should be drooping. The color of all Angoras is white. "Red kids" are born occasionally.

The production of unscoured mohair per goat is about 3½ to 4½ lb for the doe and kid band under range conditions, and for wethers about 5 lb. The average weight per fleece, which in the 1920–24 period was 3.8 lb, increased to 5.0 lb in the 1945–49 period. Much of the mohair is taken off in two clips per year. This is particularly true of mohair grown in the Southwest. Pure-bred herds often clip double the above quantities.

Types of Fleeces. There are three primary types of fleece based on the formation of the lock, viz.: the tight lock, the flat lock, and the fluffy fleece. Angora breeders generally prefer a well-developed tight lock or ringlet, although some prefer the flat lock, which produces a very desirable type of mohair. The tight lock is ringleted throughout almost its entire length. It is the type that is most strongly associated with extreme fineness of mohair. (See Fig. 1.) The flat lock is usually wavy and forms a bulky fleece. This lock is usually associated with heavy shearing weight and a satisfactory quality of hair. The fluffy or open fleece probably stands lowest in character, and is objectionable on the range because it is easily broken and is torn out to a greater extent by the brush. One of the most important problems in the improvement of Angora goats and their mohair is the elimination of the kemp fibers, which greatly reduce the value of the fleece. A great advance has been made in this direction since 1920.

FIG. 1. Angora goat buck. Fleece type: tight lock. (*Courtesy U. S. Department of Agriculture.*)

Management of Angora Goats. A large portion of the Angora goats in the United States are maintained under range conditions. Angora goats are especially adapted to the use of many kinds of range forage, and, since they can be handled in large herds, they lend themselves to very economical use of certain range lands. Browse furnishes most of the forage for goats on the ranges. During the summer, browse and grass are often grazed in approximately equal quantity, provided about equal amounts of palatable species of both make up the forage. In the winter, however, browse is the principal goat feed, and is absolutely necessary on any winter goat range which is subject to continual snow.

Most goat ranches in the range country, especially in the Southwest, consist of the headquarters, kidding, and shearing facilities, and sheds for winter protection. On the range, goats are grazed in herds of a few hundred head to over 2000. General range practice has shown, however, that it is most economical on timbered mountain ranges to graze goats in herds of approximately 1200 head of mature animals.

The time of year to breed the does varies for different parts of the country, but, as March and April are the months in which most of the kidding occurs, the breeding season is chiefly in the months of October and November. In the spring, goats are sheared as soon as the weather permits and when all danger of cold rains has passed. In the Southwest, on account of the warmer climate, goats are shorn twice a year, spring and fall.

In Texas, breeding takes place during the months of October and November and the kids are born in the early spring. The first shearing takes place in the fall, when the kid is 6 or 7 months old. This hair is known as Fall Kid and is the finest type of mohair produced. The next shearing takes place the following spring, when the goat is approximately 1 year old. The hair obtained at that time is known as Spring Kid. At the next shearing in the fall when the goat is 1½ years old, the hair is known as Yearling Mohair. Beginning with the fourth shearing the mohair is classified as Adult.

Shearing should be done only when the mohair is dry. Goats are shorn either with hand shears or with machine clippers. Before the body of the goat is sheared, all tags, dung locks, and stained pieces should be removed. These sorts should be packed separately. The fleeces from kids, those from the middle-aged goats, and those from old goats, which have straight and coarse mohair, should be packed separately. It is quite a general practice to pack the kid mohair by itself.

Marketing. In the farm states, where little mohair is produced, the growers usually sell directly to country buyers or assemblers, who concentrate the hair in their own warehouses or ship it to central markets where it is stored, sorted, and sold to manufacturers.

In the Southwest, mohair is generally handled by the local wool warehousemen on a commission basis. In recent years, there has been a growing tendency on the part of California mohair producers to ship their mohair to Texas handlers on consignment. In Texas, the bulk of mohair is handled on consignment by local warehousemen who charge a commission for storage, insurance, and selling. This commission usually is 1 cent per lb. Some small growers sell their clips directly to the warehousemen, who in turn resell for their own account.

Most of the mohair is purchased from the warehouses by dealers located in Boston and Philadelphia, although a substantial amount is purchased directly by mills, through brokers or order buyers. In seasons of good demand the buyers may go directly to the growers and contract for the mohair before it is shorn. This, however, is a highly speculative practice and is not favored by Texas warehousemen, who follow this method only in order to compete with out-of-town buyers.

The three principal ways in which Texas mohair is offered for sale by warehousemen are: (1) in the original bag, (2) graded, and (3) sorted.

1. Original bag. By far the most important method of marketing raw mohair is in the original bag. Original bag Texas mohair is divided into four classes, as follows: Fall kid, spring kid, yearling (or third shearing), and adult.

2. Graded. Many disadvantages of marketing mohair by the original-bag method were recognized a number of years ago. The Department of Agriculture began a program in 1922 of promoting, grading, and improving the packaging of mohair. At present, the Texas Mohair Grading Committee, an organization made up of growers and warehousemen, is carrying on and promoting a mohair-grading program.

Table 4 shows the grades, yields, and spinning counts used by the Committee as a basis for grading.

TABLE 4. Basis for Grading Yields, Spinning Counts and Grades

Grade	*Yield (per cent)*	*Spinning Counts*
No. 1 Kid	90	36–40's
No. 2 Kid	85	30–36's
No. 1 Grown	70	28–30's
No. 2 Grown	70	24–26's
No. 3 Grown	70	20–22's
No. 4 Grown	90	16's and below

Stained—discolor due primarily to absorption of urine
Kempy—contains kemp or medullated fibers

3. Sorted. Very little mohair is being sorted due to the objections of manufacturers and dealers.

Turkey Mohair. The latest available figures on the mohair-growing industry in Turkey are given in Table 5.

In order to raise the quality and to safeguard the export of mohair from Turkey the Turkish government [15] issued strict regulations relating to inspection of mohair for export on January 19, 1940.

TABLE 5. Turkish Mohair Production, 1941–46

Year	*Thousands of Goats*	*Production (thousands of pounds)*	*Average Pounds per Goat*
1941	5,534	16,451	3.0
1942	4,973	16,612	3.3
1943	4,381	14,252	3.3
1944	4,975	14,835	3.0
1945	3,997	13,200	3.3
1946	..	12,100	..

Source: Turkish Embassy, 1948.

Mohair for export is divided into two categories:

Esas tiftikler, principal mohair.
Tali tiftikler, secondary mohair.

Principal mohair is divided into the following nine classes:

1. Birinci oglak (Kids I). This mohair is of a superior quality, having fine fibers which are shiny and silky. Yield 70–72 per cent.
2. Ikinci oglak (Kids II). These are the fleeces from goats which are not first quality, having short stiff hair, and they are much lighter in weight. Yield 72–74 per cent.
3. Ince tiftik (Best Average mohair). These are mixtures of selected good-quality mohair from the regions around the cities of Karahisar, Kutahya, Eskisehir, Yozgat, and Bolvadin. Yield 78–80 per cent.
4. Iyi tiftik (Good Average mohair). These are mixtures of good-quality merchandise from the regions around the cities of Ankara, Beypazar, Polatli, and Maden and of similar quality from other regions, which for the most part are long-hair mohair of average fineness. Yield 76–78 per cent.
5. Sira tiftik (Fair Average mohair). These are mixtures of usual quality from the regions of Cankiri, Gerede, Aksehir, Bolu, and Kirsehir, and qualities from other regions which for the most part have coarser hair. Yield 74–76 per cent.
6. Kastamonu tiftigi (Kastambol mohair). These are mixtures from Kastamonu (Kastambol) or of similar quality from other regions. The fleece has separated tufts and falling hair, is light and free from grease. It has a high yield of white, shiny, open tufts. The selection is of superior quality. Yield 90–92 per cent.

7. Konya dag tiftigi (Konia Mountain mohair). This is the mohair from the mountainous regions of Konia and similar qualities from other regions. It has a high yield equal to Good mohair in respect to luster and fiber fineness. Generally, the fibers are white and in part light cream color. Yield 82–84 per cent.
8. Konya ova tiftigi (Konia Plain mohair). This mohair is from the plains of Konia and of similar quality from other regions. It is lighter (in weight) than the mohair from the mountainous regions of Konia. It is also inferior in fiber fineness and yield. Lots from this area may contain felted, reddish-brown, and white fleece. Yield 76–78 per cent.
9. Cengelli tiftigi (Gingerline mohair). This is a mixture of mohair similar to camel hair and is mostly brown.

The secondary mohair is divided as follows:

1. Renkli, colored.
2. Yagli, greasy.
3. Hafif, short and felted.
4. Sari, yellow.
5. Deri, skin. Subdivided into: shorn or torn from dead goats; and mohair from the tannery.
6. Sekeri, lightly colored.
7. Alata, Cengelli—offsorts from Gingerline.
8. Pitrakli, burry.

Istanbul is the principal mohair market of Turkey. The fineness of the grades, as in the United States, is based on the possible spinning count obtainable with the Bradford system (560 yards/lb). The finest Turkish mohair attains a 50's quality.

Cape Mohair. In spite of many difficulties, the Angora goat was successfully introduced and crossed with the South African variety to produce a breed of goats growing a good class of hair. Mohair from the Cape now bears comparison with the best Turkish qualities, the climate and general conditions of the Cape being very suitable. The color of Cape mohair is not generally as clear as white Turkey hair. There are two clips a year, summer growth and winter growth. The following list shows the principal classes:

Cape kids. The first shear from the young goat, equivalent to lamb's wool. Length 6 to 7 in.; very lustrous, brownish color, and very soft.

Cape first. The long summer growth. Length, 8 in.; very lustrous, fairly clear in color, and soft.

Cape winter. The shorter winter growth. Length, 5 in.; good luster, fairly clear color, and fairly soft.

Cape basuto. A class of hair rather stronger and coarser than Cape firsts.

Cape mixed. A class of hair between Cape firsts and Cape winter, such as a late clip or a mixture of the two clips.

Thirds. Equivalent to edges of a long wool fleece. Each fleece may be subdivided into firsts, seconds, and thirds, according to fineness, length, and luster.

Cape mohair, in fineness, reaches the same quality number as Turkey hair, viz., 50's.

Physical Properties [22]. The hair of the Angora goat grows in long uniform locks forming a fleece, which gives the animal the characteristic appearance seen in Fig. 1. The raw fiber has a brownish color caused by the presence of 10 to 30 per cent of foreign matter, such as sand, dust and grease. For the domestic kid mohair there is a difference of approximately 4 per cent in the yield between the spring and the fall clips. The spring clip yields between 80 to 82 per cent, whereas the fall clip yields 84 to 86 per cent. The grease content in the spring mohair ranges from 5 to 8 per cent, whereas the fall clip ranges from 3½ to 7 per cent. The vegetable matter in mohair very rarely exceeds 0.25 per cent, and the ash content of the scoured mohair varies between 0.3 and 0.6 per cent. After scouring, the mohair shows the silklike luster for which it is mostly valued. The best grades are clear white.

The United States Department of Agriculture [17] on November 1950 issued proposed standards for grades of mohair of 7 grades each for spring and fall. In Table 6 the fineness measurements are given of the 7 fall grades. These measurements were based on an interlaboratory test which was conducted in cooperation with industrial establishments and agricultural experimental stations, with six laboratories participating [2]. Each grade represents the average of 3600 fibers. The stock tested was taken from piles of Texas fall mohair matchings being used in making up sets of the proposed standards for grades of mohair by the Department of Agriculture.

Table 7 gives the fineness graduation of eight mohair tops obtained in the Boston market, based on the measurement of 1000 fibers each. The measurements prove that the fineness is the main factor governing the sorting of mohair.

TABLE 6. TENTATIVE UNITED STATES MOHAIR GRADES, FINENESS DISTRIBUTION TEXAS FALL MATCHINGS

Diameters (microns)	*40's*	*36's*	*32's*	*28's*	*24's*	*20's*	*16's*
10 to 20	28	19	16	7	4	2	1
20 to 30	56	53	49	41	23	17	9
30 to 40	15	25	31	42	46	35	25
40 to 50	1	3	4	9	22	33	35
50 to 60				1	4	11	22
60 to 70					1	2	7
Over 70							1
Average	24.3	26.6	27.4	30.7	34.9	39.0	44.5
Coefficient of Variation	27.0	26.4	25.9	24.3	25.3	25.7	23.7
Proposed range	23–25	25.1–27	27.1–29	29.1–31.5	31.6–35.5	35.6–39.5	39.6–45

TABLE 7. FINENESS MEASUREMENTS OF COMMERCIAL MOHAIR TOPS

Grades		*Average (microns)*	*Deviation (microns)*	*Coefficient of Variation (per cent)*	*Standard Error (microns)*	*Average Range (microns)*	*Dispersion Range (microns)*
Super kid	Kid	25.7	6.30	24.5	0.19	25.2 to 26.3	10 to 45
40's	Kid	27.0	5.29	19.1	0.17	26.5 to 27.5	10 to 45
36's	Kid	28.7	6.23	21.7	0.19	28.1 to 29.2	10 to 50
32's	Kid	30.0	6.89	22.9	0.22	29.4 to 30.7	10 to 50
28's	First	32.2	7.81	20.5	0.24	31.5 to 32.9	10 to 55
26's	First	34.0	7.99	23.5	0.25	33.3 to 34.8	15 to 55
24's	First	35.7	9.25	25.7	0.29	34.8 to 36.5	15 to 60
Low—Second		41.4	10.60	25.6	0.30	40.5 to 42.3	20 to 70

Length. The length of the fiber of kids ranges from 4 to 6 in. for a half year's growth and 8 to 12 in. for a full year's growth. Because of the differences in age of the kids at shearing time, the fleeces are not as uniform in length as those of the grown goats.

Microscopic Structure [10]. In its microscopic structure the mohair fiber is similar to wool, but it has some characteristics which make its identification possible. The epidermal scales are only faintly visible and hardly overlap. They lie close to the stem, giving the fiber a very smooth appearance. The number of scales per 100 μ is 5 as against 10 to 11 in fine wools. The scale length ranges from 18 to 22 μ. This scale [11] formation is the cause of the smooth handle of the fiber as well as the high luster. On the large, uninterrupted fiber surface the light rays are strongly reflected.

The cortical layer built up of the spindlelike cells is clearly visible as strong striations throughout the length of the fiber. In many instances, there exist between the cells air-filled cigar-shaped pockets or vacuoles of various lengths. The percentage of hairs containing such vacuoles varies within wide limits.

Medullas. The number of medullated fibers in well-bred mohair is normally below 1 per cent. In a study made on Texas and Turkish mohair the data in Table 8 were obtained.

TABLE 8. MEDULLATED FIBERS IN TEXAS AND TURKISH MOHAIR

Samples	*Average (microns)*	*Form*	*Number of Fibers*	*Medullated Fibers*	*Kemp*
Texas kid mohair	24	Roving	1000	7	..
Texas kid mohair	29	Carded	1000	16	2
Turkish mohair	9 in. staple	Root part	240	8	6
		Middle part	120	2	..
		Tip	120	..	..

As in wool, three forms of medullas are found in mohair, namely, (*a*) continuous, (*b*) interrupted, and (*c*) fragmental types. The continuous type is most common. See Fig. 2.

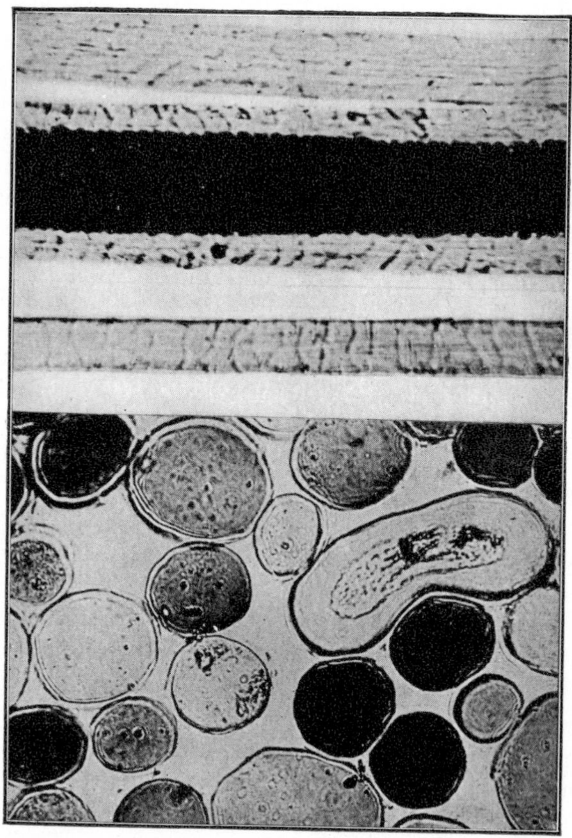

FIG. 2. Mohair. *Top,* longitudinal view (×240). *Bottom,* cross-section (×500). (*Textile Fiber Atlas.*)

Cross-Section. Mohair is recognized immediately by a skilled worker as having a cross-section of high circularity. The ratio between the major and minor diameters is usually 1 : 1.2 or lower. Many hairs show black dots or little circles, which are caused by the air-filled pockets or vacuoles already mentioned. Fibers range in diameter from 14 to 90 μ.

Kemp [7]. The manufacturer's great objection to mohair is that it commonly contains short, coarse, undesirable fibers, known as kemp. Besides taking dye poorly, these fibers often cause a loss in combing of as much as 18 per cent of the original weight. In addition, it is not possible to remove them completely from good mohair. In some of the best Texas mohair, however, the percentage of kemp is negligible.

Moisture Content. The average moisture content of the mohair fiber when exposed to standard conditions is equal to that of wool.

Chemical Properties. Chemically the mohair fiber is identical with wool. Its sulfur content seems to vary according to the origin of the mohair. Harris found that the sulfur content of Texas kid mohair is 2.92 per cent and of Turkey mohair fleece 3.58 per cent. In general, mohair is more sensitive to the various chemicals than wool; consequently, more attention should be given to the amount of chemicals used in the various manufacturing processes, such as scouring, dyeing, carbonizing, and bleaching. As with wool, the mohair fibers covering the back of the animal are more or less damaged by sunlight while still on the animal, a damage which influences the dyeing property of the fibers.

Commercial Uses. As an upholstery material, mohair—usually in the form of a pile fabric—is unsurpassed for general durability. Mohair fabrics are used for upholstery of automobile and railroad car seats, where the fabric must withstand the hardest kind of service. It is not necessary to sacrifice esthetic properties to gain a high degree of durability, for it is possible to make many beautiful coverings by variations in the pile height and structure, as well as by embossing and hand-block printing.

Mohair is also used in men's summer suitings, in all-mohair fabrics, and in numerous combinations with other fibers, sometimes mixed in the yarn structure, but usually as either warp or filling of the fabric. One of the much-advertised brands of men's suitings is made of mohair yarn in one direction and worsted yarn in the other. As a lining for suits, mohair is used extensively, woven plain or twilled, and sometimes combined with wool, cotton, or rayon. In ladies' coatings such as bouclé, mohair blends are especially suitable.

Because of its luster and because it dyes brilliantly and retains the colors well, mohair fiber serves admirably for nets, laces, and drapery materials, and produces many novel effects in decorative trimmings for coats, hats, and shoes. The long lustrous pile is bound into the base of the fabric and then curled and embossed, by ingenious construction and dyeing methods, to imitate furs and to produce materials which are not only attractive but serviceable.

The long-fibered mohair is particularly desired for use in the manufacture of wigs and switches which are used extensively for theatrical purposes. The value of the mohair entering into the manufacture of these products probably represents a larger amount of money for the weight of mohair used than that used in any other branch of the industry.

Rugs of beautiful appearance, with long pile, are made from mohair. The design is frequently effected by hand-block printing. These rugs compare favorably in appearance with handmade oriental rugs. Leather made from the pelt or skin of the Angora goat is useful for ornamental purposes and for the manufacture of gloves, purses, bookbinding, and novelties.

Cashmere [20]

Cashmere hair is obtained from the Cashmere goat (*Capra hucus laniger*), which is found in Tibet. Although the name comes from the Province of Kashmir in northern India, actually the main portion of the cashmere of commerce comes from the northwestern provinces of China, particularly from the provinces of Ningsia, Sui Yuan and Kausu, where the goat is kept as a domestic animal. The hair obtained its fame through the beautiful cashmere shawls made from it in the mountain valleys of Kashmir.

The Cashmere is somewhat smaller than the Angora goat. It has straight, round, pointed horns and large pendent ears. It is covered with straight coarse long hairs, with a fine undercoat or down. This undercoat alone constitutes the fibers from which the celebrated shawls are made and is known in Kashmir as pashm. The natural color of the hair is white, gray, or tan, with the gray and tan mixtures prevailing. Every spring the animal loses this undercoat and part of the outer coat through molting, which takes place early in June. The actual shedding time spreads over a period of several weeks. The hair, when loose enough, is combed by hand from the animals. During this combing process much of the coarse outer hair, which is not suitable for fine fabrics, is separated from the down. A considerable amount of this coarse cashmere hair is used by the natives for hand weaving of coarse, heavy bags about 5 ft long and 2 ft wide, which are strong, durable, and water resistant and are used for carrying grain on donkeys' backs. The remainder of the coarse hair, not used by the natives, is exported as goat hair.

Fig. 3. Cashmere goat. Lidor Valley, India. (*Courtesy American Wool Handbook.*)

The normal cashmere down consists of a mixture of the fine wool hair with coarse beard hair. The amount of beard hair depends upon the care with which the hand combing was done and may vary from 10 to 50 per cent of the total. The yield of this mixture per animal is probably not more than ½ lb.

It is impossible to make an estimate of the number of goats yielding cashmere wool because no statistical data are available. Probably the most reliable figures for the amount of cashmere wool produced are those which were given to R. Burns in 1946 [5] by the Foosing

Trading Corporation, a Chinese Government export trading company. The estimated production per annum for the main northwestern provinces of China is shown in Table 9.

TABLE 9. ESTIMATED ANNUAL PRODUCTION OF CASHMERE DOWN IN CHINA

(in pounds)

Province	*Color*	*Amount*
Kansu-Yuen	Purple	66,000
Kansu-Hsinfengcheng	Purple	66,000
Ningsia	White	202,000
	Purple	202,000
Sui Yuan	Purple	172,000
Sinkiang		22,000
Total		730,000

These figures agree closely with prewar average annual export figures for the years 1934 to 1937 of cashmere down from China, which amount approximated 850,000 lb. Of this amount, the United States imported about 350,000 lb annually. Data reported in the United States Department of State Publication 2249, "The Livestock of China," are considerably higher, as seen in Table 9*a*. These figures unquestionably include all kinds of goat wool and goat hair.

TABLE 9*a*. AMOUNTS OF GOAT HAIR AND GOAT WOOL EXPORTED FROM CHINA

Year	*Goat Hair* (*pounds*)	*Goat Wool* (*pounds*)
1915	..	1,366,200
1920	..	1,111,440
1925	3,118,060	3,094,960
1930	1,206,920	1,654,180
1935	2,990,020	2,628,780
1940	1,567,060	1,821,600

Source: Phillips-Johnson-Moyer, "The Livestock of China," U. S. State Dept. Publication No. 2249, 1944.

One of the main collecting centers for cashmere is the city of Lanchow. The original cashmere packages collected from the farmers, weighing about 90 lb each, are brought by camel train, each camel carrying two packages, one on each side. The cashmere is unsacked, hand or machine dusted, and then repacked into bales weighing approximately 175 lb. When the shipment has been thus prepared, it is transported to the export centers, Tiensin or Shanghai, for shipment to the market.

In normal times the main marketing center is London, although most of the cashmere wool reaching the United States following the close of World War II was handled through the Russian Government

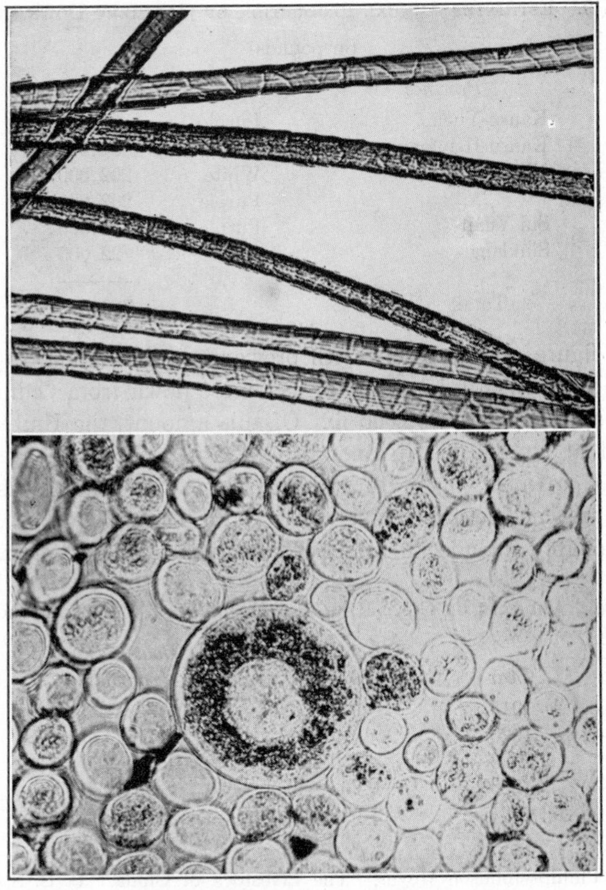

FIG. 4. Cashmere. *Top,* longitudinal view (×240). *Bottom,* cross-section (×500). (*Textile Fiber Atlas.*)

agency. The cashmere marketed by the Russians is much lower in quality because it is undusted and unsorted, containing a much higher percentage of coarse hairs. Whereas a good grade cashmere should yield 80 per cent of clean fibers, this undusted product yields only about 50 per cent. A further loss occurs in the dehairing process, which may bring the final yield from the poorest quality as low as 20 per cent.

Length. Cashmere wool hair is from 1¼ to 3½ in. long, whereas cashmere beard hair is 1½ to 5 in. The hairs are contaminated with white scales from the skin of the animal. In the light of a quartz lamp, the cashmere hair has a bluish white fluorescence, like sheep's wool. The scales from the skin show a strong white fluorescence.

Microscopical Characteristics [10]. The cashmere wool hair consists of the cortical layer and the epidermis. All the fibers show clearly cylindrical scales which slightly project beyond the cortical layer, causing a serrated effect. The number of scales per 100 μ averages 6 to 7. The number of scales is a means of distinguishing cashmere from sheep's wool. The cortical layer of the white and gray hairs shows distinct longitudinal streaks with crevices between the cells, whereas the brown hairs are covered completely with minute dye pigments (colored granules). Figure 4 illustrates three white and two brown hairs with their characteristic marks.

The diameter of the hair, a true indicator of fineness, is extremely regular with all cashmere wool hairs. The values given in Table 10 prove this very well, being based on the measurement of 1000 fibers, except in the last column, where 800 fibers were measured.

TABLE 10. FINENESS ANALYSIS OF COMMERCIAL CASHMERE SAMPLES

Types	Scoured Gray	Top Gray	Noils		Fabrics of Four Manufacturers
			Gray	White	
Average diameter, μ	14.8	15.6	15.1	15.1	15.4
Standard deviation, μ	3.0	2.9	2.7	2.9	3.1
Standard error, μ	0.09	0.09	0.09	0.09	0.11
Coefficient of variation, per cent	20.3	18.6	18.0	19.2	20.1

Since the hair is obtained by plucking from the skin of the animal, most hairs retain the root. The fibers have long fine ends which, because of their fineness, are already broken on the back of the animal. The normal cashmere wool hair grows thinner toward the root as well as toward the end.

The fiber is practically circular in cross-section; it is, therefore, possible to determine the fineness of the hair from its width without any error. The brown hair shows the brown dye pigment also in the cross-section.

Beard Hairs. The beard hair consists of three parts, the epidermis, the cortical layer, and the medulla. The medulla on the whole constitutes the larger part of the hair. The root and the extreme end do not contain any medulla. Partially medullated hair is rarely found. The diameter of the beard hairs is extremely irregular, ranging from 30 to 150 μ with an average of 62 μ.

Chemical Properties. The behavior of cashmere fibers toward chemical influences, as compared with wool fibers, is affected mainly by two factors, the great degree of fineness of the fibers and the better wetting out properties. If cashmere is brought under the surface of water, it becomes saturated within a few seconds and lumps together. Wool, on the other hand, must be manipulated for one-half to one minute before the last bubbles of air disappear.

Like wool, cashmere is extremely sensitive to alkalies, and when heated, is completely dissolved by caustic alkalies, such as caustic soda. But cashmere is markedly more sensitive toward soda ash than the finest wools. The following experiments prove this.

Five grams each of carded cashmere and Australian top were treated in 500 cc of liquor at 115° to 120° F. for half an hour. The different baths contained per 1000 cc 1 gram, 3, 5, and 10 grams of soda. Table 11 gives the values obtained with this test.

TABLE 11. EFFECT OF ALKALI ON CASHMERE

Content of Soda per Liter in Bath Liquid (grams)	*pH Number*	*Cashmere in Solution (per cent)*	*Wool in Solution (per cent)*
1	9.0	0.22	0.06
3	10.9	0.39	0.17
5	11.0	0.91	0.22
10	11.4	1.39	0.33

As a hair it is chemically identical with wool and mohair. The sulfur content of a sample was found by Harris [8] to be 3.39 per cent and the nitrogen content 16.2 per cent. The statement made about mohair being more sensitive toward the various chemicals than wool is true to an even greater extent for cashmere, because of the great fineness of the fiber.

Uses [4]. From time immemorial cashmere has been regarded as one of nature's choicest products and unquestionably it is today one of the finest fabrics, for its softness affords the wearer an extravagance of comfort, and its superb soft texture brings to the garment all that may be desired in real elegance and distinction. Owing to the limited number of animals and the high cost of obtaining the fiber, cashmere is necessarily costly. To produce sufficient yardage for only one overcoat requires the entire animal yield of no less than 30 Cashmere goats.

Cashmere is used mainly for producing high-quality ladies' dress goods and overcoats. The most expensive products in this respect are the cashmere silk velour having a silk warp and a 100 per cent cashmere filling. Occasionally cashmere is also used for men's topcoats and overcoats. The percentage of cashmere in the various products varies widely from 10 to 100 per cent. Unfortunately, the word "cashmere" is often used indiscriminately, as many products are called cashmere which actually contain no cashmere fiber at all. Such fabrics can easily be identified microscopically.

Iran Goat Hair [5, 6]. Hair derived from goats in Persia is occasionally marked as cashmere or Persian cashmere. The down is considerably coarser than the genuine cashmere down, running on an average between 19 and 20 μ, which is very close to the fineness of camel hair. Another distinction is its occurrence in such colors as cream, fawn, and dark brown, which are not present in genuine cashmere. In a 20,000-lb shipment the percentages of colors were: dark brown, 30; fawn, 30; white, 10; cream, 22; and light gray, 8.

TABLE 12. Fineness Analysis of Cashmere and Iran Goat Hair

	Genuine Cashmere	Iran Goat Hair
Number of fibers measured	1000	700
Average diameter, μ	14.8	19.5
Dispersion range, μ	Per Cent	Per Cent
5 to 10	3	..
10 to 20	92	61
20 to 30	5	37
30 to 40	..	1
40 to 50	..	0.5
50 to 60	..	0.5
Over 60 *	1	2

* Not included in the average.

Common Goat Hair. The hair of the common goat is seldom used in the manufacture of woolen and worsted goods. The coat is largely made up of beard hairs. Like the Cashmere goat, the animal goes through a shedding time, and therefore the hair is found mostly with the roots attached. The beard hair of the white animals is used in place of kemp as an effect fiber for ladies' sport clothes. This hair ranges in fineness from 7 to 20 μ for the down, from 50 to 200 μ for the beard hair of the full-grown animal, and from 15 to 90 μ for the kid. It resembles cashmere closely.

Camel Hair [12]

The camel hair used in the American wool industry is grown chiefly in Mongolia, Chinese Turkestan, and the Chinese northwestern provinces. The camel bred in north China and Mongolia is of the Bactrian type, with two humps, as distinguished from the dromedary or one-hump camel (see Fig. 5).

Fig. 5. Bactrian camel, Gobi Desert, Mongolia. (*Courtesy American Museum of Natural History.*)

The ancestry of the domestic camel is unknown, but neither the Arabian nor the Bactrian exists any longer in the wild state, though there are some semi-wild herds which have escaped from captivity. Wild camels are said to have existed in Arabia at the start of the Christian era. This coupled with the fact that camels do not appear to have been known to the ancient Egyptians makes an Asiatic origin of both types plausible.

The first person, perhaps, to make a systematic study of the Bactrian camel of Asia, of its fine hair, and of its probable relation and importance to fine and beautiful fabrics was an English Army officer of India, Captain Thomas Hutton. In his travels and studies he discovered that the hair of neither the dromedary nor the pure Bactrian camel of antiquity possessed the dual characteristic of warmth against cold and coolness in the face of heat. The ancient Bactrian, he found, could not stand heat, and the dromedary was equally at a disadvantage in cold climates. But he did learn that the age-old crossbreed of the two camels, producing great herds of the hybrid, or Bokhara type, known natively as the Boghdi, had for thousands of years possessed their individual and rare combination of heat-resisting, cold-resisting shaggy coats of hair.

Today this Boghdi or crossbred native of ancient Bactriana is the generally known Bactrian camel of Asia.

The Bactrian is found in nearly all desert regions of central Asia lying between Afghanistan, Turkestan, China, and southern Siberia, where it is as important to the nomad inhabitants of this region as the Arabian camel is to the Arabs. It feeds chiefly on the bitter plants of the steppes, which are rejected by most other animals, and has a curious partiality for salt, drinking freely of brackish water and salt lakes. The young are so helpless at birth as to be unable even to eat for about a week; they do not attain their full size and vigor before the fifth year.

Once a year the better kind of camel hair is gathered from the living animals in the molting season in late spring or early summer. It is interesting to note the manner in which the hair is obtained; it is neither sheared nor plucked, as with other fleece-bearing animals. In the spring, as the temperature grows milder, the hair begins to form matted strands and tufts, hanging from head, sides, neck, and legs, from which it falls off in clumps. By the time warm weather has definitely set in, the animal has almost completely lost its coat.

Photographs of caravans often show a man trailing the last camel. He is the "trailer." It should be observed that the animal sheds its fleece not only in the spring, when the greatest quantity is shed; the year round it is rubbing off chunks of hair. The task of the trailer is to pick up the hair as it drops from the camel and place it in baskets provided for that purpose. These baskets are strapped to the last camel in the caravan, and therein is transported the accumulation of the entire journey. The hair is also to be found in the morning at the spot where the caravan rested for the night, the camel having rubbed it off. Where batches appear ready to fall, they are pulled free and stuffed into the baskets. The first town reached by the caravan is usually where the hair is sold, generally to traveling compradores, who, in turn, forward it to the terminals across mountain and desert. Eventually the hair is brought to Tientsin, or to other points of shipment, where it is sorted and graded preparatory to export.

The average yield of hair from each animal per year is about 5.3 lb. In 1930 it was estimated that there were more than 1 million camels in the regions mentioned. Paotowehen and Kweihwa, in the provinces of Ningsia and Kansu, on the Peking-Suiyuan railway, are the chief collecting centers for northwest China, with an estimated production of 1 million lb in 1946 [6]. Table 13 gives an idea of the size of the camel hair market.

TABLE 13. CAMEL HAIR EXPORT AND IMPORT

(thousands of pounds)

	1934	*1935*	*1936*	*1937*
China export	2094	3641	2338	1404
U. S. import	206	586	526	307

Marketing of Camel Hair. The camel hair trade is dominated by English interests, and most of the hair is shipped directly to London, which is the main marketing place. The hair is marketed either in its loose raw form or in semi-manufactured products such as camel hair top and camel hair noils. The trade grades are Fine, Medium, and Coarse, or Qualities 1, 2, and 3.

The camel carries a mixed fleece similar to the Cashmere goat. The outer hair of the animal is very coarse, tough, and wiry. It may reach a length up to 15 in. Beneath the outer hair is a short, soft down of great fineness which varies in length from 1 to 5 in. The soft down fibers are the valuable product known as "camel hair wool." As the camel loses both coats together during the shedding time, it is very difficult to separate the hairs from the wool fibers. A separation to the extent effected in cashmere is not possible, because a high percentage of heterotypical fibers is present. The type with the thickened tip predominates. The sudden need for a covering after the shedding is probably the stimulating factor of producing hairy medullated fibers, especially with the severe climatic conditions prevailing in Mongolia and Siberia. The best way to separate the down from the hair is through the combing process. In the combing machines the two types of hair are separated, the coarse and long hairs producing the top and the short fibers combing out as noils. The trade grades are based on the amount of coarse fibers still present. The fine camel hair consists mainly of fine down or camel hair wool, of a very characteristic light, reddish-brown color. The fineness variation within a 15-in. staple is an excellent illustration of the mixed nature of the camel hair based on the measurement of groups of 100 fibers, shown in Table 14.

Microscopic Characteristics. The wool fibers are uniform in width and range from 9 to 40 μ. The epidermal scales are poorly visible.

TABLE 14. Fineness Variation in a 15-In. Camel Hair Staple

Position in staple from root (inches)	1½	6½	11½
Number of fibers	100	100	160
Average diameter, microns	25.1	49.5	72.5
Percentage Dispersion			
10 to 20 μ	23	..	..
20 to 30 μ	64	5	..
30 to 40 μ	9	26	..
40 to 50 μ	2	34	1
50 to 60 μ	2	12	4
60 to 70 μ	..	14	19
70 to 80 μ	..	2	20
80 to 90 μ	..	7	21
90 to 100 μ	..	..	22
100 to 110 μ	..	..	13

The diagonal edges of the scales are more or less sharply bent. The cortical layer is regularly striated and filled with color pigments. Some hairs show interrupted medulla. The presence of these medullated fibers and the wider dispersion range are the characteristics that identify the fibers. Beard hair is dark brown to black, 30 to 120 μ broad, with a wider and mostly continuous medullary cylinder. The thin fiber layer contains strong accumulations of dark brown to black granules. The medullary cells are short but broad, and are filled with color pigments.

TABLE 15. Fineness Analysis of Commercial Camel Hairs

Types	Scoured and Carded	Top		Noils		
		Fine	Coarse	No. 1	No. 2	No. 3
Number of fibers	1000	1000	1000	1000	500	500
Average, μ	19.7	18.2	23.1	18.0	20.9	22.8
Deviation, μ	6.60	5.48	9.46	5.38	7.75	9.31
Stand. error, μ	0.21	0.17	9.30	0.17	0.34	0.42
Variation, per cent	33.4	30.1	40.9	29.9	37.1	40.8
Dispersion, μ	10 to 45	6 to 40	10 to 55	8 to 40	8 to 50	10 to 55

The data in Table 15 illustrate clearly the variation in fineness of commercial camel hair of the various grades.

Chemical Properties. Raw camel hair contains on the average 15 to 25 per cent sand and dust, 4 to 5 per cent fat; 75 to 85 per cent is fiber. Harris [8] established the sulfur content at 3.47 per cent and the nitrogen content at 16.48 per cent for purified camel hair. These amounts are nearly identical with those found in cashmere and mohair. It is therefore logical that camel hair shows the same behavior toward chemicals as cashmere and mohair.

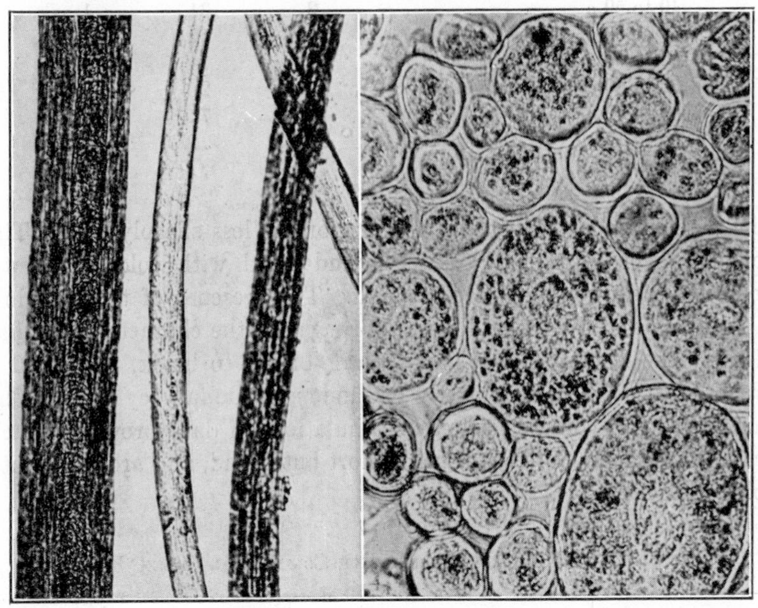

Fig. 6. Camel hair. Longitudinal (×240). Cross-section (×500). (*Courtesy American Wool Handbook.*)

Uses. Camel hair has found its greatest use in men's high-grade overcoating. Because of their high insulating properties, these fabrics are especially preferred by Arctic explorers. Probably no other fabric is as badly misrepresented in the market as camel hair. The public is becoming more and more conscious of this fact and is insisting on properly labeled goods. The characteristic tan color does not insure the consumer against buying a cheaper substitute because the color can very easily be matched by any experienced dyer. A proper microscopic analysis is the only way to disclose the real presence of the camel hair.

THE LLAMA FAMILY [3, 7, 10, 9, 13]

The llama constitutes one branch of the small family of animals known as Camelidae, the Old World camels constituting the other branch of the family. Whether camels and llamas are the descendants of a single progenitor has not been definitely established, but the discoveries of fossil forms of the true camel in various parts of the Western Hemisphere seem to lend strength to the contention. The two branches, however, are now quite distinct.

FIG. 7. Peruvian llamas. (*Courtesy American Wool Handbook.*)

Today four distinct and two hybrid species of llamas exist. These species are llama and alpaca, the domesticated members of the tribe, guanaco (or huanaco as it is known in Peru) and vicuña, the wild members. The hybrids are huarizo, known to the Indians as huaro—progeny of a llama father and alpaca mother—and paco-llama, or misti in Quichua, the language of the aborigines—offspring of an alpaca father and a llama mother. Unlike most hybrids, these two animals are productive, but after a few generations they usually revert to type. The vicuña and alpaca have also been crossed to produce two other hybrids, paco-vicuña and vicuña-paco, depending on whether the father was alpaca or vicuña. The intention of this interbreeding, of course, was to produce an animal that would combine the stature and heavy fleece of the alpaca with the magnificent hair of the vicuña.

But these expectations were not realized, and today these two hybrids are practically extinct.

There has always been a good deal of confusion as to the origin and classification of the various llamas, but today scientists are in general agreement that the llama and alpaca are the direct descendants of the guanaco, and the vicuña is a distinct species. No doubt a long period has elapsed since their evolution, for both the llama and alpaca have been domesticated for probably 1200 years, and today there is a pronounced difference between the wild and domesticated species in both physical characteristics and behavior.

The habitat of all the llama tribe, except the guanaco, is the high Andean regions of southern Ecuador, Peru, Bolivia, and northwestern Argentina. The guanaco once roamed the pampas and other open areas from Ecuador to Patagonia (southern Argentina), including all the above-mentioned countries, and Chile, but today it is confined chiefly to Patagonia. It is also seen in the rocky islands to the south of the Strait of Magellan.

The Andean mountain system has two principal chains, the western, or Cordilleras, situated 60 to 75 miles from the Pacific, and the eastern or Andes proper, paralleling it, but with a slightly eastward slant. Between these two chains lies the puna, the vast, almost uninhabitable 300-mile wide tableland that stretches from southern Ecuador to the Argentine. This plateau is not absolutely arid, however, for upon it are found various mosses and lichens, including the grass ichu, chief diet of the various llamas, and a few stunted trees and bushes. Their growth is made possible by the moderately heavy precipitation during the rainy season (from late November until about the middle of April) and, to some extent, by the thick mists that intermittently sweep down from the mountain heights.

The llama, *Lama glama glama,* is the largest of the Andean Camelidae, weighing about 250 lb and being approximately one-third the size of the Old World camel. The body, which tapers like that of the greyhound, is about equal in length and height, giving the animal a finely proportioned and exceedingly graceful appearance. The llama stands 4 to 4½ ft high, although occasional specimens attain a height of 5 ft.

The llama has a thick, coarse coat, which terminates abruptly along the bottom line of the body. Its long neck is well covered, but its throat is bare. Its fleece is valuable as fur and is erroneously known in the fur trade as vicuña fur. The hair closely resembles that of the alpaca, with a mixture of fine hairs and kemp.

Although of variegated colors, the llama fleece has a tendency to run to browns. Some fleeces are lighter, of course, some are pure brown and others are black; and some are pure white or a mixture of colors. The hair under the belly is generally white.

The llama's economic importance is as a burden carrier, and apparently always will be, for today the llama remains the only reliable draught animal of the upper Andes; it is able to live at altitudes of over 2½ miles above sea level without being subject to mountain sickness.

There are about 2 million llamas in Bolivia today, and probably a little less than half that number in Peru, with another 100,000 distributed throughout the higher areas of Ecuador, Chile, and Argentina. They are owned almost exclusively by the Indians, who alone appear able to understand and manage them.

Alpaca

Equally as important and surely of more specific importance to the textile industry is the alpaca, *Lama glama pacas,* the second of the domesticated species. This animal has always occupied a major position in the economic life of the great Andean plateau. It was indispensable to the general welfare in both Inca and pre-Inca days and has been almost equally so in the centuries that have intervened. Even today, although the sheep of the lower altitudes have increased immeasurably in number, its position as a fleece bearer is unchallenged. (See Fig. 8.)

Physical Characteristics. The alpaca is somewhat shorter than the llama, seldom being more than 3½ ft high. Its body, however, is proportionately larger, and of greater bulk. Like the llama, it is variegated in color, with grays and fawns predominating. Sometimes it is of a coffee color, sometimes pure white or black, and not infrequently piebald. Its soft fleece is remarkably beautiful, fine, and strong. The average weight of the animal is 175 lb.

The hair of the alpaca hangs down its sides, rump, and breast in long, glossy, and more or less tangled strands, measuring from 8 to 12 and, not infrequently, 16 in. in length, and when left unsheared for long periods it attains lengths of nearly 30 in. This hair differs from that of the llama in having no coarse or brittle fibers, which are common in the fleece of the llama. It shears from 4 to 7 lb every second year.

There are two distinct types of alpaca, the huacaya (or bacaya, as it is called in some districts) and the suri. The huacaya is bigger than the suri, heavier in weight, and in a general aspect more closely resembles the llama. The suri, however, produces a fleece that is finer, more lustrous, and thicker. The comparative weights of the fleeces yielded by these animals are: huacaya 5½ lb, suri 6½ lb, for the same period of growth and the same length of staple.

It is estimated that there are well over 2 million alpacas in Peru, 250,000 in Bolivia, and a small number on the high plateaus of Chile

FIG. 8. Alpaca, Peru. Suri breed. (*Courtesy Pan American Union.*)

and Argentina. Neither Peru nor Bolivia has ever made a census of the animal, so it is impossible to estimate the number of head with any degree of accuracy.

The alpaca does not thrive in regions lower than 12,000 ft, being in its own element in the lofty regions of 13,000 to 16,000 ft. It often ascends to heights of 17,000 ft or more, just below the snow line. The animal is not found north of the equator because of the absence of the grass ichu, its principal source of food. Nor has its acclimatization been found possible elsewhere, although attempted in various parts of the world, notably in England and Australia. Further efforts, however, are not likely to be made in the future, for under a law enacted by the government of Peru, the animals' exportation is now rigorously prohibited.

Until shearing time, the alpacas roam the limitless range throughout the day, and in the evening return to their corrals, dilapidated structures of stone for the most part, many of them antedating the Inca regime. The sixth sense of the alpaca is uncanny, and the flock knows instinctively when the time has come to follow the leader, called haino by the Indians, to the fold; unfailingly they return on the minute. The reason for enclosing the flocks at night is to obtain the excrement, the principal and, before the coming of the railroad, the only fuel of the puna. This product of the alpaca finds its chief use in the mines.

Efforts to raise the alpaca on a large commercial scale have been made from time to time, but invariably without success. A few years ago, for example, a British company leased thousands of acres from the Peruvian Government for this purpose, expecting to raise the alpaca as one does sheep, but the enterprise failed.

Hybrids of the Family, Huarizo and Misti

Being members of the same family and endowed with the same instincts and habits, llamas and alpacas mix freely, and out of the association come two hybrid animals, each possessing certain of the characteristics of both animals. As has been stated, these animals are huarizo, born of a llama father and an alpaca mother, and misti, the progeny of an alpaca father and a llama mother. In some remote regions, the huarizo is employed as a beast of burden, but the misti is never so used. The fleeces of these hybrids are not as fine, generally speaking, in either texture or quality as that of the alpaca.

All these animals produce a certain amount of fleece, but by far the preponderant portion is derived from the alpaca, which, in 1935, accounted for 93 per cent of the total Peruvian clip of approximately 8,200,000 lb. This included first, second, and inferior qualities. The actual figures were: alpaca, 93 per cent, huarizo and misti 5 per cent, and llama 2 per cent. The amount of fleece actually available for any manufacture of fine fabrics, after eliminating inferiors, approximated only 4 million lb per annum in recent years. From 1938 to 1942 the total annual export from Peru amounted to approximately 7,100,000 lb, of which 88 per cent was alpaca, 8 per cent huarizo, and 4 per cent llama.

The puna country stretching north and northwest of Lake Titicaca in an almost illimitable sweep is the chief fleece region, the most important collection points being Cusco, Sicuani, Checacupe, Santa Rosa, Juliaca, Ayravire, and Puno; the fiber obtained from Puno, however, is not considered of high grade. Eventually all these fleeces are shipped to Arequipa, via Cusco and Puno, for grading and sorting for color, after which they are baled for export to the markets of the world. Arequipa, a city in southwestern Peru, is situated at an altitude of 8000 ft, about 100 miles from the port of Mollendo.

Shearing. The alpacas are sheared during the warmest months of the year, late November and early December, just after the rains. Until recently, shearing was done in a most primitive manner by cutting the wool with knives, but at the present time shears are being used.

The fleece arrives in Arequipa in bulk, having been turned in and wound up into small bundles, resembling hands, for easier transportation. As the sacks are emptied, the fleece is examined very carefully to see that it has been properly represented for grade and that it has not been "loaded," a time-honored practice of increasing weight. The procedure here is to dampen the fleece and load it with sand, which, when it dries, adheres to the fleece and becomes like clay in effect. The fleece is then weighed, after which it is graded for color, each color being piled separately for later careful sorting. In this preliminary sorting the seven basic colors are obtained. They are white, fawn, gray, light brown, dark brown, black, and piebald. After the alpaca fleece is sorted, it is put up in the form of "bumps" and sent to the press for baling. Each bale weighs 100 kilos, or 220 lb. Llama, huarizo, coarse fleeces, and short pieces are handled separately.

Of the total yield of llama fleeces, including the various grades, it is estimated that more than 80 per cent passes through Arequipa to the port of Mollendo, Peru. The remainder, shipped from Callao and Tacna, other Peruvian ports, is known as Callao fleece and Tacna fleece. These are inferior in quality and poorly sorted. The packers put these various colors into lots of 100 bales each. The approximate percentage of the various colors present in such round lots is: white, 12 per cent; piebald, 10; light fawn, 13 to 14; light brown, 13 to 14; dark brown, 21; gray, 20, and black, 10. In order to get rid of all the colors, the packers will not break up their round lots and sell separate colors. In the period from 1938 to 1942, Peru exported a yearly average of 6,230,000 lb of alpaca, 320,000 lb of llama, 91,000 lb of short huarizo, and 470,000 lb of fine huarizo wool [1].

Vicuña [17, 10, 14, 21]

Vicuña wool is obtained from the smallest and most agile species of llama, the vicuña (*Lama vicunna*). It is the rarest and finest fiber classified as wool and is therefore very much sought after.

The animals are found in the wild state throughout the Andes mountains of Peru, their greatest concentration being in the Departments of Puno, Cuzco, Apurimac and Arequipa.

The habitat of the vicuña is at elevations of from 13,000 to 16,500 ft, where climatic conditions are not extremely variable. They abound where short grasses are found in the high damp prairie areas known as bofedales. Although they usually live at higher elevations, they are often found grazing in flocks with alpacas and llamas.

Fig. 9. Vicuñas, Peru. (*Courtesy S. Rosenfelder & Son.*)

Smaller than its three relatives, the vicuña stands less than 3 ft high and weighs from 75 to 100 lb. It is the most timid as well as the most graceful in appearance, having a fine, slender form (Fig. 9). The bodies are covered with a short wool; on the necks of the animals it has the appearance of fine down. On the flanks toward the chest and belly, the exquisitely soft coat is much longer and of a light cinnamon, known as vicuña, color. The color shades to a pallid white on the belly and the insides of the thighs. The average weight of a vicuña fleece is 1 lb, consisting of the cinnamon color as well as the white belly part. These two colors are present in a ratio of approximately 1 to 1, and both colors have the same degree of fineness. Between the chest and forelegs, almost down to the knees, and continuing along its flanks, are fringes of long white hair which form an apron, giving the vicuña a distinctly characteristic appearance. The apron is accentuated in the males. The long white hairs are also found intermixed with fine down in small percentages. The vicuña differs from the other three species also in having no callosities or bare spots on its hind legs.

The amounts of vicuña wool exported during the period 1933 to 1941 illustrate the rarity of this fiber (see Table 16).

TABLE 16. VICUÑA WOOL EXPORTS

	Countries of Destination			*Total*
Year	*Great Britain*	*United States*	*Italy*	*(pounds)*
1933	1107	..	..	1107
1936	3881	1173	..	5054
1938	1916	1379	132	3427
1939	246	1173	..	1419
1940	..	7995	..	7995
1941	..	906	..	906

Source: H. W. Alberts, American Consular Report 313, Lima, Peru (July 1944) [1].

The prices in Peru fluctuated: in 1933 the wool sold for approximately $10.00 per kilo; in 1936, $7.00 per kilo; in 1938, $7.50 per kilo; in 1939, $7.50 per kilo; in 1940, $9.50 per kilo; and in 1941, $10.00 per kilo. (1 kilo = 2.2 lb.) In Peruvian money a kilo in 1941 cost 21 soles; 1 sole is equal to $0.474.

Vicuñas can be domesticated only when captured very young or when they are born in the fold. Numerous attempts have been made at domestication, but only recently has it been a comparative success.

Most of the vicuñas being found in Peru, it is natural that the Peruvian Government should be most active in protecting the animal. It is exerting every possible effort to foster the vicuña and to this end is insisting that the law of 1921 be rigorously enforced. This law, one of the finest conservation measures ever placed upon the statute books of any country, should have most beneficial and far-reaching effects. Peru is now taking an animal census of the various flocks of vicuñas. According to figures released by the Peruvian Department of Agriculture at Lima, the total number of vicuñas in Peru at present is approximately a million. It is hoped that with adequate enforcement of the legislation referred to above and even stricter hunting and breeding regulations, the flocks will continue to increase. The available supply of vicuña fleeces in 1950 was very small indeed—approximately 10,000 lb—and was sold exclusively under license from the Peruvian Government.

Under present laws in Peru and neighboring countries the vicuñas are increasing. It is not uncommon to see as many as ten to fifteen flocks in crossing the mountains between Arequipa and Juliaca. If the present system of raising vicuñas under domestication proves to be successful, the number of animals can be increased enormously. The area suitable for raising them is extensive.

TABLE 17. Alpaca, Vicuña, Llama, and Huarizo Imports from Peru by the United States

(In the grease; thousands of pounds)

	1938	*Per Cent* *	*1942*	*Per Cent* *	*1943*	*Per Cent* *	*1944*	*Per Cent* *
Alpaca	1237	19	4084	80	5235	89	6295	94
Vicuña	1	33	0	0	0	0	0	0
Llama	0	0	177	72	190	79	142	92
Huarizo	11	24	195	39	429	80	455	95
Total	1249	17	4456	76	5854	88	6892	94

* Of total export. The remainder of the Peru export went to the United Kingdom, Germany, and Belgium.

Source: H. W. Alberts, American Consular Report 313, Lima, Peru (July 1944) [1].

Guanaco [25]

The fibers of the guanaco (*Lama huanaco*) have only recently been introduced by the woolen industry as one of the luxury fibers. The guanaco is thought to be the original stock from which came the llama and the alpaca. It is smaller in size than the llama, never growing to a height of more than 4 ft, but is larger than either the alpaca or the vicuña.

In general the guanaco is scattered over a much larger territory than the other auchenias. It is found in its wild state as far south as the Strait of Magellan. It seems that the animal has migrated southward because, in the llama land proper, it is very rarely found. It is quite plentiful in Patagonia where the animal furnishes the natives with food and raiment. See Fig. 10.

Although it resembles the llama somewhat in its outer form, the back of the guanaco is more arched and its body is less tapered at the waist. Guanacos are by far the swiftest of the four species, are very shy, and travel in small herds. The mixed coat is rather shaggy, but the down is of unusually fine texture. The color of the wool is reddish-brown on the upper and white on the lower portions of the body much like the vicuña, but the white area is larger. The pelts, especially the baby guanaco, known as guanaquito, resemble those of the red fox.

Some of the peltries taken in Chubut are very red; in fact almost copper colored.

Argentina is the principal source of guanaquito furs, and the guanaco fibers used in the woolen industry are obtained from Argentina peltry by the cutting and blowing process described for rabbit hair in Chapter XIV. The peltry of the guanaquito is used for trimming cloth coats. Their use for fur purposes is possible because the hairs of animals a

Fig. 10. Guanaco (*Lama huanacho*). (*Courtesy New York Zoological Park.*)

few weeks old are rather straight and lack the woolly texture. The best grade of peltry is that which, in general, resembles the fox and in which the beard hair is similar to the guard hair and the fine down, the fur fiber. The peltries are known by the names of the collecting sections. These sections are: Rio Gallegos, Chubut, Punta Arenas, Rio Negro, Santa Cruz, and Pampas. The finest type of peltry is produced in the Rio Gallegos district, which extends from southern Santa Cruz southward to the Punta Arenas area.

There has been confusion about the proper name of this peltry because certain concerns in the trade have adopted the name vicuña for it. This name is naturally misleading when used for the fibers cut from the guanaquito peltry.

The hair is a mixed type containing approximately 10 per cent beard hair. Microscopically, the guanaco is similar to vicuña, the only difference being in the fineness and color. Fineness measurements made on guanaco fibers place it between the alpaca and vicuña. Fiber width averages vary from 18 to 24 μ.

The commercially available product which is cut from Argentine pelts and then blown averages 19 μ with a fiber dispersion from 5 to 60 μ.

Physical Properties. The fleeces of the llama and alpaca are similar in character to the Angora goat hair. During the years of breeding, the undercoat has disappeared and the hairs have become quite uniform in diameter and length. A high percentage of kemp is present in the llama, whereas the fine alpaca has practically none. The raw fiber contains a small amount of natural grease (less than 4 per cent), and the total amount of impurities does not exceed 25 per cent. The average yield of fiber is 80 per cent.

The vicuña fleece has two distinct types of hairs, similar to camel hair: the outer or beard hair and the under or wool hair. Beard hair is not used, whereas the wool hair, which grows close to the skin, is the softest and finest wool fiber used in wool manufacturing. The average length is about 2 in.

Strength. The figures given in the literature regarding the strength of these specialty hair fibers vary considerably. Table 18 shows results, establishing the strength factor on a more scientific basis, obtained in the laboratory of the Forstmann Woolen Co.

TABLE 18. BREAKING STRENGTH OF SPECIALTY HAIR FIBERS

[Standard conditions: 70° F. at 65 per cent R.H.; bundle test on tops.]

Quality	*Average Fineness (microns)*	*Average Bundle Size (grams)*	*Average Breaking Strength* * *(pounds per square inch)*	*Coefficient of Variation (per cent)*
Mohair, super kid	25.4	0.0889	35,610	2.4
Mohair, 32's	30.0	0.0896	35,220	1.1
Mohair, 22's	36.4	0.0891	35,330	2.5
Cashmere down	15.0	0.0296	23,870	3.3
Camel hair, fine	20.7	0.0578	29,590	3.2
Camel hair, coarse	26.6	0.0603	29,880	3.2
Alpaca, white	27.0	0.0944	30,090	0.7
Alpaca, light brown	27.0	0.0885	28,870	2.6
Alpaca, black	27.0	0.0915	27,810	3.4

* Calculated on a dry basis.

NOTE: Length of the test specimen: Camel hair, 2 in.; mohair and alpaca, 3 in.; cashmere, 1 in.

The specialty hair fibers were found to be generally stronger than the wool of the same fineness, with the mohair fibers leading in strength. It is interesting to note that the fineness does not influence the strength, as it does in wool. The amount of dye pigments present has a clear influence on the alpaca fiber, with the black alpaca approximately 8 per cent weaker than the white. The fineness of the various hairs yielded by the members of the llama family is indicated in Table 19.

TABLE 19. FINENESS OF COMMERCIAL HAIRS FROM LLAMA, ALPACA, AND VICUÑA

Types	Llama		Alpaca		Huarizo Scoured Carded	Vicuña Scoured Carded
	Raw Mixed	Baby Scoured	Scoured Piebald	Tops Various		
Number of fibers measured	500	400	1000	1200	500	1100
Average, μ	27.0	20.1	26.7	27.3	25.8	13.2
Standard deviation, μ	6.3	4.4	7.1	8.0	6.1	2.3
Standard error, μ	0.28	0.22	0.22	0.23	0.27	0.07
Coefficient of variation, per cent	23.3	21.9	26.6	29.3	23.6	17.4
Dispersion, μ	10 to 60	10 to 40	10 to 60	10 to 60	10 to 50	6 to 25

Expressed in wool fineness terms, llama, alpaca, and huarizo range between a 56's and a 60's wool grade, with the baby llama as fine as 70's. The vicuña is between a 120's and a 130's wool quality, which indicates that the vicuña is by far the finest fiber of all wools and specialty fibers.

Microscopic Properties. The epidermal scales of all hairs of the llama family are very indistinct, although present, as in camel hair. The cortex is regularly striated and filled with color pigment except in the white. The main characteristic is the presence of interrupted medulla. In general, less than 10 per cent of the fibers are nonmedullated. In the beard hairs, this medulla shows a contraction in the middle, appearing as a double channel, as seen in the cross-section of the alpaca hair. This form of medulla is of great aid in fiber identification (see Figs. 11 and 12).

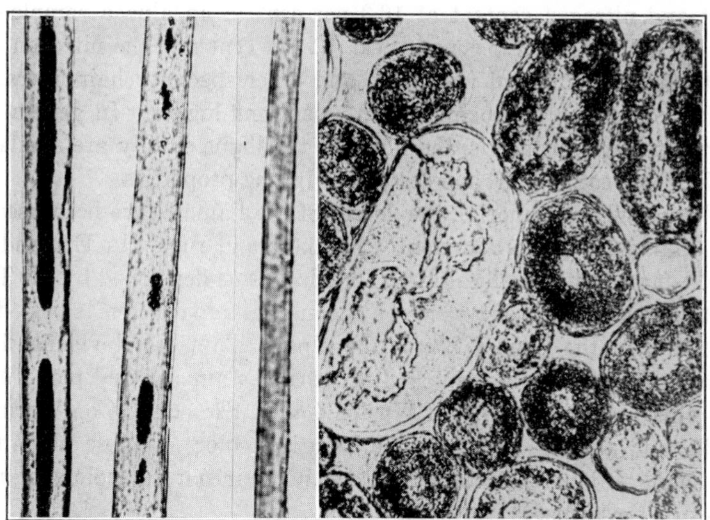

FIG. 11. Alpaca. White hair, longitudinal (×240). Fawn and white, cross-section (×500).

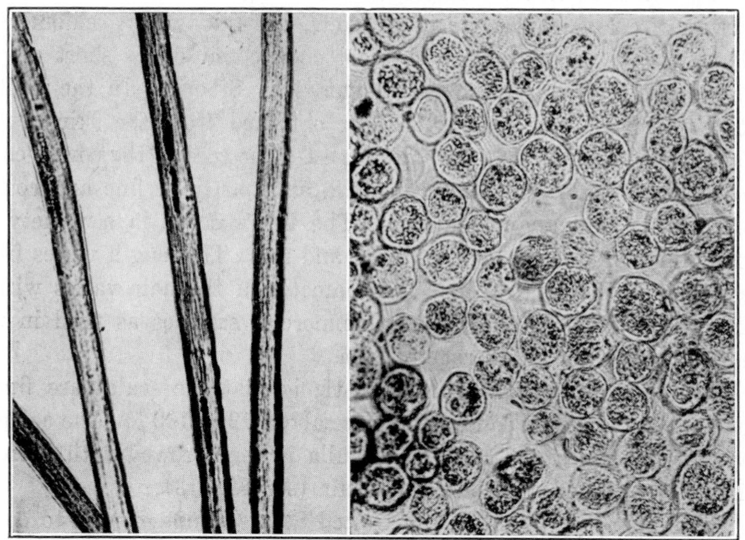

FIG. 12. Vicuña. Longitudinal (×240). Cross-section (×500). (*Courtesy American Wool Handbook.*)

Chemical Properties. Harris [8] found a sulfur content of 4.17 per cent and nitrogen content of 16.3 per cent in an alpaca sample. In vicuña hairs the sulfur content was 4.1 per cent and the nitrogen content 16.26. Compared with wool and other specialty hair fibers, the sulfur content is approximately 0.5 per cent higher. In general behavior toward chemicals, the fibers of the llama family are similar to mohair and camel hair, and show poor fulling properties.

From time immemorial, the fleeces of the llamas have been used by the Indians in the production of blankets and rugs. In England the world-famed village of Saltaire, Yorkshire, was developed by Sir Titus Salt, following his discovery of the use of alpaca for ladies' dress fabrics. In the United States the alpaca, llama, and vicuña fibers have been extensively employed for women's apparel and men's coats by mills such as Forstmann Woolen Co., S. Stroock & Co., Worumbo Mills, and others. Owing to the beautiful colors of these fibers they are employed to the best advantage in their natural colors or mixtures of the same.

Cow Hair

Cow hair is extensively employed as a low-grade fiber for the manufacture of coarse carpet yarns, blankets, and felts. It is seldom used alone, always in mixtures with wool on account of its short staple. The world supply is principally covered by Siberia. In the United States domestic cow hair is used as obtained from the skin of the slaughtered animals by a pulling process. The coat of the cow is composed partly of hairs without medulla and partly of fine and coarse beard hairs strongly medullated. The fibers occur in a variety of colors, including white, brown, black and red. The length varies from less than ½ in. up to 2 in. The diameter of the hair varies within wide limits from 12 to 180 μ. Commercial samples as used in the carpet trade show an average of 36 μ.

The main microscopic characteristic is that the scales are finely toothed and arranged so that there are about 12 in 100 μ. The cortical layer is finely striated and the medulla is single-rowed with narrow, distinctly outlined cells, filled with air (see Fig. 13).

The amount produced in the United States is not enough to cover the demand, therefore large quantities have to be imported, mainly from Canada, Japan, Germany, England, and Spain. The average imports of cattle hair in the 5-year period from 1931 to 1935 are given in Table 20.

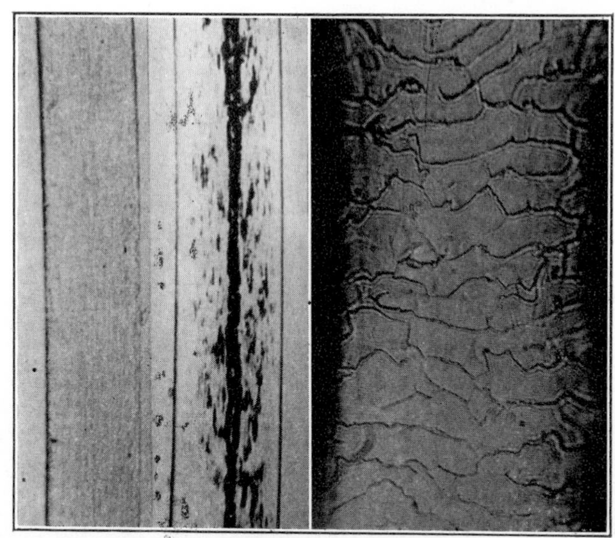

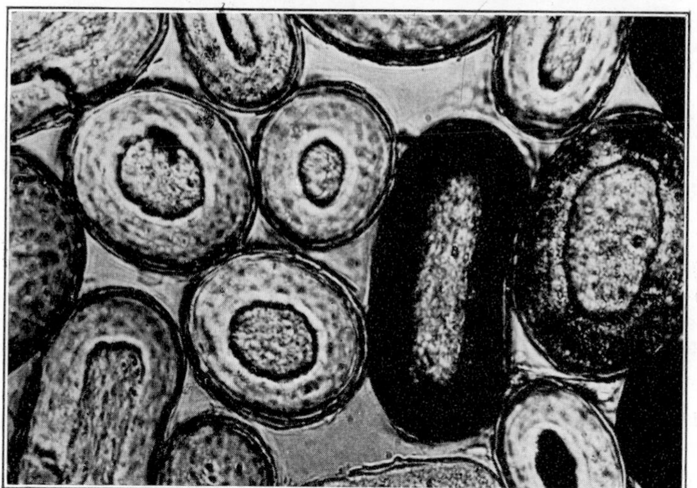

Calf's hair cross-section (×500).

FIG. 13. Cow hairs. (*Courtesy Textile Fiber Atlas.*)

TABLE 20. IMPORTS OF CATTLE HAIR

[Source: U. S. Tariff Commission, Comparative Statistics, Vol. V, pt. 3, "Wool and Hair."]

	Pounds (millions)
Body hairs at $0.05 per lb	3.127
Cattle switches, i.e., long tail hair at $1.15 per lb	3.190
Total	6.317

Horsehair

Horsehair finds little use in ordinary woolen and worsted goods. The mane and tail hair is used in manufacturing of upholstery cloth

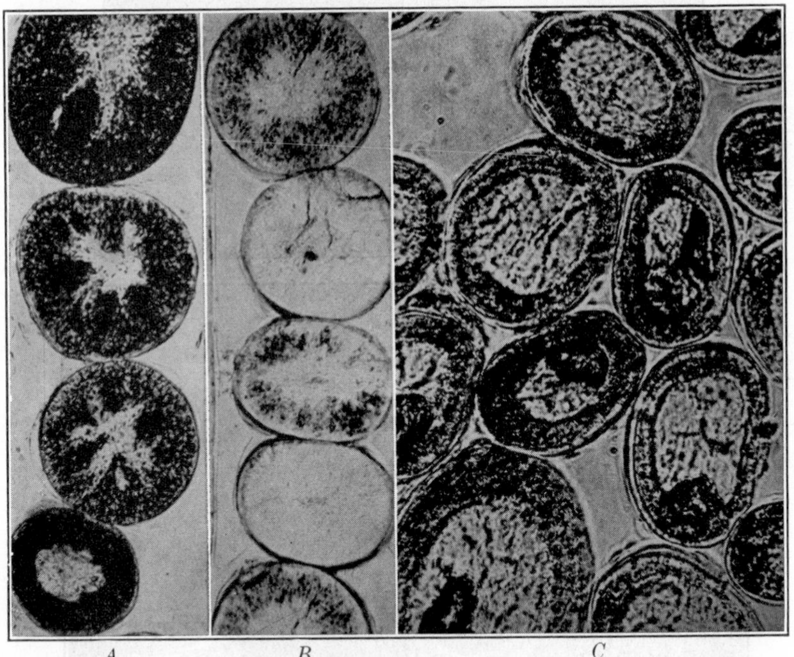

A B C

FIG. 14. Cross-sections of horse hairs. *A*, black hair (×115); *B*, white hair (×115); *C*, pony hair (×500). (*Courtesy Textile Fiber Atlas.*)

for railroad car seats, whereas the much shorter body hair is used mainly as upholstery stuffing. Horsehair is also used as stuffing in men's suits and coats (see Figs. 14 and 15).

In their microscopic structure horsehairs are very similar to the human hair, but in cross-section they differ. The human hair is mostly

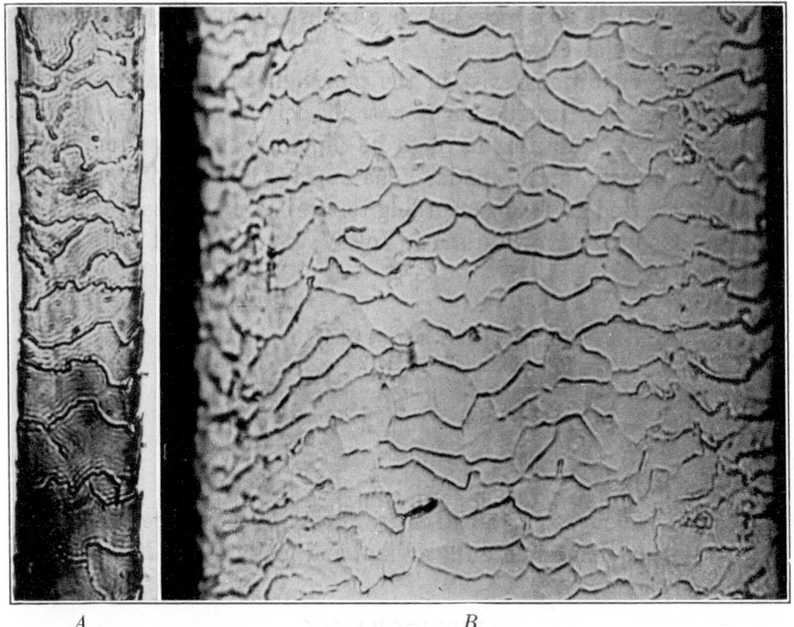

FIG. 15. Horsehair epidermis. *A*, pony epidermis (×500); *B*, horse epidermis (×500). (*Courtesy Textile Fiber Atlas.*)

elliptical; horsehair is highly circular, and strongly medullated. The dispersion range for mane hair is 50 to 200 μ; for tail hair 75 to 280 μ.

TABLE 21. WIDTH VARIATIONS IN HORSEHAIR *

Type of Hair	*Age of Animal (years)*	*Average Diameter (microns)*	*Coefficient of Variation (per cent)*	*Dispersion Range (microns)*
Tail	1	149	11.2	113 to 188
Tail	11	167	11.0	123 to 213
Tail	19	183	10.4	133 to 233
Mane	1	121	19.7	73 to 168
Mane	11	129	14.9	93 to 173
Mane	19	124	17.8	98 to 158
50% tail, 50% mane	..	147	29.6	68 to 253

* Courtesy of Appel, National Bureau of Standards.

In a special study made at the National Bureau of Standards on the fineness of mane and tail hair from three horses, the results shown in Table 21 were obtained by measuring groups of 100 fibers, which indicates clearly that it is possible to establish from which part of the body the hair was taken.

The same conditions exist in the horsehair market as in the cow hair market. Our production is not sufficient to cover the demand; therefore large quantities have to be imported, mainly from China, Argentina, Russia, and Canada. The average imports of horsehair in the 5-year period 1931–35, according to the United States Tariff Commission (Comparative Statistics, Vol. V, pt. 3, "Wool and Hair"), amounted to:

	Million Lb
Tail and mane hair at $0.47	1.217
Raw horsehair at $1.12	1.593
Total	2.810

Musk-Ox [23]

Musk-ox is not a commercial fiber. Attempts have been made from time to time to domesticate the animal and make use of its hair.

BIBLIOGRAPHY

1. Alberts, H. W., American Consular Report #313, Lima, Peru (1944).
2. American Society for Testing Materials, D-13, Wool Section I, Subcommittee A-3.
3. Barker, A. F., *The Prospective Development of Peru as a Sheep-Breeding and Wool Growing Country,* Leeds (1927).
4. Barker, A. F., *The Cottage Textile Industries of Kashmir,* Leeds (1933).
5. Burns, R., personal correspondence.
6. Burns, R., "Glimpses of Iranian Livestock," *Nat. Wool Grower* (July and Aug. 1950).
7. Hardy, J., "Studies of the Occurrence and Elimination of Kemp Fibers in Mohair Fleeces," U. S. Dept. Agr. *Tech. Bull.* 35 (1927).
8. Harris, Milton, personal correspondence.
9. Hodge, W. H., "Camels of the Clouds," *Nat. Geog. Soc.* (May 1946).
10. Plail, J., "Microscopic Appearance of Goat's Hair, Mohair and Cashmere Wool," *Melliand Textilber.,* **8,** 197–200 (1927).
11. Skinkle, J. H., "The Determination of Wool and Mohair by Scale Size and Diameter," *Am. Dyestuff Reptr.,* **25,** 620 (1936).
12. Stroock, S. I., *The Story of Camel Hair* (1936).
13. Stroock, S. I., *Llamas and Llama Land* (1937).
14. Stroock, S. I., *Vicuña—The World's Finest Fabric* (1937).
15. Turkish Embassy, "Reglement relativ au controle des exportations de Mohairs," Decret No. 2/12699 (Jan. 19, 1940).
16. U. S. Dept. Agr., "The Angora Goat and Mohair Industry," *Bull.* 50 (March 1929).

17. U. S. Dept. Agr., "Proposed Standards for Grades of Mohair," *Federal Register* **15** (202) (Oct. 18, 1950).

18. U. S. Dept. Commerce, "The Interdepartmental Angora Goat and Mohair Committee," *Misc. Circ.* 50 (March 1929).

19. von Bergen, W., and Mauersberger, H. R., *American Wool Handbook,* 2d ed., Textile Book Publishers, New York (1948).

20. von Bergen, W., "Cashmere," *The Melliand,* **1** (6), 855 (Sept. 1929).

21. von Bergen, W., "Vicuña," *The Melliand,* **2,** 353 (June 1930).

22. von Bergen, W., "Wool and Mohair," *Am. Dyestuff Reptr.,* **26,** 271–279 (May 17, 1937).

23. von Bergen, W., "Musk-Ox Wool and its Possibilities as a New Textile Fiber," *Melliand Textile Monthly,* 3, 6, 7, 8, 9, 10 (Sept., Oct., Nov., Dec. 1931; Jan. 1932).

24. Williams, G. P., "The Angora Goat," U. S. Dept. Agr. *Farmers' Bull.* 1203 (1936).

25. Whitford, A. C., "Guanaco Fibers," *Textile Research* (Nov. 1939).

CHAPTER XIV

TEXTILE FUR FIBERS, ANIMAL BRUSH FIBERS, AND DOWN

MAX BACHRACH

History

The use of the hair covering of fur-bearing animals for textile purposes dates far into antiquity, and the early natives of western South America are known to have used the various breeds of the chinchilla family to make a soft, warm fabric. In Europe, the hair covering of rabbits and hares has been used in mixtures with other fibers, chiefly wool, for many centuries, but it has never been an article of large fabric production until recent years.

During the early 1920's, rabbit hair and rabbit fur, as well as that of the hare, and lately muskrat and other fur fibers were used in special fabrics both in France and the United States. The aim in these fabrics was to produce a furry or hairy appearance and a soft handle. At first, a comparatively small percentage of fur fibers was worked into the fabrics because of mechanical difficulties, such as flying during carding and static electricity, but this has since been practically overcome.

Angora rabbit has been used extensively in the manufacture of knitting yarns since the late 1800's. Rabbit fibers, as well as fibers from other fur-bearing animals, have been used for hundreds of years in the manufacture of hats, but this subject will not be given consideration in this chapter.

It is necessary to understand, however, that fur-bearing animals have two types of hair covering: (1) the long spikelike hairs, known as guard hairs, which serve as the raincoat of the animal, and (2) the soft downy fibers, which are shorter than the guard hairs and serve to give warmth to the animal during the cold season.

The seasonal weather changes cause corresponding changes in the texture and amount of hair of fur-bearing animals. During the warmer, wet spring weather, the fur fibers are molted and the guard hairs take on a more prominent appearance. With the advent of the fall and winter, the fur fiber is again fully developed and the new guard hairs are silkier than in the spring.

The use of muskrat guard hair dates since about 1937, and the conditions described for the rabbit prevail in the hair covering of this animal. Since the muskrat is a water rodent, the best quality of fur and hair is found during the spring months, when the water in the streams and lakes is at its coldest.

Raw Material Varieties

Cutting or plucking the fibers of fur-bearing animals solely for textile purposes is too expensive for the general run of clothing fabrics. This disadvantage has been overcome by using hair and fur by-products of the fur and hat industries. These have become the most important sources of supply for the so-called rabbit hair fabrics.

In the manufacture of men's and ladies' hats, the skin is shredded from the hair covering which, after being graded into different qualities, is put into a blowing machine, which separates the guard hair from the fur fiber. The fur fiber is retained by the hat manufacturer because of its excellent felting qualities, but the nonfelting guard hair is discarded. Such hair as can be used by the textile industry is sold for the manufacture of fabrics. Other types of hair, such as that of the Australian rabbits, are generally disposed of for fertilizer and glue stock.

The type of hair desired by the textile industry is from the white "French" type of rabbit. It is obtained from France, Belgium, Germany, Poland, Italy, North America, China, and Japan. The better rabbit pelts are used for manufacturing fur garments. The general trade term for this fur is "coney." The less expensive grades are sold to the hatters for cutting and blowing.

Garments of rabbit fur are made either from peltries having the guard hairs intact, or those which are sheared to simulate the more expensive furs such as seal and beaver. In processing these latter peltries, the guard hairs are either sheared off to the height of the fur or they are pulled out with a plucking machine; these plucked hairs are much longer than those which are sheared.

The great majority of fur skins are sheared, as plucking is much slower and more expensive. The stubs, which remain in the sheared product, are later removed by a "guillotining" process (known as "unhairing"). Since this is done after the peltries are dyed, the value of these hairs is low, varying with the staple and the dye. The length of these stub hairs is usually from 0.39 to 0.59 in.

The hair blown out in the hat-manufacturing processes is longer in staple, inasmuch as the skin is shorn away from the basal portion of the hair. The cutting machine has spiral knives which whirl against the skin, slicing it away in thin fine shreds.

Not all the fur fibers which go into the making of felt hats is cut fur; in order to get proper felting it is required that very short-staple fur be mixed into the batch. To reduce costs it is frequently necessary to put in fur, which otherwise would be wasted. This fur is obtained from various sources but principally from what is known as "boiled fur."

Boiled fur is obtained by boiling in sulfuric acid (3 per cent technical grade solution) the tails, ears, snouts, and paws of the raw skins. Pieces of dressed skins obtained from the fur factories as waste are handled similarly. This fur is washed and dried, then blown, and later mixed with the cut fur.

The guard hair remaining after blowing is sold for textile purposes; microscopical examination should be made to see that it has not been overboiled, which produces cracked and shattered fibers. These may cause difficulties in the finished yarn and cloth, especially after fulling, when the hair points will be missing, spoiling a desired appearance.

Fur fibers without the guard hair have also been blended with practically all vegetable, animal, and man-made fibers used in cloth manufacture. Fur fibers have no special appearance, but they give an exceptionally soft handle to the yarn when used in mixtures greater than 15 per cent. In some novelty yarns the fur fibers create a nubby appearance, which is accomplished by matting the fur while it is being processed in the boiling plant.

Commercial Classifications

Zoologically, hares and rabbits belong to the order Lagomorpha, although they resemble the Rodentia. They are generally catalogued under the family of Leporidae, genus *Lepus*. No special zoological classification is made between the large, domestically raised European and American rabbits and hares, except to designate locale and the subgenus nomenclature. The small common rabbit, which has brown guard hair and bluish fur, is imported in great quantities from Australia and is classified as *Lepus cuniculus*.

Rabbit hair is supplied in two natural colors: white and gray. It is also dyed; the dyed hair is nearly always boiled from skin pieces, but the natural hair may be either cut or boiled.

There are three general classifications of length: (1) The long cut from the hatters' stocks, (2) the plucked hairs from the plants of the fur processor, and (3) the sheared or short cut, a by-product of the fur dyer's plant, which may be very short or of medium length, depending on the type of skin originally processed.

Sectional grades are practically never kept separate, as in the fur-processing plants the skins from different sections, including many types and places of origin, are thrown together into the same dye vats, later on to be separated into the different quality grades as required. The shearing and plucking operations, which precede the vat manipulations, do not permit the separation of the different grades of hair. In some hatters' cutting shops facilities may permit keeping these grades separate, inasmuch as the grading of the fur is carried through the cutting operations and the hair is blown out before the final mixtures are made. This is not necessarily true of all fur-cutting plants, especially in those cutting up smaller quantities or those cutting up lower-priced hat products.

The sectional grades used by furriers and hatters do not always have a bearing on the desirability of the hair for textile use, inasmuch as some cloths require a coarse hair, whereas others are preferably made with soft grades. Seasonal differences in all sections cause changes in hair from coarse to fine. Males or bucks produce coarser hair than does. Since these hairs are a by-product, no standard classification has been attempted. The individual millman has to use his own discretion in buying rabbit hair.

Rabbit fur which is not mixed with the hair can be bought in regular hatters' grades, and these grades vary with the individual fur cutter. These grades in general are the backs, sides, rump, and neck, each of which has a different staple and different felting properties; the back is considered best by most hatters.

Mixed staples will be found among the boiled products, into which go the heads, snouts, ears, paws, and tails.

For textile purposes the white and gray French, Belgian, and American rabbits offer the longest staples; the Polish and German hair is somewhat shorter; the Japanese is about the same, and the Chinese is the shortest.

Australian rabbits are used in largest quantities and provide the most important products of the hatters' trade as well as the fur trade. The guard hair is short and bristly and not especially useful for textile purposes. The fur is grayish but may be bleached into a pale beige or a pale gray white.

An interesting type of hair and fur is obtained from the Russian hares known by the name of *Zayats;* they come chiefly from the Siberian regions of Ob and Yenisei Rivers. The raw skins like other Russian furs are controlled by the Soviet Government and are offered either at public bidding or are obtained by private contract with the U.S.S.R.

The belly hairs are longer and softer than those of the back in most of the hare species and are usually sorted separately after the skin is clipped away. The Russian hares and the Scandinavian and Finnish hares have soft long belly hairs like the short Angora rabbit hair. The back hairs are slightly longer than those of the French rabbit inasmuch as they have a longer shaft, but a shorter, broader diameter in the medial and apical hair regions.

Angora Rabbit

Angora rabbit guard hair and fur fiber are the longest and softest of the rabbit fibers. Erroneously, the fiber is called "angora wool." Obviously it is not a wool and therefore does not come under the wool tariff regulations. The Angora rabbit, which originated from the type of animal coming from Asia Minor, has been raised for over 100 years by the peasants of France, Belgium, Switzerland, and neighboring countries. Since 1930, the United States has shown more interest in its home-grown product although previously angora was not raised here to any great extent. Angora rabbit hair has brought the highest price of any fiber. The exact quantity produced annually is not definitely known.

Grades. The fibers are graded according to length and cleanliness. Fibers to be of first-grade classification must be at least 2 to 3 in. or better in length, averaging 2½ in., of soft texture, and not tangled or matted. The fibers of second grade must be 1½ to 2 in. long and also must contain no matted or tangled hairs. The fibers of third grade are 1½ in. or under and free from tangled or matted hairs. Fibers of fourth grade are clean and pure white, but are matted. Fifth grade includes fibers that are not clean, whether matted or unmatted.

Angora rabbits can be sheared four times a year, depending upon weather conditions and geographical location. In the winter, the shearing is done by leaving half an inch of hair on the skin. In the summer the rabbit is sheared close to the skin and care must be exercised to shear just before the rabbits molts, otherwise the hairs will become matted. Plucking of angora fur just prior to molting is said to produce longer, livelier fur.

A large part of the American flocks are obtained from the Pacific coast area, where the climatic conditions are more uniform throughout the year. The French and Belgian spinners in Rhode Island are the principal processors.

Muskrat

The muskrat belongs to the order Rodentia, super-family Muroidae, family Cricetidae, genus *Ondatra*. The northern variety is known as *Ondatra zibethica*, and the southern variety as *Ondatra rivalicia*.

Muskrat hair can be classed into two general textures, the soft and medium soft from the northern variety (*Ondatra zibethica*) and coarse shorter hair from the southern variety found chiefly in the delta of the Mississippi River (*Ondatra rivalicia*). The Canadian types offer the finest texture of guard hair, but guard hair cannot be assorted as to sectional grades because it is not feasible to keep different types of skins separate in the fur-processing plants. It is simpler for the furrier to have his skins processed all together; he can then assort them into the types he will require for his garments, after they are returned to him already processed.

Muskrat hair is more bristly than any of the rabbit hairs. The color of the hair is dark brown and the fur a deep bluish gray. This fur can be bleached into a pale beige, and sometimes a grayish white. It is a by-product of (1) boiling in the hatters' plants, (2) piece-cutting and blowing from hatters' plants, and (3) the shearings from fur-processing plants when the muskrat peltries are to be dyed into seal simulations.

The hatters' plants offer a full-length staple because the skin is cut away from the hair; since muskrats are too expensive to use in their entirety for the average felt hats, only the waste natural-color pieces which fall from the furriers' table are used. These pieces are pasted on paper by machine or manually, and are put through the cutting machines, following which the guard hairs are blown separate from the fur. Some plants do not cut their muskrat pieces, preferring to boil them.

The hairs obtained from the fur dye plants are sheared down to the tip length of the fur, so that it is actually cut at the lower portion of the medial hair region, i.e., slightly above where the lower terminus of the fusiform shape of the middle of the hair continues into the basal third. The serrated lower part of the guard hairs, which is of great assistance in the spinning process, is thus absent.

Other types of furs which are occasionally used in the hatters' trades and can be used by the textile industry are the fox, wolf, mink, and skunk; in these furs the guard hair and fur can be used. These furs are always boiled products of the waste pieces which come from the furriers' factories.

Nutria and beaver pieces are either pasted and then cut, or else may be boiled for hatters' purposes. The fur is used in the more expensive felt hats, but the guard hair is too bristly and stiff to find use in textiles.

Economics and Statistics

The cost of preparation of fur hair is usually absorbed entirely in the direct product from which these hairs are a by-product; the market prices charged are dependent almost entirely on the available supply at the time of the demand. The exception is the Russian hares and Angoras, which are processed for textile purposes.

The cost of producing the hair and fur is based upon the yield after the skin is clipped away; the hair is blown from the fur, and both may be bought separately as in some instances more hair is desired than fur. The fur has no appearance value, but gives the soft handle desired in certain fabrics.

The cost of clipping the skin varies with the original weight of the skins and the yield varies greatly, depending on the thickness of the skin and the profusion of the hair covering. The net yield of the hair and fur runs anywhere from 15 to 35 per cent, and each lot of cut hair and fur is assayed separately.

Statistics are lacking as to the quantities which have been sold to the textile industry in this country or abroad. At times of great demand the same lot of hair may be resold between dealers selling the textile trades. There is usually a foreign demand, but the export statistics give only the number of pounds of pieces and cuttings collectively and no definite figures of quantities of either cut hair or the pieces containing the hair.

The chief market in the United States for the trading of the pieces and some of the cut fur is located in New York. The cut fur is obtained from the hatters' cutting plants in Danbury, Bethel, and South Norwalk, Conn. Several hat plants doing cutting are also located in Philadelphia, Pa., and Newark, N. J.

Rabbits from Australia are sold by the pound in the raw state; the white rabbits from Europe and Asia are generally sold on a per-skin basis; those from the United States are sold both by the pound and by the skin.

MICROSCOPIC APPEARANCE AND PHYSICAL CHARACTERISTICS

Rabbits

The European and United States varieties of white and gray rabbits have fur and hair of varying length, according to the season and origin. The full winter quality for fiber averages from 0.65 to 0.75 in.; the guard hair from 1.00 to 1.25 in. These hairs have three physical sections: apical, medial, and basal. The shape of the rabbit guard hair in the apical region, sometimes extending to half the medial region, is fusiform. The section below this down to the skin is generally uniform in contour. Just before molting, the shaft of the hair gets thinner where it protrudes from the skin, owing to the contraction of the follicular orifices.

The cuticular scales have a varied pattern in the different sections of the guard hair, but all are imbricated, flattened scales with wavy edges, and for the most part semi-coronal in their contour. The cuticular scales vary in shape in the different regions of the hair. In the basal third they run slightly diagonal to almost horizontal, and this continues into the lower part of the medial section where the bulge of the hair diminishes.

TABLE 1. Fineness Analysis of Rabbit Hair in Percentages *

Details	*Various Rabbit Hair*	*Angora Rabbit*
Number of fibers	1000	400
Per cent of fibers from:		
5 to 10 μ	11	15
10 to 15 μ	52	60
15 to 20 μ	29	22
20 to 25 μ	6	2
25 to 30 μ	2	1
Per cent of coarse fibers	4 over 30 μ	2 over 30 μ
Average microns	14.3	13.2
Standard deviation	4.0	3.3
Standard error	0.13	0.16
Coefficient of variation, per cent	28.1	24.6

* Courtesy of Forstmann Woolen Co. laboratory.

In the lower part of the medial section, the edges of the scales run upward in a series of hills and valleys, and are not easily photographed. The reason for this is that the contour of the medial section of the hairs is in many instances either like a dumbbell or else so extremely ovoid as to have both edges of the oval draw out almost to a point; sometimes it has a bananalike appearance (see Figs. 1 to 4). The scales on the apical tip of the hair make this pattern still more exaggerated.

The intermediary hairs are really guard hairs that do not attain their full growth but otherwise have the characteristics of the guard hair.

The medulla of both the guard hairs and the intermediary hairs is a series of long columns of cuticular air spaces, separated by the solid connected medullary tissue. These cells start as a single column in the basal section of the hair and divide into a series of columns, which may range from 3 or 4 to 19 or 20 in the medial section of the hair. These columns are generally twisted like a rope at one or two places, giving the hair its dumbbell shape. This multiple formation in the medullary extends usually to about halfway up the apical section. There it may become double or single column, generally the latter, in the tip of the hair. See Fig. 2.

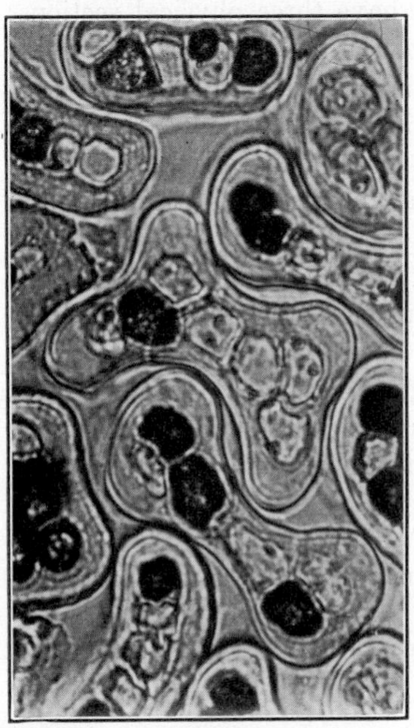

FIG. 1. Cross-section of angora rabbit guard hair. (×500.) (*Krauss.*)

Each of the air vesicles, which are found in the medial and lower apical sections, may show a small amount of pigmentation along the bottom edges. The color of this pigment in the white rabbit is extremely faint, whereas in the gray rabbit it is a deep gray, almost black. In the gray rabbit there is a secondary, pale yellowish tinge, but this is generally absent in the white rabbit. This diffused color appears to be in the cortex cells as well as in the medulla; it is definitely due to protein coloration rather than distinct pigment granules, such as are found in the air vesicles and the medullary tissues.

The fur fibers have more of a general equalized contour throughout, becoming only very slightly larger in the upper half of the medial region and gradually tapering to a fine tip. The contour runs from round to oval in the basal region, to ovoid and square-ovoid in the medial section, and continues to an oval shape in the apical section. The scales are imbricated of semi-coronal formation and fairly uniform throughout; the edges of the cuticular scales run quite close to each other.

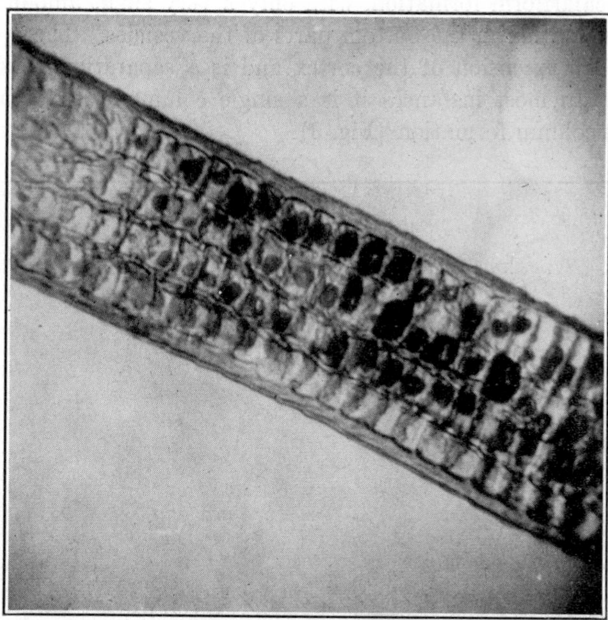

FIG. 2. Rabbit guard hair showing construction of air spaces and multiple medulla.

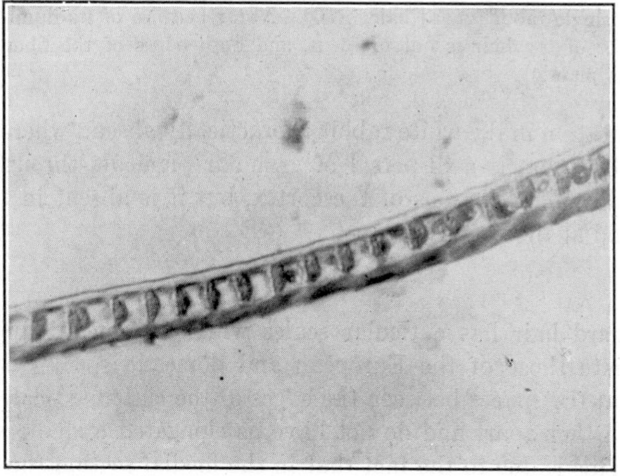

FIG. 3. White rabbit fur fiber.

The medullary formation consists of large-sized air vesicles of a square scalariform formation, with only a very slight amount of pigment granulation in the bottom parts of the vesicles. The medullary tissue is an extension of the cortex and is a separation between the vesicles. In most instances it is a single column, with occasionally a double column formation (Fig. 3).

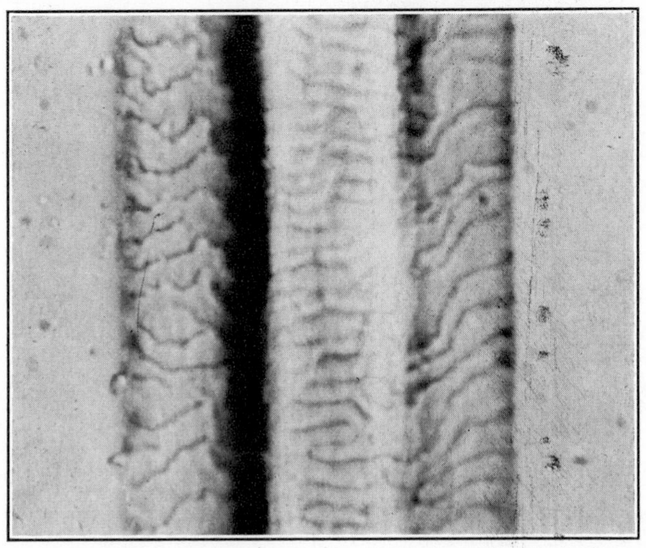

FIG. 4. A single rabbit guard hair, ×300. *Note:* because of its dumbbell shape the center of the hair is out of focus, and both edges of the fiber show the serrations plainly.

Pigmentation in the white rabbit is practically absent, whereas in the gray rabbit there is a dispersal of granular pigments throughout the medial and apical sections of the cortex, but it is absent in the basal section and at the very tip.

Hare

The guard hair has cuticular scales which in general appearance approximate those of the European and domestic species of rabbit, except that the spaces between the edges of the cuticular scales are set slightly farther apart and do not have as elongated a shape as in the rabbit. This is due to the fact that in the medial section the hair has only a slightly bulbous shape.

The medulla in the hare guard hair has a series of columns starting as a single column in the basal region, gradually dividing into a series of columns running from 5 or 6 to as many as 18 or 20. The air vesicles are rectangular with rounded sides, and the gray species show a diffusion of pigment granules scattered chiefly along the lower edges of each vesicle. The columns are set very close together, showing that the medullary tissue has only a very thin formation. The moisture content of uncarroted rabbit fur, at standard conditions of 72° F. and 65 per cent R.H., is on the dry side 10.9 per cent, and from the wet side 12.5 per cent.

Angora Rabbit

The guard hair is softer in texture than that of any other rabbit fiber; it ranges in length from 1 to 3 in. The hair shaft runs uniform in diameter for the lower three-quarters of its length, the upper quarter bulging upward and coming to a sudden fine tip. The hair has a high luster. The medulla in the lower half of the hair is often discontinuous, especially in the intermediary type of hair. Ordinarily it has a single series of cells formed in a scalariform pattern which changes into two and then into numerous columns in the apical section. They have somewhat the appearance of the columnar formation of the air vesicles found in the hare.

The fur fiber, which is also lustrous, varies from 0.5 to 1½ in. or occasionally longer. The medulla is arranged in a single column of saccate cells. Pigmentation is generally absent throughout.

The scales on the guard hair have the general formation of those found in hare, especially those in the bulging apical region, although in the lower three-quarters of the shaft, the scale edges are placed slightly farther apart.

The scales in the fur fiber are imbricated and the edges are also set farther apart than those of the hare; they run approximately halfway around the shaft.

Muskrat

The cuticular scales of the guard hair are imbricated; the scales are broad with slightly toothed edges, and form about one-quarter to one-third of the circumference. In the medial third, the edges are set closer together than in the base or apex. The length of the hair varies in different parts, the longest hair coming from the rump and the shortest toward the neck. The color is a deep brown, darker toward the tip, and lighter, rather bluish, toward the base. The broadened area starts about ¾ in. from the tip and tapers to a point.

The fur fiber has approximately the same diameter throughout, with a light beige coloration in the apical region, turning to a dull gray in the basal part. The scales are imbricated, running usually about one-half the circumference of the hair. The medulla is saccate throughout the lower and upper sections. At approximately the middle, some of the hairs show a distinct narrowed medullary canal with long pigment-filled air vesicles. Pigmentation is scattered throughout the cortex as separated granules, whereas in the air vesicles, it is concentrated in the bottom of the pockets.

It is possible to ascertain the method by which the hair and fur have been prepared. In the boiled fur, the root bulb is wholly or partly present, whereas in the cut fur, the basal end of the hair shows a straight or jagged cut. Bleached fur shows a varied percentage of hairs having fissures or split cortexes in the apical bulge. The fissures may appear as fine longitudinal cracks or may be total separations held together at both ends of the fissure. Such hairs have become brittle and may shatter further during manufacturing operations.

CHEMICAL COMPOSITION AND CHARACTERISTICS[1]

Fur keratin is believed to be a mixture of several more or less closely related proteins, still not differentiated satisfactorily. This would

TABLE 2. Chemical Analysis of Common Varieties of Keratin *

Sources of Keratin	*Carbon*	*Hydrogen*	*Nitrogen*	*Sulfur*	*Oxygen*
Feathers	52.46	6.94	17.74	....	22.86
Quills	51.70	7.20	17.90	....	.....
Wool	50.65	7.30	17.71	4.61	20.00
Human hair	50.65	6.36	17.14	5.0	20.00
Rabbit fur	49.45	6.52	16.81	4.02	23.20

* Barritt, *J. Textile Inst.*, March 1926.

TABLE 3. Per Cent Composition of Animal Proteins *

Types	*Carbon*	*Hydrogen*	*Nitrogen*	*Sulfur*	*Oxygen*
Irish wool	49.80	7.20	19.10	3.00	19.90
Southdown wool	51.30	6.90	17.80	3.80	20.20
Rabbit fur	49.45	6.52	16.81	4.02	23.20

* Barritt, *J. Textile Inst.*, March 1926.

account for the differences in the properties of the epithelium, cortex, and medullary regions. The fur keratins are insoluble in customary solvents.

[1] Personal correspondence: Thomas R. LeCompte, Chief Chemist, Jonas & Naumburg Corp., New York, manufacturers of hatters' furs.

Fur responds to the xanthoproteic and Millon tests, both tests being more strikingly discernible on white furs. Upon hydrolysis, fur keratin yields comparatively large amounts of the amino acids, cystine and tyrosine.

Heat, Light, and Aging

Prolonged aging of white fur results in some discoloration and degradation, with increased felting power. Exposure of raw rabbit fur to heat rays increases the acidity roughly proportional to the temperature and duration of exposure.

After 20 seconds at 210° F., the *p*H changes from 6.4 to 6.3
" 30 " " 280° F., " " " " 6.3 to 6.1
" 40 " " 360° F., " " " " 6.2 to 5.8

The *p*H was measured on the water extract of 1 gram of fur boiled in 100 cc distilled water.

Singeing of fur is accompanied by the characteristic odor of burning feathers.

Rabbit fur, in still air, singes in 3 min at 275° F., in 2 min at 290° F., in 1 min at 320° F.

Water Content

The relation of water content of rabbit fur to relative humidity of the air is somewhat lower than that of wool. At 70° F., raw rabbit fur in equilibrium with atmospheric moisture shows the following approximate water contents.

% R.H.	*Water Content % on dry wt*	*% R.H.*	*Water Content % on dry wt.*
30	7.0	60	12.1
40	8.8	70	14.3
50	10.5	80	17.3

Hot Water

Fur keratin is apparently not altered by water below 212° F. Fur wets rapidly in water at temperatures of 140° F. and above, thus closely resembling wool. Boiling water causes the fur fiber to change from a more or less rigid elastic condition to one of greater plasticity. Fur fibers, when immersed in cold water and subsequently dried, will revert to their former coiled condition. However, as a result of exposure to steam or boiling water, the internal strains and stresses are destroyed, and upon cooling in a new physical configuration will retain the newly imposed shape. Dyed fur wets less readily than undyed fur. It also combines with less sulfuric acid. Fur may be dyed with both acid and basic dyes. This in addition to its reactions with strong acids and alkalies proves its amphoteric character. Carroted or chemically degraded fur accepts acid dyes with much greater ease and thoroughness than raw fur.

Acids and Alkalies

Fur resists the action of boiling strong acetic acid and of cold dilute hydrochloric acid; a 20 per cent solution causes a partial decomposition, and 39 per cent solution completely transposes the fur. Dilute nitric acid causes the fur to turn yellow (xanthoproteic reaction). Concentrated sulfuric acid decomposes fur into a charred mass; boiling solutions of 3 to 4 per cent do not seem to affect the cellular fur structure materially. Dilute sulfuric acid combines with the fur; in industrial production washing out this combined acid is an impracticable, slow, and tedious operation. Raw fur has some felting power, but a chemical treatment, known as carroting, is necessary to confer adequate speed and tightness of felting. Formerly a mercuric nitrate carrot was almost universally used, but since about 1942 this carrot has been obsolete in the United States.

Alkalies affect fur fibers as they do wool. Warm caustic alkali solutions break down the fiber structure, and concentrated solutions dissolve it. Fur swells in alkaline oxidizing solutions; observations under the microscope show that 0.1 N alkali causes carroted or chemically degraded fur to swell and curl to a much greater degree than unaltered fur.

Static Electricity

Fur, like casein, becomes electrified by friction. On the basis of the general similarity of fur to wool, it is believed that the charge on electrified fibers, where found, is positive.

Mold Growth

Raw fur is subject to becoming sour and moldy. Hydrolyzed fur is outstandingly subject to mold development, the degradation products serving as a food supply to the mold colonies.

Dye Affinity

Von Bergen [2] has found in his mill experience that, in dyeing rabbit hair and wool mixtures with most acid and chrome dyes, a two-tone

[2] Personal correspondence.

The European bristle, which is of medium softness, was formerly obtained from Poland, Lithuania, and France.

American bristle has been neglected because of the difference in cost of domestic and foreign labor. A part of this neglect is claimed to have been caused years ago. When American bristle was first used, it was so poorly dressed that it was usable only in cheaper brushes. Since World War II American bristle has come into the market, where it is expected to become a factor. Some of it is as hard as the Siberian bristle, and in general it is better than the Polish, Lithuanian, and French, or the softer Chinese grades.

Other sources of bristle are the Near East, Germany, Rumania, and India. South America currently supplies sizable quantities, but the dressing is poor.

Hog bristles obtained from the older hogs are longer and have a better strength and springiness than those from young hogs. See Figs. 5 and 6. Bristles are "dragged" or assorted into different lots according to their lengths, with differences of ¼ in. between lots. Fine European and Chinese bristles range in length from 2 to 7 in.; the domestic bristle ranges in length from 2¼ to 4¼ in., with a small percentage of the latter size. (See Table 4.)

Seasonal differences are noticeable in the bristle texture. The winter collection, which usually contains the full-grown hog bristle, is of superior quality. The summer collection, which is usually obtained from the younger hogs, is of inferior quality, owing to its softness.

Hair Fibers

Hair fibers are divided into those obtained from domestic animals and those from wild animals. The domestic type is obtained from horses, cattle, and goats. Horsehair, Fig. 7, is separated into that from the mane and that from the tail. The hair from the mane is the softer, whereas that from the tail is more springy and bristly. Cattle hair, known commercially as ox hair, is the tuft of bristly hairs from the inside of cattle ears (see Fig. 8). This hair as it comes from the slaughter house is usually so clogged with blood and dirt that it loses about 40 per cent of its weight in the cleaning process. Ox hair is soft and straight and has good resiliency.

Goat hair is obtained from the beard or whiskers of the goat and is used for cheap brushes. The belly hair is softer and not as strong as the others. China and Tibet have been the main sources of supply, and in the past most of this hair was prepared in China. Cow hair,

TABLE 4. Bristles, Sorted, Bunched, or Prepared

(United States exports of foreign merchandise, and imports for consumption, by principal sources, specified years, 1939 to 1951.)

Year	Exports of Foreign Merchandise [1]	Imports for Consumption				
		All Countries	China	Soviet Union	India [2]	Argentina
	Quantity (1000 lb)					
1939	764	5,163	4,632	140	48	2
1943	144	1,386	534	2	288	337
1947	1,823	6,167	5,884	201	19	1
1948	1,151	7,307	7,122	58	16	9
1949	2,266	4,828	4,479	57	30	8
1950 [3]	1,746	7,357	6,918	11	29	[4]
1951 [3]	572	3,654 [5]	2,767	21	33	15
1952 [3]	42	5,368				
	Value ($1000)					
		Foreign Value				
1939	1,044	7,337	6,116	333	199	2
1943	620	3,729	1,100	7	758	1,201
1947	3,288	19,093	18,429	380	148	2
1948	3,016	22,956	22,135	210	99	14
1949	6,036	18,278	16,528	271	238	43
1950 [3]	4,763	28,317	26,581	68	270	1
1951 [3]	2,269	19,812 [5]	16,038	62	365	31
1952 [3]	197	25,093				

[1] Includes exports reported as "domestic merchandise" believed to consist of imported dressed bristles, slightly further processed before reexport.

[2] Includes Pakistan in 1930–47. There have been no imports from Pakistan since 1948.

[3] Preliminary.

[4] Less than 500 lb.

[5] Includes 223,000 lb, valued at $1,720,000, from Manchuria.

Source: Compiled from official statistics of the U. S. Department of Commerce; supplied by Unites States Tariff Commission.

which is not suitable for brush purposes because of its curly nature, is used for the stuffing of mattresses and furniture.

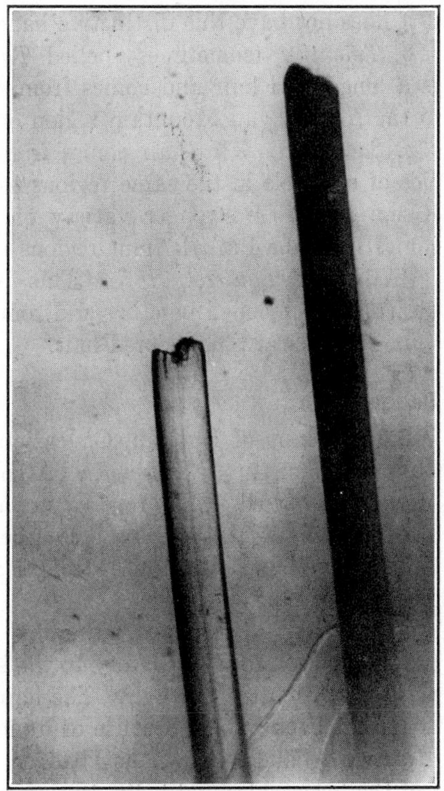

FIG. 7. Horse hair, ×27.

Wild Animal Hairs

The following animal peltries supply soft brush hairs from the tail portions: squirrel, kolinsky, fitch, skunk, and little spotted skunk (American civet). The hairs from all parts of the badger, however, are used for brushes.

Squirrel Tail

Squirrel tail, incorrectly known as "camel hair," is derived chiefly from the Siberian squirrel (see Figs. 9 and 10). Four general grades are recognized as follows:

a. Kazan Hair. There are two grades, "prime" and "ordinary." The prime hair, sometimes called French camel hair, comes from the brown-tail squirrels, which originate in the Obsky, Yeniseisk, and Lensky regions of Siberia. The highest grade of this hair is identified by the light golden band below the tip. The ordinary grade is the same quality, but it does not have this distinctive band.

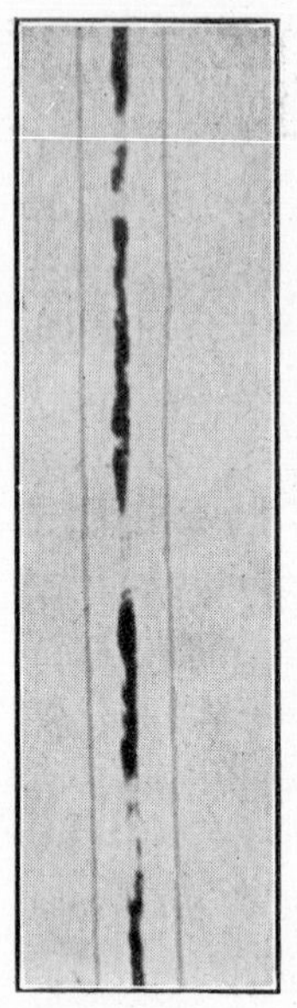

FIG. 8. Longitudinal of white ox ear hair. (×100.)

b. *Teleutky* (sometimes spelled *Taloutky*). This is a longer tail hair and comes from a giant squirrel in the Altai-Sayan Mountain region of Siberia.

c. *Sacamina.* This hair comes from the dark species of squirrels in the same regions that produce the Kazan hairs. A stronger variety of the black hair comes from the Baikal-Amur regions of Siberia.

d. *Blended Squirrel Hair.* This is all types of squirrel hair blended together and sometimes dyed to simulate natural blue-colored hair.

Badger Hair

Badger skins of Russian, Caucasian, Turkish, and Chinese origin supply this hair. A small percentage of the soft-haired skins are used in the fur industry. The Turkish badgers are considered best. They have a distinctive band. They are stronger and give a better yield of hair.

Badger hair is removed either by clipping or by the application of a depilatory to the skin side of the pelts which loosens the hair. The hair from the center of the back is best because of its longer and more distinctive bands, known as "badger casings." The stripe on the hair of the lower sides and belly, known as "badger middle," is shorter and not as distinctive as the preceding. The choicest badger hair is known as the "silver type," because of its distinctive white tip. Its use is limited to expensive shaving brushes.

Kolinsky Tail

The kolinsky is an Asiatic mink found in its best qualities in the Siberian regions of Ob and Yenisei and in the Ural Mountain region and also in Turkestan. A short-haired type is obtained from skins originating in the Baikal-Amur-Irkutsk regions of eastern Siberia. China mink comes from the middle and northern parts of China and Manchuria. It supplies a short tail hair, coarser than the previous grades, which is often sold to the brush trade as kolinsky. The kolinsky hair is known by the erroneous commercial name of "red sable hair"; in fact, the term "red sable hair" often includes other types of dyed hair, such as ox hair or little spotted skunk hair (civet), which is used commercially as "black sable."

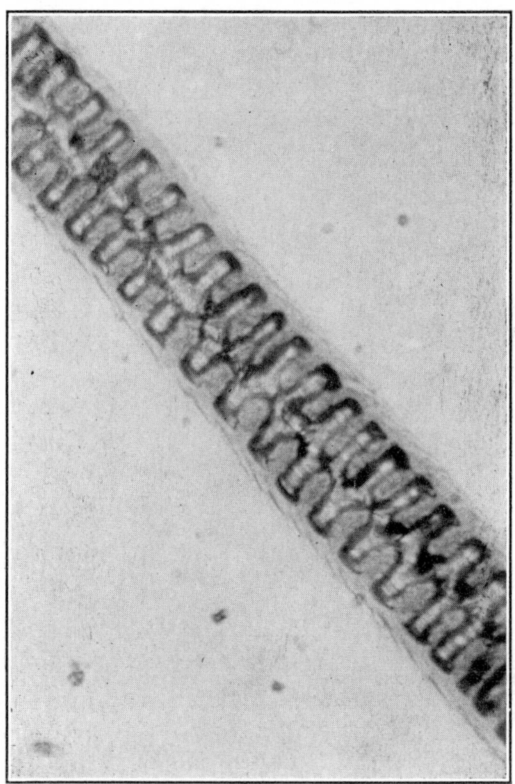

FIG. 9. Squirrel guard hair medulla.

Fitch Tail

This hair is obtained from the tails of both the European and the Russian fitch, preferably the latter. This animal is found in the same regions as the kolinsky.

Skunk Tail

This hair is obtained from the tails of the American skunk in three qualities, depending upon the origin of the animals. The Eastern is the strongest and best quality and comes from the New England States and surrounding areas. The second best comes from the states bordering the Great Lakes and is known as the Northern. The third and cheapest comes chiefly from the Mississippi Valley and is known as the Western. Skunk hair is also known commercially as "fitch" hair.

Little Spotted Skunk (Incorrectly Named Civet Cat)

This animal is a subspecies of the skunk. Its tail hair is stronger, straighter, and has greater resilience than that of the true skunk. The

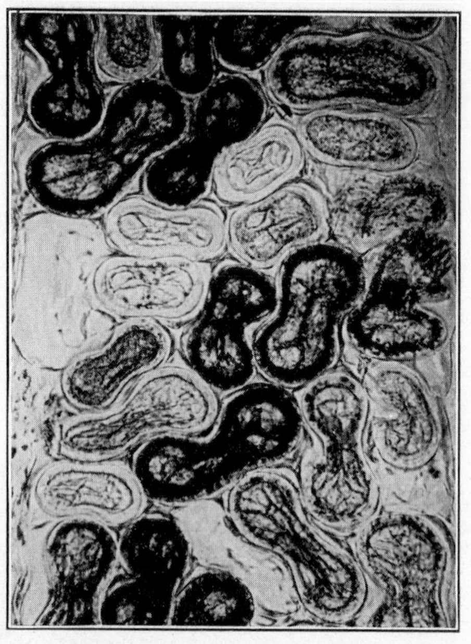

Fig. 10. Squirrel tail hairs. Fibers taken from a "camel's-hair" brush. (×230.) (*Krauss.*)

northern variety coming from the states in the northern part of the Mississippi Valley has an all-black tail; the skunks in the central and southern parts of the Mississippi Valley have a white tip at the end of the black tail and the tail hair is somewhat coarser than the previous grade.

A substitute for this hair is brown goat hair, but it is not a good simulation.

Dressing of Bristle and Hair. The dressing process varies with different types of bristles and hair; it consists in first cleaning, then washing and combing, then tying into small bundles and immersing for a short time in boiling water to straighten. After this the bristles and hairs are placed in ovens to dry at a moderate temperature. The dry hairs are pulled and knifed, a process which cleans the bristles of dead hairs.

In the "dragging process," the sharp edge of a knife is used by the operator to pull out the long hairs first, and then each hair is further drawn out with a knife and a fine comb to graded sizes, differing by a quarter of an inch for each size.

Natural flags are found on hog bristle. The "flag" on bristle is split or forked, and, as the brush is used, the bristle continues to split. Horsehair and tail hairs from fur-bearing animals have only tips and no flags, and the tips wear off with use. The brush becomes useless for such paintwork as requires an edge or point.

FIG. 11. Ostrich feather fibers showing growth from shaft. (×100.)

Blending of different kinds of hair, or of bristles and hairs, is required to meet the purposes for which brushes will be used. This gives either a softer or a stiffer texture to the brushes. It also allows tapering of the brushes, that is to say, it combines hairs of different lengths to form an edge or point on the finished brush.

Brushes are classified generally as follows: *PERSONAL brushes,* such as tooth, hair, shoe, nail, shaving, and similar brushes; *UTILITY brushes,* used by surface painters and artists; *INDUSTRIAL brushes,* as for example, comb dabbing brushes used in textile plants; *HOUSEHOLD brushes,* such as those used for cleaning and dusting of floors and ceilings, windows, and other home uses.

FEATHERS AND DOWN [4]

Feathers were first combined with other textile fibers in America in the early 1930's. Their use in cloth, however, originated in Europe,

[4] The above information is from the files of the National Feather and Down Co., Brooklyn, N. Y.

particularly France; it is difficult to fix the exact date of their first appearance.

The raw material is composed of two types of covering, namely, feathers and down. The types used in the past for textile purposes were obtained chiefly from the ostrich, the goose, and the duck. The

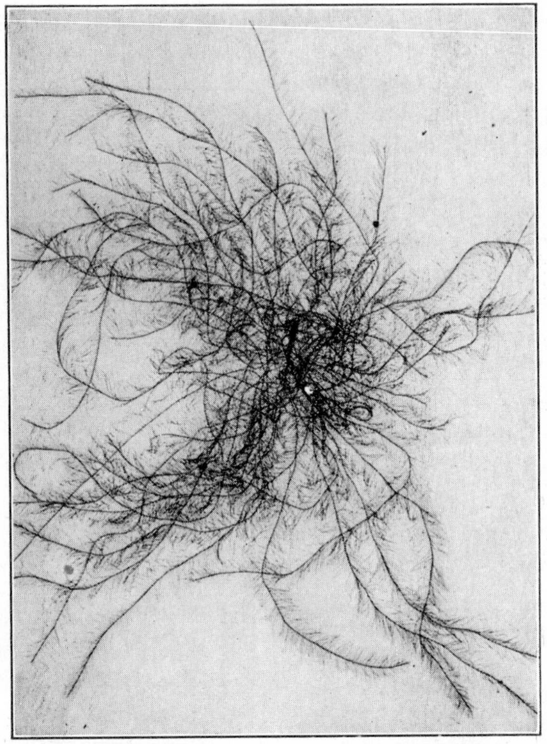

Fig. 12. Goose down. (×8.) (*von Bergen.*)

ostrich product is actually a feather, whereas for textile purposes the down from the goose and duck has been used. Finely chopped feathers have also been used in mixtures with down.

Down and feathers are obtained from large collectors who dress large quantities of geese and ducks for the consumer markets, or they are purchased from local slaughter houses and butchers who sell live and dressed poultry locally. Ostrich feathers, because of their extremely high cost and the difficulty of obtaining them, are seldom used, although some of the cloths have been given the erroneous name of "ostrich." (See Fig. 11.)

The feathers of birds differ from the down in that they have a quill from which protrude coarse, threadlike fibers. The down, which is the undercoating of water birds, serves as a warmth-giving undercoat. Down grows from a separate small pointed quill in a sort of clusterlike formation. Each cluster has varying lengths of fibrils.

Feathers do not offer much opportunity for conversion into a textile yarn, inasmuch as they are too coarse and too resilient, even though removed from the quill; if the quill is included with the feather, it has a tendency to break sharply while being felted, causing difficulties in spinning and weaving, through unevenness and shedding. Down is more compressible and has a softer handle and only a partial tendency to buoyancy.

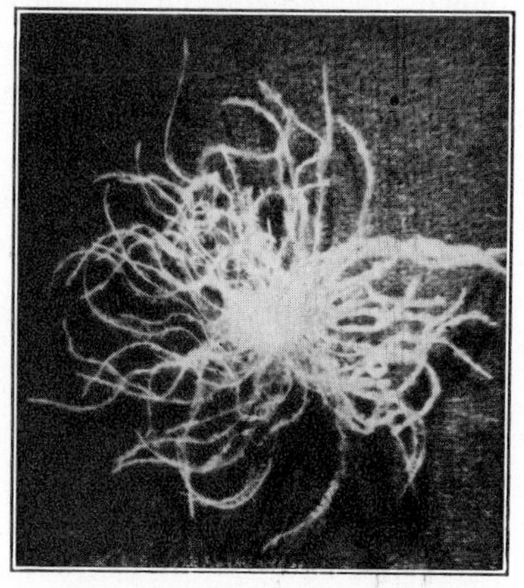

Fig. 13. Duck down. Note absence of quill formation. (×10.)

Of the feather fibers, the goose down is considered most adaptable. It has a fluffier texture and generally is taken from the adult animals (see Fig. 12). The duck produces a thinner-textured fiber owing to the fact that most of the ducks are killed up to 12 weeks of age before the down has developed to its fullest fluffiness (see Fig. 13).

The color in demand is mostly white, although some gray has been used; the difficulty with the gray type is that it sometimes has off shades of brown in it. It is suitable only in mixtures where such off-color is desirable.

The goose down is obtained from various regions throughout the Northern Hemisphere, and its quality is based upon the distance north of the equator at which the birds live; fluffiness is the most important qualification, and this is found at its best in the more northerly regions.

The sections for the duck are similar to those for the goose; however, the sections are not as well defined and do not run as uniform. There is an exception, however. The Long Island duck growers, who are among the largest producers of ducks, have a rather more uniform product. The large duck and goose producers market their feathers and down usually in a good condition, inasmuch as they scald the birds before plucking, then rinse the feathers and dry them properly. Butcher feathers are carelessly handled, generally bloody and wet, in which condition they may lie around for some time, causing a partial disintegration to take place and resulting in a putrefactive odor which is often offensive even after the feathers are washed and sterilized. The down in the average adult bird amounts to about 20 per cent.

Attention must be given to the fact that in the cleaning and blowing of down for textile purposes, very often adulterants are mixed in to lower the cost. The most common adulterant is the stripped and blown fiber of chicken and turkey feathers. Also the shredded and ground quills and fibers from the large 4-in. goose feathers are mixed in. This shredded or ground fibrous mass, which may escape detection unless carefully examined, will cause unevenness in the subsequent dyeing processes.

BIBLIOGRAPHY

A.S.T.M., Tentative Standards D276–41T and D276–43T (1943).

Bachrach, M., *Fur* (1938).

Buchwalter, L., *The Story of Downs and Feathers* (1936). National Feather and Down Co. booklet.

Gilbert, A., *American Angora Handbook* (1942).

Hardy, J. I., and Plitt, T. M., "An Improved Method for Revealing the Surface Structure of Fur Fibers," *Wildlife Circular 7*, U. S. Dept. Interior (1940).

Hausman, L. A., "Microscopic Identification of Commercial Fur Hairs," *Sci. Monthly*, **10** (1919) (March 1930).

Lochte, T., *Atlas der Menschlichen und Tier Haare* (1938).

Lomuller, L., "Fur Hair Identification," *Bull. sci. pharmacol.*, **31** (1924).

von Bergen, W., and Krauss, W., *Textile Fiber Atlas* (1942).

von Bergen, W., and Mauersberger, H. R., *American Wool Handbook* (1939).

CHAPTER XV

THE SILK FIBERS AND YARNS

CHARLES J. BRICK

History of Silk Culture

Chinese myths date the culture of silk back to 2640 B.C., when the Empress Si-Ling-Chi learned not only how to rear the caterpillars but, what is more important, how to unwind the filament that formed their cocoons. The Chinese monopolized the art for over 3000 years, but during the early period of the Christian era the cultivation of the silkworm (or sericulture) was introduced into Japan. It gradually spread throughout central Asia to Persia, Turkey, and Arabia. In the eighth century it was carried into the countries influenced by the Moorish rule, including Spain, Sicily, and the African coast. In the twelfth century sericulture was practiced in Italy and was introduced into France in about the thirteenth century [1].

Silk production was started in America early in the seventeenth century, when bounties were offered to settlers in Virginia, Georgia, and Carolina. Probably the greatest boom took place in the decade following 1830, concentrated largely in the states of Connecticut and New Jersey, which ended in the financial crash of 1840. Since then sporadic attempts have been made to develop a sericultural industry in the United States, several of which have centered in southern California. It is contended that mulberry leaves may be grown for nine months of the year in California. During World War II when no Asiatic silk was available, efforts were made to develop silk raising in the United States, Mexico, Cuba, Venezuela, and Brazil, but with little success. Since the resumption of trade with Japan and China, practically all silk has been imported from these two countries with small amounts from Italy.

The silk industry is divided into a number of separate enterprises:

a. Mulberry culture.
b. Egg production.
c. Sericulture—the rearing of silkworms and the production of cocoons.
d. Silk reeling or filature, where the silk filament is unwound from the cocoon to form the raw silk thread.

e. Throwing, which takes the raw silk thread and converts it into suitable yarns for manufacturing purposes.

f. The manufacturing of fabrics from the thrown yarns by weaving, knitting, braiding, etc., and finishing by bleaching, weighting, dyeing, and printing.

The Silkworm

The silk fiber is a continuous protein filament produced by various insects, especially by the larvae of a caterpillar (known as the silkworm), in forming their cocoons. The silkworm is not really a worm but a caterpillar having eyes and legs, which no true worm possesses [2].

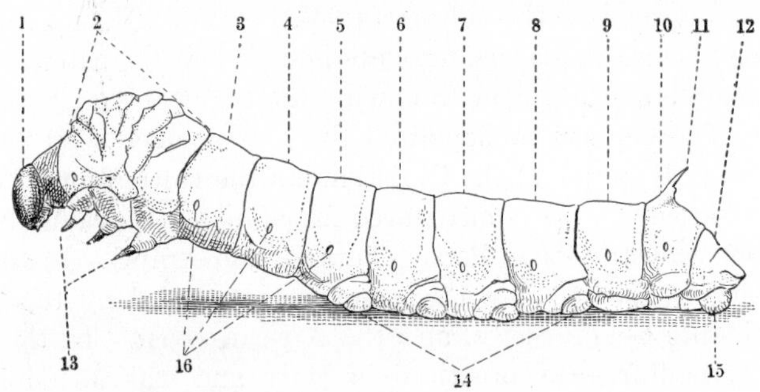

Fig. 1. The silkworm. 1, Head; 2–10, 12, rings; 11, horn; 13, articulated legs; 14, abdominal or false legs; 15, false legs on last ring.

All the true silkworms belong to the order Lepidoptera, or scale-winged insects, and more specifically to the genus *Bombyx*, of which the principal species is *Bombyx mori*, or mulberry silkworm, which produces by far the major portion of the silk used in the trade.

Bombyx mori species are divided into *two* classes:

Monovoltine, which produce only one generation each year.
Polyvoltine, which reproduce several times annually.

Silkworm culture, which starts with the proper selection and care of the eggs, has developed into a large, scientifically controlled industry.

Silkworm eggs are of two types: (1) those used for reproduction and (2) those used for cocoon production. The former are used as stock by egg producers, whereas the latter are hatched by cocoon farmers where the egg stock has simply passed a cocoon inspection. In Japan in 1934, the production of industrial eggs used by cocoon raisers consisted of 57 per cent egg sheets and 43 per cent grain method where the eggs are distributed in 10-, 20-, and 30-grain unit receptacles [3].

Besides rearing the worms very carefully for reproductive purposes,

Quercus serrata. This general type is divided into several different species which grow in different parts of the tussah district but which have little effect on the cocoons produced. The kind and quality of cocoon are largely controlled by the climatic and soil conditions in the locality in which it is grown. The colder weather of Manchuria produces a darker, heavier cocoon than is raised in the mild climate of Shantung with its sandy soil.

The tussah silkworm is very different from the domesticated mulberry silkworm. It will feed only out of doors on oak trees of shrub type which are kept at a height of 5 to 6 ft by pruning. On maturity, it ranges in length from 3 to 5 in., is of soft green color, and is covered with tufts of reddish brown hair.

There are two crops of cocoons produced annually—the spring and autumn crops. The spring crop is small and is used almost entirely for producing the autumn crop [15].

The moth from the cocoon of the autumn crop emerges about the end of March. The eggs hatch about April 30. The worm life cycle is shown in Table 4.

TABLE 4. TUSSAH WORM LIFE CYCLE

Stage 1	6 days' feeding	2 days' sleep
Stage 2	6 days' feeding	2 to 3 days' sleep
Stage 3	7 to 8 days' feeding	2 to 3 days' sleep
Stage 4	8 to 9 days' feeding	2 to 3 days' sleep
Stage 5	10 to 12 days' feeding	2 to 3 days' spinning

Total time required for the spring crop is about 45 days from hatching to spinning. The moth emerges from these cocoons in about 15 days, and the eggs are hatched in about 10 days. The autumn crop is harvested in Shantung between the first and the middle of September, whereas in Manchuria it is around the first of October.

The basic data on tussah silk are as follows:

Average number of eggs laid by each mother moth—150
Ratio of seed cocoons to cocoons produced—1 to 15
The number of oak trees per acre, average—1500
Oak tree reaches maturity in 7 to 8 years.
The life of an oak tree is from 30 to 50 years.
One acre of oak trees produces about 60,000 cocoons.
10,000 cocoons (average fresh) produce about one picul [1] of silk.
Yield of fresh cocoons: 20 units of fresh cocoons produce one unit of raw silk.

Practically the entire cocoon supply for the Chefoo filatures comes from Manchuria and is shipped in large, cylindrical, woven willow

[1] One picul is equivalent to 132.25 English pounds.

baskets holding from 5 to 10 piculs of green cocoons. A medium-sized basket is 40 in. in diameter, 60 in. high, and weighs about 100 lb empty. This monstrosity of a container is the outgrowth of a tax regulation based on the number of units or baskets, so that a saving is made by shipping the cocoons in the largest possible packages. They are extremely awkward to handle, besides crushing many cocoons and staining many others with the fluid which exudes from the crushed ones.

The filatures store the fresh cocoons in several different ways. Inasmuch as the climate is crisp and dry, most of the cocoons are left in the baskets, which are stood on end and covered with matting. Sometimes platforms are built in the storage yards, raised about a foot from the ground; the cocoons are piled on them and then covered with mats held down with rope. Some of the cocoons (though only a small portion of the whole quantity used) are stored in ventilated warehouses containing 8 or 10 tiers of bins about a foot deep.

The tussah worm in spinning its cocoon leaves one end open, which it seals with sericin as the last act of its worm life. In emerging from the cocoon, the moth softens this sericin, and the cocoon fiber is not broken. For this reason the so-called pierced tussah cocoon may be reeled, but in general the reeling is done while the chrysalis is dormant.

The tussah cocoons differ from the domestic or mulberry-worm cocoons in that they contain more gum and also calcium compounds, which makes it necessary to treat them chemically in the boiling operation so that the filament may be unwound. One picul[1] of cocoons is shoveled into a large willow basket and set into an iron tank containing a solution of sodium carbonate and boiled for 1½ hr, then thoroughly rinsed in fresh water, again brought to a boil, and then allowed to stay in this water for about 16 hr before reeling.

Although many of the chop (brand) tickets on tussah silk bear the inscription "Steam Filature," it is entirely a misnomer, since in none of the tussah filatures is steam or electric power used for operating the reels. All are driven by foot power supplied by the operator. In two other respects there is a fundamental difference between the reeling of domestic or mulberry silk and tussah silk.

a. All the reeling in the tussah industry is done by men.

b. All the cocoons are reeled in a semi-dry condition while lying on a piece of board instead of while floating in a basin of water as is the case with mulberry silk.

New cocoons are easier to reel, and they give better yield and color. Pierced or opened cocoons are reeled in small quantity, and, although the color is light, the silk is apt to be full of defects as the cocoons are hard to unwind.

The reeling room is invariably low, dingy, exceedingly untidy, and crowded with workers. The small so-called windows, which are paper covered, allow very poor illumination. These rooms are not only used for reeling but also as sleeping quarters for the workers. They are purposely kept hot and humid so that the cocoons will not dry out and so they will unwind easily.

The reels are very inexpensive wooden foot-power machines which use the *tavelle* system of reeling with eight as the usual number of cocoon filaments forming a single end 30 to 35 denier in size.

Only one end is reeled by an operator at one time into the standard American skein with diamond crossing, ready for exportation.

Other Wild Silks

Besides the *Antheraea pernyi,* there are still other varieties of caterpillars which produce silk. These silks are called wild, because these worms are not capable of being domesticated and artificially cultivated. Some of the more important types are given below:

Antheraea yama-mai, a native of Japan, whose silk was formerly exclusively used by Japanese royalty, is a green caterpillar which feeds on oak leaves. Its cocoon is large and bright greenish. The silk bears a close resemblance to that of the *Bombyx mori,* but it is not as readily bleached or dyed.

Antheraea assama or muga moth is a native of India and in importance is next to the tussah moth. It produces a large cocoon, almost 2 in. long.

Antheraea mylitta is another Indian species which feeds on the leaves of the castor oil plant and produces cocoons over 2 in. long and over 1 in. in diameter.

The *Attacus ricini* is found in both Asia and America. It produces a very white silk of good quality, known as eria silk. A variety of this species, *Attacus atlas,* is perhaps the largest moth known; it spins open cocoons and gives the so-called Fagara or Ailanthus silk.

There is a silkworm found in Uganda and other parts of Africa belonging to the *Anaphe* genus. It feeds principally on the leaves of a species of fig tree. The caterpillars construct large nests inside of which they form their cocoons in considerable numbers. The entire nest, together with the cocoons, is composed of silk, and the whole of the product is capable of being used for waste silk [17]. In southern

Nigeria this Anaphe silk is used by the natives in conjunction with cotton for making the so-called *soyan* cloths.

SPIDER SILKS [2]

More than two centuries ago attempts were made by the French to utilize spider silk in the textile industry. With a great deal of patience a pioneer, Monsieur Bon of Languedoc, France, collected a large number of spider cocoons and from the fine gray silk he made some stockings and gloves, which were exhibited before the Academy of Sciences at Paris in 1710. That body showered M. Bon with honors and became excited over his idea of starting a spider silk factory. René Réaumur, the physicist and entomologist, was commissioned to investigate the possibility of raising spiders for their silk.

Historic

Although Réaumur began his investigation with enthusiasm, he found so many insurmountable difficulties that he was compelled to render an adverse report. The spiders were difficult to manage, became belligerent, easily excited, and cannibalistic. It was found difficult to provide them with proper food and to keep them in large groups. Furthermore, the silk produced was small in quantity and was so delicate in quality as to be difficult to utilize in spinning.

All spiders spin silk, but members of the subfamily Nephilinae spin so much that they have been used in attempts to establish a spider silk industry. In 1864, Dr. Wilder, an American Army surgeon stationed in South Carolina, revived the idea of using spider silk in textiles. He selected the brush-legged *Nephila clavipes* and proposed the "milking" method of reeling the filaments directly from the spider, instead of collecting the cocoons. He found that the life product of about 450 spiders would be required to produce 1 yd of silk goods. A pair of spider silk hose would cost more than $100, and they would be so sheer that they would render little service.

More recently another species, *Nephila madagascarensis,* found in Madagascar, has been used in making silk cloth. The female, a spider about 2½ in. long, alone produces the silk. The silk is reeled from the spider by native girls, five or six times during a month, after which the spider dies, having yielded about 4000 yards of filaments. About a dozen spiders are locked in a frame in such a manner that on one side

[2] Contributed by John G. Albright, Professor of Physics, and Head of Physics Dept., Rhode Island State College.

protrudes the abdomen, while on the other side the head, thorax, and legs are free. The ends of the web are drawn out, collected into one thread, which is passed over a metal hook, and the reel is set in motion. The extraction of the silk apparently does not inconvenience the spider. The cost of the material is high, because about 55,000 yd of 19 strands thickness weighs only 386 grains, and 1 lb of the silk is worth $40. At the Paris Exposition in 1900 a fabric 18 yd long by 18 in. wide was shown containing 100,000 yd of spun thread of 24 strands, i.e., the product of 25,000 spiders. It was golden yellow in color.

Uses

Although spider silk has proved impractical for textile use, it has found a field of usefulness in the optical industry as crosslines in various instruments. The intersection of the two taut fibers of spider silk is used to mark the optical center of telescopes, microscopes, and other instruments used in astronomy and surveying.

David Rittenhouse, of Philadelphia, a world-famed instrument maker, astronomer, and clock builder, first used crosslines of spider silk in his transit instruments in 1786. His priority in regard to this use was acknowledged by E. Traughton, the famous instrument maker of England, who brought spider lines into universal use in astronomical instruments. However, this use of spider silk had been anticipated in 1775 by Felice Fontana, professor of physics at the University of Pisa.

Spider silk for crosslines depends upon several factors for its usefulness: fineness, uniformity, strength, and ability to withstand changes in humidity and temperature. Only a few spiders have been found whose silk meets the rigid requirements of the astronomer and optical instrument maker. They are all orb weavers, producing webs of fine strong filaments in which to ensnare their prey. One of the best of these is the large golden garden spider (*Miranda aurentia*), a beautiful black and yellow spider with a body almost an inch long (female).

Microscopic

The silk for crossline use is "milked" or harmlessly drawn from an adult female spider and wound on reels, where it can be kept indefinitely. The silk is stranded as it comes from six nipplelike spinnerets, arranged in a circle near the posterior end of the spider's abdomen. For use as crosslines, a single filament of the strand is separated from the rest and mounted on the ring or reticle. (See Fig. 9.)

The silk taken from the golden garden spider has a diameter of about 0.0001 in. or 2.5 μ. Under the microscope it appears solid, almost

Fig. 9. Spider silk for crosslines wound directly on a reel for transportation or storage. Two-thirds natural size. (*Albright.*)

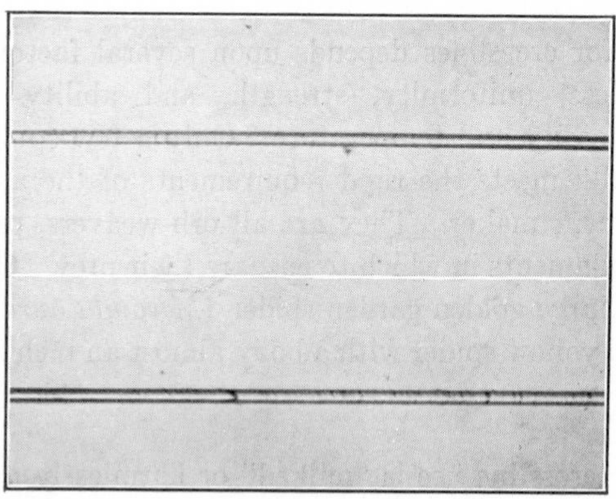

Fig. 10. Single filaments of spider silk. (×320.) (*Albright.*)

transparent, without any internal structure, of approximately circular cross-section, and uniform in diameter (see Fig. 10). It has a specific gravity of about 1.30 to 1.37 and an ultimate breaking strength of about 60,000 lb per sq in. It has a considerable amount of elasticity, but also shows some flow properties. It continues to be extended under a constant stress for some time, but recovers upon the removal of the stress.

Physical Properties

A century and a half of use as crosslines has tested the reliability of spider silk, its ability to withstand changes in temperature and humidity, and its ability to withstand oxidation, the bane of artificial and metal fibers used as crosslines. In many installations spider lines have been known to last more than half a century, often outlasting the instruments themselves.

Spider silk is not surrounded by an enveloping substance like the sericin of ordinary silk. In microchemical tests it has been found to be similar in composition to true silk. In very humid atmosphere the silk absorbs moisture. This causes the crosslines in the surveyor's transit to sag, when water gets into the telescope; however, their tautness is restored on drying out the telescope.

Chemical Properties

The filaments spun by the *Nephila madagascarensis* closely resemble ordinary silk in external appearance. The silk is orange-yellow, which is intensified by alkalies and is destroyed by acids. It differs from ordinary silk principally in its small amount of silk glue (or water-soluble substances). According to Fischer [18] spider silk when hydrolized with acid gave the products shown in Table 5.

TABLE 5. Chemical Components of Spider Silk

Chemical Elements	*Per Cent*
Glycocoll	25.13
d-alanine	23.40
e-leucine	1.76
Proline	3.68
e-tyrosine	8.20
d-glutaminic acid	11.70
Diamino acids	5.24
Ammonia	1.16
Fatty acids	0.59

Glutaminic acid, which is present in rather a large amount in spider silk, has not been found in ordinary silk. Spider silk, on ignition, gave 0.59 per cent of ash.

Dupion Silk

Dupion silk is reeled from double cocoons or cocoons produced by two worms. From 5 to 9 per cent of the Japanese annual crop of cocoons are of this type. They are hard to reel and produce a very slubby raw silk thread which, owing to these imperfections or defects, is used in weaving many novelty fabrics.

SILK THROWING

The raw silk as received from the primary market is soaked in an oil or soap emulsion to soften the thread without, however, dissolving the silk gum. It is then wound onto bobbins, and several threads are doubled together to give the desired size of yarn, and then twisted. The "throwster" simply converts the raw silk thread into a yarn of proper size for manufacturing, or, by regulating the twist, produces various qualities of silk yarn for the several purposes required for the weaving or knitting of various kinds of fabrics. The term "throwing" is apparently derived from an Anglo-Saxon word "thrawan," meaning to whirl or spin, and the word in this connection means to twist the silk.

Silk throwing requires special skill and knowledge, as well as expensive machinery, and consequently it has developed into a separate and distinct business. In the several years prior to World War II the major portion of the raw silk imported into the United States was used for hosiery. Since the end of the war and with the advent of nylon, very little silk is used for hosiery.

Classification of Silk Yarn

Hosiery yarns are known in the trade as 2, 3, or more thread yarns, where each thread refers to a 14-denier raw silk thread. These yarns may be designated as "tram," having 3 to 5 turns of twist per inch of length or higher twists known as "crepe."

In the Trade Practice Rules for the Hosiery Industry as promulgated May 15, 1941, by the Federal Trade Commission, "crepe" is defined in respect to hosiery as silk yarn in which the total number of turns in both the initial and final twists is at least:

100 turns per inch for two-thread,
80 turns per inch for three-thread,
60 turns per inch for four-thread,
50 turns per inch for five-thread or over.

At least 50 per cent of these minimum twist requirements must be in the initial twist, which may be either "S" or "Z" or both.

d. Average size test
e. Evenness test
f. Cleanness test
g. Neatness test
h. Tenacity and elongation test
i. Cohesion test.

(The cohesion test shall be omitted for raw silk of 34 denier, or of a coarser size.)

QUALITY TEST

Article 1. Sample Skeins and Test Pieces

The sample skeins for mechanical tests shall consist of 50 original skeins drawn from a lot, in case the lot consists of skeins of approximately 70 grams each, and 25 original skeins in case the lot consists of skeins of approximately 140 grams each. They shall be taken after the completion of the lot inspection.

In order to take out the sample skeins and test pieces for mechanical test uniformly from every part of a lot, books, and skeins, the following methods are employed:

1. Sample skeins shall be taken out in the following manner:

a. Draw from different books, taken uniformly from various parts of the lot, not more than one skein from any one book. In case of a lot with the test result of color slightly un-uniform in the visual inspection, bales shall be assorted into groups according to the color, and special attention shall be given so that the number of sample skeins to be drawn from each group be proportional to the bales.

b. In case 50 skeins are to be taken, 5 skeins are drawn from the corners of the books, 25 skeins from the outer surface of the books, excepting corners, and the remaining 20 skeins from the inner part of the books.

In case 25 skeins are to be taken, 6 skeins are drawn from corners of the books, 13 skeins from the outer surface of the books, excepting corners, and the remaining 6 skeins from the inner part of the books.

2. Test pieces shall be taken from the sample skeins in the following manner:

a. Lot consisting of skeins of approximately 70 grams each:

20 skeins shall be wound from the outer surface of the skeins, 20 skeins from the inner surface of the skeins, and 10 skeins from the middle part of the skeins, of which 5 skeins shall be wound toward the inside, beginning at about one-quarter part from the outer surface of the skeins, and the remaining 5 skeins toward the outer side, beginning at about one-quarter part from the inner surface of the skeins.

b. Lot consisting of skeins of approximately 140 grams each:

10 skeins shall be wound from the outer surface, 10 skeins from the inner surface and the remaining 5 skeins from the middle part of the skeins, beginning at about one-quarter part from the outer-surface. In order to take 50 test pieces, the above-mentioned winding operation shall be repeated on another 25 bobbins.

Article 2. Visual Inspection

1. Object. The object of this inspection is to inspect visually and by hand the uniformity, general finish, and characteristic nature of a lot of raw silk, and to make such sorting as to provide proper value as a lot of merchandise.

The visual inspection shall be made on the books and skeins of a whole lot.

2. Equipment. The visual inspection shall be conducted in a standard visual inspection room. The standard visual inspection room shall have a window facing directly north, which enables the inspector to utilize the skylight free from reflection of any surrounding object.

3. Inspection. The inspection shall be conducted on the following items. In case there are any books or skeins considerably defective or irregular in uniformity and unsuitable to form a lot, they shall be removed and replaced.

a. Uniformity. The general condition of the uniformity as to color, luster, and hand of a lot shall be inspected.

b. General Finish. The condition of the general finish of a lot and the presence and degree of the following defects shall be inspected.

1. *Re-reeling.* Hard gum spots; gummed skeins; irregular traverse; double ends; partial lack of traverse.
2. *Finish.* Improper skein-lacing; dropped threads; pulled threads; disturbed traverse; loose ends; double skeins.
3. *Make-up.* Irregular skeins or books; improper skein twisting or making of books; raised threads; lacing of booking cord through skeins; cut ends; dissimilar skeins; streaky threads; dissimilar threads; sooty skeins; gum knots on skeins; adhered substance on skeins; skeins or books of different nature or sort.
4. *Damage.* Damage by friction: injured skeins; insect-eaten threads; discolored skeins; browned skeins; musty skeins; soiled threads; shrunk threads; books out of shape; gummed books.

c. Nature. The nature of a lot shall be inspected on the following characteristics:

1. *Color:* shade and degree.
2. *Luster:* kind and degree.
3. *Hand:* nature (hardness) and smoothness.

The visual inspection as described is intended for the producing market where the skeins are easily available previous to final packing. Such modifications as may be necessary, due to conditions in the consuming market, are permissible.

4. Record. The results of the visual inspection of a lot which is completely sorted shall be recorded in the following manner:

a. Uniformity. The uniformity of a lot shall be indicated by Excellent, Good, Fair, Slightly Inferior, or Inferior.

b. General Finish. The general finish of a lot shall be indicated by Excellent, Good, Fair, Slightly Inferior, or Inferior; outstanding defects shall be mentioned in the test certificate.

The inspection for gums shall be made on the lot, on the sample skeins during visual inspection, and on the open skeins on the swifts during the winding test.

In case hard gum spots are found, they shall be indicated in degree and quantity as follows:

1. *Degree:* slight, hard, or very hard.
2. *Quantity:* few, many, or very many.

5. Nature. The nature shall be indicated in the following manner:

a. Color

1. *Shade:* white raw silk—white, greenish, creamy, brownish, or grayish Yellow raw silk—yellow, reddish, or darkish.
2. *Degree:* extremely light, light, medium, deep, or very deep.

b. Luster

1. *Kind:* full, moderate, or light.
2. *Degree:* bright, medium, or dull.

c. Hand

1. *Nature:* hard, ordinary, or soft.
2. *Smoothness:* smooth, ordinary, or rough.

Article 3. Winding Test

1. Object. The object of this test is to determine the number of breaks which occur in the raw silk thread in the winding operation.

2. Apparatus—Winding Frame. The winding frame upon which the test is to be performed shall be capable of being adjusted to a winding speed of 110, 140, or 165 meters per min. It shall be equipped to drive the bobbins from both ends and run smoothly at a uniform speed.

Swifts. The swifts used in the test shall be automatic, self-centering, pin-hub swifts, and each swift shall weigh about 530 grams.

Bobbins. The bobbins used for the test shall be smooth and well balanced so as to give uniform tension and speed. The dimensions shall be as follows:

Diameter of head	60 mm
Diameter of barrel	38 mm
Length between heads	85 mm
Weight	105 grams

3. Sample. The sample for the test shall be 40 skeins out of the 50 skeins, omitting the 10 skeins to be wound from the middle, as specified in Quality Test, Article 1-2. These 10 skeins shall not be used for the winding test.

4. Test. Twenty sample skeins shall be wound from the outer surface of the skeins, and an additional 20 skeins from the inner surface of the skeins. The winding shall be continued for a certain period, after a preliminary winding operation, and the breaks occurring during the period shall be counted and recorded. The time of the preliminary winding operation, the winding period and the average winding speed shall be determined by the size under test, as shown in Table 8.

During the winding test, the room in which the test is conducted shall be maintained at as nearly a standard atmosphere as possible. The condition in which the raw silk contains moisture equivalent to 11 per cent of the absolute weight is called the standard condition of raw silk. The atmospheric condition in which the raw silk maintains a standard condition when remaining exposed for a reasonable period of time is called the standard atmosphere.

TABLE 8

Size under Test (denier)	*Preliminary Winding (minutes)*	*Average Speed (meters per minute)*	*Winding Period (minutes)*
12 or finer	10	110	60
13–17	10	140	60
18–27	10	165	60
28–33	5	165	60
34–69	5	165	30
70–99	5	165	20
100 or coarser	5	165	10

5. Record. The record shall show the number of breaks in each skein by a table of frequency distribution, and the total number of breaks in 40 sample skeins occurring during the specified period.

Article 4. Size Deviation Test

1. Object. The object of this test is to determine the degree of size variation within the test pieces of sizing skeins of definite length of raw silk.

2. Apparatus—Sizing Reel. The measuring machine for making the sizing skeins shall have a reel 1.125 meters in circumference (400 revolutions equals 450 meters), revolving at a uniform velocity of 300 rpm, provided with a dial showing the number of revolutions, and equipped within an automatic stop-motion to stop the reel immediately in case the thread breaks or when the skein is complete.

Balance. The balance for determining the total weight of sizing skeins shall have a sensitivity of 5 mg and a capacity of 50 grams.

Scale. The scale for weighing the individual sizing skeins shall be of the quadrant or other suitable type and have the capacity and sensitivity mentioned below:

Capacity (denier)	*Sensitivity (denier)*
40	0.25
80	0.5
160	1.0
400	2.5

3. Sample. In 33 denier, or a finer size, the sample for the test shall consist of a total of 200 sizing skeins out of 50 sample skeins, taking 4 sizing skeins of 450 meters each from every sample skein (total length of 90,000 meters). In 34 denier, or a coarser size, the sample for the test shall consist of 400 test pieces, taking 8 sizing skeins of 112.5 meters each out of 50 sample skeins (total length of 45,000 meters).

4. Test. The total sizing skeins shall be divided into 10 groups. Each individual sizing skein of a group shall be weighed separately on a quadrant scale, and then the weight of each group of skeins as a whole is obtained by an analytical balance. The number of sizing skeins in a group, the graduation of the scale for weighing each individual skein and a group of skeins as a whole, shall be determined by the size under test as shown in Table 9.

TABLE 9

Size (denier)	*Number of Skeins in a Group*	*Graduation of Scale for Weighing*		*Difference (denier)*
		One Skein (denier)	*Group (denier)*	
33 or finer	20	0.5	0.5	1.5
34–49	40	1.0	2.0	4.0
50–99	40	2.0	2.0	8.0
100 or coarser	40	5.0	2.0	19.0

In case the sum of the weights of the individual skeins of a group should differ from the weight of the group of skeins as a whole by more than the denier difference as shown in Table 9, the weighing of the individual skeins and group of skeins as a whole shall be repeated.

5. Record. A table of frequency distribution shall be made, showing the number of individual sizing skeins which come under the respective denier.

The size deviation can be obtained by the following formula:

$$\frac{2n}{N}(M - m)$$

N is the number of sizing skeins;
M is the arithmetic mean of the sizes of these N sizing skeins;
n is the number of sizing skeins the size of which is lower than the average size;
m is the arithmetic mean of the sizes of these n sizing skeins.

The result of size deviation test shall be calculated down to two places of decimals.

Article 5. Maximum Deviation Test

1. Object. The object of this test is to determine the degree of spring size in 450 or 112.5 meters sizing skeins.

2. Apparatus. Same as given in Quality Test, Article 4-2.

3. Sample. Same as given in Quality Test, Article 4-3.

4. Test. Same as given in Quality Test, Article 4-4.

5. Record. The difference between average size and average of four coarsest size, and also the difference between average size and average of four finest size shall be obtained. Both differences are now compared, and the larger one represents the result of maximum deviation. In 34 denier and coarser, eight coarsest and finest sizes respectively shall be taken for the test.

The result of maximum deviation shall be calculated down to one place of decimals.

Article 6. Average Size Test

1. Object. The object of this test is to determine the average size at conditioned weight.

2. Apparatus—Conditioning Oven. A conditioning oven with forced ventilation, positive valve control, capable of drying the sample skeins at 140° C. The conditioning oven shall be equipped with a balance arranged to weigh the skeins with an accuracy of one (1) centigram while suspended within the drying chamber, the holder of the skeins to be of such type as to insure free access of the dry air to all skeins.

Sizing Reel. The same as given in Quality Tests, Article 4-2.

3. Sample. The same as given in Quality Test, Article 4-3.

4. Test. The 200 skeins shall be placed in the conditioning oven, dried to constant weight as determined by two successive weighings at 5-min intervals. The first weighing shall be made at the expiration of the first 10 min of drying. The second weighing shall be taken as the dry weight provided the loss between the first and second does not exceed one-quarter per cent (¼%) of the total first-dry weight. If the loss between the first and second weighing exceeds one-quarter per cent (¼%) the skeins shall be weighed at 5-min intervals until the losses between two successive weighings are within one-quarter per cent (¼%).

5. Record. The average size shall be indicated by the conditioned average size of the total sizing skeins, and it shall be recorded in deniers by omitting the figures beyond the second place after the decimal point.

Article 7. Evenness Test

1. Object. The object of this test is to determine the degree of evenness of raw silk within approximately the same length as the sizing skein.

2. Definitions—Evenness Defects. Evenness defects are those portions of raw silk threads on an inspection board which show stripes caused by variations on the size of raw silk to such a degree as is easily noticeable by visual inspection. The degree of such size variations of raw silk is called the intensity of variation.

For the purpose of determining the intensity of variations, the following four standards are established and shown as the standard variation photographs as mentioned below:

Variation 0 (V0): The intensity of variation which corresponds to or contains less variation than the V0 panel of the standard variation photographs.

Variation 1 (V1): The intensity of variation which corresponds to the VI panel of the standard variation photographs.

Variation 2 (V2): The intensity of variation which corresponds to the V2 panel of the standard variation photographs.

Variation 3 (V3): The intensity of variation which corresponds to or contains more variation than the V3 panel of the standard variation photographs.

Panel. A panel is a section of raw silk 127 mm wide by 450 mm long uniformly wound from a bobbin on to an inspection board.

Inspection Board. An inspection board is a flat board 1 meter in circumference upon which the inspection panels may be wound. It shall have a uniformly flat black surface without streaks, bars, or other imperfections which might influence the estimator or give a false effect.

3. Apparatus and Equipment—Seriplane. A seriplane is a frame designed to revolve an inspection board in such a manner that the raw silk threads of fixed length can be wound upon it with uniform spacing. The inspection board shall revolve at a uniform speed of 100 rpm. In case of excessive breaks, the speed may be reduced to 80 rpm. The machine shall be equipped *with a device to secure uniform tension on the thread and may be equipped* with a counter to indicate the number of raw silk threads wound on the panel.

Standard Photographs. The following standard photographs prepared by the Silk Conditioning House of Yokohama and Kobe shall be used:

a. Standard variation photographs indicating the intensity of variations.
b. Standard evenness photographs indicating relative values of evenness expressed in percentages.

4. Sample. The sample for the test shall consist of a total of 100 panels from 50 sample skeins, taken at the rate of 2 panels from each sample skein.

The thread shall be spaced on the inspection panel according to the size under test as follows:

Denier	*Threads per 25 mm*
9 or finer	133
10 to 12	114
13 to 16	100
17 to 26	80
27 to 36	66
37 to 48	57
49 to 68	50
69 to 104	40
105 to 149	33
150 to 197	28
198 or coarser	25

5. Test. The test shall be conducted by the estimator, taking a position of about 2 meters distance directly in front of the inspection panels placed in such lighting conditions that the two extremities of the panel receive the same intensity of light by indirect lighting. Each panel on any one side of the inspection board shall be carefully compared with the standard evenness photographs, and its evenness value shall be estimated in percentage. From 100 per cent to 50 per cent the estimate shall be made to the nearest 5 per cent. Below 50 per cent it shall be made to the nearest 10 per cent.

In estimating any panel which is markedly different from the standard evenness photographs, each uneven place or stripe of such panel shall be compared with the standard variation photographs to determine the intensity of variation, and each stripe or variation shall be penalized according to the table of unevenness penalties (Table 10). In case the total penalty percentage of one panel is

TABLE 10. Table of Unevenness Penalties

	Intensity of Variation					
Width of Stripes	V½ *(per cent)*	V1 *(per cent)*	V1½ *(per cent)*	V2 *(per cent)*	V2½ *(per cent)*	V3 *(per cent)*
4 mm and below	3	5	7	10	15	20
12 mm and below	5	10	12	15	20	25
25 mm and below	7	15	17	20	25	30
Above 25 mm	10	20	22	25	30	35

30 per cent or below, it shall be deducted from 100 per cent, and in case the total penalty percentage exceeds 30 per cent, one-half of such excess percentage plus

30 per cent shall be deducted from 100 per cent, for obtaining the value of respective panels. If such value is found to be 50 per cent and above, it may be modified within the scope of + or − 5 per cent, and shall be rated for every 5 per cent; while, if such value is found to be below 50 per cent, it may be modified within the scope of + or − 10 per cent, and shall be rated for every 10 per cent.

Note. V½ denotes the intensity of variation which is about midway between V0 and V1, V1½ between V1 and V2, and V2½ between V2 and V3.

6. Record. The record shall show the estimated evenness percentage of each panel, the average evenness percentage of a total of 100 panels, and the low evenness percentage which is the average percentage of low panels corresponding to one-quarter of the total panels inspected.

Article 8. Cleanness Test

1. Object. The object of this test is to determine the kind and the number of cleanness defects of raw silk.

2. Definitions—Cleanness Defects. The cleanness defects are classified into three general groups, viz., Super Major Defects, Major Defects, and Minor Defects.

a. Super Major Defects. The super major defects are defects which are ten or more times as large as the minimum size of major defects in length or in size.

b. Major Defects. The major defects are divided into five kinds as follows:

Waste is a mass of tangled cocoon filament or fibers attached to the thread.

Large slugs are considerably thickened places in the thread, 7 mm and above in length, or extremely thickened places with less length.

Bad casts are abruptly thickened places in the thread due to the cocoon filaments not being properly attached to the raw silk thread, or made by adding more than one cocoon filament at a time.

Very long knots are knots which have loose ends, 17 mm and above in length, or those caused by improper tying of threads.

Heavy corkscrews are places in which one or more cocoon filaments are longer than the remainder, and give the appearance of a very thick and large spiral form.

c. Minor Defects. The minor defects are divided into four kinds as follows:

Small slugs are considerably thickened places in the thread from 2 to less than 7 mm in length, or extremely thickened places less than 2 mm in length.

Long knots are knots which have loose ends, from 3 to less than 17 mm in length.

Corkscrews are places in which one or more cocoon filaments are longer than the remainder, and give the appearance of a thick spiral form.

Long loops or loose ends are loops or split ends 20 mm and above in length when measured along the filament.

3. Apparatus and Equipment—Standard Photographs. The standard photographs for cleanness defects prepared by the Silk Conditioning House of Yokohama and Kobe shall be used.

Lighting Equipment for Cleanness Test. The lighting equipment shall consist of a horizontal reflector, with a set of special lamps and a corrugated glass cover uniformly illuminating the inspection board from above.

Seriplane. The same as given in Quality Test, Article 7-3.

4. Sample. The same as given in Quality Test, Article 7-4.

5. Test. The test shall be conducted by the inspector, taking a position of about 0.5 meter (2 ft) distance directly in front of the inspection panels, under the lighting for cleanness test. The actual number of cleanness defects of each class and kind described in the above definition shall be counted on the threads of both sides of the inspection board, omitting the parts on its edges. The class and kind to which each defect belongs shall be determined by comparing with the standard photographs for cleanness defects.

6. Records. The record shall also show the number of defects in 100 panels found by test and also show the cleanness percentage, which is determined by deducting from 100 per cent the total penalty calculated by penalizing each defect with the following rate:

For each Super Major Defect	1.0%
For each Major Defect	0.4%
For each Minor Defect	0.1%

Article 9. Neatness Test

1. Object. The object of this test is to determine the neatness percentage of raw silk.

2. Definitions—Neatness Defects. The following imperfections or similar thereto, in the raw silk threads, which are smaller than those classified as minor cleanness defects are called neatness defects.

Nibs are small thickened places or spots in the thread less than 2 mm in length.

Loops are small open places in the thread due to the excessive length of one or more cocoon filaments, less than 20 mm in length when measured along the filament.

Hairiness and fuzziness is the condition of the thread which shows small loose ends and fine particles of cocoon filaments projecting from the thread.

Raw knots are knots which have loose ends, less than 3 mm in length.

Fine corkscrews are places in which one or more cocoon filaments are longer than the remainder and give the appearance of a fine spiral form.

3. Apparatus and Equipment—Standard Photographs. The standard photographs for neatness defects prepared by the Silk Conditioning House of Yokohama and Kobe shall be used.

Artificial Lighting for Neatness Test. The same as given in Quality Test, Article 8-3.

Seriplane. The same as given in Quality Test, Article 7-3.

4. Sample. The same as given in Quality Test, Article 7-4.

5. Test. The test shall be conducted by the estimator, taking a position of about 0.5 meter (2 ft) distance directly in front of the inspection panels, under the lighting for neatness test. Each panel on any one side of the inspection board shall be carefully compared with the standard photographs for neatness defects, and its neatness value shall be estimated in percentage. From 100 per cent to 50 per cent the estimate shall be to the nearest 5 per cent. Below 50 per cent it shall be made to the nearest 10 per cent.

6. Record. The record shall show the estimated neatness percentage of each panel together with the average neatness percentage of a total of 100 panels.

Article 10. Tenacity and Elongation Tests

1. Object. The object of these tests is to determine the tenacity and elongation of raw silk.

2. Apparatus—Serigraph. The apparatus for these tests consists of a tensile strength testing machine with an automatic attachment recording simultaneously the pulling force and corresponding elongation of the thread. The distance between the upper and lower clamps shall be 10 cm. The pulling speed of the lower clamp shall be 15 cm per min.

Sizing Reel and Scale. The same as given in Quality Test, Article 4-2.

3. Sample. Ten sample skeins shall be taken out of 50 sample skeins drawn from a lot. From every one of these 10 sample skeins, a sizing skein, or a total of 10, shall be prepared for tenacity and elongation tests.

4. Test. The sizing skeins to be tested shall be placed for a sufficient time in a place where standard humidity can be maintained, in order to allow them to become adjusted to standard condition. Each sizing skein shall be carefully weighed for sizing and then tested for tenacity and elongation by the serigraph which is placed in the room where the same standard humidity is maintained.

5. Record. The tenacity shall be expressed in grams per denier, while the elongation shall be expressed in percentage of total stretch of the portion tested. The result shall be indicated by the average results of 10 test pieces.

The result of the tenacity shall be calculated by omitting the figures beyond the second place after the decimal point.

Article 11. Cohesion Test

1. Object. The object of this test is to determine the degree of agglutination of cocoon filaments forming the thread.

2. Apparatus—Duplan Cohesion Tester. The cohesion tester consists of a framework upon which a continuous thread of raw silk is placed zigzag between a set of 10 hooks on each side of the frame, under constant and uniform tension in such way that the thread can be subjected to a friction action at 20 different places simultaneously, and the number of strokes is recorded automatically. The total load to be given for tension is 180 grams.

3. Sample. The sample for the test shall consist of 20 test pieces taken from 20 skeins out of 50 skeins drawn from a lot. The thread shall be free from any cleanness or pronounced evenness defect in the portion which is to be tested.

4. Test. The test shall be performed in a room where standard humidity can be maintained during the test and the maximum speed of stroke shall be 140 strokes per min. The machine shall be stopped every 10 strokes, and every thread inspected very carefully to see if there is any open place. As soon as 10 different open places 6 mm long and above are observed, they shall be recorded with the number of strokes which shall be considered as the strokes of the thread opened.

5. Record. The record of the test shall be indicated by the average number of strokes of 20 test pieces.

The result of cohesion shall be calculated by omitting decimals.

RAW SILK CLASSIFICATION

Article 1. Grades

The grades shall be expressed in the following order, viz., 6A, 5A, 4A, 3A, 2A, A, B, C, D, E, F, and G for raw silk of 33 denier, or of a finer size, and 4A, 3A, 2A, A, B, C, D, E, F, and G for raw silk of 34 denier, or of a coarser size.

Article 2. Method of Classification

The grade of a lot shall be determined in the following manner:

1. Grading in Accordance with the Results of the Major Tests. The grade of a lot in sizes 33 denier and finer shall be determined according to the lowest respective percentage of its evenness, low evenness, cleanness, and neatness, whereas the grade of a lot in sizes 34 denier and coarser shall be determined according to the lowest respective percentage of its evenness, low evenness, cleanness, neatness, size deviation, and maximum deviation as tabulated in the classification table, Table 11. Should any one or more of these percentages fall below the minimum limits prescribed for a grade, the lot shall be degraded to the lowest grade wherein such a less or insufficient percentage is given in the classification table.

2. Degrading in Accordance with the Results of the Auxiliary Tests.

a. If any one of the size deviation, maximum deviation, winding, tenacity, elongation or cohesion tests of a lot in sizes 33 denier and finer, or if any one of the winding, tenacity or elongation tests of a lot in sizes 34 denier and coarser is found to be lower than the required value listed in the grade of the auxiliary tests, then the grade provisionally established in accordance with the preceding paragraph shall be lowered by as many grades as the difference that exists between the required auxiliary test grade and the grade actually found.

In case two or more auxiliary test grades are found to be lower than the required value listed in the grades of the auxiliary tests, then the lot shall be degraded to the lowest auxiliary test grade actually found.

b. In case the result of the visual inspection of a lot is found to be *Slightly Inferior* in its uniformity, and/or its general finish, the grade of the lot shall be one below that as determined in accordance with the preceding paragraphs.

c. In case the result of the visual inspection of a lot is found to be *Inferior* in its uniformity, and/or its general finish, or in case the number of breaks in the winding test exceeds the limits mentioned in Table 12, the lot shall be determined as G grade.

TABLE 11. Classification Table of Raw Silk

Major Tests	Grade											
	6A	5A	4A	3A	2A	A	B	C	D	E	F	G
Average Evenness, per cent	95	94	92	90	87	85	83	81	78	73	67	below 67
Low Evenness, per cent	87	86	83	81	77	75	73	70	66	60	54	below 54
Cleanness, per cent (denier)												
33 and below	96	95	94	92	90	88	86	83	80	76	70	below 70
34 and above			93	91	89	86	83	79	75	70	64	below 64
Neatness, per cent (denier)												
33 and below	95	94	92	90	88	87	85	83	81	77	73	below 73
34 and above			92	90	88	86	83	80	77	74	70	below 70

Auxiliary Tests	Grade								
	(I)	(II)	(III)	(IV)	(V)	(VI)	(VII)	(VIII)	(IX)
Size Deviation (denier)									
12 and below	0.75	0.80	0.85	0.95	1.05	1.15	1.25	1.35	above 1.35
13–15	0.80	0.85	0.90	1.00	1.10	1.20	1.30	1.40	above 1.40
16–18	0.90	1.00	1.10	1.20	1.30	1.40	1.50	1.60	above 1.60
19–22	1.05	1.15	1.25	1.35	1.45	1.55	1.70	1.90	above 1.90
23–27	1.25	1.35	1.45	1.55	1.70	1.85	2.00	2.20	above 2.20
28–33	1.45	1.55	1.70	1.85	2.00	2.20	2.40	2.60	above 2.60
Maximum Deviation (denier)									
12 and below	3.0	3.2	3.4	3.8	4.2	4.6	5.0	5.4	above 5.4
13–15	3.2	3.4	3.6	4.0	4.4	4.8	5.2	5.6	above 5.6
16–18	3.6	4.0	4.4	4.8	5.2	5.6	6.0	6.4	above 6.4
19–22	4.2	4.6	5.0	5.4	5.8	6.2	6.8	7.6	above 7.6
23–27	5.0	5.4	5.8	6.2	6.8	7.4	8.0	8.8	above 8.8
28–33	5.8	6.2	6.8	7.4	8.0	8.8	9.6	10.4	above 10.4

Major Tests	Grade									
	4A	3A	2A	A	B	C	D	E	F	G
Size Deviation (denier)										
34–49	2.40	2.70	3.00	3.40	3.90	4.60	5.40	6.40	7.60	above 7.60
50–69	3.20	3.60	4.00	4.50	5.20	6.10	7.20	8.50	10.10	above 10.10
70–99	3.90	4.40	4.90	5.50	6.30	7.50	8.80	10.40	12.30	above 12.30
100–199	5.90	6.60	7.30	8.30	9.50	11.20	13.20	15.60	18.50	above 18.50
200 and above	9.50	10.70	11.90	13.50	15.40	18.20	21.40	25.30	30.10	above 30.10
Maximum Deviation (denier)										
34–49	9.0	10.0	11.0	13.0	15.0	18.0	21.0	25.0	30.0	above 30.0
50–69	12.0	14.0	16.0	18.0	21.0	24.0	28.0	34.0	40.0	above 40.0
70–99	15.0	17.0	19.0	22.0	25.0	30.0	35.0	41.0	49.0	above 49.0
100–199	23.0	26.0	29.0	33.0	38.0	44.0	52.0	62.0	74.0	above 74.0
200 and above	38.0	42.0	47.0	54.0	62.0	72.0	85.0	101.0	120.0	above 120.0

TABLE 11. CLASSIFICATION TABLE OF RAW SILK (*Continued*)

Auxiliary Tests	Grade						*
	(I)	(II)	(III)	(IV)	(V)	(VI)	G
Winding (breaks) (denier)							
12 and below	20	25	30	40	60	above 60	above 80
13–17	15	21	27	35	50	above 50	above 70
18–33	12	17	23	30	40	above 40	above 60
34–69	5	7	10	15	20	above 20	above 30
70–99	3	5	7	10	15	above 15	above 20
100 and above	2	4	6	8	10	above 10	above 15

Auxiliary Tests	Grade			
	(I)	(II)	(III)	(IV)
Tenacity (grams	3.6	3.5	3.4	below 3.4
Elongation, per cent (denier)				
17 and below	19	18	17	below 17
18 and above	20	19	18	below 18
Cohesion (strokes) (denier)				
13–17	40	35	30	below 30
18–33	60	50	40	below 40

Auxiliary Test	Grade	
	(I)	(II)
Cohesion (strokes) (denier)		
12 and below	30	below 30

* The values indicated in this column are only applicable under the conditions laid down in Raw Silk Classification, Article 2-2*c*.

TABLE 12

Size (denier)	*Breaks*
12 or finer	80
13 to 17	70
18 to 33	60
34 to 69	30
70 to 99	20
100 or coarser	15

3. Average Size Variation. The conditioned average size of a lot shall not vary more than the following limitations either way from the contract size:

20/22 denier and finer	4% either way is allowed
21/23 to 26/28	3.5% either way is allowed
27/29 and coarser	Unless by special agreement, the average size shall fall within the limits specified.

PHYSICAL PROPERTIES

Microscopy of Silk Fiber

When *Bombyx mori* raw silk is examined under a microscope it exhibits an appearance which readily distinguishes it from other textile fibers. The longitudinal view shows a very irregular surface structure, mostly in the sericin layer, which consists of traverse fissures, creases, folds, and uneven lumps. These markings are largely due to the reeling operation when the soft gum is slipped or broken in the crossing or croissure. Frequently the two fibers of a cocoon filament are distinctly separated from one another for considerable distances, the intervening space being filled in with sericin. All of these markings are in no wise structural, and occur only in the sericin layer.

The cross-sectional view of a cocoon filament is roughly elliptical, showing the two triangular brins completely surrounded by sericin normally facing each other with the flat side of the triangle. The ellipticity of the cross-section varies from the outside which is nearly circular to the inside of the cocoon which is usually very much flattened. The innermost layers are not capable of being reeled, so are used for waste silk. The cross-sections of the fiber from the middle portion of the cocoon, constituting the reeled silk, are much more rounded in form.

When raw silk is degummed or boiled off the thread always has an even number of filaments because the original cocoon filament consisted of two triangular fibroins or brins. It was found by Mennerich and Hougen [21] that both the size and shape of these brins are very important to the manufacturer of silk fabrics. Yarns made from brins larger in diameter or flatter in cross-section dye darker than those made from smaller brins or those having a more nearly round cross-section. By carefully measuring the ratio of the smaller to the larger diameter of each silk filament for a group of 100 fibers, it was found that Japanese silks showed an extreme range of diameter ratios from 0.61 to 0.40 and that a difference of diameter ratios of only 0.04 was sufficient to cause a visible two-tone dyeing in fabrics. This shade variation was also noticeable when the difference of the mean diameters of the filaments of two yarns exceeded 0.7 μ.

The longitudinal view of the degummed fiber shows a smooth, structureless, translucent filament with occasional constrictions as well as swellings or lumps. The *Bombyx mori* fiber is rarely striated longitudinally, but when such striations do appear they always run parallel to

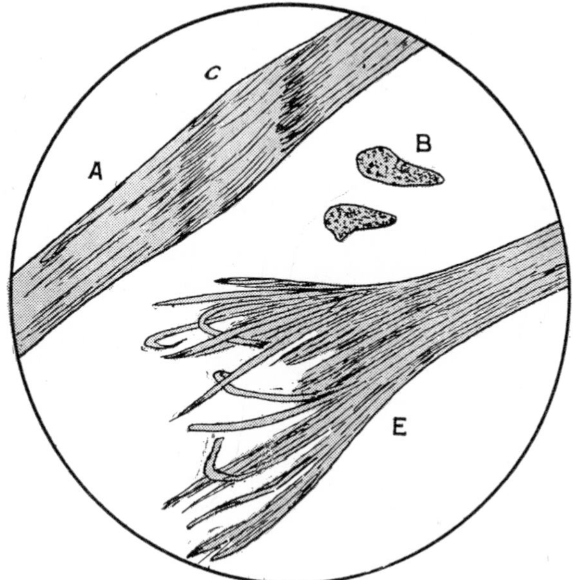

Fig. 11. Tussah silk. (×400.) *A*, view of broad side; *B*, cross-sections; *C*, cross-mark; *E*, torn end showing fibrillae. (*Micrograph by Matthews.*)

the axis of the fiber; and, when such fibers are treated with dilute chromic acid, very fine striations appear.

The microscopic appearance of the wild silks is very different from that of *Bombyx mori*. The fibers are broad and show distinct longitudinal striations, also peculiar flattened markings, usually running obliquely across the fiber, which more or less obliterate the striations. These cross-markings are caused by the overlapping of one fiber on another before the substance of the fiber has completely hardened, in consequence of which these places are more or less flattened out. The striated appearance of wild silk is evidence that structurally the fiber is composed of minute filaments, often referred to as fibrils or, more recently, as micelles. In fact, the fibrils may be readily isolated by maceration in cold chromic acid.

According to Höhnel these structural elements are only 0.3 to 1.5 μ in diameter; they run parallel to each other through the fiber and are rather more dense in the outer portion of the fiber than in the inner part. Besides the fine striations on the fibers of wild silk caused by their structural filaments, there are also a number of irregularly oc-

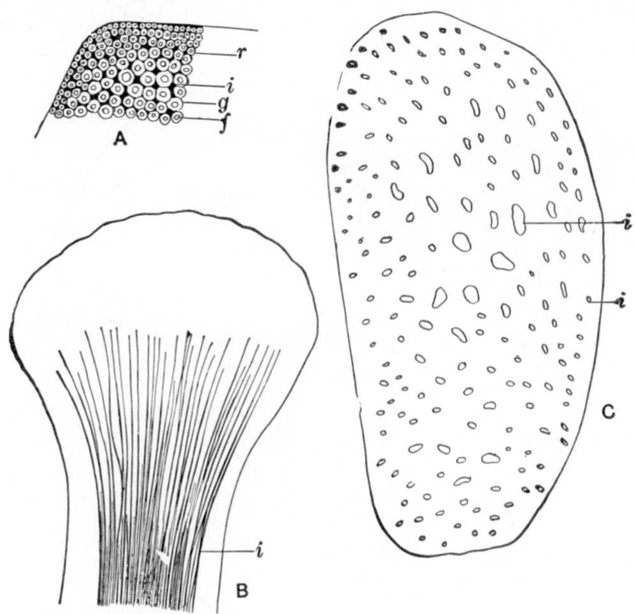

Fig. 12. Cross-section of wild silk. *A*, diagrammatic drawing of section; *i*, air space; *g*, ground matrix; *f*, fibrillae; *r*, marginal layer; *B*, end of fiber of tussah silk swollen in sulfuric acid; *C*, cross-section of fiber of tussah silk swollen in sulfuric acid. (*After Höhnel.*)

curring coarser striations, which appear to be due to air canals or spaces between the fibrils of the fiber.

Höhnel is of the opinion that there is really no difference in kind between the structure of wild silk and that of cultivated silk; that is to say, the fibroin fiber of the cultivated silk is also composed of structural fibrils, but they fuse into one another in a more homogeneous manner on emerging from the silk glands, thus rendering it more difficult to recognize them superficially. This view is confirmed both by the appearance of a slight striation when the silk fiber is macerated in chromic acid solution and by modern X-ray technique.

The cross-sectional contour of tussah silk is definitely wedge-shaped. In the raw silk, according to Von Bergen and Krauss [22], the two small sides of the wedge face each other and are surrounded by the silk glue. The filament structure can be easily recognized in the cross-section by the grainy inner structure of the fiber and the sawtoothlike contour of some of the fibers. Taken collectively, wild silks are all similar in their microscopical structure and it is difficult to differentiate between the various species. They are distinguished from cultivated silk in that they are darker in color, have a ribbonlike form, and are strongly fibrillous, with a wedge-shaped cross-section.

X-Ray View of Silk

The X-ray photographs of natural silk fibroin as made by Astbury [23] show definite X-ray "spots," which prove at once that silk is really crystalline in structure. The protein fibroin, from which the fiber is made as it exudes from the spinneret of the silkworm, is built into invisible crystals which are sufficiently perfect to reflect X-rays in definite directions; it is then possible, by the application of the Bragg law, to deduce the dimensions of the molecular pattern. All the invisible crystals in a silk fiber point in the same direction directly along the axis of the fiber and may be up to 700 A long [24]. X-ray studies have given a much clearer concept of many of the important physical characteristics of silk fibroin, such as stress-strain load curve, moisture absorption, and electrical resistivity.

Hygroscopic Nature

Silk is quite hygroscopic, and under favorable circumstances will absorb as much as 30 per cent of its weight of moisture and still appear dry. It is therefore customary to determine the amount of moisture in each lot at the time of sale. This is called conditioning, and is usually carried out in official laboratories. The amount of "regain" officially permitted is 11 per cent; this would be equivalent to 9.91 per cent of moisture in the silk. Boiled-off silk appears to contain somewhat less moisture than raw silk, the silk gum having a greater power of absorbing water than the fiber proper. The amount of moisture in boiled-off silk is usually regarded as about 8.45 per cent, which would correspond to a regain of 9.25 per cent. The Milan Commission (1906) adopted a temperature of 140° C. for the conditioning of silk, as it is found to be difficult to dry the fiber completely at 110° to 120° C.

The X-ray studies have shown that silk fibroin is made of crystals less than 0.1 μ long and only a few thousandths of a micron thick. A single fiber thus contains an incredibly large number of crystals giving an internal surface, i.e., the sum total of all the surface area of the invisible particles, which from water absorption standpoint is enormously greater than the external visible surface of the fiber. Also inasmuch as the crystals are about twenty times as long as they are thick, it explains the pronounced lateral swelling of the fiber compared with the slight increase in length [25].

The amount of water absorbed by silk, or its regain, depends on its previous history, i.e., on its molecular state, as well as on the surrounding atmospheric humidity. To describe the phenomena more completely, the term "adsorption" is used when moisture equilibrium is approached from the dry state and "desorption" when approached from the wet state.

Table 13 gives the adsorption and desorption data in per cent at various relative humidities and constant temperature of about 65° F. [26].

TABLE 13. Adsorption and Desorption of Silk

	Per Cent Relative Humidity						
	40	45	50	55	60	65	70
Japanese raw silk:							
Adsorption	7.3	8.0	8.6	9.1	9.7	10.3	11.2
Desorption	9.3	9.9	10.5	11.2	11.8	12.4	13.1
Raw organzine:							
Adsorption	7.5	8.1	8.7	9.2	9.8	10.5	11.4
Desorption	9.7	10.3	10.8	11.4	11.9	12.5	13.1
Degummed organzine							
Adsorption	6.3	6.8	7.3	7.8	8.3	8.9	9.6
Desorption	7.7	8.0	8.4	8.9	9.4	10.1	10.7

Tensile Strength

Silk is also distinguished by its considerable strength, having a tensile strength equal to many engineering materials. Its breaking strength is about 4 grams per denier, which is about 65,000 lb per sq in. The conversion formula is:

$$\text{Tensile strength (psi)} = 12{,}800 \times \text{Density} \times \text{Grams per denier}$$

Silk has an elongation of about 20 per cent, i.e., it will stretch about 20 per cent of its original length before breaking. It has a relatively low true elasticity. It can be stretched only 1 to 2 per cent, before it has a permanent set. The X-ray studies [27] show that the silk crystals or micelles are extended to the maximum possible in the normal state; so, when the fibers are stretched, extension can take place for the most part only by means of internal slipping. Beyond an extension of 1 to 2 per cent, the micelles slip over one another or "draft" exactly as is done in the familiar spinning operation. There is, however, an elastic aftereffect or a tendency of strained fibers, even after the true elastic limit has been exceeded, to creep back slowly toward their original length when the stress is removed. This is due to imperfect alignment of all molecules parallel to the axis of the fiber.

Density

The density of silk in the raw state is 1.33, whereas boiled-off silk has a density [28] of 1.25. Silk fibroin, therefore, is somewhat lighter than cotton, linen, or rayon. Silk is also slightly lighter than wool and hair fibers, which have a density of 1.33 to 1.35. The figures given here for the density of silk apply, of course, to the pure unweighted fiber. In weighted silks the density increases with the degree of weighting, as all the metallic weighting materials have a much higher relative density than the fiber itself.

Scroop

Another property of silk, and one which is peculiar to this fiber, is what is termed its "scroop"; this refers to the crackling sound emitted when the fiber is squeezed or pressed. To this property is due the well-known "rustle" of silk fabrics. The scroop of silk does not appear to be an inherent property of the fiber itself, but is acquired when the silk is worked in a bath of dilute acid (acetic or tartaric) and dried without washing. A satisfactory explanation to account for the scroop has not yet been given; it is probably due to the acid hardening the surface of the fiber. Mercerized cotton can also be given a somewhat similar scroop by such a treatment with dilute acetic acid. Wool, under certain conditions of treatment, in some degree can also be given this silklike scroop, as, for instance, when it is treated with chloride of lime solutions or with strong caustic alkalies. In many manufactured articles scroop is considered as a desirable property; by some it is supposed to indicate a high quality of silk, but this is not the case, as the scroop, crunch, or rustle of silk is purely an acquired property added by artificial treatment; it does not enhance the real value and quality of the silk.

Electrical Properties

Silk is a poor conductor of electricity and accumulates a static charge by friction, which at times renders it difficult to handle in manufacturing processes. The charge can be dissipated by high humidity. Owing to its insulating properties, silk has been much in demand for covering wire in electric apparatus.

The difference in electrical behavior of different textile fibers, according to Walker [29], may be illustrated by a comparison of the adsorption of moisture on the internal surfaces of silk and cotton fibers. From Astbury's pictures of the structure of protein molecules as compared with cellulose molecules, it appears that although there are more points per unit of surface for moisture to condense on the protein surface, there are also possibilities of separation of adjacent moisture chains in a manner similar to that for cellulose; and furthermore there appear to be side chains which may act as barriers to the ready contact of adsorbed water chains. Consequently silk might be expected to have a higher electrical resistance than cotton for a given moisture content, and a higher dielectric breakdown.

CHEMICAL PROPERTIES AND NATURE

Chemical Constitution

Chemically, silk fibroin and silk sericin are similar compounds, both belonging to the protein group. Generally proteins are insoluble; and being amphoteric, they have the property of combining with both acids and bases to form salts. There is also present in raw silk about 2 per cent of wax, which is thought to act as a water repellent for the cocoon [30], and about 1 per cent of mineral matter.

Analyses of samples of mulberry silk are given in per cent by H. Silbermann [31] in Table 14.

Sericin

Sericin is an albuminoid protein insoluble in cold water. Like all proteins, sericin may be broken down into various amino acids of which at least 12 have been isolated: alanine, tyrosine, glycocoll, and leucine are the most abundant [32]. The empirical formula as given by Grover [33], for sericin, is $C_{15}H_{25}N_5O_8$. According to Mosher [34], it may be completely dissolved by acid solutions having a *p*H below 2.5 and by alkali solutions having a *p*H above 9.5. Shelton and Johnson [35] definitely established the presence of two proteins, which they named Sericin A and Sericin B. Sericin A is more soluble, hygroscopic,

TABLE 14. Chemical Components of Mulberry Silk

	White		Yellow	
	Cocoons	Raw Silk	Cocoons	Raw Silk
Fibroin	73.59	76.20	70.02	72.35
Ash of fibroin	0.09	0.09	0.16	0.16
Sericin	22.28	22.01	24.29	23.13
Wax and fat	3.02	1.36	3.46	2.75
Salts	1.60	0.30	1.92	1.60

and plastic; has the isoelectric point of *p*H 3.8 but is of little value commercially.

Sericin B is a stiff, hornlike protein with an isoelectric point of *p*H 4.5 and forms, with oils and waxes, an excellent buffer solution for dyeing. It acts as a reservoir for dyestuffs in the dye bath as they are slowly and evenly supplied to the fabric. Sericin B is converted into Sericin A on prolonged heating in water at a temperature above the normal boiling point or by the action of strong alkali.

The total amount of sericin present in raw silk ranges from about 15 to 25 per cent, depending on the type of silk and the country or district of its origin. It is the material that causes the fiber to feel stiff and harsh, yet it forms a most essential protective agent through the various steps in the manufacturing process. Different types of soaps and oils are applied in soaking solutions so as to soften the sericin. This enables the twists to be inserted in the throwing operation to produce a smooth pliable yarn which on fabrication will give uniform interlacings and loops without distortion.

Degumming. In order to make a silk fabric soft and glossy, it is necessary to remove the sericin or gum by a treatment called discharging, stripping, or degumming. It is really a scouring operation, the silk being worked in a soap solution at a temperature of 205° F. Successive scourings charge the soap solution heavily with sericin, and this solution is subsequently utilized in the dye-bath as a buffer agent under the name of "boil-off liquor." The boil-off of thrown silk is greater than that for raw silk, owing to the absorption of soaps and oils from the soaking bath; it may range from 18 to 36 per cent, depending on the type of yarn made.

Tables 15 and 16 give average boil-off data taken from tests made by the United States Testing Co., Inc., for both raw and thrown silk yarns. These tables should be used with caution. Although the values given are the average for a large number of tests, the individual samples do vary widely.

In the removal of sericin from raw silk by a hot alkaline bath, the active alkali content of the solution is lowered by its reaction with sericin to form an alkali-sericin compound of indefinite composition. Wolf and Hougen [36] consider the degumming of silk a chemical reaction, because the rate of boil-off is more than doubled by an increase of 10° C. rise in temperature, by the reduction of active alkali, by the formation of free oleic acid from reaction with soap, and by the

TABLE 15. Average Per Cent Loss in Boil-Off (Degumming) of Raw Silk *

Years	Japan		China		Italy	Canton	Tsatlee	Tussah
	White	Yellow	White	Yellow				
1932	18.49	21.10	18.50	..	23.09	23.40	..	..
1933	18.99	21.91	18.69	21.50	23.78	23.33	..	..
1934	19.03	20.91	17.17	..	..	23.50	19.86	..
1935	19.35	21.11	16.98	23.00	..	..	..	..
1936	19.49	22.17	17.30	..	22.75	23.25	19.00	..
1937	19.36	22.30	17.85	..	22.95	..	20.00	..
1938	20.10	22.88	18.57	..	24.50	..	21.20	..
1939	21.08	23.65	18.98	21.04	24.00	..	21.17	..
1940	21.34	23.73	19.51	22.50	24.47	23.44	21.63	16.00
1941 †	21.26	23.12	20.27	..	..	23.60	21.25	13.50
1945	..	..	..	..	..	..	..	..
1946	21.60	..	..	..	..	..	..	..
1947	22.44	..	..	..	..	..	..	..
1948	22.63	..	..	..	..	..	..	..
1949	22.23	..	..	..	..	..	..	..
1950	22.03	..	..	..	..	..	..	..

Variation or range in percentages:

Japan: White	14 to 25	Italy	22 to 35
Yellow	17 to 28	Canton	22 to 25
China: White	14 to 27	Tsatlee	19 to 23
Yellow	20 to 24	Tussah	10 to 16

* Unpublished data, U. S. Testing Co., Inc.
† January to July, inclusive.

TABLE 16. AVERAGE PER CENT LOSS IN BOIL-OFF OF THROWN SILK *

Year	Organzine		Tram				Crepe			
	Japan, White	China, White	Japan, White	China, White	Italy	Tsatlee	Japan, White	China, White	Italy	Canton
1932	22.29	....	24.61	....	....	....	25.51	28.25	30.07	29.93
1933	24.17	....	26.10	....	....	....	26.55	27.33	....	30.27
1934	24.35	....	25.00	....	....	....	27.15	25.67	....	31.00
1935	24.71	20.00	25.18	....	....	....	27.58	27.50	....	29.67
1936	25.07	23.67	25.41	....	....	....	27.74	26.14	30.00	30.00
1937	24.59	22.67	25.57	....	29.40	....	27.09	....	29.00	....
1938	25.18	26.14	28.31	....	32.38	....	27.29	....	....	....
1939	27.14	24.90	28.87	....	....	....	28.83	....	33.00	....
1940	26.67	25.42	29.79	28.61	32.75	25.20	28.15	....	....	....
1941	26.20	21.38	30.16	29.37	....	24.93	30.06	....	....	....

Variation or range in percentages:

Organzine	Japan 18 to 32	China 17 to 30	Italy 27 to 36	Tsatlee 24 to 29
Tram	Japan 18 to 36	China 21 to 35	Italy 29 to 33	Canton 26 to 33
Crepe	Japan 18 to 33	China 24 to 31		

* Unpublished data, U. S. Testing Co., Inc.

liberation of carbonic acid by reaction with sodium carbonate. The chemical reaction is complicated by the presence of at least two sericin fractions and by the progressive degradation of the sericin particle after it enters solution.

In general, the conclusions reached by many investigators is that the boil-off solution should have a *p*H value between 9.5 and 10.5, and that there is little degumming at temperatures under 180° F. A solution of this type is sufficiently potent to remove the gum expeditiously and, yet, will not attack and degrade the protein fibroin. Wolf and Hougen state that the coefficient of degumming depends on the temperature, yarn size, degree of agitation, water-silk ratio, and nature of alkali. For small laboratory tests conducted at normal boiling point, at constant weight on 140 denier tubing with a water-silk ratio of 100 to 1, the values of this coefficient were found to be as shown in Table 17 for the various alkalies and to be nearly independent of concentration:

For soap solutions, the value of the coefficient decreases with increasing normality of soap.

Soaking Baths and Tints. Raw silk is usually soaked prior to throwing in order to secure a yarn with greater flexibility, pliability, hygroscopicity, and lubricity. In addition, the bath must neutralize the

TABLE 17. COEFFICIENT OF DEGUMMING OF RAW SILK

Sodium hydroxide	984
Sodium carbonate	873
Sodium silicate (SiO_2/Na_2O ratio 3.73)	427
Trisodium phosphate	349
Borax	189
Sodium bicarbonate	173

natural acidity of the raw silk, give a distinct shade or color value to yarn, and also contain a fungicide to prevent mildew.

Owing to the many different sizes and twist constructions of silk yarns in a modern throwing plant, it is most essential for identification purposes that a tint be placed in the soaking bath that has a distinctive tinctorial value and further is definitely "fugitive." It must hold its color throughout the various steps of manufacture, including the steam setting of the twist and then be completely removed in the degumming bath.

In the knitting field the rapid absorption and release of moisture are prerequisites of good functioning yarn. The moistened hosiery yarn is flexible, giving smooth and perfect loop formation, which will retain its shape on rapid drying. All these requirements are met in a modern soaking bath by using carefully selected chemical ingredients under rigid control.

Fibroin

The long molecular chain of fibroin is made up by the linkage of many α-amino acid residues, the units that are left after the elimination of water from the α-amino acid molecules [37]. All the numerous proteins taking part in biological processes appear to be built up mainly by the combination of the residues of α-amino acids having the general formula

$$
\begin{array}{c}
\mathrm{H} \\
| \\
\mathrm{NH_2{-}C{-}COOH} \\
| \\
\mathrm{R}
\end{array}
$$

in which R stands for an atom or group of atoms having only one remaining valence free for attachment to another atom. Two or more amino acid molecules may be made to react, eliminating water molecules and being held together with the linkage —OO—NH— to form long chains of high molecular weight known as polypeptides. By hydrolysis, the water molecule may be restored to the amino acid residues of a polypeptide chain and may thus give the original amino acids. By this method, chemists have been able to estimate the various amino acid residues in fibroin.

Cohnheim, in his tables of the percentage composition of various albumins, gives the following for fibroin of silk:

TABLE 18. CHEMICAL COMPOSITION OF SILK FIBROIN ELEMENTS

	Per Cent
Glycocoll	36.0
Alanine	21.0
Leucine	1.5
Phenylalanine	1.5
α-Pyrrolidine carboxylic acid	0.3
Serine	1.6
Tyrosine	10.0
Arginine	1.0

The occurrence of the following compounds in indeterminate amounts is also given: lysine, histidine, tryptophane, and amino-valerianic acid.

Mulberry silk fibroin has an isoelectric point at *p*H 2.5 [38], is colored pink by Millon's reagent; is dissolved in an aqueous solution of calcium thiocyanate of specific gravity of 1.20 at 70° C. [39]; and is insoluble in ammonia, in solutions of the alkaline carbonates, and in a 1 per cent solution of caustic soda.

Fibroin is dissolved by stronger (5 per cent) caustic soda solutions, especially at boiling temperature. It is also soluble in hot glacial acetic acid, strong hydrochloric, sulfuric, nitric, and phosphoric acids, and in alkaline solutions of the hydroxides of such metals as nickel, zinc, and copper.

Coloring Matter

According to Dubois the yellow coloring matter of silk is similar to carotin. He obtained five different bodies from the natural coloring matter of silk, as follows:

(1) A golden-yellow coloring matter, soluble in potassium carbonate and precipitated by acetic acid;

(2) Crystals which appear yellowish-red by transmitted light and brown by reflected light;

(3) A lemon-colored amorphous body, the alcoholic solution of which on evaporation gave granular masses;

(4) Yellow octahedral crystals resembling sulfur;

(5) A dark bluish-green pigment in minute quantities and probably crystalline.

Levrat and Conte [40] have shown that the color of natural silk is due to the coloring matter present in the leaves on which the silkworms feed, chlorophyl being the coloring matter in green silks and yellow silks containing the yellow coloring matter of the mulberry leaves. These investigators made experiments by feeding silkworms with leaves stained with with various artificial dyes, and it was found that the silk produced was more or less colored. The silk from the *Atlacus orizaba* gives a more pronounced color than that from the ordinary silkworm.

Action of Heat

In its general chemical behavior silk is quite similar to wool. It will stand a higher temperature, however, than the wool fiber, without injury; it can be heated, for instance, to 140° C. without danger of decomposition; at 170° C., however, it is rapidly disintegrated. On burning, it liberates an empyreumatic odor, which is not as disagreeable as that obtained from burning wool.

Action of Water

Silk is a highly absorbent fiber and readily becomes impregnated or wetted by water. Dissolved substances present in the water also are rather readily absorbed or taken up by silk; therefore, it is easy to understand that hard and impure waters are sources of contamination for silk goods with which these waters come in contact during processes of washing, dyeing, or finishing. The softness and luster of the fiber are quite easily affected by these impurities; consequently it is to be recommended that, wherever water is employed in connection with silk, the water be as soft as possible. So thoroughly is this fact realized at the present time that most modern silk factories use water softened by the zeolite process whereby the hardness may be reduced practically to zero. The character of the water employed in reeling silk from the cocoons is also said to have considerable influence on the quality of silk produced. The best results are obtained with soft water.

Action of Acids

Silk readily absorbs dilute acids from solutions, and in so doing increases in luster and acquires the scroop of which mention has previously been made. Unlike wool, it has a strong affinity for tannic acid, which fact is utilized for both weighting and mordanting the fiber.

The reaction of tannic acid with silk is different from that with other textile fibers. Heermann [41] points out that vegetable fibers absorb only small amounts of tannic acid, a state of equilibrium being produced which depends on the relative amounts of water, tannic acid, and fiber. The tannic acid absorbed by vegetable fibers is also readily removed by cold water [43]. Wool absorbs but little tannic acid from cold solutions, and when treated with hot solutions the fiber becomes harsh. The silk fiber, however, behaves somewhat like hide, in that it absorbs a large amount of tannic acid from cold solutions, and as much as 25 per cent of its weight from a hot solution. Furthermore, the tannin absorbed by silk is not readily removed by treatment with water. Heermann experimented on the absorption of various tannins by silk, the following tannins being employed: Gambier, gambier substitute, Aleppo gall extract, sumac extract, and divi-divi extract; the samples of silk used for the purpose being (1) pure silk which had been degummed, (2) silk dyed with Prussian blue, and (3) silk mordanted with tin chloride and sodium phosphate.

The following conclusions were deduced: Most tannin is absorbed by all three samples of silk from the gambier extract; pure silk absorbs almost as much from gall extract and from sumac extract, but the prepared samples of silk showed only a slight absorption of these two tannins. Divi-divi comes next to gambier in amount of absorption. Gambier substitute is peculiar, as tannin is absorbed from it only when the solutions are concentrated.

Concentrated sulfuric and hydrochloric acids dissolve silk; nitric acid colors silk yellow, as in the case with wool, probably owing to the formation of xanthoproteic acid. This color can be removed by treatment with a boiling solution of stannous chloride. The action of nitric acid on silk is rather peculiar. When treated for 1 min with nitric acid of sp. gr. 1.33, at a temperature of 45° C., the silk acquires a yellow color, which cannot be washed out and is also fast to light. Pure nitric acid free from nitrous compounds, however, does not give this color. On testing the yellow nitro-silk with an alkali, the color is considerably deepened. Vignon and Sisley [42] found that the purified fibroin of silk when treated with nitrous nitric acid increased 2 per cent in weight.

With strong sulfuric acid nitro-silk swells up and gives a gelatinous mass resembling egg albumen. The solubility of silk in strong hydrochloric acid is very rapid, a minute or two sufficing for complete solution. Under such conditions wool and cotton fibers are but slightly affected, hence such a treatment may be used for the separation of silk from wool or cotton for the purpose of analysis. Though silk is soluble in concentrated acids if their action is continued for any length of time, it appears that if silk is treated with concentrated sulfuric acid for only a few minutes, then rinsed and neutralized, the fiber will contract from 30 to 50 per cent in length, without otherwise suffering serious injury beyond a considerable loss in luster. This action of concentrated acids on silk has been utilized for the creping of silk fabrics, the acid being allowed to act only on certain parts of the material. It appears that the acid does not affect tussah silk to the same degree as ordinary silk, and hence creping may be accomplished by mixing tussah with ordinary silk, and treating the entire fabric with concentrated acid.

Hydrofluosilicic acid and hydrofluoric acid in cold 5 per cent solutions do not appear to exert any injurious action on the silk fiber; these acids, however, remove all inorganic weighting materials and their use has been suggested for the restoring of excessively weighted silks to their normal condition, so that they may be less harsh and brittle.

According to Farrell [43], when silk is treated with hydrochloric acid of a density of 29° Tw. it shrinks about one-third without any appreciable deterioration in the strength of the fiber. With solutions of acid below 29° Tw. no contraction occurs, while with solutions above 30° Tw. complete disintegration of the fiber results. In the production of "crepon" effects by this method, the fabric is printed with a wax resist, and is then immersed in the hydrochloric acid; the contraction is complete in one to two minutes, after which the fabric is well washed in water. Nitric acid and orthophosphoric acid may also be employed for the creping of silk fabrics [44]. According to a French patent a similar effect may be obtained by treating silk with a solution of zinc chloride of 32° to 76° Tw. [45].

When silk is treated at ordinary temperatures, with 90 per cent formic acid, the silk swells, contracts, and becomes gelatinous, and can be drawn out into threads which, however, have little strength. The action is complete in 2 or 3 minutes. If the acid is then drained off and the silk is thrown into water, the rinsing restores it nearly to its original condition with sufficient elasticity to enable it to be stretched to its original length by hand. On drying, silk so treated becomes stiffer and generally more lustrous, without any loss of tensile strength. The original shrinking ranges from 8 to 12 per cent of the length before treatment. Formic acid has the same action on natural silks, whether degummed or not; but "Schappe" silk, which is not very strong to begin with, may lose somewhat in strength. The treatment has very little effect on tussah. The best results are obtained with greige (whether degummed or not), treating with 90 per cent formic acid for

b. Direct colors dye silk preferably in neutral or weak alkaline solutions. They are better for washing than acid dyes and by careful selection, a line of colors may be obtained satisfactory for light fastness.

c. Basic colors may be dyed in either weak acid, neutral, or slightly alkaline solutions. They are noted for their brilliancy; usually fast to washing but quite fugitive to light.

d. Vat colors are soluble only in fairly strong alkaline solutions. The alkalinity should be kept as low as possible to dissolve the dyestuff. While vat colors are the fastest type of dyes known, it is necessary to select carefully to have all the colors in the line fast.

Weighting of Silk

The weighting of silk may be best considered a finishing process developed by the trade to meet the demands of fashion for a fabric having a full hand and superb draping qualities. There are many materials that are readily absorbed and held by silk, which add weight or fix color as a mordant, but the method most generally used in commercial practice is the tin-silicophosphate process.

In continental Europe, where the practice of weighting silk had been in vogue for a long time, it was considered perfectly proper and legitimate to replace the gum removed in the boil-off process with a metallic or organic material. This was thought of as a finishing process and simply as bringing the silk back to "par." The reason for this contention was based on the fact that most weavers send their goods in the gum as cut from the loom to the converter to be dyed and finished. Before sending the pieces from the weaving mill, they are all measured and weighed. When they are returned, they are again measured and weighed, and if these figures agree with those obtained as cut from the loom, the goods are considered to have normal or standard weight, or to be "par weighted."

During the late twenties such a large amount of weighting was added to silk fabrics in America that the buying public considered it an adulterant and that this excessive weighting had a detrimental effect on the durability or wearability of these fabrics. The Silk Association of America appointed a technical committee to study this problem.

It was found that fabrics were weighted 10 to 60 per cent above par or that 35 to 55 per cent of finishing materials were in the fabric as sold over the counter. Other items that proved important in this study were the size and construction of the yarn; the weave of the fabric; the method of degumming; and the amount and process of applying the weighting, dyeing, and finishing materials. Hard-twisted threads and close weaves will not absorb the weighting materials readily and, if weighted excessively, will tend to produce weak goods. However, fabrics properly designed and processed by experienced converters will not only have excellent draping qualities, but will also give good serviceability.

The Federal Trade Commission Rulings adopted at the Trade Practice Conference held April 21, 1932, state:

> Goods containing in the finished state (*a*) silk, or silk and other fiber or fibers, and (*b*) more than 10 per cent of any substance other than silk or such fiber or fibers except black color, which shall not exceed 15 per cent, shall not be designated by a designation containing reference to silk or such other fiber or fibers unless there be added to such designation the word *weighted* or some other qualification which shall reasonably indicate that such goods contain an addition of metallic salts or other substance above mentioned.
>
> Goods containing silk, or silk and other fiber or fibers, shall not be designated *pure dye,* if they contain in the finished state more than 10 per cent of any substance other than silk or such other fiber or fibers except black color, which shall not exceed 15 per cent.

According to Holterhoff [49], the tin-weighting process is based on simple lines. The degummed silk is first immersed in an acid solution of tetrachloride of tin. The fiber is permitted to absorb the salt to the point of saturation. Excess solution is now removed by centrifugal hydroextraction. The material is then thoroughly washed with cold water which hydrolizes the tetrachloride of tin into stannic oxide and hydrochloric acid. The insoluble oxide remains precipitated in the fiber, while the acid is carried off in the wash water. A treatment in a hot solution of disodium phosphate follows, which adds a phosphate radical to the tin, already present in the silk.

It is interesting to note that, after the phosphate radical has been introduced, the silk is capable of absorbing more tin tetrachloride, and after another phosphating is capable of absorbing still more. Thus, weight may be added almost indefinitely by merely repeating the routine. Each round of such treatment is called a "pass." Thus, it is common to designate silk as one, two, three, or four pass, as the case may be. Afterward, it is customary to treat the material in a hot solution of sodium silicate to increase the weight still further and to fix the tin salts properly. Since the temperature and concentration of the silicate bath govern the amount of weighting added in this treatment, it serves as a medium to adjust the total of weighting ingredients to the exact amount which is specified.

The following gives a brief summary of the materials used and their concentrations:

Tin Bath. Tetrachloride of tin ($SnCl_4$), called commercially anhydrous stannic chloride, is a colorless liquid having a specific gravity of 2.26 and containing 45.5 per cent tin. When exposed to air, it gives off copious white fumes, which are very penetrating and irritating to the respiratory system. To avoid these fumes, a concentrated stock solution of sp. gr. 56° Bé is made by forcing with compressed air the tetrachloride from shipping drums directly into water containing muriatic acid (20° Bé) to prevent hydrolysis. The tin bath is made by diluting the stock solution to 30° Bé (13 per cent tin) and the bath held at a temperature of 50° to 60° F.

Phosphate Bath. The phosphate of soda ($Na_2HPO_4 12H_2O$) is dissolved in water at a temperature of 140° to 160° F., having a concentration of 4 to 7° Bé.

Silicate Bath. Sodium silicate "water glass" is a clear liquid which is used at a concentration of about 42° Bé and which contains about 10 per cent Na_2O and 30 per cent SiO_2.

CHEMICAL PROPERTIES OF WILD SILKS

Tussah Silk

Tussah silk presents a number of differences, both physical and chemical, from ordinary silk. It has a brown color and is considerably stiffer and coarser. It is less reactive, in general, toward chemical reagents, and consequently presents more difficulty in bleaching and dyeing. Tussah silk requires a much more severe treatment for degumming than cultivated silk, and the boiled-off liquor so obtained is of no value in dyeing.

Tussah silk is largely used in the weaving of a pile fabric known as "sealcloth," which consists of a tussah silk plush woven into a cotton back, and is a material of most useful character for wraps and mantles. It is a fabric having a rich and handsome appearance, and, if injured by wetting or pressing, is readily restored by drying before a fire and brushing. Tussah silk is also extensively used for rug and carpet making, and as its fiber is nearly three times as thick as mulberry silk, it gives a much firmer and better pile. It is also used in the manufacture of woven cloths such as mandarine and grenadine fabrics. It furthermore finds extensive use for fringes, damasks, millinery pompons, tassels and cords, chenille for upholstery, and for embroidery silks.

Tussah silk is scarcely affected by an alkaline solution of copper hydrate in glycerol, whereas ordinary silk is readily soluble in this reagent [50].

Shroff [51] describes the properties of a variety of oriental wild silk in the manufactured form. The cloth examined is often spoken of as "Kashmere silk"; it is of a yellow-reddish tint. It is almost entirely unaffected by concentrated hydrochloric acid, chromic acid, and zinc chloride, all of which dissolve mulberry silk. The action of boiling 10 per cent caustic soda is slow. Soda ash and soap, both followed by hydrogen peroxide, partly bleach it, reducing the luster. Hydrogen peroxide and sodium silicate preserve the luster and are equally good in reducing the color. The best result is obtained by boiling with 1° Tw. hydrochloric acid, then treating with 3° Tw. caustic soda for a few minutes and finally with ½° Tw. ammonium hypochlorite, washing after each.

Muga (or Moonga) Silk

This is a wild silk next in importance and value to tussah. It is indigenous to Assam, but is also to be found in some other provinces. The fiber is fawn-colored when the worm feeds on the common plants in the districts of which it is a native, but the fiber is whiter and of better quality when the worm is fed on leaves on which other silkworms are reared. Champa-fed worms produce the celebrated champa pattea moonga, a white silk of very fine quality used only by the rajahs.

Eria Silk

This is, perhaps, the third in importance among the wild silks. It is produced by a worm which feeds on the castor-oil plant, and, like the muga silk, is indigenous to Assam, but it is also found in other districts. In Assam the fiber is white, but in Singapore it is brown. Eria silk does not dye very readily, being inferior in this respect to tussah. Owing to its rather loose cocoon, eria silk cannot be reeled, but has to be combed and spun.

Other varieties of wild silk come from the *Bombyx textor,* known as the pat silkworm, a native of Assam. It is probably a variety of the *Bombyx mori,* though its cocoon is of a different shape and is yellow in color. The silk is of excellent quality and is quite valuable.

The *Cricula trifenestrata* is abundant in British Burma, where the cocoons literally rot in the jungles for want of gathering. The silk is strong, rich, and lustrous; it is spun in the same way as eria silk and is yellow in color.

Byssus Silk

This is also known as sea-silk or pinna silk; it is obtained from a marine mollusk, *Pinna nobilis* and related varieties. The shellfish possesses a long slender gland which secretes woolly fibers known as the byssus or beard. These fibers are of a brown color and are 4 to 6 cm in length. The brown color is said to be due to an external covering which when removed leaves a colorless fiber. Sea-silk is somewhat used in southern Italy and in Normandy for the making of various ornamental braided articles. Though this fiber somewhat resembles silk in appearance, it is easily distinguished by the presence of natural rounded ends. The fibers vary considerably in diameter (10 to 100 μ), are elliptical in cross-section, and are often twisted. Fine longitudinal striations are apparent, but as the fiber is solid, no empty lumen or air canals are present. The finer fibers are smooth, but the coarser ones are rough and corroded. Frequently very delicate fibrils are to be observed branching from the larger fibers.

The manufacture of materials from pinna silk was carried on at Taranto in Italy. The "fish wool," as it was called, was washed twice in water, once in soap and water, and again in tepid water, and finally spread out on a table to dry. While moist, it was rubbed and separated with the hands and again spread on the table to dry. When quite dry, it was drawn through a wide bone comb and then through a narrow one. It was then spun into a yarn with distaff and spindle. As it was not possible to procure much of the material of good quality, the manufacture was limited to a few articles such as gloves and stockings, and these were quite expensive. The fabrics were very soft and warm and of a brown or glossy gold color [52].

Another animal fiber of a somewhat silklike nature is the so-called sinew fiber. This product is obtained from sinews which consist of fibrous connective tissue made up of wavy elements united in bundles. Hanausek [53] calls attention to the fact that sinew fiber was utilized in ancient times, the Israelites using a yarn twisted from sinews under the name of "gidden" for their religious rites. In recent years, sinew fiber has been spun into yarns by mixing with wool or hemp. The fiber is very silky in luster and varies much in length (from 1.18 in. to 7.08 in.). Such yarns have great tensile strength and are rough in feel.

UTILIZATION AND LABELING OF SILK

Silk has a wide variety of uses in the apparel, drapery, upholstery and military fields. Until the introduction of nylon the largest portion of silk imported into the United States was made into hosiery. Since World War II, only a small amount of silk has been used in hosiery, the vast majority of hose being made from nylon.

Table 20 gives raw silk consumption in bales excluding reexports, and average prices in dollars per pound. From 1930 through 1933, prices are Japan's 13/15 crack double-extra grade (new name for this grade is Japan's 13/15 denier white, Grade D), as computed by the United States Bureau of Labor Statistics. From 1934 to August 1941, the silk prices shown have been computed by the Textile Economics Bureau. The silk price given from August to December 1941 is the ceiling price of $3.08 per pound set on August 3 by the Office of Price Administration under Price Schedule No. 14, and represents the government's purchase price for impounded silk under the silk freeze order.

For the war period and to mid-1946, there were no quotations. The prices for July 1946 to January 1947 are average prices received by the USCC for the D grade, 13/15 denier, at 7 midmonth auctions; for February 1947 through December 1947, the price shown is for this grade as set by the USCC under the price stabilization program; for

TABLE 19. PERFORMANCE DATA OF SILK FABRICS

Types of Fabrics	Breaking Strength, in Pounds, Grab Method		Per Cent Shrinkage, Hand Shaped		Slippage, Pounds	Per Cent Finishing Material
	Warp	Filling	Warp	Filling		
Canton crepe	120	80	2	4	20	5
Flat crepe	80	50	2	2	15	5
Satin crepe	120	60	2	2	15	5
Satin	100	60	1	1	15	3
Printed crepe	80	40	2	2	10	5
Georgette	40	40	1	1	15	3
Taffeta	80	60	1	1	15	3
Voile	20	20	3	2	7	2
Chiffon	25	20	2	3	7	2

the year 1948, the price is for this grade of silk as set by SCAP plus 15¢ per pound for transportation and certification. Since that time, the quotations cover the AA grade, 20/22 denier size.

Silk is a poor conductor of heat and for this reason it has a high warmth factor. It is very hygroscopic, which enables it to be saturated with perspiration and yet not feel clammy.

Silk fabrics are luxurious in appearance and lend themselves readily to style changes. When fluffy evening dresses are in vogue, they are made from chiffons, georgettes, and voiles, whereas satins, Canton crepes, and velvets are more apt to be used for regal dinner dresses.

The average performance data for some of the more important silk fabrics of standard constructions as compiled by the United States Testing Co., Inc., from many tests, are given in Table 19.

ECONOMICS AND STATISTICAL DATA

Prices

Up until the stocks of silk were frozen by the Office of Production Management on July 26, 1941, the United States was still the largest single purchaser of raw silk in the world. However, the deliveries to the mills had shrunk in 1940 to less than one-half of the all-time high consumption of over 600,000 bales in 1929. The average price of this

TABLE 20. Deliveries and Prices of Silk, United States [54]

Year	*Consumption (bales)*	*Average Price * (pound*	*Year*	*Consumption (bales)*	*Average Price * (pound)*
1920	220,089	9.08	1935	470,997	1.63
1921	319,629	6.57	1936	437,331	1.76
1922	363,290	7.65	1937	405,288	1.86
1923	355,219	8.65	1938	390,668	1.69
1924	361,118	6.25	1939	357,838	2.71
1925	496,186	6.57	1940	270,704	2.77
1926	495,732	6.19	1941	183,190	2.94
1927	541,548	5.44	(Ceiling price from October 1941)		3.08
1928	562,832	5.07	1946	44,167	6.79 †
1929	611,302	4.93	1947	20,818	4.55
1930	571,548	3.41	1948	59,397	2.60
1931	580,989	2.40	1949	36,551	3.00
1932	533,147	1.56	1950	67,214	3.46
1933	449,673	1.61	1951	44,030	4.81
1934	439,984	1.29			

* Prices based on 13/15 denier, D grade, white, 78 per cent.
† Average of July to December 1946.
Sources: Rayon Organon, Commodity Research Bureau, American Silk Council.

commodity fluctuated through a wide range from a high of $9.08 per lb in 1920 to $1.29 per lb in 1934 and to $4.20 from 1946 to 1951, as shown in Table 20.

Production

The world's raw silk production data are shown in Table 21.

TABLE 21. WORLD'S RAW SILK PRODUCTION

Year	*Million Pounds*
1940	130
1945	24
1946	32
1947	35
1948	42
1949	43
1950	43
1951	44

Source: 1940, League of Nations *Statistical Yearbook*, 1941–51, Textile Economics Bureau, Inc.

According to the Census Bureau there were 80 mills in the United States weaving broad silk fabrics as of December 31, 1949, and they had 2149 looms on silk as of that date.

TABLE 22

	Number of Mills	*1947 Production*		*1948 Production*		*1949 Production*	
		Thousands of Linear Yards					
All-silk, and silk mixture fabrics, total	33	5017	100%	8677	100%	7075	100%
All-silk fabrics, *not* jacquard woven, total	31	4549	91	7579	87	6453	91
Habutai	5	312	6	384	4	248	4
Flat crepes	20	2313	46	2909	33	2075	29
Triple sheers	6	56	1	137	2	345	5
Georgette crepes	3	151	3	50	1	22	..
Satin crepes	11	299	6	605	7	436	6
French crepes	5	303	6	592	7	679	10
Twills (tie fabrics)	11	543	11	1160	13	1013	14
Shantung	6	263	5	1066	12	747	11
All others	12	309	7	676	8	888	12
All-silk fabrics, jacquard-woven, total	8	314	6	442	5	368	5
Silk mixtures, total	9	154	3	656	8	254	4

Courtesy National Federation of Textiles.

In a survey conducted by the National Federation of Textiles, Inc. [55], the only present source for detailed information, 33 of those 80 mills weaving broad silk fabrics submitted data. These mills accounted for 70 per cent of the 2149 active looms.

Of the 33 mills participating in the survey, 19 had "30 per cent or more" of their loom production on broad silk fabrics; and they accounted for 71 per cent of the total broad silk production. Six of this group had from 90 per cent to 100 per cent of their production on broad silk fabrics.

See Table 22 for fabric types that were woven by the sample group in three years.

According to the Census Bureau, following is the postwar production of broad-woven silks, in linear yards:

1946	9,400,000
1947	10,400,000
1948	18,800,000
1949	15,900,000
1950	29,338,000
1951	26,521,000
1952	35,559,000

REFERENCES AND NOTES

1. Manchester, H. H., *The Story of Silk and Cheney Silks* (1924).
2. *Fortune,* **XI,** 3, 70 (1935).
3. Iketani, M., *The Japan Silk Yearbook,* 41 (1935–36).
4. Howard and Buswell, *A Survey of the Silk Industry of South China,* 74 (1925).
5. Huber, C. J., *Raw Silk Industry of Japan,* 10 (1929).
6. In tropical and subtropical countries such as India and South China, all stages of the silkworm's life cycle are shorter than those in Central China or Japan.
7. Iketani, M., *The Japan Silk Yearbook,* 9 (1935–36).
8. U. S. Testing Co., *A Survey of the Silk Industry of Central China,* 87, 89 (1925).
9. *A Survey of the Silk Industry of South China,* 97 (1925).
10. *A Survey of the Silk Industry of South China,* 99 (1925).
11. The denier is a unit of weight equal to 0.05 gram. As used in the textile field, it indicates the size of a thread or yarn by giving the weight in denier of the standard length of 450 meters.
12. Huber, C. J., *The Raw Silk Industry of Japan* (1929).
13. U. S. Testing Co., *A Survey of the Silk Industry of Central China* (1925).
14. Howard and Buswell, *A Survey of the Silk Industry of South China* (1925).
15. Huber, C. J., unpublished data, U. S. Testing Co. (1926).
16. Wardle, Sir T., *Divisibility of Silk Fibre,* 54 (1908).
17. The Imperial Institute has made an extensive investigation on the utilization of *anaphe* wild silk. There is an outer layer or nest which contains the

cocoons located within, and as this outer layer is more difficult to degum than the cocoons, it is advisable to separate it from them and work it up for the fiber by itself. When the nests of the *anaphe silk* are handled in the dry state they cause an intense irritation of the skin and mucous membrane, presumably due to the enclosed hairs of the caterpillars; therefore, before the nests are separated from the cocoons they must be soaked in water, or better yet, it is advised to boil the envelopes for two hours in a one per cent solution of sodium carbonate.

18. *Z. physiol. Chem.*, 126 (1907).
19. Huber, C. J., unpublished notes, U. S. Testing Co. (1935).
20. "Standard Method of Raw Silk Testing and Classification," International Silk Assoc. (July 1950).
21. Mennerich, F., and Hougen, O. A., *Textile Research,* **5,** 223 (1935).
22. Von Bergen, W., and Krauss, W., *Textile Fiber Atlas,* 24 (1942).
23. Astbury, W. T., *Fundamentals of Fibre Structure,* 79 (1933).
24. A equals Angstrom unit of length. One A equals 0.0001 μ.
25. Astbury, W. T., *Fundamentals of Fibre Structure,* 91 (1933).
26. Weltzien, W., *Monatsh. Seide Kunstseide,* **39,** 343, 390, 435 (1934).
27. Astbury, W. T., *Fundamentals of Fibre Structure,* 123 (1933).
28. International Critical Tables, II, 237.
29. Walker, A. C., *Textile Research,* **7,** 294 (1937).
30. Bergmann, W., *Textile Research,* **6,** 198 (1938).
31. Silbermann, H., *Seide,* **2,** 210 (1885).
32. Walters-Hougen, *Textile Research,* **5** (2), 93 (1934).
33. Grover, P. F., *Am. Dyestuff Reptr.,* **17,** 555–557 (1928).
34. Mosher, H. H., *Am. Silk J.,* **49** (7), 53 (1930).
35. Shelton, E. M., and Johnson, T. B., *J. Am. Chem. Soc.,* **47,** 412 (1925).
36. Wolf, H. W., and Hougen, O. A., *Textile Research,* **V** (3), 134–148 (1935).
37. Astbury, W. T., *Fundamentals of Fibre Structure,* 116 (1933).
38. Harris, M., *J. Research Natl. Bur. Standards,* **9,** 557 (1932).
39. ASTM Designation D–629–42T, 29 (1942).
40. *J. Soc. Chem. Ind.,* **2,** 172.
41. *Faerber Zeitung,* 4 (1908).
42. Vignon and Sisley, *Compt. rend.* (1891).
43. *J. Soc. Dyers Colourists,* 70 (1905).
44. See C. and P. Depoully, *J. Soc. Dyers Colourists,* 8 (1896).
45. *J. Soc. Dyers Colourists,* 214 (1899).
46. Harris and Jessup, *J. Research Natl. Bur. Standards,* **7,** 1179 (1931).
47. *Chem.-Ztg.,* 400 (1901).
48. Gianoli, *Chem.-Ztg.,* 105 (1910).
49. Holterhoff, *Am. Dyestuff Reptr.,* **26,** 358 (1937).
50. Filsinger, *Chem.-Ztg.,* **20,** 324.
51. *Posselt's Textile J.* (1922).
52. Gilroy, *History of Silk,* 182.
53. *Microscopy of Technical Products,* 150.
54. Rayon Organon, 1942 Annual Rayon and Textile Statistics. Textile Economics Bureau.
55. National Federation of Textiles, Inc., survey (1949).

CHAPTER XVI

REGENERATED RAYON FIBERS, FILAMENTS, AND YARNS

A. R. Macormac

Terminology. Rayon is a coined word with an interesting history. Before 1924 rayon was variously known as artificial silk, art silk, glos, wood silk, and fiber silk. The National Retail Dry Goods Association felt there was a need for a better name for the then known man-made fibers. Their artificial silk committee appointed a special subcommittee with S. A. Salvage of the American Viscose Corporation as chairman. This subcommittee after considerable discussion recommended the word "rayon," suggested by Kenneth Lord of Galey and Lord, Inc., New York commission merchants. The recommendation was approved by the artificial silk committee and submitted to the Board of Directors of the National Retail Dry Goods Association, which adopted the report on May 21, 1924. Although this action had no legal status, it did mean that members of the association would use the word rayon and publicize it.

In March 1925, du Pont renamed its Fiber Silk Division the Rayon Division. In 1926 Committee D-13 on Textiles of the American Society for Testing Materials tentatively defined rayon as "a generic term for filaments made from various solutions of modified cellulose by pressing or drawing the cellulose solution through an orifice and solidifying it in the form of a filament." In 1933 A.S.T.M. made this definition official. In 1937 the Federal Trade Commission adopted and promulgated the first "Rayon Trade Practice Rules," thus giving the word official and legal status. In these rules it was definitely stated that rayon included fibers with a cellulosic base made by the viscose, acetate, cuprammonium, nitrocellulose or other process.

However, the manufacturers of rayon by the acetate process accepted this classification under protest, claiming their product is not regenerated but is used in the form of cellulose acetate and is different both chemically and physically; hence it should not be classed as rayon. When the term was adopted in 1924 the world production by the various processes was viscose 76 per cent, nitro 18 per cent, cuprammonium 5 per cent, and acetate less than 1 per cent. Celanese Corporation of America, the first successful producer of acetate in the United

States, did not get into production until 1925, so that at that time the above distinction was purely academic, but by 1937 over 20 per cent of the United States "rayon" production was acetate and this percentage has increased to 34 per cent in 1950.

In 1949, A.S.T.M. acknowledged the justice of the contention of difference by modifying their definition of rayon to read "generic term for man-made fibers, monofilaments, and continuous filament yarns composed of regenerated cellulose with or without lesser amounts of non-fiber-forming materials" and introducing a new term, "Estron," for fibers of cellulose esters (acetate). In 1951 the new definition of rayon was made official. Finally, in 1952 the Federal Trade Commission adopted and promulgated new "Rayon and Acetate Trade Practice Rules" to be effective on and after Feb. 9, 1952. These rules include the following definitions:

Rayon: Man-made textile fibers and filaments composed of regenerated cellulose, and yarn, thread, or textile fabric made of such fibers and filaments.

Acetate: Man-made textile fibers and filaments composed of cellulose acetate, and yarn, thread, or textile fabric made of such fibers and filaments.

Since these rules were instituted upon application of the National Retail Dry Goods Association and the Rayon Producers Group and after public hearings, an unambiguous definition of rayon acceptable to all appears to have been achieved.

History. The first commercial and successful artificial silk, as it was then known, was made by the nitrocellulose process in France in 1891 by Count Hilaire de Chardonnet. By 1900 the total world production was 2,200,000 lb. Most of it was made by the nitrocellulose process, but the cuprammonium process was also used. The viscose process was developed in England by Cross and Bevan who were employed by Courtaulds and Company from 1904 on. In 1909 American imports were over 1,000,800 lb. The first successful American producer was the American Viscose Company in 1910. In 1911 their production was 375,000 lb, and the total world production was 18,700,000 lb. American imports and production increased steadily during the following years (see Table 2). Imports dropped during World War I, rose again in the late 1920's, and since 1930 have been only a small fraction of consumption. Staple fiber was developed in Germany and Italy during World War I but did not become important in the United States till the late 1930's. Since 1940 world production of staple and filament yarn has been approximately equal. Between 1920 and 1930 a number of other concerns including du Pont and Industrial Rayon entered the field. In 1924 the distribution of rayon according to trades was: broad silk 20 per cent, hosiery 20 per cent, knit outerwear 15 per cent, converters and throwsters 20 per cent, narrow fabrics 7 per cent, underwear 6 per cent, cotton goods 10 per cent, and miscellaneous 2 per cent. The world production was 97 million pounds, of which 75 per cent was viscose, 18 per cent nitro, 5 per cent cuprammonium, and 1 per cent acetate.

DULL AND HIGH-TENACITY YARNS

During the 1930's the use of titanium dioxide to produce dull and semi-dull yarn became common, and by 1936 half of the United States production was dull and semi-dull. In 1937 du Pont produced Cordura the first high-tenacity viscose yarn. This was also the period which saw the greatest development of rayon crepe and spun rayon fabrics.

Even before World War II several rayon producers had been developing special high-tenacity rayon primarily for use in industrial fabrics. Du Pont has offered its Cordura since 1937, and Enka produced Tempra, a high-tenacity 275-denier rayon in 1938. The program on a high-tenacity tire cord rayon got under way in 1943 with a request for an annual production of 240 million lb as soon as possible. This goal was not reached until 1947. At first, rayon tire cord was made in 275 denier, but soon the standard sizes were established as 1100, 1650, or 2200 denier. Currently, 73 per cent of the tire cord yarn is 1650 denier. American Viscose Corporation, du Pont, Rayon Department, Industrial Rayon Corporation; American Enka Corporation, and North American Rayon Corporation cooperated in the program and converted current production or built new plants. Production increased from 38 million lb in 1942 to 202 million lb in 1944 and has increased continuously since then (see Table 2), but production has never been able to meet demand.

In February 1952 National Production Authority increased by 20 per cent the amount of high-tenacity rayon which may be used by tire manufacturers. Of the 93 million lb expected to be produced in the first quarter of 1952, 91 million were allotted to rubber manufacturers. An increase in the production to an annual rate of 400 million lb by April 1952 was reached.

INCREASED USE OF STAPLE FIBER

The increased importance of staple fiber and tow was an outstanding development of the post-World War II years. New types of staple were developed, with specific end uses an important factor. One of the most important was the use of rayon in rugs and carpets. This development was due at least in part to the inability to obtain carpet wools. Asia is our chief source of such wools. Several manufacturers experimented with rayon and rayon-wool blends, but the types of rayon staple available were not then suitable. For carpets a high-denier, smooth rayon staple was required. The producers in cooperation with the carpet manufacturers have since developed products which have been highly successful. In 1948 Celanese Corporation of America produced for this purpose Celcos staple fiber, a 4-in. staple of 15 denier per filament. It is a surface-saponified acetate with properties between viscose and acetate staples. In 1951 Celcos was produced in 3, 5½, 8, 12, and 17 denier per filament. In 1949 American Viscose Corporation offered a 15 denier, dull, crimped, viscose staple. These and other special staples for carpets and rugs have proved successful, as is shown by the fact that from January to August 1951 22,300,000 lb of such staple was used. This represents 22.7 per cent of the surface fibers in these products as compared with 1.6 per cent in 1949 and 6 per cent in 1950 (*Textile Organon*). Another indication of the importance of this development is the fact that in February 1951 Bigelow Sanford Carpet Company purchased the Hartford Rayon Corporation, and in April 1951 Mohawk Carpet Mills purchased New Bedford Rayon Company and Delaware Rayon Company for the manufacture of carpet staple.

Rayon staple was also finding increasing use in suiting fabrics. Many experiments were made, and much development work was done, especially by the Textile Research Department of American Viscose Corporation. In 1948 the information and experience obtained were summarized and published in their book, *Rayon Technology*. In the worsted industry the common practice is to make both the wool and rayon into tops and blend them on gill boxes. In such cases the rayon is frequently used as the form of a tow, which is a large group of a hundred thousand or more continuous filaments. In 1949 American Viscose Corporation produced a 190,000-denier tow of 10 denier per filament.

In the same year du Pont announced the commercial production at Old Hickory, Tenn., of "Fiber E," which is a special viscose rayon staple. It acquires a crimp on treatment with a dilute caustic soda solution, thus giving it a fuzzy woollike feel. The success of rayon in the clothing field is indicated by the estimate that, in 1949, 50 per cent of men's summer suits made up contained rayon. Data on the use of rayon in the wool and worsted industry for 1949 and 1950 is given in Table 1.

TABLE 1. INCREASE OF RAYON STAPLE IN WOOL FABRICS

	1949 (million pounds)	*1950 (million pounds)*	*Per Cent of Increase*
Woolen industry	20	25.9	28
Worsted industry	4.9	10.0	105
Carpet industry	2.87	12.5	336

In February 1952 American Bemberg Company, a subsidiary of Beaunit Mills, announced plans to make a cuprammonium staple rayon in 1½ and 3 denier to be sold at 42¢ per lb. These staples have a natural crimp and resemble wool. They have been used 100 per cent in linenlike fabrics and mixed with acetate staple in flannels. The planned production has reached approximately 9 million lb annually. Beaunit Mills started production in their Coosa Pines, Ala., plant in May 1949, and reached 60 per cent of its annual capacity of 10 million lb of textile yarn. During 1951 a shortage of wood pulp and sulfur reduced rayon production. In 1952 the wood pulp shortage eased somewhat but the sulfur shortage gives every evidence of being present for some time. In September 1951 Courtauld, Ltd., of England announced plans to build a staple rayon plant near Mobile, Ala., which is expected to be in production in 1953 at a rate of 50 million lb per yr. This represents the return of Courtaulds to the American market after selling out their interests in the American Viscose Corporation several years ago.

STATISTICS AND ECONOMICS

The general characteristics of the rayon industry in this country have been constant growth, continual price reductions, improved properties and greater field of uses. Production is confined to the East, principally from Ohio and Massachusetts south to Alabama and Georgia, with Pennsylvania and Virginia being the most important States. It is primarily an industry of large units. In 1950 there were 10 producers with 32 plants, and 95 per cent of the production came from the 7 large producers.

Although rayon was first produced in Europe and in some countries was aided by government subsidy, because of the precarious supply of other fibers, nevertheless the United States under a free competitive system became the largest producer in 1919. Except for the 1937 to 1943 production of Germany and the 1937 to 1940 production of Japan, it has held the lead to the present time. In 1950 United States accounted for 36 per cent of the world production. These records apply to combined rayon and acetate filament and staple material. By process, the 1949 production was 66 per cent viscose, 33 per cent acetate, and 1 per cent cuprammonium. Seventy-six per cent of American rayon production is filament yarn, whereas only 55 per cent of the world production is filament yarn.

Production, Imports and Exports. In Table 2 are given United States production, imports, and exports, and the world production of regenerated rayons since 1900. Up to 1910 most of the world production was by the nitro process. After 1910 the viscose process rapidly replaced the nitro process and soon became the most important. Rayon was made by the nitro process in this country from 1921 to 1934. Cuprammonium rayon has been made continuously by the American Bemberg Corporation since 1926; production has never been more than 5 per cent of the total and generally only 1 or 2 per cent. From Table 2 it will be noted that after 1915 filament yarn imports were relatively unimportant. However, imports of staple fiber which started in 1928 continued in appreciable quantities until World War II and revived afterward. Exports have been relatively unimportant with no evident general trend. Except for occasional leveling off or slight recession, both United States and world production of filament and staple rayon show a remarkably consistent growth, and this is the most important fact demonstrated by Table 2.

Distribution. The markets for rayon yarn and staple fiber are many and varied. In the early years rayon was used chiefly for decorative effects, ribbons, and fillingwise, where its high luster was an advantage and its low strength was not too great a disadvantage. During these years all-rayon fabrics were rare. Figure 1 shows the distribution of regenerated rayon filament yarns since 1915. Hosiery was the first most important use. After 1921 circular knit goods became more important than hosiery. Since the early 1930's broad woven materials have accounted for the greatest amount of filament rayon.

The outstanding recent trend has been the phenomenal growth of high-tenacity or tire cord rayon. In 1948, it was 4 per cent and, in

TABLE 2. United States and World Rayon Production; United States Imports and Exports

(Millions of Pounds)

Year	United States							World Production	
	Production			Imports *		Exports *			
	Filament	High-Tenacity	Staple	Filament	Staple	Filament	Staple	Staple	Filament
1900									2.2
1905									11.1
1910				1.54					17.6
1911	0.36			1.76					18.7
1915	3.89			2.50					18.5
1920	10.00			1.5					33.1
1921	14.87			3.3					48.2
1922	23.95			2.1					76.6
1923	34.83			3.0					103.0
1924	36.21			1.9					138.3
1925	49.43			5.4		0.15			185.1
1926	60.07			9.3		0.40			211.7
1927	70.41			15.0		0.40			295.7
1928	91.23		0.2	12.1	0.05	0.19			360.5
1929	113.0		0.5	15.1	1.05	0.22		7.2	435.4
1930	117.5		0.4	6.3	0.43	0.35		6.3	415.0
1931	135.2		0.9	1.8	0.66	0.32		8.0	454.0
1932	116.4		1.1	0.2	2.18	0.65		17.3	465.0
1933	172.4		2.1	0.9	3.30	1.11		27.9	583
1934	170.3		2.2	0.08	0.21	2.51		51.8	682
1935	202.6		4.3	0.03	1.45	2.19		139.0	814
1936	214.9	0.4	9.8	0.25	12.72	1.73		300	892
1937	238.2	0.9	16.6	0.57	20.61	1.28		626	1038
1938	214.4	5.0	26.4	0.26	23.19	1.35	0.96	930	847
1939	221.0	10.0	45.3	0.18	47.40	1.69	1.40	1091	972
1940	247.0	10.0	70.8	0.04	17.74	1.57	2.29	1282	968
1941	267	20.0	105.3	0.03	11.69	3.25	3.39	1535	1017
1942	272	38.0	127.6	. .	0.17	5.46	1.43	1452	960
1943	276	62.0	129.6	. .	. .	9.25	3.02	1392	926
1944	258	126	128.4	. .	. .	16.77	2.33	1053	805
1945	247	202	129.1	. .	2.44	20.57	4.64	504	677
1946	265	228	132.7	0.11	33.89	15.26	4.39	530	860
1947	285	240	168.2	0.31	36.06	25.78	4.86	600	1004
1948	299	263	184.5	10.15	38.67	14.80	7.44	813	1161
1949	255	289	129.8	0.34	15.60	17.48	15.59	891	1272
1950	319	308	188.5	6.38	91.19	12.31	10.10	1433	1474
1951	325	333	207.3	5.32	102.47	14.70	29.00	1752	1626
1952	182	412	211.8	0.68	74.11	11.43	24.50	1634	1471

N.A. Not available.

Source: Data from *Textile Organon.*

* Includes acetate.

1950, 48 per cent of the total, and still the demand is greater than the supply. It should be emphasized that, although the percentage of

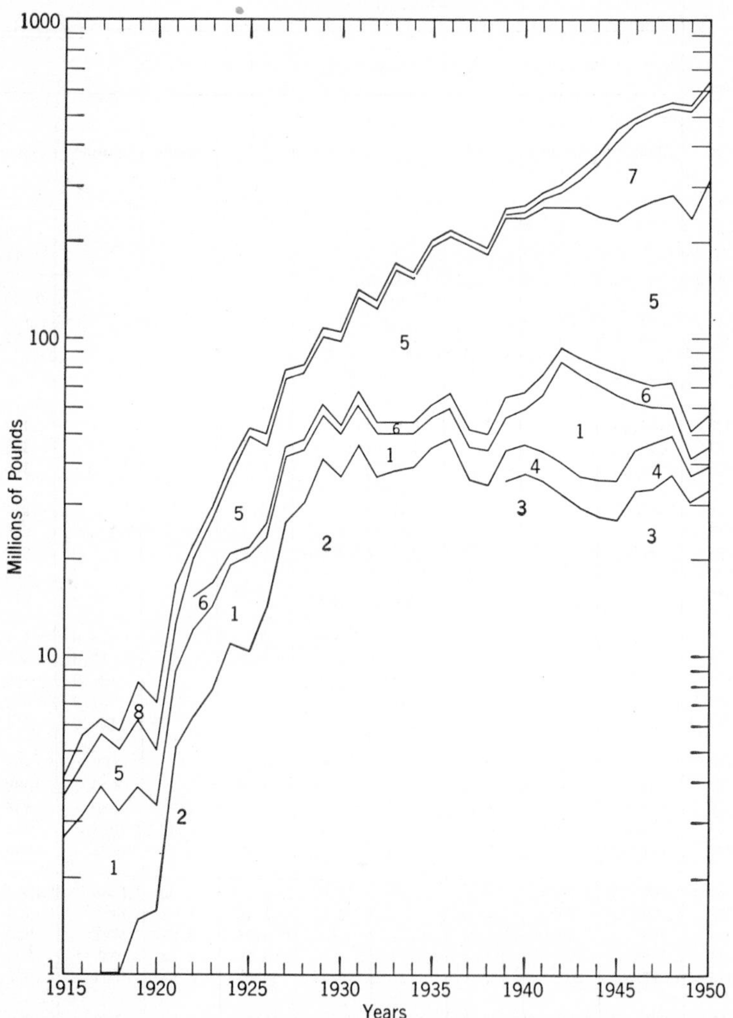

FIG. 1. Regenerated filament rayon—distribution by trade. 1, Hosiery; 2, knit goods; 3, circular knit; 4, warp knit; 5, broad woven; 6, narrow woven; 7, tire (h.t.) yarn; 8, miscellaneous. (Data from *Textile Organon,* February 1952, p. 53.)

total production used in certain industries may show a decline, the actual number of pounds used has generally increased. This is borne out by Fig. 1, where the distribution is given in millions of pounds.

Information similar to that given in Fig. 1 is not available for staple fiber. At first staple fiber was used primarily in blends with cotton, but soon fabrics made entirely of spun rayon became increasingly available as replacements of spun silk and in some cases cotton apparel fabrics. Since 1940 the entrance of rayon staple or tow into new fields has been remarkable. Its use in carpets and rugs and in the woolen and worsted industries has already been mentioned. An idea of this growth can be formed from Table 3, taken from *Textile Organon,* May 1951 Supplement.

TABLE 3. END USE CHANGES IN FIBER CONSUMPTION—1937 COMPARED WITH 1949

(Millions of pounds and per cent change)

Classifications	1937 (pounds)	1949 (pounds)	Change from 1937 to 1949					
			Total		Man-Made		Natural	
			Pounds	Per Cent	Pounds	Per Cent	Pounds	Per Cent
Men's and boy's	1115	1234	+119	+11	+84	+179	+36	+3
Women's and children's	931	1178	+247	+27	+202	+89	+45	+6
Household uses	1015	1268	+253	+25	+48	+165	+205	+21
Industrial uses	1556	1592	+36	+2	+313	+929	−277	−18
Exports	98	467	+369	+377	+96	+2469	+273	+289
Total consumption	4715	5739	+1024	+22	+743	+218	+282	+6

This table shows that the total poundage of fibers used in men's and boy's apparel increased 22 per cent from 1937 to 1949. During this same period the poundage of man-made fibers, which includes rayon, acetate, nylon, etc., increased 84 million lb, or 174 per cent, whereas the poundage of natural fibers increased only 35 million lb, or 3 per cent. In industrial uses the 950 per cent increase of the man-made fibers while the natural fibers were decreasing 28 per cent is due primarily to the replacement of cotton by rayon and nylon tire cords.

Prices. From an industrial and economic viewpoint one of the great advantages of both rayon and acetate fiber has been their relative stability. This is clearly illustrated in Fig. 2, which shows the range in price per pound of viscose and acetate staple fiber. Figure 3

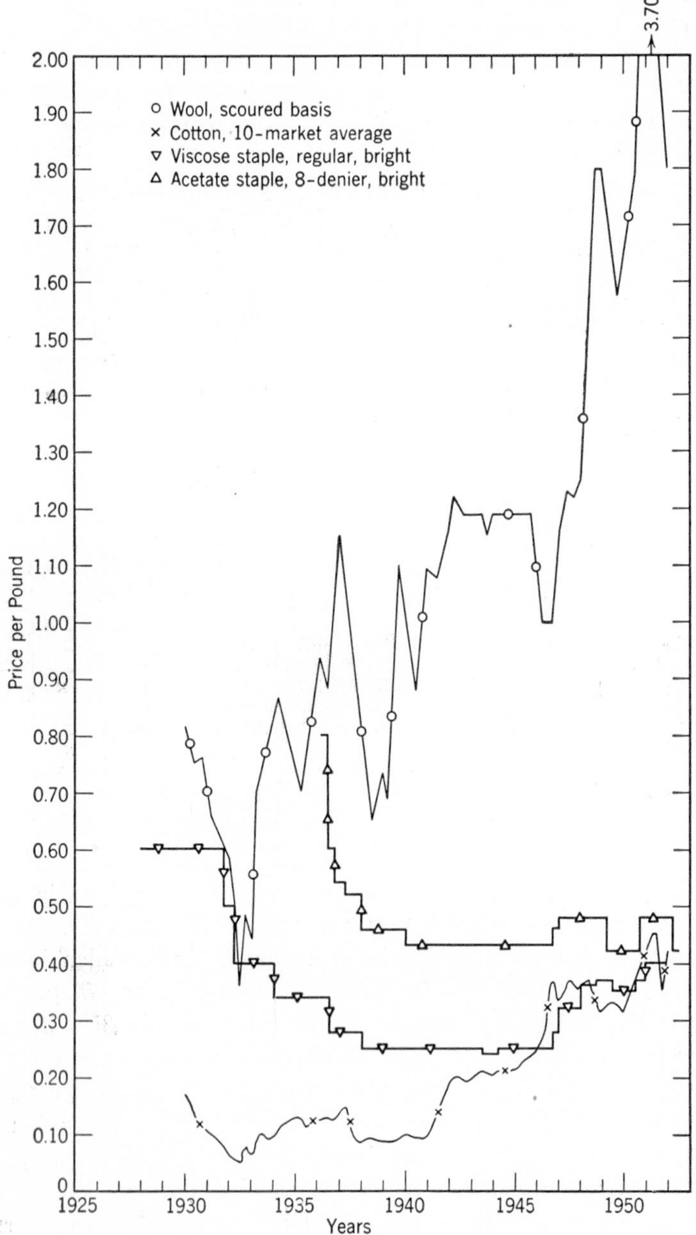

Fig. 2. Prices of cotton, wool, and staple rayon. (Data from *Textile Organon.*)

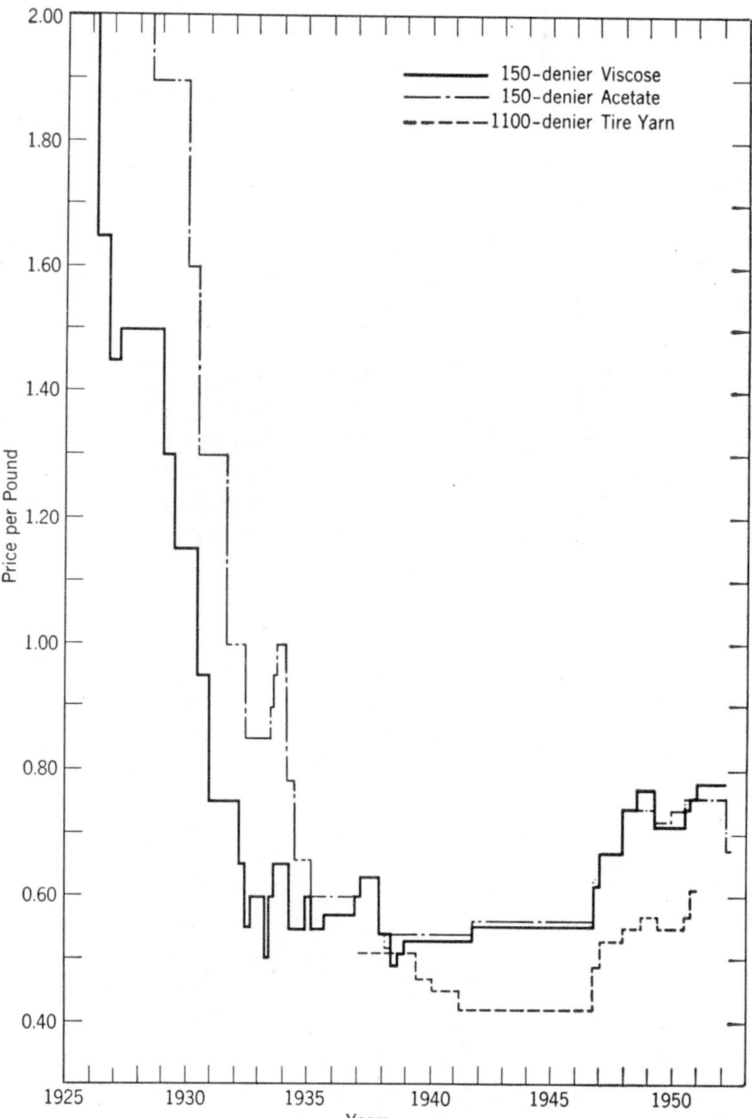

FIG. 3. Prices of filament rayon, acetate, and tire yarn. (Data from *Textile Organon.*)

plotted on the same scale gives the price range of 150-denier viscose and 150-denier acetate since 1925 and of 1100-denier high-tenacity (tire cord) rayon since 1937. All these materials show a continued downward trend, reaching low points between 1940 and 1945. Since then the trend has been generally upward, but the advance has been less than the general cost of living indexes, so that actually on a real economic basis it may be stated that costs have continued downward.

The price of 150-denier viscose rayon rose from $1.85 in 1911 steadily to a high of $6.00 in February 1920, then dropped sharply to $2.55 in October 1920, back to $2.80 in September 1921, and down to $2.05 in February 1924.

Rayon yarns are sold on a spot basis or during a futures period from 60 to 90 days ahead. There are actually no contracts as there is in the sale of cotton and silk futures. There has been a narrowing of the price differential between different deniers, but the difference is still appreciable. For instance, in August 1950 when 150 denier was selling for $0.78 per pound, 50 denier was $1.48; 75 denier $1.09; 100 denier $0.96; 300 denier $0.63, 600 denier $0.59 and 900 denier $0.58. At the same time 1100 denier high tenacity was selling for $0.63 and 2200 denier for $0.61. Cuprammonium yarns are generally higher, for instance, in August 1950, 50 denier was $1.47; 75 denier $1.15; 100 denier $1.02 and 150 denier $1.01.

Deniers. Regenerated rayon filament yarns are produced in a wide variety of deniers and filament numbers. They never remain identical each year, and the relative proportions of the various deniers change from year to year as shown in Table 4.

Information on all deniers and filament numbers of regenerated rayons produced in the United States is given in Table 5 for textile yarns and Table 6 for tire cord yarns. These two tables are from *Modern Textiles Magazine* and are dated September 1952.

Staple Fiber and Tow. Staple fiber is classified by the denier of the single filament and the length of the staple. Frequently it is possible at a slight increase in cost to obtain the staple cut to any desired length or of varied length, such as 3 in. to 6 in. It may also be bright, dull, crimped, etc. When desired, it may be purchased in large groups of uncut continuous filaments which are cut or broken by the textile manufacturer in processing. In this form, it is called "tow." Table 7 gives the types of rayon staple made in the United States as of September 1952. At that time tow of 190,000 denier was being produced by the American Viscose Corporation, either bright or dull, in 1.5, 3, 5.5, and 15 deniers.

TABLE 4. Regenerated Rayon Filament Yarn Production by Denier

(Millions of Pounds)

Denier	*1930*	*1935*	*1940*	*1945*	*1950*	*1952*
50	2.4	0.6	4.1	5.1	2.2	2.2
75		3.3	20.7	29.9	42.6	8.6
100	11.2	26.7	50.2	51.3	72.0	7.9
125	4.5	5.3	3.7	12.7	4.1	2.8
150	83.3	124.1	141.3	95.2	142.2	101.2
200	1.9	15.8	3.8	1.5	0.4	1.5
250	12.6	21.7	21.5	3.4	3.3	2.0
300				37.6	27.0	22.6
450	1.6	4.5	2.3	34	6.7	7.9
600			2.3	34	7.6	7.4
900			2.9	6.9	9.2	15.6
H.T. 1100	0	0	4.3	180.8	53.0	49.3
H.T. 1650	0	0	0	6.2	229.4	365.5
H.T. 2200	0	0	0	17.4	27.6	
Average Denier	148	149	129	129	130	170
Average Denier, H.T.	..	..	384	1085	1554	1585

Source: *Textile Organon* (Feb. 1953).

THE VISCOSE RAYON PROCESS

Although the viscose process for making rayon was the last of the three commercial processes to be developed, it has since about 1910 been by far the most important. The process was developed first in England by Cross, Bevan, Topham, and others employed by Courtaulds, Ltd., from 1900 to 1910. Although the process is rather lengthy (several days to a week) and requires careful control throughout, all the raw materials are fairly cheap, with the result that viscose rayon can generally be made to sell below the price of all other rayons. This is the chief reason for its greater success.

One pound of rayon yarn uses about 1.15 lb pulp, 1.0 lb caustic soda, 0.4 lb carbon disulfide, 1.5 lb sulfuric acid, 1.0 lb sodium sulfate, 0.5 lb glucose, and 800 to 1700 lb water. Small quantities of various other chemicals are used, depending on the manufacturer's preference. Briefly, the process consists in treating wood pulp and/or cotton linters with sodium hydroxide to give alkali cellulose, converting this into cellulose xanthate by means of carbon disulfide, and dissolving the xanthate in a caustic solution to give the viscose spinning solution. This solution is forced through a spinneret into an acid bath which coagulates it into filaments. The xanthate is decomposed and

TABLE 5. Deniers and Filament Numbers of United States Continuous Rayon and Acetate Yarns

Companies	30	40	45	50	55	60	65	75	90	100	120	125	150	200	250	270	275	300	450	600	900	1100	1150	1650	2200	4400	Qualities
													Deniers														
RAYON YARN																											
American Viscose Corp.	..	..	..	20	..	..	..	30	..	40–60	..	..	24	44	60	..	..	44–120	..	100	100	..	..	..	..	..	Avisco, Bright, Dull, and Semi-dull
	..	..	..	..	..	..	..	10	..	14	..	..	40–90	..	..	..	..	..	100	..	150	..	..	..	..	..	
E. I. du Pont de Nemours & Co.	..	..	..	..	..	..	..	30	..	40	..	50	40	..	..	..	..	50	72	96	144	..	..	..	..	..	Bright and Dull
	..	..	..	..	..	..	..	..	..	60	..	..	90	..	..	..	..	..	..	..	50	..	..	..	..	..	
Industrial Rayon Corp.	..	..	..	..	..	..	..	..	..	..	..	..	..	..	60	..	..	44	..	..	66	..	..	..	..	..	Dul-tone, Premier, Spun-lo
	..	..	..	..	..	..	..	..	..	..	..	..	..	..	..	..	..	80	60	100	150	..	..	..	..	..	
	..	..	..	..	..	..	..	..	..	..	..	..	40	..	..	..	..	80	..	..	..	..	..	..	..	..	
American Enka Corp.	..	..	..	18	..	..	..	18–30	..	40–60	..	40	40	..	60	..	..	60	..	..	..	..	..	..	..	..	Briglio, Perlglo, Englo
	..	..	..	..	..	..	..	45	..	100	..	..	90	..	..	..	..	40	..	..	..	..	..	..	..	..	
North American Rayon Corp.	..	..	..	..	..	..	..	30	..	60	..	..	42	..	..	..	..	75	..	98	98	..	..	..	..	..	Bright, Xtra-dul
	..	..	..	..	..	..	..	..	..	..	..	52	..	..	..	..	..	..	75	..	..	..	..	..	..	..	
Delaware Rayon Co.	..	..	..	..	..	..	..	..	..	24–44	..	..	24–44	30–44	120	..	120	120	..	..	..	..	..	..	..	..	Bright, Dull, Delustra, Delvisca, Delragal, Delastra
	..	..	..	..	..	..	..	..	..	60	..	..	60–90	60–90	..	..	..	44–60	..	..	..	..	..	..	..	..	
Skenandoa Rayon Corp.	..	..	..	..	..	..	..	..	..	..	..	..	..	..	..	..	..	75	75	98	98	..	..	..	..	..	Bright, Veri-Dul
	..	..	..	..	..	..	..	..	..	..	..	..	40–90	..	..	..	..	..	..	..	..	..	..	..	..	..	Veri-Dul
Celanese Corp. of America	..	..	..	..	..	..	..	30	..	60	..	..	40	..	..	..	..	..	..	..	..	..	..	..	..	..	Bright
	..	..	..	..	..	..	..	..	..	60	..	..	40–90	..	..	..	..	..	..	..	..	..	..	..	..	..	Dull
New Bedford Rayon Co.	..	..	..	..	..	..	..	..	..	..	..	..	..	..	..	..	..	..	..	..	..	..	..	..	..	..	New Bray
	..	..	..	..	..	..	..	..	..	..	..	..	40	..	..	..	..	..	..	..	..	..	..	..	..	..	New Dull
Eastern Rayon Mills, Inc.	..	..	..	..	..	..	..	..	..	..	..	..	..	..	..	..	..	50	..	90	90	..	..	..	..	..	Bright, Dull, and Spun-dyed
ACETATE YARN																											
American Viscose Corp.	..	..	11	..	14	..	..	20	..	28	32	..	41	54	..	..	..	80	..	..	..	..	..	..	..	..	Avisco, Bright, and Dull
	..	..	..	..	..	..	..	..	..	..	..	..	..	..	..	..	..	..	..	..	..	..	..	..	..	..	
Celanese Corp. of America	..	..	13	..	15	..	..	20–50	..	26–40	40	..	40	52	..	..	..	80	120	160	..	..	..	..	..	..	Celanese
	..	..	..	..	..	..	..	..	..	..	..	..	..	..	..	..	..	..	..	..	..	..	..	..	..	..	
E. I. du Pont de Nemours & Co.	..	..	..	..	18	..	..	24	..	32	40	..	40	..	..	..	..	50	..	..	..	..	..	..	..	..	"Acele," Bright, and Dull
	..	..	..	..	..	..	..	50	..	66	50	..	..	..	..	..	..	..	..	..	..	..	..	..	..	..	
Tennessee Eastman Co.	..	..	..	..	..	..	..	19	..	25	30	..	38	50	..	..	..	75	114	..	..	..	..	..	..	..	Dull and Bright
	..	..	..	..	13	..	..	49	..	..	..	..	..	..	..	..	..	..	..	..	..	..	..	..	..	..	Estron
CUPRAMMONIUM YARN																											
American Bemberg		30	..	36	..	..	45	60	..	74	..	..	120	..	..	..	..	..	..	..	..	..	..	..	..	..	Bemberg, Matesa
		..	..	36	..	..	45	54	..	60	..	..	90	..	..	..	..	..	..	..	..	..	..	..	..	..	Bemberg
	..	..	..	..	..	..	..	45	..	..	..	..	120	..	..	..	..	..	..	..	..	..	..	..	..	..	Continuous

Source: *Modern Textiles Magazine* (Sept. 1952).

TABLE 6. DENIERS AND FILAMENT NUMBERS OF SEMI-HIGH AND HIGH-TENACITY YARNS

Companies	*Deniers* 30	40	50	60	90	120	150	270	300	900	1100	1150	1650	2200	2700	4400	*Process and Trade Names*
American Viscose Corp.	..	..	..	..	..	..	..	..	..	..	490 †	490 †	980 †	980 †	..	..	Avisco tire †
E. I. du Pont, Rayon Div.	..	..	20 *	..	..	..	..	..	120 *	..	480 †	..	720 †	960 †	..	2934 †	Viscose; Cordura †
	..	..	..	..	..	..	60 *	..	50 *	50 *	..	..	..	..	270 *	..	Fiber E
	..	..	..	..	..	..	..	..	..	90 *	..	..	..	..	..	..	Bright
Industrial Rayon Corp.	..	..	..	..	..	..	40 *	..	..	..	..	..	720 †	..	..	..	Viscose; Tyron †
American Enka Corp.	..	..	..	..	..	..	..	..	..	..	480 †	..	720 †	..	..	..	Viscose Tempra †
North American Rayon Corp.	..	..	..	..	..	..	..	..	75 *	..	480 †	..	720 †	..	..	..	Viscose; Super-Narco †
	..	..	..	..	..	..	..	..	..	..	..	..	..	..	..	..	Hi-Narco *
Beaunit Mills	..	..	..	..	..	..	..	..	..	..	..	..	720 †	..	..	..	Viscose
Celanese Corp. of America	40 †	60 †	..	80 †	120 †	160 †	..	360 †	..	..	..	..	..	..	..	..	Acetate; Fortisan †
Eastern Rayon Mills	..	..	..	..	..	..	..	..	..	..	..	..	720 †	900 †	..	3200 †	

* Means semi-strong or semi-high-tenacity yarns; † means high-tenacity or tire-cord yarn.
Source: *Modern Textiles Magazine* (Sept. 1952).

TABLE 7. Types of Viscose Staple Fibers Produced

American Viscose Corp.

Deniers	*Length (inches)*	*Luster*	*Crimp*	*Spinning Systems*
1.00	1 9/16	Bright	none	Cotton
1.25	2¼	Dull	yes	Asbestos
1.50	1⅛	Bright	none	Cotton
1.50	1 9/16	Bright	none	Cotton
1.50	1 9/16	Dull	none	Cotton
1.50	2	Bright	none	Cotton
1.50	2	Dull	none	Cotton
1.50	2½	Dull	none	Cotton
3.00	1⅛	Bright	yes	Cotton
3.00	1 9/16	Bright	yes	Cotton
3.00	1 9/16	Dull	yes	Cotton
3.00	1 9/16	Dull	none	Cotton
3.00	2	Bright	none	Cotton and wool
3.00	2	Dull	none	Cotton and wool
3.00	2½	Dull	none	Cotton and wool
3.00	3	Dull	none	Cotton and wool
5.50	1 9/16	Bright	yes	Cotton and wool
5.50	2	Bright	yes	Cotton and wool
5.50	2	Dull	none	Cotton and wool
5.50	3	Bright	none	Cotton and wool
5.50	5–7	Bright	none	Worsted
5.50	5–7	Dull	none	Worsted
8.00	1 9/16	Bright	yes	Carpet
8.00	2½	Bright	yes	Carpet
8.00	5–7	Bright	yes	Carpet
15.00	1 9/16	Bright	yes	Carpet
15.00	3	Dull	yes	Carpet
15.00	5–7	Bright	yes	Carpet
		The du Pont Co.		
1.50	1½	Bright	none	Cotton
1.50	1½	Dull	none	Cotton
1.50	2	Dull	none	Cotton
1.50	2	Bright		
3.00	1½	Bright	none	Cotton
3.00	1½	Dull	none	Cotton
3.00	2	Dull	none	Cotton
3.00	2	Bright		
3.00	2½	Bright	none	Cotton and wool
3.00	2½	Dull	none	Cotton and wool
5.50	1½	Bright	none	Cotton
5.50	2	Bright	none	Cotton

Courtesy *Modern Textiles Magazine* (Sept. 1952).

the sulfur removed by a sodium sulfide solution; then the yarn is bleached with hypochlorite, washed, and finished as desired.

Alkali Cellulose Formation

The first step in the manufacture of viscose rayon is the formation of alkali cellulose. The raw materials used in this process are cellulose pulp, sodium hydroxide, and water. The cellulose pulp in the form of sheets about 30 x 20 x 0.125 in. is made from cotton linters, Northern spruce, Western hemlock, or Southern pine by a bleaching and purifying process (see Chapter II, on cellulose). Normally, the alpha cellulose content varies from 91 to 99 per cent, but the viscose manufacturers purchase this pulp under rigid specifications as to alpha cellulose content, ash content, color, impurities, etc. The sheets are stored in a room under controlled temperature and humidity conditions, i.e., generally 70° F. and 65 per cent R.H., for several weeks. The exact condition may be varied to suit the manufacturer's preference. The important point is that a uniformly distributed moisture content is attained. The sodium hydroxide is prepared as an 18.5 per cent solution free from heavy metals and containing not more than 1 per cent hemicellulose or sodium carbonate. The water used here and in all other processes in rayon manufacture must be soft, neutral, and free from heavy metals and other impurities. (W. S. Habbard, *Rayon Textile Monthly* **26,** 579–581, 1945.)

Steeping. The cellulose sheets are placed in a long rectangular vat divided into sections by perforated plates. A number of sheets are put in each section, and a batch varies from 500 to 1000 lb. The NaOH is run in from the bottom at a rate which permits proper wetting. After the sheets have soaked 60 min at 70° F. a hydraulic ram forces the sodium hydroxide solution out of the sheets until their weight is five to six times the original conditioned weight. The caustic solution, which is now a dark-brown color due to the hemicelluloses in the pulp, is usually purified by dialysis and reused.

Shredding. The pressed cellulose sheets shrink in length and width as well as swell considerably from their original thickness. They are broken up, but not cut, and mixed in a cast-iron, brine-jacketed shredder by rotating serrated spirals to give a white fluffy, powder-like material known as "crumbs." The temperature is kept at 70° F.

Aging. The crumbs are placed in containers and aged at 85° F. for 40 to 80 hr. The completion of the aging process is determined by viscosity measurements on samples of viscose solution made from the crumbs. During the aging process the caustic soda reacts with the cellulose to form alkali cellulose. At the same time there is a drop in degree of polymerization of the cellulose from 850–1100, to 350–400 and an increase in the carbonyl content from around 7.5 to 15–20 milliequivalents per kg. Thus it appears that in aging the oxidizing action which increases the carbonyl content and decreases the degree of polymerization is equally as important as the formation of alkali cellulose. For this reason, the aeration of the crumbs during aging is very important. In fact there is evidence that, by controlled oxidation with hydrogen peroxide, aging time can be greatly reduced. H. A. Wannow and C. Feickert, *Kolloid-Z.* **108,** 103–113, 1944; *Chem. Abst.* **40,** 7609, 1946.)

Cellulose Xanthate Formation

A charge of 600 to 1000 lb of properly aged crumbs is placed in the xanthator (see Fig. 4). This is a hexagonal drum arranged on a stand

FIG. 4. Xanthating churn with cover plate open, showing interior. (*Courtesy Baker Perkins, Inc.*)

so that it can be revolved. It has openings through the shaft so that the carbon disulfide can be run in without opening and the air can be exhausted to give a reduced pressure. There is a sight panel in one side of the drum through which the condition of the contents can be noted. The charge fills the drum about ¾ full. At the start, the temperature is 70° F. Air is exhausted to give 400 mm of mercury pressure, and 35 per cent carbon disulfide based on the weight of alpha cellulose is run in while the xanthator is revolving slowly. Gradually the white crumbs turn yellow, then orange as the xanthate is formed. Xanthation requires 1 to 2 hr, and during the process the temperature may be allowed to rise to 85 to 90° F. Some water is also added during xanthation. The crumbs decrease to about half their original volume. The excess carbon disulfide vapors are drawn off before the xanthator is opened.

The entire batch is then discharged into a large, brine-jacketed tank provided with stirring and mixing elements. This tank, the dissolver, contains a weak caustic solution (see Fig. 5). A batch will dissolve in 2 to 3 hr. The resulting solution is a viscous, dark, yellowish-brown liquid containing 6½ per cent NaOH and 7¼ per cent cellulose. At this stage it is customary to blend a number of batches and store the solution at 70° F. until it ripens. This will require 12 to 24 or more hours. During this blending and ripening, the solution is filtered eight to ten times. It is then stored under a vacuum to remove air bubbles. It is extremely important that any impurities be removed so that the filaments do not break during spinning.

The chemistry of the formation of cellulose xanthate and its subsequent ripening is complex. The reaction is fundamentally as follows:

$$\text{Cellulose (ONa)} + CS_2 = \text{Cellulose—S—}\overset{\overset{\text{ONa}}{|}}{C}\text{=S}$$

It is generally assumed that only the primary OH group in cellulose reacts. During ripening CS_2 is given off, and the indications are that the ripened solution contains one xanthate group to each cellobiose unit. Alkaline solutions of cellulose xanthate are quite stable at 40° F., but under ripening conditions they are decidedly unstable. When the xanthate is decomposed, cellulose hydrate is formed and will precipitate. The object of the ripening process is to obtain a partially colloidal solution which will have a viscosity and rate of coagulation suitable for spinning.

The most important factor in viscose viscosity is the degree of polymerization. This is established in the aging of the crumbs and is not appreciably changed in subsequent processing. During the ripening process it falls at first and then rises. Of course, the cellulose and caustic content of the solution will affect the viscosity. About 8 per cent NaOH gives the minimum viscosity and also the maximum xanthate stability. Under such conditions coagulation is too slow

FIG. 5. Large Vissolver for dissolving cellulose xanthate in sodium hydroxide solution. (*Courtesy Baker Perkins, Inc.*)

and the maximum concentration of acid and salt is required in the coagulation bath. Such conditions are not desirable.

Ripening is retarded by an increase in NaOH and by lower initial cellulose content. Higher temperatures and longer times result in quicker ripening. The degree of ripeness test is used as a method of control in this process. It is determined by adding a 10 per cent solution of ammonium chloride to 20 grams of viscose in 30 ml of water. The number of milliliters required to coagulate the viscose is the degree of ripeness. Values of suitable spinning solution will run from 5 to 20 ml. The object of ripening is to obtain a viscose solution with a viscosity and ripeness that will give a good spinning solution. Both of these properties vary independently, so that it is frequently a matter of experiment based on past experience to obtain the proper viscosity and ripeness at the same time. If delustered rayon or spun-dyed rayon is desired, the delusterant, dye, or pigment is added during the dissolving and ripening process.

Spinning

The ripe viscose solution is pumped from storage tanks to the spinning machine. An accurate gear metering pump is used so that the viscose solution is supplied at a definite controlled rate. The spinning machine (see Fig. 6) also has a special "candle filter" which gives one final filtration. The spinneret is a platinum alloy cup containing a number of holes equal to the number of rayon filaments being spun. This may vary from 10 to 120 for ordinary filament rayon and from 500 to more than 3000 for tire cord and tow. The holes are generally cylindrical or countersunk and 0.002–0.004 $\pm$ 0.0001 in. in diameter. The final denier of a rayon filament depends more on the rate of supply of the solution by the pump and the amount of stretching during coagulation than it does on the size of the spinneret holes (see Fig. 7).

The spinnerets are immersed in a long tank containing the coagulating solution maintained at 40°–45° C. This is always an acid solution containing additional salts. The exact composition will vary, depending on the results desired. The normal range in composition is within the following limits: 9 to 12 per cent sulfuric acid, 17 to 20 per cent sodium sulfate, 4 to 10 per cent corn syrup or glucose, and 1 per cent zinc sulfate. There is a rapid and continuous countercirculation in the tank so as to keep its concentration uniform. As the cellulose xanthate emerges from the spinneret and travels through the bath it gradually coagulates due to the neutralization of the caustic soda by the sulfuric acid, and solid threads of cellulose xanthate are formed. The three common treatments of the thread as it leaves the bath are pot, bobbin, and continuous spinning.

Pot spinning. This is the most popular method. The emerging filaments are led through the bath to a hook at the surface and from

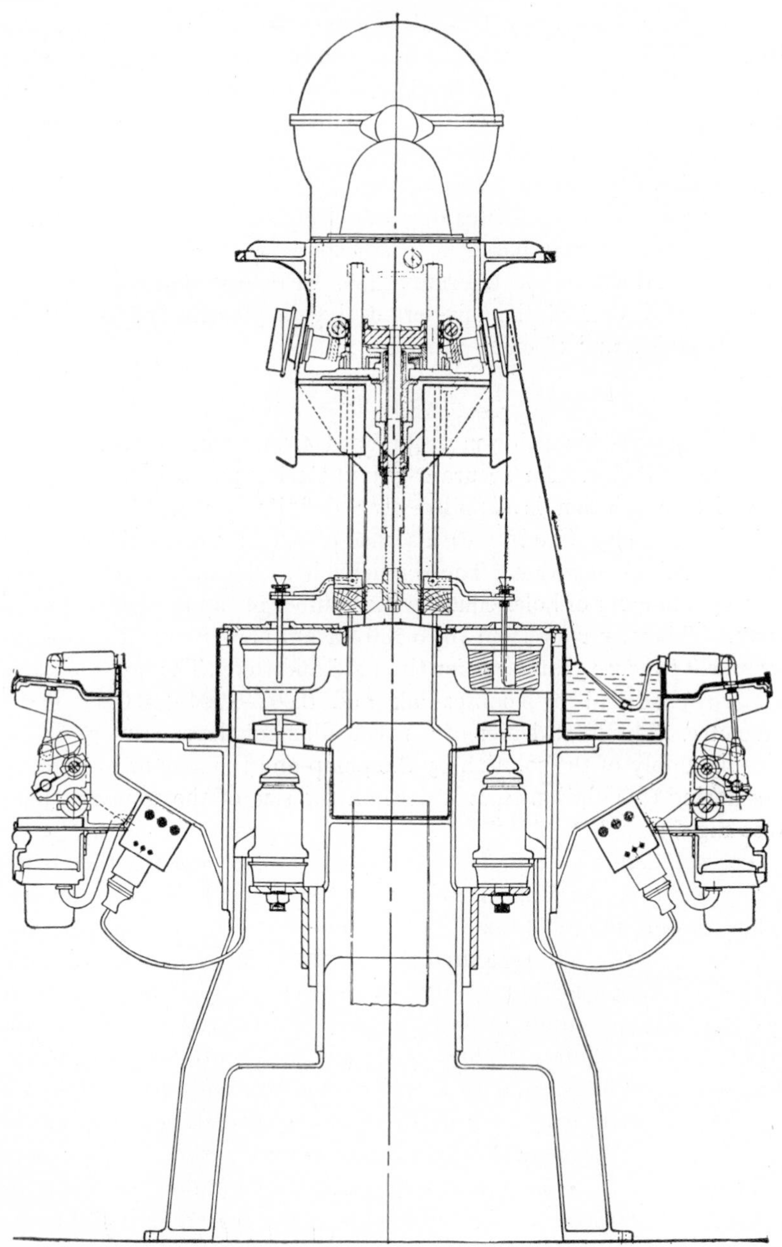

Fig. 6. Modern pot spinning machine. (*Courtesy H. W. Butterworth & Sons Co.*)

it up to the power-driven drawing or Godet wheel, as shown in Fig. 6. The filaments are wrapped around the wheel, the speed of which controls the take-up of the filaments at a rate of 80 to 100 yd per min. For high-tenacity yarns, the yarn is stretched between this wheel and another Godet that runs at a higher speed. The group of filaments, at this point still plastic, can be stretched by as much as 100 per cent. Special stretching devices have been invented to insure

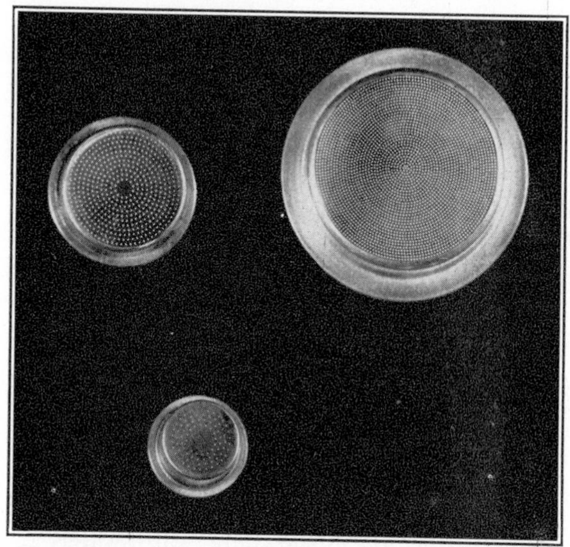

FIG. 7. Three types of spinnerets or jets for rayon filament spinning. (*Courtesy Baker & Co.*)

absolute uniformity and control of this stretch. The purpose of stretch here is twofold, *first,* to reduce the thickness of the filaments, and *second,* to create a stronger yarn.

From the second Godet wheel the group of filaments goes downward through a glass funnel into a spinning pot, the English "Topham box." About 22 in. in circumference, this pot rotates at 8000 to 10,000 r.p.m. It is hollow and smooth, is usually made of reinforced Bakelite or aluminum, and is provided with a removable plastic cover with a hole in its center. See Fig. 8.

In the rotating glass funnel the filaments are twisted to the extent of 2½ to 3 turns per in. The twisted yarn is then laid by centrifugal force against the side of the pot and is distributed by vertical reciprocation of the funnel to form a "cake," which is removed every 4 or 5 hours when the pot is stopped and the lid is taken off. At this time it weighs from 1 to 2 lb, 29 per cent of this weight being yarn and the rest spinning-bath fluid.

The final treatments that are given to the yarn in finishing vary, of course, with different plants. For instance, some producers used to wind the cakes into skeins for treatment, and, although this practice has been largely done away with, it is still followed by some. The following is a brief outline of one common series of treatments.

Some of the excess liquid has already been removed, by centrifugal force, through perforations in the sidewalls of the Topham box. The

Fig. 8. Construction of spinner pot or bucket.

remainder is now washed off in soft, pure, warm water, and the yarn is dried in a tunnel drying machine. Residual sulfur compounds are removed in a solution of sodium sulfide. The fiber at this stage has a rather pronounced yellow color, which is removed by bleaching with a neutral solution of sodium or calcium hypochlorite. Then the fiber is soured with dilute hydrochloric acid.

Finally, it is thoroughly washed with warm and cold water and soap, and then carefully dried. If in skeins, it is wrapped in cheesecloth and excess water is removed in a centrifuge. Cakes are centrifuged in individual buckets. After a more thorough and slow drying in a second tunnel drying machine, it is cooled and rehumidified to 11 per cent moisture regain.

Bobbin Spinning. An important difference between bobbin spinning and pot spinning is that the filaments are not twisted until later. They are merely laid externally on a perforated bobbin, which revolves more slowly than the Topham box. The bath fluid, 79 per cent of the total weight of a finished bobbin, is then washed off, and the ensuing treat-

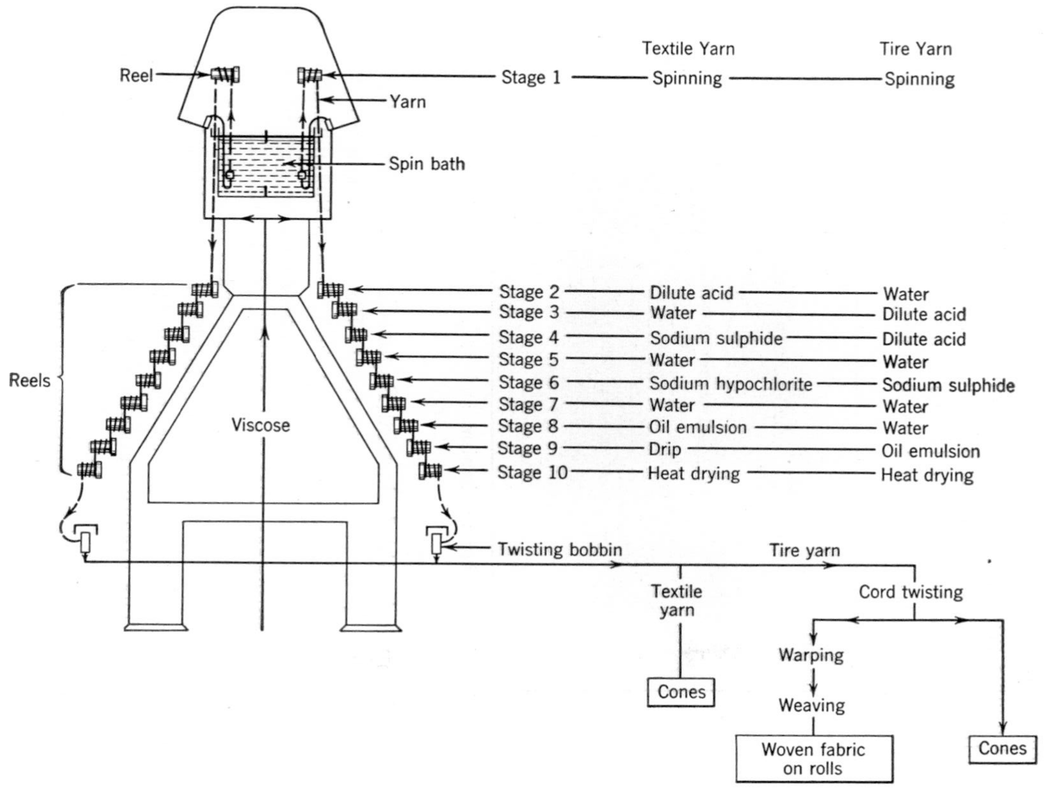

Fig. 9. Schematic view and flowsheet of continuous-process machine for viscose rayon filaments. (*Courtesy Industrial Rayon Corp.*)

ments, much the same as for pot spinning, are done without taking the yarn off the bobbin. After the last drying it is oiled, twisted, and wound on commercial packages.

Continuous Processing. It will be noted that the viscose process just described is a batch process, and efforts have been made to make it a continuous process. Considerable progress has been made at both ends but a completely continuous viscose process has not as yet been attained. The most notable advance has been in the steps following coagulation. The first continuous spinning machine was developed

Fig. 10. Thread-advancing mechanism and reel. (*Courtesy Industrial Rayon Corp.*)

and put into use by the Industrial Rayon Corporation in 1938. The machine in Fig. 9 is an A-shaped frame 108 ft long and 20 ft high with 200 spinning positions on the top deck. From the spinning bath the yarn passes over a series of 10 reels, as shown in Fig. 10, where it is washed, desulfurized, bleached, washed, oiled, dried, twisted, and wound on a large twister bobbin. All this takes place in 5 to 6 min. The length of yarn from the jet to the bobbin is several hundred yards. Several other methods for continuous spinning have been developed and patented. The Kohorn machine (Fig. 11) is a much more compact unit, using a similar series of reels. The operator stands in an alley with the spinning bath and the wet processing reels on one side. From these reels the yarn passes over his head through a finishing trough and down the other side of the machine, where it is dried and twisted. The whole treatment takes about 5 sec. In the Kuljian or Nelson machines, a still more compact arrangement is attained. Instead of a number of reels, the yarn is processed on a single 24-in. drum separated into various sections, so that stretching, regeneration, bleaching, washing, and drying are accomplished in rapid succession. Then the yarn is delivered to a cap twister. The process is completed in about 3½ min. In all of these processes, stretch during coagulation can be controlled. In general continuous processes have been more successful on tire yarns or other heavier high-tenacity yarns than on fine denier textile yarns. Of course, they have resulted in greatly increased production.

Fig. 11. Kohorn continuous spinner. (*Courtesy Oscar Kohorn & Co., Ltd.*)

Considerable work was done in Germany during World War II in making continuous the steps from mercerizing to xanthating. Information on these investigations is given in the reports of the postwar industrial teams which investigated the rayon industry. They were summarized in a publication by the Textile Research Institute, "Synthetic Fiber Developments in Germany," edited by LeRoy H. Smith. In one procedure the pulp in the form of continuous sheets supported on endless belts is passed through a caustic soda solution flowing in the opposite direction. The excess NaOH is pressed out by rolls, and the sheet passes into a conditioning chamber so arranged that the material ages as it passes through the chamber. After shredding it is ready for xanthation. Several similar methods have been described.

In all of these, temperature and time of treatment are carefully controlled. In most cases aging is done at higher temperature for a shorter time.

Special Products. A number of special products and novelties have been produced at various times. Yarns have been made with a flat-holed spinneret. They are known as rayon straw, rayon bands, or monofilament yarns such as artificial horsehair. There are also the "thick and thin" yarns which are being used in shantungs and other dress fabrics. Another specialty which appears to be increasing in importance is spun-dyed or solution-dyed yarns. "Spun-dyed" means that a colored pigment is added to the viscose solution just as the titanium dioxide is used in dulling. Such yarns eliminate the necessity for dyeing and give colors of superior fastness. Pink, rose, and black are the most common colors. Finally, there is the continuous cellulose bubble or bead yarn, for which the viscose solution is extruded through a single large spinneret hole. A small amount of air or a gas is injected into it at regular intervals just as the monofilament is coagulated by the acid bath. The bubbles or beads, which are streamlined, may be any size and spaced according to choice, i.e., an endless chain of disconnected bubbles, each bubble tightly sealed from adjacent units, or a continuous tubular yarn. Such a yarn was used by the Navy in life jackets and in air compartments of lifeboats and rafts.

Viscose Tow or Staple Fibers

Process. Basically, the production of rayon staple is the same as for regular or continuous-filament rayon, in that the raw materials (cotton linters and/or wood pulp) are chemically treated in such a way as to put the cellulose into solution, to extrude it through the fine holes of a spinneret into an acid coagulating bath, and to recover the cellulose in the regenerated form as a large group of continuous filaments. The main difference comes in the collecting and handling of these filaments as they are spun. In viscose staple fiber manufacture, the filaments from *each jet* are formed into continuous tow or a rope of continuous filaments. The number of holes per jet is much greater—2000 or more holes per jet (see Fig. 12).

The tow, at the end of the spinning machine, may receive additional treatments before it is sold as staple fiber. Two methods are in use in the viscose process, the *wet-cut* and *dry-cut*. In the wet-cut method, where the wet filaments in rope form are cut immediately after spinning or cut after a purification process, the "green" fibers have a chance to shrink and crimp freely as they are desulfured, bleached, washed, oiled, and dried in loose form.

In the dry-cut method, the continuous rope of filaments is handled in that form and led through various continuous desulfurizing, washing, bleaching, neutralizing, washing, drying, and lubricating baths, and then cut in the *dry* state or left in the continuous tow form and shipped

FIG. 12. Three-roll stretching assembly on staple spinning machine. (*Courtesy Oscar Kohorn & Co., Ltd.*)

that way to textile spinners or industrial users, who do their own cutting, as required.

Cutting of Staple. The continuous rayon filament rope can be cut to produce uniform-length staple, meaning that all fibers are cut to the same *equal* length, say, 2 in. In 1943 one viscose company offered what is described as a "varied staple length," which is specially designed for use in the worsted spinning trade and is now in commercial use. The new fiber differs from regular types in that each lot manufactured contains fibers that vary in length instead of all being of the same length.

The controlled varied staple length achieved in this product provides a blend of fiber lengths that complements those found in wool and is claimed to produce a more evenly spun yarn. It is also a distinct aid in achieving a more thorough blending of the rayon fibers with the various grades of wools with which they are blended on the worsted system of spinning. An additional advantage of this development is that there are no over-length fibers to be broken in the drawing, and no under-length fibers to add to the noilage. The varied-staple-length fiber is suitable for both the Bradford and the French process of worsted yarn spinning.

There is also a product known as rayon flock, which consists of rayon fiber cut 0.02 to 0.079 in. in length. It can be cut directly to any required short length by the rayon producer; it is also obtainable from shearing operations of rayon pile fabrics and may consist of a mixture of varying lengths. Such rayon flock is used by textile and paper converters for suède, pile, and napped effects, for relief printing to simulate embroidery, and for linings in instrument and jewelry cases.

Use of Continuous Tow. Staple fiber was first made by cutting up continuous tow and was sold to the textile manufacturer in the form of bales of staple fiber. At present, however, an increasing quantity of this material is purchased in the form of continuous tow by the textile industry and processed by it. Three processes are used: (*a*) a tow-to-top cutting system; (*b*) a tow-to-top breaking system; and (*c*) a direct spinning system. In all three systems there is an elimination of some of the usual textile processes, especially carding, and a decrease in labor and machine cost which result in gross savings in operating costs that has been estimated at 2¢ per lb of yarn on the worsted system and 10 to 15 per cent on the cotton system.

In the tow-to-top cutting system a number of tows, up to a million or more denier, are run through a machine which cuts and shuffles the cut fibers and then forms the lap into a top. The cut may be uniform or variable, and the machine is easily adjusted to give any desired staple length. The Pacific converter is an example of a machine for this process. In the tow-to-top breaking system, instead of the tow being cut it is stretched until it breaks. This system gives a variable staple length which is not under good control, and the resulting yarn shows improved strength and a greater tendency to shrink than yarn spun in the normal way. The Perlok system is an example. Both of these systems result in a top or roving which can be handled by the usual textile drawing and spinning processes.

In the direct spinning system the tow is processed directly on a specially constructed spinning frame. Saco-Lowell has experimented with this system. All three of these processes have been used to a limited extent and have given satisfactory yarns, although in some cases the yarns have certain faults when compared with normally processed yarn. The tow-to-top cutting process has been used to the greatest extent with the Pacific converter in the United States and the Greenfield system in England.

Microscopic Characteristics

Viscose rayon filaments or fibers exhibit special microscopic characteristics. Since viscose rayon filaments and staple fiber are "filaments composed of regenerated cellulose, which has been coagulated and solidified from a solution of cellulose xanthate," and are made in varying lusters and denier sizes, microscopic examination has been found to be the easiest, quickest, and most positive means of identification.

The medium for mounting regenerated cellulose rayons, i.e., viscose and cuprammonium, is glycerine, colorless mineral oil (refractive index 1.46), or monobromonaphthalene (refractive index 1.66). Microscopic examination is valuable and indispensable for identification of such fibers in blends, for width measurements and denier determination, for swelling action in various mediums, process of manufacture, and degree of dullness.

The longitudinal examination is best made at magnifications of 100 to 500 diameters and with monobromonaphthalene as a mounting medium. This brings out a number of channels or striations parallel to the fiber axis, produced by the shrinking of the filament after it leaves the spinneret. These are more visible in bright than in dull filaments. They are particularly clear and sharp at 500 magnifications and may vary in a random manner. Therefore, they cannot be used for identification purposes or for determining the producer of any viscose rayon filament. Dullness is readily ascertained by scattered black specks in a longitudinal view (see Fig. 13).

When water is employed as an embedding mounting, the filaments swell from 25 to 45 per cent. In crimped staple fiber, prominent dents are found, which are caused by a mechanical crimping process.

The cross-section of viscose rayon filaments and staple is particularly characteristic and valuable for identification. In fact, it is the only positive means of identification. The cross-section may vary in size, according to the denier, and may vary greatly in outline or shape. The major factors responsible for its shape are the nature and strength of the coagulating bath and the composition and age of the viscose solution. The size and shape of the spinneret hole and the amount of stretching that is given after or during coagulation have only a minor

Fig. 13. Viscose rayon yarn, longitudinal and cross-sectional views. *A*. Bright filaments (×115). *B*. Dull filaments (×115). *C*. Cross-sections, bright (×1000). *D*. Bright filaments showing striations (×500). *E*. Dull filaments showing striations. (*Courtesy Textile Fiber Atlas.*)

effect. The chief distinguishing characteristic is the strongly serrated contour or outline (see the cross-sections in Fig. 13), which may vary from almost round or circular, irregular, or oval to flat or ribbonlike. The semi-dull and dull types show dark or black specks, dispersed throughout the section, more in the very dull than in the semi-dull sections. The indentations in the viscose rayon cross-sections are irregular, sharp, numerous, and not very deep. To get a sharper outline it may be necessary to dye the filaments lightly, because the dye will penetrate the outside but not penetrate completely to the inside.

The cross-section method is preferred for the determination of the denier size of a viscose staple fiber. This method has been adopted by the A.S.T.M. for testing rayon staple. (See Designation D540-44.)

Physical Properties

Structure. When a viscose solution is made by mercerizing and xanthating native cellulose, the crystallinity of the original fiber is disrupted; and when the cellulose is regenerated, a *new crystallization* takes place according to Sisson. This recrystallization consists first of a coagulation, followed by a regeneration. Since these reactions usually take place simultaneously in a comparatively short time from a viscous solution, the degree of crystallinity in viscose cellulose is never as great as in native cellulose.

According to available data the cellulose chains in a rayon fiber do not lie in an entirely unoriented condition, but are partly oriented parallel to the fiber axis, depending on the degree of stretching to which they have been subjected. It has been found that mechanical and chemical treatments may change the crystalline and amorphous parts in a rayon fiber.

Sisson points out that *increased strength* and *decreased elongation* of an oriented rayon and improved water resistance may be due partly to a shifting of a large number of amorphous cellulose chains, which are easily swollen and deformed, toward the more rigid crystalline state, where they are more strongly bound by polar forces and hydrogen bonds. Strength and elasticity are thus associated with crystalline cellulose, whereas reactivity and extensibility are associated with the amorphous portions (see Fig. 14).

Freund and Mark point out that the crystallized areas give to rayon a high modulus of elasticity, rigidity, and ultimate tensile strength; the amorphous parts are responsible for its flexibility, recovery, elongation, and swelling. If the internal mobility of the cellulose chains is increased by appropriate measures, such as swelling or a temperature increase, a certain amount of rearrangement will take place and the viscose rayon will undergo a change in its internal structure, in its external shape, and in its physical properties. Hence, viscose rayon is

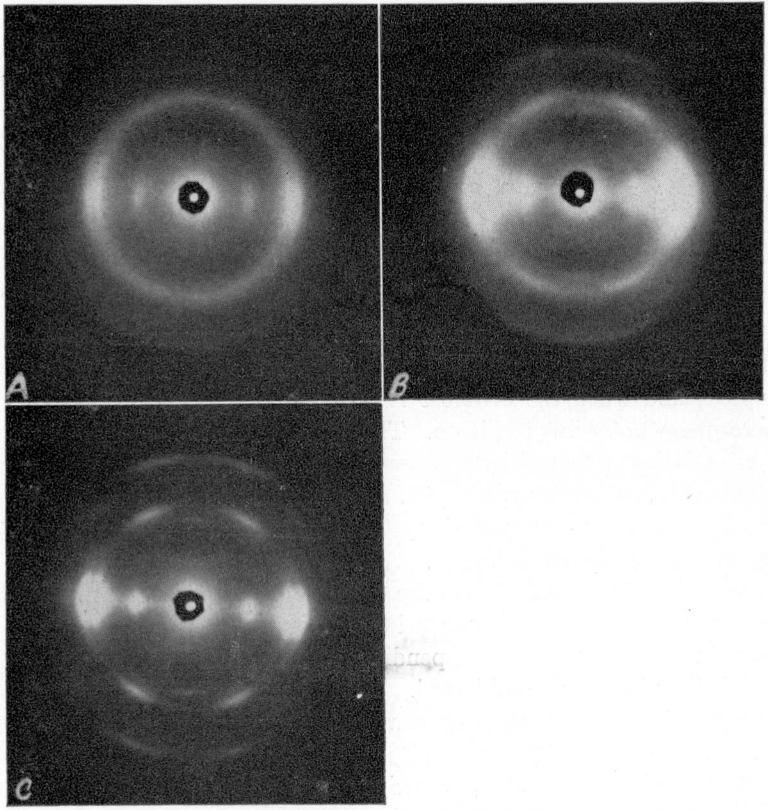

Fig. 14. Typical X-ray diffraction patterns of viscose rayon. *A*. Regular bright viscose rayon showing a medium amount of orientation and crystallinity. *B*. High-tenacity (tire cord) yarn showing a higher degree of orientation but a lower degree of crystallinity. This type of structure gives combined strength and extensibility (toughness). *C*. High-strength (Lilienfeld type) yarn showing a very high degree of both orientation and crystallinity, giving high strength but low extensibility. (*Courtesy American Viscose Corp.*)

a very complicated system of certain intrinsic meta-stability, which makes it very sensitive to any change of the external conditions, such as humidity, temperature, and presence of swelling agents. The complex structure of the interface between the crystallized and amorphous portions effects their swelling and setting properties.

Tensile Strength. Tensile strength where specifications are set up for textiles, either yarns or fabric, is by far the most important property included and frequently it is the only one for which strict limits are established. These facts give some idea of the importance of this property.

When rayon was first put on the market as a commercial item, one of its great disadvantages was its low tensile strength, especially when wet. The gradual improvement in breaking strength of rayon has been remarkable, especially in the development of high-tenacity yarns since 1940. Table 8 gives data on both strength and elongation from

TABLE 8. Strength (Grams per Denier) and Elongation (Per Cent) of Regenerated Rayons

			1920	*1924*	*1928*	*1932*	*1938*	*1941*	*1943*	*1945*	*1949*
Regular Viscose	Strength	Wet	0.40	0.66	0.83	0.95			0.7–1.0	0.7–1.0	0.7–1.2
		Dry	1.50	1.81	1.88	2.00	2.05	2.41	1.5–2.0	1.5–2.4	1.5–2.4
	Elongation	Wet				24–33			20–35	20–35	20–35
		Dry				20–37	27	23	15–30	15–30	15–30
Cuprammonium Rayon	Strength	Wet			0.36	0.6			0.8–0.9	0.95–1.25	0.95–1.25
		Dry			1.5	2.0	1.84		1.7–2.3	1.7–2.3	1.7–2.3
	Elongation	Wet							17–32	17–32	17–32
		Dry					23		10–17	10–17	10–17
High-Tenacity Viscose	Strength	Wet							1.9–2.0	1.9–2.4	1.9–3.0
		Dry						3.07	3.0–3.6	3.0–4.0	3.0–4.6
	Elongation	Wet							14–20	14–20	14–20
		Dry						17	9–17	9–17	9–17

1920 to 1949. Data in this table were taken from several different sources, which may explain some of the inconsistencies. The general trends are evident. From 1920 to 1940 there was a steady increase in both wet and dry strength. Since 1940 the regular viscose has remained practically stationary with both high and medium considerably stronger than the regular. Cuprammonium rayon has shown only a slight increase in strength.

Moisture Regain. Viscose rayon absorbs considerable water from the air. This amount varies with the relative humidity. A.S.T.M. has set up a standard 11 per cent regain at 70° F. and 65 per cent R.H. This is lower than the actual regain, as is shown in Table 9. It is to be noted that there is a slight difference in the regain of the different samples.

Elasticity and Elongation. When a stress is placed on a rayon yarn or filament it becomes longer. As the stress increases the elongation becomes greater until finally the yarn breaks. Scott tensile-strength testing machines and most other similar machines have automatic

TABLE 9. Per Cent Water Absorption of Viscose Rayon Filaments

Relative Humidity (per cent)	*Viscose Yarns* A	B	C	*Average (per cent)*
10	3.9	4.2	3.8	3.9
20	5.7	6.1	5.5	5.7
30	7.3	7.7	7.2	7.4
40	8.7	9.2	8.7	8.8
50	10.2	10.8	10.3	10.4
60	11.9	12.5	12.2	12.2
65	12.8	13.4	13.2	13.1
70	14.0	14.4	14.4	14.3
80	16.9	17.2	17.4	17.1
90	22.1	21.6	22.0	21.9

recording devices which record the relation between the force stretching the yarn and the amount of elongation. Such curves are frequently called stress-strain curves. The stress-strain curve is characteristic of the fiber being tested, and such curves give much useful information about the properties of fibers. All these curves can be divided into several parts. *First,* there is a region of perfect elasticity. Within this region if the strain is removed the yarn returns instantaneously to its original length. This is also the Hooke's law region where the elongation is directly proportional to the stress. *Next,* there is a region in which the return is not instantaneous but takes place over a period of time. *Finally,* there is a region up to the point of rupture where permanent deformation takes place.

Both elongation and elasticity are altered by changes in fiber structure. Elongation is dependent on molecular orientation. Some figures on elongation are given in Table 8. It will be noted that the high-tenacity yarns which have a high degree of orientation have the lowest elongation. It should also be noted that wet yarn elongates more than dry.

Leaderman defines the instantaneous modulus of elasticity as the ratio of the instantaneous elastic strain to the stress causing the deformation. This modulus expressed in dynes per square centimeter depends only on the state of the filament and is independent of time. Leaderman gives the following two values for viscose filaments: 1.50×10^6 and 1.56×10^6. Mark gives the following values for normal rayon: 1.2 to 1.6×10^6 dynes per sq. cm.

When a constant load is applied to a viscose filament, the deformation is not constant but decreases gradually with time. Such behavior is described as "creep," "plasticity," or "cold flow." Immediately upon removal of load, the viscose filament is found to have taken a "set" or "residual" deformation. The magnitude of this residual deformation depends on the *magnitude* of the load and the *length of time* that it was applied. Upon removal of the load a marked reduction in residual deformation takes place gradually; deformation may disappear entirely in the course of considerable time. This gradual reduction of residual deformation following removal of the load is called *creep recovery.*

Leaderman suggests that such reversible delayed elastic effects, together with the associated relaxation behavior, be referred to as *primary creep phenomena.*

Viscose filaments exhibit a large primary creep, which increases gradually with time, and the rate of increase of deformation decreases continuously with time. In other words, viscose filaments are *plastic* rather than elastic. The application of a longitudinal load for more than a momentary interval of time does result in a permanent elongation of the filament or yarn. Temperature and moisture have a considerable influence. A change in temperature appears simply to alter the time scale of creep, provided that irreversible flow and thermo-recovery phenomena are absent. Moisture causes swelling, which increases the plasticity and therefore increases the primary creep.

All these phenomena tend to show that viscose filaments are more plastic than elastic. The elasticity of viscose is in all probability less than 2 or 3 per cent, after which creep develops and permanent elongation sets in until rupture. This is a very important consideration in the handling of rayon yarns in processes like winding, oiling, rewinding, warping, and sizing, as well as weaving and tentering of goods, or all processes where sudden tensions are applied, particularly when the rayon is moist or wet. Permanent attenuation of the yarn must be avoided, as such attenuation changes the appearance, luster, and chemical reaction of the yarn. This results in shiners in weaving or knitting, streaky dyeing and printing, and shifting of yarns in the goods in final finish.

Fineness or Diameter. The diameter or fineness of rayon filaments is expressed in denier units. For instance, a 150-denier, 24-filament yarn would have a filament denier of 150 divided by 24, or 6.25 denier. Such a yarn would be considered to have coarse filaments. The finest filament produced in a viscose process yarn is the 100-denier, 100-filament yarn, where the individual filament is 1 denier. The finer the size of the individual filament the softer the yarn feels to the touch.

In viscose staple fiber the fineness can be adjusted or matched to the diameter of the fiber with which it is to be mixed or spun. In cotton mixtures or if spun alone on the cotton system, viscose staple fiber is made in 1.0-, 1.25-, 1.5-, and 3-denier sizes. For use with fine wools on the French system, 3, 5, and 5.5 denier are used. For carpet wools or on the Bradford system of spinning, 5-, 5.5-, 7-, 10-, 12-, and 15-denier diameters are employed.

The actual diameter can also be expressed in microns, which is the more common method used by microscopists. Mennerich has calculated and determined the diameter of various denier staple fibers in microns. He found the values given in Table 10, which are helpful in matching viscose with natural fibers.

TABLE 10. THEORETICAL AND ACTUAL DIAMETERS OF VISCOSE STAPLE FIBERS

Filament Deniers	*Theoretical Microns*	*Cross-Section Microns*	*Longitudinal Microns*
1.5	11.8	11.3	12.5
2.5	15.3	14.9	16.5
3.0	16.7	16.6	18.9
4.0	19.3	20.4	23.9
5.5	22.6	22.1	24.9
10	30.6	31.0	34.0
20	43.2	42.9	47.8
25	48.3	46.3	52.1

This means that a 62's quality wool, which is 23.3 μ in diameter, will require an approximate 5.5-denier viscose staple to match its size.

Degradation. Since cellulose is extremely sensitive to the action of acid and also to oxidation, acids produce *hydrocellulose* and oxidizing agents produce *oxycellulose.* In either case a breakdown of the molecular chain is brought about, which is commonly described as "degradation." In the case of acids the cellulose chain is attacked at the oxygen linkage, whereas oxidizing agents attack the two secondary alcoholic or hydroxyl groups. Hydrocellulose and oxycelluloses are weaker than cellulose, and their formation is a destructive process. (See Chapter II.) Photocellulose is another type created by partial oxidation with light.

Ash Content. The quantity and type of ash in viscose yarns vary somewhat with each producer and each method of production. Ash content depends a great deal on the quality of water used, since hydrated cellulose will adsorb dissolved substances, such as calcium and iron compounds. Dry viscose rayon yarns have proved to be exceptionally uniform in ash content, ranging from 0.15 to 0.25 per cent, normally.

Effect of Light. According to Grempe, light has a deteriorating influence on all regenerated cellulose products, and degradation takes place on the surface exposed to the light. It is due both to water and to the ultraviolet rays of the sun. The damage to viscose rayon is slightly greater in an atmosphere of 45 per cent R.H. than in one of 65 or 90 per cent R.H. according to Huezel. Eichler points to his experiments on deterioration of various textile fibers and fabrics resulting (1) from 6-hr exposures to mercury-vapor lamps and (2) after exposure of 250 hr to daylight through a window glass. His results are shown in Table 11 and represent losses in per cent of original strength.

TABLE 11. DEGRADATION OF TEXTILE FIBERS DUE TO LIGHT

Fibers	*Ultraviolet Light, 6 Hr*	*Daylight, 250 Hr*
Natural silk	28	62
Cuprammonium rayon	11	57
Viscose rayon	4	35
Acetate rayon	35	24

According to these data acetate rayon loses the greatest amount of strength in ultraviolet rays, whereas it loses the least under daylight exposure. Viscose rayon seems to lose little strength when exposed to ultraviolet rays and loses more when exposed to daylight. This is due to the formation of photocellulose.

Action of Dry Heat. Most regenerated celluloses, under the influence of heat as well as light, show rapid loss in strength, these changes being accompanied by an increase in copper number and alkali solubility. In a study of effects of drying conditions of textile yarns, Wiegerink in 1940 showed that the quality index [1] of cellulosic fibers decreases either as the temperature is increased or as the moisture content of the surrounding atmosphere is increased. Both the breaking strength and fluidity of viscose rayon appear to be functions of the relative humidity to which the samples are exposed.

Degradation of cellulose is slower in the absence of oxygen. Continued heating, however, in the absence of oxygen leads to deteriora-

[1] Defined as the percentage of the original breaking strength retained after drying multiplied by the percentage of the original elongation retained after drying.

tion of the cellulose, but little is known about the course of the reactions. If cellulose is exposed to relatively high temperatures, drastic degradation of the material occurs. Short heating at high temperatures, such as 140° C., is less harmful than long heating at lower temperatures. A decrease of tenacity and eventually a yellow to brown discoloration occurs on aging.

Absorbency. Viscose rayon is highly absorbent and takes up water readily without the aid of any assistants, such as wetting agents. Oven-dry cellulose is extremely hygroscopic and comparable to the best drying agents. When water is adsorbed by viscose rayon, a swelling occurs—0.4 to 7 per cent axial swelling in normal viscose rayon, but only 0.7 to 2 per cent in highly oriented rayon, according to Valko. The presence of water in regenerated cellulose increases the penetration of reagents into the cellulose, increases the electrical conductivity, reduces the breaking strength, and changes other mechanical characteristics. Cellulose is wet by all types of oils, and when oil is imparted as a dulling agent, it is held very tenaciously. Its removal is not always easy because of uneven application and absorption.

Action of Acids. The resistance of regenerated cellulose rayons to acids is generally less than that of cotton to the same concentrations of the same acids. Therefore, acid treatments must not be too drastic with respect to concentration, temperature, and time. Organic acids (acetic and formic) can be safely used in 1 to 2 per cent concentration (on the dry weight of the goods) without injury to the fiber. Inorganic acids, such as sulfuric, hydrochloric, and nitric, can be used in surprisingly strong concentrations provided the temperatures are not too high and the treatment is brief. In all cases, acids must be neutralized thoroughly and must certainly not be allowed to dry on the material or serious weakness will result. Oxalic acid for removal of iron stains is not recommended except at temperatures lower than 150° F.

At high temperatures and concentrations all acids will destroy or carbonize regenerated rayons. Sodium bisulfite is applied to regenerated cellulose rayons as an antichlor and to remove manganese dioxide from permanganate-bleached goods. No harmful action will result if applied at ½ to 3 per cent solutions at room temperature. Acids in contact with yarn cause rayon to become hard and brittle. Acids tend to prevent swelling of rayon filaments.

Oxidizing Agents. Although regenerated rayon fibers, filaments, and yarns are usually a good white, because they are made from bleached pulp and are bleached by the producers, it does become necessary to subject them to bleaching agents to restore their whiteness after soiling or when they are used in conjunction with real silk, cotton, or wool. Peroxide solutions can weaken regenerated cellulose rayons when applied at 150° F. Hence, hydrogen peroxide is employed at temperatures not exceeding 130° F. Sodium peroxide is not as well suited for this purpose, although it is used by some in the last 10 min of a scouring operation, for instance.

Regenerated rayon yarns are bleached with sodium hypochlorite solutions. Neutral sodium hypochlorite solutions exert a good bleaching action and will not harm regenerated rayon yarns when applied at or below room temperatures in concentrations not exceeding 1¼ per cent available chlorine, based on the dry weight of the goods in a 20 to 1 bath volume.

Sodium hypochlorite in acid solution has a violent bleaching action and can only be applied cold and in great dilution. Alkaline hypochlorite solutions are much milder in their action than the acid. When time permits and gentle treatment is required, alkaline sodium hypochlorite solutions are preferred. Potassium permanganate can be used also, but caution is necessary; this bleach should be used only in mild acid solution, as the formation of manganese dioxide prevents the bleaching action from proceeding.

As a stripping agent for redyeing or removal of reduced sulfur compounds or light colors before dyeing into dark shades, sodium hydrosulfite is most commonly used. Its action is gentle at or near the boil in an alkaline bath. Hydrosulfite compounds, such as sodium hydrosulfite, sodium sulfoxylate-formaldehyde, basic or normal zinc sulfoxylate-formaldehyde, as well as other reducing compounds, form small quantities of hydrocellulose in regenerated cellulose yarns when treatment is too drastic.

Action of Soaps. Ordinary soaps in usual textile concentrations have no direct effect on regenerated cellulose materials. Improper use of soap or use of poorly made soap results in rancidity and odor in rayon fabrics or yarns. When soap alone is used, there is a tendency for the ionized fatty acid from the soap to adhere tenaciously to the individual rayon filaments. During the drying of such materials and subsequent storage, the free fatty acid radical is very likely to turn rancid and to give the goods an objectionable odor. This phenomenon is especially prevalent on oil-delustered rayons, because the fatty acid radical of the soap adheres tenaciously to the minute oil globules in the structure of the yarn. If given time enough the fatty acid radical will produce a pronounced "scroop" in the fabric or fiber. Rancidity can be prevented by a final rinse in hard water.

Action of Solvents. Textile solvents such as pine oil, hydrogenated hydrocarbons, benzene, toluene, xylene, gasoline, and carbon tetrachloride can be safely used on regenerated rayons. They are employed as spotting agents, before or during scouring processes, or as additions to the scouring or boil-off bath.

Effect of Iron. Direct contact with iron in the form of ferrous hydroxide tends to weaken rayon yarns. In the presence of moisture, air, and carbonic acid in the air, iron is transformed from its metallic state first into the more soluble ferrous hydroxide. In this state and in the form of a solution, ferrous hydroxide is readily absorbed by rayon. On exposure to air, this ferrous hydroxide absorbs oxygen from the air and is thus converted into the ferric hydroxide state. In the process of changing from the ferrous to the ferric state, this iron salt is very active. It can act as a catalyst under favorable conditions, adding oxygen to the cellulose molecule and forming what is known as *oxycellulose.* This form of cellulose has no tensile strength, hence the tendering of rayon by iron. Staining, marking, or touching of rayon to iron or iron surfaces, as occurs in tinting, boil-off, throwing, and dyeing, must be avoided. All traces of iron stains can be removed in 5 to 15 min by 1 to 2 per cent of oxalic acid at a temperature of 150° F. or below. This treatment is quite harsh and should be avoided on regenerated rayons.

Dye Affinity. Viscose and other regenerated cellulose fibers dye readily with all dyestuffs which are substantive to cotton. Some modifications in dyeing technique are necessary to offset the generally increased affinity of viscose and cuprammonium rayon for these dyes in order to obtain level and well-penetrated dyeings. These modifications include dyeing at *lower* temperatures, the use of retarding agents, and lower concentrations of electrolytes to affect exhaustion of color from the dye bath.

Physical variations in rayon yarn arising during manufacture become more apparent after dyeing and result in differences of depth of color on adjacent filaments. A careful selection of dyes will minimize such effects. Published information on this subject is available from most suppliers of dyestuff.

The mechanism of direct dyeing is now generally believed to be a process of diffusion, in which equilibrium is obtained between dye bath and fiber. The comparative speed at which dyes attain this equilibrium influences the quality of the dyeings. High-tenacity rayons are less absorptive of color than regular regenerated rayon yarns.

The fastness properties of direct cotton colors when dyed on rayon are generally superior to similar dyeings on cotton. The introduction of a delusterant in the yarn, however, adversely affects the light fastness of many dyes. The enhanced fastness of dyed bright yarns has been ascribed to their greater degree of light reflectance. Regenerated cellulose rayons are not injured by customary diazotizing and color-developing chemicals in commonly recommended concentrations. High twist decreases the dye penetration and increases the time of dyeing to the same shade.

Biological Properties. The effect of molds and mildew on viscose rayon filaments, yarns, and goods is an important consideration in their handling and storage. Such influences cause discoloration and stains in rayon materials and affect their strength, dye affinity, and luster. The presence of molds and mildew depends on the type of warp size, on the conditions of temperature and humidity in which viscose rayon is stored, and how it has been treated before storage. Clean dry viscose rayon is rarely attacked.

CUPRAMMONIUM RAYON

The cuprammonium process was the second process used to make rayon. The early efforts were not very successful, and it was soon replaced by the cheaper viscose process. During the 1920's the stretch spinning process for making cuprammonium rayon was commercially successful, and since that time a limited amount (5 to 8 per cent) of the annual production of rayon has been made by this process, chiefly by various branches of the J. P. Bemberg Company; hence the name Bemberg rayon. The first American producer was the American Bemberg Company founded in 1920.

Stretch Spinning. The solution for the cuprammonium process is prepared by adding basic copper sulfate and a 28 per cent solution of aqua ammonia to purified and bleached cotton linters. The cotton is first purified by pressure cooking in a mild caustic solution until it is almost 100 per cent cellulose. The chemicals are then added, and the very heavy spinning liquid that is formed must be thinned and matured as well as carefully filtered before it can be put through the spinnerets.

The metallic, large-holed spinnerets form the solution into continuous filaments, which pass through a glass funnel containing pure, soft running water that takes out nearly all the ammonia and some of the copper. In single filaments they pass into a tank containing a weak solution of sulfuric acid, where solidification becomes complete, and some more of the copper is removed. The remaining chemicals must be washed off with water after the yarn has been wound on a reel.

When the thread is removed from the reel it is tied with a colored thread that marks the denier. Next, it is twice washed with soap and water, being carefully dried each time. When properly conditioned, soft, and pliable, it is twisted, if it is to be sold in this form. Many manufacturers of knit goods now prefer it entirely untwisted. Finally, it is wound on bobbins, cones, or spools.

Several attempts have been made by others to devise a more streamlined process like the "continuous" viscose, but without success.

Statistics. Its production figures have always been merged, at first with viscose and nitrocellulose, and after 1934 with viscose production figures. The maximum production reached by the company has never been in excess of 12,000,000 lb annually.

Before 1933, Bemberg yarns were approximately 100 per cent higher in price than other rayon yarns. Since that time prices of American cuprammonium yarns became approximately the same as those of viscose yarns.

Physical Properties. Cuprammonium yarn, being a regenerated rayon yarn, assumes many of the physical properties of viscose rayon yarn described under the viscose process with the exceptions given below.

The average dry tensile strength in 1934 was 1.47 grams per denier; today the dry tensile strength has been increased to a low of 1.7 and a high of 2.3 grams per denier, or an average of 2 grams per denier, which is an increase of 36 per cent.

The average wet tensile strength in 1934 was 0.87 gram per denier, which has also increased to a low of 0.95 gram per denier and a high of 1.25 grams per denier. The average wet strength today is 1.10 grams per denier, an increase of 26 per cent. While in 1934 the comparative loss of strength from dry to wet was 41 per cent, today it is 45 per cent.

Cuprammonium yarns are made in finer deniers and with a higher number of filaments than viscose (see Table 4). The average fineness of the cuprammonium filaments is 1.25 denier, but these filaments have been made as fine as 0.40 denier. The variation in the denier of cuprammonium filament is on the average about 5 per cent. The elasticity and elongation of dry cuprammonium filaments and yarns are from 10 to 17 per cent at 65 per cent R.H. and 70° F. This is due largely to the effect of stretch spinning. The wet elongation is from 17 to 33 per cent. The moisture regain of cuprammonium yarns and fabrics is 11 per cent at 70° F. and 65 per cent R.H.

Microscopic Characteristics. Longitudinally the filaments appear fine and structureless, without striations or markings of any kind. In cross-section the fibers are circular or sometimes slightly oval, with a smooth contour, which is very characteristic of this rayon.

Utilization, Consumer Evaluation, and Labels

Cuprammonium rayon yarns in this country, known more prevalently and widely advertised as Bemberg brand cuprammonium rayons, have found extensive use in women's fine hosiery, fine warp-knit underwear, and women's sheer dress fabrics, especially. The softness, fineness, and drapability qualities have distinguished this filament rayon. Quality control plans cover finished merchandise made from this yarn. Tests for shrinkage, color fastness, tensile strength, seam strength, slippage, and yarn uniformity are made by the U. S. Testing Company, an independent testing laboratory. Labels certifying to these tests guarantee serviceability to the consumer.

BIBLIOGRAPHY

American Viscose Corp., *Rayon Technology,* McGraw-Hill Book Co. (1948).

A.S.T.M. Yearbook, American Society for Testing Materials (1950, 1951).

Avisco Rayoneers (monthly), American Viscose Corp.

Mauersberger, H. R. (ed.), *American Handbook of Synthetic Textiles,* Textile Book Publishers (1952).

Modern Textiles Magazine (monthly), Rayon Publishing Corp.

Textile Organon (monthly), Textile Economics Bureau, Inc.

Textile World (monthly), McGraw-Hill Publishing Co.

Balsom, H. P., "Warner Swasey's Pacific Converter, Pin Drafters and Modern Weaving Machines," *Canadian Textile J.,* **68** (5), 55–61 (1951).

Bendigo, C. W., "Newer Synthetics Are in the Spotlight," *Textile World,* **99** (9), 111–130 (1949).

Bendigo, C. W., "Synthetic Fibers—New and Improved," *Textile World,* **100** (9), 92–93 (1950).

Bowden, C. M., "Direct Spinning Rayon Tow to Yarn," *Textile World,* **98** (5), 114–115 (1948).

Frick, P. W., "A Review of Continuous Viscose Spinning Machines," *Rayon Synthetic Textiles,* **30** (9), 49–52 (1949).

Hermans, P. H., "Physical Properties of Skin and Core of Viscose Yarns," *Textile Research J.,* **20,** 553–569 (1950).

Jones, R. M., McConnell, R. J., Dreher, E. Hand, and Culpepper, F. S., "Processing Rayon Staple on Cotton Machinery," *Textile World,* **94** (11), 135–137 (1944).

Kennedy, J. H., "The Pacific Converter," *Textile World,* **100** (5), 75–84 (1950).

Kernan, A. J., "Carding and Combing of Staple Fiber Eliminated," *Textile World,* **96** (6), 123, 192, 194 (1946).

Lohrke, J. L., "The Perlok System of Tow Stapling," *Rayon Synthetic Textiles,* **31** (6), 41 (1950).

Meredith, R., "The Tensile Behavior of Raw Cotton and Other Textile Fibers," *J. Textile Inst.,* **36,** T 107–130 (1945).

Preston, J. M., and Narasimhan, K. I., "Orientation of Skin and Core in Viscose Rayon Fibers," *J. Textile Inst.,* **40,** T 327–337 (1949).

Rose, L., "The Structure of Textile Fibers, Part IX, Viscose Rayon," *J. Textile Inst.,* **40,** 1035–1047 (1949).

Saxl, V., "How Should Long Staple Synthetics Be Processed," *Textile World,* **102** (1), 131–133, 237 (1932).

Smith, H. DeWitt, "Physical Properties of Textile Fibers" (1944 Marburg lecture), A.S.T.M. *Proceedings,* **44,** 543–585 (1944).

Van Laer, J. A., Brown, F. R., Kline, H. B., and Appleton, W. C., "Rayon Tire Cord Developments," *Rayon Textile Monthly,* **26** (7), 81–85 (1945).

Whitehead, W., "Development and Application of Fortisan Yarn," *Rayon Textile Monthly,* **28,** 71–72, 127–128 (1947).

Wilkie, R. E., "The Pacific Converter," Papers of the American Association of Textile Technologists, **5** (5), 223–226 (1950).

CHAPTER XVII

ACETATE FIBERS AND YARNS

H. DeW. Smith and H. R. Childs[1]

HISTORY

Cellulose acetate as a chemical was first prepared by Schutzenberger in 1869 by heating cellulose with acetic anhydride in a sealed glass tube. E. C. Worden, in 1921, published a review of the early history of the art and preparation of cellulose acetate. In 1894, Cross and Bevan, in England, discovered that zinc chloride or sulfuric acid catalyzed this chemical reaction. They obtained a chloroform-soluble acetate, which they referred to as the primary acetate and which they erroneously considered to be a tetraacetate. Bronnert made the first cellulose acetate filaments at Mulhausen, Germany, in 1899. Meanwhile, Cross and Bevan had communicated with Arthur D. Little, of Boston, Mass., about their viscose discoveries. Little and a few friends began to experiment with viscose and also, at the same time, with cellulose acetate. In 1900, Little, Walker, and Morck continued the development of the acetate process and established a small plant in Boston, Mass. In 1902, they applied for a patent on the spinning of "artificial silk" from cellulose acetate, which was granted in October. In 1914, the Lustron Company was established in a small factory in Boston, which eventually produced 300 lb of 150-denier acetate yarn per day. The process involved the spinning of a chloroform solution of cellulose triacetate into a liquid coagulating bath. The hazards of chloroform and the difficulty in dyeing the triacetate defeated the commercial success of this enterprise.

Eichengruen and Becker, in 1901, patented the process of kneading cellulose with a mixture of glacial acetic acid, acetic anhydride, and sulfuric acid at low temperatures. This technique has become the basis of most commercial production of cellulose acetate.

In 1903, Miles discovered that a composition approximating cellulose diacetate is soluble in acetone and that the acetone-soluble cellulose

[1] Revised, 1952, by G. H. Hotte, Technical Director, A. M. Tenney Associates, Inc.

acetate could be prepared by saponifying the primary acetate under controlled conditions. The advantages of acetone as compared to chloroform for large-scale manufacturing operations made Miles' invention of fundamental importance for the establishment of acetate yarn manufacture. Nevertheless, more than 20 years elapsed between the idea and its commercial achievement by the Dreyfus brothers.

The development of the acetate process was advanced during the first World War when cellulose acetate was used as a "dope" or varnish to coat fabric airplane wings. The Dreyfus brothers, who had been working on cellulose acetate in Switzerland, were invited by the British Government to Spondon, England, where they established a dope factory.

About this time, the United States War Department became interested in the value of cellulose acetate for the coating of airplane wings. The Eastman Kodak Company, which had sold 35-mm acetate safety film commercially as early as 1909, possessed facilities for the manufacture of cellulose acetate, and soon after war was declared in 1917 Eastman supplied our government with large quantities of cellulose acetate for wing dope. The War Department also arranged with Camille Dreyfus to come over from England and organize the American Cellulose and Chemical Manufacturing Company of Delaware. Its plant for the manufacture of acetate dope was located at Cumberland, Md.

With the signing of the Armistice in November, 1918, the United States Government canceled its contracts for cellulose acetate before the American Cellulose and Chemical Manufacturing Company's plant had been completed [1].

Camille Dreyfus returned to England, and after a further period of development the British Cellulose and Chemical Manufacturing Company began to produce cellulose acetate yarns commercially in 1921 under the trade name "Celanese." One million pounds had been imported into the United States by 1924. The Celanese Corporation of America (formerly American Cellulose and Chemical Manufacturing Company, Ltd.) bought certain of the Lustron Company's patent rights and in 1924 completed its plant in Cumberland, Md., which commenced to produce acetate yarns. Difficulties encountered in dyeing the yarn retarded its progress at the start, but at about this time British Celanese and the British dyestuff industry solved the dyeing problem. This marked the real beginning of the commercial use of textile filaments and yarns made by the acetate process, which was the third man-made fiber process to be introduced into America.

In 1927, the production of the Celanese Corporation of America rose to 5 million lb annually, nearly double that of 1926, and the company continued to expand its production in subsequent years. The year 1929 witnessed a new expansion of the acetate industry when the du Pont Rayon Company ventured into the field by establishing a plant for the production of acetate under the trade name "Acele" at Waynesboro, Va.

The Viscose Company entered the acetate yarn field with a plant at Meadville, Pa., which started producing in June, 1930, and sold acetate yarn under the brand name "Seraceta." The first dull acetate yarns were produced by the Viscose Company in 1931 under the trade name "Sombraceta." The Tubize Chatillon Corporation began to make bright acetate filament yarn in 1930 under the brand name "Chacelon" (later changed to "Tubize"), and a dull yarn in 1932.

Tennessee Eastman Corporation (now Tennessee Eastman Company, Division of Eastman Kodak Company), Kingsport, Tenn., commenced the manufacture of cellulose acetate yarns in a pilot plant early in 1929, and the commercial production began early in 1931. Eastman's filament acetate is sold under the trade name "Estron." "Teca," a crimped acetate staple fiber, which was launched in 1935 by Tennessee Eastman, marked the entry of acetate staple into the American market on a broad scale.

The acetate yarn producers also manufacture cellulose acetate for photographic safety films, acetate plastics, and acetate foil for wrapping and for other coating or chemical uses.

Further developments in the acetate field include the marketing of abraded continuous filament yarns, thick-and-thin filament yarns, flat monofilament yarns, black solution-dyed yarn, high-impact filament yarn for aerial delivery parachutes, strong saponified acetate yarn, and plasticized staple. There is a great deal of current interest in the development of processes for converting continuous filament acetate tow into top or roving for spun acetate yarns.

STATISTICS AND ECONOMICS

The production of acetate filament yarns in the United States dates back to 1919, according to the Textile Economics Bureau Inc. [2]. The year 1925 marked the transition from experimental to commercial production. Table 1 gives the domestic production figures of acetate filament yarn in pounds and in percentage of the entire filament rayon and acetate production for each year from 1919 through

TABLE 1. ACETATE FILAMENT YARN PRODUCTION *

Year	*United States Production (millions of pounds)*	*Percentage of Total United States Combined Rayon and Acetate Production*
1919	0.1	1.2
1920	0.1	1.0
1925	1.6	3.1
1926	2.6	4.2
1927	5.1	6.8
1928	6.0	6.2
1929	8.4	6.9
1930	9.8	7.7
1931	15.6	10.4
1932	18.3	13.6
1933	41.1	19.3
1934	38.0	18.2
1935	55.5	21.6
1936	62.7	22.6
1937	82.4	25.6
1938	76.1	29.6
1939	97.3	29.6
1940	133.0	34.0
1941	163.7	36.3
1942	168.8	35.2
1943	162.6	32.4
1944	171.7	30.9
1945	174.9	28.0
1946	186.3	27.5
1947	221.5	29.6
1948	293.8	34.3
1949	256.3	32.0
1950	326.6	34.3
1951	300.1	31.3
1952	234.3	28.0

* From *Textile Organon*, February 1953.

1950. Acetate filament yarn production increased yearly for 23 years, reaching 387 million pounds in 1950, which was 34.3 per cent of the total rayon and acetate yarn produced in that year. The use of heavy-denier viscose rayon yarns for military purposes, such as tire cords and parachute shroud lines, has increased the viscose yarn production rapidly since 1941, with a consequent reflection in the percentage figures for acetate production. There are 4 producers of acetate yarns, namely, Celanese Corporation of America, Tennessee Eastman Company, E. I. du Pont de Nemours and Company, and American Viscose

Corporation. The first two mentioned also produce acetate staple fiber. Figures are published for acetate staple fiber production, including tow, and these data are presented in Table 2.

TABLE 2. United States Acetate Staple and Tow Production [3]

Year	*Production (millions of pounds)*
1946	43.7
1947	60.2
1948	83.7
1949	65.3
1950	117.0

Prices. Previous to 1934, prices for acetate filament yarns in the United States were considerably higher than for viscose and cuprammonium, whereas, after 1934, the list prices came down to approximately the same level. The price history of the most common acetate yarns in this country is shown in Table 3, from *Rayon Organon.*

TABLE 3. Price Levels of Acetate Weaving Yarns

	Dollars per Pound			
Dates	*75 denier*	*100 denier*	*150 denier*	*300 denier*
May 1, 1925	3.95	3.85	2.90	2.70
Jan. 1, 1926	3.95	3.85	2.90	2.70
Feb. 1, 1927	3.95	3.85	2.90	2.70
Jan. 1, 1928	3.45	3.35	2.90	2.70
Aug. 10, 1928	2.75	2.60	1.90	2.20
Jan. 15, 1930	2.45	2.20	1.60	1.50
Sept. 9, 1931	1.40	1.30	1.10	1.00
June 24, 1932	1.00	0.95	0.85	0.85
July 20, 1933	1.15	1.10	1.00	1.00
April 17, 1935	0.90	0.77½	0.60	0.60
Oct. 7, 1936	0.80	0.72	0.60	0.60
April 1, 1937	0.83	0.75	0.63	0.63
May 20, 1938	0.75	0.68	0.52	0.52
Sept. 20, 1939	0.80	0.73	0.56	0.56
Dec. 1, 1939	0.78	0.71	0.54	0.54
Nov. 1, 1941	0.80	0.73	0.56	0.56
June 27, 1942	0.80	0.73	0.56	0.56
Dec., 1947	0.98	0.91	0.74	0.70
July, 1950	1.06	0.97	0.76	0.68

As recorded in Table 3, the price of acetate yarns dropped steadily from a high of $2.90 in 1925 (for 150-denier) to a low of 52¢ in 1938. Since then it has increased to 76¢ (July 1950). The price history of

3-denier acetate staple fiber is given in Table 4, which shows a gradual decrease from the introductory price of 80¢ per lb in 1936 to a low of 38¢ per lb in 1944 [4].

TABLE 4. PRICES OF ACETATE STAPLE FIBER (3 DENIER) [4]

Dates	*Price per Pound*
March, 1936	$0.80
July, 1936	0.60
November, 1936	0.54
February, 1937	0.52
January, 1938	0.46
January, 1940	0.43
October, 1944	0.38
January, 1947	0.48
August, 1950	0.42

Dull acetate yarns were introduced in 1932 and at first commanded a price premium. Soon afterward, however, dull and bright acetate yarns were sold at the same price.

Distribution. In 1931 the distribution of acetate filament yarn to the knitting and weaving trades was 41 per cent and 58 per cent, respectively. The weaving percentage increased to 91 per cent in 1940, declined by about 9 per cent in 1946 but returned to 88.5 per cent in 1950. Thus, the major outlet for acetate yarns has always been for weaving. During 1944 acetate yarn had found increased use; in tricot fabrics, it is very successful. The principal uses of acetate filament yarns in woven fabrics have been in satins, sharkskins, taffetas, ninons, for warp in viscose rayon-filled crepes, and twisted with viscose crepe for the warp and filling of "combination" fabrics.

Acetate staple fiber has been spun alone and in blends with other fibers on all systems of spinning. Its principal outlet, however, has been in blends with viscose staple, spun on the cotton system or on new, modern machinery for weaving into sportswear, children's dresses, men's shirts, sports slacks, and shirts. Men's wear, particularly summer suitings, has increasingly employed acetate staple in its fabrication. Some spun acetate yarns have also been knitted for outer wear. Acetate staple is desirable for the cross dyeing, the wrinkle resistance, pleat retention, and the stability to shrinkage or stretching in laundering which it confers on properly finished fabrics.

Denier. The production of acetate filament yarns and their respective filament numbers has not changed as much as that of the viscose yarns. Since 1940 the deniers and filament numbers have remained rather stationary; they are shown in Table 5. The tendency toward

TABLE 5. Acetate Deniers and Filament Numbers Produced in United States

Company	45	55	75	100	120	150	200	300	450	600	900	Qualities
American Viscose Corp.	..	14	20	28	32	41	54	80	..	..	..	Avisco, acetate, Brt & Dull
Celanese Corp. of America	13	13	20–50	26–40	40	40	52	80	120	160	..	Celanese, Brt & Dull
du Pont Co.	..	18–36	24–50	32–66	40–50	40	..	80	..	..	..	Acele, Brt & Dull
Tennessee Eastman Co.	11	13	19–49	25	30	38	50	75	114	152	230	Estron, Brt & Dull

finer filaments is not so prevalent in acetate yarns as in viscose rayon yarns, the finest filament in Table 5 having 1.5 deniers per filament. This is undoubtedly due to the fact that acetate is inherently softer than viscose, hence the need for finer filaments is not so great. The greatest variety of filament sizes exists in 120-, 100-, and 75-denier yarns.

Acetate yarn production figures by denier are shown in Table 6, covering the years 1942 to 1950, inclusive. It can be noted that the 75 and 150 deniers have been consistently popular through the years.

TABLE 6. Acetate Filament Yarn Production by Denier [5]

(Units are Millions of Pounds and Average Denier Thereof)

Denier	1942	1943	1944	1945	1946	1947	1948	1949	1950
55 (62 and less)	13.9	12.5	13.5	13.9	16.4	17.0	22.7	17.3	24.5
75 (63 to 87)	51.6	48.7	52.7	53.5	59.1	70.1	82.8	95.0	104.6
100 (88 to 112)	21.7	20.8	26.1	25.3	24.5	30.3	35.1	29.1	40.2
120 (113 to 137)	20.5	28.7	28.4	34.8	29.4	23.5	25.0	13.4	9.2
150 (138 to 162)	56.5	45.4	44.5	37.4	51.2	65.1	97.9	63.9	104.7
200 (163 to 237)	2.7	4.3	3.6	3.6	1.6	2.5	5.0	4.1	5.9
300 (238 and over)	1.9	2.2	2.9	6.4	4.1	13.0	25.3	32.2	37.5
Totals	168.8	162.6	171.7	174.9	186.3	221.5	293.8	255.0	326.6

Acetate staple fiber is made in a range of lengths to suit the type of machinery on which it is to be spun, and in 3, 5, 8, 12, 16, and 20 deniers.

PROCESS OF MANUFACTURE

Raw Materials

Seven major raw materials are necessary for the manufacture of acetate, namely, purified cellulose from cotton linters or wood pulp, glacial acetic acid, acetic anhydride, sulfuric acid, acetone, titanium dioxide, and water. The recovery of acetic acid, its reconversion into acetic anhydride, and the recovery of acetone are essential to the commercial success of the process.

Purified Cellulose. The purification of cotton linters and wood pulp is discussed in Chapter II.

Glacial Acetic Acid (highly concentrated acetic acid crystallizes partially into icelike flakes) is used as a solvent in the production of cellulose acetate. It is obtained, however, in the course of reclaiming the total dilute acid formed during the process. Its recovery is essential in order to make the acetate process economically possible. One of the earliest sources of acetic acid was the wood distillation industry.

Acetic Anhydride is a highly reactive modification of acetic acid. Synthetic processes starting with acetylene, petroleum gases, or ethyl alcohol, which produce free acetic acid rather than its salts, have stimulated the production of acetate anhydride by new methods. One method of producing it is the direct thermal decomposition of acetic acid. Acetic acid in the presence of a catalyst is vaporized and increased in temperature to a point where ketene and water are formed. The ketene and water are separated, and the ketene is absorbed in acetic acid, forming anhydride. Another method starts with acetone, which is converted by heat to ketene, which is then combined directly with acetic acid to form the anhydride. Specifications for purity which acetic anhydride for acetate manufacture must meet include freedom from iron and other metals, because they affect the whiteness of the cellulose acetate.

Sulfuric Acid. Chemically pure sulfuric acid in relatively small amounts is the normal catalyst for promoting the chemical reaction between the cellulose and the acetic anhydride. Other substances, such as zinc chloride, have been proposed and used as catalysts, but sulfuric acid seems to retain its position as the simplest and most effective.

Acetone. This is a volatile solvent obtainable from wood by destructive distillation or from corn by a fermentation process. At present, however, most of it is made by synthetic methods from the oxidation of isopropyl alcohol, from acetylene, or from petroleum gases. For acetate manufacture, it must be water white and free from turbidity, suspended matter, and dissolved metals. Each shipment is checked by tests for distillation range, moisture content, and specific gravity.

Titanium Dioxide. This substance is used in the manufacture of dull yarns. It is very satisfactory because of its inertness, high refractive index, small particle size, and ease of dispersion. It is used in a very finely divided state (of the order of 1 μ or less in average particle size) and must meet strict specifications, such as freedom from iron and other impurities, chemical neutrality, and uniformity and fineness of particle size.

Water. Water is required in large quantities. It is obtained from natural sources and treated to free it from hardness and impurities. This treatment includes settling to remove coarse suspended matter, aerating to oxidize organic matter and iron, and filtering for final clarification. The treated water must be very low in color and in iron.

The approximate quantities of these raw materials required per pound of acetate yarn (with no recovery) are given in Table 7.

TABLE 7. GROSS CONSUMPTION OF RAW MATERIALS PER POUND OF ACETATE FIBER OR YARN

Raw Materials	*Per Pound of Fiber or Yarn*
Purified cellulose	0.65 lb
Acetic anhydride	1.60 lb
Glacial acetic acid	4.00 lb
Sulfuric acid	0.05 lb
Acetone	3.00 lb
Titanium dioxide	0.02 lb
Water (processing)	10.00 gal

The consumption of chemicals is too great to make the process of manufacturing acetate economically practicable without efficient recovery of the acetone and of the dilute acetic acid formed during the reaction and the reconversion of part of the acid to glacial acetic acid and part to acetic anhydride. The actual net consumption of chemicals per pound of acetate yarn (after recovery) is approximately 0.65 lb of purified cellulose; 0.70 lb of glacial acetic acid; 0.05 lb of sulfuric acid; and 0.30 lb of acetone lost during processing and recovery.

The manufacturing procedure varies in respect to the size of batches, the chemicals used as solvents or diluents, the time, the temperature, et cetera, but the following description of the several steps in the conversion of purified cellulose into acetate gives a general view of the steps and principles involved.

Manufacture of Cellulose Acetate

The cellulose is acetylated in batches in closed mixing tanks equipped with large stirrers. The acetylator is completely jacketed and cooled with a circulating medium capable of temperature control between 35° and 120° F. The blending process begins with the charging of the acetylator. Each batch of cellulose which goes into an acetylator is drawn from ten or twelve bales of cellulose, each bale of which is from a different lot.

An acetylator, holding from 250 to 300 lb per batch, is first charged with the acetylating mixture containing acetic anhydride and glacial acetic acid to which a small amount of concentrated sulfuric acid is added. To this mixture, which has been cooled to 45° F., the linters or pulp (which usually have been activated by a pretreatment such as soaking in acetic acid or some other chemical) are added gradually, with constant mixing. The temperature is held below 68° F. for the first hour and thereafter under 86° F. for the remainder of the time required to complete the acetylation. Five to eight hours are needed to allow the reaction to progress until a clear solution of the required viscosity is secured. The critical factors in the production of a uniform product are correct time, temperature, and amount of catalyst.

In general, yarn esters have to be high enough in viscosity or chain length to give the necessary tensile strength to the yarn. There is a slight correlation between viscosity, or chain length, and tensile strength—high viscosity giving high strength.

The viscosity of acetone solutions is correlated with the viscosity of the acetylation mixture (which can be controlled). The chain length of the starting cellulose is considerably greater than the chain length of the end product because degradation occurs during the acetylation reaction. Control of the reaction is directed toward the attainment of the desired chain length, or inherent acetone viscosity, in the finished product by measurement of the viscosity of the acetylation mixture and, subsequently, by the viscosity in acetone.

When acetylation has been completed, the fibrous structure of the linters has disappeared, and the charge, as it flows from the acetylator, is a viscous, semi-transparent, and acrid-smelling fluid. Cellulose is capable of combining with three molecules of acetic acid to form cellulose triacetate. This can be precipitated from the acetylated mixture by dilution with water and then washed free of acid. It is unsuitable for the manufacture of acetate yarn, *first,* because it is soluble only in solvents which are impracticable from an industrial standpoint, and, *second,* because it is too impervious to moisture and to dyes to permit practical finishing and dyeing.

The practical range of acetyl content for acetate manufacture is quite narrow. Cellulose acetate yarn must meet the following criteria:

1. It must be soluble in acetone.
2. It must be sufficiently water-sensitive to swell slightly in the dye bath, permitting the fiber to imbibe dye.
3. It must be sufficiently high in acetyl content to have stability, or resistance, to boiling water.
4. It must be sufficiently high in acetyl content so that the hydroxyl groups will not function when exposed to cotton dyes.

Hydrolysis of Triacetate. In order to obtain the desired acetyl content, the finished batch from the acetylator is run into a container in which it is diluted with acetic acid and water, and allowed to stand for 10 to 20 hr at an elevated temperature. During this time, the water present in the diluted mixture gradually reacts with the triacetate, reducing its acetyl content with the consequent liberation of acetic acid. Periodically, samples are taken and tested. When an acetate of the desired composition is obtained, the hydrolysis is arrested by precipitation into water in the form of finely divided, chalky-white flakes. The object of this hydrolysis is to produce a cellulose acetate that will meet the criteria previously enumerated. It results in an acetyl content which is about halfway between the triacetate and the diacetate. This is commonly designated as the "secondary" acetate.

The secondary acetate is run into large washing vats in which the flakes are allowed to settle without stirring. The clear waste liquor containing dilute acetic acid is drawn off and piped to the acid recovery plant. The cellulose acetate is then washed free of uncombined acid by stirring the flakes in a vat full of fresh water, stopping the stirrer, waiting for the acetate to settle to the bottom of the vat, drawing off the clear liquid above it, refilling with pure water, and again agitating thoroughly.

Finally, the suspension of acetate flakes in water is run into a centrifuge, from which the flakes are fed to a drier. The dry flakes are conveyed to storage bins for packaging into shipping containers. In this form the cellulose acetate is delivered to the yarn department, and each package of acetate carries the number of the acetylating batch of which it was a part. Each batch is analyzed for acetyl content, viscosity of a standard solution in acetone, and ash.

Spinning Acetate Yarn

Preparation of Spinning Solution. To convert the cellulose acetate into yarn, a solution is prepared which can be forced through fine holes into a coagulating medium. The best solvent for yarn-type cellulose acetate is acetone containing a small amount of water. The high volatility and flammability of acetone vapor necessitates that all operations in the preparation and spinning of acetate yarn be carried out in closed containers. The volatility of acetone has the great advantage of permitting the use of the *dry-spinning* process.

The spinning solution is prepared in a heavy, closed mixing vessel. It is charged with acetone, and flake cellulose acetate is added gradually, with the mixing blades constantly rotating. For one batch of spinning solution, an equal number of packages of flake acetate are drawn from ten to twelve different batches of acetate in order to blend the material more thoroughly. The cellulose acetate content of the spinning solution may vary from 15 to 30 per cent, being constant for a given type of yarn. The mixing is continued until the solution is clear and homogeneous, which requires 12 to 24 hr. Samples of the solution are taken periodically and tested for freedom from undissolved fibers, viscosity, and acetate content, until solution is complete.

For dull-luster yarns the spinning solution contains a small amount of white pigment (usually less than 2 per cent of the weight of cellulose acetate) which is added to the charge in the mixer. The titanium dioxide, the pigment generally used, is thus dispersed uniformly and renders the solution opaque and white instead of clear and glassy, like the spinning solution for bright-luster yarns.

Colored filaments and fibers (called "solution-dyed") can be made by incorporating suitable dyes or pigments in the spinning solution during the dissolving or blending processes. Although any shade can thus be produced, the differences in hue demanded by customers, the varieties of colors required by changing fashions, and the great number of colors that would be required for a complete range of shades in many lines of textiles make the inventory problem very difficult for the yarn producer. The principal exception is black, for which there is a steady demand. Solution-dyed filament and staple acetate possess excellent fastness to light, perspiration, washing, wet and dry crocking, atmospheric fumes, and commercial cleaning fluids.

The charge from the mixer is run into a large blending tank, accommodating several batches. The blender is kept full of spinning solution by drawing off just enough blended solution to make room for each new batch from the mixer. The spinning solution is, therefore, a homogeneous blend, not only of the number of batches which the blending tank will hold at one time, but of a far greater number, because each batch becomes thoroughly distributed through the batches which follow it as well as through those that have preceded it into the blender.

From this blending tank, the spinning solution, or "dope," is filtered several times, deaerated, and then run into the feed tank of the spinning machines.

Spinning. Cellulose acetate solutions are converted into filaments by dry spinning into warm air. Spinning machines have 25 to 50 spinnerets and spindles on each side. Each unit consists of a pump and spinneret at the top of a tall shaft about 6 in. in diameter and from 9 to 15 ft high. This shaft is provided with ducts near the bottom for the intake of warm air and, also, near the top for the disposal of the air containing acetone vapor. The winding device is outside the shaft, at the bottom.

The spinning solution is forced under pressure from the storage tank to the spinning pump, which produces the desired spinning pressure and acts as a precise metering pump for delivering the "dope" at a uniform rate to the spinneret.

The spinneret is a round jet, made of suitable metal, containing a number of small holes. These holes, about 0.003 in. in diameter, may be arranged in one or more concentric circles. The number of holes is determined by the number of filaments desired in the acetate yarn. The fineness of the filaments is determined partly by the diameter of the holes but primarily by the relation between the rate at which the solution is forced through the spinneret and the rate at which the coagulated filaments are withdrawn from the spinning cabinet. (See Fig. 1.)

The fine streams of spinning solution, issuing from the spinneret, meet the warm air rising through the shaft. The air temperature is higher than the boiling point of acetone (134° F.). Temperature, moisture content, and velocity of air are so regulated that the evaporation of the acetone and, hence, the coagulation of the filaments are completed and the filaments become dry before they reach the bottom of the shaft. At this point they are collected and guided out of the shaft to the winder. As they leave the shaft they are lubricated with a suitable emulsifiable oil to reduce static and friction during subsequent processing.

The filaments that come from the spinning machine are a finished product from the chemical standpoint. They are then twisted and packaged as continuous filament acetate for weaving and knitting mills. The dry-spinning operation permits a very effective control of the uniformity of physical and chemical characteristics of both continuous-filament yarn and staple fiber; it also favors freedom from tangling and breakage of filaments.

The number of filaments in the final yarn from every spindle is checked periodically by actual count. The denier is tested as the yarn

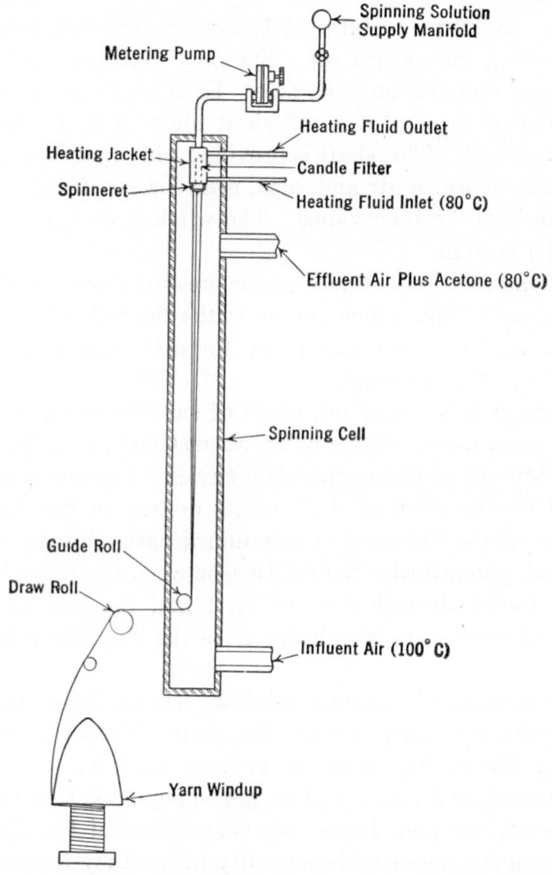

FIG. 1. Diagrammatic view, showing basic principle of dry spinning of acetate.

is delivered from the spinning room, and, in addition, the control laboratory makes independent denier tests daily. Other tests include twist, moisture content, strength, elongation, dye absorption, lubricant content, visual appearance, and density of the packages ready for shipment.

Finishing Operations for Continuous-Filament Yarns. Yarn from the spinning room is twisted by the usual methods employed in the textile trade, i.e., up-twisters or down-twisters. The full twisting bobbins are sent to the packaging department, where the yarn is wound on cones, spools, or cops, or into skeins, according to requirements. For certain purposes, particularly hosiery knitting and throwing, the yarn is tinted with fugitive tint to distinguish it from other lots or kinds of yarn. The textile departments are air-conditioned to a definite atmosphere, usually 75° F. and 60 per cent R.H. The bobbins are so designed that the yarn is drawn off "over end." This prevents the strain on the yarn that would be caused by an unrolling bobbin and permits proper tension control in twisting, coning, spooling, and copping. A continuous check on winding tensions is made by periodically testing the tension and the density of the packages from each spooling, coning, or copping spindle. Each package is now subjected to an examination for wind, broken filaments, evenness of tint, and condition, before it is carefully wrapped and packed in shipping cases.

Staple Fiber Production. For some years the production of acetate was confined to the making of continuous-filament yarns, but, inevitably, the producers began to explore its possibilities as a staple fiber. Natural fibers, like cotton and wool, are graded for several characteristics, including fineness, degree of cleanliness, and staple length. Acetate fiber can be made with the desired diameter (fineness), staple length, and crimp, permitting it to function on the textile systems originally designed for the natural or man-made fibers.

The chemistry and mechanics of producing both continuous-filament yarn and staple are identical or similar up to and including the process known as spinning. In the manufacture of staple fiber, the filaments, after having been withdrawn from the spinning cabinet by the Godet roll, pass to a cutting operation. At this point the common ancestry of continuous-filament and staple ends.

The cut fiber, as it emerges from the cutting unit, is not ready for shipment to the mills until it has been subjected to a series of opening, crimping, lubricating, and drying operations.

After opening, it is necessary to crimp and lubricate the staple in such a manner that it is suitable for the various textile systems such as cotton, woolen, and worsted. All fibers require the use of a lubricant for successful conversion into yarns. The lubricant serves two purposes: (1) it acts as an antistatic agent; and (2) it eases the strain on the fibers in drawing and spinning, thus allowing uniform drafting, reducing fiber breakage and contributing to the production of a level or even spun-acetate yarn. The lubricated fiber is then dried or conditioned and baled. After baling or other packaging as required for the trade, it is ready for shipment.

Yarn and Fiber Varieties

In addition to the varieties of acetate already discussed, there are several other types which are either in commercial production or of interest experimentally.

Abraded Yarn is filament acetate which has been subjected to abrasion during winding or twisting. The abrasion, or cutting of the filaments, is controlled in such a way that, although a good part of the strength of continuous filament yarn is retained, there are sufficient fiber ends to give the yarn some of the characteristics of spun yarn made from staple fiber.

Plasticized Acetate Staple Fiber is a type that is rapidly increasing in commercial importance for blending with other textile fibers, both natural and manufactured. It is used to form a batt, or mass, which can then be converted into a felted sheet by subjecting the batt to heat and pressure under controlled conditions that cause the plasticized fibers to soften and bond to one another and to other fibers. By varying such factors as the amount of plasticized acetate staple in the mixture, the weight of the batt, and the pressure, temperature, and time of the bonding treatment, a wide variety of feltlike materials, ranging from thin, papery textures to soft, porous felts, can be produced. The use of plasticized acetate staple fibers in the making of thin, bonded materials has been discussed by Bendigo [6].

Acetate Tow. The development of several different machines for converting a heavy strand of continuous filaments, known as tow, directly into a sliver, or top, which can then be drafted and spun into yarn, has resulted in a demand for acetate tow. This can be produced in any desired filament fineness and in a total denier per end of tow which varies from one manufacturer to another, depending upon spinning-machine details. The tow is made without twist but with a crimp, which helps the fibers to cling together to form a coherent strand, and the denier per end of tow ranges, in general, from 25,000 denier upward.

Flat Filament Acetate Yarn. Experimental quantities of a flat-filament yarn have been made as monofils of about 200 denier per filament. Filaments of approximately 20 denier fineness have also been made—for example, 100 denier 5 filament and 150 denier 7 filament. This yarn combines the sheen of a flat monofil with some of the suppleness of a multifilament yarn for use where novelty glistening effects are desired.

Metallic Yarn. In the field of tinsel and lamé yarns, where metallic effects are desired, a new type of metallic yarn has been made experimentally and is now in commercial production. It is composed of two layers of cellulose acetate-butyrate foil secured to a layer of aluminum foil by a transparent white or colored adhesive. The foils are combined in wide rolls, and the "sandwich" thus formed is slit into yarns of the desired width—for example, 1/64 in. wide. This ribbon-shape monofil has a thickness of approximately 0.003 in. Its fineness is approximately 450 denier, which corresponds to 10,000 yd per lb. This product can, of course, be made in any wider widths, also. It can be furnished in silver and in gold colors, and the silver can be dyed to any color with acetate dyes. When used alone, or wrapped in a spiral around a core yarn, it can be woven into metallic-type fabrics. This yarn does not tarnish, even after long exposure. It will withstand wet processing when used to decorate fabrics that are to be scoured and piece-dyed, and it will withstand dry cleaning and mild washing.

High-Impact (High-Elongation) Acetate Yarn. See section on Mechanical Properties, below.

Other Cellulose Derivative Fibers. Extensive experimentation with many cellulose derivatives other than cellulose acetate has, thus far, failed to produce any other cellulose derivative fiber as versatile for general textile purposes as cellulose acetate.

With respect to the cellulose esters, the plasticity of the ester increases with increasing molecular weight of the acyl group, and cellulose acetate has, therefore, remained the best ester for general textile use.

Ethyl cellulose has been spun into fibers under the trade name Ethofil.

MICROSCOPIC CHARACTERISTICS

Appearance. Under the microscope, cross-sections of regular commercial cellulose acetate filaments or fibers are revealed as having two, three, four, or occasionally more, smoothly rounded lobes which are readily distinguishable from the serrated edges of cross-sections of the usual viscose rayons. In lateral view, the fiber surface is smooth and the lobes are visible as gently rounded longitudinal ridges and valleys. (See Fig. 2.)

Bright-luster acetate is clear and transparent, as is evident from Fig. 2. In dull-luster fibers, Fig. 3, the pigment particles can be seen as tiny specks, distributed throughout the fiber substance. The dimensions of the pigment particles are so small in comparison to the width of the fibers that even those particles that lie in or near the fiber surface do not appreciably affect the smooth contours of the surface. The general shape of the acetate cross-section is much the same for fine or coarse fibers, as is seen by comparing the 3-denier-per-filament and 20-denier-per-filament fibers in Fig. 4.

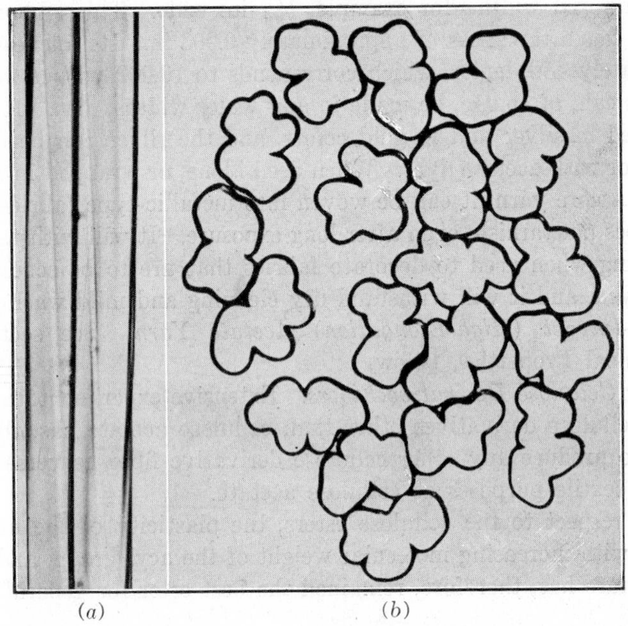

(*a*) (*b*)

FIG. 2. Bright luster acetate. (*a*) Longitudinal view, (*b*) cross-sections, ×500.

Solution dyed fibers in black or in colors are usually indistinguishable microscopically from fibers dyed by the regular stock, yarn, or piece-dyeing methods, because the dyes and pigment particles used to color the dope before extrusion either are soluble in cellulose acetate or are so finely dispersed that they are not readily resolved by the microscope.

When a filament of acetate is examined by polarized light, a longitudinal view shows only dark, first-order gray polarization colors, which may be almost invisible. However, when a "first-order red" plate is inserted between the crossed nicols, the fibers appear purple and orange against a red field [7].

A cross-section illuminated with plane-polarized light will appear light in some places and dark in others, as shown in Fig. 5. When the plane of polarization is rotated 90 degrees, the dark places become

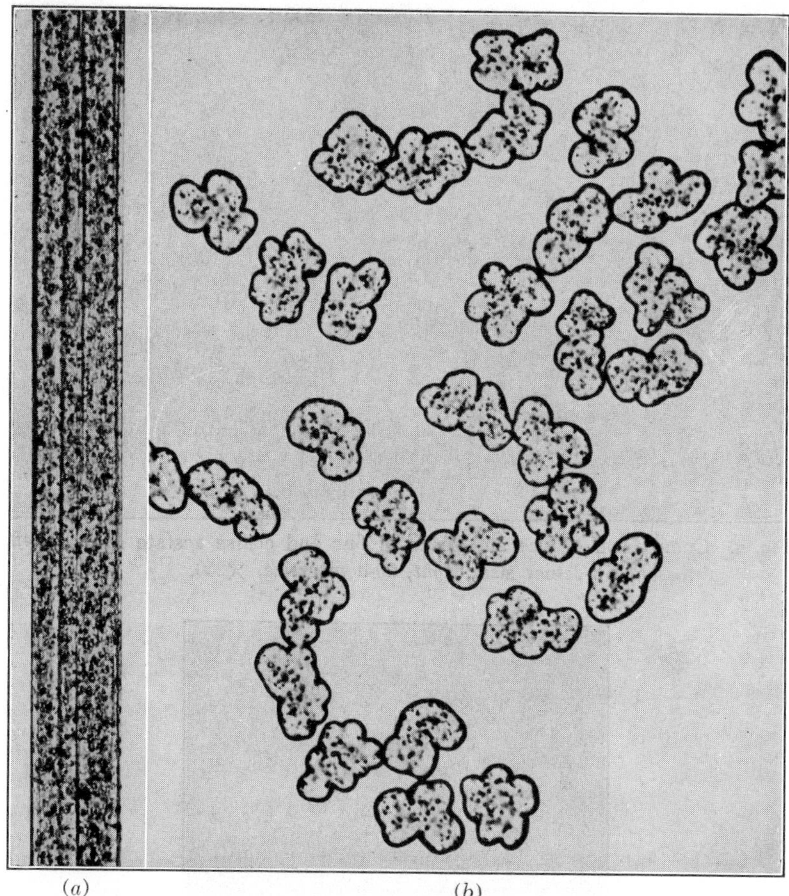

FIG. 3. Dull-luster acetate. (*a*) Longitudinal view; (*b*) cross-sections, ×500.

light and the light places become dark [8]. This phenomenon is due to the fact that the micelles in the fiber appear dark when they are at right angles to the axis of the fiber and lie in the plane of vibration of the light.

Refractive Indices. From Table 8, which lists some published measurements of refractive indices of acetate fibers, it appears that the specific index of birefringence (specific double refraction) for ordinary

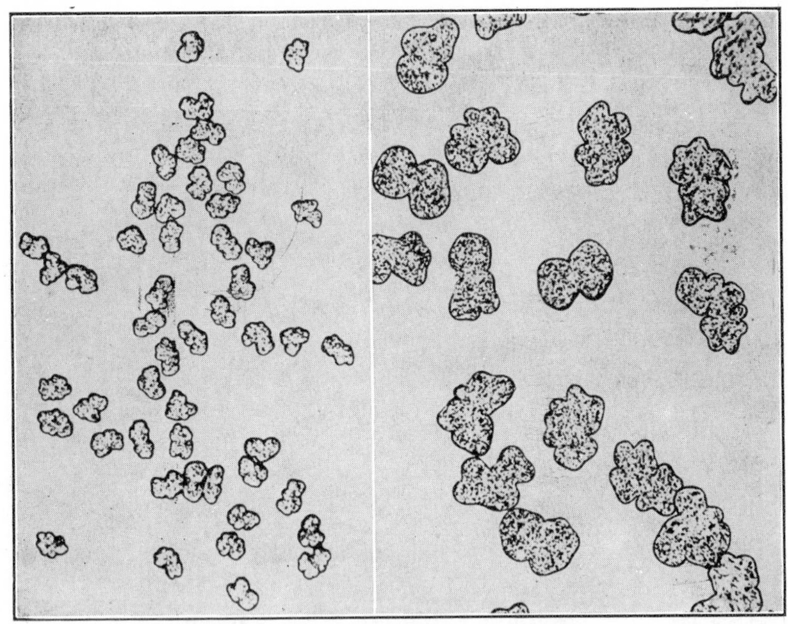

FIG. 4. Comparison of size and shape of fine and coarse acetate fibers. *Left,* 3-denier size; *right,* 20-denier size, ×250.

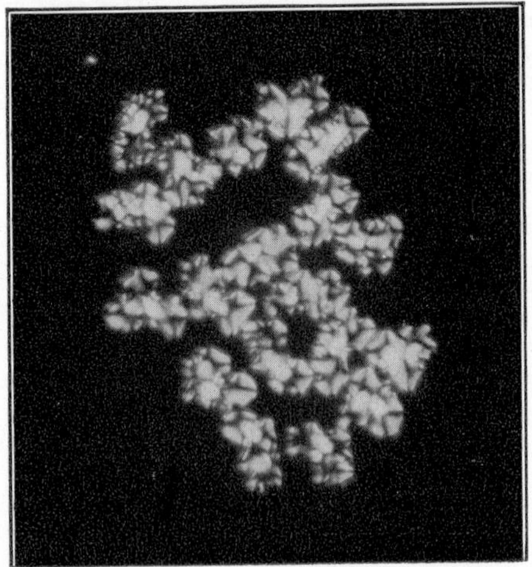

FIG. 5. Acetate cross-sections viewed in polarized light, ×300.

TABLE 8. Refractive Indices of Acetate

Refractive Indices				
Max. N_2	Min. N_1	Specific Index $(N_2 - N_1)$	Observer	Year
1.48	1.475	0.005	Chamot	1930
1.476	1.470	0.006	English worker	....
1.4794	1.4732	0.0059	Schwarz	1934
1.4794	1.4732	0.0059	Schwarz	1935
1.478	1.473	0.005	Schwarz	1940

acetate lies between 0.005 and 0.006. To obtain accurate results, monochromatic light must be used. Values as low as 0.004 are obtained with white light. According to the table of refractive indices of eight common textile fibers [9] published by A.S.T.M. Committee D-13, this value is the lowest of all birefringent fibers. The nearest is wool, whose specific index is about twice that of acetate. Vinyon and glass, however, show no birefringence.

Identification. Acetate of the usual type can usually be identified readily by microscopic examination because of the characteristic shape of the cross-sections. Confirmatory tests include solubility in acetone (if vinyl fibers such as Vinyon are present, use glacial acetic acid at room temperature, which dissolves acetate but does not dissolve vinyl fibers). Selected acetate dyes which have little or no affinity for cotton, viscose, wool, and silk can also be used for identifying acetate by staining. Such dyes will stain nylon, which, however, because of its circular cross-sections, is readily distinguishable from acetate under the microscope.

Identification of fibers by microscopy is discussed and illustrated by von Bergen and Krauss [10]. Confirmatory tests by other methods are often desired. A scheme of identification by simple burning, solubility, and chemical tests has been tabulated by Skinkle [11]. See also Chapter XX.

Solubility and staining reactions are, of course, affected by partial or complete saponification of acetate, which is sometimes effected in finishing and dyeing operations as well as in the manufacture of high-strength saponified acetate yarns. Although the overall degree of saponification can be studied by comparing the color of a sample of acetate fiber, yarn, or fabric, after dyeing with a selected direct dye, such as Cotton Blue FF, with the color of a series of similarly dyed standards of known degree of saponification, a study of fiber cross-sections under the microscope is essential if it is desired to know how and where the acetate fibers have been affected.

If the specimen is undyed, it may be dyed either before or after sectioning on the Hardy microtome but before mounting on the slide. The dye chosen should be either a viscose dye which does not stain cellulose acetate or an acetate dye which does not stain viscose but, in either event, one that will dye readily to a deep shade. A viscose dye is generally used. Examination of sections prepared in this way will reveal whether the fibers are saponified and, if so, whether the saponification has occurred uniformly throughout the fiber mass or is confined to the surface layers of the fiber without affecting the core. Controlled saponification is used by some dyers and finishers to get certain effects. The results obtained for a given degree of saponification vary greatly according to the distribution of the saponified part within the fiber substance.

PHYSICAL PROPERTIES AND CHARACTERISTICS

Acetate is produced chiefly in two forms: continuous-filament yarns, whose straight, endless filaments lie parallel and packed closely together by a few turns per inch of twist to form a smooth, sleek yarn; and staple fibers, whose appearance when pulled from a bale is that of a fluffy, matted tuft or mass of crinkly fibers.

The fiber substance of both filament acetate and staple acetate from any one producer is at present identical or, at least, very similar; hence the chemical properties of both types are similar so far as they depend only on the fiber substance. Differences in behavior during processing into yarns and fabrics and differences in texture and in physical properties of filament acetate fabrics and spun acetate fabrics are, therefore, due to the differences in fiber form and yarn structure rather than to differences in composition and internal structure between filament and fiber.

Length

Acetate Filament Yarns. Acetate issues continuously in an unbroken strand of endless filaments from each cabinet of a spinning (extruding) machine. The length of the unbroken filaments, therefore, depends only on the capacity of the winding mechanism on which the yarn is collected. Inasmuch as the take-up bobbins on modern acetate machines hold several pounds of yarn, the 3- and 4-lb cones on which the bulk of the filament acetate is shipped have an average of only one or two knots per cone.

Acetate Staple Fiber. The continuous strands of acetate filaments which issue from the spinning machines are cut to any desired length, depending upon the type of textile machinery on which the staple is to be spun into yarn. Common commercial lengths are 1½, 2, 2½, and 3 in. for use on cotton spinning machinery; 3, 3½, 4, 4½, and 5 in. for use on woolen and on worsted spinning machinery; and 5, 6, and 7 in. for use on schappe or spun silk spinning machinery.

Inasmuch as the cutting is done with great precision, the staple length of acetate staple is very uniform. Acetate staple is far cleaner and has greater uniformity of length than natural fibers, thus eliminating the necessity for much of the processing to which natural fibers are subjected to remove short fibers and trash. There is some difference of opinion as to whether, in processing on worsted-type machinery, a uniform fiber length or an assortment of lengths within certain limits gives the better results in processing and in yarn quality. The length distribution of acetate staple can be adjusted as desired by blending fibers of different lengths after cutting.

Fineness

The fineness of individual fibers of commercial acetate ranges from 1.5 to 4.1 denier for filament yarns and from 1.5 to 20 denier for staple fibers.

Filament Yarns. The fineness of commercial acetate filament yarns ranges from 45 to 600 denier.

Filament yarns are usually designated by yarn denier, number of filaments, and twist per inch. Thus 55/20/3*S* designates a 55-denier yarn composed of 20 filaments with 3 turns per inch *S* twist. Similarly, 150/54/2*Z* designates a 150-denier yarn composed of 54 filaments with 2 turns per inch *Z* twist.

Except for a few duplications, each acetate manufacturer has selected a different number of filaments for a given yarn denier in order to provide a ready means of identifying the different brands of yarn in fabrics. This is illustrated in Table 9, which lists the deniers and filament counts offered commercially at the present time by the four producers of acetate filament [12]. For example, Eastman (Estron) makes 75/19 and 75/49; du Pont makes 75/24 and 75/50; whereas both Celanese and American Viscose (Avisco) make 75/20. The figures in parentheses in Table 9 give the filament fineness (in denier) for each yarn. The filament fineness ranges from 1.5 to 4.10 denier per filament.

TABLE 9. Commercial Sizes of Continuous-Filament Acetate Yarns [12]

(As of September 1951, with number of filaments per yarn and consequent fiber fineness.)

	Yarn Denier															
	45		55		75		100		120		150		200		300	
	Fil. Count	*Fil. Denier*	*Fil. Count*	*Fil. Denier*	*Fil. Count*	*Fil. Denier*	*Fil. Count*	*Fil. Denier*	*Fil. Count*	*Fil. Denier*	*Fil. Count*	*Fil. Denier*	*Fil. Count*	*Fil. Denier*	*Fil. Count*	*Fil. Denier*
American Viscose Corp. (Acetate Div.)	14	(3.22)	14	(3.93)	20	(3.75)	28	(3.57)	32 36	(3.75) (3.33)	41	(3.66)	60	(3.33)	80	(3.75)
Celanese Corp. of America	13	(3.46)	15	(3.67)	20 50	(3.75) (1.50)	26 40	(3.85) (2.50)	40	(3.00)	40	(3.75)	52	(3.85)	80	(3.75)
E. I. du Pont de Nemours & Co.			18	(3.05)	24 50	(3.13) (1.50)	32 40 50	(3.13) (2.50) (1.50)	40	(3.00)	40	(3.75)	64	(3.13)	80	(3.75)
Tennessee Eastman Co.	11	(4.10)	13	(4.23)	19 49	(3.95) (1.53)	25	(4.00)	30	(4.00)	38	(3.95)	50	(4.00)	75	(4.00)

Staple Fiber. Table 10 lists the denier sizes in which acetate staple is commercially available.

TABLE 10. Commercial Sizes of Acetate Staple Fiber [13]

(as of October 1951)

Producer	*Brand Name*	*Fineness—Denier per Filament*
Celanese Corp. of America	Celanese	All deniers
Tennessee Eastman Co.	Estron staple	3, 5, 8, 12, 16, 20

In yarn mills which operate on the cotton-spinning system or on the newer types of spinning machinery, the bulk of the acetate staple used is 3 denier for counts up to 30's cotton count, where soft, fine textures are desired. Five denier is used for yarns up to 20's cotton

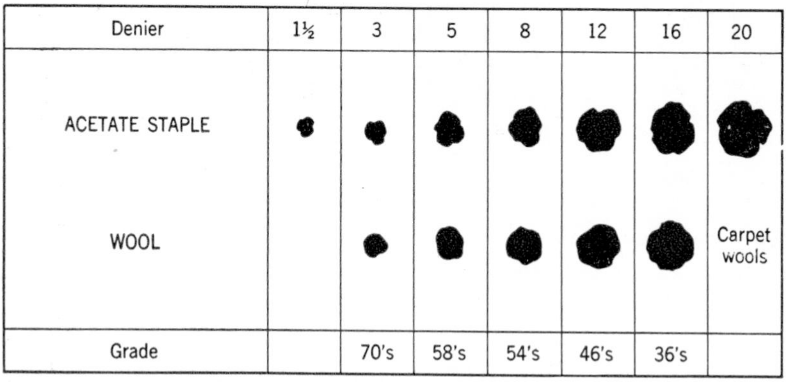

Denier	1½	3	5	8	12	16	20
ACETATE STAPLE	●	●	●	●	●	●	●
WOOL		●	●	●	●	●	Carpet wools
Grade		70's	58's	54's	46's	36's	

Fig. 6. Comparative fineness of acetate staple fiber and wool. (Sketched at ×250.)

count for fabrics in which a firmer body and more crispness are desired. For yarns made on the worsted system, 5 denier is most common, although some 3 denier and some 8 denier have been employed. Acetate staple fibers of 8 denier and coarser are used chiefly in blankets and in carpets, although 12 denier has been blended with finer viscose or acetate staple in summer dress and suiting fabrics. Blends of different deniers have been explored, and it is believed that skillful blending of acetate fibers of two or more sizes will find increasing favor as a means of creating texture, hand, and drape in apparel and household fabrics.

In Fig. 6 the average fineness of the several commercial qualities of wool and of the several commercial sizes of acetate staple is compared by diagrammatic representation of their cross-sections drawn to the same scale.

The fineness distribution of acetate staple is much more uniform than that of either cotton or wool, as shown in Fig. 7.

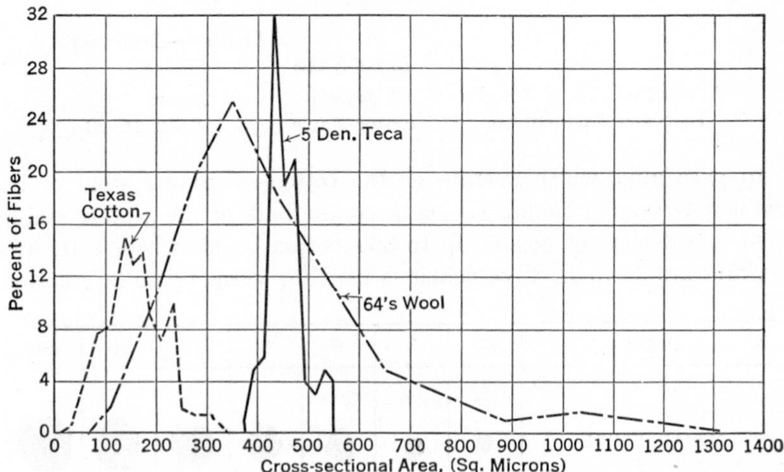

FIG. 7. Per cent fineness distribution of acetate, cotton, and wool fibers.

Appearance and Color

Acetate is made in bright and in dull luster. Intermediate degrees of luster can be made, if desired. Maximum luster is obtained with bright filament yarns of little twist. Dull filament yarns give a chalky appearance to the fabrics. Spun yarns made of bright acetate staple are not as lustrous as bright filament yarns because the fiber crimp and the more irregular orientation of the fibers in the yarn break up the light reflection.

Most acetate staple fibers are crimped during manufacture to produce a wavy or crinkled fiber. This crimp is of primary importance in improving the drafting and spinning qualities of the staple, and it contributes also to the loftiness of the spun yarns.

Acetate fibers and filaments are very white, and the whiteness gives the dyer a free hand in the production of clean, pure colors, ranging from the palest tints to heavy shades.

Density

The published values for density of acetate range from 1.25 to 1.33 grams per cc. The differences are undoubtedly due in part to the methods of measurement, in part to differences in moisture content of the sample at the time the test is made, and in part to actual differences in the specific gravity of specimens of different origin and, therefore, of different composition. For general use in computations involving the density, or specific gravity, of the various textile fibers, the value of 1.32, as determined in helium gas [14], which is also the calculated density of cellulose acetate containing 38.5 per cent acetyl content [15], is recommended.

Sorption and Swelling Behavior

In Water Vapor and Water. The hygroscopicity, or sorptive power, of cellulose acetate is qualitatively similar to that of cellulose itself, but the quantity of moisture absorbed at any given relative humidity is much less because of the fact that part of the water-attracting hydroxyl groups of the cellulose have been replaced by non-attracting acetyl groups. In common with all hygroscopic fibers, cellulose acetate exhibits hysteresis in moisture absorption; that is, the equilibrium moisture content of the fibers at any given relative humidity is less if equilibrium is approached from a lower relative humidity than it is if approached from a higher relative humidity.

Moisture content of textile fibers is almost always expressed as moisture regain, which is defined as the amount of moisture present in the fiber, expressed as a percentage of the dry weight. For this purpose, the dry weight is determined by heating the material to constant weight in an oven at 105° C.

Figures 8 show the sorption curves, or moisture isotherms, as they are sometimes called, for a typical cellulose acetate. The exact location of these curves may vary slightly from one brand to another because regain is dependent on acetyl content. The adsorption curve (*a*) gives the relation between equilibrium moisture regain at all relative humidities from 0 to 100 per cent when equilibrium is approached from the drier side. The desorption curve (*b*) gives the relation between equilibrium moisture regain and R.H. when approached from the moister side. It will be seen, for example, that, at 70° F. and 65 per cent R.H., the equilibrium regain may be any value between 5.4 and 7.1 per cent. The mean value between absorption and desorption is usually cited as the regain, in this case 6.3 per cent.

The standard moisture regain for acetate as specified in A.S.T.M. Standard D-258-50T is 6.5 per cent. This is the commonly accepted basis for the sale and purchase of yarn and staple fiber. Although the apparent net weight of yarn or fiber in a case or bale depends upon the actual moisture regain and the amount of oil or finish present at the time of weighing, the invoiced net weight on the producer's invoice is the weight of the dry, clean fiber plus 6.5 per cent (standard moisture

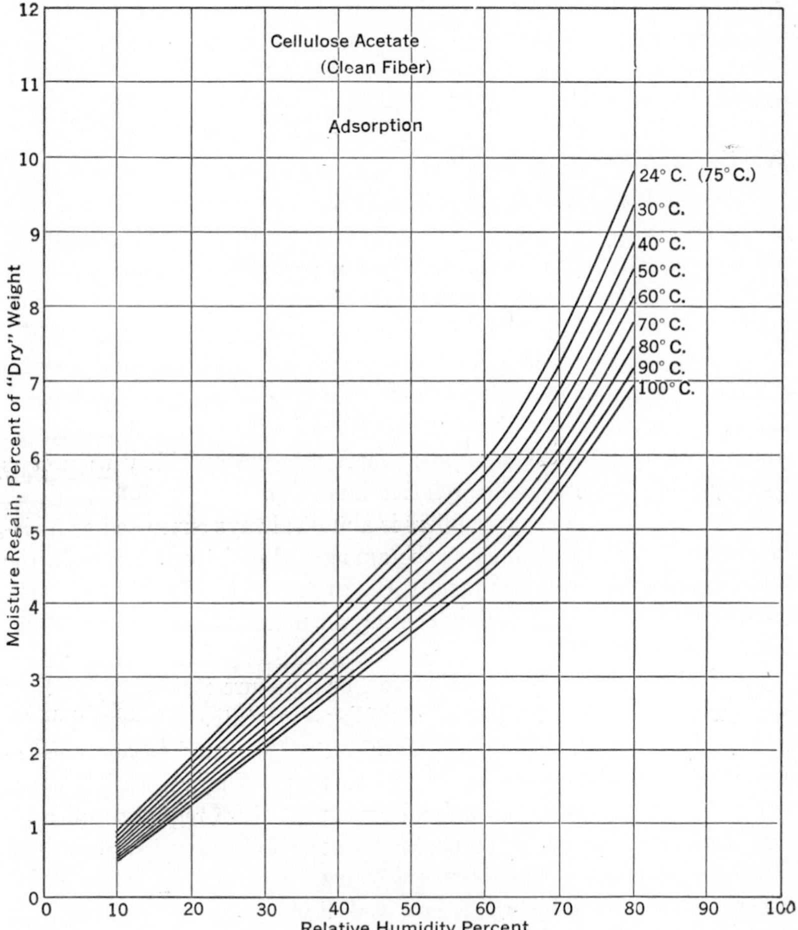

FIG. 8(*a*). Adsorption curves for typical acetates at several temperatures. (*Courtesy American Viscose Corp.*)

regain). It will be noted that all oil or finish on the yarn is thereby included in the tare weight.

The equilibrium moisture regain at 100 per cent R.H. represents the maximum absorptive capacity for the fiber substance for water at the given temperature and may be considered equal to the amount of water retained *within* the fiber substance after immersion in water at this temperature and subsequent removal of *all* extraneous water held

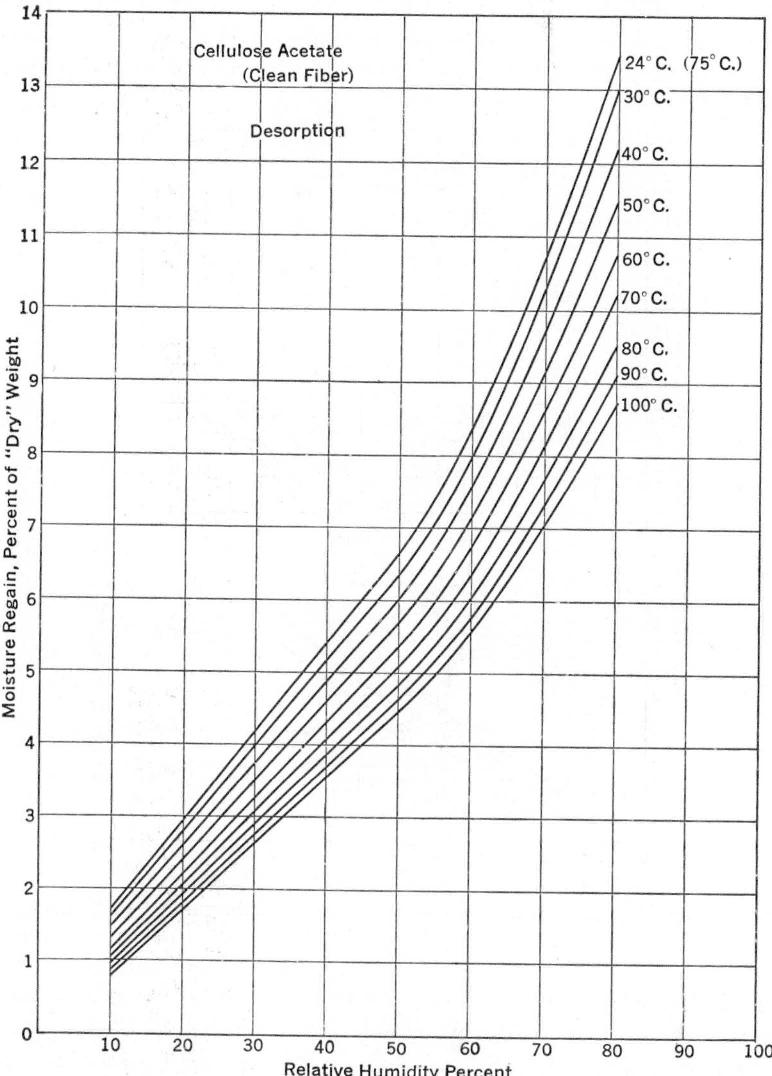

FIG. 8(*b*). Desorption curves for typical acetates at several temperatures. (*Courtesy American Viscose Corp.*)

between the fibers by capillary attraction. It is not easily determined by direct experiment because of difficulties due to condensation at such high humidity.

At any given relative humidity, the moisture regain of acetate (like that of all hygroscopic fibers) decreases with increasing temperature. This is clearly shown in Fig. 9, which gives the relation between relative humidity and moisture regain of cellulose acetate at several temperatures ranging from 96° to 302° F., as determined by Wiegerink [16].

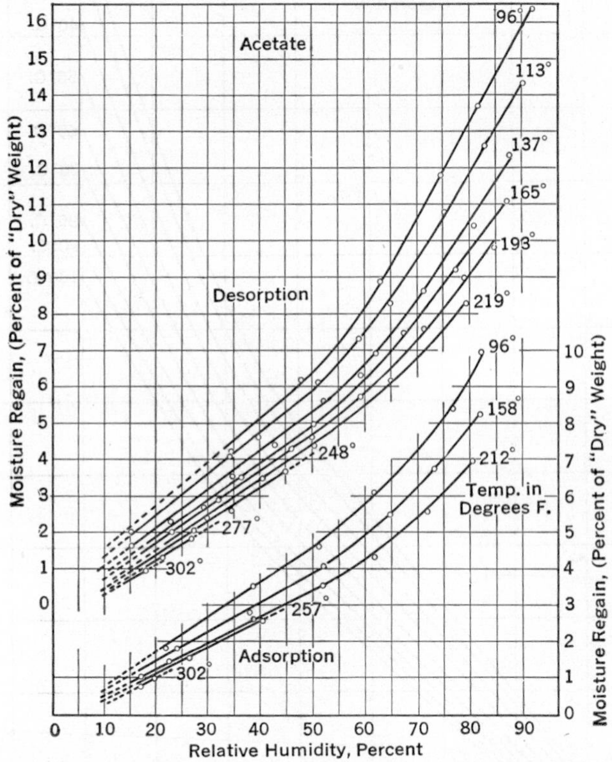

FIG. 9. Equilibrium moisture regain of cellulose acetate yarn at different R.H. and temperatures.

Cellulose acetate in any form—loose fibers and yarns, compressed masses of fibers in bales and closely wound packages of yarns, or fabrics of varying weights and textures—attain the moisture regain indicated in Figs. 8 and 9 if allowed to come to equilibrium in an atmosphere of constant temperature and R.H. The rate of absorption or desorption and, therefore, the time required to reach equilibrium depend on the density of packing of the fibers and the dimensions of the fiber mass, that is, upon the bulk density and the exposed surface per unit volume, and also on the velocity of the air surrounding the material. This statement is, of course, equally true for all hygroscopic fibers.

For a single fiber or a loosely twisted group of fibers, such as a single end of filament yarn or of a soft spun yarn, where the surface exposed to the atmosphere is large in proportion to the mass of fiber substance, the pick-up or loss of moisture with changes in moisture content of the surrounding air is extremely rapid, the major part of the absorption or desorption occurring within a few seconds or a few minutes. Cassie [17] points out that, because of the very large surface-volume ratio of textile fibers, the time required for a single fiber to come within 80 per cent of its final water content, when a change in water-vapor concentration occurs at its surface, is less than 0.1 sec, provided that complications due to heat of sorption are neglected. A 3-lb cone, on the other hand, will pick up or lose moisture slowly and will require hours to reach equilibrium with the surrounding atmosphere, whereas a bale of fibers, even with the wrappings removed, will take days. Absorption or desorption by the fiber substance at the surface is rapid, but diffusion of adsorbed moisture through the interior of a mass of fibers is much slower.

Because of the importance of moisture content in processing, in testing, and in the determination of commercial weights in buying and selling, these considerations with respect to equilibrium regain and rate of pick-up or of loss of moisture are of importance in the handling of all hygroscopic textile fibers, including acetate.

The absorption of moisture by textile fibers is always accompanied by swelling of the fiber substance. Longitudinal swelling is relatively unimportant, being of the order of 1 or 2 per cent for most textile fibers. (If the fiber has been previously stretched, the absorption of moisture may actually result in a longitudinal shrinkage because the swelling of the fiber substance releases internal contractile forces.)

The major swelling effect is transverse to the fiber axis and results in marked enlargement or contraction of the cross-sectional area of the fiber as the moisture content increases or decreases. The magnitude of the swelling of different kinds of textile fibers varies, being affected not only by the amount of moisture absorbed but also by the composition and structure of the fiber substance. The data on lateral swelling are not very plentiful, and there is considerable variation in the data from different sources. Measurements are usually made of changes in fiber diameter or in cross-sectional area from the "air-dry" to the wet state, the relative humidity at the time of the air-dry measurement not always being given.

Table 11 presents the results of two different workers for a number of fibers. Acetate, which has approximately one-half the moisture

TABLE 11. Lateral Swelling of Fibers in Water

Kind	*Country of Origin*	*Percentage Increase in Area of Air-Dry Cross-Section Caused by Immersion in Water*	*Observer*	*Date*
Cuprammonium	Germany	61.8	A. Herzog [18]	1929
Viscose	Germany	65.9	A. Herzog [18]	1929
Acetate	Germany	5.7	A. Herzog [18]	1929
Cuprammonium	England	53.0	L. G. Lawrie [19]	1928
Cuprammonium	England	41.0	L. G. Lawrie [19]	1928
Viscose	England	35.0	L. G. Lawrie [19]	1928
Viscose	Germany	52.0	L. G. Lawrie [19]	1928
Acetate	England	9.0	L. G. Lawrie [19]	1928
Acetate	England	11.0	L. G. Lawrie [19]	1928
Acetate	France	14.0	L. G. Lawrie [19]	1928

content of viscose rayon at any humidity, shows about one-quarter of the lateral swelling of viscose. Cotton, whose moisture regain is only slightly above that of acetate, swells more than twice as much.

This low swelling affects the physical and chemical behavior of the fiber in many ways. It accounts, in part at least, for the lack of affinity of acetate for acid, vat, and direct cotton dyes when applied by the methods employed for cotton and viscose, and for the indifference of acetate toward crease-resistant resin finishes which are readily taken up by cellulose fibers.

On the other hand, the low swelling power of acetate gives it better resistance to the penetration of stains and soil and also results in a better degree of dimensional stability in properly finished fabrics because shrinkage and stretching of fabrics or garments during washing and wear are directly connected with the degree of swelling caused by the absorption of water. This is illustrated in Fig. 10, which shows the shrinkage during boil-off in the same boil-off bath of a series of spun-yarn fabrics of the same construction except for the composition of the fiber blend in the warp and filling yarns. The lower moisture absorption and swelling of acetate have found a practical application in increasing the dimensional stability of washable spun-staple fabrics. The presence of sufficient acetate staple in the blend reduces not only the laundering shrinkage of properly finished fabrics but also the shrinking, sagging, or stretching of such fabrics when wet by rain or perspiration during wear.

The lower moisture absorption and swelling of acetate fiber also result in faster drying of acetate fabrics.

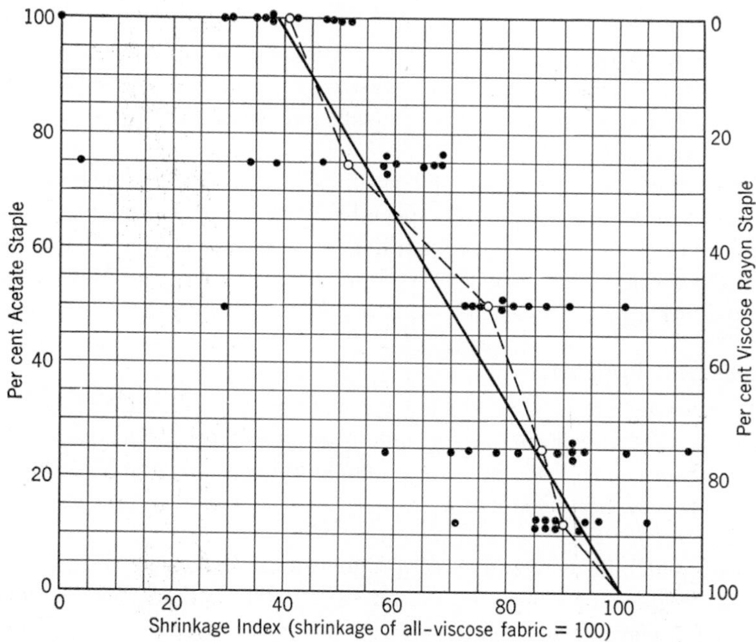

FIG. 10. Effect of acetate staple on the shrinkage in boil-off of spun acetate-viscose. Note: ○ = average shrinkage in warp and filing of six pieces of the same blend, boiled off in two different finishing plants, using three different boil-off methods in each plant. Each dot represents an individual shrinkage determination, i.e., either warp or filling of one of the six pieces.

A good survey of the moisture relations of textiles and the influence of moisture on behavior in processing and in use has been made by P. W. Carlene [20].

Swelling and Solubility in Nonaqueous Liquids. Organic liquids can be classified generally, with respect to their effect on acetate, into solvents, semi-solvents which act as swelling agents or plasticizers, and nonsolvents or inert liquids. (See section, "Chemical Constitution and Properties," below.) Mixtures of water with water-soluble solvents like acetone can be chosen which will swell acetate without dissolving it, but they are seldom used commercially because close control is required to avoid damage. Mixtures of water with water-soluble organic swelling agents like methyl alcohol are less critical and are commonly used as swelling media in the process of dyeing acetate with selected acid dyes. These dyes are not taken up by acetate from a water bath, but the swelling of the fiber substance in the water-alcohol dye-bath permits the penetration of the dye, which is then "locked" within the fiber by removal of the swelling medium by rinsing and drying. After drying, it can be washed thoroughly to remove surface dye. Such dyeings are extremely fast to washing because subsequent swelling in water or soap baths is insufficient to permit the removal of the dye particles.

The wider use of solvent and swelling media in the processing of acetate yarns and fabrics for special effects offers interesting possibilities but would require the installation of special equipment to provide close control of bath composition, the recovery of solvents, and the reduction of hazards from toxic and flammable vapors.

Mechanical Properties

In studying the mechanical behavior of any textile material such as acetate, it is important to consider separately the properties of the fiber substance itself in the form of single fibers or continuous-filament yarns and the behavior of fiber masses such as batts, felts, yarns, and fabrics.

The great bulk of commercial production of acetate, which may be called "regular tenacity" (RT), has a dry strength in the neighborhood of 1.4 grams per denier and an elongation in the neighborhood of 25 per cent. The wet strength is approximately 65 per cent of the dry strength, or approximately 0.9 gram per denier, and the wet elongation is in the neighborhood of 34 per cent. There are some differences in strength between yarns of different producers, but in general they are no greater than the differences between different yarn sizes and filament structures of the same brand. The strength range is between 1.2 and 1.7 grams per denier. Higher strength is usually accompanied by lower elongation.

Stronger acetates, which might be classed as "medium tenacity" (MT), have been made experimentally with tenacities ranging up to 2.6 grams per denier and elongations ranging down to 12 per cent. Such MT acetates, when commercially available, should find a ready market in fabrics where higher strength per unit weight is important.

During World War II another type, known as "high-impact" (HI) acetate yarn, was developed to a commercial status and used as an emergency raw material for aerial delivery parachutes, for which use it passed all the performance tests demanded of MT and high-tenacity (HT) viscose chutes. This yarn is essentially a high-stretch yarn, having a tenacity equal to that of RT acetate, namely, 1.4 grams per denier, with an elongation of about 50 per cent, which is twice the normal elongation. The success of this yarn in parachutes is due to the fact that the work of rupture under impact (extremely rapid loading) is higher than that of MT or HT viscose, despite the fact that its tensile strength is lower than RT viscose.

The saponified acetates that have been in production for some time are, strictly speaking, regenerated cellulose yarns since the acetyl groups are almost completely removed and replaced by hydroxyl groups during manufacture. They are made by stretching acetate yarns in the plastic state at high temperatures, followed by saponification. They are extremely strong, with tenacities between 6 and 7 grams per denier. The elongation is correspondingly low, being in the neighborhood of 6.5 per cent. These saponified acetates lose less strength in the wet state than RT acetates, the wet strength being about 75 per cent of the dry.

The *stress-strain behavior* of textile fibers as members of the class of substances known as high polymers has been discussed by various workers in this field. The complexity of the interrelated phenomena within the fiber substance which underlie the familiar shape of a typical stress-strain curve or a curve showing the flow of a fiber under constant load is analyzed by Press and Mark [21]. They tabulate six elementary processes of elasticity and six elementary processes of viscous flow and then proceed to interpret the observed behavior of acetate and of viscose filaments under load in terms of roles played by these several types of molecular processes. In summing up the experiments on acetate filament yarn, they conclude that the yarn shows excellent elastic recovery as long as the stresses are of short duration and are small (between 0.5 and 1.0 gram per denier or within an elongation of 5 per cent). Under these conditions, elastic recovery is complete within a few seconds. If the load is applied for longer times, however, creep occurs, and recovery upon release of the load is very slow. Hence the "springiness" of acetate is limited at higher elongations, and, if even small loads are applied for very long times (several days or weeks), the viscous or plastic flow which occurs results in permanent deformation or rupture.

Comparable conclusions drawn by these authors on a similar study of viscose filament yarns are that viscose is a stiffer and more rigid fiber whose elastic extensibility under small stresses of short duration is about 3.5 per cent as compared to 6.5 per cent for acetate, and that the rate of recovery after removal of the load is much slower. Creep occurs at a slower rate than for acetate but is less recoverable. At small loads there is no evidence of viscous or plastic flow, even after very long times.

The data and conclusions of these authors substantiate and elucidate the textile industry's subjective evaluation of acetate with respect to

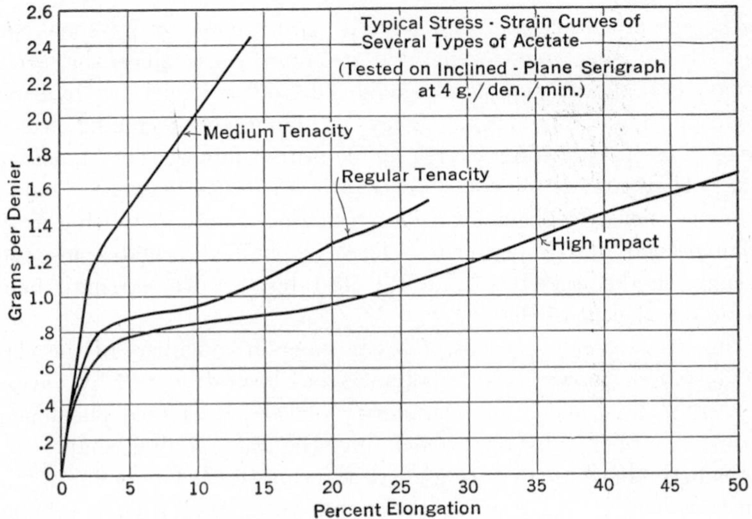

FIG. 11. Typical stress-strain curves of several types of acetates, tested at 4 grams per denier per min on inclined-plane serigraph.

its contribution to the hand, draping qualities, and wrinkle resistance which it imparts to properly constructed fabrics because these textile characteristics of fabrics are directly related to the elasticity and resilience of the fiber substance under small and moderate loads of short duration.

Figure 11 reproduces a stress-strain curve of each of three types of acetate as determined at the commonly specified rate of loading of 4 grams per denier per min on a constant-rate-of-load-type machine. These curves illustrate that a wide variety of mechanical properties is obtainable with cellulose acetate as a fiber-making material.

Table 12 gives some data computed in accordance with a system proposed by Smith [22] from the original serigraph charts from which these curves were taken. This system lists strength, stiffness, toughness, elasticity, and resilience as the basic criteria of the mechanical behavior of textiles because these fiber qualities affect the textile quali-

TABLE 12. Comparison of Mechanical Properties of Several Types of Cellulose Acetate *

(Tennessee Eastman Co. Laboratories)

	Symbol	*High Impact* (HI)	*Regular Tenacity* (RT)	*Medium Tenacity* (MT)
Description: denier, filaments, twist		340/52/3	150/52/3	170/52/3
Denier per filament		6.5	2.9	3.3
Mechanical Properties				
Elongation at break				
$\left(\text{Ratio } \frac{\text{Extension}}{\text{Original length}}\right)$	E	0.500	0.270	0.145
Tenacity (g/den)				
At breaking point	P	1.65	1.51	2.45
At 0.01 elongation	p_1	0.40	0.45	0.70
At 0.02 elongation	p_2	0.60	0.71	1.10
At 0.04 elongation	p_4	0.75	0.85	1.43
At 0.08 elongation	p_8	0.84	0.93	1.85
Stiffness (g/den/unit elongation)				
To breaking point (average stiffness)	S	3.3	5.6	16.9
At 0.01 elongation	s_1	40.0	45.0	70.0
At 0.02 elongation	s_2	14.0	16.0	23.0
At 0.04 elongation	s_4	4.0	3.0	13.0
At 0.08 elongation	s_8	1.2	1.4	10.0
Toughness (g. cm/den/cm)				
To breaking point	W	0.553	0.288	0.238
To 0.01 elongation	w_1	0.0016	0.0020	0.0040
To 0.02 elongation	w_2	0.0072	0.0080	0.0144
To 0.04 elongation	w_4	0.0172	0.0220	0.0396
To 0.08 elongation	w_8	0.0532	0.0544	0.1060

* Rate of loading: 4 grams per denier per minute.

ties of hand, drape, resilience, and durability of fabrics. Table 12 shows the tenacity (unit strength), the stiffness (resistance to deformation), and the toughness (unit work absorbed), as computed from these particular curves, to the breaking point and also to several points along the first part of the curves, namely, to 1, 2, 4, and 8 per cent elongation. Although it is impossible to determine the elastic limit from this type of curve, and hence to compute the elasticity and resilience of the three fibers, it is safe to assume that the stiffness and toughness at elongation up to at least 2 per cent are recoverable and that these values, therefore, are elastic stiffness and resilience.

The curves and the data show that the breaking tenacity of RT and HI are about the same, whereas that of the MT is considerably higher. Because of the differences in elongation, however, the unit breaking toughness, or work per denier per unit length, required to rupture the HI yarn is twice that of the RT. The unit breaking toughness of the MT yarn is somewhat less than that of the RT.

The overall or average stiffness (as measured by the ratio of breaking tenacity to breaking elongation) of the MT is three times that of the RT, whereas the average stiffness of the HI is one-half that of the RT. This stiffness is a measure of resistance of the fiber substance to stretching or to bending. Bending stiffness is dependent upon fiber fineness as well as upon inherent stiffness, and an HI yarn or fabric would be markedly more pliant than an RT yarn or fabric if the filaments of which it is composed were as fine as the RT filaments.

The yield point for all these yarns under the conditions of this test occurs at about the same elongation, namely, between 2 and 3 per cent elongation; the tenacity at 2 per cent elongation, however, is 0.6 for HI, 0.7 for RT, and 1.15 for MT.

Therefore, in the region from 0 to 2 per cent elongation in which all these fibers are undoubtedly elastic, the elastic stiffness and the resilience of HI and RT are approximately equal to one another, and about half of the corresponding values for MT. For the tensile stresses of processing, such as warping, winding, and weaving, this means that HI can be handled safely at the same tensions as RT and that MT will withstand greater tensions. In terms of the hand and draping qualities of similar fabric construction, which usually involve small stresses, it means that, for filaments of equal fineness, the HI and RT fabrics will feel and drape alike, whereas the MT fabrics will be markedly crisper and stiffer.

In contrast to this behavior below the yield point, an examination of the mechanical properties at 8 per cent elongation, which is beyond the yield region, reveals that the stiffness of the MT is seven times that of the HI and RT, which are very pliant and, therefore, easily stretched or distorted in the region beyond 5 per cent elongation. A load of 1 gram per denier produces an elongation of 2 per cent in MT, 12 per cent in RT, and 23 per cent in HI acetate.

Inasmuch as the stress-strain behavior of textile fibers, including acetate, is the result of overlapping and interrelated plastic and elastic phenomena, it is drastically affected by the rate of loading or unloading. Almost all published data so far on the mechanical properties of acetate are based on tests made at or near the standard testing speeds of 4 grams per denier per min for constant-rate-of-load testers and 12 in. per min for pendulum-type testers. The military uses of textiles in tires and parachutes have focused attention on the need for data obtained under very high rates of loading and has led to an interest in impact tests and in determination of the "dynamic modulus," i.e., the inherent stiffness of the fiber substance under instantaneous changes in load. Few or no data have yet been published on longitudinal impact tests.

A paper by Ballou and Silverman [23] describes a method of determining the instantaneous stiffness of fibers by measuring the velocity with which sound travels along them and gives some preliminary data to illustrate the use of the method. Table 13 and Fig. 12 have been

TABLE 13. Dynamic or Instantaneous Stiffness of Some Fibers as Determined by Sound Velocity Measurements

Computed from data by Ballou and Silverman [23].

	Instantaneous Elastic Stiffness (grams per denier per unit elongation)			
	Acetate RT	Viscose RT	Viscose HT	Nylon
Specimen tested at elongation of				
0.5 per cent	60	77	163	67
1 per cent	61	86	166	70
2 per cent	63	101	174	73
3 per cent	65	110	181	81
4 per cent	66	116	188	92
6 per cent	70	123	206	120
8 per cent	74	129	...	147

compiled from that paper. These values represent the true *elastic* stiffness of the fiber substance at each elongation indicated in Table 13 because the frequency of the loading-unloading cycle which is set up by the sonic waves is so high that plastic flow is eliminated. The data show that the instantaneous elastic stiffness of each fiber, including acetate, is higher than the elastic stiffness (s_1 per cent) as determined at 4 grams per denier per min.

Figure 12 shows that the true elastic stiffness increases with increasing elongation. Figure 11 shows that, at the normal rate of loading, the stiffness decreases with increasing elongation. This difference in behavior is due to the fact that, at the normal rate of loading, plastic flow is occurring simultaneously with elastic extension. The faster the rate of loading, the less important is the plastic component of the extension. Table 14 compares stiffness data on RT acetate and RT viscose rayon at the two rates of loading.

Fiber Masses. The mechanical properties of a mass of fibers in the form of a batt, a yarn, or a fabric are affected not only by the inherent

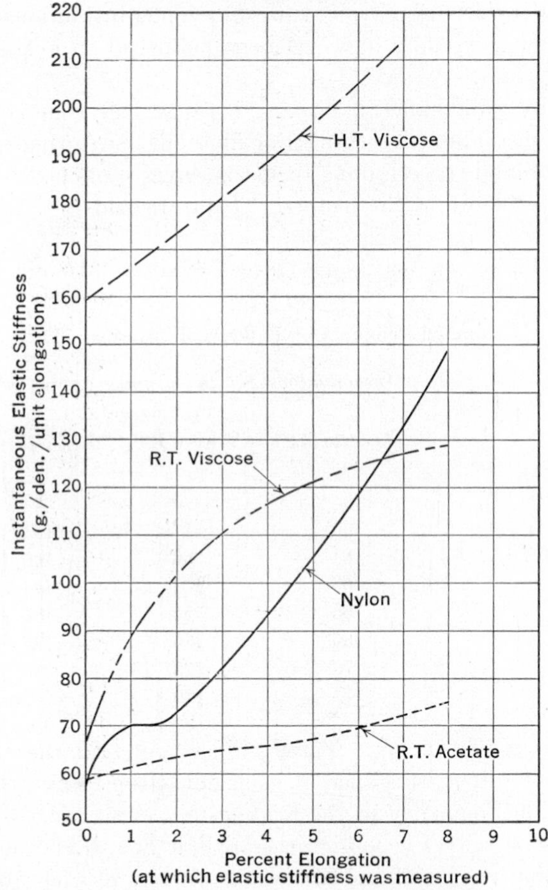

FIG. 12. Instantaneous stiffness (modulus of elasticity) of some fiber substances, computed from data of Ballou and Silverman, and obtained by the sonic method [23].

mechanical properties of the fiber substance and the dimensions of the individual fibers but also by the frictional force between the fibers, which is complex, involving the nature of the fiber surfaces and of the finish or lubricant on them, the shape of the fibers with particular reference to crimpiness, and the arrangement of the fibers within the mass.

TABLE 16. RELATION BETWEEN ACETYL CONTENT OF CELLULOSE ACETATE AND SOME MECHANICAL AND CHEMICAL PROPERTIES OF ACETATES MADE THEREFROM UNDER COMPARABLE SPINNING CONDITIONS

(Tennessee Eastman Co. Laboratories)

Sample	*A*	*B*	*C*	*D*	*E*
Acetyl content (%)	39.5	37.7	36.0	35.4	34.4
Acetyl groups per glucose unit	2.42	2.25	2.12	2.02	1.95
Dye take-up (increase in absorption of light expressed as percentages of reflectance of undyed fabric)					
Acetate dye	31.3	34.4	39.5	39.4	42.0
Viscose dye	0	4.0	7.0	6.4	7.6
Resistance to boiling 0.01 *N* NaOH *	60	13	0	0	0
Mechanical properties					
Tenacity (g/den) dry	1.36	1.30	1.32	1.30	1.25
wet	0.93	0.89	0.72	0.69	0.64
Ratio $\frac{\text{wet}}{\text{dry}}$	0.68	0.68	0.55	0.53	0.51
Elongation (%) dry	27	26	27	28	29
wet	42	41	43	45	48
Ratio $\frac{\text{wet}}{\text{dry}}$	1.55	1.57	1.59	1.60	1.65

* Percentage of NaOH unconsumed after boiling 1-g sample for 60 min in 100 cc of 0.01 *N* NaOH.

of the undyed white acetate at 500 $\mu\mu$ is 80.7 per cent. Each value for dye take-up in Table 16 is the increase in absorption of light (decrease in reflectance) of the dyed acetate expressed as a percentage of the undyed reflectance (80.7). Thus, sample *A* shows complete resistance to the viscose dye and takes up acetate dye to an extent that absorbs 31.3 per cent of the light reflected by the undyed acetate.

As expected, the acetate dye take-up increases as the acetyl content decreases. Immunity to viscose dye is already lost at 37.7 per cent acetyl, and the take-up of viscose dye increases as the acetyl content decreases further. Stability to alkali decreases with decreasing acetyl content.

With respect to mechanical properties, dry strength decreases and elongation increases with decreasing acetyl content. The wet strength and elongation are affected to a greater degree because of the increased swelling that results from the presence of more hydroxyl groups. The relative wet strength drops rapidly from two-thirds to one-half that of the dry strength.

An increase in swelling with decreasing acetyl content occurs not only in water but also in other polar solvents like methyl and ethyl alcohol. This is of interest in connection with the commercial method of dyeing acetate with direct wool dyes in an alcohol-water bath that swells the fibers sufficiently to permit the entry of acid dyes to which the fibers are otherwise immune.

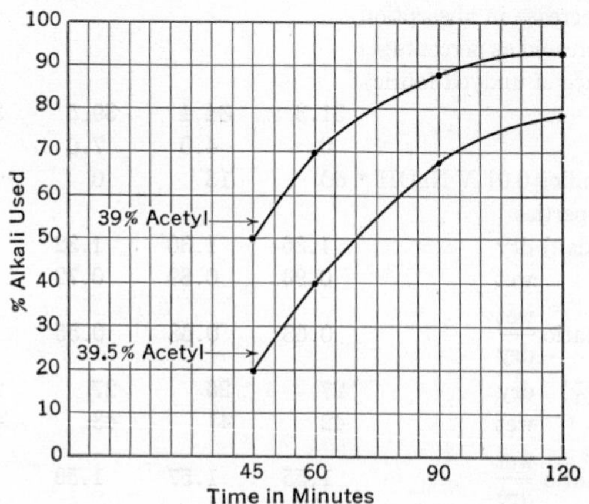

Fig. 16. Reactivity of acetate yarn to boiling alkali. (*Tennessee Eastman Co. Laboratories.*)

Modern commercial acetate yarns have an acetyl content in the neighborhood of 39 per cent. Figure 16 shows how the rate of chemical reaction of commercial acetate yarns is influenced by even slight variations in acetyl content. Two such yarns having an acetyl content of 39.5 and 39.0 respectively were exposed to boiling 0.01 *N* NaOH under quantitatively controlled conditions. The curves show that the yarn having 39.5 per cent acetyl is definitely more resistant to hydrolysis.

Whereas Table 16 indicates the relation between the chemical and mechanical properties of acetate and the acetyl content of the cellulose acetate from which the yarn is made, Table 17 shows the effect, on mechanical properties, of hydrolyzing an acetate the original acetyl content of which is 39.5 per cent. The tenacities in this table are based on the denier of the hydrolyzed yarn. Hydrolysis was effected by exposure to NaOH solutions of different concentrations at a constant temperature until virtually all the NaOH present had reacted. The experiment was carried out at 50° C. (122° F.) and also repeated at 83° C. (181° F.).

TABLE 17. EFFECT OF HYDROLYSIS (SAPONIFICATION) ON MECHANICAL PROPERTIES OF ACETATE

(Tennessee Eastman Co. Laboratories)

Grams NaOH in Bath at Start. Grams per 100 Grams of Acetate Staple	*Bath Temperature 50° C.*					*Bath Temperature 83° C.*				
		Dry		Wet			Dry		Wet	
	Per Cent Acetyl	Tenacity (g/den)	Elongation (%)	Tenacity (g/den)	Elongation (%)	Per Cent Acetyl	Tenacity (g/den)	Elongation (%)	Tenacity (g/den)	Elongation (%)
5	35.9	1.37	25	0.73	37	35.7	1.24	25	0.74	39
10	31.6	1.27	23	0.66	39	33.3	1.33	24	0.73	40
15	27.0	1.31	23	0.53	34	27.3	1.21	20	0.54	26
20	18.5	1.35	22	0.46	28	23.4	1.26	21	0.46	20

The photomicrographs of cross-sections of the fibers after saponification reveal that the reaction at the higher temperature resulted in concentrating the hydrolysis near the fiber surface rather than diffusing it throughout the fiber cross-section. See Fig. 17. The photomicrographs show that the saponified layer is not continuous but is broken at the "valleys" between the lobes. The most probable explanation for this is that the swelling of the fiber in the NaOH bath closes the bottom of these "valleys," thus preventing further direct contact of the bath with this portion of the fiber surface.

Although no definite trend of dry tenacity is indicated by these data, the dry elongation and the wet tenacity and elongation are all reduced by hydrolysis at both temperatures. The fiber substance becomes stiffer and less tough as hydrolysis increases, and the effect is more marked at the higher temperature. The relative wet tenacity, which is approximately two-thirds that of the dry tenacity of the original yarn, drops to one-third that of the dry tenacity for yarn in which half of the original acetyl groups have been removed by hydrolysis.

With these general observations on the stability of cellulose acetates and the influence thereon of such controllable factors as degree of polymerization and acetyl content, the chemical behavior of the modern commercial acetates may be described.

Effect of Water and Alkalies. In its early days acetate was readily delustered and partially saponified by prolonged treatment in water or mild alkaline baths at temperatures above 180° F. Acetate is now chemically stable to water even at the boil. It will also withstand treatment in soap solutions or other alkaline baths the *p*H of which is not above 9.5, at temperatures up to the boiling point for periods long enough for normal scouring and dyeing operations without suffer-

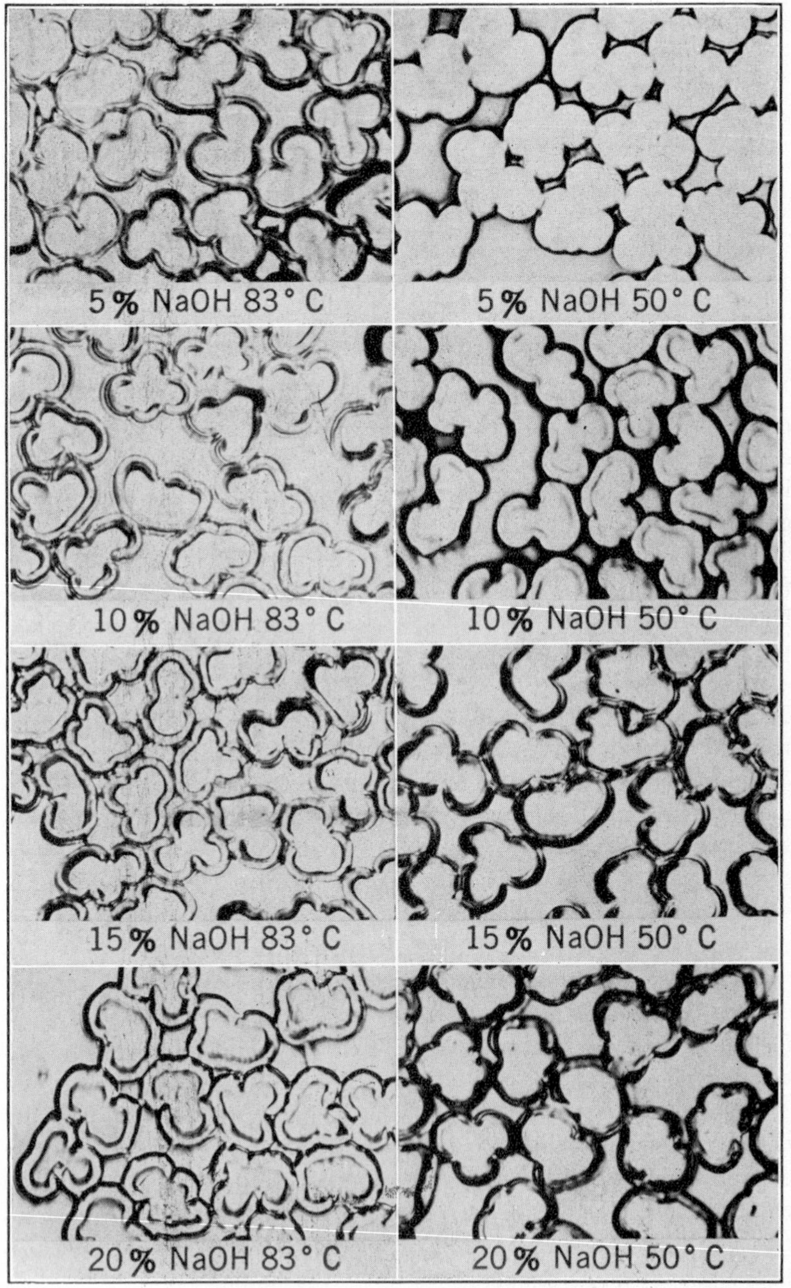

Fig. 17. Cross-sections of saponified acetate yarn in Table 17 after exposure to direct cotton dye (×700).

ing either appreciable delustering or sufficient saponification to impair its immunity to viscose and cotton dyes. Stronger alkalies cause saponification, the extent and distribution of which depend upon the combined factors of time, temperature, alkalinity, and amount and type of alkali present. Controlled saponification, localized on the fiber surfaces, has been used as a method of raising the fusing point and of imparting affinity for dyes that do not dye cellulose acetate. This principle is finding increased application in the printing of vat colors on the discharged portions of print patterns and in the pad dyeing of vats in solid shades.

Effect of Acids. Acetate is unaffected by dilute solutions of weak acids but is attacked by strong acids. Apart from the chemical effect of acidity, concentrated organic acids like acetic and formic will cause excessive swelling and solution. Nonvolatile, inorganic acids, such as sulfuric, if left on the fibers, will become concentrated upon evaporation or drying of the wet material, with consequent degradation by breakdown of the chain molecules. The resistance of cellulose acetate to tendering and charring when impregnated with H_2SO_4 and heated is considerably greater than that of natural or regenerated cellulose, which makes it difficult to remove acetate fibers from wool by the usual carbonizing processes.

Sulfuric acid should not be used in dyeing and finishing operations because, even if the goods are thoroughly washed, the absorbed residue of acid will make the cellulose acetate unstable. After storage of such goods, particularly at higher temperatures, the odor of acetic acid will reveal the decomposition which has been caused by the mineral acid.

The effect of acid and alkaline processing baths on the fastness properties of dyed acetate is discussed in the section "Dyeing," below.

Effect of Oxidizing Agents. The whiteness of scoured acetate, either bright or dull luster, is such as to make bleaching of this fiber for its own sake entirely unnecessary. However, if bleaching is required for other fibers present or to remove "fugitive tints" or soil, mild oxidizing agents may be used. If chlorine is used, the reaction should be carried out in the cold, on the acid side, and at a concentration of not more than 1 gram of available chlorine per liter. A mild peroxide bleach may also be used. With permanganate bleach, which is sometimes used to clear color stains on cross-dyed goods in which the acetate is desired in full white, particular care must be taken to clear the goods completely by means of sodium bisulfite, followed by an additional treatment in a 1 per cent solution of zinc sulfoxylate at

TABLE 18. Effect of Solvents on Cellulose Acetate

(Tennessee Eastman Co. Laboratories)

Solvent	*Effect*
Methanol ANH	No solution (60° C.)
Ethanol 2-B	No solution (60° C.)
N-propanol	No solution (60° C.)
Isopropanol	No solution (60° C.)
N-butanol	No solution (60° C.)
Isobutanol	No solution (60° C.)
sec-Butanol	No solution (60° C.)
tert-Butanol	No solution (60° C.)
N-amyl alcohol	No solution (60° C.)
Isoamyl alcohol	No solution (60° C.)
tert-Amyl alcohol	No solution (60° C.)
Ethyl acetate	Partial solution (60° C.)
Isopropyl acetate	No solution (60° C.)
N-propyl acetate	No solution (60° C.)
N-butyl acetate	No solution (60° C.)
sec-Butyl acetate	No solution (60° C.)
Isobutyl acetate	No solution (60° C.)
Isoamyl acetate	No solution (60° C.)
Ethyl lactate	Solution (room temperature)
Cellosolve acetate	Partial solution (60° C.)
Methyl cellosolve acetate	Solution (room temperature)
Acetone	Solution (room temperature)
Methyl ethyl ketone	Solution (room temperature)
Methyl propyl ketone	Swelling (60° C.)
Methyl isobutyl ketone	No solution (60° C.)
Methyl N-butyl ketone	No solution (60° C.)
Di-isopropyl ketone	No solution (60° C.)
Methylene chloride	Partial solution (60° C.)
Chloroform	Partial solution (60° C.)
Ethylene chloride	Partial solution (60° C.)
Propylene chloride	No solution (60° C.)
Diethyl ether	No solution (60° C.)
Di-isopropyl ether	No solution (60° C.)
1,4-Dioxane	Solution (room temperature)
Methyl cellosolve	Solution (room temperature)
Cellosolve	Swelling (60° C.)
Methyl acetate	Solution (room temperature)

Notes: "No solution" means that the solvent has no visible effect. In many cases classed as "no solution" in this table, swelling, though not visible, may be sufficient to affect dye penetration and physical properties.

"Swelling" means that the flakes or fibers are visibly swollen or softened but retain their general shape.

"Partial solution" means that parts of the flakes or fibers actually dissolve to produce a hazy solution with many fibrous particles.

"Solution" means that the flakes or fibers dissolve completely, to form a clear solution.

190° F. for 20 min in order to avoid the subsequent yellowing due to the formation of manganese dioxide.

Effect of Solvents. Because of the cost of acetone and its general suitability as an industrial solvent as compared to other solvents for cellulose esters, the production of yarn-type cellulose acetates has been dominated by the tendency to design acetylation reactions that will yield esters having the desired physical and chemical properties when extruded as acetone solutions. The behavior of these yarn-type esters (39–40 per cent acetyl and medium viscosity) in other common organic solvents is given qualitatively in Table 18. Acetate fibers, yarns. and fabrics (unless altered chemically, as by hydrolysis, in processing) will respond to solvents in the same way as the ester of which they are composed.

Although Table 18 classifies organic liquids into solvents, partial solvents, swelling agents, and nonsolvents, when used individually, it should be noted that mixtures of two or more such liquids are not necessarily additive in solvent or swelling effects. Such mixtures, when used for industrial processing where softening or solution is desired, must be studied in connection with the particular processing conditions. It should also be emphasized that the term "swelling," as used in this table, signifies drastic swelling, and that the term "no solution" does not necessarily signify the complete absence of swelling. For example, methanol, which is listed as "no solution" rather than as "swelling," does swell acetate fibers sufficiently to permit the absorption of acid dyes.

As a result of research by the Celanese Corporation of America in collaboration with the laboratories of the National Institute of Cleaning and Dyeing, during the early years of the commercial development of acetate, the effect of cleaning solvents and spotting agents on acetate was carefully studied. The dissemination of the results of this work to the dry-cleaning industry enabled it to adjust its choice of solvents and its processing so that for years the dry cleaning of all fabrics has been done by methods that are safe for acetate. (See Table 19.)

With respect to the manufacture of acetate, the viscosity of the solution of cellulose acetate in acetone as prepared for yarn spinning depends upon the solubility properties (acetyl content) and the inherent viscosity (chain length) of the ester and upon the concentration of the spinning solution. Spinning solutions range in viscosity from 1000 to 4200 poises (calculated from ball-drop determinations).

One of the criteria used to indicate the solubility of a cellulose ester in a solvent is the relationship between solution viscosity and ester

TABLE 19. Spotting Agents for Acetate [31]

	Safe	
Acids	Carbon disulfide	Potassium permanganate
28% acetic	Carbon tetrachloride	Sodium hydrosulfite (stripper)
28% formic	Castor oil	Sodium hypochlorite (Javelle water)
Alkalies (dilute)	Chlorine bleaches	Soluble oils (monopole, tetrapole, etc.)
soap in water	Digestive agents	Synthetic detergents
soda	Glycerine	Toluol
washing soda	Hydrofluoric acid (erusticator)	Trichloroethylene
Ammonia (26°)	Oleic acid	Turpentine
Amyl acetate (pure banana oil)	Oxalic acid	Xylol
Benzol	Perchloroethylene	
Butyl acetate	Petroleum ether	
Butyl cellosolve		
	Semi-Safe	
Butyl alcohol	Grain alcohol	Sulfuric ether
Cyclohexanol (Hexalin)	Isopropyl alcohol	Wood alcohol (methyl)
Fusel oil (amyl alcohol)		
	Unsafe	
Acetic ether (ethyl acetate)	Alcohol-benzol	Cresol
Acetone	Alcohol-volatile type paint remover	Ethylene dichloride
Acids	Aniline oil	Lactic acid
formic (conc.)	Benzaldehyde	Lysol
glacial acetic	Chloroform	Pyridine (full strength)
		Tetrachloroethane

The Dilution of Unsafe and Semi-Safe Chemicals. If a mixture is to contain these chemicals, the total amount of them should not be more than 30% of the total volume of the mixture. The safe chemicals should evaporate as slow or slower than the unsafe or semi-safe chemicals. The unsafe and semi-safe chemicals must be soluble in the safe chemical.

concentration. This is dependent both on chemical composition and on chain length of the ester.

Figure 18 shows the viscosity-concentration curves for several esters of the same chemical composition but of different intrinsic viscosities. The intrinsic viscosity $[\eta]$ is defined by Kraemer [32] as follows:

$$[\eta] = \left(\frac{\ln \eta_r}{c}\right)_{c \to 0}$$

where η_r = viscosity of the solution, relative to that of the solvent and c = concentration, grams cellulose ester per 100 cc of solution. In general, the intrinsic viscosity is now accepted as a good indication of the molecular chain length, or molecular weight, of high polymers such as cellulose esters. Hence, Figure 18 shows the effect of molecular weight on the viscosity-concentration relationship in the range of viscosities used commercially and when the chemical composition is held constant.

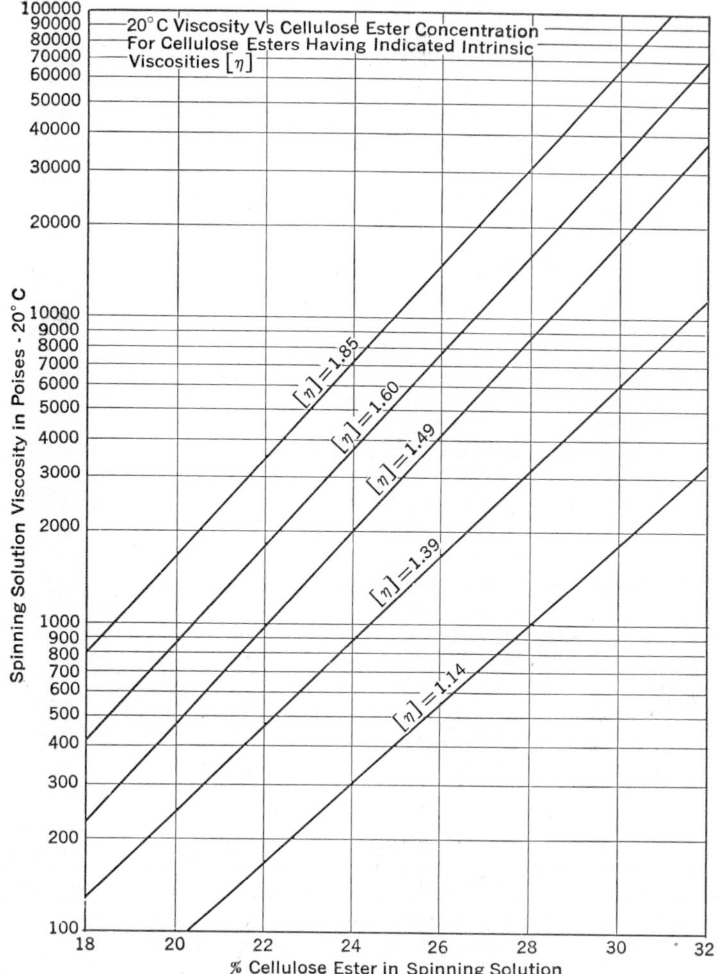

FIG. 18. Viscosity-concentration curves for several esters of the same chemical composition but of different intrinsic viscosities.

Effect of Light. Long exposure to sunlight produces a tendering effect on almost all fibers, both natural and man-made, but the various fiber substances are affected to different degrees. In the early history of dull acetate (delustered with titanium dioxide pigments), the tendering effect was very pronounced. Developments in the manufacture of titanium pigments involving the introduction of small quantities of other metallic oxides have eliminated this effect. Modern dull acetate is as resistant as bright acetate to tendering by light, as shown in Table 20, which indicates the effect of exposure to the light of a Fade-Ometer on the mechanical properties of acetate.

TABLE 20. Effect of Light (Fade-Ometer Exposure) on Mechanical Properties of Acetate

(Tennessee Eastman Co. Laboratories)

Type	*Early* Dull Luster	*Modern* Dull Luster	*Modern* Bright Luster
Unexposed			
Dry tenacity (g/den)	1.40	1.38	1.48
Dry elongation (%)	25.2	23.7	27.0
Wet tenacity (g/den)	0.95	0.91	1.03
Wet elongation (%)	35.0	32.8	34.9
50-hr exposure			
Dry tenacity (g/den)	1.06	1.31	1.30
Dry elongation (%)	19.6	22.7	24.5
Wet tenacity (g/den)	0.68	0.87	0.87
Wet elongation (%)	25.2	30.7	32.3
100-hr exposure			
Dry tenacity (g/den)	0.93	1.24	1.31
Dry elongation (%)	15.4	20.8	23.0
Wet tenacity (g/den)	0.52	0.83	0.77
Wet elongation (%)	23.6	29.7	27.7
200-hr exposure			
Dry tenacity (g/den)	0.70	1.22	1.20
Dry elongation (%)	9.5	21.6	19.8
Wet tenacity (g/den)	0.37	0.82	0.83
Wet elongation (%)	17.3	30.6	31.6

Note: Although the data in this table are comparable because the procedure of preparation and exposure was the same for all three specimens, they are not necessarily comparable with other data determined elsewhere because the effect of light on textile materials depends not only on the nature of the fiber substance but also on other materials, such as dyes, present in the fiber as well as upon the dimensions and bulk density of the textile material, since light absorption is essentially a surface phenomenon.

Dyeing

An excellent review of the status of dyes and dyeing of acetate in 1941 is contained in a paper by Ellis [33], who was responsible for much of the pioneering research in dyeing acetate during the preceding twenty years. Modern methods of dyeing acetate are also discussed in a paper by Scull and Smith [34] on the dyeing of manufactured fibers.

The preparation of acetate textiles for dyeing is based on the considerations discussed above under the heading "Chemical Reactivity." When necessary, sizing materials are solubilized before boil-off treatment with diastatic or proteolytic enzymes, depending upon whether a starch-base or protein-base size has been used. Boil-off is carried out in a bath containing soap or a synthetic detergent; the use of strong fixed alkalies should be avoided except where saponification is intended. Modern boil-off equipment is designed to minimize tensions, thus permitting natural fabric shrinkage for the preservation of hand and fullness, and also to "set" the cloth in open width so as to prevent creasing during subsequent processing at temperatures below the "setting" temperature.

The classes of dyes being used commercially include direct acetate dyes, developed acetate dyes, naphthols, acid dyes, vat dyes, and pigments.

Acetate has little or no affinity for direct viscose and cotton dyes but is readily dyed by certain direct acetate dyes, which are soluble in the solid cellulose acetate. Some of these are water-soluble, but most are not and are, therefore, applied from a bath containing a dispersion of the finely divided insoluble dyes in the presence of soap, synthetic detergents, or soluble oils. Since acetate dyes in general do not dye cellulosic fibers, mixtures of acetate with viscose rayon or cotton can be either cross-dyed or dyed to a solid shade by the judicious selection of dyes and dyeing techniques.

Direct Acetate Dyes. These are of three general chemical types: aminoanthraquinone, nitroarylamine, and azo. Until recently, the azo dyes provided principally the color range from yellow to violet, and the aminoanthraquinones the range from orange through the blues and blue-green; the nitroarylamines ranged in shade between greenish-yellow and yellowish-orange. Blue azo dyes are now available. One of the difficulties in the selection of direct acetate dyes is the limited range of blues, greens, and violets possessing all-round dyeing and fastness properties, particularly with respect to fume fading and light fading.

Fume fading (sometimes called atmospheric fading, gas fading, or acid fading) is caused by chemical reaction between certain dyes and minute amounts of gases present in air that has been polluted by combustion fumes. The reaction results in a change in shade or in actual color of the dye. Fume fading is not confined to dyed acetate but occurs also in textiles composed of other fibers. With these other fibers, however, the problem is less acute, because the choice of suitable dyes is great enough to permit the elimination of the offending ones. Among direct dyes for acetate, the blues and violets which have been valued for good working properties and light fastness are anthraquinones, which are subject, as a class, to a color change toward red as a result of the reaction with atmospheric fumes. Several blues of the azo type are commercially available which are not reddened by atmospheric fumes, and these are finding increased use within the limits imposed by the higher dyeing temperatures, which they require, and their lesser fastness to light.

Within the anthraquinone group, there is a great difference in the degree of reddening. Therefore, a judicious choice of the best anthraquinones with respect to fume fading is essential.

Resistance of the dyed fabric to fume fading can be increased by after-treatment with suitable protective agents, which, when properly applied, will double or treble the time of exposure necessary to produce a visible change of shade.

In general, it has been found that superior light- and fume-fastness properties for the greenish-yellow to yellowish-orange shades can be obtained by employing the nitroarylamines (including nitroacridones); for the yellowish-orange to reddish-orange range, azo dyes. In the reddish-orange to green-blue range, azo dyes are used that have fair light-fastness and good fume-fastness properties. Dyes that couple good light- and inferior fume-fastness properties are available in the range orange to blue-green by employing various amino- and alkylated aminoanthraquinone dyes. Therefore, direct acetate dyes must be selected carefully with respect to the end use of the fabric. Fabrics for linings, evening wear, bedspreads, high-style dress goods, and neckties do not require as much light fastness as sportswear and drapery fabrics, but excellent fastness to atmospheric fumes is desirable. Therefore, azo blues should be used. A moderate degree of combined light and fume fastness is attainable by combinations of carefully selected anthraquinones, azo, and nitroarylamine dyes with the use of a protective agent.

The principal protective agents in common use are amines, which are divided into two classes, the semi-permanent and permanent types. The semi-permanent group contains water-soluble materials such as melamine, diethanolamine, and triethanolamine, and are most effective when applied to a dyed fabric that has been rinsed in a bath made slightly alkaline with sodium carbonate. However, the washfastness properties are such that they are removed with normal laundering. Melamine is suitable for use on fabrics containing a mixture of acetate and rayon, as well as on all-acetate fabrics. The other two, as well as other amines which give satisfactory results on all-acetate fabrics, are not suitable in the presence of rayon because of an adverse effect on the shade and the light fastness of some direct dyes.

The permanent-type inhibitor is represented by diphenyl-ethylene diamine which is dyed onto the acetate fiber and is very resistant to washing and dry cleaning.

Developed Acetate Dyes. In addition to the use of azo compounds as direct acetate dyes, certain members of this class are used for producing black and navy by applying them as a base, followed by diazotization and developing with beta-oxynaphthoic acid or other developers, such as *m*-acetaminodi-beta-hydroxyethylaniline and phloroglucinol. Such developed blacks and navy blues have excellent fume fastness and, if properly selected, also have good light fastness.

Acid Dyes. Acetate is dyed with a selected group of acid dyes in the presence of an agent that swells the fibers sufficiently to permit the absorption of the dye, which is mechanically entrapped within the fiber by the subsequent removal of the swelling agent. Alcohol is commonly used for this purpose in concentrations up to 75 per cent in water. The use of formic acid is covered in a patent [35].

Acid dyes have been applied by these methods in stock dyeing and in yarn dyeing of skeins or packages. Work on piece dyeing is in progress. The colors thus obtained are bright and highly resistant to fume fading, peroxide bleaching, washing, and cross dyeing, and, if the dyes are carefully selected, good light-fastness can also be obtained.

Vat Dyes. The increasing use of acetate, particularly in the form of staple fiber, for sportswear, work clothes, and summer suitings, as well as for draperies, calls for a combination of fastness as to light, washing, and perspiration, and fume fastness, for which the better qualities of vat dyes are desired. However, the basic stumbling block to the general application of vat dyes to cellulose acetate is that the alkalinity necessary for application of the fast-to-light types of vats causes excessive saponification of the cellulose acetate. Several solutions of this general problem are being used under certain limitations.

The indigoid vats can be applied to acetates under mild conditions of alkalinity, to produce light shades, but under such conditions the viscose or cotton in a mixed-fiber fabric has little or no affinity for the dye.

Mixer-fiber fabrics containing less than one-third acetate have been dyed in light shades with selected vats by permitting a partial saponification of the cellulose acetate.

Intensive work is in progress in several quarters on the application of the best types of vat dyes by pigment padding methods involving the controlled surface saponification of the acetate fibers to a degree that permits the production of solid shades on mixed-fiber fabrics as well as on all-acetate fabrics without any appreciable loss of the stabilizing properties and the characteristic hand and resilience contributed by the acetate fibers.

Pigments. Acetate fabrics are colored with resin-bonded pigments by processes similar to the pigment dyeing and printing of cotton and viscose fabrics. This method of applying color to textiles is essentially a surface coloration and involves little or no penetration of the pigment particles into the fiber substance.

Another pigment dyeing process which is close to commercial application is based on the principle of padding the fabric with a pigment dispersed in a medium that acts both as an agent to swell the fibers to the point where the pigment can enter the fiber substance and as a bonding resin to hold it there. The fact that pigments can be chosen for superlative general fastness qualities makes the results of these pigment dyeing methods excellent, except for the problem of crocking.

Biological Reactivity

Effect of Microorganisms (Mildew). Acetate is inherently resistant to attack by bacteria and fungi attack such as mildew. If such growth occurs, it is confined to a discoloration of the surface and does not appear to damage the physical properties of the fibers. Although the low moisture content of cellulose acetate may contribute to its resistance to mildew, the primary reason for this desirable property is undoubtedly that the compound cellulose acetate is not a nutrient for bacteria and fungi.

The only evidence contrary to this generally established immunity of acetate to mildew damage is mentioned by Marsh and Duske [36], who stated, in a paper dealing principally with viscose rayon, that an organism classified as a species of *Aspergillus* was found to tender acetate (but to a lesser extent than viscose rayon) when both were incubated in contact with Czapek's agar medium at 30.5° C. and 80–90 per cent relative humidity for 6 days.

Borlaug [37], on the other hand, in an extensive investigation of acetate fabric in several states, including greige, scoured, commercially finished, and purified by washing and ether extraction, found that acetate is highly resistant to soil burial tests for 21 days and also to laboratory exposure for 14 days at 27° C. and 50 per cent R.H. when exposed separately to *Chaetonium globosum, Metarrhizium, Stachybotrys* sp., and to a mixture of *Aspergillus* and *Penicillium.* The acetate fabric was badly discolored by *Stachybotrys,* but no appreciable reduction in tensile strength occurred with this or the other fungi. Borlaug also exposed skeins of acetate for 7 weeks at 27° C. and 80 per cent R.H. in air containing a high population of mildew spores and found no visible evidence of fungus growth and no deterioration in tenacity or elongation.

Heuser [38] cites investigations of the effect of aerobic bacteria in which cellulose acetate was not attacked by organisms that convert cellulose into a mucilage-like material.

Effect of Insects. Acetate appears to be immune to attack by insects except that in a few instances it has been shown that moth or carpet beetle larvae will cut their way through acetate or other nonnutrient fabrics to get at wool fibers.

Effect of Acetate Yarns and Fibers on Humans. Acetate is indigestible, but harmless if ingested (by infants, for example). It is also nontoxic and nonirritating to the skin, and no case of allergy attributable to cellulose acetate has ever been reported.

UTILIZATION

The rapid rate at which the consumption of cellulose acetate has increased from year to year during its existence as a commercial textile fiber has been due to the versatility of its usefulness.

Apparel Textiles. In the field of women's apparel, filament acetate is used in a wide variety of fabrics for evening gowns, daytime dresses, blouses, lingerie, bathing suits, linings, and ribbons. A very large proportion of dress crepes is made with acetate filament warp and viscose crepe filling. Acetate staple fiber is widely used, alone and in blends, with viscose staple in women's sportswear and daytime dress fabrics.

In men's apparel, filament acetate is used in linings, shirts, neckties, hatbands, socks, pajamas, and dressing gowns. Acetate staple fiber, alone or in blends with viscose, is used in an increasing variety of men's summer suitings, slacks, and sport shirts. One of the specific uses of acetate is in stiffened fabrics such as semi-soft collars, in which a layer of fabric containing acetate is laminated between two layers of cotton or other fabric, and the whole welded, or fused, into a composite structure with a permanent stiffening effect by the action of a partial solvent, or heat, which bonds the acetate fibers to the adjacent fabrics. Acetate staple is being employed in the floor-covering field.

Fabrics are often constructed with filament and spun yarns in combination as warp and filling respectively, or in other ways. In addition to the woven fabrics, acetate filament yarn has been very successful in tricot knit fabrics, known as acetate jerseys, for women's dresses and gloves.

In children's apparel filament and staple acetate are used in a variety of garments, ranging from party dresses to play clothes.

Another development has been the increasing use of fabrics derived from sportswear types for work clothes for both men and women, and for uniforms for such services as air transport, messengers, and building employees.

The thermoplasticity of acetate is utilized in the making of ribbons, hatbands, and tapes from broad woven goods by cutting the wide fabric into the desired widths with heated blades, which simultaneously cut the fabric and fuse the edges into an almost invisible selvage that prevents raveling.

Household Textiles. In this field, filament acetate yarn has long held a place in fine ninons, glass curtains, taffetas, and satins for draperies and bedspreads, and acetate staple fiber is being used in blankets. As a result of recent improvements in the fastness qualities of dyed acetate fabrics, the use of acetate in both draperies and upholstery is increasing.

Industrial Textiles. The most important industrial application of acetate is undoubtedly in the field of electrical insulation, because of the outstanding electrical characteristics of this fiber. It is used in the form of yarn for covering wires, and in the form of tape for covering coils. Plasticized acetate staple is employed for the manufacture of teabags, filter cloths, and certain types of industrial felts. Lint-free wiping cloths, and uniforms for workers in industrial operations in which the products being manufactured must be protected from contamination by the lint produced by the abrasion of clothing made of short fibers are made from filament acetate yarns.

Woven textures range all the way from sheer chiffons through fine satins, taffetas, and crepes, to velvets and heavier pile fabrics. Acetate staple fiber is used in a range of weaves of the types encompassed

which the fiber will dye and the amount of dyestuff it will take up in reasonable commercial times is very measurably increased. In many cases the hand of the fabric is improved as to fullness and soft silkiness.

The Opus treatment is of particular advantage in sewing thread. Fortisan sewing threads which have had this treatment have excellent sewability and extremely uniform sewing results. Yarns which have a high, quick elastic recovery yet stretch rather readily at low loads constitute quite a problem in sewing in that the tension in sewing results in a residual energy in the sewn seam which in turn results in a tightening and puckering or gathering of the sewn material. Fortisan threads have a high resistance to stretch and thus this problem does not arise. The Opus treatment causes a longitudinal contraction of the yarn, a moderate reduction in breaking load, and substantially higher elongation. Resistance to stretch, however, still remains high, and this coupled with the higher elongation improves sewing qualities, does not lower the stitched or looped strength, and increases the resistance of the sewn seam to ripping.

Printing presents no special problem, and all usual types of printing have been applied to Fortisan yarn and fabrics.

Normal Aging. All textiles are slowly degraded and weakened by aging. This rate of degradation is slow, and garments even 100 years old or more, especially those of cellulosic origin, are frequently found having considerable residual strength. This degradation is hastened by the action of light, ultraviolet rays, heat, moisture, organisms, etc. Fortisan yarn and fabric have been carefully tested for the effects of normal, everyday aging, and yarns and fabrics have shown no apparent weakening.

Solubility. In this respect Fortisan behaves like cotton or regenerated cellulose.

Resistance to Exposure, Visible Light, and Ultraviolet. These factors of resistance are high on Fortisan yarns and fabrics which have higher strength, after severe exposure, than other fibers.

Resistance to Molds, Mildew, Fungi. The structure of the Fortisan filament imparts improved resistance to mildew, fungi, molds, soil organisms, etc. The usual fungicides and other proofing agents may be added with satisfactory results to such products as they are to cotton, etc., to provide high resistance to different kinds of organisms. Again, the high original strength offers an advantage over other yarns under conditions of abnormal exposure to rotting organisms.

Organic Solvents. Fortisan yarn and fabrics are inert to organic solvents including, of course, those used in dry cleaning. Launderability is excellent, and fabrics may be ironed as easily as cotton or linen. The fine filaments give high covering power, and thus garments of lighter weight can be employed.

Uses. See "History."

CHAPTER XVIII

SYNTHETIC FIBERS, FILAMENTS, TOW, AND YARNS

In this chapter have been grouped and described all American man-made fibers, filaments, and yarns that do not have a natural base, nor are derived or regenerated from a natural base, but are strictly synthetic raw materials.

Varying space has been allotted to these fibers, depending on the information available at the time and their relative importance. These fibers have been classified in various ways by different authorities, but a convenient and simple grouping is shown in Fig. 1.

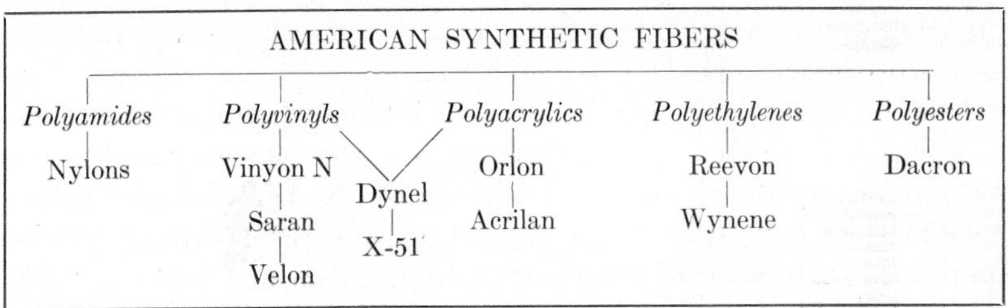

FIG. 1. Classification of synthetic fibers.

All of the fibers in Fig. 1 are currently produced commercially in the United States, and their production reached at least 200 million lb in 1952, with an estimated plant capacity of 385 million lb. Fibers still in the experimental stage have not been included because of their relative unimportance or because they will never be produced commercially. Aralac (casein) and Soylan (soybean) fibers described in the fifth edition have been omitted because they are no longer made in the United States. For information on Plexon see fifth edition, pages 905 to 908. For a summary of all non-cellulosic yarns, staple, and tow, see Table 48.

Much of this chapter is devoted to nylon. A large part of the material in the *American Handbook of Synthetic Textiles* (Textile Book Publishers, New York, 1952) that concerns the manufacture of the synthetic fibers and their physical, chemical, and microscopic properties has been used.

Although much information has been available on some fibers, less was available on some of the newer fibers, and the latest or additional information should be obtained directly from the producer when needed. It was found impossible to keep all the information up to the minute, because of the time required to complete this section. However, the information used has been gathered from reliable sources and is subject to revision from time to time after publication, because of changes in the product made by the manufacturer.

The synthetic fibers have gained in commercial importance and are definitely here to stay. Their commercial importance and industrial progress in the future will depend largely on price relationships, evaluation of properties, and fields of application or end uses.

None of them will serve all purposes at one time, each one having its own distinctive qualities and properties, which are depicted in this chapter in great detail. Since this is an extremely lucrative field, it is possible that more and more synthetic fibers, filaments, and yarns will be created by the advance of chemistry and plastics in all its branches and by more intensified chemical research. For X-ray diagrams of these fibers see Chapter XXI.

Due to wide price differences and various desirable properties, blending of these fibers among themselves as well as with the principal natural fibers will be practiced to a great extent, until the proper combinations have been found to meet specifications of price, special properties such as weight, feel or handle, finish, and other requirements desirable for apparel or industry. This is one of the advantageous aspects of the synthetic fiber, in that each producer can and no doubt will modify each fiber to meet special needs and requirements, which is not possible with the natural fibers. Foreign makes of these same fibers may have different properties.

The synthetic fibers are discussed in the following order: nylon, Orlon, Dynel, Vinyon, vinylidene chloride filaments and yarns (Saran and Velon), Acrilan, X-51, Vicara, Caslen, Dacron, and polyethylene monofilaments (e.g., Reevon).

NYLON FILAMENTS, YARNS, AND STAPLE[1]

History. Nylon is the culmination of an expanded program of fundamental research instituted by the E. I. du Pont de Nemours & Co. in 1928 at Wilmington, Del., by Dr. W. H. Carothers, formerly

[1] This section is based on information furnished by the Textile Fibers Department, E. I. du Pont de Nemours & Co.

an instructor at Harvard University. He became interested in a study of long-chain polymers and found that they were composed of large molecules in the form of chains of smaller units. In the spring of 1930, it was discovered that the dibasic acids and polyhydric alcohols combine, when heated in a molecular still, to form polyesters having molecular weights up to 25,000. Dr. Carothers designated them "super" polymers. Similarly, other super polymers were made. (See section on Dacron polyester fiber, below.) Finally, a polymer from adipic acid and hexamethylene diamine was made in 1935 and called "Polymer 66," because there are six carbon atoms each in the diamine and the adipic acid.

The first nylon filaments were made by forcing the molten polymer through a hypodermic needle. In 1936, the Rayon Department of the du Pont Company assumed sponsorship of the research, previously under the direction of the Chemical Department. In March 1937, fifty batches were run and 86 hours of continuous spinning were reached. In February the first experimental stockings were knitted. In January 1938, a pilot plant was authorized and the new building was finished in July. Meanwhile, toothbrushes, bristled with the new material, had been manufactured. This new product was named "nylon," and its first use was announced by du Pont. The name was chosen because it is distinctive and easy to pronounce and became a new word in the English language, a name for an entirely new family of chemicals, staple, yarns, and materials.

A nylon plant in Seaford, Delaware, started production in January 1940. In the meantime the first women's nylon hosiery made from experimental yarn was produced and put on preliminary sale in a Wilmington store in October 1939. By May 1940, women's nylon stockings were available in all principal cities. About 64 million pairs of nylon hose were sold during the first year. In October 1940, announcement was made of a second plant for the manufacture of nylon yarn, to be built at Martinsville, Va. This plant went into production in November 1941.

Then nylon went to war, and its first application for military uses was as a replacement for silk in parachutes. Both Seaford, Del., and Martinsville, Va., plants were diverted entirely to the production of yarn for military uses in February 1942. During World War II nylon found extensive uses in escape parachutes, not only in the canopy cloth but also in shroud lines, harness webbing, and belting. Later, it was used in bomber tires as a tire fabric; as tow rope for gliders; pup tents in the tropics; shoe laces and uppers for army shoes. It was

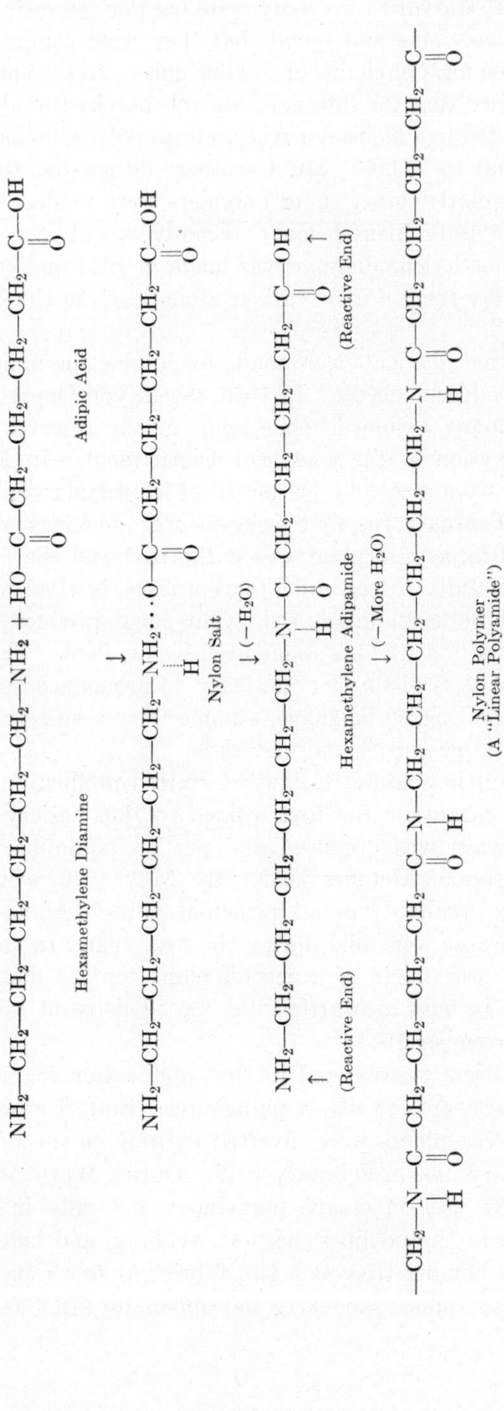

$$NH_2—CH_2—CH_2—CH_2—CH_2—CH_2—CH_2—NH_2 + HO—\underset{\underset{O}{\|}}{C}—CH_2—CH_2—CH_2—CH_2—\underset{\underset{O}{\|}}{C}—OH$$

Hexamethylene Diamine   Adipic Acid

$$\downarrow$$

$$NH_2—CH_2—CH_2—CH_2—CH_2—CH_2—CH_2—\underset{\underset{H}{\vdots}}{N}H_2\cdots O—\underset{\underset{O}{\|}}{C}—CH_2—CH_2—CH_2—CH_2—\underset{\underset{O}{\|}}{C}—OH$$

Nylon Salt

$$\downarrow (-H_2O)$$

$$NH_2—CH_2—CH_2—CH_2—CH_2—CH_2—CH_2—\underset{\underset{H}{|}}{N}—\underset{\underset{O}{\|}}{C}—CH_2—CH_2—CH_2—CH_2—\underset{\underset{O}{\|}}{C}—OH$$

↑ (Reactive End)   Hexamethylene Adipamide   ↑ (Reactive End)

$$\downarrow (-\text{More } H_2O)$$

$$—CH_2—\underset{\underset{H}{|}}{N}—\underset{\underset{O}{\|}}{C}—CH_2—CH_2—CH_2—CH_2—\underset{\underset{O}{\|}}{C}—\underset{\underset{H}{|}}{N}—CH_2—CH_2—CH_2—CH_2—CH_2—CH_2—\underset{\underset{H}{|}}{N}—\underset{\underset{O}{\|}}{C}—CH_2—CH_2—CH_2—CH_2—\underset{\underset{O}{\|}}{C}—$$

Nylon Polymer
(A "Linear Polyamide")

FIG. 2.

brush was still in active service after a year's operation, whereas natural bristles in some cases lasted only a week.

Nylon ropes used as drive ropes on spinning mules have been known to show no signs of wear after 1 year in service, whereas the rate of replacement of cotton ropes was 1 rope each 24 hr.

This resistance is attributed to the inherent toughness, natural pliability, and the ability of nylon to undergo a high degree of flexing without breakdown. Coupled with these properties the smooth-filament surfaces do not readily create friction when rubbed against themselves or other surfaces.

From Table 3, it appears that nylon yarn should be bulkier and give more coverage than any other common textile fiber for yarn of a

TABLE 3. Fiber Densities *

Fiber	*Density (Grams/ Cubic Centimeter)*	*Fiber*	*Density (Grams/ Cubic Centimeter)*
Acetate	1.33	Nitrate (cellulose)	1.54
Aralac	1.29	Nylon	1.14
Asbestos	2.10–2.80	Orlon acrylic fiber †	1.17
Camel hair	1.32	Permalon	1.72
Cotton	1.50	Ramie	1.51
Cuprammonium	1.52	Saran	1.72
Dacron polyester fiber †	1.38	Silk, raw	1.33
Fiberglas	2.56	boiled-off	1.25
Fortisan	1.52	tussah	1.27
Hemp	1.48	Velon	1.72
Jute	1.48	Vinyon	1.35
Linen	1.50	Viscose rayon	1.52
Mohair	1.32	Wool	1.32

* Obtained from various sources.

† From E. I. du Pont de Nemours & Co.

given weight. But such is not the case. First, nylon is comparatively translucent, particularly in the low-twist, bright yarn form. Second, the thread is extremely compact due to the fact that each individual filament is uniformly circular in cross-section and is free from surface irregularities, being similar to glass rods in this respect. Thus, nylon hose possesses greater sheerness than silk hose of comparable gauge and weight.

When nylon is compared with materials outside the textile field, such as copper wire, its advantage in light weight shows up quite markedly. For instance, where nylon monofilament yarn (specific gravity 1.14) is substituted for copper wire (specific gravity 8.9) as in industrial filter screening, equal weights of these two materials will result in a much greater yardage of finished nylon screening.

Elastic Recovery

Elastic recovery is the ability of a material to regain its original length after being stretched. The length of time required for the yarn to recover its original length is important. Without elastic recovery, it is not possible to produce fabrics which will maintain their original shape or conform to specific contours of the body. The cling or fit of nylon and silk hose results from the inherent elastic recovery of these two fibers.

Data from tests on the elastic recovery for nylon and silk at various conditions are shown in Tables 4 and 5.

TABLE 4. Recovery against No Load, Stretch 100 Seconds, Recovery within 60 Seconds

Per Cent Stretch	*Per Cent Elastic Recovery* Silk	Nylon
2	..	100
4	76	100
8	56	100
16	47	91

TABLE 5. Recovery against a Load of 0.25 Gram/Denier, Stretch for 30 Seconds, Recovery in 60 Seconds

Fiber	*After Stretch of* 1 Per Cent	2 Per Cent	4 Per Cent
Nylon	38%	63%	73%
Silk	82%	74%	59%

Delayed Recovery. When nylon yarn is allowed to relax against no load after it has been held under tension for several days, it does not immediately return to its original length, but *creeps back slowly.* However, it almost instantly recovers approximately 50 per cent of the stretch imparted and will during the first 24 hr recover a total of approximately 85 per cent, of the amount of the stretch. It will require approximately 2 weeks for the stretched yarn to recover completely and return *to its original length.* These results were obtained from yarn held under constant R.H. conditions of 72 per cent. Subjecting the yarn to high temperature or high R.H. will hasten its return to original length.

The delayed recovery should be considered a part of the total residual shrinkage. When testing yarn for per cent residual shrinkage, the original length of the sample should be measured immediately (within 5 min); otherwise some recovery will take place and the results will be in error by the unknown amount of recovery which takes place before the original measurement.

Stretchability; Modulus of Stretch

Nylon yarn requires less tension for a given amount of stretch than most common textile fibers. (This refers to unsized nylon; the effect of size on modulus varies with the amount and type of size. See Table 6.)

TABLE 6. MODULUS OF STRETCH

Fiber *	*Modulus of Stretch (Grams/Denier per 1 Per Cent of Stretch)*
Silk	0.75–1.16
Wool	0.30–0.40
Nylon (at 50% R.H.)	0.31
Cotton	0.50
Glass yarn	2.75
Cellulose acetate	0.40
Viscose rayon	0.70
Ramie and cuprammonium	0.90

	Modulus for Low-Stretch Range		*Modulus for High-Stretch Range*	
*Nylon * Package*	*Modulus*	*Stretch Range*	*Modulus*	*Stretch Range*
Pirns	0.41	0–5%	0.63	5–9%
Skeined and relaxed	0.22	0–6%	0.56	6–11%
Skeined-steam shrunk	0.14	0–7%	0.20	7–14%
Skeined-steam shrunk-backwound	0.17	0–10%	0.30	10–19%

* *Note:* Nylon samples conditioned at 72 per cent R.H. and 78° F. All other fibers conditioned at 50 per cent R.H. and 25° C. (77° F.).

The "modulus of stretch" may be defined as the ratio of the increase in load to the increase in elongation.

Thus, if an initial load of 2.05 grams/denier produces 5 per cent elongation, the modulus is 2.05/5, or 0.41 gram/denier per 1 per cent stretch, between zero per cent and 5 per cent elongation. If a further increase in load of 2.52 grams/denier produces an additional 4 per cent elongation, the modulus is 2.52/4, or 0.63 gram/denier per 1 per cent stretch, between 5 per cent and 9 per cent elongation. The over-all average modulus is $(2.05 + 2.52)/(5 + 4)$, or 0.51 gram/denier per 1 per cent stretch, between zero per cent and 9 per cent elongation.

Nylon's stress-strain curve as obtained with an IP-4 Scott Tester has two rather straight portions with different slopes, one for the lower range and one for the higher range. In Table 7 are listed some modulus data representing nylon yarns with different yarn histories. There are also listed some modulus data on several other fibers for comparison. Hence, the history of a nylon sample has great influence on its modulus of stretch. The R.H. of the atmosphere in which nylon yarn is conditioned also greatly affects its modulus of stretch, as illustrated by an actual test in Table 7.

TABLE 7. MODULUS OF STRETCH AT VARIOUS RELATIVE HUMIDITIES

Relative Humidity (Per Cent)	*Modulus of Stretch (Grams/Denier for 1 Per Cent Stretch)*
0	0.48
50	0.31
100	0.116

From the above tables, it is seen that thread tensions should be as uniform as possible in order not to introduce large variations in the amount of stretch. Although it possesses elasticity, as does rubber, nylon yarn does not recover or snap back after release of tension as quickly as rubber. Like rubber, it constantly tries to return to its original length when held in stretched condition, and will exert a relentless, crushing force upon any packages on which it is wound, until allowed to contract. In view of the crushing force exerted by stretched nylon, it is extremely important that tensions employed in winding cones, spools, bobbins, beams, etc., be held to a minimum consistent with proper performance, and that proper consideration be given to the quantity of yarn per unit package. The more wraps the package contains, the greater the potential crushing force.

Flammability

Experience has shown that nylon yarn is more resistant to burning than cotton, rayon, silk, or wool. This is confirmed by tests on woven fabrics conducted by the Associated Factory Mutual Fire Insurance Companies as reported in their Bulletin No. 10646, August 15, 1940, entitled, *The Fire Hazard of Nylon*.

The natural flammability of clean, undyed, finish-free nylon and of nylon dyed and finished with properly selected materials is very low and is considered highly satisfactory for practically all textile purposes. Nylon will not flash burn. It will melt at a temperature of approximately 480° F., if a flame is applied. However, as soon as the igniting flame is removed, the melt will drop away from the yarn or fabric and harden with very little tendency for further flame propagation. The term "flameproof" as applied to fabrics implies a resistance to any spread of flame after the fabric has been ignited. Undyed, unfinished nylon yarn or fabric may, therefore, be considered flameproof since it does not support spread of the flame after the igniting source has been removed. Cotton, paper, and wood are distinctly different in this respect.

If pigments, dyes, oils, finishes, salts, or other materials are present on the fiber, there is always the possibility that the resulting treated yarn or fabric may support combustion due to their presence. Some of these materials may be flammable themselves, or may release oxygen on ignition, thereby speeding the burning of nylon or other fibers on which they are present. Other materials, which are not flammable, such as antimony oxide, talc, etc., in powder form on nylon may increase its tendency to burn. Apparently, the molten drops of nylon are thickened by the powder and, instead of dropping off before the flame is propagated to adjacent fabric, the drops cling to the fabric due to increased viscosity. Additional material is then melted and ignited, thus propagating the flame. This explains why certain flame-retardants for other materials may increase the flammability of nylon.

As a further illustration of the principle involved in the latter part of the preceding paragraph, it has been found that combination nylon-Fiberglas fabrics may burn when ignited, although neither nylon fabric nor Fiberglas fabric will support combustion alone. The same is true for combination nylon-asbestos fabrics. It has also been found that the inclusion of other fibers, such as cotton, rayon, or wool, with nylon in combination fabrics may make the fabrics more flammable even though the other fibers are treated with flame-retardants.

Some tests were made in the laboratory to determine the effect of various types of dyestuffs on the flammability of nylon fabrics. In general, it was found that most of the acetate, acid, and direct dyes had only slight or no effect on flammability, but many of the chrome and other metallized dyes appreciably increased the flammability.

In other laboratory tests, it was found that the flammability of flammable chrome-dyed nylon fabric could be reduced to the same flammability level as that of undyed control fabric by the application of a thioureaformaldehyde resin to the dyed fabric. The amount of resin required varied with the type of fabric sample. In some cases satisfactory results were obtained with as little as 2 per cent resin. The experimental thioureaformaldehyde method of treating nylon fabric is discussed in an article entitled, "A New Way to Flameproof Nylon," *Textile World,* March 1951.

In view of the many variables affecting flammability, it is considered advisable for each manufacturer of products made from nylon to have *flammability tests conducted on his own products as ready for the market,* wherever flammability is an important factor.

Heat Resistance and Related Properties

Melting Point. The melting point in air of nylon 66 polymer (the nylon ordinarily used in the textile industry) is approximately 250° C. (482° F.). The range of temperature over which nylon (66 polymer) softens and melts is very narrow.

Heat Capacity. The average "heat capacity" of nylon between 20° C. (68° F.) and 250° C. (482° F.) is 0.555 calories/grams/°C.

Heat of Fusion. The heat of fusion of nylon (66 polymer) is 22 calories/gram.

Heat Yellowing. After heating for 5 hr at 150° C. (302° F.) in dry air the relative color change of a series of undyed fabrics are as shown in Table 8.

TABLE 8. HEAT YELLOWING OF VARIOUS FIBERS

Silk	Brown
Wool	Yellow
Nylon	Light yellow
Viscose and Acetate	Still lighter yellow
Cotton	Very slight yellowing

Resistance to Deterioration from Heat. The resistance of nylon (66 polymer) to deterioration due to heat may be summed up as follows:

100° C. (212° F.)	Exposure to steam for 6 days produced slight if any change in tenacity.
200° C. (392° F.)	Oxygen-free atmosphere for 3 hr resulted in no change in tenacity.
225° C. (437° F.)	Oxygen-free atmosphere (nitrogen) for 1 to 3 hr caused some decrease in strength.
245° C. (473° F.)	Oxygen-free atmosphere (nitrogen) for 1 to 3 hr caused a considerable loss in strength.
250° C. (482° F.)	In air, nylon melts.

65° C. (149° F.) (in the dark) Air at this temperature (yarn stored in the dark) caused losses in yarn from various fibers as shown in Table 8.

Table 9 shows, for one test, the percentage loss in tenacity on yarns stored in the dark for 16 months at 65° C. (149° F.).

TABLE 9. LOSS OF TENACITY DUE TO STORAGE *

Yarn	*Not Boiled Off*	*Boiled Off*
1/40 Worsted	+9	12
25/1 Combed American cotton	25	11
Silk—200 denier 6 turn	18	16
65/1 Linen	14	35
Cordura † rayon (textile yarn) 200–80–6Z	20	4
Cordura † rayon (tire yarn) 275–120–5Z	26	4
Nylon—Semi-dull (70–23–200–5S)	13	12
Nylon—Bright (70–23–300–5S)	+3	14
Nylon—Bright (210–69–300–5S)	7	5
Nylon—Bright (210–23–300–5S)	7	16

* Exposure data of the type listed here are not believed to be quantitatively reproducible, and are intended to serve only as *indications of the order of magnitude* of percentage loss in tensile strength.

† Du Pont trade mark.

Ironing. In a laboratory test, no effect on tensile strength for temperatures up to 180° C. (356° F.) was noted. At this temperature, very slight sticking began. Sticking, of course, is undesirable.

Three very important factors to be considered in connection with ironing are: (*a*) pressure applied, (*b*) time of contact of iron with surface of fabric, and (*c*) amount of moisture present in the fabric or any covering cloth.

Exposure to Air at Elevated Temperatures. Figure 8 was made from averaged data covering several types of nylon yarn, including bright, semi-dull, regular, and high-tenacity yarns. The curves for the various nylon yarn types were so similar that it was not felt worth while to present them separately. It is seen that at temperatures above 140° C. (284° F.) the rate of loss increases rapidly with an increase in temperature. It is also seen that the percentage loss in tenacity at 140° C. (284° F.) varies roughly as the logarithm of the time of exposure.

Resistance to Insects

It is believed that nylon is as free from attack by insects as any other textile fiber, with the possible exception of Fiberglas. There is no known instance where an insect has derived nourishment from nylon. There are insects which are known to flourish and reproduce in California crude oil, whereas the same crude oil can ordinarily be used as an insecticide. There is an organism which will grow in lime-sulfur spray. Thus, there may very well be insects somewhere in the world which may thrive on nylon.

It has been demonstrated in the laboratory that several species of insects will cut their way through fabrics made of various fibers if

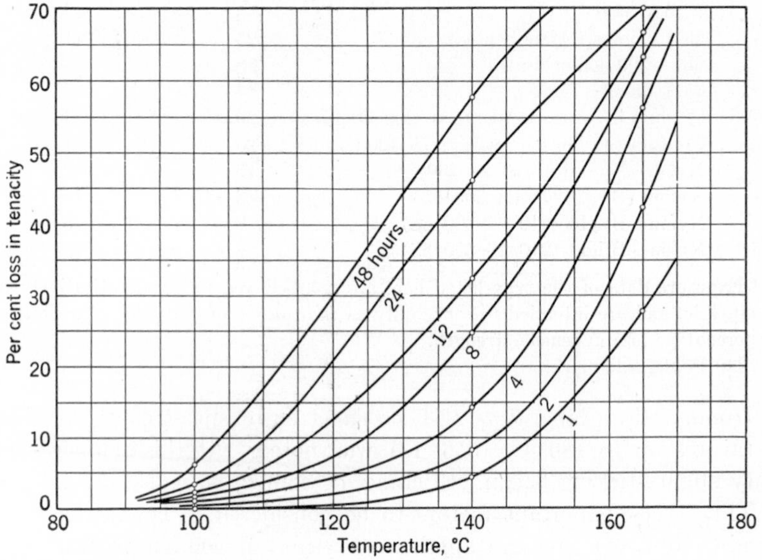

FIG. 8. Tenacity *vs.* temperature *vs.* time, nylon yarns. Permanent loss in tenacity upon exposure to air for various lengths of time at various temperatures.

entrapped within them. Insects will often attack fibers which are normally very unattractive if they are first coated with an attractive or preferred material. This sometimes occurs when sizings, finishing oils, or other materials are applied to fabrics. Damage to cloth by *leaf feeding* beetles which had accidentally been trapped in the folds of the fabric has been observed. A number of types of beetle larvae quite often cut holes in fabrics and other soft materials to assist in shedding their skins during moults. Thus, there are many cases in which insects damage fabrics and other materials without utilizing the base as food.

A few typical comments on specific insects are given below.

Clothes Moths. Endeavor to cut their way out of scoured nylon cloth when trapped or imprisoned in the folds, causing moderate damage. Neither the larvae nor the moths appear to eat the nylon for food as they do in the case of wool.

German Cockroaches. Cause little or no damage to nylon.

Black Carpet Beetles. Damaged nylon and silk during imprisonment by cutting the fibers in an attempt to release themselves. Experiments have demonstrated that this species of insect cannot live on a diet of nylon from which the spinning oils and finishes have been removed.

Firebrats. Slowly cut their way out of nylon and silk fabric, if imprisoned.

Ants. Certain varieties of ants in some localities of the United States cut their way out of nylon, silk, and other fabrics when imprisoned.

Varied Carpet Beetle (Anthrenus verbasci). This beetle has shown more tendency to eat nylon from choice than any other insect. Nylon which is perfectly free from oils or other attractive materials is not attacked by Anthrenus verbasci except upon entrapment. However, if oils which are attractive to this insect have once been applied to nylon, it appears extremely difficult to scour them off the nylon to the point where the danger of attack is completely removed. The important factor in attractiveness is not olfactory stimulation. It appears that the tactile senses of the insect are of great importance; therefore, the finish imparted to the fiber is probably the critical factor.

Resistance to Mildew, Mold, and Fungus

Undyed, unfinished nylon yarns and fabric have been found to be remarkably resistant to molds and other microorganisms, showing insignificant loss in strength after severe exposure to *Chaetomium, globosum, Metarrhizium, Stachybotyrs* sp., *Aspergillus niger* and *penicillium,* and to the microorganisms (particularly the cellulose-destroying organisms) encountered in a soil-burial test. Fabrics exposed to soil-burial tests for 21 days retained from 95 to 99 per cent of their original strength and were relatively bright and clean after rinsing in cold water.

Molds. Molds can be induced to grow upon nylon yarn by applying suitable food materials, but such growth causes little if any loss in strength of the yarn. *The use of certain finishes on nylon fabric might induce or support the formation of mold on the finish.* Each finish should be individually tested to determine possible reaction.

Bacteria. Controlled tests have shown no bacteria that readily attack nylon.

Resistance to Marine Deterioration and Fouling. Nylon fishing lines, both waterproofed and not waterproofed, when exposed to both fresh and salt water intermittently for a period of 6 months, lost only about 20 per cent of their original tensile strength. The waterproofed line accumulated a 4- or 5-in. growth of marine moss during this period; the moss was apparently feeding on the waterproofing material, *as the unwaterproofed line was perfectly clean.*

Light Resistance

Nylon yarn, like other textile fibers, is subject to degradation on exposure to light. Prolonged exposure causes a loss in strength and elongation and affects other properties of the yarn, but does not cause discoloration of the nylon. The degradation is due, primarily, to the effect of light in the visible violet and blue range of wave lengths.

Du Pont data from sunlight-exposure tests indicate that bright nylon yarns have essentially the same sunlight durability as cotton, linen, and bright textile rayon yarns of the same denier; better sunlight durability than silk and dull textile rayon yarns; and poorer sunlight durability than Orlon acrylic yarns.

Outdoor exposure tests on comparable samples of nylon and Manila (abaca) ropes showed that both lost strength on a percentage basis at about the same rate. The nylon rope remained stronger at the end of a year of atmospheric exposure, having the same percentage advantage over Manila at the end as it had for the original strength.

The degree to which nylon resists deterioration by light depends on a number of factors among which are the following (these factors are not necessarily listed in order of importance):

1. Type of fiber or yarn (bright or semi-dull).
   Bright nylon is considerably more resistant to sunlight degradation than semi-dull nylon. For this reason it is important to select bright nylon, rather than semi-dull, for uses where resistance to sunlight is obviously important, such as for window curtains, tarpaulins, awnings, and tents.
2. Filament size (denier per filament) and thickness of the thread or fabric.
   High-denier-per-filament fibers are more resistant to sunlight degradation than low-denier-per-filament fibers. Normally, the resistance is also better with thicker (heavier) cords and fabrics because of the protection afforded by the outer fibers. This would, of course, depend somewhat on the construction.

3. Dyes, finishes, and other agents in or on the fibers.
   The rate of deterioration of nylon may be appreciably affected (increased or decreased) by the presence of dyes, finishes, and other agents in or on the fibers. Some dyestuffs which in du Pont tests definitely improved the light durability of nylon yarn are as follows:

   Du Pont Brilliant Paper Yellow Extra Conc. 125%
   Pontamine[3] Fast Yellow 5GL
   Pontamine Fast Brown BRL Conc. 175%
   Pontamine Fast Red F Conc. 125%
   Pontamine Fast Orange 2GL

   In limited tests, most of the Capracyl[3] dyestuffs also improved the light durability of nylon.
4. Type of exposure, i.e., outdoors, indoors behind glass, or indoors out of direct sunlight.
   Nylon has slightly better resistance to sunlight when exposed behind window glass than when exposed outdoors. Indoors out of direct sunlight the rate of degradation is much slower, although some light deterioration may result from reflected sunlight and from lamps, especially those which emit considerable light in the visible violet and blue range of wave lengths, such as fluorescent lamps.
5. Geographical location.
   Sunlight deterioration is more rapid at certain locations than at others because of differences in duration and intensity of the particular wave lengths which damage the fiber. In du Pont tests nylon deteriorated more rapidly in Florida sunlight exposure than in Delaware exposure. Location may also affect the relative light resistances of the different fibers.
6. Time of year when exposed.
   At most, but not all, locations in the United States, deterioration due to sunlight is much more rapid in summer than in winter. A rough comparison based on comparative outdoor and Weather-ometer durability results with the same nylon yarns gave the ratios shown in Table 10 for outdoor exposure in Wilmington, Del., and exposure in a single carbon arc Weatherometer. This is by no means to be considered authoritative, but only tentative and subject to change as additional information indicates.

[3] Du Pont trade marks.

TABLE 10. Time Required for Equivalent Degradation of Nylon Outdoors in Wilmington and in a Weatherometer

Month	*Outdoors Wilmington (Weeks)*	*Weather-ometer (Hours)*	*Month*	*Outdoors Wilmington (Weeks)*	*Weather-ometer (Hours)*
January	10	100	July	0.8	100
February	8	100	August	1.5	100
March	3.6	100	September	2.5	100
April	1.0	100	October	4	100
May	0.9	100	November	7	100
June	0.8	100	December	9	100

Comments on Exposure Tests. Du Pont experience indicates that it is impossible to draw valid conclusions from the results of exposure of any two fibers or fabrics unless the items to be compared are concurrently given identical conditions of exposure. Even then, such factors as the wave lengths of the particular light may affect the relative light degradation of the fibers.

In testing products such as tents, tarpaulins, sails, and flags, where light resistance is obviously important, degrading factors other than light should also be considered. In many cases these other factors may cause more damage to some of the textile fibers than light. Examples are mildew and mold, industrial fumes, smoke from burning fuel, constant flexing, abrasive wear, and sand carried by the wind. Sand may not only abrade but also may exert a shearing action on filaments under stress during testing. Some items are in storage longer than out of storage. Under certain conditions, many fibers are damaged more by storage rot (mildew, mold, fungus, etc.) than by longer periods of actual use.

In selecting a fiber for any particular use, full consideration should be given to *all* the conditions which the material will have to undergo. Wherever possible, it is advisable to make durability tests under the same conditions as those which will be encountered in actual use of the product.

Shrinkage and Swelling

Boiling nylon fibers with 10 per cent Glauber's salt caused a 3 per cent swelling. Nylon yarn which was immersed in 5 per cent cresylic acid solution for 5 to 10 minutes at 50° C. shrank to almost one-half of its original length. The wet length varies from about a 3 per cent gain to an actual loss in length as compared with bone-dry nylon, depending upon the degree of previous relaxation and removal of residual shrinkage. Fully shrunk nylon yarn gains in length when wet.

The *unrelaxed* residual shrinkage of current nylon yarns as removed from shipping pirns, as determined in boiling water, is between 8 per cent and 12 per cent and is usually 9.25 per cent ± 0.75 per cent.

Relaxation of the yarn in air for 24 hr under zero tension, after being removed from pirns, results in 2–2.5 per cent relaxation (contraction), which reduces the residual shrinkage still remaining in the yarn by this amount.

Some *actual shrinkage data* on completely unshrunk yarn (pirns) and on partially shrunk yarn (cones) are given in Table 11 and Fig. 9.

TABLE 11. SHRINKAGE TESTS ON YARNS

Treatment				*Per Cent Shrinkage*			
				Pirns		*Cones* *	
Temperature (°C.)	*Steam Pressure Gauge*	*Shrinking Medium*	*Time (minutes)*	*Actual*	*Residual*	*Actual*	*Residual*
25		Water	3	4.7	4.4	0.3	3.9
80		Water	3	7.5	1.0	2.3	1.2
100		Water	3	8.8	0.2	3.5	0.0
100	Atmos.	Sat. steam	3	7.9	0.8	3.6	0.8
100	Atmos.	Sat. steam	10	8.5	0.0	3.6	0.6
100	Atmos.	Sat. steam	30	8.4	0.4	4.4	0.0
121	15 lb	Sat. steam	3	9.7	0.3	5.4	0.3
121	15 lb	Sat. steam	10	10.0	0.2	5.8	0.0
134	30 lb	Sat. steam	3	11.5	0.2	7.3	−0.3
134	30 lb	Sat. steam	30	11.7	0.0	8.1	−0.3

* Cones: Twist-setting conditions—180° F. dry bulb, 170° F. wet bulb—for 2 hr before sizing.

Note: Original yarn lengths were measured within 5 min after removing yarn from packages. The actual shrinkage values above represent "unrelaxed" yarn shrinkages.

Effects of Variable Relative Humidity. Changes in length with changes in relative humidity are experienced with nylon yarns and materials. This is believed to be a fundamental physical-chemical characteristic of the polymer. It is believed to affect monofilament and multifilament yarns in the same manner and to approximately the same degree.

Figure 10 shows what happened in an actual test on 11-mil diameter monofilaments cold drawn from nylon 66 polymer.

In three different styles of nylon sail *fabric,* a fluctuation between 35 per cent and 100 per cent R.H. caused an average change of approximately 1.1 per cent in linear measurements, the greater measurements corresponding with the higher R.H.

The linear measurements of these three sail fabrics when soaked in water of varying temperatures increased about ½ per cent in water

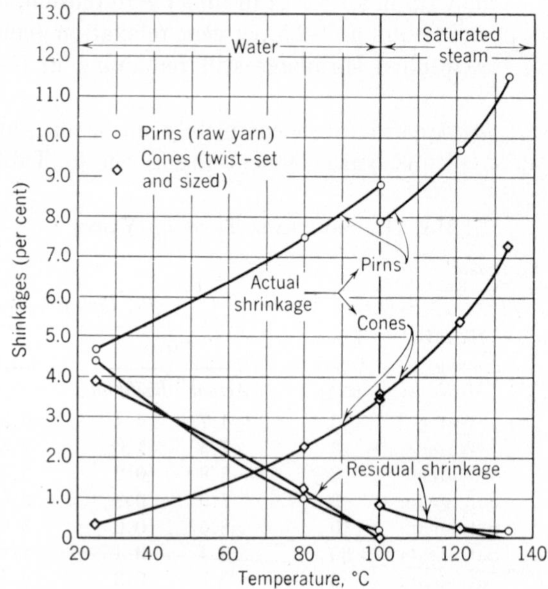

Fig. 9. Three-minute shrinkages of nylon yarn. Actual shrinkage *vs.* shrinkage conditions, and residual shrinkage remaining in yarn (as determined by the boiling-water method) *vs.* shrinkage conditions.

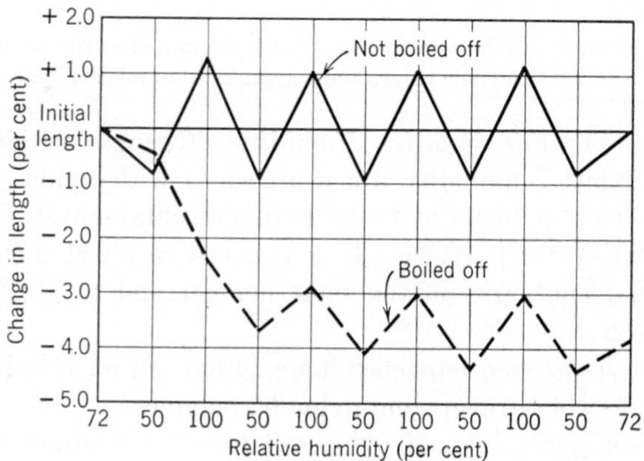

Fig. 10. Nylon 66—11 mil diameter—cold drawn.

at 7° C. as compared with water at 45° C. The measurements were longer in cool water than in warm water.

Extractable Matter

When nylon is given a scour to remove size and/or oil, there is a slight loss of water-soluble material in the nylon itself. The amount of this loss is related to the temperature, time, and constituents (soap or plain water) of the scour bath. Under a very specific set of conditions, it is found that approximately 1.0 per cent of extractable material was removed in addition to size and oil. More drastic boil-off procedures may result in a slightly greater loss, whereas less drastic procedures approaching something like soaking in water at roon temperature may result in a lower loss of extractable material. This is a basic characteristic of nylon and does not indicate weakening of the fiber. Net billed weights take into account this loss, since the billing factors are arrived at by scouring the yarn using a typical scour formula under controlled laboratory conditions.

Toxicological Properties

Before nylon was introduced, tests were conducted by du Pont's Haskell Laboratory of Industrial Toxicology on undyed and unfinished nylon, using, as a control, rayon and degummed natural silk. There were definitely no greater number of positive reactions from nylon than from the control fabrics. These and other toxicological studies demonstrated that the use of nylon itself by humans involved no greater hazard than that of rayon or degummed natural silk. Repeated experiments and continued experience have proved that the type of polymer which goes into the nylon yarns does not possess harmful toxicological properties, and is incapable of causing skin reaction. Nylon has met the rigid suture requirements of the medical profession, and is now being successfully used in surgical work. Nylon is not the causative factor of any of the conditions which are reported, and, furthermore, any references to "nylon dermatitis" or "an allergy to nylon" are distinct misnomers. In fact, any cases which have been traced back invariably have been associated with dyeing and finishing materials.

Dr. Louis Schwartz, formerly in charge of dermatosis investigations for the U. S. Public Health Service, Bethesda, Md., has conducted some investigations, and his reports [4] entitled "An Outbreak of Derma-

[4] *J. Am. Med. Assoc.*, **115**, 906–911 (Sept. 1940); **128**, 1209–1217 (Aug. 25, 1945).

titis from New Resin Fabric Finishes" and "Dermatitis from Wearing Apparel" confirm the statement that nylon does not possess harmful toxicological properties.

TABLE 12. Electrical Properties of Nylon Film

Volume resistivity: 18% R.H.	4×10^{14} ohms-cm
Wet	5×10^{9} ohms-cm
Breakdown strength: Unrolled, 9 mils	1300 volts/mil
Rolled, 2 mils	3000 volts/mil

Dielectric Properties	*Power Factor (per cent)*	*Dielectric Constant*
1000 cycles, 18% R.H., 22° C.	5	4
1000 cycles, wet, 22° C.	11	20
60 cycles, dry, 33° C.	1.8	3.8
60 cycles, dry, 90° C.	13	7

Resistance to Perspiration

Synthetic perspiration prepared in both acid and alkaline solution was found to have virtually no effect on the tensile strength and color of a woven nylon slip fabric during exposure under a wide range of temperatures in the laboratory. Single end tensile strength tests made after overnight soakings at room temperature and following exposures for 2 hr at 212° F. in the two solutions showed substantially no strength loss in the warp direction of the fabric under any of these conditions, and only a negligible loss (approximately 8 per cent) in the filling following exposure to the most severe conditions, namely, the acid solution at 212° F. for 2 hr. A slight loss in color from the original pink shade of the fabric resulted from the action of the perspiration. The slip fabric used in these tests contained 40-denier, 34-filament nylon in the warp and 60-denier, 20-filament nylon in the filling. Its finished construction was 330 x 125.

The solutions were made up as follows: *Acid:* 10 grams sodium chloride, 1 gram lactic acid, U.S.P. 85 per cent, 1 gram disodium orthophosphate, anhydrous, made up to 1 liter with water. *Alkaline:* 10 grams sodium chloride, 4 grams ammonium carbonate, U.S.P., 1 gram disodium orthophosphate, anhydrous, to 1 liter with water.

Residual Shrinkage

Delayed recovery should be considered a part of the total residual shrinkage. When testing yarn for percentage of residual shrinkage, the original length of the sample should be measured immediately (within 5 min); otherwise, some recovery will take place and the results will be in error by the unknown amount of recovery which takes place before the original measurement. Below is the procedure which is employed in determining residual shrinkage of yarn.

Skein Shrinkage Method for Determining Residual Shrinkage

Sampling. Samples of yarn for shrinkage consist of 450-meter denier-skeins. These skeins are wound on a denier reel with or without traverse; tied loosely with a single, colored tie; and the length is measured on the shrinkometer immediately, i.e., within 5 min of reeling. Colored yarn has been used for identifying skeins. Serially numbered brass tags simplify the identification procedure. These tags are tied to the skein with a single lace of thread.

Number of Samples. Two or preferably three skeins are taken from single packages of yarn to be samples. In lot sampling the number of skeins would depend upon the size of the lot and the certainty with which the shrinkage was to be established.

Relaxation. Nylon yarn, when wound off a package into skein form, shrinks or relaxes as much as 2.8 per cent on hanging under no tension for 3 days. The amount of relaxation depends upon the tightness of the package from which the yarn was removed, presence or absence of size, amount of twist and other factors, *being greater for drawtwister* packages and at least for soft spools. Data indicate that approximately 85 per cent of this relaxation takes place within 24 hr and that the rate of relaxation is relatively slow after this length of time. Since allowance of complete relaxation would be inconvenient because of the time involved, a 24-hr relaxation period has been standardized.

Second Measurement. At the end of 24 ± 1 hours, the skeins are remeasured on the shrinkometer to obtain the relaxed length, wrapped in cheesecloth, and boiled off.

Boil Off. The skein is twisted once into a "figure 8," folded on itself, twisted and folded again, giving a four-coil loop about 2½ in. in diameter. This loop is laid flat on a piece of cheesecloth approximately 11 in. square, leaving about 4 in. of cheesecloth border around the skein. Two horizontal folds are made over the skein, giving a package about 2½ in. wide by 11 in. long; then the ends are folded over the skein, and the two overlapping ends fastened with a paper clip. The final package is flat and about 5 in. square. The wrapped samples are placed in boiling water and remain there for 1 hr and 10 min.

It has been determined that 1 hr is sufficient by reboiling samples and obtaining no additional shrinkage, and the 10 min were added to this because the bath requires 6 min to regain the boil on the introduction of 15 samples. The bath in use is a converted domestic pressure cooker about 14 in. in diameter, 7 in. deep, provided with a cover containing four ½-in. holes to allow the escape of steam. It is heated on an electric hot plate. Since the wrapped samples often float, a heavy wire screen (about ½-mesh), supplied with legs so that it rests horizontally about ½ in. below the surface of the water, is placed over the samples to insure their thorough wetting at all times during the boil-off period. A maximum of 15 skeins per boil off is specified to insure no interference during the shrinkage reaction.

FIG. 11. Shrinkometer.

Drying of Skeins. Upon removal from the boil-off bath, the skeins are centrifuged (still wrapped) for 5 min, removed from their cheesecloth wrappers, scutched to straighten them out, and hung to dry in a conditioned area (72 per cent R.H. 74° F. dry bulb). For convenience and to insure complete drying, a period of at least 24 hr is specified, although data indicate that drying is substantially complete in 7 hr.

Final Measurement. When the skeins are completely dry and conditioned, they are again measured on the shrinkometer to obtain the final shrunk length.

Calculations. Per cent shrinkage is reported on the unrelaxed and relaxed bases. Calculations are as follows:

L_1 = Original length of skein
L_2 = Length of skein after relaxation, before boil off
L_3 = Length of skein after boil off

$$\text{Unrelaxed \% shrinkage} = \frac{(L_1 - L_3)(100)}{L_1}$$

$$\text{Relaxed \% shrinkage} = \frac{(L_2 - L_3)(100)}{L_2}$$

Shrinkometer. The shrinkometer (see Fig. 11) consists of two arms, the lower arm movable, attached to a vertical upright. The lower arm is connected to a dial calibrated to read in centimeters, the smallest division on the dial being 0.05 cm. The skein to be measured is placed over the upper (fixed) arm, and the lower one lifted and allowed to fall repeatedly until a constant reading is obtained. Successive measurements on the same skein are reproducible to within about 0.06 cm maximum discrepancy—usually to within 0.03 cm.

Moisture Regain.

The moisture regain of nylon fibers at any given R.H. is considerably less than that of most of the common textile fibers, but greater than that of some of the newer synthetic fibers. Some moisture regain data for various textile fibers at 65 per cent R.H. and room temperature are summarized in Table 13.

TABLE 13. AVERAGE REGAIN OF VARIOUS FIBERS

Fiber	*Approximate Average Regain at 65 Per Cent R.H. and Room Temperature (per cent)*
Wool	16
Viscose rayon	13
Silk and mercerized cotton	11
Cotton and linen	8
Acetate	6
Nylon	4
Orlon acrylic fiber	1–2
Dacron polyester fiber	0.4

Figure 12 summarizes moisture regain data for several nylon yarns at a temperature of 75° F. and under various R.H. conditions.

Nylon fibers, like most other textile fibers, undergo changes in length with changes in moisture content. If the moisture content of nylon fibers, previously boiled off to eliminate shrinkage, is increased, the fibers will increase in length. They will decrease in length when the moisture content is reduced.

Table 14 summarizes some data obtained in the du Pont laboratory on the increase in length of various "preshrunk" fibers with an increase in R.H. from zero per cent to 100 per cent at room temperature. The fibers returned to their original lengths when conditioned again at zero per cent R.H.

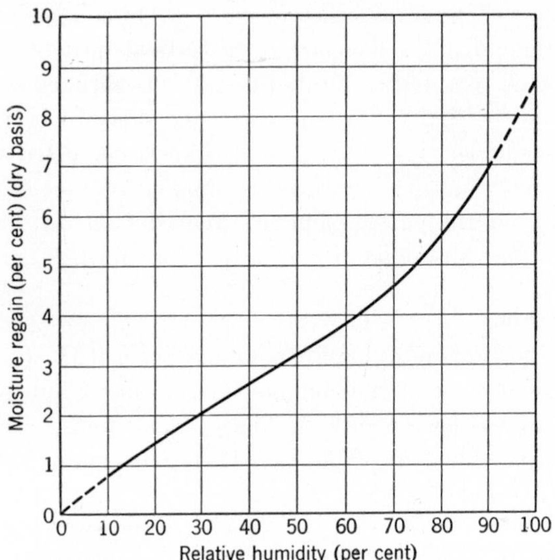

FIG. 12. Drawn nylon yarns. Moisture regain *vs.* relative humidity. Average values at 75° F.

TABLE 14. INCREASE IN LENGTH DUE TO RELATIVE HUMIDITY

Fiber	*Average Increase in Length of the Samples Tested* * *(0–100 Per Cent R.H.) (per cent)*
Viscose rayon	3.4
Nylon	2.4
Acetate	2.1
Wool	1.1
Silk	0.7
Orlon acrylic fiber	0.3
Cotton	0.2
Dacron polyester fiber	0.1

* In some cases significant differences were noted with different samples of the same fiber.

A change in the moisture content causes only a slight change in the diameter of nylon fibers. Limited tests indicate that the diameter of thoroughly wet nylon is approximately 2 per cent greater than that of the dry fiber.

The rate at which nylon yarn will pick up moisture from the air is largely dependent upon the type of package on which it is wound, particularly the density of the package. For instance, it was found that continuous-filament yarn packages originally at equilibrium with 72 per cent R.H. which were transferred to an atmosphere of 50 per cent R.H. reached equilibrium as follows:

Cones, after approximately 300 hr.
Spools, after approximately 320 hr.
Shipping bobbins, practically no change after 530 hr.

The time required for unsized, unfinished nylon fabric weighing 1.4 oz/sq yd, either saturated at 100 per cent R.H. or essentially dry, to reach equilibrium at 72 per cent R.H. was approximately 20 min. This may be compared with 450-meter skeins, which took 60 to 85 min to reach equilibrium. This would indicate, therefore, that any conditioning treatment should be dependent on the type, as well as the size, of the package.

Apparently, the low moisture regain of nylon as compared with rayon, silk, or cotton makes nylon fibers more susceptible to static electricity. Therefore, in processing nylon it is usually advisable to maintain the R.H. in the storage and processing rooms at as high a level as is consistent with good performance. Sized yarn may have a lower ceiling of R.H. for good performance than unsized yarn because of the effect of moisture on the size.

Heat Stabilization

It is usually necessary to set nylon fabric to prevent the formation of permanent wrinkles during scouring, dyeing, and finishing, and to make the product dimensionally stable. Setting enables the ultimate consumer to launder nylon materials in warm or hot water without excessive wrinkling. The dimensional stability of properly set nylon fabrics precludes trouble due to shrinkage or change in shape. Wearers of nylon hosiery are already familiar with the smooth condition of the hose following washing and drying in the conventional manner. Women are likewise finding that they do not need to stretch nylon curtains after laundering since they are dimensionally stable. They need to give curtains, slips, and other nylon things only a light pressing with a warm iron to smooth out the few "shadow" wrinkles which may develop during laundering.

It is important for the commercial finisher to be familiar with the physical properties of nylon which are involved in the finishing of fabrics. It is also helpful for him to know the yarns and construction of the fabrics which he is finishing so that he may adjust his procedure accordingly, to obtain finished fabrics with the best possible physical characteristics and qualities.

Stabilization of nylon goods is accomplished by various processes which subject the fabric to varying degrees of moisture, heat, and pressure, at varying lengths of time, depending upon the type of fabric being processed and the desired finishing qualities. Most woven and warp-knit fabrics made from nylon filament yarns are now being heat-set with dry heat, usually at temperatures above 400° F. Hot roll equipment is generally used for woven fabrics and tenter equipment for warp-knit fabrics.

Saturated steam is also used for setting nylon. As an example, full-fashioned nylon hose in the greige state are mounted on metal forms of suitable dimensions and shape, and are usually subjected to steam under 15 to 30 lb pressure for periods of approximately 1.5 to 3 min.

Certain fabrics such as lace or warp knit are sometimes set in smooth condition while on rolls, in boiling water or in pressure chambers with live saturated steam under 10 to 20 lb pressure for 10 min to ½ hr.

The use of dry heat applied in any one of a number of ways constitutes a *third* possible method of setting nylon fabric. One point about dry-heat setting (or dry-heat finishing) is that the effect on the fabric is quite different from the effect obtained with wet heat. Dry-heat treatment in the proper range usually improves the hand and drape of nylon fabric to a remarkable degree.

The fabric may be passed over heated rolls, or subjected to hot air as on an enclosed tenter frame, at temperatures ranging from 400° F. to 475° F. Heat may also be supplied by radiation or by induction, although dry-heat finishing by induction does not seem feasible at present. In any case, the length of time for which the fabric is subjected to dry heat is short, usually a matter of seconds. Because of the possible effect of high temperatures on the strength of nylon and its subsequent processing, temperatures over 400° F. must be used cautiously.

"Set" and "setting" are relative terms as applied to nylon. Nylon is never absolutely set. If a set is imposed on nylon, its effect will not be entirely overcome unless the original setting conditions are greatly exceeded by subsequent setting conditions.

An unset fabric must not be allowed to wrinkle during the boil off because the wrinkles will be permanently set in the fabric, that is, unless they are subsequently removed by a considerably more drastic setting procedure.

Dyeability

Nylon is dyed by practically every class of dyes, including acetate, neutral-dyeing acid, acid-dyeing acid, chrome, premetalized, direct, and other colors. Vat colors dye nylon but not with a fastness comparable with their fastness on cellulosic fibers.

For continuous-filament nylon, as in hosiery, for example, acetate colors are almost exclusively used because of their good leveling properties on nylon. When the occasional use of cellulosic fibers in combination with nylon is resorted to, a careful selection of dyes for these cellulosic fibers must be made, to avoid unlevel dyeing.

Applications and Uses

In Apparel. Continuous-filament nylon has an unusual combination of strength, elasticity, toughness, and abrasion resistance. The great toughness and abrasion resistance are unique properties which should be considered in designing fabrics. These properties are believed to stem, in part, from the low elastic modulus, which enables the fibers in a fabric to deform easily and thus spread the load over a number of fibers. The low bending modulus gives nylon a luxurious suppleness and softness which is particularly attractive in knitted fabrics. The success of nylon filament in women's hosiery is now well known. Nylon is also of interest in tricot-knitted lingerie and intimate apparel. Its high strength-to-weight ratio is translated into sheerness; high abrasion resistance into long wear and durability; ability to be heat-set into stability of dimension and shape; and its relatively low water insensitivity into ready launderability, quick drying, and, in many instances, no necessity for ironing.

Industrial. High-tenacity nylon is used in airplane tires where its high strength per unit weight and ability to withstand shock loads upon landing are utilized. These properties, together with its high resistance to fatigue, are especially attractive in tires. The initial high elongation and the development of creep under sustained loading hinder full capitalization of the favorable properties. Nylon has been utilized successfully by making a carcass sufficiently strong to stop growth. At the present time nylon is being successfully used in "off the road" tires, which require great strength, excellent flex life, and high impact resistance.

The combination of light weight, high strength per unit volume, flexibility, and elasticity are utilized in conveyor belts to obtain better troughing characteristics. The high resistance to impact and toughness of nylon contribute increased resistance to shock loads and longer wear life.

Nylon Staple. The use of nylon staple in blends with wool, cotton, rayon, and other fibers offers possibilities for future development in both knitted and woven structures. Essentially the same properties possessed by the filament yarn apply to the staple, with durability, resistance to abrasion, ease of care, and dimensional stability being paramount.

Major uses for staple are socks, sweaters, hand knitting yarns, upholstery, and as a blending component to complement certain properties of other fibers. Nylon staple in blends with wool permit the spinning of finer yarns and consequently the production of lighter fabrics. Blends of the staple with other fibers to increase abrasion resistance are particularly indicated in children's clothing, sportswear, uniforms, and upholstery. Types of nylon staple and tow are shown in Tables 15 and 16.

TABLE 15. NYLON STAPLE FIBERS *

Denier	*Lengths*	*Luster*
1.3	1½	S.D.
3.0	1½, 2½, 3, 4½	S.D.
6.0	3, 4½	Bright
15.0	3	Bright

* Furnished in crimpset and noncrimpset.
S.D., semi-dull.

TABLE 16. DU PONT NYLON TOW

Tow Denier	*Filament Denier*	*Number of Filaments*	*Luster*
330,000	1.5	220,000	S.D.
430,000	3	143,333	S.D.
330,000	6	56,000	Bright

S.D., semi-dull.

Nylon staple now ranges from 1.5 denier to 15 denier and in lengths from 1½ to 4½ in. It is made in semi-dull luster in the finer deniers up to 3 denier, and in bright luster in 6 and 15 denier. All nylon staple is crimped in its manufacture. Du Pont offers its staple as crimpset or noncrimpset. The average tenacity of nylon staple is approximately 4 grams per denier. Nylon staple has been spun to extremely fine counts because of its excellent tensile strength and light weight, which causes it to have more fibers per cross-section of yarn.

Nylon Brush Fibers

Du Pont nylon fibers for paint and household use come in lengths of ¼-in. differences starting at 2½ in. The 3-in. length is the most popular, and the 5-in. the longest. The tips are blunt and must be tapered by special machining.

Nylon brush fibers come in three dimensions. Tapering is shown in Table 17.

TABLE 17. NYLON BRISTLE TAPERS

Butt	*Tip*
0.009″	0.005″
0.012″	0.008″
0.015″	0.010″

These fibers are black when used for paint or industrial brushes and generally white for personal brushes.

ORLON[5] ACRYLIC FIBER[6]

History. This acrylic fiber became a commercial reality with the discovery in the du Pont Laboratories of suitable organic solvents which can be employed for preparing solutions of polyacrylonitrile. With such encouraging results, exploratory studies were continued. In 1944, a semi-works, using the dry-spinning process, was built in Waynesboro, Va., under the auspices of the Acetate Research Section of the du Pont Company. Until August 1945, development work was concerned mainly with determining how it could be used to aid the war effort. It was found that the possibilities for Orlon in military applications, especially in the Pacific theatre, were of far-reaching importance. This development had not been brought to fruition when World War II ended. By early 1946, it looked promising enough for commercialization, and process development continued. In October, a decision was made to build a plant for its production in Camden, S. C. Approximately 18 months were required to complete the plant, and it went into production in July 1950. The first yarn produced was a 200-denier 80-filament yarn. The first five years of market explora-

[5] Trade mark of du Pont acrylic fiber.

[6] Specially prepared from information furnished by the Textile Fibers Dept., E. I. du Pont de Nemours & Co.

tion, employing a large poundage of Orlon fiber, showed that the fiber has a combination of properties for a wide diversification of markets, which cause it to be suitable for many purposes in which nylon and the rayons will not equal its performance.

Orlon is a trade mark selected by du Pont for its synthetic, orientable fibers from polymers which contain a preponderance of acrylic units, particularly acrylonitrile units, in the polymer chain. Acrylonitrile is a fairly volatile liquid derivable from ethylene or acetylene with HCN, and has the formula:

$$CH_2{=}CH{-}CN$$

It can be polymerized, alone or in combination with other polymerizable acrylic or vinyl units under the influence of a catalyst, to yield a product of the following type:

$$\left[\cdots{-}CH_2{-}\underset{\displaystyle CN}{\underset{|}{CH}}{-}\left(CH_2{-}\underset{\displaystyle CN}{\underset{|}{CH}}\right)_n{-}CH_2{-}\underset{\displaystyle CN}{\underset{|}{CH}}{-}\cdots\right]$$

Polyacrylonitrile

These polymers, like other vinyls, are the products of an addition type of polymerization; that is to say, the molecules are added directly together without condensing out some by-product (e.g., water, as in the polymerization of nylon).

When acrylonitrile polymer was first recorded some years ago, a feasible process for transforming it into a commercially useful product was not known. It was described as being intractable, infusible, and insoluble. The general belief was that it had a three-dimensional structure. Later, it was established that the polymer has a linear structure and that its insolubility results from the strong interchain forces between the nitrile groups. A broad investigation for non-reactive organic solvents disclosed several from which the polymer could be spun. The intractable nature of the polymer and the strongly interacting nitrile groups required the development of solvents which were different from those normally used for polymers—acetone, ethyl alcohol, aromatic hydrocarbons, and water. A number of patents have been issued, disclosing a variety of compounds possessing solvent properties for polyacrylonitrile and copolymers, containing predominant proportions of acrylonitrile. Among these may be mentioned dimethoxyacetamide, tetramethylene cyclic sulfone, dimethylacetamide, dimethyl formamide and the meta- and paranitrophenols. These solvents made it possible to produce concentrated solutions amenable to conventional yarn-spinning techniques.

The initial work on acrylic fiber disclosed that it was orientable, leading to strong structures which are dimensionally stable, resistant to common solvents, acids, dilute bases, and ultraviolet light. (See flow chart, Fig. 13.)

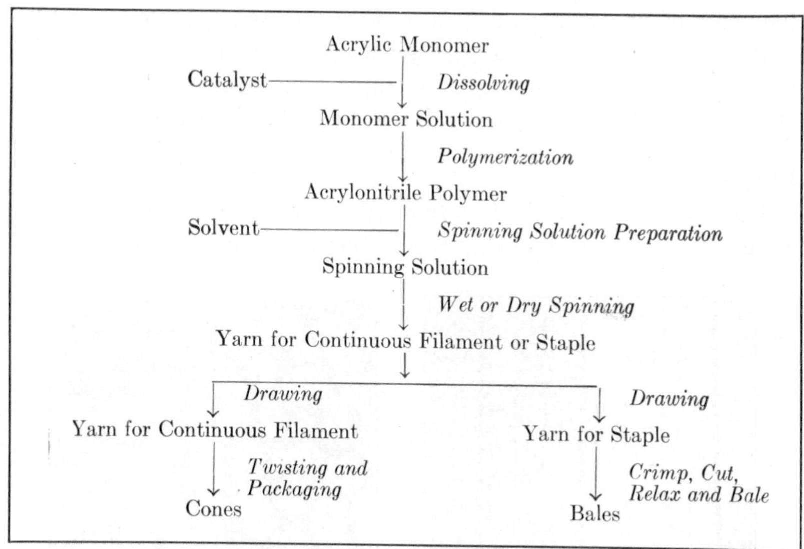

FIG. 13. Flow chart for production of Orlon acrylic fiber.

Manufacture

Polymerization. Monomeric acrylonitrile, alone or together with monomers selected for copolymerization, is polymerized in the presence of a suitable catalyst under appropriate temperature and time conditions. The polymer is blended and then dissolved in a suitable solvent. This solution is filtered to insure uniformity and cleanliness for spinning.

Spinning. Because of its relative infusibility, polyacrylonitrile is not readily adaptable to the method of spinning by melt extrusion used for nylon. This acrylic fiber may be spun by either the wet or dry processes, both of which require solution of the polymer. Both processes involve precise metering of the concentrated solution through a spinneret into a medium where solvent is removed and the solid filaments are formed.

Continuous Filament. After spinning, the yarn is drawn to orient the polymer molecules along the filament axis, thus establishing intermolecular forces which increase the yarn strength. High draw ratios are possible, since large amounts of plastic flow occur during drawing, in addition to that required for orientation. Dimensional stability is imparted to the yarn by allowing it to relax a controlled amount after the drawing operation.

Staple. The preparation consists of combining a large number of filaments of undrawn yarn in a rope or tow which is drawn. After drawing, the necessary crimp is imparted to facilitate processing and to give the proper loftiness to the staple. The staple is then relaxed, cut into the desired length, dried, and baled for shipment.

Properties

The continuous-filament acrylic fiber possesses a very pleasing, warm, dry hand; fabrics made of this fiber in continuous-filament form

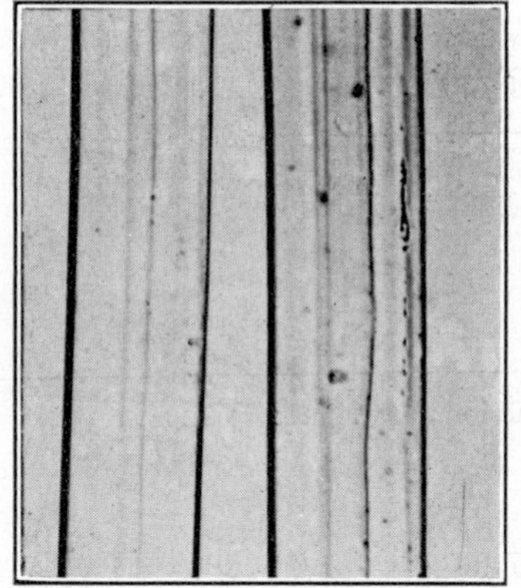

Fig. 14. Orlon fiber. Longitudinal view, ×500.

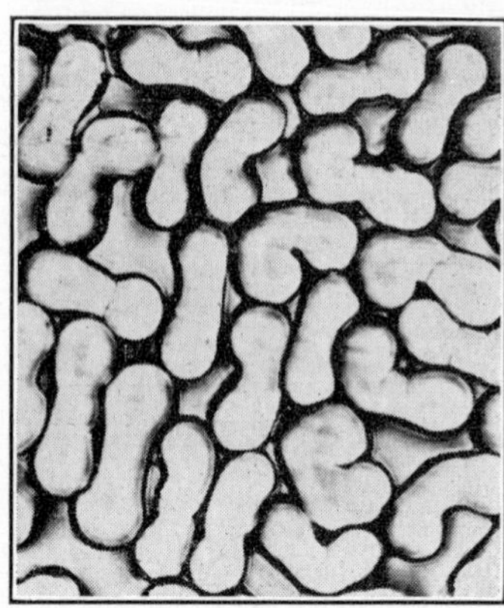

Fig. 15. Orlon fiber. Cross-sections, ×500.

exhibit a silklike luster, hand, and drape. In addition to these outstanding aesthetic properties, Orlon has many excellent physical characteristics that place it in a prominent position in the textile field. Specific physical properties of current standard production bright yarns follow.

Microscopic Properties. In its microscopical structure, the fiber has some characteristics which make its identification possible. The general appearance is similar to Vinyon, but the surface of Orlon is irregularly striated to varying degrees. See Fig. 14. The shape of the majority of the cross-sections is "dog-bone" or "dumbbell" in character as shown in Fig. 15. Clover-leaf-shaped cross-sections are also present.

Structure. The X-ray diffraction diagrams of the polymer indicate that the polymer is unoriented and partially crystalline. See Fig. 16. The diffraction diagram of the drawn fiber is, on the other hand, highly oriented and indicates the complicated type of order which characterizes the Orlon filament yarn. See Fig. 17.

Specific Gravity. The specific gravity is 1.17, compared with 1.14 for nylon.

Identification. Microscopic Test. This acrylic fiber can be identified by its dog-bone-shaped cross-section.

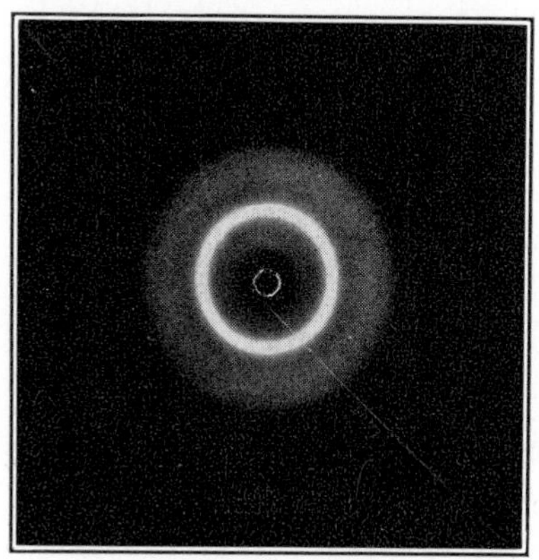

FIG. 16. Polyacrylonitrile, X-ray diffraction diagram.

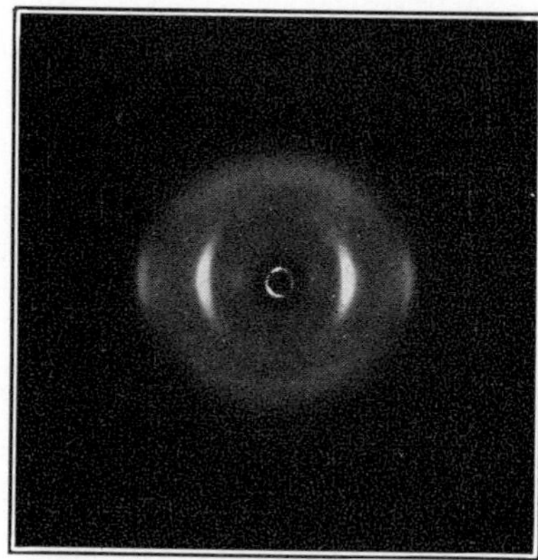

FIG. 17. Orlon fiber, X-ray diffraction diagram.

Burning Test. Orlon will melt and burn, leaving a hard, beadlike ash similar to that of cellulose acetate.

Chemical Test. (*a*) Orlon is not affected by acetone or 88 per cent formic acid. (*b*) Nylon dissolves in 88 per cent formic acid. (*c*) Acetate dissolves in acetone.

TABLE 18. TENSILE STRENGTH AND ELONGATION, CONTINUOUS FILAMENT

		Tenacity (grams per denier)	*Tensile Strength (pounds per square inch)*	*Elongation (per cent)*
Straight	dry	4.7–5.2	71,000–79,000	15–17
	wet	4.6–5.0	69,000–75,000	15–17
Loop	dry	3.3,3.7	49,000–55,000	11–13
	wet	3.3–3.7	49,000–55,000	11–13
Knot	dry	2.7–3.0	41,000–45,000	9–10
	wet	2.7–3.0	41,000–45,000	9–10

Note: A Scott IP4 testing machine (at 16 grams/denier/min rate of loading) was used for this testing at 75° F. and 65 per cent R.H. Results may vary considerably depending on the type of machine used and the conditions in testing.

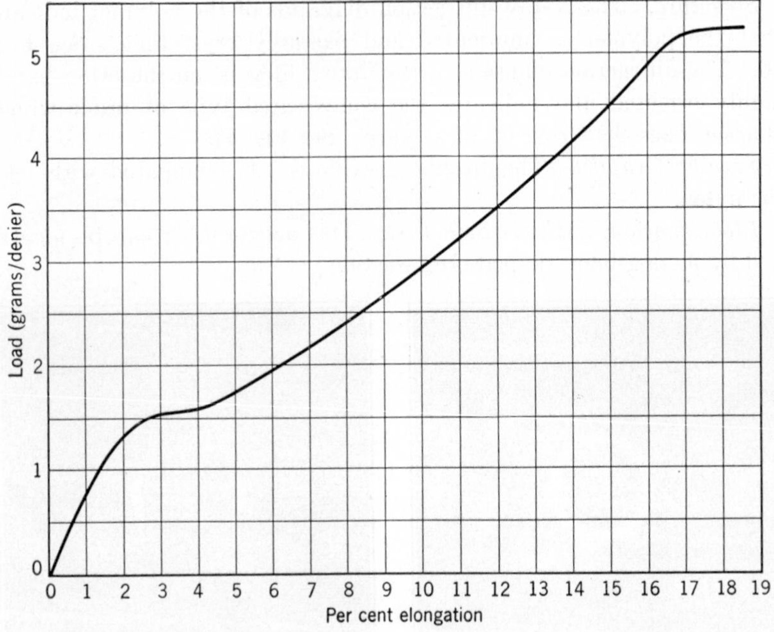

Fig. 18. Stress-strain curve of Orlon acrylic fiber.

Strength. The strength and elongation, measured at the breaking point, are shown in Table 18 and in Fig. 18.

Stretch Resistance. Figure 18 presents the stress-strain data for standard Orlon acrylic continuous filament. It will be observed in

TABLE 19. Stretch Resistance at Various Elongations, Continuous Filament

Per Cent Elongation	*Grams/Denier*
0.5	0.4
1.0	0.8
1.5	1.1
2.0	1.3
2.5	1.5

Table 19 that Orlon possesses a high resistance to stretching during mill processing with normal tensions.

Recovery from Stretch. Orlon exhibits a good recovery from stretching, as shown in Table 20.

Impact Strength. Orlon continuous filament has very good transverse impact properties. Measured on a pendulum-type tester of

TABLE 20. STRETCH RECOVERY OF CONTINUOUS FILAMENT

Per Cent Stretch	Per Cent Recovery	
	Instantaneous	*Retarded*
2	97	85
4	84	66
8	75	57

Note: The yarn was stretched and released *instantaneously and after* 100 *sec.* Measurements were made 60 sec after release.

special design (5-cm strands) at 75° F. and 65 per cent R.H., the impact strength was 2.4–2.9 gram cm per denier cm.

Toughness. The toughness, which is the work of rupture as determined from the area under the stress-strain curve, is considered excellent. (See Fig. 18.)

Abrasion Resistance. Measured by laboratory tests, the resistance of this fiber to degradation by abrasion is good. However, there are many variables which can affect the performance of any given material. Consequently, if abrasion resistance is a critical property, it is suggested that finished products be subjected to tests. Hot calendering improves the abrasion resistance of fabrics.

Flex Life. The resistance to degradation by flexing is excellent; however, this property should be studied in particular end uses to establish final performance data.

Moisture Regain. The moisture regain in comparison with nylon 66 is shown in Table 21.

TABLE 21. MOISTURE REGAIN

Per Cent Relative Humidity at Room Temperature	*Per Cent Moisture Regain*	
	Orlon Acrylic Fiber	*Nylon*
65	1.5	4
95	2.5	8

Fabrics are exceptionally stable under extreme changes in humidity. Fabrics were subjected to humidities of 15, 35, and 60 per cent. The 35 per cent conditioning was conducted at 75° F.; the tests at 15 per cent and 60 per cent were conducted at 70° F. The samples were rotated weekly from 60 per cent R.H. to 15 per cent R.H. to 60 per cent R.H. and to 35 per cent R.H. No dimensional change could be detected after any of these periods.

Residual Shrinkage. The amount of shrinkage of yarn (as shipped), induced by boiling water, is low. In a standard test of 30 min boil off at 212° F., skeins of Orlon shrink 2 to 4 per cent. Further boiling for 1 hr or more shows little change in shrinkage characteristics.

Effect of Temperature. Ironing temperatures of 275° F. (low rayon setting) are normally satisfactory. After prolonged heating at 230° F. and after short-contact ironing at 392° F., some yellowing of the fabric will occur.

This fiber is resistant to degradation by elevated temperatures, for both long and short exposure periods, up to 300° F. Only brief exposures, however, are possible at temperatures over 300° F., such as are used for heat treatments during finishing, since long periods of exposure can result in degradation of the fiber. Table 22 illustrates

TABLE 22. Exposure to High Temperatures

Temperature (°F.)	*Time (days)*	*Loss of Strength (per cent)*
212	16	0
257	32	0
302	2	0

the effect of severe conditions of exposure (static air) on the strength of yarn. Physical testing was done at 75° F., 65 per cent R.H.

When this fiber is exposed in high-temperature atmospheres for periods of time long enough to bring about chemical and consequent physical degradation, extreme shrinkage occurs. A decrease in the rate of shrinkage has been accomplished by heat treatment during fabric finishing. Consequently, this procedure is suggested for all industrial fabrics made of this acrylic fiber which will be subjected to high temperatures.

Only limited data are available regarding the effect of *low temperatures* on the physical properties. The preliminary information, however, can serve as an indication. Low-temperature exposure (−70° F.) resulted in a slight increase in breaking tenacity and a slight decrease in breaking elongation. Secondary creep (the permanent yield or lengthening of the fiber after repeated stress expressed as a per cent of the original) is less, however, at lower temperatures than at normal temperatures. Other tests have indicated that the excellent flex life of this fiber is not measurably impaired by low temperatures.

Flammability. The fire hazards [7] of textile fabrics made from this fiber are in a class with those presented by cotton, acetate, and viscose

[7] "List of Inspected Gas, Oil and Miscellaneous Appliances," p. 207, Underwriters Laboratories, Inc. (Nov. 1950).

rayon fabrics of similar weight and weave. The life hazards of the combustion and thermal decomposition products of these fabrics under fire conditions are judged to be similar to those presented by the fumes evolved during combustion or thermal decomposition of silk or woolen fabrics. This fiber has a higher ignition temperature (926.6° F.) than cotton and the rayons. The application of special dyes and finishes, however, may change the burning characteristics, and tests should be made on the end product.

Resistance to Sunlight, Weathering, and Industrial Fumes. An outstanding property of this acrylic fiber is its remarkable resistance to degradation by sunlight, weathering, and industrial fumes. This important characteristic has been proved in exposure tests under several climatic conditions. The unique combination of resistance to degradation by chemicals, sunlight, and weathering permit wide use of Orlon in areas where industrial fumes are prevalent. In an outdoor exposure test of yarn, conducted in Wilmington, Del., involving Orlon, silk, nylon, linen, cotton and viscose rayon, Orlon retained 77 per cent of its strength at the end of 1½ years after all of the other fibers had completely failed. Exposure tests conducted on awning fabrics in Florida, where the effects of ultraviolet light are intense and industrial fumes are nil, have shown that Orlon has excellent resistance to sunlight alone; other exposures of the same fabrics in the heavy, fume-laden areas have shown the remarkable resistance of Orlon to the combined influence of sunlight, smoke, soot and acidic fumes.

Additional tests, involving acrylic awning fabrics versus cotton fabrics, exposed for over a year in Florida, have also corroborated the great superiority of Orlon over cotton with respect to resistance to ultraviolet light, mildew, and molds.

This inertness to degradation by light shows up in a manner which is quite revealing. For example, some delusterants which catalyze the photodegradation of many other fibers and often catalyze the fading of many dyes not only fail to catalyze the photodegradation of this material but generally do not catalyze the fading of dyes in the Orlon.

Effect of Microorganisms and Insects. Orlon has good resistance to degradation by bacteria and insects. In evaluations with aerobic bacteria, soil bacteria, fresh-water and salt-water bacteria, feredo (a cordage-destroying shipworm), and insects, the fiber was very resistant.

Fabrics were buried for 21 days in soil containing an active flora of microorganisms with no apparent harmful effects.

TABLE 23. Acid and Alkali Exposure Tests

Chemical	*Temperature*	*Time*	*Effect on Strength*
100% Aqua regia	Room	20 weeks	None
100% Aqua regia	167° F.	7 days	Degraded
30% Aqua regia	176° F.	6 days	None
30% Aqua regia	176° F.	4 weeks	Degraded
37% Hydrochloric acid	Room	3 days	None
37% Hydrochloric acid	Room	5 weeks	Appreciable
18% Hydrochloric acid	77° F.	30 weeks	None
37% Hydrochloric acid	77° F.	2 days	None
37% Hydrochloric acid	77° F.	3 weeks	Degraded
40% Nitric acid	Room	30 weeks	None
40% Nitric acid	104° F.	4 weeks	None
40% Nitric acid	104° F.	8 weeks	Appreciable
10% Nitric acid	167° F.	4 weeks	None
10% Nitric acid	167° F.	8 weeks	Appreciable
20% Nitric acid	167° F.	2 weeks	None
20% Nitric acid	167° F.	8 weeks	Degraded
40% Nitric acid	167° F.	1 day	Appreciable
40% Nitric acid	167° F.	2 days	Degraded
10% Nitric acid	194° F.	1 week	None
10% Nitric acid	194° F.	2 weeks	Moderate
40% Nitric acid	194° F.	4 hr	None
40% Nitric acid	194° F.	8 hr	Appreciable
40% Nitric acid	194° F.	20 hr	Degraded
10% Nitric acid	223° F.	1 day	None
10% Nitric acid	223° F.	6 days	Appreciable
10% Nitric acid	223° F.	8 days	Degraded
85% Phosphoric acid	210° F.	3½ hr	None
85% Phosphoric acid	210° F.	6 hr	Appreciable
85% Phosphoric acid	210° F.	8½ hr	Degraded
5% Sodium hydroxide	Room	5 weeks	None
5% Sodium hydroxide	Room	15 weeks	Appreciable
10% Sodium hydroxide	Room	10 days	None
10% Sodium hydroxide	Room	8 weeks	Appreciable
10% Sodium hydroxide	Room	15 weeks	Degraded
20% Sodium hydroxide	Room	9 days	None
20% Sodium hydroxide	Room	21 days	Moderate
10% Sodium hydroxide	77° F.	4 days	None
10% Sodium hydroxide	77° F.	8 days	Moderate
5% Sodium hydroxide	176° F.	4 hr	Appreciable
5% Sodium hydroxide	176° F.	1 day	Degraded
20% Sodium hydroxide	212° F.	8 hr	Degraded

Firebrats, carpet beetles, and clothes moths will eat through this fiber when entrapped; entrapped German cockroaches did not damage it. Starvation and subsistence tests indicate that it has a very limited attraction for insects as a source of food.

The presence of certain dyes and finishes may modify these characteristics.

Chemical Resistance. An outstanding property of this acrylic fiber is its resistance to degradation by chemicals. Although excellent results have been observed in preliminary tests, each specific end use may comprise a unique combination of variables which will have an effect on fabric performance. Therefore, tests under specific conditions of use are suggested in order to confirm durability for the particular product involved. Orlon has: good to excellent resistance to mineral acids; fair to good resistance to weak alkalis; excellent resistance to common solvents, oils, greases, neutral salts, and some acid salts.

This acrylic fiber has been subjected to immersion tests in many chemicals including hydrochloric, nitric, and sulfuric acids, sodium hydroxide, ammonium chloride, hydrofluoric acid, ferric chloride, soybean oil, cottonseed oil, and many combinations of chemicals. In Tables 23, 24, and 25 and Fig. 19 are given the results of the immersion

TABLE 24. SOLVENT EXPOSURE TESTS

Solvent	*Temperature*	*Time*	*Effect on Strength*
Acetone	Room	75 hr	None
Ethanol	Room	75 hr	None
Ether	Room	75 hr	None
Toluene	Room	75 hr	None
"Triclene"	Room	75 hr	None

tests. It is very important, however, to remember that *any changes in testing conditions may alter the results obtained.* Therefore, the data should be used only as a guide for further trials under specific end use conditions. The effects of the chemicals are rated as: None—10 per cent or less loss in tenacity; Moderate—11–30 per cent loss in tenacity; Appreciable—31–75 per cent loss in tenacity and Degraded—over 75 per cent.

Dry Cleaning. Fabric made from this fiber, in tests by the National Institute of Cleaning and Dyeing, was found to be unaffected by dry-

TABLE 25. Effect of Solutions of Salts

Chemicals	*Temperature*	*Concentration*	*Time*	*Effect on Strength*
Ferric ammonium sulfate	257° F.	Saturated	20 min	None
Ferric chloride	212° F.	40%	20 min	Dissolved
Ferric chloride	Room	50%	5 days	Degraded
Ferric chloride	212° F.	8%	10 min	Appreciable
Ferric chloride	167° F.	8%	10 min	None
Ferric chloride	194° F.	4%	10 min	None
Ferric citrate	257° F.	Saturated	20 min	None
Ferric nitrate	257° F.	Saturated	20 min	Dissolved
Ferric oxalate	257° F.	Saturated	20 min	None
Ferric phosphate	257° F.	Saturated	20 min	None
Ferric sulfate	257° F.	Saturated	20 min	Moderate
Nickel chloride	257° F.	Saturated	20 min	None
Nickel sulfate	257° F.	Saturated	20 min	None
Potassium permanganate	Boiling	1.7%	15 min	None
Potassium permanganate	Boiling	2.7%	15 min	Appreciable
Soap solution	Room	2.0%	50 days	None
Sodium chloride	Room	3.0%	50 days	None
Stannous chloride	257° F.	Saturated	20 min	None
Zinc chloride	Room	50%	15 weeks	None
Zinc chloride	167° F.	50%	1 day	Dissolved
Zinc chloride	176° F.	30%	4 weeks	None
Zinc chloride	176° F.	30%	6 weeks	Degraded

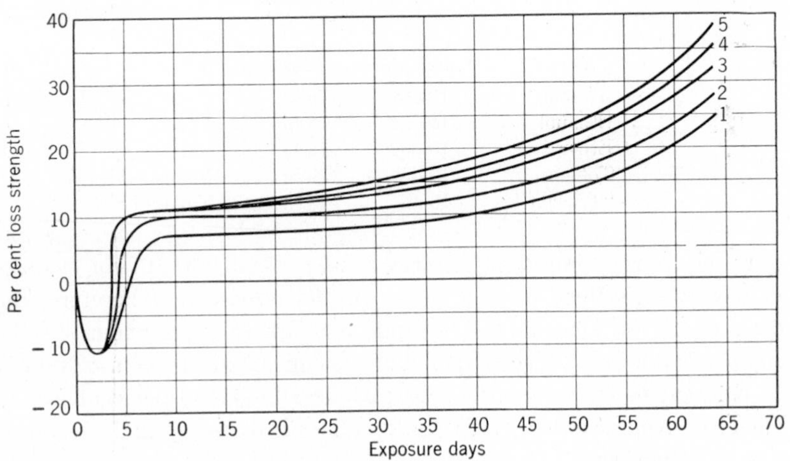

Fig. 19. Effect of sulfuric acid on Orlon acrylic fiber. Immersion test bath temperature, 86° F. Original fabric (strip) tenacity, 146 lb.

cleaning solvents or the common chemicals used in spotting. The following materials were applied to nondyed fabric with no visible effects:

Acetone	Paint removers
Ammonia	Perchlorethylene
Amyl acetate	Pyridine
Carbon tetrachloride	Sodium bisulfite
Chloroform	Sodium hypochlorite
Commercial rust remover	Sodium perborate
Concentrated formic acid	Stoddard solvent
Digestive agents	Titanium stippers
Ethyl acetate	Trichlorethylene
General formula	28% acetic acid
Glacial acetic acid	Water and synthetic detergent
Hydrogen peroxide	Water and soap
Methyl alcohol	Wet spotter

Dyeability

At conventional dyeing temperatures, that is, with the maximum obtainable temperatures of 212° F., or slightly lower, continuous-filament yarn can be dyed in light shades with dispersed acetate dyes, basic dyes, and vat colors. Azoic dyes yield very light shades. Acid dyes stain the fiber very lightly, or not at all.

By using assistants or "carriers" such as phenolic compounds and aromatic amines, especially metacresol, paraphenyl-phenol and aniline, stronger dyeings are obtained, but they are still in the light-shade range. These assistants are most effective with acetate dyes, somewhat effective with basic colors, and less so with vat dyes. The "carriers" have limited solubility in the dye bath, but they penetrate the fiber readily. Metacresol must be used in about 2 per cent concentration, based on dye-bath volume, for this purpose. The amount of "carrier" absorbed is proportional to the dye-bath concentration. Thus, the partition coefficient for metacresol in a bath containing the fiber is considerably greater than one. Although the "carriers" can be removed efficiently by scouring procedures, they are quite obnoxious and difficult to handle.

The dyeing at raised temperatures under pressure, usually about 15 psi, corresponding to 250° F., has shown considerable advantage. The acetate dyes can be applied in heavy shades under pressure. Two to three times as much dye is taken up by the fiber at 250° F. as at the boil, or 212° F. A few examples of the many dyes which can be applied by using this method are Acetamine Yellow CG, Acetamine Orange GR and Celanthrene Pure Blue BRS. Although the depth of shade obtainable under pressure is greatly increased, the exhaustion efficiency of the acetate dyes is low, in the 30 to 40 per cent range.

Acetate dyes, in general, show light fastness about equal to that for the same dyeings on acetate yarns. The wet fastness of acetate dyes is excellent, being far superior to the wet fastness of these dyes on acetate and nylon.

Basic dyes can be applied in full, heavy shades under pressure. These colors exhibit very good wet fastness properties and a few of them are moderately fast to light.

The application of vat dyes to continuous filament is limited to the thio-indigoid type of vat colors plus a few members of the anthraquinone series. Dyeings at the boil in the *p*H range of 9.5–12 produce light to medium shades with good light fastness and washfastness, but poor fastness to crocking. The vat dyes do not penetrate the Orlon fiber under these conditions. At high *p*H, using caustic and hydrosulfite, deep shades result, probably because there is some surface degradation of the fiber. There have been some indications that "carriers" such as metacresol and β naphthol assist the dyeing, and the use of potassium carbonate in relatively large amounts also greatly improves the depth of shade, but the application of heavy shades with good fastness properties is still not attainable.

Vat dyeings have been markedly improved in depth of color and in fiber penetration (resulting in good crock fastness) by the use of pressure, 15 psi for 30 to 45 minutes. The exhaustion of color by this method is of the order of 70 per cent.

The method by which pressure dyeings are obtained involves the use of package dyeing machines for coloring yarn, sewing thread, and raw stock, in aqueous baths under pressure at high temperatures. In order to operate package dyeing machines under pressure, the dyeing chamber or kier is isolated by means of appropriate valves and the dye liquor is circulated in the normal manner. The kier is heated indirectly either by a steam jacket or closed steam coil.

At 250° F., or above, the acetate colors yield fairly heavy shades such as OD#7 and Shoe Brown. Black and olive-drab shades are applicable with vat colors. Bright, full shades have been obtained with basic dyes.

A modified pressure-dyeing method using fabric has been developed on a laboratory scale. This method consists of padding the fabric with dye, drying, and then subjecting the dried fabric to steam under pressure, such as in an autoclave. The results of dyeing by this method are similar to those obtained in aqueous baths under pressure.

Another important development in the dyeing of Orlon continuous-filament materials involves the application of vat dyes in light shades. This is accomplished with soluble vat dyes or the vat-acid forms of the insoluble vat dyes. Fabrics made of Orlon may be dyed in light shades with excellent fastness to light and very good fastness to washing simply by padding the fabric with solutions or dispersions of the vat dye and then developing in a short treatment on a jig at a raised temperature. In the case of soluble vat dyes, the fabric is padded with color and sodium nitrite, the fabric is dried, and then the color is developed by treating with hydroxyacetic acid at 200° F., two ends on a jig. The vat-acid forms of insoluble vat colors are prepared in the usual manner, padded, the fabric is then dried, and the colors are oxidized by treatment on the jig at 200° F., with peroxide and hydroxyacetic acid.

Employing the *cuprous-ion method,* Orlon filament may be dyed with acid colors and a few direct dyes. Fastness properties may vary depending upon the depth of shades and the colors involved. The acid colors offer a fairly broad range for dyeing filament yarn in shades up to medium depth having good wet fastness and fairly good fastness to light. Under pressure, at 250° F., acid dyes even in heavy shades exhibit very good wet-fastness properties.

Acrylic staple exhibits a considerably greater degree of affinity for the various dyes. At dyeing temperatures at or near the boil, acetate colors are absorbed more readily, giving light to medium shades. These colors show the usual good wet-fastness and moderate light-fastness properties. Basic dyes are applicable at the boil, giving medium to heavy shades, having good wet-fastness properties and, with selected dyes, moderate light fastness. Other basic dyes have poor light fastness. The dyeing of staple with vat colors is more satisfactory than that of continuous filament. At the boil, a number of good deep shades can be applied. These have light fastness of a high order, considering that the same dyes, usually of the thio-indigoid type, exhibit a lower order of fastness on cotton.

Staple is not only more receptive than the continuous filament to dyeing with acetate, vat, and basic dyes, but it is also dyeable with a fairly broad range of acid dyes and a few direct colors, as well as being dyeable in full, heavy shades with naphthanil colors. The acid and direct colors exhibit affinity when applied by the so-called cuprous-ion technique, in which the copper apparently forms a bridge between the nitrile groups in the fiber and the dye anions. Thus, staple is suitable for wide textile use in the form of fabric, yarn, or raw stock.

Staple exhibits its best dyeing behavior in the range of 200 to 212° F., and it is, therefore, readily dyed in existing mill equipment.

In the dyeing of staple with acid and direct dyes, cuprous ions are obtained by heating together cupric sulfate and hydroxyl-ammonium sulfate, and then dyeing at the boil in the presence of acid. Selected dyes give suiting and outerwear shades of satisfactory fastness, but there are few colors which show good light fastness in the lighter shades. It is anticipated that vat colors will be used to supplement the acid colors in the lighter shades and naphthanil colors will find use in full, bright shades for hosiery and other uses.

Filament Yarn Uses

Industrial. The excellent resistance to degradation by chemicals—particularly acids—and to degradation by sunlight and weathering cause Orlon to be of great interest in window curtains, awnings, auto-tops, outdoor fabrics, filter fabrics, acid-resistant and marine cordage, signal halliards, sewing thread for outdoor fabrics and fertilizer bags, leader cloths, dyebeck reel covers, back greys, hosiery dye nets, tennis nets and tapes, tents, tarpaulins, tobacco nettings, work clothing, yacht sails, and channel fabrics.

Domestic and Apparel. Filament yarn possesses a warm, dry, silk-like hand, a subdued luster, excellent recovery from wrinkling, and dimensional stability in the dry and moist states. The silklike properties of filament yarn appear to reside in a similarity in the stress-strain curves of Orlon and silk (see Fig. 20) and perhaps also in the fact that both fibers have a rough surface and a high fiber-to-fiber coefficient of friction, which gives these fabrics a "scroop" or "rustle."

The following domestic and apparel fields are indicated: glass curtains, casement cloths, draperies, fine dress fabrics, combination fabrics. Orlon with other fibers increases dimensional stability and resistance to wrinkling in rainwear, sportswear and Venetian blind tapes.

Staple Fiber Uses

There is a plant for the commercial production of acrylic staple fiber, as well as continuous filament, at Camden, S. C.

By variations of processing conditions, it is possible to produce a wide range of properties. The curve (Fig. 20) for the sample marked Orlon Staple shows that it approximates wool rather closely in stress-strain behavior, and it has been found to exhibit woollike behavior in fabrics. Complete physical properties for staple are not available at this time since the staple is still under development.

Properties. The outstanding features of this staple are its warm hand, high bulking power, and its recovery from wrinkling in both the dry and wet states. The bulking power is translated into high insulating power, high coverage, and increased yardage per pound.

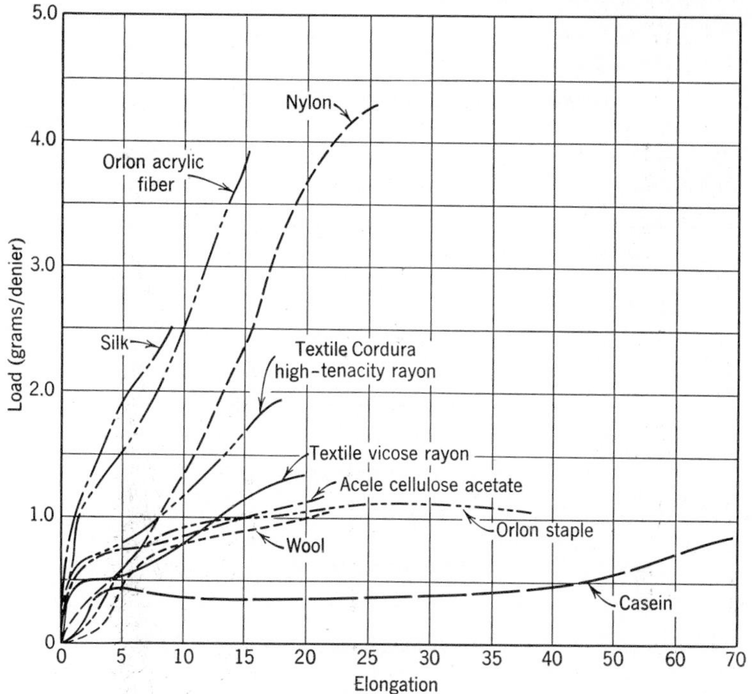

Fig. 20. Stress-strain curves of various textile fibers.

The high bulking power results from the dog-boned cross-section, which does not pack readily, and the low specific gravity. Where thermal insulation is important, i.e., in blankets and overcoats, etc., this staple has the advantage of giving greater bulk with low weight. In making suiting fabrics of the thickness normally used today for winter or summer wear, this staple will permit the manufacture of these fabrics in lighter weights for the same thickness.

The above properties of Orlon staple indicate that it will find utility in sweaters, blankets, dresses, suitings, and overcoatings. Although the staple is especially indicated for winter suitings and overcoatings, it will not be confined to these thicker fabrics. Tropical-type light-weight summer suitings and blends with other fibers have been wear-tested with promising results.

Since staple is insensitive to moisture and takes creases which are substantially permanent to water, suitings made of Orlon have easy maintenance. In blends with rayon, wool and other hydrophilic fibers, acrylic staple will produce fabrics which have better dimensional stability in high humidity, easier maintenance, greater strength, and durability.

DYNEL STAPLE FIBER AND VINYON N

Dynel [8] is a strong, pliant, and extremely tough staple fiber made from two important large-volume synthetic organic chemicals—vinyl

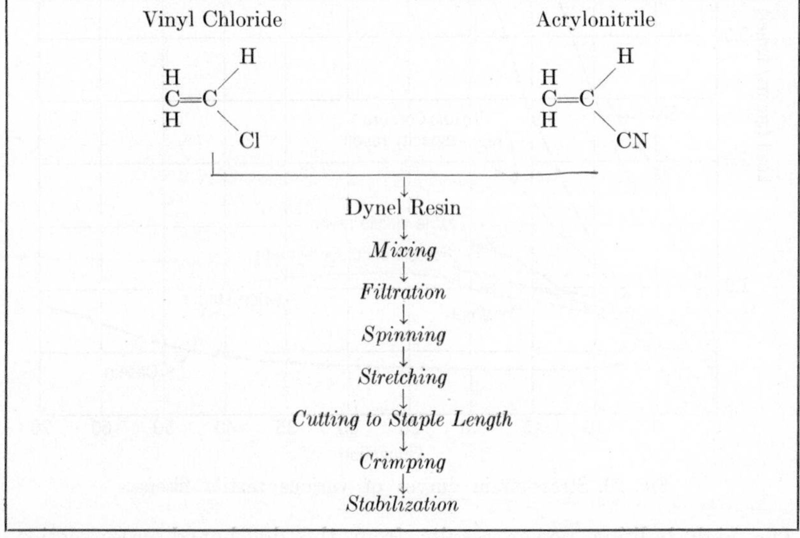

Fig. 21. Flowsheet of manufacture of Dynel staple fiber. (*Courtesy Textile Fibers Dept., Carbide and Carbon Chemicals Co., Division of Union Carbide and Carbon Corp.*)

chloride and acrylonitrile. The flowsheet in Fig. 21 outlines the basic steps in its commercial manufacture. The 60 : 40 copolymer resin is mixed with acetone and filtered. Wet-spinning techniques are employed in forming the filaments. The tow collected is stretched and stabilized, then cut to the desired staple lengths for textile spinning and processing.

[8] Trade mark of Union Carbide and Carbon Corp.

Production

In April 1952, Carbide and Carbon Chemicals Company, a division of Union Carbide and Carbon Corporation, expanded its raw materials units and fiber-producing plant to a capacity of 4 million pounds of staple per year. The engineering work on another plant with a capacity of 20 million pounds per year is planned.

Availability

Staple is currently supplied in fiber sizes of 2, 3, 6, 12, and 24 denier and in lengths from 1½ to 6 in. It is also available as tow.[9]

Staple fiber is shipped in corrugated cartons, baled with steel tape. Bales contain approximately 400 lb of fiber. Smaller shipments for sampling are made in fiber drums containing 100 lb net.

Properties (Table 26)

Texture. Fabrics feel warm to the skin. Many fabrics have a texture, warmth, and hand like that of fine vicuña. Tests comparing napped fabric of natural fibers of comparable weight, construction, and thickness indicate that Dynel rates well with respect to both warmth and compressional resilience. The irregular ribbon-shaped cross-section (Fig. 22) of these filaments provides higher covering power than round fibers, and the high resilience of the fibers gives an unusual permanent loftiness to fabrics.

Finished fabrics can be soft or harsh, because this staple fiber is extruded in various filament deniers and cut to length, because yarns can be spun on any standard equipment, and because fabrics are amenable to a variety of finishes. The fiber is relatively light. (See Table 26.)

Moisture Regain and Action of Water. The moisture regain is less than ½ of 1 per cent at 77° F. (25° C.) and 65 per cent R.H. This resistance to the action of water makes it one of the fastest drying fibers. In certain fabric constructions, water is held mechanically. If such fabrics are wet and subjected to centrifuging, most of the water is removed immediately. Heavy napped or knitted fabrics whirl-dried and hung up at room temperatures dry with remarkable rapidity.

Water has no adverse effect on this fiber. Yarns and fabrics retain well over 85 per cent of their dry strength when wet. Properly stabilized fabrics are shrinkproof in hot water.

[9] Latest information is obtainable from the Textile Fibers Dept., Carbide and Carbon Chemicals Co., a Division of Union Carbide and Carbon Corp., New York.

TABLE 26. PROPERTIES OF DYNEL STAPLE FIBER

Filament shape	Irregular ribbon-shaped cross section.
Specific gravity	1.31 at 81° F.
Tenacity, wet or dry	3.0 grams per denier.
Elongation, wet or dry	36 per cent.
Stiffness	9.7 grams per denier.
Toughness	0.52 grams per denier.
Flammability	Fire resistant; will not support combustion.
Moisture regain	Less than 0.5 per cent at 77° F. and 65 per cent R.H.
Resistance to water	High—nonfelting and nonshrinking except at temperatures above 212° F.
Resistance to chemicals	High for strong detergents and soaps and wide variety of inorganic acids, bases, and salts.
Resistance to solvents	Unaffected by hydrocarbons and most organic solvents. Acetone, cyclohexanone, and dimethylformamide are solvents in varying degrees. Other cyclic ketones and certain amines exert solvent or swelling action at higher temperatures.
Resistance to insects	Excellent. Completely resistant to carpet beetle and clothes moth larvae.
Resistance to mildew and fungus	Excellent.
Effect of dry heat	Strain release starts at 240° F., softening range is 300–325° F.
Electrical properties	Medium-grade dielectric; comparable to cellulose acetate and nylon under normal conditions.

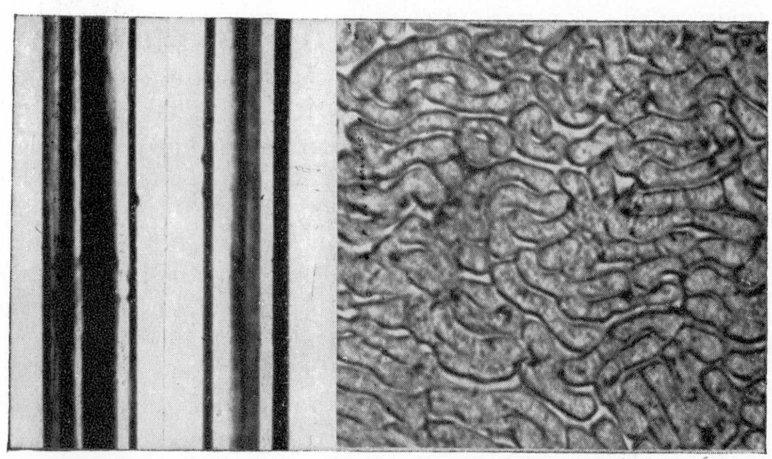

FIG. 22. Dynel staple, longitudinal and cross-section (×500).

The fibers are nonfelting and nonshrinking. This, coupled with high resistance to chemical attack and high wet strength, makes possible repeated launderings even with strong detergents under vigorous conditions. Fabrics may be disinfected with sodium hypochlorite solutions without affecting tensile properties or hand.

Napped fabrics may pill if subjected to extreme agitation in automatic "home laundries." With the proper fabric construction, however, napped fabrics can be washed with confidence in automatic machines.

Color. The natural color of the fiber is a light cream, but near whites can be made by bleaching, or by bleaching and dyeing with a white dye. Fiber, yarn, pieces, or finished goods can be dyed in a full range of colors from light through dark shades with excellent fastness to fumes, crocking, and washing, and good fastness to light. Almost the entire range of acetate-type dyes, a large number of the acid-type dyes, many of the direct dyes, and certain vat dyes can be used. As a result, dye can be selected to match nearly any color and withstand nearly every type of service required of the finished fabric.

Flammability. Dynel resists burning, burns slowly while directly exposed to a flame, but stops burning quickly when the flame is removed. It does not melt or drip. It will not support combustion.

Fabrics made entirely of this fiber pass the A.S.T.M. Test D 626–41 T for flame-retarded textiles, but, because some dyes contribute to flammability, fabrics should be tested thoroughly. (See Table 27.)

TABLE 27. FLAME RESISTANCE OF FABRIC

	A.S.T.M. D 626–41 T		
100% Dynel	*After-Flame* (*seconds*)	*Length of Char* (*inches*)	*Modified AATCC Burning Time* (*seconds*)
Blanket	0	3¼	*
Crib blanket	0	4	*
Drapery fabric	0	4	*
Heavy filter fabric	0	½	*
Light filter fabric	0	3	*
Knitted fabric	0	3	*

* Burns only during contact with flame.

Effect of Heat. This staple fiber is not a definitely crystalline material and, therefore, does not have a sharp melting point. Upon the application of heat, a strain-release temperature is reached at which the fiber will shrink slightly. At the temperature of boiling water, the shrinkage of unstabilized fiber is also dependent upon the length of exposure. Further elevation of the temperature causes greater shrinkage to occur, and so on until finally all strains imparted to the fiber are relieved. When this fiber has had strains relieved at a given temperature and time, it becomes dimensionally stable thereafter up to this temperature for that time. Fibers held under tension may be heated considerably above their strain-release temperatures with only minor changes in molecular structure. Fabrics stabilized by dyeing at the boil or by boiling off are dimensionally stable in boiling water and to dry-heat temperatures up to 240° F.

The application of heat to fabrics at temperatures below their strain-release temperatures may be utilized to mold a fabric, or to impart creases or permanent pleats. These shaped fabrics are resistant to change due to wetting, and their forms are relatively permanent until the shaping temperature is again equaled or exceeded.

Utilization of both the shrinkage and the thermoplastic properties is well exemplified in the molding of such articles as hats where the fabric is made to shrink to a form and then set in this shape. For hats and similar articles, high temperatures are employed to provide fabric stiffness and rigidity.

Heat and pressure may be employed to obtain selective fusion of parts of a fabric. In this manner such articles as panels may be prepared from both woven and knit fabrics with a border of fused yarn.

The controllable shrinkage characteristics and the thermoplastic nature are valuable properties for many purposes. Thus fabrics may be woven and stabilized by shrinking to give extremely tight constructions. Mixtures with other synthetic and natural fibers extend the range of novel fabrics.

Under prolonged exposure to air at high temperatures, this fiber gradually darkens and loses weight. Its mechanical properties, however, are preserved to a remarkable degree. The strength at elevated temperatures increases when it is heated for prolonged periods under tension.

Pressing. Wrinkles disappear from such fabrics under ironing with little effort and at low ironing temperatures. High ironing temperatures, however, will cause this fiber to stiffen and shrink. To preserve the beauty and luxurious hand of fabrics these pressing and ironing instructions should be closely followed:

When ironing all-Dynel fabrics, the lowest iron setting and a dry cover cloth of cotton or other fabric should be used. If no cover cloth is used, an iron with a lower than "rayon" setting is necessary. Dynel fabrics can be steam-pressed at reduced pressures, and wrinkles can be removed by jet-steaming, but steam irons, mangles, or hot-head presses should not be used.

The resistance to shrinkage by heat of fabrics containing this fiber is increased markedly by stockblending with more heat-resistant fibers. When 25 per cent to 50 per cent of this fiber is present, the fabric will be stabilized to washing and will retain creases set by an iron. In general, such fabrics can be ironed at the normal temperature setting for the other fiber in the blend.

Light Stability. After Florida exposures of 400 sun-hours (approximately 80 days) on low-denier fibers, Dynel retained approximately 50 per cent of its original tenacity. These observations are not in complete agreement with those obtained with "Fadeometer" tests, for it has been found that exposures to the Fadeometer constitute highly accelerated aging conditions.

Deterioration by Chemical Reagents. This fiber has a high degree of resistance to a wide variety of inorganic acids, bases, and salts. It is unaffected by such industrial chemicals as concentrated hydrochloric acid, concentrated phosphoric acid, and concentrated aqueous solutions of sodium hydroxide. Laboratory tests with pure reagents are guides for determining the suitability of fabrics for use under many conditions. However, where impurities, localized high temperatures, and chemical reactions are of critical importance, field tests should be made.

A porous, woven fabric was tested by an impartial testing research organization to determine its resistance to immersion in various chemicals at specified concentrations and temperatures. Visual appearance, shrinkage, and deterioration after 20 hr of immersion were recorded. Control strips and immersed strips were cut to identical thread counts for all shrinkage and tensile measurements. These results are summarized in Table 28.

The fabric strips were immersed by covering them with reagents in tall form beakers fitted with heavy watch glasses. The beakers were then placed in ovens at the designated temperatures. Volatile reagents were refluxed, as necessary, to maintain the concentration. The strips were conditioned for 4 hr in an atmosphere of 65 per cent R.H. at 70° F. before breaking. Tensile strength tests were made by the strip method in accordance with Federal Specification CCC-T-191a.

Despite these precautions and duplicated tests (10 on control samples and 3 on immersed samples), normal yarn variation is such that the precision of the tensile test measurements is limited to plus or

TABLE 28. EFFECT OF SPECIFIED CHEMICALS ON DYNEL AFTER 20 HOURS' IMMERSION *

Reagents	*Concentration (per cent)*	*Temperature (°C.)*	*Appearances and Effect of Reagent*	*Shrinkage (per cent)*		*Tensile Strength (pounds)*		*Loss in Strength (per cent)*	
				Warp	*Filling*	*Warp*	*Filling*	*Warp*	*Filling*
Original (control)	..	..	..	..	..	93.2	91.0	..	..
INORGANIC ACIDS									
Sulfuric acid	70	50	No effect	0.0	0.0	85	88	8.8	NL
Sulfuric acid	25	100	Stained brown	0.0	0.0	82	80	12	12
Sulfuric acid (100 hr)	25	100	Stained brown	5.0	5.0	76	70	18	23
Sulfuric acid	5	100	No effect	0.0	0.0	93	92	NL	NL
Hydrochloric acid	38	100	Stained brown	5.0	5.0	83	80	11	12
Hydrochloric acid	38	50	No effect	0.0	0.0	89	89	NL	NL
Hydrofluoric acid	50	Room temp.	No effect	0.0	0.0	90	89	NL	NL
Nitric acid	40	50	No effect	0.0	0.0	93	89	NL	NL
Nitric acid	20	100	Slight bleaching	2.5	2.5	84	84	9.9	7.7
Aqua regia	25	100	Bleached white	7.5	7.5	83	81	11	11
Chromic acid	25	50	Stained brown	0.0	0.0	86	86	7.7	5.4
Chromic acid	5	50	Stained brown	0.0	0.0	88	86	5.4	5.1
Phosphoric acid	85	100	Slight darkening	0.0	0.0	96	89	NL	NL
ORGANIC ACIDS									
Acetic anhydride	100	50	Stiffened, shrunk and curled	40	35	30	30	68	67
Acetic acid	75	100	Shrunk, curled, stained brown	7.5	7.5	81	78	13	14
Acetic acid	25	100	Bleached white	2.5	2.5	90	87	NL	NL
Formic acid	100	50	Slight bleaching	5.5	5.0	85	86	8.8	5.1
Formic acid	25	50	No effect	0.0	0.0	91	89	NL	NL

Adipic acid in ethanol	25	50	Slight bleaching	0.0	0.0	86	85	7.7	6.6
Benzoic acid in ethanol	25	50	Slight bleaching	0.0	0.0	89	88	NL	NL
Oxalic acid in ethanol	25	50	No effect	0.0	0.0	91	90	NL	NL
Salicylic acid in ethanol	25	50	Slight bleaching	0.0	0.0	90	89	NL	NL
Phenol	5	Room temp.	Stiffened and shrunk	12.5	10.0	63	69	32	24
Benzene sulfonic acid	50	50	No effect	0.0	0.0	91	89	NL	NL
Bases									
Sodium hydroxide	50	50	No effect	0.0	0.0	89	85	NL	6.6
Sodium hydroxide	25	100	Stained dark brown	2.5	2.5	77	76	17	17
Ammonium hydroxide	28	Room temp.	No effect	0.0	0.0	92	89	NL	NL
Copper ammonium hydroxide	5	Room temp.	No effect	0.0	0.0	93	89	NL	NL
Inorganic Salts									
Potassium acetate	50	100	Slight darkening	0.0	0.0	90	89	NL	NL
Sodium bichromate	50	100	Stained brown	0.0	0.0	90	87	NL	NL
Calcium chloride	50	100	No effect	0.0	0.0	90	91	NL	NL
Stannous chloride	50	100	Slight bleaching	0.0	0.0	89	86	NL	5.5
Zinc chloride	50	100	Slight darkening	0.0	0.0	89	91	NL	NL
Ferric nitrate	50	100	Stained brown	0.0	0.0	95	91	NL	NL
Trisodium phosphate	pH13	43	No effect	0.0	0.0	89	88	NL	NL
Calcium thiocyanate	50	100	Stained brown	2.5	2.5	89	87	NL	NL
Oxidizing Agents									
Hydrogen peroxide	90	Room temp.	Slight bleaching	1.2	1.2	86	86	7.7	5.5
Hydrogen peroxide	30	Room temp.	Slight bleaching	0.0	0.0	88	90	5.3	NL
"Clorox" bleach (5.25% sodium hypochlorite)	100	50	No effect	0.0	0.0	91	91	NL	NL

NL = No significant loss.

TABLE 28. EFFECT OF SPECIFIED CHEMICALS ON DYNEL AFTER 20 HOURS' IMMERSION * (*Continued*)

Reagents	*Concentration (per cent)*	*Temperature (°C.)*	*Appearances and Effect of Reagent*	*Shrinkage (per cent)*		*Tensile Strength (pounds)*		*Loss in Strength (per cent)*	
				Warp	*Filling*	*Warp*	*Filling*	*Warp*	*Filling*
MISCELLANEOUS ORGANIC CHEMICALS									
Acetaldehyde	40	50	Partially dissolved, stiffened, and curled white	30	35	35	40	62	56
Acetamide	25	50	No effect	0.0	0.0	93	91	NL	NL
Acetone	10	50	No effect	0.0	0.0	89	89	NL	NL
Acetone	100	Room temp.	Dissolved	100	100	0	0	100	100
Aniline	5	50	Reddish plastic, partially dissolved	20	25	5	5	95	95
Aniline hydrochloride	10	50	Stained yellowish gray	0.0	0.0	92	91	NL	NL
Benzophenone	100	50	Stiffened and bleached	3.2	3.2	80	77	14	15
Butyl Cellosolve	100	50	Slight darkening	0.0	0.0	89	90	NL	NL
Carbon bisulfide	100	Room temp.	Slight bleaching	2.7	2.5	91	87	NL	NL
Cyclohexanone	5	50	Slight stiffening	0.0	0.0	64	60	31	34
Diethanolamine	25	50	Stained tan	0.0	0.0	93	92	NL	NL
Diethyl ether	100	Room temp.	No effect	0.0	0.0	96	92	NL	NL
Ethyl acetate	100	50	Bleached white	0.0	0.0	81	80	13	12
Ethyl benzoate	100	50	No effect	0.0	0.0	90	89	NL	NL
Ethylenediamine	10	50	No effect	0.0	0.0	91	91	NL	NL

Ethylene dichloride	100	50	Partially dissolved, fused yellow, stiffened	35.0	40.0	27	28	71	69
Formaldehyde	40	50	Slight yellow staining	0.0	0.0	90	89	NL	NL
Gasoline (leaded)	100	Room temp.	Stained slightly red	0.0	0.0	91	91	NL	NL
Hexamethylenediamine	25	50	No effect	0.0	0.0	94	90	NL	NL
Hydrazine	25	50	No effect	0.0	0.0	93	92	NL	NL
Isophorone	100	Room temp.	Slight bleaching and stiffening	0.0	0.0	60	58	36	36
Methyl Carbitol	100	50	Slight bleaching	0.0	0.0	91	91	NL	NL
Methyl ethyl ketone	100	Room temp.	Stiffened and curled	15	15	30	29	68	68
Monochlorbenzene	100	50	Color altered to grey	0.0	0.0	87	85	6.6	6.6
Naphthalene	100	100	Stiffened, shrunk, and curled	30	30	30	28	68	69
Nitromethane in water	Saturated	50	Dissolved into a plastic mass	100	100	0	0	100	100
Perchlorethylene	100	50	No effect	0.0	0.0	95	93	NL	NL
Pyridine	5	50	No effect	0.0	0.0	92	89	NL	NL
Stoddard solvent	100	Room temp.	No effect	0.0	0.0	95	90	NL	NL
Toluene	100	50	Slight bleaching	0.0	0.0	90	87	NL	NL
Urea	25	50	No effect	0.0	0.0	89	89	NL	NL

* Better Fabrics Testing Bureau, Inc., Report No. 43164; text references BR/LB-cc, 5.11.51, BR/LB-cc, 4.12.51, and BR/LB-cc, 6.14.51.

NL = No significant loss.

minus 5 per cent. Losses in strength less than 5 per cent may or may not be significant. Only significant losses are recorded in the columns headed "Loss in Strength."

Dye Affinity

There are many ways of dyeing Dynel, and the application of color to these fibers requires the exercise of the usual good practices followed in a well-managed dye house. Emphasis is placed on the temperature of 205° F. as no color will go on Dynel at lower temperatures. For proper color fixation and color yield in commercial operations, lower temperatures are usually inadequate except where special techniques are employed. Many dyes can be "crocked" onto Dynel in fairly heavy amounts at the lower temperatures, and it is for this reason that the usual cautions must be exercised to prevent unevenness.

Acetate Colors. The easiest dyes to apply to Dynel are the acetate colors. Almost the entire range of acetate dyes, with the exception of those requiring development, can be applied. They have the great advantage of leveling well. Commercial application is accomplished in a dyebath at 205° F. or above with about 1 per cent of a good dispersing agent. Excessive amounts of dispersing agent will retard or even prevent dyeing. In short baths, such as in package and stock dyeing, the use of a high *p*H to maintain the dispersion of the dyes is recommended.

Dyeing is usually carried out for 1 hr; then 40 to 60 per cent of sodium sulfate on weight of fiber is added to improve exhaustion and to maintain fiber luster. The salt addition is particularly desirable for heavy shades. Relustering may also be accomplished by drying the fabric at a temperature below 200° F. and then heating it to 230–240° F. for a brief period. The dyed goods are rinsed, scoured at 175° F., and, where maximum washfastness is required, given a second treatment at 160° F. with 1 per cent of Tergitol wetting agent 7, and 2.0 per cent of sodium hydrosulfite. From 1 to 2 per cent of Amide PES is finally applied as an antistatic finish.

The light fastness of acetate dyes cannot be judged from their fastness properties on acetate. Most of the yellows are excellent, and selected blues, reds, and violets have been found that have acceptable light fastness to complete the range.

Basic Colors. Basic dyes are of interest primarily for fluorescent and brilliant shades where light-fastness requirements are not important. Their application requires a low starting-bath temperature. The dyebath is maintained at a low *p*H with acetic acid, and the color is slowly exhausted onto the fiber with additions of Tergitol wetting agent 7 and with a gradual increase of bath *p*H. *p*-Phenylphenol (2.25 per cent) is often used as a swelling agent to obtain better dyestuff penetration. Commercial dyeing time is 1½ hr at 205° F. or above. The relustering processes may or may not be used, as desired.

Acid Colors. A large number of acid dyes can be applied. While the list is extensive, only a few metallized dyes are included at present. As the fastness properties of the acid dyes vary with the color, dye selection is very important.

Four different procedures are employed for the application of acid colors according to the shade and end-use requirements. Each of the procedures, of course, requires the use of proper dyeing temperatures.

For pastel shades the dye is usually applied at a *p*H of 6 without the aid of assistants other than an anionic disperser to prevent the color from exhausting too rapidly. It is important that the goods be thoroughly wet out before the dye is added to the bath. After addition of the color the dyebath temperature is raised to 205° F. or above, and dyeing is continued for 1 to 1½ hr. The dyed goods are scoured and finished as described for the acetate colors. Certain of the whitening dyes are often employed to brighten pastel shades.

For medium shades two procedures may be employed. In the first, 2.25 per cent of *p*-phenylphenol is introduced into the cold dyebath as the sodium salt or in the micronized form as Purasist. When micronized *p*-phenylphenol is employed, the assistant is pasted with a disperser stable to a boiling acid dyebath and added directly to the bath. When crystalline *p*-phenylphenol is used, it is mixed with one-third its weight of sodium hydroxide and dissolved in a small amount of hot water. The solution is added to the bath.

After the swelling agent has been dispersed in the bath, acetic or formic acid is added to adjust the *p*H to an initial value of about 6. The dyestuff is then added, and the bath temperature is raised to the dyeing temperature. Additions of acid may be made to improve color exhaustion.

In the second method for obtaining medium shades, reduced copper is employed to form a bond between the dyestuff molecule and the fiber. In a typical case 1 or 2 per cent of a cupric salt, such as cupric sulfate, is dissolved and added to the bath containing a wetting agent. To this bath is then added one-half as much reducing agent as cupric sulfate, the reducing agent being zinc formaldehyde sulfoxylate. The dyestuff is finally added, and the temperature of the bath is raised to the dyeing temperature. Color exhaustion may be improved by additions of acid, and, where desirable, additions of copper salt may be made, provided it is reduced with reducing agent before addition to the dyebath. Dyeing time is usually 1½ hr at the dyeing temperature.

Each of the methods for obtaining medium shades has merit for certain applications.

For very heavy shades the two methods used for obtaining medium shades are consolidated. Thus, reduced copper and *p*-phenylphenol are employed together to obtain very striking increases in color build-up.

Salt may be employed for maintaining luster during dyeing for some colors, but care must be exercised as salt will reverse or retard dyeing with others. It is quite commonly used at the end of dyeing, usually in a new bath. In cleaning up the material after dyeing employ a stripping agent where washfastness requirements must be met.

Direct Colors. Certain direct cotton dyes may be applied by acid-dyeing procedures. As in the case of the acid dyes, light fastness varies with the dye.

Soluble Vat Colors. General Dyestuff Corporation has developed procedures for applying Algosols in a range of light and medium shades. They have good fastness to washing and to light but are rated only fair to poor in resistance to crocking. Hence, they should not be used where crock fastness is important.

Vat Dyes. Heavy shades with good light fastness and washfastness have been obtained, but these are poor on fastness to crocking.

Pigment Colors. Resin-bonded pigment colors can be used and good light fastness is obtained. American Cyanamid Company, Calco Chemical Division, has made runs and matched shades with these colors.

Mildew, Fungus, and Insects

When 100 per cent fabrics were buried in soil and held under tropical conditions of 87° F. (31° C.) and 97 per cent R.H., no deterioration of the cloth was detected after 6 months. In other types of tests, such as the mineral-base-agar and free-hanging tests, no fungus attack has been observed. Many tests indicate that Dynel fabrics are immune to insect attack.

Toxicological Action

Both the resin from which Dynel is manufactured and the acrylonitrile-vinyl chloride fibers themselves have been carefully studied by authoritative toxicologists and rated as nonhazardous. No dermatitis or allergic effect has ever been reported by toxicological laboratories or by many individuals who have worn or used Dynel fabrics. Thus, there is every indication that Dynel is relatively nonallergic.

Uses

Among Dynel's outstanding characteristics are: warmth, resilience, dyeability, strength (wet or dry), dimensional stability, resistance to acids and alkalis, resistance to combustion, mothproofness, and mildewproofness. Its applications are shown below.

Apparel	*Home Furnishings*	*Industrial Uses*
Socks	Blankets	Filter fabrics
Work clothing	Draperies	Chemical-resistant clothing
Suiting blends	Upholstery	Anode bags
Knitted jerseys	Rugs and carpeting	Water-softener bags
Knit underwear	Filling for pillows and comforters	Dye and laundry nets
Rainwear		Valve and flange covers
Pile and napped fabrics		Paint roller covers
Dresses		Dust-fume bags
Doll wigs and chignons		Felts and nonwoven fabrics

The percentage breakdown of 1952 distribution of this fiber is as follows: 10 per cent, knit pile fabrics and fleeces including trim; 10 per cent, men's hose; 5 per cent, underwear and miscellaneous knit goods; 5 per cent, circular and tricot knit fabrics; 20 per cent, woven apparel fabrics, one-quarter of this quantity each for blends with wool, blends with cotton, blends with rayon and acetate, and 100 per cent Dynel fleeces; also 50 per cent, industrial, household, and domestic uses, including drapery fabrics and uniforms.

A Dynel tow is produced by Union Carbide and Carbon in vinyl resin filaments in 135,000-total deniers and 2-, 3-, 6-, 12-, and 24-individual deniers, semi-bright luster of a light amber color. It is shipped in fiber cartons. See Table 29.

TABLE 29. Dynel Tow

Total Denier	*Number of Filaments*	*Denier/Filament*
135,000	67,500	2
135,000	45,000	3
135,000	27,500	6
135,000	11,250	12
135,000	5,625	24

TABLE 30. Vinyon-N Filament Yarns

Total Denier	*Filaments*
100	60
140	60
250	240
270	240
500	200

TABLE 31. Vinyon N Characteristics

Tensile strength, grams/denier	Std.	2.8 to 3.2
	Wet	2.8 to 3.2
Elongation, per cent	Std.	25 to 35
	Wet	25 to 35
Elastic recovery, per cent		97% at 2%
Tensile stress, psi		51,000 to 59,000
Average stiffness, grams/denier		10.5
Average toughness		0.45
Specific gravity		1.32
Regain (adsorption)		0.3% at 78° F., 60% R.H.
Water absorbency		0.1%
Effect of heat		Will not support combustion. Shrinks above 275° F.
Effect of age		Virtually none.
Effect of sunlight		Darkens only after prolonged exposure.
Effect of acids		Excellent resistance even at high concentrations.
Effect of alkalis		Excellent resistance even at high concentrations.
Effect of other chemicals		Generally good resistance.
Effect of organic solvents		Softened by warm acetone and certain other ketones. Unaffected by common dry-cleaning solvents.
Dyes used		Acetate, acid, direct, basic, some vat.
Resistance to moths		Wholly.
Resistance to mildew		Wholly.
Typical uses		Continuous filament: filter fabrics, dust fume bags, work clothing, dress goods, resist yarns, sail cloth, draperies, thread, pile fabrics, molded fabrics, auto-window channels, and military fabrics.
Method of manufacture		A copolymer of vinyl chloride and acrylonitrile is dissolved in acetone, filtered, and then dry spun by means of extrusion.
Identification		Shrinks from flame leaving a hard black irregular bead. Self-extinguishing; it will not support combustion.

Vinyon N—Continuous Filament

Union Carbide and Carbon also produces a continuous-filament yarn under the trade name Vinyon N, at its South Charleston, W. Va., plant. See Table 30 for specifications and Table 31 for characteristics.

Vinyon Staple

From its Vinyon yarn American Viscose Company produces a staple the details of which are given in Table 32.

TABLE 32. VINYON * STAPLE

Deniers	*Length (inches)*	*Luster*	*Crimp*	*Spinning Systems*
3	1	Bright	none	Cotton
3	1¼	Bright	none	Cotton and Wool
3	1½	Bright	none	Cotton and Wool
3	2	Bright	none	Cotton and Wool
3	7	Bright	none	Cotton and Wool
5½	1½	Bright	none	Cotton and Wool
5½	3½	Bright	none	Carpet

* Trade mark of Union Carbide and Carbon Corp.

VINYLIDENE CHLORIDE FILAMENTS AND YARNS

History. About 1840, the French chemist Regnault encountered a strange new fluid which was later determined to be unsymmetrical dichloroethylene, now more commonly known as vinylidene chloride. This material received practically no mention in literature until 1922, when Brooks indicated that halogenated ethylenes, in addition to vinyl chloride and vinyl bromide, showed a tendency toward polymerization. In 1930, Staudinger and Feisst reported on the polymerization of an apparently impure unsymmetrical dichloroethylene. Feisst reported the polymer to be crystalline. This was later confirmed by Natta and Rigamotti.

Chemists of the Dow Chemical Company investigated vinylidene chloride as a phase of an extensive program on chlorinated aliphatic compounds. The early work showed that a more thorough investigation on vinylidene chloride was justified, and as a result of later work the first commercial vinylidene chloride polymers were introduced about 1940. The practical commercial plastic material is a copolymer of vinylidene chloride and vinyl chloride known by the generic term "Saran."

Utilization. Among the first commercial applications of vinylidene chloride were fishing leaders made of monofilaments and produced by Pierce Plastics, Inc., of Bay City, Mich., under the trade name of Permalon. This company also used Saran for the production of tapes, as well as catheters for surgical purposes. Irvington Varnish & Insulator Company produced filaments in a rattanlike cross-section for use in upholstery fabrics. The success obtained with this material in specialty fields soon led to its adoption for the manufacture of narrow webbing in decorative fabrics such as belts and suspenders, as well as specialty braids and some knitted fabrics. It was found possible to weave the material on metal wire looms through minor loom modifications. A durable insect screen was made for war purposes, which outlasted metal in adverse tropical and humid climates. Among the first extruders producing monofilaments for this use were the Firestone Industrial Products Company, now Firestone Plastics Company, of Pottstown, Pa., under the trade name Velon. Shortly after the work on metal wire looms was started, it was found possible to weave this fabric on slightly modified standard textile looms. The use of vinylidene chloride in insect screens is a typical example of the utility of this material for military applications. Other companies have taken up the manufacture of Saran monofilaments and brush bristles: Lus-Trus Extruded Plastics, Inc.; Bolta-Saran, Inc., and Dawbarn Brothers, Inc.

Process. Petroleum and brine are the basic raw materials. Ethylene, made by cracking petroleum, and chlorine, obtained by the electrolysis of brine, combine to form trichloroethane, which is converted to vinylidene chloride as shown in Fig. 23.

Monomeric vinylidene chloride is a clear, colorless liquid having a boiling point of 31.7° C. (89° F.). The structural formula is $CH_2{=}CCl_2$. It can be readily polymerized to form a long, linear, straight-chain polymer. By selection of copolymers and control of the polymerization conditions, polymers can be formed which have softening points ranging from 70° C. (156° F.) to at least 180° C. (356° F.). An average commercial polymer has a molecular weight of approximately 20,000 and a softening point of 120 to 140° C. (248 to 284° F.). The basic vinylidene chloride resin is practically odorless and tasteless, and is nontoxic.

The fabrication method of particular interest in the textile field consists of extrusion with subsequent mechanical or heat treatment for improved properties. The extrusion of vinylidene chloride produces a long, continuous-length monofilament, either of circular cross-section or of flat shapes for special purposes. A typical set-up for the extrusion of such fibers is indicated in Fig. 24.

Vinylidene chloride being a crystalline material, mechanical working procedures may be employed, giving exceptional physical properties.

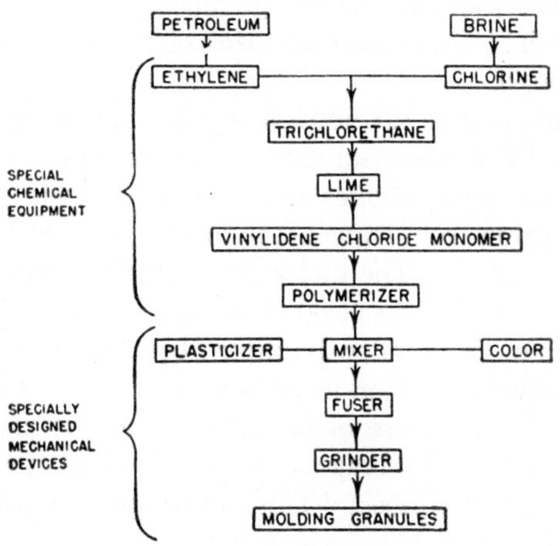

FIG. 23. Flowsheet for the production of vinylidene chloride polymers.

During the extrusion process, the material, as it leaves the die, must be completely molten. The extrusion temperature is on the order of 350° F. After the material has left the die, it is immediately quenched in a water bath to produce a supercooled, amorphous strand, free from crystal formations. This supercooled strand is then mechanically

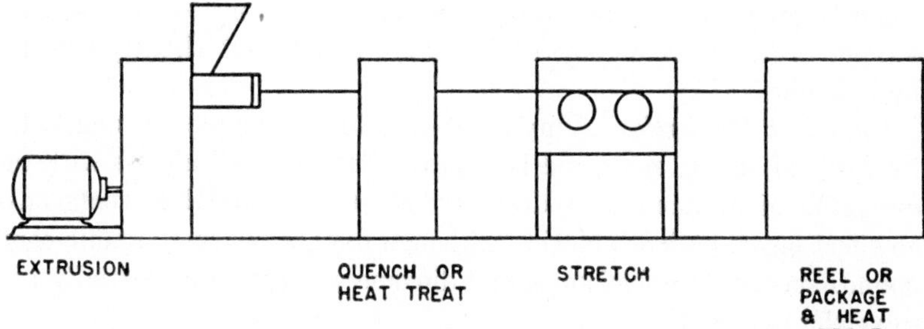

FIG. 24. Orientation process for Velon filaments.

"stretched" to produce an oriented, fully crystalline monofilament. This filament has high tensile-strength values, resulting from the longitudinal alignment of the crystals within the filament. Subsequent heat treatment may be employed to alter somewhat the physical properties of the extruded material. Experiments with multifilament extrusion methods are under way. Single filaments 1 mil in diameter have been extruded.

After winding and spooling, the extruded fibers are ready for textile processing. The filaments so far produced ranged in diameter from 0.005 to 0.080 in. Corresponding sizes of special cross-sections may also be fabricated.

The material, as it is extruded, is a pale gold or straw color with a glossy surface. The filaments are translucent, with a lustrous appearance. Through the use of dyes and pigments, a wide variety of colors and shades ranging from translucent to opaque may be obtained.

Physical Properties. The dielectric strength of vinylidene chloride is 3 to 5. The power factor at 60 cycles ranges from 0.03 to 0.08. The tensile strength of the smaller-diameter fibers is in excess of 40,000 psi, decreasing somewhat with an increase in diameter. Oriented filaments retain at 212° F. in excess of 50 per cent of the room-temperature strength, but severe shrinkage is encountered above 170° F. unless the filaments are restrained. This shrinkage is a function of both time and temperature.

Vinylidene chloride has a specific gravity of 1.68 to 1.75 and an average refractive index of 1.60 to 1.63 n_D. The elongation will be in the order of 15 to 25 per cent. The thermal conductivity is 2.2×10^{-4} cal/sec/cm^2/°C./cm. This is approximately 1/4500 the conductivity of copper. The heat resistance of the material is satisfactory up to 170° F., and heat distortion is observable from 150 to 180° F., depending on the section involved. Vinylidene chloride presents no fire hazard and is self-extinguishing. The water absorption is less than 0.1 per cent. It is unaffected by aging and is but slightly affected by sunlight.

Chemical Properties. Vinylidene chloride is completely unaffected by weak or strong acids and is highly resistant to all alkalis with the exception of ammonium hydroxide. Most commercial solvents have no effect on vinylidene chloride, although oxygen-bearing organic compounds such as cyclohexanone and dioxane will soften or partially dissolve the material.

Microscopic Characteristics. Microscopic examination of the extruded monofilament shows a round, uniform cross-section with a smooth outer surface. (See Fig. 25.)

Economics and Statistics. When vinylidene chloride was first introduced as an experimental material, it was sold at about $1.75 per lb for the basic resin. As production increased and fabrication efficiency improved, there was a steady decline in price. Filaments produced from this resin were originally introduced at prices ranging from $3.25 to $5.00 per lb, depending on the size and quantity involved, but can now be purchased at less than $1.00 per lb. The present use of vinylidene chloride in insect screens, drapery fabrics, filter cloths, narrow webbings, upholstery fabrics, and a host of other applications indicates the wide versatility of this material in the textile field.

FIG. 25. Velon monofilament yarn, bright, longitudinal and cross-section. ×75. (*Flynn.*)

CHEMSTRAND ACRILAN STAPLE

Acrilan, a new acrylic textile fiber of The Chemstrand Corporation, became available in limited commercial output in 1952 following an extended period of research and development, and pilot plant production.

History. Chemstrand, by the end of 1952, completed commercial manufacturing facilities for this fiber at Decatur, Ala., where the company has established its administrative headquarters and a multi-unit research and development center. Initial capacity output of the Acrilan plant was planned at 30,000,000 lb of staple.

Since 1949, Acrilan fiber and the various production processes have undergone extensive research and development in laboratories at Dayton (Ohio), Springfield (Mass.), and Marcus Hook (Pa.). As buildings were completed at Decatur, these research functions were transferred to the newly completed commercial facilities.

Process

Acrilan manufacture involves the copolymerization of acrylonitrile with small quantities of other monomers, and dissolving the copolymers thus produced in a solvent. This results in the formation of the "spinning dope," which is introduced to spinnerets submerged in a coagulation bath, constituting a "wet"-spinning operation. The filaments are stretched, crimped, cut into staple lengths, dried and opened, and baled for shipment to textile mills for processing into fabrics containing 100 per cent Acrilan or Acrilan blended with other commercial fibers—cotton, wool, rayon, acetate, nylon, and others.

Acrilan processing is shown in the flowsheet of Fig. 26.

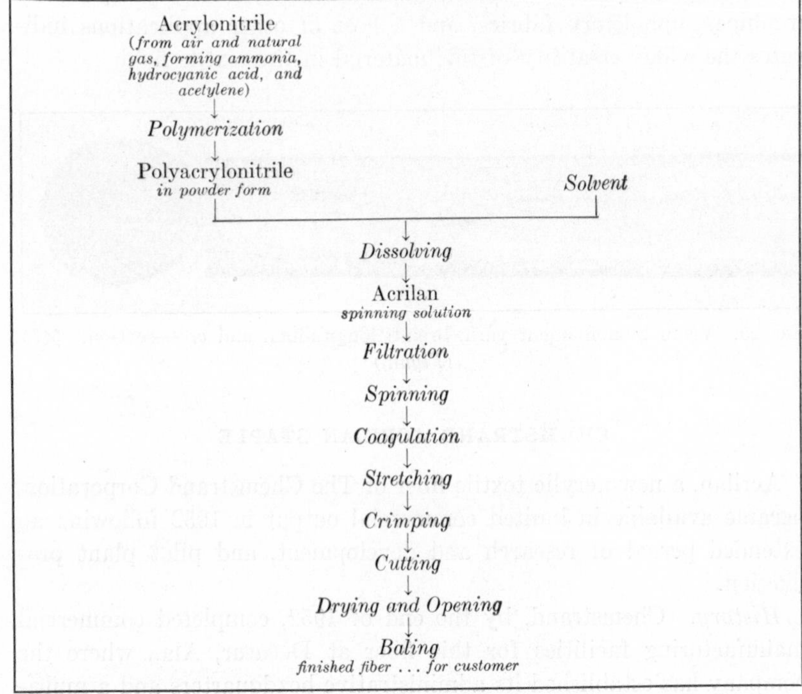

FIG. 26. Flowsheet of Acrilan staple process. (*Courtesy: The Chemstrand Corp.*)

Physical Properties

The tensile strength of this staple fiber is 3.5 grams per denier in the dry and wet state. Its dry and wet elongation is 25 per cent. Its tensile stress ranges between 44,000 to 66,000 psi. Its average stiffness is 30 grams per denier. Its specific gravity is 1.171, and its regain at 58 per cent R.H. and 70° F. is 1.7 per cent. Its elastic recovery is 80 per cent at 2 per cent extension, 50 per cent at 5 per cent extension, and 40 per cent at 10 per cent extension. Its average toughness is 0.32 gram/denier/cm. Its cross-section is nearly elliptical, with an axis ratio of 2 : 1, as shown in Fig. 27.

Chemical Properties

At ordinary room temperatures acids have no effect on this fiber, except concentrated sulfuric acid. Some effect has been observed at elevated temperatures. Acrilan is resistant to weak alkalis and generally very resistant to all other chemicals. It is generally very resistant to common solvents and dry-cleaning agents. Sunlight causes a slight degradation in time, and no aging effect has been discovered as yet. Acrilan softens at 455° F. and tends to discolor in dry heat.

Selected acid and acetate dyes can be used in coloring the fiber. Acrilan is completely resistant to mildew and moths.

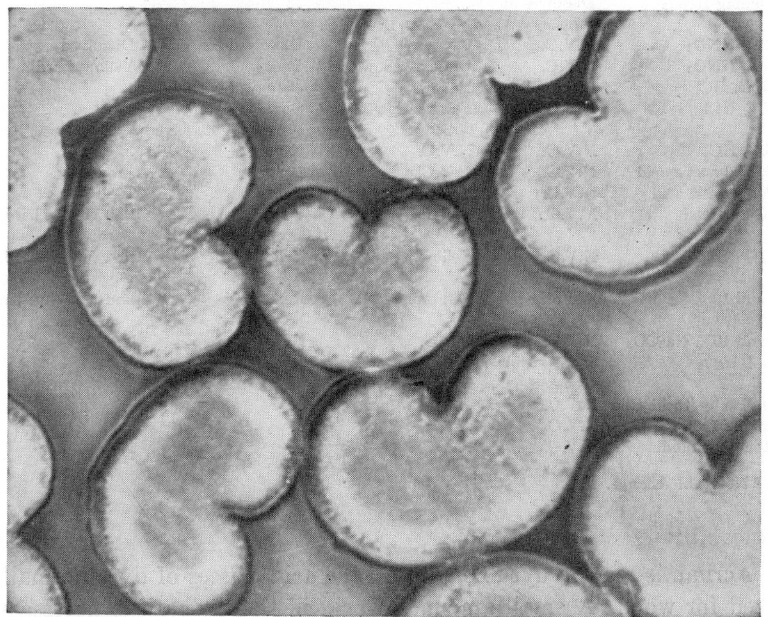

FIG. 27. Cross-section of 3-denier Acrilan staple, ×750. (*Courtesy: The Chemstrand Corp.*)

Water swells the fiber about 5 per cent, and its water retention is about 17 per cent after centrifuging. The fiber shrinkage in boiling water is about 2 per cent. Additional shrinkage in air is about 5 per cent at 180° C. (356° F.) and increases gradually to 11.5 per cent at 240° C. (464° F.), when it softens. The fiber turns yellow to orange to brown on prolonged heating at elevated temperatures.

Its thermal properties are about the same as those of wool. The following solvents have no apparent action on this fiber: acetone, ethyl acetate, dioxane, methyl formate, formaldehyde, benzene, petroleum ether, ethanol, methanol, tetra hydrofuran, nitromethane, carbon tetrachloride, Freon 113, furfuryl alcohol.

The chemical resistance is given in Table 33.

TABLE 33. Chemical Resistance of Acrilan

Chemical	*25° C. 12 Days*	*50° C. 48 Hr*	*75° C. 48 Hr*	*100° C. 48 Hr*
Conc. H_2SO_4	Dissolved	..	..	..
50% H_2SO_4	N.V.C.*	Dissolved partially	Dissolved in 20 hr	Dissolved in few hr
10% H_2SO_4	N.V.C.	N.V.C.	N.V.C.	N.V.C.
Conc. HNO_3	N.V.C.	Dissolved	Dissolved	Dissolved
Fuming HNO_3	Dissolves at once	..	..	..
35% HNO_3	N.V.C.	Gummy	Dissolved	Dissolved
10% HNO_3	N.V.C.	Orange-yellow	Yellow	Yellow, hard
Conc. HCl	Bleached	Yellow	Dissolved partially	..
18% HCl	N.V.C.	Faint yellow	Gummy yellow, partially dissolved	..
10% HCl	N.V.C.	N.V.C.	N.V.C.	..
Glacial acetic acid	N.V.C.	N.V.C.	Brown	Brown
50% Acetic acid	N.V.C.	N.V.C.	Tan	Tan
5% NH_4OH	N.V.C.	Yellow	Yellow	Red yellow, hard, brittle
10% NH_4OH	N.V.C.	Yellow	Yellow	Red yellow, hard, brittle
5 and 10% NaOH	Red orange	Red orange	Red orange	Red, gummy, hard on cooling
5 and 10% Na_2CO_3	N.V.C.	N.V.C.	N.V.C.	N.V.C.
60% H_2O_2	Slight visible change	..	..	..
Aniline hydrochloride	N.V.C.	..	..	..
Aniline 10%	N.V.C.	..	..	..
Monoethyl aniline	N.V.C.	..	..	..

* No visible change.

Dyeability

Acrilan is readily dyeable with all the acid classes of dyes normally used for wool. A small amount of acid in the dyebath is necessary, however, even when the neutral dyeing types of wool dyes are used. Because of the hydrophobic nature of the fiber, the washfastness of the acid dyes on Acrilan are very much better than on wool. Sunlight fastness properties are generally equal to those of the same dyes on wool, although Fade-Ometer tests may indicate a lower order of fastness for Acrilan. Union dyeings with wool are readily accomplished with most of the leveling acid types and with some selected metallized types.

Like all acrylic fibers, Acrilan may be dyed with the dispersed acetate dyes. Most of these dyes show good washfastness properties, and selected ones give reasonable sunlight fastness properties (20–40 hr). Vat dyes and soluble vat dyes show considerable promise on this fiber, their light fastness in many cases being better than is found on the natural fibers.

Processability

Acrilan can be processed on the cotton system similar to rayon staple with little change in machinery. On the woolen and worsted system, no additional finish should be added, unless the fiber was stock dyed.

In finishing, hot pressing or drying should be avoided. A 30-second semi-decating is all that should be used. Temperatures in excess of 300° F. should be used only for a few minutes, because of the danger of yellowing at high temperatures.

Uses

Due to its warm hand and bulky character, this acrylic fiber will find its widest application in apparel, outer wear fabrics, blankets, and inner linings, in blends with cotton, wool, rayon, and other fibers. Its good outdoor and chemical resistance indicates many uses in tents, awnings, filter cloths, fume bags, and chemical-resistance clothing.

X-51 ACRYLIC FIBER [10]

This acrylic fiber is produced by the American Cyanamid Company at Stamford, Conn. Commercialization is handled by the New Product Development Department, New York. The fiber was announced publicly at the March 5th, 1952, meeting of the American Association of Textile Technologists in New York.

X-51 acrylic fiber is presently produced in *two* forms, staple of 3 and 1.5 denier, and continuous-filament yarn of 75/45, 100/60, and 150/90 denier and filament numbers. The color of the staple is almost white with a bluish cast, that of the filament almost white with a yellowish tint (Table 34). Both can be easily bleached. Both are naturally semi-dull in luster with the staple slightly duller than the filament. The staple contains a permanent crimp.

Process

An acrylonitrile resin is copolymerized and dissolved. The dope is spun into a *frigid* bath, and the filaments are subsequently stretched. The filament is produced on a continuous machine. The staple is crimped and crimp set, in addition to inherent crimp produced by the wet-spinning method. So far seven patents have been issued by the

[10] Trade mark of American Cyanamid Company. Other trade marks for this product are Creslan and Cyana.

TABLE 34. COLOR

Conditions *	Continuous Filament Lightness † (per cent)	Continuous Filament Yellowness ‡ (per cent)	Staple Fiber Lightness † (per cent)	Staple Fiber Yellowness ‡ (per cent)
Original	78–82	0.16–0.22	81–88	0.04–0.10
After 0.5 hr at 240° F.	74–78	0.18–0.24	75–80	0.11–0.17
After 6 hr at 275° F.	55–65	0.39–0.45	53–57	0.38–0.41

* Tests were made on material containing the lubricating and antistatic agents put on it to improve its running properties in textile equipment. Tests without such agents indicate much less effect of heat on its color.

† Lightness is based on reflectance, with MgO taken as 100 per cent.

‡ Yellowness is measured according to Federal Specifications TT-P-141a. Method 425.2 (June 16, 1944) and would have a value of 0.00 for a pure white body.

company on this process as follows: U. S. #2,558,730 to 2,558,735 inclusive, also U. S. #2,558,781.

Properties

The cross-section of the fibers is round, and they have a pronounced ring structure. Specific gravity in liquids is 1.17. The fiber, however, has a greater bulking factor than is indicated by these two aspects.

This acrylic fiber has excellent resistance to outdoor exposure, to microorganisms, to acids, to insects, and to most solvents. It has fairly good resistance to caustics. Acids tend to bleach, caustics tend to yellow it.

Shrinkage is very low and, once manufacturing stresses are relieved, the fiber and properly constructed textile products have exceptional stability. Washed fabrics should retain their size and shape, and retain creases well.

The filament can be processed on conventional equipment and with standard procedures. It forms good stitches on both warp-knitting and filling-knitting machines if the needles are not crowded. The yarn is unusually bulky.

Staple can be spun on all conventional types of equipment: cotton, spun rayon, woolen, and worsted. No major changes in procedures are required. The important thing is to allow for the great bulkiness of the fiber, both in the amount of fiber fed through machines and the twists used. Tables 35 and 36 show effect of twist on strength, spinning limits for 3-denier staple, and the superior evenness of yarn that can be expected.

TABLE 35. EFFECT OF TWIST ON STRENGTH

(30's Cotton Count from 3-Denier, 1½-Inch Staple)

Twist Multiplier	*Turns per Inch*	*Lea Product (Count × Strength)*	*Yarn Evenness * (per cent)*
2.22	10.06	1687	74.4
2.59	11.65	1722	62.4
3.08	13.79	1756	48.6
3.56	15.74	1633	55.0
4.62	19.49	1543	57.1
6.34	28.80	1016	51.1

* Yarn evenness was measured on a Uster Tester, and the results are expressed in per cent variation from the normal.

TABLE 36. SPINNING LIMITS

(3-Denier, 1½-Inch Staple)

Yarn Number	*Twist Multiplier*	*Turns per Inch*	*Skein Break (pounds)*	*Lea Product (Count × Strength)*	*Yarn Evenness * (per cent)*
9.80	3.44	10.60	218.12	2138	47.9
20.10	3.08	13.79	87.36	1756	48.6
29.36	3.39	18.37	46.56	1367	72.0
35.94	3.70	22.19	28.96	1041	..
40.50	3.39	21.53	22.86	926	..

* Yarn evenness was measured on a Uster Tester, and the results are expressed in per cent variation from the normal.

The most common mistakes made in processing this acrylic staple are to use too much twist and to overconstruct fabrics—both woven and knit. The fault of overconstructing seems to be aggravated in X-51 because of an observed tendency to full somewhat. The acrylic staple is expected to make the best blends with rayon, wool, cotton, and Vicara.

Both staple and filament can be dyed by means of conventional dyestuffs at temperatures up to the boil, and with ordinary techniques. The cuprous-ion method and high temperatures can be used to advantage. Scouring and bleaching present no unusual problems. Staple and filament, however, dye differently. Tables 37 and 38 show the results that can be expected with several classes of dyes.

TABLE 37. DYEABILITY OF STAPLE

Dyestuff Class	Build-Up	Fastness to		
		Light	Wash	Crocking
Acetate	Good	Fair to moderate	Good	Good
Acid *	Good	Moderate to good	Good	Good
Direct *	Good	Moderate to good	Good	Good
Basic	Good	Fair to good	Good	Good
Vat	Moderate to good	Good	Good	Moderate to good
Soluble vat	Moderate to good	Good	Good	Good

* Cuprous-ion method.

TABLE 38. DYEABILITY OF FILAMENT

Dyestuff Class	Build-Up	Fastness to		
		Light	Wash	Crocking
Acetate	Fair to good *	Moderate to good	Good	Good
Acid †	Fair to moderate	Moderate to good	Good	Good
Direct †	Fair to moderate	Moderate to good	Good	Good
Basic	Moderate	Moderate	Good	Good
Vat	Fair to moderate	Good	Good	Good
Soluble vat	Fair to moderate	Good	Good	Good

* Only moderate unless temperatures above the boil are used.
† Cuprous-ion method.

Exposure to alkalis at high temperatures while scouring this acrylic fiber can cause yellowing. However, yellowing can be prevented or, if it does occur, can be corrected by subsequent treatments. The clean whiteness need not be lost. Several good scouring methods are available. In dyeing, dye assistants, such as *p*-phenylphenol, are not needed.

For two classes of dyes, acid and direct, the cuprous-ion method of dyeing is recommended. On filament yarns, better depths of shade are obtained if temperatures above the boil can be achieved. X-51 is unique among acrylic fibers in that it can be dyed a wide range of shades with vat dyes. Fastness to washing, perspiration, and crocking is excellent. Fastness to light will be in the range expected for vat colors if the depth of shade is taken into account.

This fiber, although easily dyeable, certainly for a hydrophobic fiber, dyes differently from any other fiber and may give many surprising results, both as to color obtained and to fastness. When examined microscopically, both forms have a fairly smooth surface. The continuous filament appears optically nearly clear; the staple presents a slightly hazy appearance.

The *cross-section* of this acrylic fiber is substantially circular in both staple and continuous-filament forms. Both forms exhibit a certain skin effect, this being somewhat more pronounced in the continuous filament. The cross-section shape is distinctive from the other acrylic fibers which are currently available (Fig. 28). Other properties which are of interest to the microscopist is the approximate refractive index of 1.51; birefringence is relatively low.

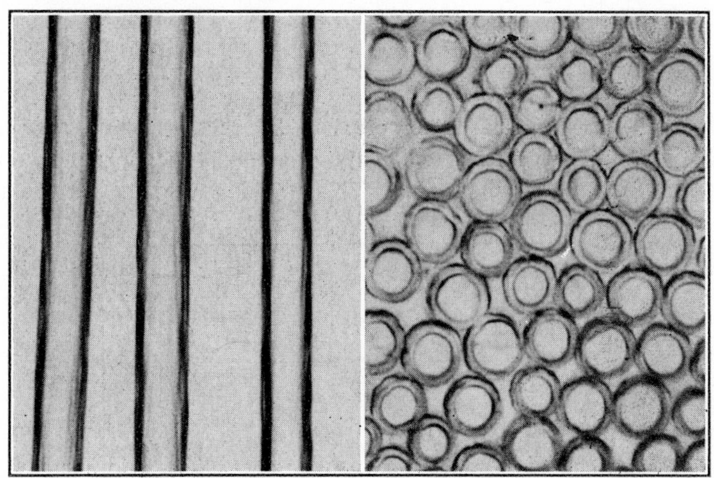

Fig. 28. Acrylic fiber X-51, longitudinal and cross-sections, ×500. Note skin effect.

The *specific gravity* of this acrylic fiber as determined by buoyancy in liquids is approximately 1.17 for both staple and continuous filament, the staple being slightly over and the continuous filament slightly under this average. However, it is of great practical interest to note that the apparent density of staple in air is appreciably lower than the true specific gravity would indicate; this is evidenced by a greater cross-sectional area, i.e., greater bulkiness, than would be expected from the true specific gravity.

The incipient melting point or *sticking temperature* of X-51 acrylic fiber is about 560° F. as determined on a hot surface. However, the fiber shrinks and shrivels below this temperature, in common with other thermoplastic fibers.

The average dry tenacity is about 3.6 grams per denier with an elongation of about 22 per cent (Table 39). This is determined with

TABLE 39. TENSILE PROPERTIES *

Conditions	Continuous-Filament Yarn Tenacity (grams per denier)	Continuous-Filament Yarn Elongation (per cent)	Staple Fiber (Single Filament), 3 Denier * Tenacity (grams per denier)	Staple Fiber (Single Filament), 3 Denier * Elongation (per cent)
Dry	3.4–4.4	20–24	2.7–3.5	25–35
Wet	2.9–4.0	20–23		
Dry knot	1.7–2.3	11–15.5		
Dry loop	2.6–2.9	16.5–19		

* An Instron testing machine, Model TT-B, was used at 73° F. and 50 per cent R.H. The rate of elongation was kept constant at 100 per cent per minute. The tensile properties may vary appreciably under different testing conditions.

yarn having a filament denier of 1.66. The stress-strain curve exhibits a definite knee or yield point of about 1.2 grams/denier and elongation of about 2 per cent. The modulus as given by the first

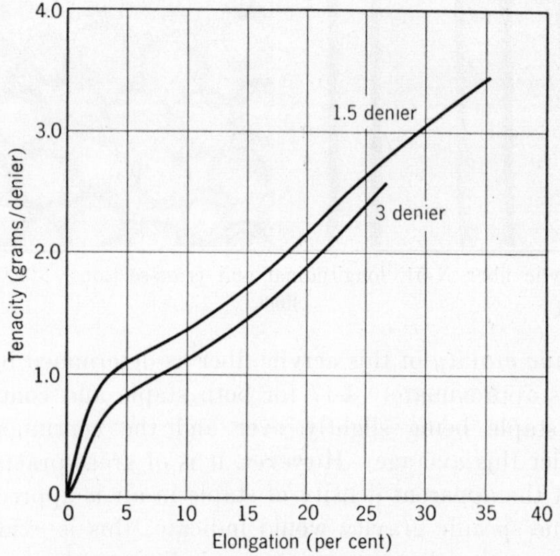

FIG. 29. Stress-strain curve of X-51 staple.

slope of the stress-strain curve (Fig. 29) is about 60 grams/denier, and the stretch resistance at 2 per cent elongation is 1.1 grams/denier. This shows that the continuous-filament yarn has a fairly firm hand and also rather good resistance to deformation under stresses associated with fiber handling. The 1-min recovery from 2 per cent stretch is 95 per cent complete from instantaneous release and 71 per cent

TABLE 40. STRETCH RESISTANCE

Elongation (per cent)	*Continuous Filament (grams per denier)*	*Staple Fiber, 3 Denier (grams per denier)*
0.5	0.3	0.1
1.0	0.6	0.3
1.5	0.9	0.4
2.0	1.1	0.5
2.5	1.2	0.6

TABLE 41. RECOVERY FROM STRETCH

	Continuous Filament (per cent)		*Staple Fiber (per cent)*	
Stretch (per cent)	*Instantaneous Release* *	*Delayed Release* *	*Instantaneous Release* *	*Delayed Release* *
2	95	71	92	53
4	84	52	80	42
8	69	43	70	35

* The filament was stretched the indicated amount and released instantaneously, or after 100 sec. Measurements were made 60 sec after release.

after 100 sec of holding under tension (Tables 40 and 41). Longer periods permit even more recovery. The *wet* tenacity of continuous filament is about 3.2 grams/denier with an elongation of about 22 per cent, which is not greatly different from dry yarn. The knot and loop tenacities are 2.0 and 2.8 grams/denier, respectively; the loop elongation, an important property in determining knitting properties, is about 18 per cent.

Resistance to *outdoor exposure,* involving radiation, moisture, changes in temperature, and so forth, is exceptionally good. One year direct exposure in Florida of continuous-filament yarn showed a retention of 60 per cent of its initial tenacity and elongation, while the loop and knot properties were affected still less. Under glass, the per cent retention of initial properties was higher. The initial tests reported were for filament yarn containing antistatic finish. Current tests being made without finish will show even better results.

The *electrical properties* of X-51 acrylic fiber are dependent to some extent on moisture conditions. At R.H. up to 50 per cent the resistance is 450,000 megohms; the equilibrium moisture in the fiber at 50 per cent R.H. is about 1.1 per cent. Above this point the resistance drops rather quickly.

The *dimensional stability* of this acrylic fiber as determined by relaxation shrinkage is good. Staple is produced with a stabilized crimp and withstands boiling water; furthermore, no fiber shrinkage takes place. Continuous-filament yarn in general will show shrinkage of less than 2 per cent in boiling water and has been produced with no residual shrinkage. In common with other thermoplastic fibers, this acrylic fiber shrinks at high temperatures with loss of tenacity; however, it can be pointed out that exposure of continuous-filament yarn to a temperature of 275° F. for 6 hr gave no change in physical properties when tested at room temperatures.

This acrylic fiber, being thermoplastic, melts and may ignite when an open flame is applied; in general, cigarette sparks and glowing embers will not ignite fabrics produced from staple or cause pinholes.

Resistance to *attack by insects or by mildew* and other microorganisms is excellent. The black carpet beetle will not eat fabric constructed of this fiber. Soil-burial test of fabric in the severe A.S.T.M. vertical method showed no change after 6 weeks' exposure to soil microorganisms.

Due to the exceptional solvent resistance of polymers comprising principally acrylonitrile, X-51 acrylic fiber is neither dissolved nor softened by the usual organic solvents such as hydrocarbons, alcohols, esters, ketones, ethers, or chlorinated hydrocarbons.

Chemical resistance is of great importance in determining not only the general utility of a fiber but also the conditions under which fabrics can be handled in dyeing and finishing. In general, it can be said that resistance to acids is very good, with a tendency to bleach; resistance to alkalis is fair to good with a tendency to yellow under severe conditions. Higher concentrations and higher temperatures cause more severe attack. For example, 2 months' exposure of continuous-filament yarn to 40 per cent sulfuric acid at 122° F. showed a retention of more than 75 per cent of the initial tenacity; at the same temperature 1 per cent caustic soda effected about the same attack in 1 month. In general, it can be said that, under normal alkaline conditions, such as those encountered in vat dyeing, no appreciable loss in tenacity or color should be expected.

Uses

The spun yarns made from staple are used in blankets, sweaters, knitted jerseys (brushed and pile types), draperies, filter fabrics, hand knitting yarns, hosiery, and bathing suits.

MANUFACTURE OF VICARA FROM ZEIN

Zein is an odorless, nontoxic protein derived from corn. It is a by-product of corn processing, and it is made into a vegetable protein fiber, primarily used in blends.

The Virginia-Carolina Chemical Corporation did extensive industrial research on it, and in 1948 began to manufacture a zein fiber under the trade name Vicara.[11] A large fiber plant in Taftville, Conn., was purchased and retooled, and the fiber brought into commercial production.

Process

In producing Vicara, powdered zein is mixed with a caustic solution until complete suspension is secured. This solution is allowed to age until the proper viscosity is obtained. The spin solution is then extruded through spinnerets with thousands of holes, producing a great number of filaments, which are combined into a tow containing as many as 270,000 filaments.

The spin solution is passed through an acid coagulation bath which hardens the protein molecule and separates it from its alkaline solution. The tow is cured and then exposed to a series of stretching and orientation processes which align the molecules, resulting in a stronger filament or fiber. Upon stretching the tow is dehydrated to prevent shrinkage after stretching. It undergoes a subsequent curing operation and is washed with large amounts of water to free it from acids and salts. It is then dried and finished and, if desired, cut into uniform staple lengths and baled.

The process involves hydroxylation, filtration, coagulation, and cross-linkaging as well as stabilization under rigid control of temperature, concentration, and stretch to assure a uniform product.

Physical Properties

Vicara is produced as an extremely soft, uniform fiber, light golden in color, being manufactured either bleached or unbleached. Deniers and staple lengths are carefully controlled. Under the microscope, it appears as a cylindrical, translucent rod with a nearly circular cross-section.

It is clean, free of noils and contains no foreign matter. A crimp is imparted to the fiber to facilitate carding and spinning.

[11] Registered trade mark of Virginia-Carolina Chemical Corp.

The specific gravity of the fiber is 1.25. Its toughness index is 2.8 grams/denier/elongation. It has an elasticity comparable to animal fibers. Its tensile strength is 17,600–19,200 psi, and its dry tenacity is 1.10–1.20 grams/denier. The elongation of the fiber is 30–35 per cent in the dry state and 30–40 per cent in the wet state.

Vicara is resilient and resists deformation to a marked degree. Young's modulus is 0.24 gram/denier.

The fiber has warmth equal to wool. Laboratory tests indicate that its insulating value is similar to that of animal fibers in a fabric of like construction.

Vicara may be had as water repellent as wool. This does not interfere with warm wet processing, such as washing, dyeing, or scouring, because the repellency is not apparent at temperatures above 110° F. The water repellency is permanent at room temperature and is not removed by dry cleaning or repeated laundering.

Vicara has a moisture regain of 10 per cent. Its moisture absorbency is approximately 16–18 per cent at 95 per cent R.H. and 75° F. Total water retention is estimated at 40 per cent.

The fiber is odorless, except in warm aqueous solution where it has a faint, pleasant odor which disappears completely after processing. It is insoluble in organic solvents. It is less flammable than the cellulosic fibers. Vicara is not seriously affected by temperatures up to 350° F., and the melting point is reached at 470°–475° F.

It is resistant to mildew and bacteria; moths and carpet beetles will not eat it. It is not affected by age, and its degree of sensitivity to sunlight is similar to that of animal fibers.

Chemical Properties

Vicara resists acids and has an affinity for most dyes. It can be dyed with acid, chrome, vat, naphthol, sulfur, or direct colors, allowing a wide variety of choice. Since it is easily dyed the problem is only one of selecting the proper dyes from the types mentioned above, and most dye houses and dye manufacturers are acquainted with the proper dyes for the various blends. The dye shrinkage in acid dyeing is less than 5 per cent. Vicara is nonfelting.

Unlike animal and all other protein fibers, it is not drastically affected by alkalis. Normal procedures used in scouring are adaptable to blends containing this fiber.

Because of Vicara's resistance to most chemicals, acids or alkalis, and its stability at high temperatures, no caution is necessary in laundering and ironing.

Fiber Types

The fibers are supplied in three types or codes differing principally in their dyeing shrinkage; in deniers of 3, 5, 7, and 15; in tow form or in any staple length from ½ to 6 in. It is shipped in 300- and 500-lb bales.

Because of its great versatility Vicara is used chiefly in blends with other fibers. When blended with wool Vicara upgrades the finished product and increases the wear life of these fabrics by enabling them to wear without pilling, stringing, or fraying, making these blends ideal for women's and men's suitings and outerwear. In blends with cotton, Vicara adds drape, softness, elasticity, mildew resistance, and a better hand and feel.

To an acetate or viscose blend it adds unusual loft, fullness of body, lively softness, greater compliance, resilience, recovery, and a richer appearance.

To the great strength and abrasion resistance of nylon, it adds its unique softness, moisture absorption, and resilience.

Being a smooth-surfaced fiber it differs from wool, which is a scaly fiber. Its relatively low resistance to bending and relatively low friction contribute to a tendency to lie down smoothly and present a cooler, smoother surface than a wool fabric in the same range of fiber fineness. On the other hand, by choice of fiber diameter and yarn twist, it is possible to secure a woollike feel.

Vicara has many properties that are similar to wool; nevertheless it has many other fine properties of its own and under no circumstances should be considered as a substitute for any other fiber. It poses no difficulties in spinning and weaving as it can be used on any commercial machinery today; i.e., that for worsted and woolens, or the Bradford, French, rayon, and cotton systems.

Vicara is being produced in four types, designated as codes. Some codes are in bright fiber, some in dull, and some in both. The several codes differ slightly in their characteristics, and each is suggested for a particular end use. Each code is likewise available in several deniers. This is summarized in Table 42.

TABLE 42. Vicara Staple

Code	*Deniers*	*Luster*	*End Use*
500	3, 5, 7	Dull or Bright	Soft woven fabrics; knit goods
600	3, 5, 7	Dull only	Knit goods; soft woolen types
700	3, 5, 7	Dull or Bright	Hard-finish woven fabrics
800	7, 15	Bright only	Upholstery; floor coverings

All the above codes and deniers are available in any staple length from ½ to 6 in., as designated by the customer. While natural color of Vicara is pale yellow, it is available in bleached form. A permanent crimp is applied to all staple fiber to facilitate processing.

A suitable textile finish is applied to Vicara before shipment—the particular finish used depends on the manner in which it is to be processed.

Vicara is being blended commercially with practically all the natural and man-made fibers. Both woven fabrics and knit goods are in large-scale production for men's wear, women's wear, upholstery, blankets, and many special fabrics.

Virginia-Carolina Chemical Corporation produces a tow the total denier weight of which varies with the filament denier as shown in Table 43.

TABLE 43. Vicara Tow

Denier	*Total Denier Weight*
3	810,000
5	540,000
7	588,000
15	594,000

Uses

Vicara is currently being utilized in men's suitings, knit goods, infants' wear, sport clothes, upholstery, women's wear, suitings, men's slacks, sweaters, men's and children's hosiery, filter cloths, blankets, and pile fabrics.

MANUFACTURE OF CASEIN MONOFILAMENTS

Work done by the U. S. Department of Agriculture suggested the development by Rubberset Company and Arthur D. Little, Inc., of a casein fiber, both curled and uncurled, known by the trade name Caslen.

Process

Casein is a protein by-product of skim milk. It is coagulated from fluid milk by the addition of acids or rennet. The resulting curd is washed, dried, and granulated to a fairly fine particle size. Water is added to the casein powder and forced under heat and pressure through fine jets. The resultant filaments are hardened in a tanning agent such as formaldehyde, and taken up in straight form after drying, or curled and dried to a permanent set.

Properties

The properties of Caslen monofilaments are given in Table 44.

TABLE 44. PROPERTIES OF CASLEN MONOFILAMENT

Diameter range, inches	0.005–0.020
Lengths	Any length
Filament shape	Round
Specific gravity	1.29
Tensile strength, psi	8000–14,000
Tenacity, grams/denier	0.5–0.9
Wet strength, per cent	50
Elongation at 65% R.H., 70° F., per cent	6–10 (curled), 15–20 (straight)
Knot strength at 65% R.H., 70° F., per cent	75
Impact strength at 65% R.H., 70° F., ft-lb/sq in.	50–75
Flammability	Burns slowly
Moisture regain at 65% R.H., 70° F., per cent	11–12
Effect of dry heat	Damage starts at 300° F. (discoloration starts at 200° F.)
Color possibilities	Natural color white. Affinity for dye similar to wool. Colored fiber can be extruded.
Resistance to insects	Excellent. Complete resistance to carpet beetle and clothes moth larvae.
Resistance to mildew and mold	Excellent
Resistance to water	Develops elasticity
Resistance to solvents	Excellent resistance to most solvents used in painting and dry cleaning

Uses

The straight fiber was intended primarily for use as a synthetic bristle in various types of brushes. In curled form, the fiber possesses properties of resiliency and springiness superior to natural horsehair and other curled animal hairs. It is used as a filler material in upholstered furniture and bedding and also for elements in various types of filters. There are many other more specialized applications.

A staple fiber of dull luster and irregular crimp, of any length (12-in. standard), is extruded in diameters of 0.005, 0.008, 0.010, 0.012, and 0.016 in.

For most purposes curled Caslen is used alone, although it has been blended with hair and wool. Its natural color is white, but it is also available in a tan color similar in shade to cattle tail hair. It is supplied in compressed bales covered with burlap, weighing approximately 175 lb each.

DACRON POLYESTER FIBER[12]

History. Dacron is the du Pont Company's trade mark for its polyester fiber, a new and versatile textile fiber, manufactured from a chemical composition of ethylene glycol and terephthalic acid. The groundwork for the development of this polyester fiber was laid by the late Dr. W. H. Carothers, du Pont research chemist, in his work with macromolecules. Rather than investigate all the possibilities of polyesters, Dr. Carothers elected to devote the major portion of his efforts to polyamides—a course which resulted in the development of nylon. British research chemists, after studying the published works of Dr. Carothers, decided to examine further the possibilities of polyesters. Their work resulted in a fiber known in England as "Terylene." These investigations were carried out by J. R. Whinfield, J. T. Dickson, W. K. Birtwistle and C. G. Ritchie, in the laboratories of the Calico Printers Association, Ltd., during the period of 1939–41.[13]

In 1946 the du Pont Company bought the United States patent to this polyester fiber. Under the provisional title of "Fiber V" and in essentially the same chemical form, du Pont has conducted intensive development work.

Commercial Production

In December 1950, the du Pont Company announced plans to use a 635-acre tract on the Neuse River, near Kinston, N. C., for the manufacture of this fiber. Construction began in the spring of 1951. Commercial production of the fiber was expected to begin during 1953 provided no unforeseen delays occurred. Limited quantities of continuous-filament and staple yarns required for development work were made in an experimental operation at the Seaford, Del., plant. On February 28, 1951, it was announced that an expansion of chemical facilities was being made at the Repauno Plant at Gibbstown, N. J., for increased production of nitric acid and dimethyl terephthalate, a

[12] This section is based on information furnished by the Textile Fibers Dept., E. I. du Pont de Nemours & Co.

[13] "Chemistry of Terylene," *Nature,* **158,** 930, No. 4026 (1946).

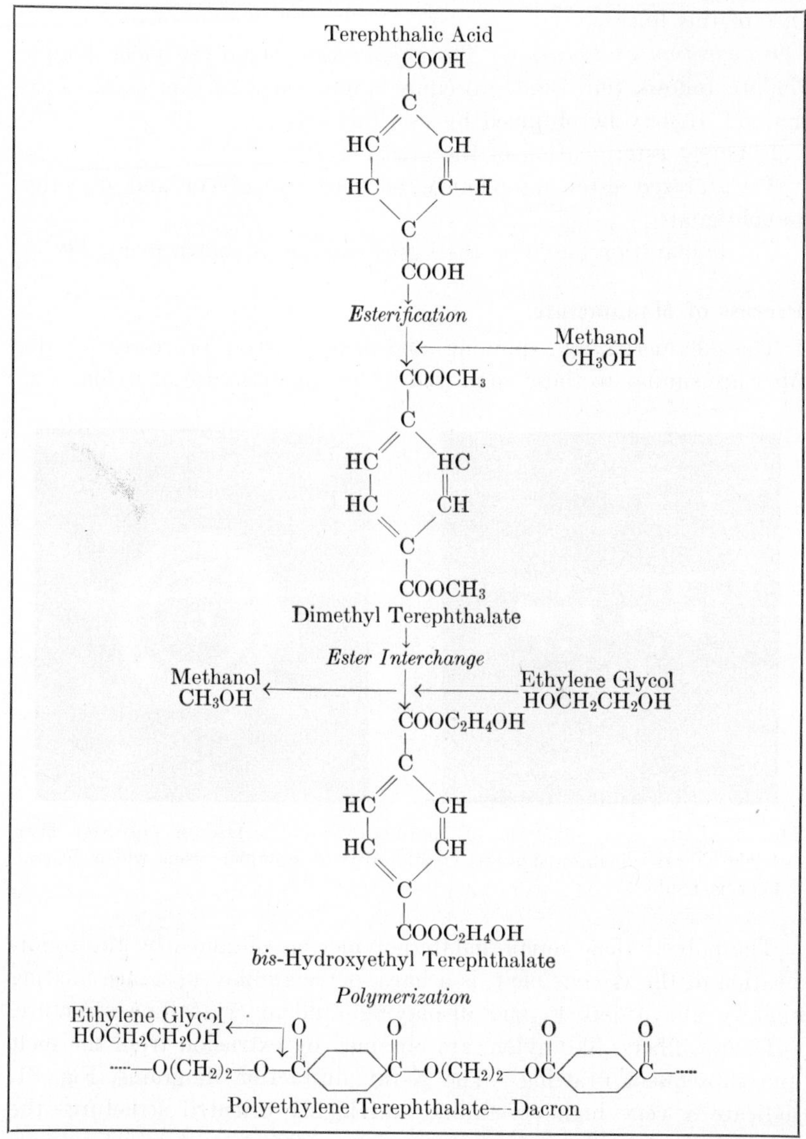

FIG. 30. Preparation of polyethylene terephthalate for Dacron polyester fiber.

white, flaky powder produced from nitric acid, xylene, and methanol. Dimethyl terephthalate is a principal raw material for the manufacture of this fiber.

Preparation of Polymer. The preparation of polyethylene terephthalate follows the usual procedure appropriate to this class of reaction. It may be obtained by *two* methods:

1. Direct esterification of the glycol.
2. Catalyzed ester interchange between the glycol and dimethyl terephthalate.

The preparation based on the latter reaction is shown in Fig. 30.

Process of Manufacture

The polymerization, spinning, and draw-twisting processes for this fiber are similar to those employed in the manufacture of nylon.

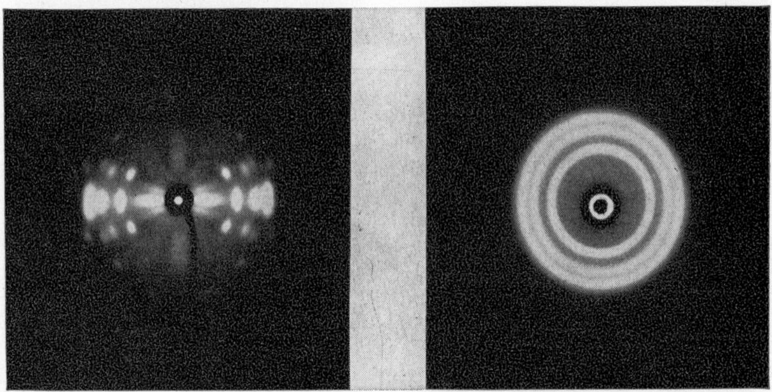

Fig. 31. *Left,* X-ray diagram of continuous-filament Dacron polyester fiber. *Right,* X-ray diagram showing crystallinity of polymer from which Dacron fiber is made.

The polyethylene terephthalate polymer, as obtained by the solidification of the viscous melt, is a hard, porcelainlike substance melting slightly above 480° F. and displaying random crystalline structure.

Dacron fibers, like nylon, are obtained by extrusion from the melt and subsequent drawing. The X-ray diffraction diagrams, Fig. 31, indicate a very high crystalline and highly oriented structure—the amount of crystalline being between 70 and 80 per cent, which is comparable to nylon.

The continuous-filament and staple fibers produced have microscopic properties similar to those of nylon. See Figs. 32 and 33.

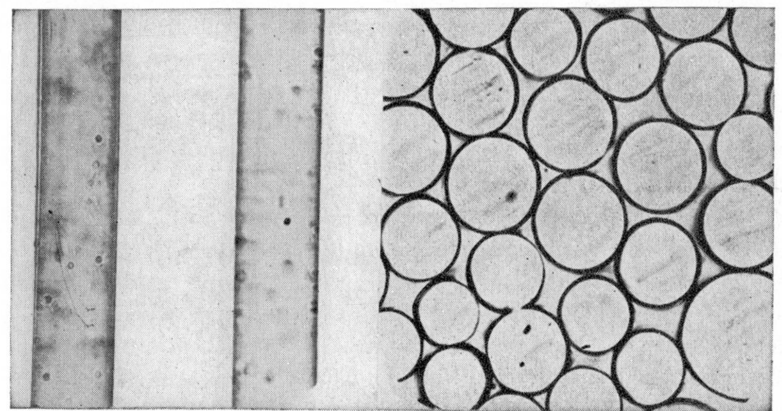

FIG. 32. Longitudinal section of Dacron polyester fiber, ×500.

FIG. 33. Cross-sections of Dacron polyester fiber, ×500.

Physical and Chemical Properties

Types Produced. This fiber can be made in all forms—continuous-monofilament and multifilament yarns, staple, and tow.

Tenacity and Elongation. This polyester fiber has the following approximate tenacity and elongation ranges, as shown in Table 45.

TABLE 45. TENACITY AND ELONGATION OF DACRON POLYESTER FIBER

(Conditioned at 72% R.H. and 75° F., on a Suter Tester)

	Tenacity (grams/denier)	*Elongation at Break (per cent)*
Filament	4.8–6.0	12–20
Uncrimped tow	3.8	38

Resistance to Stretch. Dacron continuous-filament (type 5500 and 5600) yarns have high resistance to stretch. To stretch these yarns 1.0 per cent, a force of 1.0 grams/denier must be applied.

Resistance to Chemical Degradation. Laboratory tests indicate that most compounds of the following general types have little or no effect on the strength of Dacron polyester fibers under ordinary conditions of exposure:

- Alcohols
- Bleaching agents
- Dry-cleaning solvents
- Halogenated hydrocarbons
- Hydrocarbons
- Ketones
- Soaps and synthetic detergents
- Water, including sea water
- Weak acids
- Weak alkalis

Dacron has good resistance to most weak acids, even at boiling temperatures, and to moderately strong acids at room temperature. It is disintegrated by concentrated (96 per cent) sulfuric acid.

The fiber has good resistance to weak alkalis and moderate resistance to strong alkalis at room temperature, but is degraded by strong alkalis at elevated temperatures.

Dacron has excellent resistance to oxidizing agents and is not degraded by bleaching treatments normally used for other fibers.

Resistance to Heat and Flammability. Dacron has remarkable resistance to heat. High temperatures cause little discoloration or degradation. A fabric kept for 30 days at 300° F. in a hot air oven retained 74 per cent of its original tenacity. It has a sticking temperature of 460° F. and it will melt at 480° F.

Experiments and experience have shown that the flammability of clean, undyed, finish-free Dacron polyester fiber and of Dacron dyed and finished with properly selected materials is very low and considered highly satisfactory for practically all textile purposes. Dacron will melt if a flame is applied. However, as soon as the igniting flame is removed, the burning melt will usually drop away from the yarn or fabric and harden with very little tendency for further flame propagation.

If oils, finishes, pigments, dyes, or other materials are present on the fiber, there is always the possibility that the resulting treated fabric will support combustion because of their presence. It is also possible that considerable amounts of nonflammable solid materials, even materials that are fire retardants for other fibers, may cause propagation of a flame by increasing the viscosity of the molten drops or by otherwise preventing the molten polymer from dropping away from the fabric. For example, a combination fabric of Dacron and Fiberglas may burn when ignited, although neither the Dacron nor the Fiberglas alone would support combustion.

Toxicological Properties. The fiber is physiologically inert. Tests have revealed no poisonous or other harmful effects when used internally. Applied externally, there is no evidence of irritation or skin reaction. The addition of other materials to this fiber may create a health hazard; therefore, finished fabrics should always be checked for dermatitis and toxicological reactions.

Moisture Absorption. This polyester fiber has a moisture regain of 0.4 per cent at 65 per cent R.H. and 70° F. Generally, such fabrics are quick drying, the extent depending on construction and whether or not continuous-filament or spun yarns are used. Even fabrics from spun yarns dry relatively fast when the excess water is removed by extracting.

Shape and Crease Retention. The symmetrically disposed, recurring benzene nuclei in the linear chain of this polymer cause less flexibility in the chains, since there are fewer points of rotation in a given length than are found in the purely aliphatic fiber-forming polymers. The fiber has an inherent stiffness which resists bending and causes rapid recovery from bending. These qualities contribute to the unusual resiliency of this fiber.

Stabilized fabrics made of continuous filament or staple have excellent resistance to wrinkling and recovery from wrinkling. Essentially permanent creases can be pressed into fabrics at ordinary ironing temperatures (about 300° F.), and remain sharp even after the fabric is washed. Such creases, however, can be pressed out, if desired. Suits made of the staple have held their shape and press in abnormally damp weather and even when wet.

Processability. Process experience to date on this polyester fiber has been most encouraging. The staple lends itself to efficient processing on all standard spinning systems. In both knitting and weaving, the continuous-filament yarn has given good performance. Certain antistatic finishes have proved effective.

Stabilization and Setting by Heat. Fabrics made of continuous-filament yarn can be stabilized and set by heat on substantially the same equipment and with the same techniques that are used for nylon. Setting at temperatures in the range of 375° F. to 425° F. on a hot roll has resulted in fabrics that are dimensionally stable to repeated washing and ironing. Fabrics made of staple are effectively stabilized in normal dyeing and finishing operations.

General Properties

Good sunlight resistance in general—excellent behind glass.

Excellent electrical insulating properties.

Freedom from damage by insects or microorganisms.

Yarn shrinkage in boiling water; for continuous-filament yarns it is about 13 per cent.

Excellent adhesion to natural and synthetic rubber can be obtained.

Fabrics are subject to accumulation of static electricity. Antistatic agents are recommended where this property is objectionable.

Washable or cleanable with standard dry-cleaning fluids.

Ironing and pressing temperatures should be approximately 250° F. for staple fabrics and 275° F. for filament fabrics.

Continuous-filament yarn is capable of 12 to 14 per cent shrinkage in boiling water. Greater shrinkage is possible, depending on temperature and tension.

Dyeing Properties

This fiber can be dyed to most of the desired shades with good-to-excellent washfastness and fair-to-good light fastness. Dispersed acetate dyes have been successfully applied to this fiber from an aqueous bath.

Three dyeing methods are currently used:

1. Aqueous dyeing with carrier. This method has been especially satisfactory for dyeing suiting fabrics on a beck. Filament fabrics, sewing thread, filament and staple yarns, raw stock, and top have also been dyed successfully with benzoic acid as the carrier.
2. Pressure dyeing without carrier. Pressure dyeing of sewing thread, yarns, and raw stock has been accomplished in machines adapted to operate under 15 lb pressure at 250° F.
3. The "Thermosol" process has been successfully demonstrated in small mill-scale operations. Acetate dyes are recommended for application by this method and can be used either alone or combined with selected vat color pigments. The Thermosol process consists of padding the color, drying, and then heating the fabric for a short time at a high temperature, such as 440° F., in a hot-air, flue-type drier.

Uses of Filament Yarn

This yarn is unique in regard to its dry hand, its high resistance to stretching, high elastic recovery, and high tensile strength. This combination of properties permits the manufacture of sheer, extremely light-weight fabrics like glass curtains, tulle, voiles, organdies, shirting, and blouse fabrics which are inherently crisp, bouffant, highly wrinkle-resistant and retentive of shape without superficial treatment of the resultant fabrics.

Like nylon, this filament can be made with a tensile strength higher than silk and linen (see Fig. 34). The high tensile strength and resistance to stretching possessed by filament yarn cause it to be an interesting possibility for sewing thread in wearing apparel, in certain V-belts which cannot be adjusted readily; and as a covering for high-pressure fire hose, where resistance to stretching under high pressures and a smaller bulk of hose are desired.

Excellent resistance to abrasion in the wet condition and to bleaching solutions are properties utilized in laundry nets. The high resistance to heat is of interest in pressing fabrics. Sail fabrics utilize the favorable properties—high tensile strength, resistance to stretching and mildew, and dimensional stability in the dry and wet states.

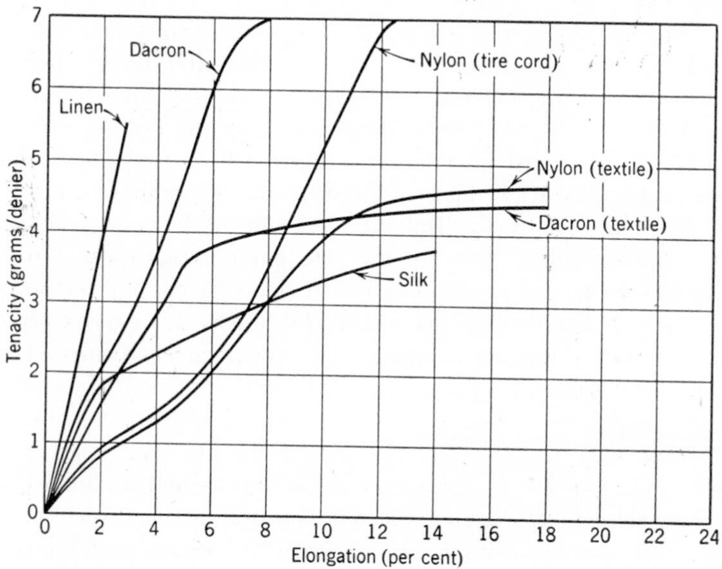

Fig. 34. Dacron polyester fiber, hot stretched, compared with nylon and other fibers.

Uses of Staple Yarns

The staple version of this fiber produces men's and women's suiting fabrics which have outstanding resilience. This encompasses excellent resistance to and recovery from wrinkling in suitings worn in hot, humid weather. The staple is indicated for light-weight fabrics for summer suitings which require unusual resiliency and dimensional stability to prevent puckering and change in shape in humid weather. It is also of interest in the heavier weight fabrics, and it seems evident that it will have a wide versatility in outerwear.

Knitting yarns have excellent elastic recovery which is of special interest from the standpoint of excellent retention of shape in sweaters, hose, and other knitted garments.

Full-scale production began during 1953. Yarns have been spun on all systems. Fabrics made of 100 per cent Dacron as well as blends of Dacron with wool, rayon, and cotton are being introduced in suitings, dresses, shirts, socks, sweaters, sportswear, work clothes, and industrial fabrics.

POLYETHYLENE MONOFILAMENTS

History

Polyethylene or polythene is produced by polymerization of ethylene under heat and pressure to build up predominantly linear chains of CH_2— groups with molecular weights ranging, approximately, between 1000 and 40,000. Originally developed in England by Imperial Chemical Industries under the name Alkathene, it is produced in this country by E. I. du Pont de Nemours & Company under the name Alathon, and by the Bakelite Division of Union Carbide and Carbon Corporation. Several other companies are expected to become suppliers of this resin. The use of polyethylene for textile purposes was first promoted in this country by American Viscose Corporation, by National Plastics Company (Wynene), and is being actively developed by Reeves Brothers, Inc. (Reevon).

Process

Polyethylene of low molecular weight is grease- and waxlike. With increasing chain length the polymer forms soft and then harder thermoplastic resins, which exhibit fiber-forming properties at a molecular weight of 16,000 and higher. Polymers of molecular weights ranging from 19,000 to 23,000 and higher are used for the industrial production of continuous monofilaments. The resin is extruded in the molten state, the filaments are cooled in air or water, then, in most instances, oriented by cold drawing, and set by annealing them, usually in a hot-water bath. These operations greatly increase tensile strength and abrasion resistance of the filaments. They permit control of their elongation to break, and improve their dimensional stability. Polyethylene monofilaments have considerable flexibility even at low temperature without addition of plasticizers. They are supplied clear in dull or bright luster or colored by incorporation of finely dispersed pigments. They are round or elliptical in cross-section, with a thickness ranging from approximately 0.006 in. upward. Production of thinner and multifilament yarns is considered.

Properties

Some of the properties of these filaments are listed in Table 46.

TABLE 46. PHYSICAL PROPERTIES OF POLYETHYLENE

Specific gravity	0.92 gram/cc
Melting point	230 to 250° F. (depending on molecular weight)
Softening point	220 to 240° F. (lower under high load)
Decomposition temperature	Above 600° F.
Brittleness temperature	Below minus 30° F.
Tensile strength of oriented filaments	1.5 to 2.8 grams/denier (17,000 to 30,000 psi)
Elongation to break	
Not oriented	500 to 800%
Oriented	20 to 150% (adjustable)
Elastic recovery	90 to 95% at 5% stretch
Moisture content and water absorption	Less than 0.01%

Thin filaments of clear, translucent polyethylene lose in tensile strength upon prolonged exposure to sunlight, especially under subtropical conditions. Ultraviolet absorbing agents and antioxidants can act as stabilizers to a certain extent. Yarns colored with selected pigments have satisfactory aging properties with excellent light fastness. The low specific gravity gives yields of yards per pound greater than for any other of the known synthetics, as shown in Table 47.

TABLE 47. SIZES AND YARDS PER POUND OF MONOFILS

Diameter of Round Monofils (inches)	*Denier Range*	*Average Yield (yards per pound)*
0.008	250–300	17,000
0.012	550–600	7,500
0.015	850–950	4,700
0.020	1,600–1,800	2,700
0.030	3,500–4,000	1,200

The filaments are readily twisted to yarns and ropes, braided to cords and ribbons, and woven or knitted into fabrics of a wide variety of constructions and patterns. These goods can be subjected to temperatures quite close to the melting point of the resin without chemical deterioration. The greige goods have a tendency to shrink when heated to temperatures beyond about 160° F. This shrinkage, however, can be controlled by the construction and can be reduced to an acceptable degree by adequate processing of the goods.

TABLE 48. Summary of Deniers and Filament Numbers of Noncellulosic Yarns *

Companies	15	20	30	40	50	70	75	100	150	200	210	250	260	270	300	400	500	540	610	770	Types and Quality
	Deniers																				
American Cyanamid Co.	..	..	..	..	..	..	45	60	90	..	..	..	..	..	..	..	..	..	..	..	Acrylic Fiber X-51
Carbide and Carbon Chemicals Div., Union Carbide and Carbon Corp.	..	..	..	..	..	..	..	..	..	..	..	..	..	..	..	..	..	..	..	..	Vinyon N stretched
	..	..	..	..	..	..	..	..	..	..	..	..	..	..	..	..	..	..	..	..	Vinyon N stretched
	..	..	..	..	..	..	..	40	..	..	..	..	..	240	..	..	..	..	..	..	Vinyon N stabilized
	..	..	..	..	..	..	..	..	..	..	..	240	..	..	..	..	..	..	..	..	Vinyon N stabilized
E. I. du Pont de Nemours & Co.	1	7	10	13	17	34	..	34	..	34	34	..	17	..	..	..	..	..	..	..	Nylon, various types †
	..	20	..	34	..	..	..	..	..	..	..	..	..	..	..	..	..	..	..	..	
	..	..	..	..	..	..	30	40	..	80	..	..	..	..	..	..	..	..	..	..	Semi-dull Orlon acrylic fiber
	..	..	..	34	..	34	34	..	..	..	..	34	..	..	..	..	..	..	..	..	Dacron, semi-dull and bright
Owens-Corning Fiberglas Corp.	..	..	..	..	102	..	..	204	..	204	..	..	..	..	204	408	..	..	408	..	Fiberglas yarns
	..	..	..	..	..	..	..	..	..	408	..	..	..	..	612	816	..	..	612	..	
	..	..	..	..	..	..	..	..	..	..	..	..	..	..	..	..	..	..	1224	..	
Libbey-Owens-Ford Glass Co.	..	..	..	..	..	..	..	..	..	120	..	..	..	..	170	250	..	..	350	..	Glass Fiber ECE 225
	..	..	..	..	..	..	..	204	204	204	..	..	..	612	204	408	612	..	408	..	Glass Fiber ECG 150
Glass Fibers, Inc.	..	..	..	..	..	..	..	..	..	408	..	..	..	..	408	816	..	..	612	..	Vitron
	..	..	..	..	..	..	..	..	..	..	..	..	..	..	612	..	..	..	816	..	
	..	..	..	..	..	..	..	..	..	..	..	..	..	..	..	..	..	..	1224	..	
Firestone Plastics Co.	..	..	..	..	..	..	..	..	..	..	..	..	..	..	..	..	0.008	..	..	0.010	Velon (Saran)
	..	..	..	..	..	..	..	..	..	..	..	..	..	..	..	..	..	0.012	..	..	
Lus-Trus Extruded Plastics	..	..	..	..	..	..	..	..	..	..	..	..	..	..	..	..	0.008	..	..	0.010	Saran
Reeves Bros.	..	..	..	..	..	..	..	..	..	..	..	0.008	..	..	..	0.010	..	0.012	..	..	Reevon
Plexon Corp.	..	..	..	..	..	..	..	..	..	..	..	..	..	..	..	..	..	..	..	0.010	Plexon
Bolta-Saran, Inc.	..	..	..	..	..	..	..	..	..	..	..	..	..	..	..	..	0.008	..	..	0.010	Saran
Dawbarn Bros.	..	..	..	..	..	..	..	..	..	..	..	..	..	..	..	..	0.008	..	..	0.010	Saran

Companies	815	840	880	915	1120	1220	1225	1540	1560	1650	1750	1835	1900	2050	2465	2770	2920	3320	3624	3675	3720	Types and Quality
	Deniers																					
E. I. du Pont	..	140	..	..	..	..	..	..	..	..	..	..	..	..	..	..	..	..	..	..	..	Nylon
Owens-Corning Fiberglas Corp.	816	..	..	612	..	..	816	3060	..	..	..	1224	..	4080	2448	1836	..	..	..	2448	..	Fiberglas yarns
	1632	..	..	1836	..	..	1224	..	..	..	..	..	..	..	..	..	..	..	..	..	..	
	..	..	..	..	..	..	2448	..	..	..	..	..	..	..	..	..	..	..	..	..	..	
Libbey-Owens-Ford Glass Co.	450	..	..	..	..	..	700	..	..	950	..	1050	..	..	1200	..	..	1950	..	..	..	Glass Fiber ECE 225
	..	..	..	500	..	..	700	..	..	..	..	1050	..	..	1400	1600	..	..	1850	..	..	Glass Fiber ECG 150
Glass Fibers, Inc.	816	..	..	612	..	..	816	3060	..	..	..	1224	..	4080	2448	1836	..	..	..	..	2448	Vitron
	..	..	..	1224	..	..	1224	..	..	..	..	1836	..	..	..	..	..	..	..	..	..	
	..	..	..	1836	..	..	2448	..	..	..	..	..	..	..	..	..	..	..	..	..	..	
Firestone Plastics Co.	..	..	..	..	0.012	..	..	..	..	0.015	..	..	..	..	..	..	0.020	..	..	..	..	Velon (Saran)
	..	..	..	..	..	..	..	..	..	..	..	..	0.020	..	..	..	..	..	..	..	..	
Lus-Trus Extruded Plastics	..	..	..	..	0.012	..	..	..	..	0.015	..	..	..	..	..	..	0.020	..	..	..	..	Saran
Reeves Bros.	..	..	..	0.015	..	..	..	..	..	..	0.020	..	..	..	..	..	..	..	0.030	..	..	Reevon
Plexon Corp.	..	..	..	..	..	..	..	..	..	0.015	..	..	..	..	..	..	0.020	..	..	..	..	Plexon
Bolta-Saran, Inc.	..	..	..	..	0.012	..	..	..	..	0.015	..	..	..	..	..	..	0.020	..	0.030	..	..	Saran
Dawbarn Bros.	..	..	..	..	0.012	..	..	..	..	0.015	..	..	..	..	..	..	0.020	..	..	..	..	Saran

* Courtesy *Modern Textiles Magazine* (Sept. 1952).

† Note: Types of nylon: Type 100 is bright, normal tenacity, no size or oil; Type 109 is bright, normal tenacity, no size or oil, ✱S-139 spin finish; Type 200 is semi-dull, normal tenacity, no size or oil; Type 213 is semi-dull, normal tenacity, 2.0% size to 2.5% oil; Type 219 is semi-dull, normal tenacity, 0.2% size, 1.25% oil; Type 300 is bright, high tenacity, no size or oil.

These polymers are odorless, nontoxic, and practically inert at room temperature to most of the commonly used chemicals, e.g., salt solutions, alkalis, acids, hydrogen peroxide, vegetable and mineral oils, and solvents. Exceptions are, for instance, fuming sulfuric and nitric acids, bromine, and chlorine. Only at elevated temperature do the polymers become soluble in organic solvents such as toluene, xylene, chlorinated hydrocarbons, and esters. This in turn renders the application of adhesives and coating materials more difficult than for other plastic materials.

Uses

The uses of these filaments are determined by their particular physical properties, such as flexibility and their chemical inertness. The economic factor has additional importance, because the resin is comparatively low in price per yard.

Uses are diversified, and the market is developing. Woven and braided fabrics have appeal due to their appearance and comparative softness. Antistatic finishes can be applied but must be renewed. Such fabrics in a wide variety of styles are used for automobile and furniture upholstery, curtains, mattings, ribbons, and miscellaneous items. Densely woven fabrics find acceptance as filter cloth in chemical plant equipment where other types of fabrics are not or are less resistant to chemical attack. Certain leno-type fabrics are used in tow targets for aircraft, because of their flexibility at low temperature and toughness under severe strain. Other fabrics are developed for special electric equipment where the insulating properties of polyethylene are as important as the chemical inertness. Filaments twisted or braided to cords or laces are used as such or in fabrics for an infinite variety of articles, especially in the novelty field. Laid polyethylene ropes are of interest in chemical plants and for marine purposes. Combination of polyethylene filaments with other fibers, natural or synthetic, are under study.

BIBLIOGRAPHY

For books, commercial literature, technical manuals, and patents, see the bibliography in Mauersberger, *American Handbook of Synthetic Textiles,* Textile Book Publishers, New York, 1952.

CHAPTER XIX

MINERAL OR INORGANIC FIBERS AND YARNS

ASBESTOS

A. S. Rossiter

Spinning may have been done first with the long hairs or wool of some prehistoric animal, or it may have been done with the fibers of vegetable origin, from a plant which nature had endowed with especially long fibrous leaves, or with tall stalks, from which long fibers could be obtained.

It was not very strange that when man discovered a "cotton stone"[1] his first thought was to use it as a textile fiber. In fact, both legend and story, as well as history, confirm that asbestos was thought of as a textile from its earliest discovery. Other uses came later, but it is said that the lamps of the vestal virgins had wicks made of asbestos. Pausanius speaks of a golden lamp, made by the Greek sculptor Callimachus for Minerva, which "though it was kept ever burning, as well by day as night, was only once a year supplied with oil, and had a wick made of Carpasian linen, the only linen which is not consumed by fire." This linen, called Carpasian, is said to have been made of asbestos mined in Cyprus. The lamp was supposed to have been made about 430 B.C.

Early Use

The Chinese are said to have used asbestos cloth as sleeve ruffles which could be cleansed, according to legend, by fire. One can only guess at the reason for this use as sleeve ruffles, but it is rather safe to believe that when the Chinese warmed their hands over the hot coals, other materials would catch fire, whereas ruffles of asbestos cloth would not. It might have been that, because of their cost, asbestos ruffles were used simply in an ornamental way, as the rich of today would use costly hand-woven lace, for asbestos cloth was by no means common in those ancient times, but a rarity, mysterious as to origin, and regarded with superstitious awe. Pliny refers to asbestos cloth

[1] The French Canadians call asbestos *pierre à coton.*

as a rare and costly cloth *"linum vivum,"* "the funeral dress of kings." In the Imperial Treasury at Vienna there was exhibited at one time an asbestos napkin which belonged to Ferdinand III, who was said to have paid 18,000 gulden for it. Ferdinand, according to story, called to his court a Carmelite monk from Sicily who understood the method of weaving asbestos.

Another well-known story of the early use of asbestos as a textile is that of Charlemagne's tablecloth, which was made of asbestos. Often he mystified his guests after the meal was over by throwing the tablecloth into the fire and drawing it out later, cleansed. At one time, war was averted by this tablecloth. Charlemagne's country was threatened with invasion by the savage hordes of Harun-al-Raschid, Emperor of the East. Charlemagne called a "peace conference" to hear the demands of Al-Raschid's ambassadors, and during the course of the conference tossed the tablecloth into the fire, drawing it out unharmed. The ambassadors were convinced that they were dealing with a great magician and subsequently advised Al-Raschid not to attempt the invasion of Charlemagne's country.

Origin [2]

The legends surrounding asbestos ascribe to it almost supernatural powers and occurrence, and, indeed, even sciestists are not agreed entirely as to its real origin. Because of its fibrous structure and appearance, asbestos has often been considered, erroneously, of fossil origin, some students postulating that a prehistoric type of cotton fiber had collected under favorable conditions and then, under the influence of temperature, pressure, and mineralizing solutions, had petrified in a manner similar to the petrification of forests in the western part of the United States.

Chemical and mineralogical studies, however, clearly show that asbestos fiber is *not of vegetable or animal origin,* but entirely of mineral origin. Taking as an example the chrysotile asbestos mined in Canada, the observed facts lead to the following explanation of its formation.

In the greenstone region of Canada, covering hundreds of square miles, the present surface rock was at one time thousands of feet below its present elevation, and under very great pressure due to the weight of the overlying rock and soil. This rock, a variety of olivine called *peridotite,* is composed of iron, magnesia, and silica. In certain ex-

[2] "The Origin of Asbestos," by M. F. Smith, *Asbestos,* p. 2 (July 1940).

tensive areas this rock was acted on by hot ground waters under high pressure and carrying dissolved salts and carbon dioxide. The pressure is easily understood when it is realized that the rock was very far below the earth's surface; the high temperature is explained by the fact that the temperature of the earth increases about 1° F. for every 50 ft of depth. From depth alone, this would give a temperature increase of at least 20° F. for every 1000 ft, not to mention the hot intrusive rocks, also present.

These ground waters gradually changed the original rock from the iron-containing peridotite to the magnesia-silica-water ($3MgO \cdot 2SiO_2 \cdot 2H_2O$) mineral, serpentine.

During the alteration the volume of the rock increased, causing innumerable cracks, small and large. These cracks were filled with the hot ground waters chiefly derived from the slow infiltration of rain or surface waters. This underground water circulated through the cracks in the rock, descending slowly through the smaller openings in the rocks and ascending through the larger openings and cracks. This water at high temperature and containing carbon dioxide under pressure is a very good rock solvent. The water rising in the larger cracks loses pressure and slowly cools, losing some of its solvent power and throwing out a small amount of the dissolved rock. This material deposits on the sides of the crack in the rock through which the water is flowing and, if suitable mineralizers are present (such as dissolved salts and carbon dioxide), tends to form regular crystal shapes, in which the molecules are deposited in a regular rather than a haphazard manner.

Rock salt forms cubes; diamond, octahedrons; graphite, six-sided plates; gold, octahedrons or cubes. Asbestos forms in easily separable, closely packed filaments, which when teased apart give the workable form in which asbestos is marketed and used.

The theory for the formation of asbestos fiber as given above is held by many experts, but may be and is contested in some of its minor details by others, based on slightly different conditions present where they made their own observations. In most cases the difference of opinion relates to such details as to how the waters were heated, and what the mineralizers were, rather than the theory itself. What has been stated above about the formation of Canadian asbestos fiber holds also for the Vermont, Arizona, Russian, Cyprus, and South African chrysotile fibers, as well as for some of the nonchrysotile types of fibers.

Turin. Its founder was Sir James Allport, of Midland Railway fame, who foresaw a large demand for properly manufactured asbestos articles in connection not only with steamships, but also with railways. This company succeeded in spinning, principally by hand, a yarn from Italian asbestos fiber which was completely freed from gritty particles or other impurities and twisted into a rope packing without any covering of cotton such as that originally used by the Glasgow company. This marked considerable advance.

Keen competition then set in between the original group of mining-concession hunters in Italy, headed by Furse Brothers, the Glasgow company, and the Italo-English company, for the control of supplies of the raw material. It was believed in those days that the Italian variety of asbestos was the only kind which was of real value, and the prices were being forced up to abnormal figures. This led to an amalgamation in 1879, when the United Asbestos Co. (consisting of the Glasgow and Italo-English companies and the asbestos interests of Furse Brothers) was formed. The publication of the prospectus of the United Asbestos Co. attracted considerable attention to the many possible applications of asbestos in the industrial world, and the capital was over-subscribed.

Many unforeseen difficulties were encountered in preparing and manufacturing a material about which comparatively little was known at the time, and which, chiefly owing to the peculiar qualities and construction of the fiber in its native state, proved to be very difficult and costly to manipulate on an extended scale. The use of ordinary textile machinery was out of the question. A great deal of money, time, and effort was spent in devising special machinery to spin and weave asbestos; costly machines were built only to be scrapped later, but much valuable pioneer work was done.

Discovery of Canadian Asbestos

Meanwhile, about 1860, deposits of asbestos were discovered in the Province of Quebec, Canada. A survey made in 1850 of the eastern townships (where the famous Thetford Mines are located) mentioned the presence of asbestos in quantities, but at that time it was regarded as of no value. In fact, it was only after asbestos had been discovered and developed to some extent in Italy that the importance of the Canadian asbestos deposits was realized.

The discovery of asbestos in Canada was of tremendous significance in the history of the asbestos manufacturing industry, for it brought a source of supply of asbestos near the United States and its rapidly growing industrial plants. Without Canadian asbestos the manufacture of asbestos products in the United States never would have reached its present proportions; the United States never would have been, as it is now, the largest consumer of asbestos in the world. There are, naturally, folk tales and stories surrounding the discovery of asbestos in Canada, all of which portray asbestos as a textile fiber.

The first discovery of asbestos in Canada is said to have been made at a place later known as Webb's Ledge, in Shipton Township, Province of Quebec. The owner, Charles Webb, regarded the field in which it was located as only waste land. Webb's Ledge was the present site of the town of Asbestos and of the large mine located at that point. In 1877 a forest fire laid bare the rocks in Thetford and Coleraine Townships, and a French Canadian, named Fecteau, is credited with being the first to observe the prevalence of the fiber veins. But two brothers, Alfred and Robert Ward, must be given the credit as the *practical* discoverers, for they at once turned over their discovery to their brother-in-law, Andrew S. Johnson, who in turn started a mine, which by 1878 had produced 50 tons of the mineral and is currently operating.

Although asbestos was known in Canada, as previously stated, as early as 1850, and was discovered "commercially" about 1860, there is proof that it was spun and woven (possibly by Indians) as early as 1724. The proof of this is the story of Benjamin Franklin's purse, told by Franklin himself in his autobiography. One of the earliest surviving letters of Franklin was written to Sir Hans Sloane on June 2, 1725, and mentioned the asbestos purse. In this letter Franklin told Sir Hans that he had been in the northern parts of America and had brought from thence a purse made of the stone asbestos. It appears that Sir Hans was a lover of curiosities, and, since Franklin was at that time in London, he got in touch with Franklin and bought from him a number of curious articles, among which was the asbestos purse. Since Franklin had arrived in London on December 24, 1724, he must have acquired the purse at least 6 months earlier; therefore it can safely be assumed that the purse was made during or before the year 1724—136 yr earlier than the date generally regarded as the date of discovery of asbestos. The purse is in the British Museum at Bloomsbury, near London. The purse is a small closely plaited bag in a fairly good state of preservation, with a thread running through the top. It was probably the first known asbestos textile in America.

One of the first gentlemen, if not the first, to recognize the great possibilities of Canadian asbestos was John Bell, founder of Bell's Asbestos Co., Ltd. To him belonged the distinction of being the first to succeed in spinning Canadian asbestos, a process which, through collaboration with Turner Brothers, expert cotton spinners of Lancashire, England, was ultimately developed to a state of perfection. Although Canadian asbestos and Italian fiber are similar in chemical properties, there is a marked difference in the physical characteristics. The Canadian variety proved to be much easier to manipulate by machinery, which differed only slightly in the more important details from the machinery which was then in ordinary use in the textile factories in Lancashire.

Mining

To date, by far the greatest proportion of asbestos ore has been extracted by opencast mining methods. Obviously, however, some deposits are worked more economically by underground systems even in the initial stages. Some of the older mines, where open-pit operations have been continuous for many years, are now changing over to underground systems as greater depths are reached.

Several of the larger Canadian mines are classic examples of the varied methods used, having progressed stage by stage from simple open quarries with boom or overhead cableway derricks, where boxes or skips were loaded by hand, to mechanized loading on a larger scale by power shovels into cars or trucks, with equipment ranging up to 6-yd and 8-yd shovels and standard-gauge railway cars, although the largest equipment mentioned is the exception rather than the rule.

Other means have been, and are being, used to suit special conditions. Glory-hole mining has been quite successfully employed in Canada although better suited for milder climates where snow and ice do not block the draw points in winter operations. Shrinkage and sublevel stoping systems have been discarded for more economical methods in mining some of the larger ore bodies, although satisfactory in particular cases. Deposits such as the flat-lying beds of Arizona, which outcrop on steep canyon sides, must be worked from adits with extraction by room-and-pillar or longwall methods.

In some of the larger Canadian deposits where open-pit mining has been pursued to the economic limit, a system of block caving has been very successful. By this method development is carried to a considerable depth below the surface and large blocks of ore are extracted with a minimum of drilling and blasting, by undercutting and allowing the ore to cave and crush from its own weight. The broken ore is drawn into chute raises and thus into cars that are hauled to a shaft. As caving proceeds it breaks through eventually to the surface and then, as the plug of broken ore descends, backfill of mill tailings is brought in by conveyor and the hole is kept filled to minimize subsidence of the walls. No pillars are left between blocks, but the practice is to allow the backfill of a worked-out block to consolidate before caving is started in an adjacent one.

In asbestos mining, steel and concrete are generally used instead of timber where support of the workings is required, and all forms of wood are kept out of the mine as far as possible, the reason for this being that wood splinters are difficult to separate from asbestos fiber when once admixed with the rock. Better practice, therefore, is to keep wood out.

Preparation for Market

In the early days of the asbestos-mining industry, production was mainly by hand methods, in which the veins of longer fiber only were selected and cobbed to remove adhering gangue. The grades thus prepared for market were called crudes and, in fact, the designation is still used for the small proportion that continues to be produced in this way. As uses developed for other than the longest fibers, mills were built in which the ore was crushed to free the smaller veins from the enclosing rock, and the fiber was separated by screening and other means. As markets continued to expand and new uses were progressively found for shorter grades of fiber, mills grew in size, so that in 1952 there were a number with capacities of from 2000 to 4000 tons per day, and one operation has a single mill capable of treating 10,000 tons of ore daily.

Asbestos fibers are strong and tough, and can be separated comparatively easily from the rock or gangue by a crushing action, which causes the more brittle material to shatter and leave the fibers free. Their removal from the accompanying barren material can then be effected by currents of air or water. All existing mills operate on a dry process in which the separation is largely by air suction. The usual application of this principle is by means of hoods, in effect very much like oversized vacuum cleaners, installed over the lower end of shaking screens: the screen removes fine sand and dust and the suction lifts the fiber away from the crushed rock.

Although asbestos fiber is strong and tough, the action of crushing and, to a greater extent, grinding, does to some degree cut and otherwise damage the filaments. For this reason it is the aim of operators to select milling equipment that will effect the necessary reduction with the least amount of abrasive action, within the economic limits for the particular ore being treated. The trend in asbestos milling is toward the use of machines giving more positive particle-size reduction by straight crushing action in the primary and secondary stages of milling, and moving the fiberizers—the machines that fluff or "open" the small bundles of fibers—farther along in the flow where mainly the very short grades only, and those more difficult to "open," are affected. Because of this, fewer hammer crushers, cyclone mills, and disintegrators are being used, and more of the work is done with cone crushers or other types of modified gyratories. One installation in South Africa employs pan crushers, which work on the principle of a chaser, with good results. At one time rolls were in great favor because of their almost ideal action in releasing fiber with minimum damage. Low capacity and high maintenance cost, however, has relegated these machines to a minor role, such as the preparation of some grades of crude.

Figure 3 shows in a much simplified form a typical layout of an asbestos mine and mill.

Milling Machines. No detailed description of the equipment used in asbestos milling will be given here, but it may be of interest to note certain features and to describe briefly some of the machines peculiar to the industry.

Primary jaw crushers are generally 36 by 42 in. in size but some operations are using 48 by 60-in. machines requiring 200 to 250 hp and with a capacity of 250 tons per hr on average ore. For the most part, they are of standard design, although it is preferable to have a smaller angle of nip than usually is possible with a standard frame and, at the same time, retain full size of opening. It is considered that the nip angle should be 21° to 23°. Most manufacturers of jaw crushers build machines with a special deep frame to attain this smaller angle between the fixed and the swinging jaw. The desirability of this feature arises from the fact that often there is a tendency for pieces of serpentine ore to slip as the crusher jaws apply pressure, resulting in a jumping action by the rock and therefore decreased efficiency.

Driers may be either the conventional rotary kiln type or the vertical stack. The former is of standard design, consisting of a rotating cylinder 40 to 60 ft long by 4 to 6 ft in diameter. The drier may be installed so that the hot furnace gases pass out along the outer shell before returning through the cylinder itself where they are in contact with the ore. For increased efficiency and to lessen the tube-mill action of the larger pieces of ore on the fiber-bearing fines, the drier cylinders sometimes are divided into segments, or smaller cylinders or tubes are built within the main shell, so that the ore and gases are confined to spaces of smaller cross-sectional area, in which there is a better mingling of the two as well as less grinding action on the fiber.

The vertical drier consists of a square stack, generally 7 by 7 ft in cross-section by 50 ft high. Ore is introduced at the top and falls through a rising current of heated air together with the gases of combustion from a coal-fired furnace. It is retarded and dispersed in its fall by a gridwork of cast-iron bars throughout most of the height of the stack, requiring about 20 sec to reach the discharge chute at the bottom. Forced draft is introduced under the furnace grates and the gases are drawn from the top of the drier by an induced-draft fan through a cyclone collector, where a small amount of dried fiber and dust is caught, before exhausting into a smokestack.

Storage bins to which the dried ore is conveyed, in addition to serving the normal purpose of a uniform supply of mill feed, allow time for the ore to cool and to lose up to 1 per cent of the remaining moisture. The bins often are made by depositing two high parallel ridges of mill tailings and constructing a reinforced-concrete tunnel with draw points in the valley between the ridges. The angle of repose of the tailings forms the bin bottom; a steel-frame structure covered with corrugated asbestos-cement board provides cover.

Screens, so widely used in an asbestos mill, serve a dual purpose—the normal one of sizing and secondly as planes from which the fiber can be lifted away from the rock by aspiration. For the latter reason a shaking action is preferable to a vibrating action, as it permits the fiber to bed above the rock and to be more effectively separated. Screens usually are constructed in the mine shops. They are made with wooden frames, reinforced where necessary with steel, and actuated by roller-bearing eccentric, although where a long stroke at slow speed is desired ordinary bearings and even a crank-type eccentric may be used. In size they are generally either 4 or 5 ft in width by 11 ft or more in length. The support usually is by pieces of hardwood shaped to allow the necessary degree of flexibility. Screens often are arranged in pairs, back to back, with one eccentric shaft serving both.

Suction hoods are made with an opening of from 2 to 5 in. and are sufficiently long to extend across the full width of the screen. They are suspended above the lower end of the screen and are adjustable as to height. The tapered upper section of the hood converges into an air duct, commonly 15 in. in diameter, which conveys the air to a cyclone collector where the fiber is dropped, and thus through the exhauster fan. One fan may serve a number of suctions, approximately 15 hp being required for each 15-in. pipe and suction.

Dust Collection. As a considerable amount of dust escapes collection, the air discharged from the fans is conducted usually to a settling chamber, often constructed in the form of a large shed in which there are burlap baffles to assist in the removal of the dust, before the air is exhausted to the atmosphere. These so-called dust sheds, however, are insufficiently effective and in the more populated areas are being supplemented by more positive means of filtration or precipitation. A system of electrical precipitation has proved quite efficient at one large plant; but others have favored the use of bag filters, which are built in units in which there are commonly 144 to 224 fabric tubes 8 to 10 in. in diameter by 18 ft or more in length per unit. Air is introduced into the tubes from below and filters through the fabric, depositing the dust on the inside surface. Multiple units are built, so that the air supply can be diverted periodically by a timed mechanism and, at the same time, the bags or tubes are shaken mechanically to dislodge the layer of accumulated dust. Accepted practice is to have sufficient fabric area so that not more than 4 to 5 cfm of free air is being filtered per square foot of fabric. For this reason a mill treating 3000 to 4000 tons per day and exhausting some 500,000 cfm of free air requires an extensive filter installation.

One point should be stressed, however, and that is the necessity of refraining from fracturing the fiber, as strength is one of the main requirements of good spinning fiber.

Grading and Cleaning

Both flat and rotary screens are used for grading of the milled fibers. Rotary screens may be operated at slow speed to handle a small quantity of fiber, or at high speed on a large production. Where three grades only are made, each half of the screen is covered with a wire cloth of a different mesh. Fiber is fed into one end of the screen; revolving paddles beat it up, forcing the short fiber through the screen of the first section, longer fiber through the screen cloth of the second section, and the longest fiber out at the end. Each grade falls on a flat cleaning screen where sand, dust, and unmilled fiber splinters loosened in grading are cleaned out. Extra grades may be made by allowing portions from each screen section to combine; or any grade may be split into a number of grades in a second rotary screen or on a flat screen. From the ends of the cleaning screen, the fiber is lifted by suction, the unopened fiber and rock being allowed to fall from the end of the screen and returned to a breaker and milled. The fiber lifted to a collector is dropped to a storeroom for bagging.

Early in 1932 the Asbestos Producers of the Province of Quebec (Canada) adopted a Standard Classification, which is regarded as standard in other chrysotile-producing countries. This standard classification is given below, but the first three groups are actually the only ones of interest in a discussion of textile fibers. The lower groups, i.e., shingle, paper, waste, stucco or plaster, refuse or shorts, sand, gravel, and stone are not considered spinning fibers.

Canadian Classification of Chrysotile Asbestos

Asbestos mined products are divided into two classes—crude asbestos and milled asbestos.

Crude asbestos consists of the hand-selected cross-vein material essentially in its native or unfiberized form.

Milled asbestos consists of all grades produced by mechanical treatment of asbestos ore.

Shipping test is the average, for each carload or smaller shipment, of tests of representative samples taken at the time of shipping.

Guaranteed minimum shipping test is that below which the actual shipping test shall not fall.

Crude absestos and *milled asbestos* are subdivided into groups designated and defined as follows

Group No. 1: crude No. 1 (¾ in. and longer).

Group No. 2: crude No. 2 (⅜ in. up to ¾ in.).

Crude run-of-mine: (unsorted crudes).

Crudes, sundry: (crudes not otherwise specified).

Group No. 3: spinning or textile fiber.

Standard Designation of Grades	*Guaranteed Minimum Shipping Test*
3F	7 — 7 — 1.5 — 0.5
3K	4 — 7 — 4 — 1
3R	2 — 8 — 4 — 2
3T	1 — 9 — 4 — 2
3Z	0 — 8 — 6 — 2

Standard Designation of Grades	Guaranteed Minimum Shipping Test
Group No. 4: shingle fiber.	
4H	0 — 5 — 8 — 3
4K	0 — 4 — 9 — 3
4M	0 — 4 — 8 — 4
4R	0 — 3 — 9 — 4
4T	0 — 2 — 10 — 4
4Z	0 — 1.5 — 9.5 — 5
Group No. 5: paper fiber.	
5D	0 — 0.5 — 10.5 — 5
5K	0 — 0 — 12 — 4
5M	0 — 0 — 11 — 5
5R	0 — 0 — 10 — 6
Group No. 6: waste, stucco or plaster.	
6D	0 — 0 — 7 — 9
Group No. 7: refuse or shorts.	
7D	0 — 0 — 5 — 11
7F	0 — 0 — 4 — 12
7H	0 — 0 — 3 — 13
7K	0 — 0 — 2 — 14
7M	0 — 0 — 1 — 15
7R	0 — 0 — 0 — 16
7T	0 — 0 — 0 — 16
7W	0 — 0 — 0 — 16
Group No. 8: sand.	
8S	Under 50 lb per cu ft loose measure
8T	Under 75 lb per cu ft loose measure
Group No. 9: gravel and stone.	
9T	Over 75 lb per cu ft loose measure

Testing Asbestos for Grade. A description of the Quebec Standard Asbestos Testing Machine and method of testing gives an idea of the meaning of the foregoing shipping test figures for each grade. The test is used on milled asbestos fibers only—crude asbestos is not graded on the testing machine.

The Quebec Standard Asbestos Testing Machine consists of a nest of four boxes, measuring 24½ by 14¾ in.; they rest on a table and are driven by an eccentric with 25/32-in. throw and 1 9/16-in. travel. The boxes, which are superimposed one above the other, are numbered from top down—1, 2, 3, and 4. The bottoms of boxes 1, 2, and 3 are made of brass screen of the following specifications:

Box No.	*Screen Opening*	*Diameter of Wire*
1	0.500 in.	0.105 in.
2	0.187 in.	0.063 in. (4 mesh)
3	0.053 in.	0.047 in. (10 mesh)

Box 4 is a receptacle for the fines which fall through the other three boxes.

To make a test, 16 oz of asbestos is placed on the uppermost tray (No. 1), which is then covered and tightly clamped. The machine is started and by means of an automatic device is kept going until exactly 600 revolutions have been made. (The speed of rotation is 328 rpm in the new model No. 2 machine.) At the end of this time the asbestos which remains on each tray (box) is weighed. This gives the grade of asbestos fiber; the longest fiber naturally stays on the screen with the largest opening, whereas shorter fiber, according to its length, remains on screens (or trays) 2 or 3, or drops into the pan (lowest tray). *The more fiber retained on the first screen, and the less fiber falling into the pan, the higher the grade and therefore the greater its value.*

Fig. 4. Quebec Standard Asbestos Testing Machine, Model 2.

If, for instance, a customer buys spinning fiber of the specification 4–7–4–1, it means that, in a sample of 16 oz, representing the average of a lot shipped, 4 oz will remain on the top screen, 7 on the second, and 4 on the third, and 1 oz will go through all the screens into the pan. It is evident that the figures of the test represent the proportion in ounces of the different lengths of fiber in a pound of asbestos.

Preparation of Fiber

The longer and better grades of asbestos fibers, comprising No. 1 crude, No. 2 crude, and spinning grades, are the only ones considered suitable for use in the making of asbestos textiles. Any of these, or combinations of them, in various proportions, with or without the addition of cotton, may be spun into yarns.

For a few purposes only No. 1 crude is suitable. Certain materials are made from No. 2 crude alone, whereas for other purposes both or either crude may be mixed with varying proportions of spinning fibers.

Spinning fiber may vary in grade from one which tests 4 oz out of 16 on the top screen in the standard test machine to one as low as ½ oz on the top screen. The proportions of each fiber in the mixture are governed by the price of the fiber, availability of grades, and the type of finished article to be manufactured.

The mixing of fibers of various lengths, milled fibers with crude, or, at times, different types of fibers, such as the mixing of Russian, African, or other fibers with Canadian, is called "blending." This process has reached a point where it may almost be called an "art." Manufacturers are loath to publish the details of their blending of fibers. Skillful blending means almost as much in the manufacture of asbestos textile materials as the quality of the fibers.

Crude fiber is prepared for spinning, generally at the factory where it is to be spun, by crushing to free it from rock, and to open it so that rock particles, short fiber, and dust may be cleaned out and the useful long fiber fluffed up or willowed. Bags as received at the factory are dumped and the fiber shoveled in front of the mullers of a chaser mill (or pan crusher). After crushing, the fiber is transferred to an opener or fiberizer. This opener or fiberizer carries the subdivision of the fiber to a finer point and also removes the crushed rock and sand and the fiber that is too short for carding and spinning.

The opened fiber is next passed over a shaking screen or through a trommel screen, where it is again cleaned of rock and dust, and then lifted by air suction to storage bins. It is then ready for mixing with cotton. The purpose of blending a small proportion of cotton with asbestos fibers is to give strength. The proportion of cotton added depends on the type of fiber and on the purpose for which the finished material is to be employed. It rarely exceeds 20 per cent and may be as low as 8 per cent or even 5 per cent.

The mixture of asbestos and cotton is either carried to the carding machine in batches or blown in by an air blast. Carding removes the remaining short fiber, sand, and dust and also arranges the fibers in parallel position. It also blends and thoroughly intermingles the cotton fibers with the asbestos fibers. Passing over a camel back, the fibers travel through a second card. Double carding increases the strength of the resulting yarn. From the last roll the fiber is stripped to a moving apron, where a set of reciprocating scrapers or rubbers condense it into rovings, which are gathered on a jack spool. A variation of this process passes the material from the condenser over a doffer roll and apron, making a single-ply yarn without the intermediate stage of rovings, the yarn being wound on spindles.

The jack spools of rovings from the cards are mounted on a mule. Twist is introduced, thereby converting the rovings into spun yarn, which is wound onto wooden or paper spools. The carriage on the mule travels out from the delivery rolls, drawing out the rovings a distance of 53 to 72 in., depending upon the type of mule. Then the twist is introduced and as the carriage travels in toward the rolls the yarn is wound onto spindles. Spinning frames are also used for introducing twist into rovings.

The spools of single-ply yarn are transferred to twister machines and twisted into two-ply or three-ply yarn, which is assembled on spools. Spools of twisted yarn in turn are carried in baskets and mounted on creels for weaving, or on braiding machines. The filling bobbins (or cops) are wound on a cop winder and delivered from this winder to the looms.

Prices

Prices of asbestos fiber used for textile purposes have remained fairly stable from month to month, but show an upward trend over the years. During World War I prices increased tremendously; No. 1 Canadian crude rose from a low of $275 per ton in 1913 to a peak of $2000 to $3000 at the end of 1918; No. 2 crude was quoted at $150 in 1913 and as high as $1000 in 1918; whereas the longer spinning fibers during the same period rose from $50 per ton in 1913 to a peak of $500 in 1918, although they fluctuated considerably over that period.

Prices tapered off gradually after the war, until in 1932 they reached the low level of $450 for No. 1 crude, $200 for No. 2, and $110 for the spinning stocks. Table 1, supplied by the Internal Trade Branch, Dominion Bureau of Statistics, shows that since 1932 the trend has been gradually upward.

There is no similar tabulation in existence for the blue and amosite varieties, nor for chrysotile from other producing countries.

Production and Consumption

Production [5] of all grades of asbestos fibers in Canada in 1948 [6] was 714,717 short tons; in Southern Rhodesia (Africa) it was 69,341 tons;

[5] The figures given, although designated as production, really cover sales and shipments; actual production figures might run a trifle higher or lower.

[6] This year was selected as it is the latest one for which data on production in most of the countries are available, and because it is more representative of Canadian production than 1949 when, because of the mining strike, Canada showed a very low production.

TABLE 1 ANNUAL WHOLESLAE PRICES OF CANADIAN CHRYSOTILE ASBESTOS

[Dollars per ton f.o.b. mine]

Years	*Crude No. 1*	*Crude No. 2*	*Spinning Stocks*
1933	450	200	110
1934	450	200	120
1935	500	200	120
1936	545	200	120
1937	550	200	120
1938	700	275	140
1939	700	275	140
1940	700	300	154
1941	700	300	154
1942	700	300	154
1943	700	300	154
1944	700	300	154
1945	700	300	154
1946	700	300	154
1947	791.67	407.50	207.92
1948	960	492	253
1949	960	492	285
1950	1000	541.20	314.70

in the Union of South Africa (which produces all types, i.e., amosite, blue, chrysotile, and even a small amount of anthophyllite) it was 45,735 tons. This last-named figure can be divided to show that 30,372 tons of amosite was produced, 10,909 tons of blue and 4441 tons of chrysotile, with 13 tons of anthophyllite. Russian production for 1948 is estimated at 180,000 tons; most of the Russian production is used by its own industries.

However, so far as the asbestos textile industry is concerned, these figures do not mean much, because only a certain proportion of these quantities is used as textile fibers. The rest was used in the manufacture of paper, millboard, asbestos-cement products, molded brake lining, and various other products, mostly as a binder.

Asbestos fibers are used in so many different distinct markets that it is very difficult to give adequate information on the quantities used in one particular field, especially as the various countries in their compilation of statistics group all grades together. Asbestos textiles are also sold in several distinct markets. (See section below, "Utilization of Asbestos Textile Fibers.")

The growth of the asbestos industry as a whole can be seen when it is noted that Canada produced 50 tons in 1878 (the earliest recorded production in that country); in 1908, when production started in Rhodesia with the year's total of 55 tons, Canada produced 90,773 tons. Earliest production recorded for the Union of South Africa was 693 tons, in 1910.

Much of the information given here applies to Canada, because Canada so far as chrysotile asbestos is concerned, sets the standard for all other chrysotile-producing countries. In peacetime its fibers are sent to practically every country throughout the world with the possible exception of Russia, which has sufficient supplies of its own (see Table 2).

TABLE 2. EXPORTS OF RAW ASBESTOS FROM CANADA, 1952 *

	Ton (2000 lb)	*Value*
Crude		
United States	371	$ 334,308
United Kingdom	150	224,250
South America	..	..
Central America and Mexico	..	..
European countries	114	74,585
Other countries	57	71,777
	692	$ 704,920
Milled		
United States	192,440	$30,690,024
United Kingdom	36,576	6,878,791
South America	17,834	3,254,359
Central America and Mexico	5,169	850,686
European countries	59,107	10,211,343
Other countries	28,692	4,761,727
	339,818	$56,646,930
Shorts		
United States	465,800	$22,551,058
United Kingdom	20,614	878,394
South America	7,331	556,153
Central America and Mexico	193	7,547
European countries	55,113	4,075,790
Other countries	12,497	1,088,756
	561,548	$29,157,698
Grand total—Unmanufactured asbestos	902,058	$86,509,548

* *Asbestos*, compiled from figures supplied by Dominion Bureau of Statistics, Ottawa, Canada, in "Trade of Canada," p. 35 (April 1953).

In comparison with other countries the United States produces very little asbestos. In 1948 its entire production was 37,237 tons, but a large part of this was the short grades used chiefly for molded products, such as molded brake lining, asbestos-cement building materials, or for the making of asbestos paper. The United States, however, is one of the largest consumers of both the crudes and the long-milled fibers used for the manufacture of asbestos textiles, and also of the

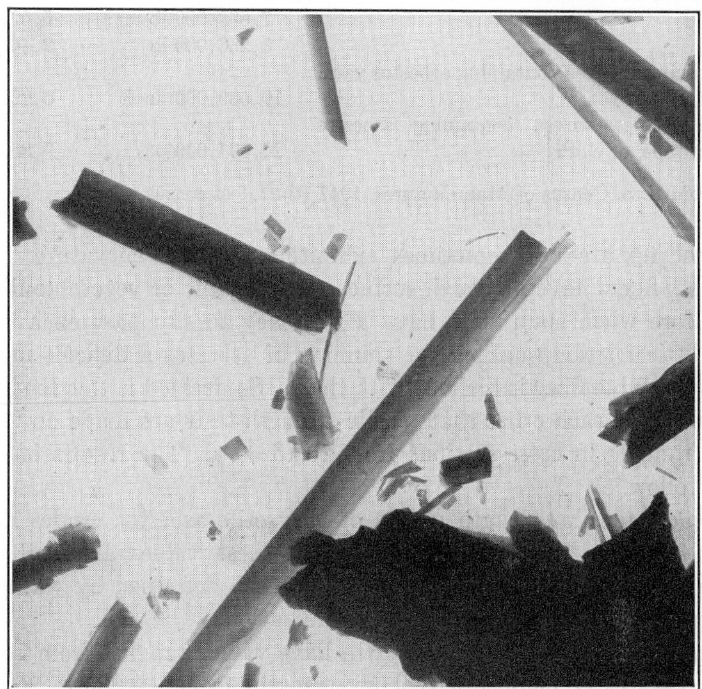

Fig. 5. Electron micrograph of crocidolite (blue) asbestos (×17,500) (*RCA Laboratories*).

short grades. In 1948 the United States imported from all sources 647,882 tons, and its apparent consumption was 678,443 tons.

The production of asbestos textiles in the United States for 1947 (see Table 3) gives an idea of the vast consumption of asbestos textile fibers.

Microscopy

Small fiber bundles of asbestos under the microscope at low magnifications vary in appearance from wavy to straight texture. At higher magnifications such as those employed by the electron microscope the fibrils appear as one or two or more slender threads approaching a

TABLE 3. UNITED STATES PRODUCTION OF ASBESTOS TEXTILES, 1947 *

	Quantity	*Value*
Carded fiber	506,000 lb	$ 178,000
Roving and lap	4,960,000 lb	1,819,000
Wick and rope	2,785,000 lb	1,291,000
Yarn, cord, and thread	9,748,000 lb	4,815,000
Cloth	7,998,000 lb	5,624,000
Tape	3,266,000 lb	2,469,000
Brake lining—woven containing asbestos yarn, tape, or cloth	19,589,000 lin ft	6,968,000
Clutch facings—woven containing asbestos yarn, tape, or cloth	20,004,000 pcs	9,851,000

* From U. S. Census of Manufactures, 1947 (the latest census taken).

straight texture but sometimes exhibiting a slight curvature. But asbestos fibers have no rough surfaces like organic or vegetable fibers. Therefore when spun they have a tendency to slip past each other with little friction, making the spinning of asbestos a difficult matter if no vegetable fiber is blended with them. So decided is this tendency to "slide by" each other that tensile-strength tests are made on "bundles" ranging in cross-sections from 10 to 30 μ. The results of such tests follow.[7]

Typical tensile strength values of chrysotile asbestos crudes range from 40,000 to 100,000 psi. Sometimes these values are well over 100,000, provided the filaments have not been deformed by wall-rock movement during the period of crystallization.

Other fibers, such as amosite, will have values ranging from 15,000 to 90,000 psi; crocidolite will show strengths from 100,000 to 300,000 psi. Some of these values are far greater than the tensile strength of the usual grades of reinforcing steel.

All types of asbestos fibers show the same characteristic of crowding or grouping together of numerous fine threads within what appears to be a single fiber. Latest figures on cross-sections vary from 285 to 214 A. Some of the diameters of the amphibole fibers are much larger and measure approximately 300 A. It has been found that the number of fibrils per linear inch will vary from 850,000 and less to 1,400,000 or more.

Recently there has been advanced a theory that asbestos fibers in the last analysis are not solid, as has been supposed for so many years,

[7] Reference: "Research on Asbestos Fibres," by M. S. Badollet, *Canadian Mining and Metallurgical Bull.* (April 1948).

but *tubular*. This was first recognized in photographs taken under the electron microscope at the University of California, and by Dr. James Hillier of the Radio Corporation of America Laboratories, Princeton, N. J. An article in February 1951 *Asbestos* gathered together the various references on the subject, from which it would appear that there is substantial foundation for the theory.

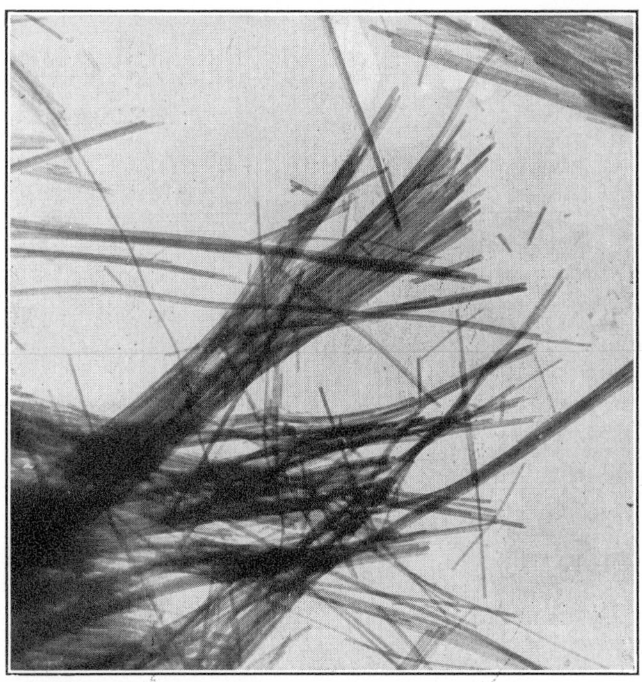

FIG. 6. Electron micrograph of chrysotile asbestos (Arizona) (×17,500), supporting the theory that these fibers are tubular rather than solid (*RCA Laboratories*).

Specifications and Tests

The A.S.T.M. has established certain standard specifications [8] and methods for testing asbestos textiles, and these are considered as standard for the industry in the United States. The grade of any asbestos textile product is based on the percentage of asbestos fiber it contains. A.S.T.M. grades are shown in Table 4.

In deciding on the grade most suitable for any given requirement, a number of factors must be taken into account, among which are tem-

[8] A.S.T.M. Standards on Textile Materials (Oct. 1944).

TABLE 4. STANDARD GRADES AND WEIGHTS OF ASBESTOS

Grades	*Asbestos Content by Weight*
Commercial	75% up to but not including 80%
Underwriters	80% up to but not including 85%
Grade A	85% up to but not including 90%
Grade AA	90% up to but not including 95%
Grade AAA	95% up to but not including 99%
Grade AAAA	99% to 100% inclusive

perature, electrical requirements, tensile strength needed, acid or caustic conditions.

To determine the *asbestos content* of any asbestos textile material, i.e., roving, yarn, cloth, tape for electrical purposes, and tubular sleeving, the following method has been adopted as standard by the A.S.T.M.

One test specimen weighing not less than 5 g is taken from each sample and dried to constant weight in an oven at 110° C. (220° to 230° F.) and the weights of the dried specimens recorded. The specimens shall be placed in an electric oven and heated for not less than 1 hr at 800° to 810° C. (1470° to 1490° F.). After removal from the oven they shall be cooled in a desiccator to room temperature and then weighed. The weight of the residue shall be divided by the factor 0.86 (this factor is based upon a proved average of 14 per cent water of crystallization in chrysotile asbestos [9]) to determine the original weight of the asbestos content. This weight of asbestos content is divided by the weight of the dried specimens to obtain the percentage of asbestos. The average of five determinations is considered the asbestos content.

Heat Resistance

H. Sommer made the following report on the heat resistance of asbestos: [10]

> The variation in the heat resistance of various kinds of asbestos depends to a great extent on the chemical composition of the asbestos, as well as on its special chemical and physical properties. The two chief kinds of asbestos, serpentine and hornblende [11] absestos, both contain, from a chemical stand-

[9] This figure has been questioned by some authorities.

[10] *Gummi-Ztg.*, No. 36, June 9, 1933. For further study of heat resistance refer to Thermal Studies on Asbestos, by D. Wolochow and W. Harold White, of the National Research Council, Ottawa, Canada, NRC 969. Reprinted from *Can. J. Research,* **B, 19:** 49–55, February 1941.

[11] Referred to previously as amphibole.

point, magnesium silicate, but—independent of the admittedly large variations in the composition of the various types of asbestos—the ratio of basic acid in serpentine asbestos amounts generally to about 1.1, in contrast with about 3.2 for hornblende asbestos. Thus it comes about also that the content of chemically combined water, conditional on the crystalline structure of the asbestos fiber, is considerably greater in the serpentine asbestos than in the hornblende asbestos. On these characteristic signs of the chemical composition depends the fundamental difference in the properties of the asbestos. For example, the preponderance of the acid portion settles the greater capability of resistance to acid of hornblende asbestos whilst the serpentine asbestos shows a greater capability of resistance to alkali. On account of the small water and MgO

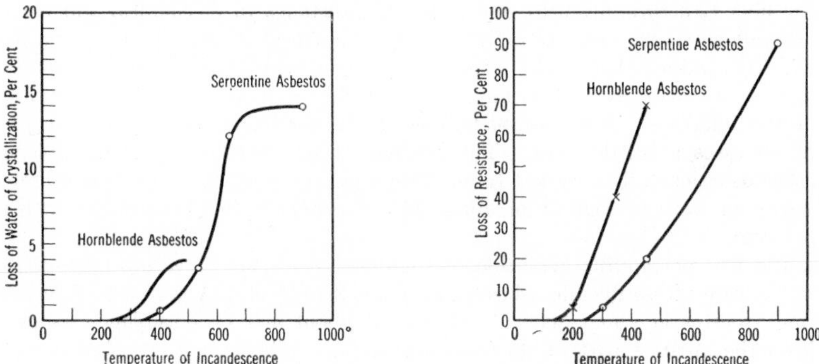

FIG. 7. Temperature of incandescence.

content, the heat resistance of hornblende asbestos is also considerably lower than that of serpentine asbestos.

If the water content of air-dried asbestos is in question, then the difference between the two forms of water content must be clearly distinguished, i.e., between the content of hygroscopic moisture only adhering to the surface, and the chemically combined water. The content of hygroscopic moisture in the asbestos has directly nothing to do with its chemical composition; it is simply a function of the superficial nature of the asbestos fiber and relative humidity of the air, as well as the temperature of the surrounding air.

By drying at temperatures little over 100° C. this hygroscopic moisture can be removed without the asbestos, whether serpentine or hornblende asbestos, suffering an injury to its chemical and physical properties. The content of hygroscopic moisture at 65 per cent relative humidity, according to experience, amounts to 1 to 1.5 per cent in the case of hornblende asbestos, but in the case of serpentine asbestos from 1.5 to 2.2 per cent. This characteristic difference can be traced simply to the different superficial nature of the asbestos fibers; the fine fiber of the serpentine asbestos, which gives it the qualities of flexibility and malleability and makes it particularly valuable for spinning, has a greater fiber surface available for taking up moisture from the air than the coarser hornblende asbestos, which is less flexible, and is, therefore, less suitable for spinning. The lower flexibility of the hornblende asbestos, increased by a brittleness dependent upon a higher content of SiO_2, on the contrary, renders the hornblende asbestos particularly suitable for the purpose of heat insulation, for example, as filling material for insulating mattresses, as it is less liable to compression, and the greater air content of a more voluminous filling gives it the preference for insulating purposes. This insulating power, the practical use of which has its limit at about 300° C., is therefore in no way of equal importance to heat resistance, which usually begins to come into question only at temperatures of over 300° C. Thus the hygroscopic moisture of the asbestos plays no part in heat resistance, whilst the water of crystallization is of much greater importance. As already mentioned, the crystalline fibrous structure of the asbestos is conditional on this chemically combined water. To the extent to which the combined water is removed from the asbestos, so the fiber structure, firmness, and power of resistance to mechanical and chemical influences are lost. Complete resistance to heat is offered by no form of asbestos; rather there exist gradual variations which are dependent on the type of asbestos, as well as on the influencing temperature and the duration of the influence. After complete loss of the combined water, there remains in all cases a brittle mass. The content of combined water in hornblende asbestos is generally very low (about 2 to 4 per cent), whilst serpentine asbestos shows an average content of about 14 per cent, varying between 11 and 18 per cent.

The first perceptible evolution of combined water upon heating takes place, in the case of hornblende asbestos, at about 200° C. and in the case of serpentine asbestos at about 300° to 350° C.; at about 400° C. hornblende asbestos loses the greatest part of its combined water, while serpentine asbestos loses only about 1 per cent. Hornblende asbestos, already brittle at about 400°, has at 450° to 500° C. completely given off its water content, whilst the serpentine asbestos only loses the bulk at 500° to 600° C., and the last traces at 800″ to 900° C.

Coincident with the loss of water is a corresponding reduction in heat resistance. According to the tests on asbestos fabrics the resistance losses amount on the average to those shown in Table 5.

TABLE 5. HEAT RESISTANCE OF ASBESTOS FIBERS

Loss of resistance after 3 hr of heating to

	200° C.	350° C.	450° C.
Hornblende asbestos	5%	40%	70%
Serpentine asbestos	0%	5%	20%

Thus it will be seen that an absolute resistance to heat in the range of temperature to 450° C. is not present in either type of asbestos but that serpentine asbestos is very considerably superior to hornblende asbestos. The loss of resistance of serpentine asbestos is, even at 450° C., still so small that it can practically be considered as heat resistant. Therefore, the claim is thoroughly justified that for asbestos products which are exposed in use to temperatures of over 300° C., serpentine asbestos alone will accomplish the purpose.

Specific Gravity [12]

The specific gravity of serpentine asbestos (chrysotile) averages close to 2.2. There is some variation in this figure for asbestos from different locations and for asbestos of different grades. The serpentine rock with which the asbestos is associated has a specific gravity of 2.5 to 2.65. This represents the highest specific gravity that may be expected for any grade of asbestos. This variation is caused partly by contamination with other minerals and partly by differences in the internal chemical composition of the asbestos itself. However, the nearer it approaches the ideal chrysotile composition, the nearer will be the gravity to about 2.2.

Acid Resistance [13]

Tests for acid resistance of various types of spinnable fibers were made in the laboratory of the Alfred Calmon Asbest- und Gummiwerke Aktiengesellschaft of Hamburg, Germany, and results obtained by this laboratory were as follows:

> Tests were made with hydrochloric acid. In the first experiment, 10 grams of asbestos fiber were treated with 200 to 500 cc of 25 per cent hydrochloric acid and allowed to remain at room temperature. After 24 hours the material was filtered, washed free of chlorides, and after drying to constant weight, the loss was determined. The residue was then treated with an equal quantity of fresh hydrochloric acid and allowed to stand for 3 days, when the loss in weight was again determined. This treatment was repeated until the acid caused no further loss in weight. The results are given in Table 6.

TABLE 6. Loss of Weight by Treatment with 25 Per Cent Hydrochloric Acid (Room Temperature)

	Bell's C (*per cent*)	*King's C* (*per cent*)	*Bell's E* (*per cent*)	*Rhod. CG2* (*per cent*)	*Russian 4* (*per cent*)	*Amosite Short* (*per cent*)	*Blue Cape* (*per cent*)
1 × 24 hr	25.2	26.3	28.8	10.3	15.6	5.9	3.4
4 × 24 hr	50.5	50.8	52.7	25.7	26.0	8.8	4.1
7 × 24 hr	55.0	55.5	56.7	40.4	46.6	9.6	4.4
10 × 24 hr	56.0	57.0	57.5	50.0	54.0	10.0	5.0
13 × 24 hr	....	....	....	56.3	58.0	10.8	5.5

> Then 10 grams of the asbestos fiber were treated with 300 cc of 25 per cent hydrochloric acid and boiled for 2 hr under the reflux condenser. After wash-

[12] *Asbestos,* p. 20 (March 1929).

[13] *Asbestos,* January 1931, p. 22, quoting from report of the laboratory of Alfred Calmon Asbest- und Gummiwerke Aktiengesellschaft of Hamburg, Germany.

ing until free of chloride, the residue was dried to constant weight, and the following *losses in weight* were established [Table 7].

TABLE 7. Loss in Weight Through Boiling Acid Treatment, in Per Cent

Bell's crude No. 1	57.0	Rhodesian CG2	54.5
Australian crude	55.0	Russian 4	56.2
Bell's B	58.0	Amosite	12.0
Canadian Z	56.3	Blue Cape Asbestos	7.0

The two kinds of hornblende (amosite and blue Cape) asbestos which were attacked but slightly were subjected repeatedly to similar 2-hour periods of treatment and the losses in weight determined. The results obtained are shown in Table 8.

TABLE 8. Loss in Weight of Horneblende (Amphibole) Treated with Boiling Hydrochloric Acid

	Amosite Long Fiber (per cent)	*Amosite Short Fiber (per cent)*	*Blue Cape Asbestos (per cent)*
2 hr	12.0	14.4	7.0
2 × 2 hr	19.1	20.5	8.4
3 × 2 hr	23.0	24.9	10.0
4 × 2 hr	27.0	30.6	13.0
5 × 2 hr	31.6	35.6	14.5
6 × 2 hr	37.6	38.8	16.0
7 × 2 hr	38.8	40.0	18.2
8 × 2 hr	....	....	20.4

At room temperature therefore the hornblende types of asbestos may be considered as relatively resistant to strong mineral acids. The decomposition proceeds very slowly after 5 to 10 per cent has been dissolved.

Hot mineral acids attack asbestos much more strongly, even the hornblende types being strongly attacked by boiling mineral acids.

The acid resistance of asbestos is important because of the use of many asbestos products in chemical factories. Asbestos fibers, or products made therefrom, are used in the actual production of acids (such as tartaric and citric, sulfuric, nitric and hydrochloric acids), the principal uses being as filtering materials and catalysts; also for bags and diaphragms in the electrolytic processes for the making of chlorine and caustic soda, peroxide and chromic acid, oxygen and hydrogen. Asbestos products are also necessary in chemical and acid plants for insulation, caulking, protective clothing for workmen, gaskets, packings, and interior linings.

Spinnability

Asbestos fibers regarded as spinnable vary from 3/8 to 3/4 in. in length. While some fibers of greater length than 3/4 in. are present in Canadian spinning grades, the percentage is small.

The common practice in the industry is to blend cotton fibers with asbestos in order to obtain good carding and spinning results. Mixes containing 5 per cent up to 20 per cent of cotton are usually employed. When only 5 per cent or 10 per cent of cotton is used, it is necessary to have only the very best and longest spinning fibers. The shorter grades of asbestos fibers, averaging about 1/2 in. in length, require 18 to 20 per cent cotton in order to obtain a satisfactory yarn and good running conditions in the mill.

The quality of cotton fiber used depends upon the quality and fineness of the asbestos yarn desired. Rough Peruvian cotton of 1 1/8-in. staple or longer is found to be satisfactory for the finer yarns. American cottons of 1-in. to 1 1/8-in. staple are widely used for asbestos yarns of average quality.

The standard designation of asbestos yarn is the "cut." The yards per pound of the standard cuts are given in Table 9.

TABLE 9. Yards per Pound of Standard Cuts of Asbestos Yarns

Cut Designation	*Nominal Yards per Pound*	*Cut Designation*	*Nominal Yards per Pound*
5 Cut	500	18 Cut	1800
6 Cut	600	20 Cut	2000
7 Cut	700	22 Cut	2200
8 Cut	800	24 Cut	2400
9 Cut	900	26 Cut	2600
10 Cut	1000	28 Cut	2800
12 Cut	1200	30 Cut	3000
14 Cut	1400	35 Cut	3500
16 Cut	1600		

Chemical Analyses

Typical analyses [14] of the three types of spinnable asbestos—chrysotile, blue, and amosite—are given in Table 10.

Color and Dyeing

Chrysotile asbestos in rock form is usually found in soft shades of green, ranging from a very pale green found in northern Ontario (Canada), Rhodesia, and Australia to the darker greens of the Thet-

[14] Taken from Oliver Bowles, *Bull.* 403, U. S. Bureau of Mines, p. 4 (1937).

TABLE 10. CHEMICAL COMPONENTS OF VARIOUS ASBESTOS FIBERS

	SiO_2	Al_2O_3	Fe_2O_3	FeO	MgO	CaO	Na_2O	H_2O	Total
Chrysotile:									
Canada *	40.36	0.21	1.35	0.66	43.86	....	....	13.45	99.89
Arizona †	41.56	1.27	....	0.64	42.05	....	....	14.31	99.83
Barberton ‡	40.05	1.90	1.60	0.40	38.35	0.15	0.40 **	16.60	99.70
Shabani ‡	40.96	1.70	....	2.44	38.73	....	0.10 **	16.07	100.00
Russia §	39.28	1.75	0.40	5.37	40.05	1.74	....	11.52	100.11
Crocidolite (Cape) ‖	51.10	....	....	35.80	2.30	....	6.90	3.90	100.00
Amosite: Penge ¶	49.72	5.72	....	37.00	3.77	1.65	....	2.29	100.15

* Ross, J. G., *Chrysotile Asbestos in Canada*, Canada Dept. Mines, Mines Branch 707, p. 20, 1931.
† Diller, J. S., "Mineral Resources of the U. S." 1918, Pt. 2, p. 302.
‡ Hall, A. L., "Asbestos in the Union of South Africa," *U. of S.A. Geol. Survey Mem. 12*, p. 31, *1919.*
§ RuKeyser, Walter A., "Chrysotile Asbestos in the Bajenova Dist., U.S.S.R.," *Eng. Mining J.*, **134**, no. 8, August 1933, p. 338.
‖ Hall, A. L., work cited, p. 19.
¶ Hall, A. L., work cited, p. 22.
** Includes K_2O.

ford district in Canada, and of Russia, Cyprus, and Vermont. Arizona asbestos is very often a pale yellow and very lustrous, although much Arizona asbestos is a pale green shade. When crushed and pulled apart, spun, or otherwise worked, however, chrysotile asbestos, regardless of its source, is invariably either white or grayish white, usually the latter.

The amosite variety in rock form runs from a dirty gray to a gray green, and when pulled apart and worked, can be described in no other way than as "dirty gray." Some amosite fibers have also been found which are a decided yellow and retain their color in any manufactured product made from it.

Blue asbestos is just that, a lavender blue, resulting from the large amount of iron in its composition. The peculiarity in blue asbestos is the fact that when worked it remains blue, and therefore products made of blue (crocidolite) asbestos, such as yarn, cloth, paper, millboard, are of the lavender blue shade.

Asbestos yarns and cloths can be dyed with little change in the normal procedures now used in the dyeing of other textile products. Dyed asbestos cloth in various colors, for draperies, curtains, towels, rugs and bedspreads is now used in ships and hotels.

Utilization of Asbestos Textile Fibers

The main reasons for the use of asbestos fiber in the manufacture of asbestos textiles are: dielectric (nonconducting) characteristics;

fire and heat resistance; chemical resistance; durability (permanence) of weathering characteristics; blendability with other fibers; cost; space-filling characteristics; wicking ability; resistance against frictional wear.

Although chrysotile asbestos fibers are the outstanding type for textiles, amosite asbestos fibers are used in large amounts for the fabrication of heavy bulky blankets for turbines, and for heavy slivers (ropelike forms) for space fillers, for bulk insulation products, etc. Also, the blue asbestos fibers (crocidolite) are fabricated into slivers, yarns, tapes, and cloth for special end use, usually in products that have to have outstanding resistance against the action of chemicals.

In the manufacture of wire, armor plate, or galvanized materials, other materials could probably be used for the wiping process, but they would need constant replacement; asbestos lasts much longer.

Asbestos is used in industrial packings. The less often pumps and other apparatus have to be "packed," the less expense and stoppage of manufacturing processes. Durability is, therefore, one of the most important qualities of asbestos and of asbestos textiles.

Basically, the only uses of asbestos textile fibers are in the making of yarn, wick, and rope packing, and felt. Yarn is made into cloth, tape and listing, brake lining, packing, gasket cloth, tubing, wick for oil-burning apparatus, twine or thread, covering for electric fixture or cable covering. Yarn is used also for the tying of gas mantles and for the edges of hair belting.

Cloth, in its turn, is the basis of sheet packing, folded and wound packings; it is folded and stitched into brake lining for heavy industrial machinery; formed into gaskets; sewed into insulation mattresses; used as a covering for insulation where temperatures are high, particularly in ships and airplanes; surfacing of conveyor belting; blankets in electrolyzer cells; and bags and diaphragms in oxygen-producing machinery. It is made into asbestos clothing, which includes suits, helmets, gloves and mittens, aprons, leggings, berets; it is used as curtains or scenery in theaters, and as hangings for firestops in various public buildings or in laboratories, cleaning establishments, and other public places where there is danger of fire; or as blankets for fire fighting everywhere. Asbestos clothing and blankets are especially useful for rescue work at building fires and in airplane crashes. All airports are equipped with them. These might be termed the principal uses of asbestos cloth. There are many special ones, i.e., for mailbags, awnings, vacuum bags in cleaning and conveyor systems, filtering, and innumerable uses where only small quantities are required, but where its durability and fire- or acid-protecting qualities are important, although hardly visible to the casual observer.

Asbestos tape or listing also finds numerous uses in industry, such as electrical tape used in practically all electrical apparatus, for the winding of coils, and for insulating armatures and underground cables. It is also used for pull strings in ovens.

Asbestos felt finds its way into acoustical work, protection of underground pipes, on paper machines, and as insulation against shock or vibration.

The largest quantities of asbestos textile fibers are therefore used principally in four basic industries—automobile, industrial packing, electrical, and insulation—but other smaller industries also use asbestos, especially for filtering, in safety apparel, and in the manufacture of acids.

Another type of asbestos textile developed for use as a protective boot in war planes, and also used for gun boots and tail-wheel boots, combines asbestos and glass fibers in the yarn, or is made by weaving asbestos yarn with glass yarn. In cord form it is used for shroud lines on military flares. The asbestos increases abrasion resistance while the glass is said to give high strength. Resistance to high temperatures and corrosive fumes is also an attribute of this unique product.

Unlike most other fibers, asbestos fibers serve their most important uses in the industrial world; in tonnage asbestos fiber is probably negligible as compared with other fibers, but its importance is tremendous and its service beyond price.

BIBLIOGRAPHY

Asbestos, a monthly magazine devoted to the asbestos industry, Philadelphia, Pa., since 1919.

Asbestos Factbook, 20 pp., 3rd ed. (April 1, 1953).

Badollet, M. S., "Research on Asbestos Fibres," *Canadian Mining and Metallurgical Bull.* (April 1948).

Bowles, Oliver, "Asbestos," U. S. Bur. Mines *Bull.* 403, 92 pp. (1937).

Bowles, Oliver, "Asbestos, Domestic and Foreign Deposits," U. S. Bur. Mines I. C. 6790, 24 pp. (June 1934).

Bowles, Oliver, "Asbestos, General Information," U. S. Bur. Mines I. C. 6817, 21 pp. (Jan. 1935).

Bowles, Oliver, "Asbestos—Milling, Marketing and Fabrication," U. S. Bur. Mines I. C. 6869, 26 pp. (Dec. 1935).

Butler, G. M., "Asbestos Deposits of Arizona," Univ. Arizona *Bull.* 126, 100 pp. (Oct. 1938).

Finucane, K. J., "The Blue Asbestos Deposits of the Hamersley Ranges," *Western Australia Rept.* 49, 16 pp. and maps (1939).

HALL, A. L., "Asbestos in Union of South Africa," *Union of South Africa Surv. Mem.* 12, 2nd Ed., 34 pp. (1930).

JENKINS, G. F., "Industrial Rocks and Minerals," *Am. Inst. Mining and Metallurgical Engs.*

MILES, K. R., and FOXALL, J. S., "The Blue Asbestos Bearing Banded Iron Formations of the Hamersley Ranges," *Western Australia Geol. Surv. Bull.* 100, 62 pp. and maps (1942).

ROSS, J. G., *Chrysotile Asbestos in Canada,* Canada Dept. Mines, Ottawa, 146 pp. (1931).

WOLOCHOW, D., and WHITE, W. H., N. R. C. 969, 970, and 972, "Thermal Studies on Asbestos I, II, and III." Reprinted from *Can. J. Research Bull.* 19, pp. 49–60, 65–67 (1941).

FIBROUS GLASS AND FILAMENTS

TYLER STEWART ROGERS [15]

Textiles of glass have been the dream of man for many centuries; their actual achievement as fabrics that could be folded, or yarns that could be knotted without breaking, dates only from 1936. In the few years that have intervened, a new industry has been born and has achieved a significant position in the textile world. The practical utility of glass as an electrical insulation material and the need for fabrics that are fireproof and resistant to rot, mildew, moisture, and stretch made the development of this industry prior to the beginning of World War II a most fortunate circumstance. Glass textiles now play an important part in military, naval, and aircraft material.

History

Though the history of the present industry is extremely short, the history of glass fibers themselves antedates human records. It is probable that the first form of glass actually shaped by the hand of man was a fiber. This probability arises from the fact that molten glass is a viscous fluid closely resembling honey or molasses. Its tendency is to string out from any implement dipped in it. It is believed that glass was discovered by some early tribe under the bed of a fire that had been built on sand containing glass-making constituents. If the discoverer, with natural curiosity, poked a greenwood stick or a stone weapon into the glowing fluid to appraise its nature, he must have drawn a fiber between the end of his implement and the mass in the fire.

Throughout many centuries man developed glassmaking to an advanced art and necessarily drew fibers for many purposes, such as for

[15] Technical Director, Owens-Corning Fiberglas Corp.

"spun glass" decoration on stemware and the enchanting millefiori (glass flowers encased in clear glass). Several attempts to make glass fibers suitable for textile purposes are recorded, but none attracted much attention until Edward Drummond Libbey made fabrics of relatively coarse glass fibers arranged in bundles and woven together with silk threads for display at the Columbian Exposition in 1893. A dress for Georgia Cayvan, reigning actress of the day, drew crowds that expected the dress would be transparent. Princess Eulalie of Spain purchased a similar gown, a duplicate of which is now preserved in the Toledo, Ohio, Art Museum. The fabrics used were impractical, since they could not be folded without breaking the filaments.

During the next four decades an increasing number of patents were issued, mostly in Europe, for processes or improvements in methods of making glass fibers. Most of these formed fibers were much too coarse for textile applications, although suitable for thermal insulating purposes. The earlier processes, including that used by Libbey, drew fibers from the heated ends of glass rods and wound them on large revolving drums. A second process, which reached a moderate state of development, produced glass fibers by centrifugal action through an orifice in the perimeter of a refractory disk or chamber revolving at high speed.

In 1931, Games Slayter, John H. Thomas, and several associates developed in America a process for drawing fibrous glass by means of jets of high-pressure steam. Within a year they had introduced coarse glass fibers formed into a pack and treated with a dust-stopping adhesive for use as an air filter. The same process, further refined, resulted in the production of a thermal insulating wool and gave rise to the establishment in America of a new glass industry.

The same group continued its research and experimental work and by 1936 had found means of drawing fine, uniform filaments and devised methods of gathering and arranging them for textile applications. A second textile fiber process followed in 1937, and the two became the basis for the production of textile fibers of glass in commercial quantities and at costs low enough to find many immediate uses. They also came into use in European countries and Great Britain and now constitute the source of practically all glass textiles.

American Processes

Two distinct types of fibrous materials are produced. One, called the continuous filament process, forms filaments of indefinite length, measurable in miles, and distinguishable by their brilliance and continuity. The other is called the staple fiber process and makes fibers of "discontinuous" length, i.e., in relatively short lengths resembling cotton or flax fibers. The length averages about 9 in. and can be made longer or shorter within limits.

In both processes, glass is formulated by precision batch mixing, using selected silica sand, limestone, and other glass-making mineral

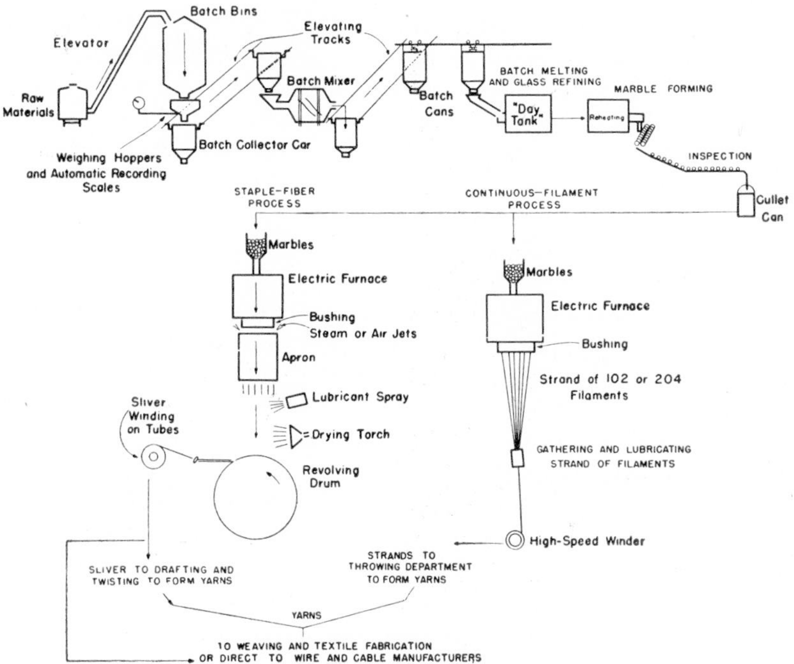

FIG. 8. Flowsheet of glass fiber processes.

ingredients to produce the type of glass required. This glass is then formed into marbles approximately ¾ in. in diameter, and these are carefully inspected to eliminate those containing "stones," "seeds," or other defects that might interrupt subsequent production operations or impair the quality of the fibers drawn from them.

In the *continuous filament process,* these marbles (or cullet) are melted in an electric furnace equipped with a bushing of high-temperature metal at the bottom of the melting chamber. This bushing is perforated with 102 or more small orifices. The glass flows through the orifices in fine streams. These streams are then caught below the furnace and the strand drawn by a high-speed winding mechanism that instantly attenuates the fibers at a point where they emerge from the hot furnace and reduces them in size to a fraction of the diameter of the orifices. This winding mechanism draws the fibers in parallel strands at a speed well over a mile a minute. The strand thus formed is ready for twisting and plying on standard textile machinery.

The *staple fiber process* begins in the same way with marbles (or cullet) melted in an electric furnace. The streams of molten glass that emerge from the bushing are attenuated into fibers by jets of high-pressure steam or air, moving at rifle-bullet speed.

These fibers are gathered below the furnace upon a revolving drum, where they form a diaphanous web that is gathered from the drum and wound on tubes to form staple fiber sliver or bands. This sliver can be drafted, twisted, and plied in much the same manner as a wool or cotton sliver. Figure 8 shows a flowsheet of the modern glass fiber production process.

Other Processes

While these specified processes are used extensively in the production of glass textiles, other processes have been developed and production of somewhat coarser textile fibers is being made by the older drum-winding or spinning processes. The production from such units, however, is devoted to the formation of mats and of insulating wools that involve no textile fabrication.

The production of fibrous glass in wool form is known as glass mineral wool or glass wool. It is made from silica sand, borates or soda ash, and limestone, with or without scrap glass (cullet) and other glass-making ingredients. Glass mineral wool is incombustible and is used principally in heat and cold insulations as well as acoustical applications.

Types of Fibers Produced

Both continuous filament and staple fibers are made in commercial fiber thicknesses and may be made from one of two or more glass compositions. Commercial fiber sizes commonly used in textile operations range from 0.00023 to 0.00048 in., as indicated in Table 11. Fiber sizes are designated by letter symbols based on a scale that starts with $A = 0.0001$ in. or less, and then rises by 0.00005-in. increments for each succeeding letter (except that I and O are omitted to avoid confusion with numbers). Any fiber of an average diameter that falls within the range separating the letters is designated by the higher letter. Thus, D fibers could have any average size between 0.00021 in. and 0.00025 in., but a fiber of a diameter averaging 0.00026 in. would be called an E fiber. (See Table 11.)

TABLE 11. TYPES OF COMMERCIAL GLASS FILAMENTS AND FIBERS

Letter Symbol	Average Fiber Diameter (in.)		Commercial Types	
	Minimum	Maximum	Ave. Diameter (in.)	Form
A	0.00006	0.00010	....	....
B	0.00011	0.00015	....	....
C	0.00016	0.00020	....	....
D	0.00021	0.00025	0.00023	Continuous and staple
E	0.00026	0.00030	0.00028	Continuous and staple
F	0.00031	0.00035	0.00033	....
G	0.00036	0.00040	0.00038	Continuous and staple
H	0.00041	0.00045	....	....
J	0.00046	0.00050	0.00048	Staple, nonstandard

Most glass fibers are drawn from a glass especially formulated to provide desirable electrical characteristics. Some types and sizes of staple fibers are also drawn from a glass especially compounded for chemical resistance. Again, letter symbols are used to designate the glass composition. *E* represents an electrical glass and *C* a chemical glass. The use of these letters is explained later under numbering systems for glass yarns. A special glass containing lead is used in limited quantities to produce fibers that are opaque to X-rays for surgical uses.

Economic Factors

Production of glass textiles rose slowly from 1936 to 1939, when the greater part of all production was being utilized as electrical insulation. The electrical industry faced a new problem in adapting its design and application techniques to make use of this new material. Once this hurdle had been passed, there was a sharp rise in consumption for electrical applications alone.

By 1940, some decorative uses had been developed, including tablecloths, shower curtains, and other specialty applications, which gave further impetus to the production of glass textile fibers. From 1941 on, the industry felt the impact of military and naval applications and steadily increased production facilities in an effort to meet these large demands. Commercial markets for glass fibers include the following:

Glass yarns for textiles provide heat resistance equal to or greater than that of asbestos with a space factor no greater than that of cotton.

Thus, glass electrical insulation materials, when properly impregnated with suitable varnishes or impregnants, provide an insulation for all class B equipment,[16] such as motors, generators, transformers, and reactors, but permit the construction of such equipment in the sizes common to class A devices. By permitting a higher temperature rise than is normally acceptable even in class B equipment, magnetic devices can be made smaller and lighter than was hitherto practical with commercial insulating materials.

As a basis for many electrical applications, glass yarns are served directly on copper wires to form glass-insulated magnet wire. This is used in forming coils for magnetic equipment; the coils are further insulated with tapes, cloths, or braided sleevings, and bound with cords constructed of fibrous glass. Glass-insulated cables of several types have been developed, some using glass-insulated conductors for space conservation or to reduce corona effect (as in high-tension cables) and some using high-bulking staple fiber slivers to replace asbestos, jute, or other filler materials, when they became scarce owing to war conditions, or to replace organic fibers in cables that required an incombustible filling material. More recently, continuous-filament yarns have come into use as a tension member in field telephone cables and other similar cords that are subjected to frequent and variable tension in service. The glass tension cord replaces steel or copper used for the same purpose.

The use of glass combined with mica to form insulating tapes and cloths for slot and phase insulation offers both mechanical and electrical advantages and conserves the use of presently scarce mica materials. Also, the use of glass fabrics as a basis for phenolic laminated materials has proved to be a sound development, because the extremely low moisture absorption of fibrous glass gives such composite materials high resistance to deterioration and excellent behavior under abnormal physical and electrical stresses.

Industrial uses range over a wide field. Glass cloths and tapes are used as a lagging or wrapping over pipe insulation and duct-work in hot locations or in tropical applications, where the usual cotton fabric will not stand up or where asbestos fabrics are undesirable because of their weight and bulk. Glass cloths are also used for connections between sections of duct-work as a sound isolator; as curtains or portières on board ship, and for similar applications requiring fireproof fabrics;

[16] Class B is the electrical industry's designation for equipment using inorganic insulation materials; class A equipment uses organic insulations such as cotton, paper, silk.

as a facing material for thermal and acoustical blankets used in aircraft and naval ships; and as a facing material on insulation boards made of glass mineral wool where a paintable, wear-resistant surface is required without the use of metal or other hard finishes. Fabrics also have found some application in dust and fume filtration, as anode bags in electroplating tanks, and for a growing number of specialized uses. Fabrics woven of glass and asbestos yarns have been developed to utilize the advantageous properties of both materials, as in fireproof fabrics subject to considerable flexing. In 1944 glass fabrics came into use as a reinforcement for certain "contact-pressure" resins to form plastic laminates and aircraft parts of exceptional strength-weight ratio, impact resistance, and dimensional stability.

Decorative applications were being developed prior to World War II. Some work was done to induce color into the glass itself, but this proved impractical because of prohibitive costs and limitations in possible color ranges. Now, new finishing techniques have made possible production of truly decorative glass fabrics, including marquisette curtains, casement cloths and printed and piece-dyed materials. Fibrous glass is also combined with certain plastic resins to make distinctive lamp shades.

It is unlikely, in light of present knowledge, that glass fabric will find a place as clothing material since its resistance to stretch and its low moisture absorption are both contrary to such requirements.

Military applications broadly parallel industrial uses. The desirability of a fire-resistant, high-strength, rot-resistant fabric is considerable in many different military, naval and aircraft applications.

Microscopic Appearance

Glass textile fibers are readily distinguished from all other textile fibers on close examination but not on casual examination of glass textiles. Close examination and simple flame or stretch tests readily reveal essential differences.

Microscopic examination of glass textile fibers (washed clear of any lubricant or binder) reveals that they are perfectly smooth, with no visible structure on the surface. The edges of the fiber under the microscope are always parallel and without any irregularities whatever. Even examination at the great magnifications possible with the electron microscope (Fig. 9) fails to discover any roughness or irregularity. See Fig. 10 for a longitudinal view of *E* fibers (normally 0.00028 in. in diameter) at $\times 2000$.

Cross-sectional examination shows that the fibers are perfectly circular. (See Fig. 11.) Fiber diameters may vary considerably from the average dimension of all in a strand, but these variations are not significant until "tramp" fibers considerably coarser than the average appear in the strand. The finer fibers merely tend to increase breaking strength and flexibility; hence, quality control standards merely seek to maintain an *average* fiber diameter within 0.00005 in. of the specified

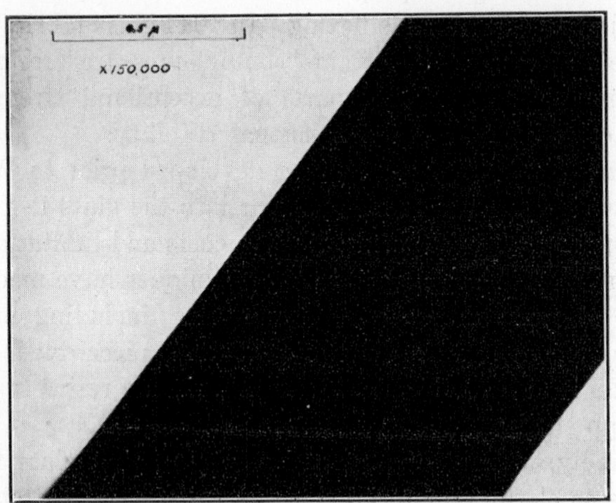

Fig. 9. Extreme smoothness of glass fibers. ×150,000.

normal fiber size and to reject only when the largest fiber present exceeds the average by 0.00010 to 0.00015 in.

An abnormality found in glass textile fibers is the occasional presence of tubular or hollow fibers, which occur in approximately 0.3 per cent of the fibers. These tubular sections are only a fraction of an inch to a few inches long; they disappear where the elongated bubbles causing them taper to a point.

The characteristic fracture of a glass fiber is a clean transverse or slightly diagonal break. The fibers rarely or never split or break longitudinally. Breaks are caused in fibers by the same stresses that break sheet glass or larger rods: if the surface is nicked by abrasion of glass against glass, or by any hard instrument, the fiber is weakened at that point just as a glazier's cutting tool causes sheet glass to break cleanly under the scratch on the surface. Similarly, a fiber is broken as any larger rod or sheet of glass is broken, simply by bending it too sharply. This characteristic will be discussed later.

Fig. 10. Longitudinal view of *E* fibers. ×2000.

Physical Properties

The utility of any textile fiber arises not from some single property but from a combination of properties that adapt it to specific uses. Properties that may be desirable for one purpose may be detrimental for another. In the study of an unfamiliar fiber it is important to note and evaluate all of the properties in order to appreciate fully its potentialities and limitations.

Incombustibility is of primary significance in glass as it is a rare property in textiles and opens up special fields of application. Glass

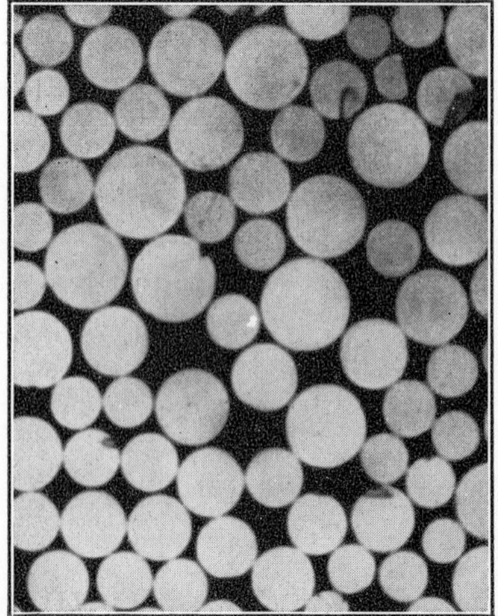

Fig. 11. Cross-sections of mixed glass textile fibers. ×1000.

is an incombustible material; it cannot burn. It is produced by great heat (about 2500° F.) in glass melting tanks in which flames pass over the molten batch. Any changes that could be caused by flames in the presence of oxygen occur during the creation of glass; thereafter the material is immune to oxidation.

Heat. In the presence of heat, glass softens and melts, without burning and without giving off smoke or noxious gases. Glass textiles will tolerate heat up to 1000° F. without material harm. They become slightly brash and embrittled on the hot surface at temperatures ranging above 850° or 900° F., but have been used successfully on high-pressure turbines and pipes at 950° F. without loss of flexibility.

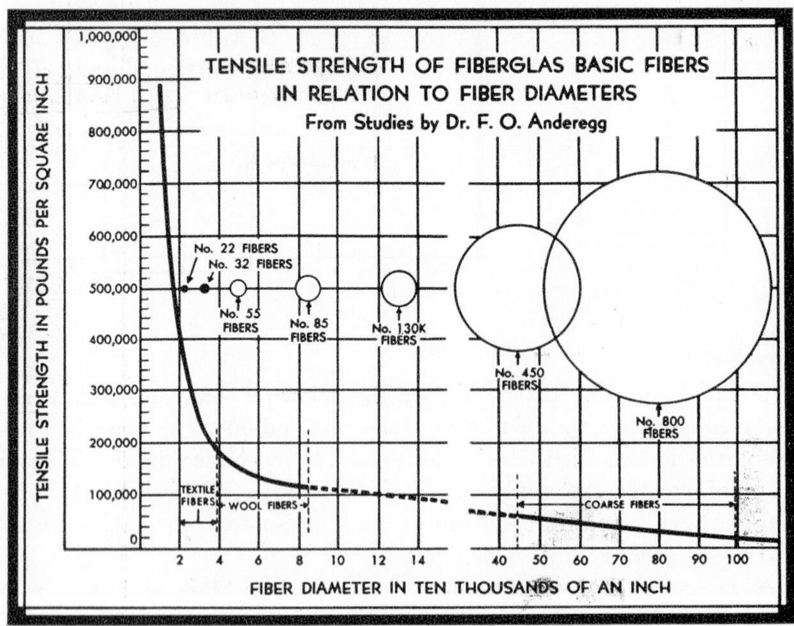

Fig. 12. Tensile strength in relation to fiber diameter.

Tensile Strength. This is the second most distinguishing characteristic, though not utilized to its capacity in the majority of applications. The tensile strength of fine glass fibers, such as *D* fibers averaging 0.00023 in. in diameter, is in excess of 250,000 psi. As the diameter decreases, strength increases very rapidly, as shown by the curve in Fig. 12 based on studies by Dr. F. O. Anderegg.[17] Fibers have been produced experimentally that show tensile strengths exceeding 2 million psi.

Conversely, as diameter increases, strength diminishes, but it should be noted that throughout the range of diameters suitable for textile applications the theoretical tensile strength remains well above 100,000 psi.

These strengths are not realized in woven fabrics or even in simple yarns because fracture points may develop in some filaments or twist and the weave may not permit uniform distribution of the stress. Nevertheless, very high tensile strengths are realized in woven fabrics, and this strength is retained at elevated temperatures. Figure 13 shows the relative tensile strengths at various temperatures of electrical glass tapes (continuous filament and staple fiber), asbestos, and cotton of approximately equal thickness.

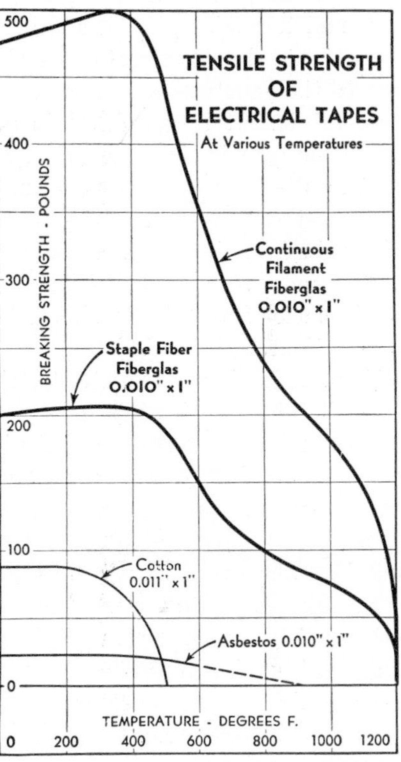

Fig. 13. Tensile strengths of electrical glass tapes at various temperatures.

Low moisture adsorption is both a negative and a positive characteristic in glass textile fibers. Since the individual fibers, with rare exception, are like very fine solid glass rods and have no cellular interstructure or pores, moisture cannot penetrate them and must therefore be limited to the surface. In the presence of water vapor, any gain in weight must be due to adsorption rather than absorption by the individual fibers. Accurate tests of clean fibers that are first heated

[17] "Strength of Glass Fiber," by F. O. Anderegg, *Ind. Eng. Chem.*, **31**, 290 (March 1939).

to absolute dryness and then exposed to atmospheres of high relative humidity (90 to 95 per cent R.H.) show that the glass fibers gain less than 0.4 per cent in weight from adsorbed moisture.

This property is valuable in electrical, aircraft, and other vehicle applications and detrimental in glass textiles for clothing purposes. Low moisture adsorption is an aid in electrical uses, because it reduces or prevents the deterioration of electrical varnishes and impregnants due to the penetration of moisture through or along the fibers of the base fabric. It is significant in aircraft applications, because it reduces the gain in dead weight of aircraft, in flight or on the ground, that results from the pick-up of moisture by hygroscopic or moisture-absorbent materials. Even in truck bodies, railroad trains, and ships this gain in weight of materials may become significant, though it applies more to thermal insulation materials than to fabrics.

The lack of absorbency deters the use of glass fabrics for clothing applications, as it would give a cold, sleazy feel in the presence of body moisture. Lack of adequate stretch is equally important in excluding most clothing applications.

Low moisture adsorption of the individual fibers should not be confused with behavior in the presence of water. A woven glass fabric may have good capillarity, as in the use of staple fiber tapes as lamp wicks for oil lamps and burners or for hydroponic cultivation of plants, but here the capillarity is through the interstices in the weave, not within the fibers themselves. Glass fabrics can be wetted as readily as others; they tend to drain off the excess moisture rapidly and to dry out quickly, since only surface moisture need be removed. In their use as pipe-lagging fabrics and as a surface finish for glass mineral wool boards used in naval fighting craft, glass cloths and tapes require very little paint to fill the pores and produce a smooth, dust-resistant surface. Likewise, in the manufacture of varnished electrical materials, less varnish is required.

Pliability is wholly dependent upon fiber diameter in relation to fiber length. Fibrous glass is just as brittle as glass rods under stresses proportioned to their size. The extreme flexibility of glass yarns is derived from the fact that the individual filaments are much finer than the yarns; that 100 to 400 fibers or filaments are required to construct even a fine yarn; and that, when such yarns are bent or knotted, it is unlikely that any single fiber will be bent more sharply than it can tolerate without breaking.

The discovery of means for achieving a yarn that could be knotted and a fabric that could be folded upon itself without breaking, by relating the yarn diameter with the fiber diameter is one of the basic inventions underlying the present glass textile industry. The patent [18] covering this point states:

> This ratio of yarn diameter to fiber diameter has a definite bearing upon the degree of bending to which the individual fibers will be subjected when the fabric is folded or creased. This ratio should be at least as high as about 10 to 1, depending upon the fiber diameter itself.
>
> The radius of curvature to which each fiber is subjected when the fabric is folded is the radius of curvature of the yarns themselves, since the yarns are folded over each other, or, at least, the smaller the yarns, the smaller will be the radius of curvature and the more likelihood of fracturing the yarns when the fabrics are folded.
>
> . . . in order to produce a usable, thin, flexible cloth, it is necessary to build up the individual yarns with a multiplicity of individual fibers having diameters below the diameter indicated. The number of fibers in each yarn which is to be woven into a textile fabric should have at least about 70 and preferably more than about 100 fibers.

This property of pliability is difficult to accept because people associate glass with rigidity. But, if one took a match stick and bent it sharply, it would break, while, if they planed off a very thin shaving from the side of that match stick, they would expect the shaving to be flexible. Similarly, a section of steel rail is extremely rigid in a short piece; the same section 40 ft long can be bent by track-layers to a moderate curve. If the same steel were stretched out into a fine wire it would become extremely flexible. Likewise, glass fibers can be pliable or flexible.

Elasticity is another property of both negative and positive value. Glass fibers are perfectly elastic; that is, their elastic limit and breaking strength coincide. A glass fiber can be bent just short of the breaking point and it will instantly recover its natural shape. If bent too far, it will break. Young's modulus for single fibers of 0.00025-in. diameter is approximately 7,200,000 psi.

Elongation is a related property. The stretch is 3 to 4 per cent maximum in the individual fibers and probably averages less than 3 per cent. Tests on typical yarns of low twist show an elongation at the breaking point of 1.7 to 2.7 per cent; high twist yarns show 2.2 to 3.3 per cent elongation. This property is helpful in such applications as drapery fabrics, either using all glass yarns or occasional warp thread of glass with other yarns, to prevent stretch after hanging. At the same time, it limits other applications where a resilient fabric is needed, as in hosiery or dress goods.

[18] U. S. Patent 2,133,238, "Glass Fabric," Games Slayter and John H. Thomas.

Durability of glass textile fibers can be expressed only in relative terms, since the durability of any fiber or fabric depends upon the specific conditions of use. An appraisal of durability of any fiber—and particularly of glass fibers—should be based upon a review of destructive influences, because fibers or textiles may be extremely durable in certain applications and yet have only limited usefulness under certain adverse conditions.

One factor affecting durability is *flexing endurance,* which is a measure of the amount of internal abrasion among fibers that a fabric can stand before it wears out from such friction. Glass cuts glass just as diamonds cut diamonds and, therefore, the individual fibers are always lubricated with a suitable mineral oil or other film-forming material to minimize fiber abrasion. Since these lubricants are less durable than glass fibers themselves, the life of glass fabrics is somewhat limited when they are employed in applications involving constant flexing.

As a rule, glass fabrics are employed in fixed applications such as for electrical insulations, pipe laggings, insulation surfacing, thermal insulating blankets, and similar uses where flexing ceases after the installation has been made. They should rarely be used, unless especially treated, for applications involving constant and severe flexing such as a flag whipping in a wind or a rope operating constantly over pulleys or sheaves. These limitations are relative, of course, as they depend upon fiber treatment.

Electrical properties of glass fibers provide one of its more important fields of use. Electrical resistance of glass is very high. Dielectric strength of a glass fabric is approximately that of air since electricity can flow through the interstices in the weave as readily as across an equivalent spark gap. Therefore, the dielectric strength of glass textiles used as electrical insulating materials depends largely upon the dielectric properties of the varnish or impregnant employed to fill these interstices.

Insulation resistance (the flow of current along the surface of glass fibers) is exceedingly high, but it is influenced in any electrical insulation by moisture or dirt accumulating on the surface of the insulator. Here the low moisture adsorption of glass fibers contributes materially to their value in electrical applications, as evidenced by the high insulation resistance of glass textiles, even under conditions of high relative humidity.

Specific gravity and refractive index for two textile glasses are given in Table 12.

TABLE 12. Specific Gravity and Refractive Index of Textile Glass Fibers

Glass Type	*Specific Gravity (grams per cu cm at 28° C.)*	*Density (lb per cu ft)*	*Refractive Index*
E	2.55	159.0	1.548
C	2.57	159.0	1.541

Biological Applications

These include surgical sutures or surgical sponges, where a tracer thread of a special lead glass that is opaque to X-rays offers a ready means of locating and removing sponges. Glass fabrics are also employed as filters in blood plasma field kits used by the Army and Navy Medical Corps.

These applications are possible for two primary reasons:

(1) Glass is readily sterilized by heat or antiseptics.

(2) Glass fibers in the blood stream or elsewhere within the body show no reaction to the blood or tissue and apparently have no biological effect whatever.

The manufacture and handling of glass textile fibers (and of other glass fibers, including glass mineral wools) introduce no new occupational hazard or industrial disease. Careful tests over an 8-yr period at Saranac Laboratory by Dr. Leroy U. Gardner show that glass fibers have no injurious effects on the lungs.

Health Hazard. In June 1941, Dr. Walter J. Siebert, Pathologist and Director of Laboratories of the De Paul and Lutheran Hospitals, St. Louis, Mo., made an investigation of possible health hazards in the manufacture and handling of glass fiber. In his report published in the January 1942 issue of *Industrial Medicine,* Dr. Siebert says:

> In submitting his best judgment, based on his professional interpretation of all facts assembled in the course of the investigation, the author finds that there is no silicosis, fibrosis, or dust hazard connected with working with Fiberglas, and that the manufacture, fabrication and application of Fiberglas products is attended by no unusual occupational hazards.

During the spring and summer of 1942, Dr. Marion B. Sulzberger, Assistant Clinical Professor of Dermatology and Syphilology, New York Post-Graduate Medical School, and Dr. Rudolf L. Baer, Junior Assistant Dermatologist and Syphilologist, New York Post-Graduate Hospital, carried out an experimental investigation of the effects of Fiberglas on animal and human skin.

In an article in the October 1942 issue of *Industrial Medicine,* Drs. Sulzberger and Baer report in part:

All of the reactions observed were of a transitory and superficial nature. The only parts of the reactions which persisted for more than a few days were slight thickening and brownish pigmentation of the skin. The latter were sometimes apparent for several weeks. No reactions or symptoms outside the rubbed skin areas were observed at any time during the experiment.

Chemical Properties

Although glass in solid form may be able to withstand surface attacks of various acids, alkalis, or even plain water to such a high degree that no apparent deterioration takes place, the glass chemist knows that some glasses are more soluble than others and that surface attacks do occur on most commercial grades of glass. That is one of the reasons for the formulation of different types of glasses; i.e., to provide resistance against exposures that are anticipated in service. For example, milk bottle glass is designed for resistance to lactic acids; a different glass is used for beer bottles because the exposure is totally different. Pharmaceutical and laboratory glassware must be highly insoluble, because of the range of substances used in medicines or chemical research work.

In the development of glasses for textile fibers, the technologists had to take into account the very great increase in surface area resulting from the reduction of the glass into the form of extremely fine fibers. The surface area of a pound of glass in the form of continuous filament fibers averaging 0.00023 in. in diameter is approximately 1370 sq ft. To meet this condition, glasses designed for textile use are given unusually high resistance to chemical attack; they may be compared in this quality to fine pharmaceutical and laboratory glassware.

Generally speaking, glass fabrics have a high resistance to all acids except hydrofluoric and have moderately good resistance to alkalis. Of the two glasses used in textile fibers, the *C* (or chemical glass) is preferred for applications involving the filtration of acid materials. Although both the *C* and *E* glasses will normally show a long life under such chemical exposures, the chemical stability of glass fibers is of primary importance to the textile mills in its bearing upon the pigmentation or dyeing of glass fibers to provide color. Here also the characteristic of nonabsorbency of fibrous glass contributes to the problem of utilizing glass in colored textiles.

Coloring. Pigmentation of glass is an old art as evidenced by the many beautiful colors found in art glasswork and in stained glass. Nevertheless, the pigmentation of glass to provide color in fibers introduces problems not present when the glass is employed in mass forms. Light refraction from the extremely fine fibers has the effect of diluting the color that may be present in the glass cullet to such a degree that only relatively light shades of color appear in the finished fibers or textiles when pigmentation is relied upon. Before World War II interrupted the production of decorative glass textiles, four permanent glass colors, in addition to the natural white, were being manufactured, namely, light and medium shades of tan or gold and light and medium shades of cobalt blue. At present, however, it appears improbable that induction of color into the glass itself will ever be satisfactory or economically practical for producing colored glass fabrics.

Because fibers of glass are nonabsorptive, the problem of getting color on materials made up of glass yarns has been principally one of surface dyeing. Processes have, however, been perfected not only for applying color to fibrous glass, but also for coating glass fabrics to assure color fastness. Screen-printed and piece-dyed fibrous glass drapery fabrics are now practical commercial items. Great progress also has been made in surface-dyeing fibrous glass for use as identification yarns in electrical wires and cables.

Binders and lubricants used with glass fibers are of two basic types. Staple fibers are lubricated with a mineral oil that can be removed by exposure to heat above 600° F. or by washing in carbon tetrachloride or similar solvents. Continuous filament yarns are lubricated and the individual filaments temporarily bound together in a strand by the use of a starch binder that can be removed by washing.

Utilization of Fibrous Glass

In spite of their extraordinary smoothness, both continuous-filament and staple fibers have proved to be practical textile materials that can be processed on standard textile machinery. Continuous filament, of course, is handled in much the same manner as silk, rayon, nylon, or other textile yarns. The strands are twisted on standard twisting equipment with only minor adjustments of speeds, tensions, and the form and material used in eyelets or other friction points. Staple fiber sliver is made in two forms.

In one, a strand of continuous filament is drawn into the sliver while it is being formed to act as a tension cord that prevents further drafting and permits the sliver to be used as a high-bulking material in certain wire and cable applications. This is called *reinforced sliver.*

The other form, lacking any such tension member, can be drafted on modified worsted frames and subsequently twisted and plied to construct yarns of desired characteristics.

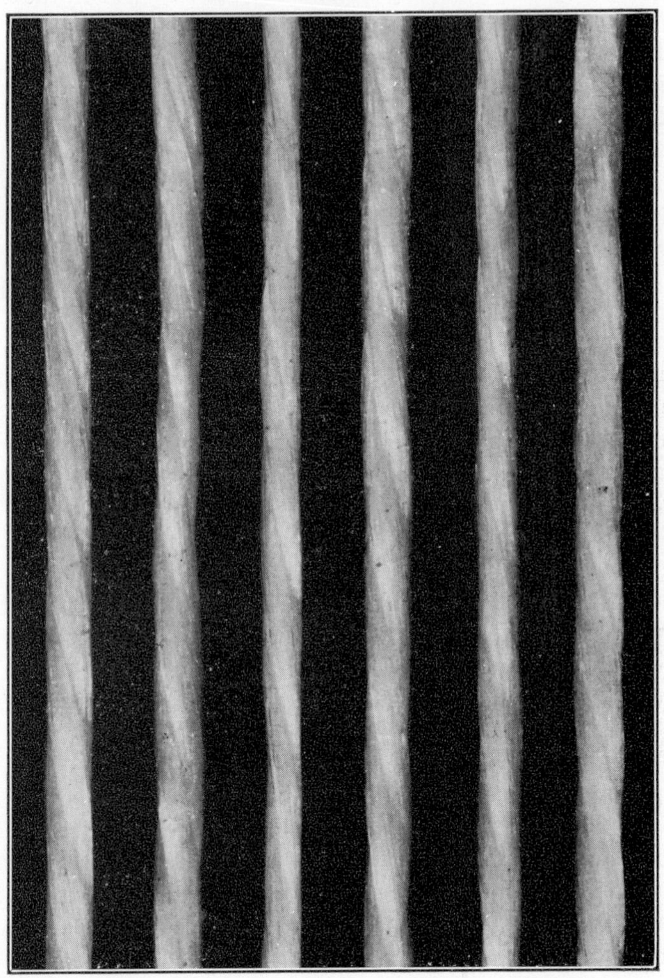

Fig. 14*a*. Continuous-filament glass yarn. Note smoothness.

Fiber nomenclature employed with glass fibers differs materially from that used with any other textile fiber. The system adopted to assist in identifying glass yarns is as follows:

A series of three letters precedes the count number of the yarn. The first letter, *E* or *C* (for electrical or chemical), identifies the glass.

The form of the fiber is identified by the second letter, *C* or *S* (for continuous or staple). The average fiber diameter is indicated by the third letter, using the diameter range noted earlier in this chapter.

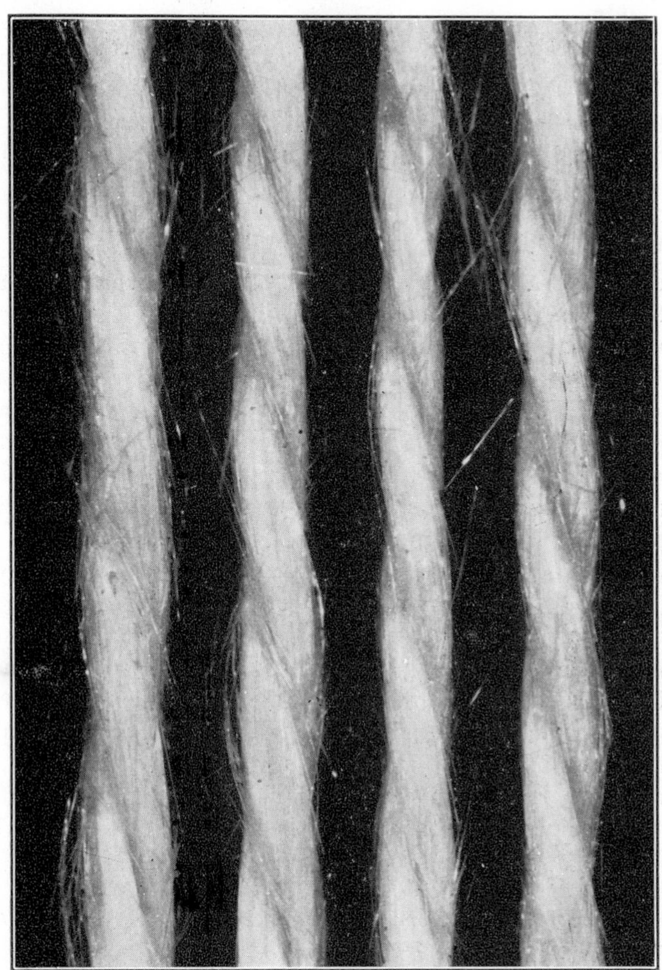

FIG. 14*b*. Staple glass spun yarn (20/2 *ESE*). Note fuzziness.

Thus, the letter symbol *ECD* would indicate a strand or yarn made of electrical glass in continuous-filament form and of fibers having an average diameter of 0.00023 in., or, properly, of an average diameter falling between 0.00021 and 0.00025 in. Similarly, the symbol *CSG* would represent a sliver or yarn made of chemical glass in staple fiber form with fibers having an average diameter of 0.00038 in. (or within the range between 0.00036 and 0.0004 in.).

This letter symbol precedes the count of a yarn or sliver using systems that need not be developed here. For identification purposes, however, typical yarn count numbers appear as follows: *ECD* 900–1/2, *ECD* 450–4/3, *ESE* 12.5/1, *ESG* 6/2. All these represent continuous-filament and staple-fiber yarns. Staple-fiber slivers would appear as *ESE* 26.5, *ESG* 6, etc. The counts give an approximate indication of the yards per pound but do not fully allow for contraction due to twist or the weight of lubricants.

Numbering System

Since glass textiles are made in continuous-filament, staple, and sliver forms, and sold by the pound, it is of interest to textile men to know in what sizes and in what counts they are available and the approximate yards per pound. The common single sizes of filament yarns and staple fiber yarns manufactured, their designations, and the yards per pound are given in Tables 13 and 14.

These tables show the diversified yarn counts that are often used and the fineness to which filament glass yarns have been spun, which is 101 denier or 52 cotton yarn count.

Care of glass textiles differs from the handling of other textile fabrics. Color fastness depends upon the characteristics of the dyes employed, but the colors used in pigmented glass fibers are entirely fast. In consequence, glass textiles of pigmented glass or uncolored fibers may be washed with ordinary mild soap and water; they do not require dry cleaning. Similarly, they may be spot cleaned or sterilized in any desired fashion.

After fabrics have been washed or cleaned and the lubricant or binder thus removed from the fibers, it is desirable to restore the lubri-

TABLE 13. Yardage of Continuous Filament Glass Yarns

Product Designation	*Nominal Yards per Pound*	*Equivalent Denier*	*Equivalent Cotton Count*
ECD 900–1/2	44,100	101	52
ECD 450–1/0	44,100	101	52
ECD 450–1/2	22,050	202	26
ECD 450–1/3	14,640	305	17
ECD 450–2/2	10,980	407	13
ECD 450–3/2	7,320	610	9
ECD 450–3/3	4,870	916	5.8
ECD 450–4/3	3,640	1,227	4
ECD 450–4/5	2,170	2,048	3

TABLE 14. Yardage of Single Staple Fiber Glass Yarns *

Product Designation	Nominal Yards per Pound	Equivalent Woolen Cut	Equivalent Cotton Count
ESE 70	7000	23.3	8.3
ESE 50	5000	16.7	5.9
ESE 40	4000	13.3	4.7
ESE 31	3172	10.5	3.8
ESE 25	2570	8.6	3.0
ESE 12.5	1250	4.2	1.5
ESE 10	975	3.2	1.2
ESE 6.2	624	2.1	0.7
ESG 12	1170	3.9	1.4
ESG 8	780	2.6	0.9
ESG 6	580	1.9	0.7
ESG 5	490	1.6	0.5
ESG 4	390	1.3	0.4
ESG 2.8	260	0.9	0.3
ESG 1.4	124	0.4	0.2

* These yarns may be made with a core of continuous filament yarn. Furnished in singles and two-ply.

cant by introducing a small quantity of mineral oil in the last rinse water. The oil picked up by the fibers lubricates them uniformly without special manipulation as the fabric dries.

Glass fabrics may be pressed to smooth out the weave, but they should not be sharply creased, because that tends to crush the fibers at the fold. Also, the resiliency of the fibers generally prevents the crease from remaining permanently in the fabric. Sewing seams requires special care if glass threads are used, because the lack of stretch in the thread or in the fabric makes it easy to introduce wrinkles that cannot be subsequently smoothed out by ordinary pressing operations. Sewing with cotton or silk is a simpler matter although, again, the lack of stretch of the fabric necessitates the equalization of the tension on both sides of the seam.

Market Evaluation

Glass textiles have found principal markets in electrical and industrial applications where materials combining fire resistance, high strength, dimensional stability and inherent resistance to rot, mildew, and fungus growth are required for more or less fixed rather than flexing applications.

However, notable advances are being made by fibrous glass in other fields. Decorative glass curtains and draperies are becoming increasingly popular, in homes and places of mass assembly, largely through their unique service properties—incombustibility, dimensional stability, resistance to rot, and wrinkle-free characteristics. A fast expanding field for fibrous glass is in reinforced plastics. Here, glass mat, cloth, and chopped fibers are impregnated with various resins to form a material combining great strength and low weight, dimensional stability, and resistance to rot and weathering.

Glass fibers themselves may undergo further development and thereby open up virgin fields of application. Processes have been developed for treating glass textile fibers so that they are reduced to almost pure silica content. Such fibers have a temperature tolerance approaching 2000° F., or almost twice the service temperature limit of standard fibers. While glass is known as a nonhygroscopic material with exceedingly low moisture adsorption, another process has been experimentally developed that converts glass fibers into a highly cellular structure with a moisture adsorption greater than that of silica gel. While these developments are still experimental, they suggest applications hitherto rarely associated with either textiles or glass.

BIBLIOGRAPHY

ANDEREGG, F. O., "Strength of Glass Fiber," *Ind. Eng. Chem.*, **31**, 290 (Mar. 1939).

"Asphalt Tank Trucks Use New Insulation," *Contractors and Engineers Monthly*, **XXXIX** (6), 13 (June 1942).

ATKINSON, F. W., *Trans. Am. Inst. Elec. Engrs.*, **58**, 277 (1939).

"Blast Cushioning Glass-Fiber Panel for Factory Blackouts," *Sci. American*, **CLXVII** (2), 76–77 (Aug. 1942).

BRAITHWAITE, K. H., "Fiberglas," *Can. Mining Met. Bull.*, **XXXV** (363), 277–280 (July 1942).

"Ceramics Aid Wartime Construction," *Ceram. Ind.*, **XXXVIII** (4), 58, 75–78 (Apr. 1942).

"Ceramics Help Industry Produce for Defense," *Ceram. Ind.*, **XXXVIII** (4), 51–56 (Apr. 1942).

FERRIS, R. E., and MOSES, G. L., *Elec. Eng.*, **57**, 480 (1938).

"Fiberglas Replacing Strategic Materials," *Chem. Eng. News*, **XX** (4), 304 (Feb. 25, 1942).

"Fiberglas Textile Yarns and Fabrics," *Am. Wool Cotton Rept.*, **LVI** (23), 9–10 (June 4, 1942).

"Fire-Safe Air Conditioning," *Buildings and Building Management*, 33–34 (Oct. 1941).

"Glass as a Textile Fiber," *Cotton (Atlanta)*, **CVI** (7), 78–79 (July 1942).

"Glass Fibre for Filter Cloth," *Fibre and Fabric*, **XCV** (2987), 8–9 (May 2, 1942).

"Glass Finds New Fields of Usefulness," *Domestic Commerce*, **XXX** (23), 11–12, 16 (Dec. 3, 1942).

Heath, D. J., "Glass Textile Fabrics for the Household," *Practical Home Economics,* **XX** (3), 93, 115–116 (Mar. 1942).

Lewison, E. F., "Rayable Gauze As a Factor of Safety in Surgical Operations," *Bull. American College of Surgeons,* **XXVII** (1), 39–40 (Jan. 1942).

"New Construction Possibilities for Chemical Plants," *Chem. Eng. News,* **XX** (19), 1236–1237 (Oct. 10, 1942).

"New Type Plasma Filter Will Aid in Prevention of Fatal Wound Shock," *Surgical Business,* **V** (5), 20–21 (May 1942).

"New Uses for Glass," *American Exporter,* **CXXIX** (6), 27, 44, 46 (Dec. 1941).

"New Work for Glass," *Technol. Rev.,* **XLIV** (1), 17 (Nov. 1941).

Phillips, C. J., *Glass: The Miracle Maker,* Chapter 17 (1941).

Phillips, C. J., *J. Applied Phys.,* **11,** 173 (1940).

"Piping Jacketed with Fiberglas Tape," *Mill and Factory,* **XXX** (2), 146 (1942).

Schneller, J. B., "Fiberglas Insulation in the Low-temperature Field," *Refrig. Eng.,* **XLIII** (5), 280–82 (May 1942).

Schols, R. P., and Mountjoy, P. S., "Fiberglas Suture Material," *Am. J. Surg.,* **LVI** (3), 619–621 (June 1942).

Sulzberger, M. B., and Baer, R. L., "The Effects of Fiberglas on Animal and Human Skin—Experimental Investigation," *Ind. Med.,* **XI** (10), 482–484 (Oct. 1942).

"Triumphs of Research," *Textile Research,* **XII** (5), 11–16 (Mar. 1942).

BASIC PATENTS

Slayter, Games, and Thomas, John H., Glass Fabric, U. S. Pat. 2,133,238 (Oct. 11, 1938).

Slayter, Games, Textile Material, U. S. Pat. 2,133,237 (Oct. 11, 1938).

Simpson, Donald C., Combined Asbestos and Glass Fiber Yarn, U. S. Pat. 2,132,702 (Oct. 11, 1938).

CHAPTER XX

IDENTIFICATION METHODS AND QUANTITATIVE FIBER ANALYSIS

WALTER KRAUSS

Identification of textile fibers, as well as subsequent quantitative determination of fibers in textile fabrics, yarns, ropes, twines, and brushes, is, with present-day competition, Fair Trade Practice Rules, and other government specifications, a necessary step in the evaluation of textiles. It also has a definite value in zoology, biology, criminology, forensic medicine, and archeology.

In routine identification of textile fibers for ultimate quantitative determination, it is usually sufficient to differentiate between major fibers or fiber types, such as wool, silk, cotton, rayon, and other man-made fibers. There are, however, occasions when further differentiation between various hairs usually classed as wool (such as mohair, camel hair, or alpaca), between various vegetable fibers, or between new synthetic fibers and filaments is desirable. Persons attempting to identify fibers should have some fundamental knowledge of the general structure of fibers, the blends possible in certain fabrics, as well as the common fiber combinations. For information on the chemical and physical structure of fibers the reader is referred to the specific chapter dealing with the physical characteristics and structure of each principal fiber.

Common fiber blends are those where two or more fibers of similar physical and chemical characteristics, such as cotton and rayon staple, are blended together. Fibers of contrasting characteristics, such as viscose rayons and acetates, are also often blended together for special effects. The occurrence of fibers in yarns, single and ply, can be classified in the following manner:

a. *One fiber type* only in a single yarn.
b. *Two or more fiber types* in a single yarn.
c. One *different fiber type* in each ply of a two or more ply yarn.
d. One fiber type in one ply and two or more fibers in the other ply or plies of a yarn.
e. Two or more types of fibers in each ply of a yarn.

These occurrences should be borne in mind when identifying fibers. Yarns of different colors, of different sizes, or different characteristics should be examined carefully and thoroughly.

METHODS OF FIBER IDENTIFICATION

There are many published methods and standards available to the reader for use in the identification of fibers. Roughly, all of these methods can be classed into *three* principal groups:

a. Simple preliminary macroscopic tests.
b. Microscopic examinations.
c. Tests employing chemical reagents, solvents, and stains.

Although microscopic and chemical methods are used for both identification and quantitative determination of fibers, the first group of tests is only a rough preliminary classification of some of the fibers or fiber groups. Differentiation between fibers of similar physical and chemical characteristics cannot be made macroscopically in this manner.

Knowledge of standard methods of identifying textile fibers, proposed by various textile associations and societies, is a definite advantage. A brief description of various methods follows.

(*A*) A.A.T.C.C. (Tentative Test Method 20-47)

Test methods for identification ("Identification and Quantitative Separation of Textile Fibers," *Yearbook* 1951) are briefly:

1. Burning tests
2. Solubility tests
3. Color reactions
4. Microscopic identification

The first test to be applied is the burning test. Advance a small bundle of the fibers slowly towards the flame. Note the behavior of the fibers in regard to burning or charring, melting or formation of bead, knob, and color.

The odor, shape, and color of the ash are given.

The second group of tests, solubility, gives differentiation between some of the newer synthetic fibers and rayon as well as natural fibers. Staining tests for differentiation of natural vegetable fibers and rayons are described under color reactions.

Finally the microscopic characteristics of the various fibers are tabulated and illustrated with longitudinal and cross-sectional views.

(*B*) A.S.T.M. ("Standard Methods of Identification of Fibers in Textiles," A.S.T.M. Designation D276-49)

This method covers 23 fibers commonly used in textile products in the United States. Emphasis is placed upon familiarity of the various fibers for successful identification of unknown samples. Reference samples of fibers are suggested for those unfamiliar with the various fibers which might be encountered in present-day textiles.

A list of reagents for mounting, staining, or dissolving of the fibers is given.

Chief emphasis placed upon identification of the fibers by means of the microscope and detailed procedures, charts, and photomicrographs make this A.S.T.M. standard method an excellent tool in fiber identification.

(*C*) Method of the Textile Institute

The present method (Tentative Textile Specification 13-1948, "Identification of Textile Materials," *J. Textile Inst.*, **39,** S1-10, March 1948) consists of four tables prepared by Technical Committee C of the Unification of Testing Methods Committee, as well as a brief explanation of the use of these tables and an appendix on the identification of manufactured fibers, along with photomicrographs of the more common fibers.

To identify single fiber sorts without the aid of the microscope the scheme as set out in Table A should be followed. It is advisable though not absolutely essential, to carry out all the chemical tests in the table on a slide while observing the results with a microscope, since much more definite conclusions can be derived from the tests made in this way. The fibers should be examined longitudinally and in cross-section and their appearance should be compared with photomicrographs of the authentic samples.

A much more difficult problem is that of mixtures in which different sorts of staple fibers have been blended before spinning into yarns. Here a mechanical separation of the different sorts, although not impossible, is not easy. It can be carried out in some cases by means of solvents which dissolve one but not the other components of a mixture.

Table A gives various preliminary tests. Table B lists the burning test, microscopic characteristics, and chemical tests for the differentiation of the major vegetable, animal, and man-made fibers. Table C is an analytical key for the identification of textile fibers. Table D gives the means of sorting pure fibers by means of flotation tests. The appendix on man-made fibers lists their physical and chemical properties as well as the microscopic characteristics.

PREPARATION OF FIBERS FOR IDENTIFICATION

Before any identification of fibers is attempted, either macroscopically, chemically, or microscopically, any foreign matter such as finishes, oils, and dirt should be removed. The agents used for the removal of such obstructive matter depend upon the fibers involved. Thus, animal fibers should not be treated with any appreciable amounts of sodium hydroxide, and, on the other hand, vegetable fibers should be treated cautiously with any concentrations of acids.

In most cases the fibers can be freed sufficiently of oils by simply immersing them in ether or in 95 per cent alcohol. Only in obstinate cases is a Soxhlet extraction with benzol or ether necessary. Latex or rubber on fabrics can be partly or entirely removed with benzol. Most starch finishes can be dissolved sufficiently by either a quick boiling of the fabric in distilled water or in a 2 per cent solution of neutral soap.

If any color reactions for identification are to be made on the fibers in question, the dye on the fibers should be removed before such tests are conducted. It should be pointed out here that any chemicals used for the reduction or oxidation of dyestuff tend to affect the fiber structure. The extent depends upon the fiber composition as well as the concentration of the chemicals. Ammonium hydroxide in low concentrations removes sufficient dye so that characteristics of the fibers are visible. If higher concentrations are employed, sufficient color may be removed to use color reactions for identification. Stripping agents can be used successfully for the removal of most dyes on fibers. If any chemical color reagents for differentiation of fibers are used, the fibers should be washed thoroughly after stripping the dyestuff to remove all of the stripping agent.

It is found advantageous, after having made a preliminary examination, to apply chemicals which, by separating the fibers into their ultimate components, bring out desired characteristics; or by destroying certain parts of the fiber, bring out others more prominently. Most of such reagents available were developed for use on vegetable fibers. There, the size and shape of the individual fiber cells, certain parts of the commercial fiber, which usually consists of cell aggregates, and extraneous vegetable matter from the plant adhering to the fiber, are of importance in identification. This is especially true with the extraneous nonfibrous vegetable matter, which at times is a valuable aid in the identification of various structural and bast (vegetable) fibers. Von Wiesner [1] and Herzog [2] have strongly emphasized the importance of such plant fragments as guides in identification. Needless to say, the chances of finding such matter are slight when the fibers have been bleached or otherwise chemically treated.

By the use of chromic acid or Schulze's reagent structural vegetable fibers can be broken down into individual cells and finally can be completely destroyed, leaving small round or star-shaped siliceous enclosures, valuable for identification. As both chromic acid and Schulze's reagent tend to act too severely on the fibers, it is recommended that a 0.5 per cent solution of sodium hydroxide be used for separation of individual fiber cells. The fibers are boiled in the solution and are washed thoroughly while being rubbed and squeezed between the fingers.

By staining hair fibers in picric acid, the scale structure or epidermis is brought out more prominently. This characteristic is a valuable aid in differentiating specialty hair fibers, where the shape of the epidermal cell is important.

SIMPLE PRELIMINARY FIBER-IDENTIFICATION TESTS

By pulling a few fibers out of the sample, holding them between tweezers, and burning the free ends in an open flame, certain fibers and fiber groups can be differentiated quickly. The odor, color, and shape of the ash should be noted; also whether or not the fibers burn slowly, fast, melt, or do not burn at all.

Simple Burning Tests

1. Fibers that burn slowly, leave lumps or blistered ashes, and have the odor of burnt hair. Wool, specialty hair fibers, fur, and minor hair fibers. Natural, cultivated, and wild silks. Man-made fibers of protein base (casein, soybean, zein).

Note: Weighted silk, when burned, leaves a whitish or brownish ash, which retains the form of the fiber or fabric.

2. Fibers that burn slowly or melt, leave beads or lumps at the ends, and do not have the odor of burning hair. Cellulose acetate (Estron)—hard knob with odor of acetic acid. Nylon—glassy bead with amine odor (boiling string beans). Dacron—irregular knob with aromatic odor. Vinyon, Dynel, Orlon, and Acrilan have an acrid, unpleasant odor and leave small, hard knobs.

3. Fibers that burn quickly, leaving very little ash and have a smell of burning paper. Man-made fibers of regenerated cellulose type, such

as viscose and cuprammonium rayons. All vegetable seed hairs, bast fibers, and structural fiber bundles.

Note: Sisal and abacá can be differentiated by the color of the ash, which is usually light gray in sisal and dark gray to black in abacá.

4. Fibers that do not burn, but melt or glow. Fibers of mineral origin such as glass fibers, asbestos, and metal threads. Metal threads, when held to an open flame, will give off a glow for some time.

Simple Tests for Vegetable Fibers

Flax and Hemp. The following wetting and torsion test can be utilized to differentiate between flax and hemp. The twist in the yarn containing one or both of the fibers mentioned is eliminated by untwisting the thread and pressing it flat. The fibers are pulled out individually and pressed down with one hand so that the free end is facing the observer. The fiber is then moistened and the direction and amount the fiber will twist while drying will be an indication of the type of bast fiber present. Flax always twists a number of turns to the right (clockwise), whereas hemp will twist very little to the left (counterclockwise). The other bast fibers, ramie and jute, can easily be identified by microscopic means.

Cotton and Flax. Simple means to differentiate between cotton and flax, as suggested by Herzog [3], are the tearing test, the untwisting test, and the oil test. Linen fabrics, when torn apart, will show torn fiber ends of uneven length, glossy and lying parallel in the yarns. Cotton, on the other hand, shows curling, lusterless threads and the torn fibers are of nearly equal length. Cotton yarns, when untwisted, show a difference in direction of each individual fiber, whereas in linen yarns when untwisted, the fibers lie nearly parallel.

To differentiate between cotton and linen fabrics, the oil test is conducted as follows: After removing the dressing in the fabric by boiling in water, place the fabric on a clean glass slide. Place a few drops of fatty oil on the fabric and, after removing the air bubbles, place another slide over the fabric. The fabric can be examined in either reflected or transmitted light. The linen fabric will assume a transparent appearance; cotton fabrics will appear opaque.

MICROSCOPE TECHNIQUES IN FIBER IDENTIFICATION

These are important tests for differentiating textile fibers. Not only can the various fibers be distinguished with the microscope, but also their fineness, any possible damage, and their proportion in fiber mixtures may be determined. In fact, where fibers of similar chemical composition are mixed together, a microscopic percentage determination is the only means of establishing the amount of each fiber present. Depending upon the fibers—whether dyed or undyed, animal, vegetable, or man made—one or more of the following methods best suited for the particular problem may be employed:

a. Examination under low-power magnification.
b. Longitudinal examination under a higher magnification by immersing the fibers in a suitable mounting medium or stain.
c. Longitudinal examination of the surface structure.
d. Cross-sectioning of the fibers.
e. Examination of outer or inner structural details of fibers by various forms of controlled light.

Low-Power Magnification

For a rapid check for fibers claimed or suspected in the sample, an examination under low magnification (about ×100) is usually sufficient. The fibers in question can be placed between two glass slides and examined. For instance, if in an "all wool" sample an appreciable amount of other fibers is detected, further microscopic methods, along with appropriate chemical tests, should be used.

Longitudinal Examination

High-power magnification is used when indications are that fibers of similar general, physical, and chemical nature, such as various types of hair fibers or vegetable fibers, are present. Magnifications of at least ×250 or ×500 are recommended. If the fibers are a dark color, much of the dye can be removed by treating with specially prepared stripping agents (see Preparation of Fibers). It is usually necessary to mount the fibers in a suitable medium. If a close study of the inner structure of the fibers is desirable for identification (chiefly in hair fibers), mounting liquid should have the same refractive index as the fibers in question. For contrast, to bring out the outer structure as well, a medium having a different refractive index—preferably higher—should be employed. Table 1 gives the refractive indices of the commonly used mounting media and the more important textile fibers. For routine work, glycerine as a mounting medium is most satisfactory. The chemical reagents given under "Reagents and Stains," when employed in conjunction with the microscopic examination, are used, in

TABLE 1. Refractive Indices of Common Mounting Liquids and Textile Fibers

Mounting Liquids		*Textile Fibers*	
Liquids	*Index*	*Fibers*	*Average Index*
Water	1.33	Acetate	1.477 *
Ethyl ether	1.35	Sisal	1.532 †
Ethyl alcohol	1.36	Viscose rayon	1.536 *
Decan	1.41	Cuprammonium rayon	1.538 *
Chloroform	1.44	Wool, chlorinated	1.549 *
Mineral oil	1.46	Wool	1.550 *
Carbon tetrachloride, Glycerine, Olive oil	1.47	Cotton	1.557 *
		Hemp	1.559 *
		Flax	1.562 *
Xylol	1.50	Cultivated silk	1.567 *
Cedar wood oil	1.51	Nylon	1.545 ‡
Canada balsam	1.54±	Vinyon	1.54 ‡
Clove oil	1.54	Casein fibers	1.54 ‡
Aniline M	1.60	Glass fibers	2.545 ‡
Monobrom naphthalene	1.66		
Methylene iodide	1.74		

* Author, A. Herzog. † Author, Himmelbauer. ‡ Author, B. Luniak.

general, in the same manner as the mounting media. A drop of the medium is spread evenly on the center of a clean slide and the fibers placed on the slide, teased apart with dissecting needles to lie parallel, then the cover glass is placed with care over the fibers so that no air bubbles are entrapped.

Surface Structure

The study of the epidermis of hair fibers, as well as the outer surface characteristics, is of definite value in identification in many cases. There are two ways of preparing fibers for such a study:

a. Impression or cast methods in quick-drying media.
b. Half mounting in media of similar refractive index as the fibers.

(*a*). A quick method of making fiber imprints is as follows: A few fibers are placed side by side on a microscope slide which has just been covered with a thin layer of plain nail polish. To prepare the slide, place a drop of the polish near one end and smooth it out into the desired thickness by using the edge of a sharp razor blade guided by a thin strip of paper fastened along each long edge of the slide. After the film with the embedded fibers is thoroughly dry, the fibers are carefully removed, leaving behind an impression of the outer surface. A little experience is required to place the fibers onto the film when it has the right consistency so that the fibers will immerse in it just halfway.

A similar method for making impressions, proposed by Lochte [4], is that of employing unexposed, fixed photographic plates. A plate is cut to microscope slide size and for use is wetted and left to dry. As soon as one corner of it is dry, place a few fibers parallel across it and cover with a clean glass plate weighted down with 3 to 5 lb of dead weight. Let the slide dry and remove the fibers. The impression is then ready for examination under the microscope.

Hardy [5] suggests that cellulose casts are especially suited for fibers of dark color. The fibers are fastened onto the slide by adhesive tape or wax and a frame of built-up layers of adhesive tape is made around the edges of the slide. Into this open frame a Celluloid solution made of 20 grams of Celluloid and 100 grams of acetone is poured. When dry, the tape is removed carefully from the slide, leaving the fastened fibers behind. The fissure on the bottom of the cast caused by the removal of the fibers does not interfere with the study of the cast.

(*b*). By immersing the fibers halfway in a mounting liquid of refractive index similar to that of the fibers, the lower part of the fibers is in optical contact with the liquid and only the surface facing the observer is visible and can be studied. Manby [6] describes various liquids which may be used for this purpose. One per cent of Celluloid in amyl acetate, 25 per cent glycerine in water, or a 3 per cent glycerine jelly is recommended. Reumuth [7] developed a new mounting liquid for this purpose called the R-O-X method, which gives excellent results. A simple method of semi-embedding fibers, especially wool and other hairs, was recently described by Herzog [8]. The fibers are first cleaned in alcohol, unless the foreign matter on the fibers is desired for observation. After drying, a number of fibers are placed parallel on a clean slide and are covered with a strip of transparent cellophane tape having an adhesive layer on one side (Scotch tape). For this purpose a 20-mm strip of the tape is cut off the roll and laid coated side down on the fibers. After moderate pressure has been applied to the strip to insure good contact with the fibers and the slide, the specimen can be studied. If the fibers contain pronounced medullae filled with air this obstructs partly the scale structure. For such fibers the cast or impression methods give better results.

Cross-Sectioning

This is a valuable aid in identification, and is especially suitable for study of dyestuff penetration, fiber fullness of man-made fibers, and fineness uniformity. In cases of dark-dyed fibers, a good cross-section will show all the structural details, not otherwise detectable without stripping the color. Fiber cross-sectioning was at one time too laborious for use in routine laboratory work. However, the development of rapid sectioning methods and devices has made it a very helpful test in the study of various fiber characteristics. While the time-consuming paraffine candle method is still employed in many research laboratories, the rapid methods are definitely responsible for making sectioning popular in mill and commercial laboratories. There are three sectioning methods used at the present time:

a. Cork method.
b. Metal plate of E. R. Schwarz [9].
c. Cross-sectioning devices of J. I. Hardy [10, 11].

All three methods give good fiber sections within a short time, but the Hardy device is best suited for making very fine sections.

Cork Method. A small cork stopper of good quality is pierced its whole length with a fine knitting needle. By means of strong sewing thread a bunch of parallel, straightened fibers are drawn through the hole formed by the needle. Thin slices can be cut from the cork with a sharp razor or a microtome. These slices with the embedded fibers are then ready for mounting.

Metal Plate Method of Schwarz [9]. A thin metal plate of the size and thickness of a microscope slide has a number of very small holes bored in rows near its center. Through these holes the fibers to be examined are drawn by means of a thin silver wire or thread. The protruding fibers are then cut flush on both sides of the plate, which is then placed on the microscope stage for examination. This method is suited only to undyed fibers, if transmitted light is used. Examination of dark fibers requires reflected light. No structural details within the fibers can be observed in this manner.

Cross-Section Devices by Hardy. The two devices here described are by far the quickest means of obtaining thin cross-sections.

The first of the devices [10] consists of a fiber holder in which is a slot 0.0085 in. wide and 3/8 in. long and of a slide holder which has a rigidly held metal slide attached to it. This slide fits into the fiber-holder slot when the two parts are brought together. In order to hold the two parts together rigidly the slide holder has guides attached to its sides. The device, when assembled, is the size of a microscope slide. The method of making the sections is as follows:

> A small tuft of the cleaned fibers is inserted in the slot of the fiber holder and the slide of the slide holder is pushed into the slot of the fiber holder so that the fibers are held securely. The fibers are then cut off flush on both sides by means of a razor blade and the device can be examined under the microscope.

Care should be taken not to pack the fibers too tightly. Fine sections can be produced with a little practice by using little or no pressure when cutting the protruding fibers. After applying a drop of collodion or other quick-drying cellulose solution, spread this into a thin film over the fibers and, after drying, cut off this film, using considerable pressure. The difference in pressure will govern the thickness of the fiber sections embedded in the film. The film can then be mounted in glycerine or Canada balsam on a microscope slide.

The other device [11], which is an elaboration of the first one, has an attachment that pushes the fiber sections out of the slot to produce any desired cross-sectional thickness. The device consists of a fiber holder and a slide holder similar to the previous one and of a mechanism containing a plunger and a micrometer screw to propel the plunger through the fiber slot. To operate the device the attached mechanism is removed and the fibers are inserted in the fiber slot as before. After the fibers have been cut off flush on both sides of the assembled device, the propelling mechanism is attached and centered over the fiber slot by means of a centering plug on one end of the attachment. The fiber plunger is propelled into the slot so that the fibers are projecting about 0.01 in. on the other side of the device. These fibers are covered with a thin film of collodion and are cut off flush with a sharp razor blade and the film is discarded. The micrometer screw is now turned to push the fibers out to the desired thickness of the cross-section. Another film of collodion is applied, and, after cutting, this film is mounted on a slide for study. The time required for making thin sections in this manner depends upon the skill of the operator.

Utilizing Controlled Forms of Light. For identification of fibers, an examination under the microscope with ordinary transmitted light is sufficient in most cases. For a more exacting study of fibers, controlled forms of light should be employed. The four different types of light or light arrangements besides the ordinary transmitted light are:

a. Reflected light.
b. Dark ground illumination.
c. Polarized light.
d. Ultraviolet light.

Reflected light is sometimes employed at low magnification for examination of fabric surfaces. When used at higher magnification, reflected light requires special attachments on the microscope. There are two general devices for transmitting light through the objective. One consists of a semi-transparent mirror attached to the bottom of the microscope tube. The light is reflected at right angles to the tube through the objective onto the object.

With the other device, reflected light, also reflected at right angles to the tube, is transmitted onto the object through special objectives (*e.g.*, Ultropack, Leitz). This form of light is for study of surface structure of fibers and cross-sectional contour of coarse fiber sections.

Dark ground illumination finds little use in routine microscopic work in textile laboratories. It is usually employed in research laboratories for study of the fine structure of fibers.

Polarized light is chiefly used in textiles for the classification of the maturity of cotton fibers, study of deterioration of rayon filaments, and for the differentiation of flax and hemp. It is helpful in emphasizing fissures and cross-marking on vegetable fibers.

Ultraviolet light, as an illuminant for textile microscopy, is at present employed only in fiber research. Its main use in textile research is for fluorescence analysis of chemicals and the detection of fungi and bacteria on fibers. As the shorter wave length of the light gives a better resolution of objects under high-power magnification the light has possibilities for the study of fibrillar and micellar fiber structure. Magnifications up to $\times 6000$ have been obtained with the ultraviolet light.

REAGENTS OR SOLVENTS

The various reagents and stains used in the methods of fiber identification are given in the following order:

a. Reagents for maceration of fibers and removal of foreign matter.
b. Fiber solvents.
c. Reagents and stains for color reactions, employed macroscopically and microscopically.

The use of a single reagent for the identification of an unknown fiber is not recommended. It is rather by a series of chemical or microchemical tests in conjunction with the microscope that any fiber can be identified positively. It should be borne in mind that the chemical tests should serve as a check for the microscopic identification.

Maceration and Removal of Foreign Matter

Alcohol. The usual 95 per cent commercial quality can be used as a reagent for removal of fatty matter, such as oil, from fibers and also for preparing solution of certain color stains.

Ammonia. Strong concentrations of ammonium hydroxide are used for removing dyes from fibers. This solution should be used before any of the other reagents for removal of dyes are employed.

Ammoniacal Copper Oxide [12]. For the differentiation of raw flax and hemp: Dissolve 5 grams of copper sulfate in 100 ml of boiling water. Add sodium hydroxide until all of the copper compound is precipitated. Filter off the precipitate and wash thoroughly. Dissolve in the smallest possible quantity of concentrated ammonium hydroxide.

The blue solution obtained should be sufficiently strong to dissolve cotton fibers quickly. As the solution is unstable, it should be prepared freshly each time. Apply a drop of the solution on the microscope slide with the fibers, put on cover glass, and examine at once. Both flax and hemp swell rapidly and are in near solution. The lumen of raw flax will appear as a tortuous tube, whereas the lumen of hemp will appear ruffled.

Chloral Hydrate. Five grams of chloral hydrate dissolved in 2 ml of water makes an excellent mounting medium for bringing out structural details in *vegetable* fibers.

Chromic Acid. Employed for isolating siliceous enclosures or the individual cells of vegetable fibers. The solution is prepared, according to Von Wiesner [1], by mixing potassium bichromate with an excess of sulfuric acid. From the resulting solution the chromic acid separates out and is then dissolved in an equal amount of water. It may be used cold. When employed with care it will not attack the cellulose too severely.

Hydrochloric Acid. Used for stripping certain dyes from animal or vegetable fibers. The acid is diluted 1 : 10 and the fibers are treated hot or cold.

Picric Acid [13]. Dissolve 0.5 gram of picric acid in 100 ml of water. The acid can be used for bringing out the scale structure of hair fibers. The fibers are placed in a few drops of the reagent on a slide, left for about 3 min, and then washed with water.

Schulze's Reagent. Employed for isolating fiber elements of vegetable fibers. It consists of concentrated nitric acid in which is added a small quantity of potassium chlorate. The fibers are heated in the solution and then washed. It rapidly dissolves lignin and attacks cellulose severely.

Sodium Hydrosulfite. Used for stripping dyes.

Sodium Hydroxide. A 0.5 per cent solution of caustic soda can be used for separating the individual cells of vegetable fibers.

TABLE 2. Solubility Chart of Fibers
[Fibers soluble as indicated]

Chemical Solutions	Hair	Silk, Cult.	Silk, Tussah	Cotton	Other Veg. Fibers	Viscose Rayon	Cupra Rayon	Acetate	Nylon	Vinyon
Acetone, conc.								X		X
Acetone (80%)								X		
Calcium thiocyanate, conc.						X	X			
Hydrochloric acid, conc.		X						X	X	
Methylene chloride										X
Nitric acid, conc.								X		X
Phenol (90%)								X	X	
Caustic soda (5%) boiling	X	X	X (partly)					Saponifies		
Sulfuric acid, conc.		X	X	X	X (slowly)	X	X	X		

Chemicals for Dissolving Fibers (See Table 2)

Acetone. The acetone in full concentration will dissolve most types of acetates as well as Vinyon. An 80 per cent solution of acetone will dissolve acetate only.

Acetic Acid, Glacial. For dissolving acetates.

Calcium Thiocyanate, Conc. For dissolving viscose and cuprammonium rayons. Must be used hot.

Hydrochloric Acid, Conc. By heating the acid to 30° or 40° C. it will dissolve silk, acetates, and nylon.

Methylene Chloride. Dissolves Vinyon.

Nitric Acid, Conc. Used for dissolving acetates and nylon.

Phenol. A 90 per cent solution of phenol (carbolic acid) dissolves acetates and nylon.

Sodium Hydroxide. Boiling 5 per cent caustic soda will rapidly dissolve wool and other hair fibers as well as silk. It saponifies acetates and decomposes tussah silk.

Sulfuric Acid, Conc. The acid dissolves cotton, viscose, and cuprammonium rayon, acetate, silk, and tussah silk. Vegetable bast and structural fibers are dissolved slowly.

Color Reactions

Brilliant Blue 6BA. A stain for the differentiation of raw and mercerized cotton, as well as cuprammonium and viscose rayon. A 0.2 to 0.5 per cent solution of the dye is applied to the fibers for 3 min. The fibers are then washed, mounted on a slide, and examined. Raw and mercerized cotton stain blue, but after repeated rinsing only the mercerized cotton will remain blue. Cuprammonium rayon stains blue; viscose rayon remains colorless or stains lavender.

Colotex B [14]. This is a dye stain made by Union Chemical Company, New York, similar to Neocarmine W, which is no longer available. The fibers are immersed for 3 to 5 min in the dye solution and washed until the water is free from color. The fibers are then passed through water containing a few drops of ammonia, rinsed again in fresh water, and dried. The color reactions are given in Table 3.

Cross-Bevan Reaction [15]. A reaction for the differentiation of vegetable fibers. By immersing the fibers in equal parts of 0.1*N* ferricyanate and 0.1*N* ferrichloride, color differences of vegetable fibers, as given in Table 3, are obtained.

Dye Stain According to Davis and Rynkiewicz [16]. A dye stain for the differentiation of principal fibers. The stain is prepared as follows:

Components	*Grams*
Acid fuchsin (color index No. 692)	6
Picric acid	10
Tannic acid	10
Soluble blue 2B extra (color index No. 707)	5

The dyes may be ground together and are dissolved in water to make 1000 ml of solution. The fibers are immersed in the cold solution for 2 min. The color reactions are given in Table 3.

Iodine and Sulfuric Acid. A reagent for differentiating vegetable fibers and certain man-made fibers. Three grams of potassium iodide are dissolved in 60 ml of water, and 1 gram of iodine is added. For use, dilute with 10 parts of water. The sulfuric acid can be prepared by mixing 3 parts of glycerine and 1 part of water to 3 parts of sulfuric acid, concentrated. After the fibers have been stained in the iodine solution, the excess liquid is blotted off and the fibers are mounted on a slide in the sulfuric acid. Color reactions are given in Table 3.

Malachite Green and Oxamine Red [17]. The fibers are immersed for 15 to 20 sec in a boiling solution of 0.1 per cent neutral malachite green (color index No. 657). After a short rinse with warm water the fibers are immersed for 15 to 20 sec in a boiling solution of 0.1 per cent oxamine red and are rinsed again in warm water. Color reactions are given in Table 3.

Methylene Blue. This dye is for the differentiation of flax and cotton. The fibers are immersed for 20 min in a cold solution of 0.1 per cent methylene blue and are then washed in warm water until no more dye bleeds from the fibers. Cotton will stay white and flax will dye blue.

Millon's Reagent [18]. A test for identification of animal and other protein fibers. One ml of mercury is dissolved in 9 ml of 94 per cent nitric acid and diluted with 10 ml of water. As this reagent decomposes very rapidly it is advisable to prepare it fresh when needed. The fibers are mounted in the solution and heated gently. Hairs, silks, and man-made protein fibers stain pink, red, or reddish brown. All other fibers remain unstained.

Morse Test [19]. For the differentiation of casein fibers and soybean fibers, a small sample of fibers is treated in 18 per cent sodium hydroxide until partly dissolved. To approximately 1 ml of the solution add 4 drops of isoamyl alcohol and 15 drops of 30 per cent hydrogen peroxide. Mix well and heat over a steam bath until foaming has subsided and most of the alcohol and water have evaporated. Add 2 ml of 5N hydrochloric acid and reheat on steam bath for 10 to 15 min and observe color. Casein fibers turn rose-red, soybean fibers remain colorless.

Neocarmine W [20]. A dye stain, similar to Colotex B, for the differentiation of the principal fiber types. The fibers are immersed from 3 to 5 min in the stain, rinsed thoroughly, and immersed briefly in a weak ammonia solution. Color reactions are given in Table 3.

Phloroglucinol and Hydrochloric Acid [12]. Two grams of phloroglucinol are dissolved in 1000 ml of alcohol. One part of this solution

TABLE 3. Color

	Wool and Other Hair Fibers	Chlorinated Wool	Cultivated Silk (De-gummed)	Tussah Silk (Un-bleached)	Raw Cotton	Bleached Cotton	Mercerized Cotton	Kapok	Raw Flax
Brilliant Blue 6BA									
Colotex B	Deep maize	Dull orange	Reddish tan	Golden yellow	Dull lavender	Dull violet	Blue violet	Greenish yellow	Bluish mauve
Cross-Bevan Reaction					Yellow to green			Light green to blue	Light green
Dye Stain Davis-Rynkiewicz	Yellow		Brown		Light blue				Light blue
Iodine and sulfuric acid	Yellow				Blue			Yellow	Greenish blue
Malachite green and oxamine red	Green	Turbid deep green	Deep green		Reddish violet				Brownish violet
Methylene blue					Unstained		Light blue	Deep blue	Blue
Millon's reagent	Red to reddish brown				Unstained				
Morse test									
Neocarmine W	Yellow	Dark yellow	Dull gold	Green	Light blue	Deep blue		Greenish yellow	Dull deep blue
Phloroglucinol and hydrochloric acid								Pink	Traces of pink
Ruthenium red					Unstained			Red	Very light pink
Swett test									
Zinc-chloride-iodine	Yellow	Dark yellow	Yellow		Red violet	Deep red violet		Yellow to brown	Brown violet

REACTIONS OF FIBER

<table>
<tr><th>Hemp</th><th>Ramie</th><th>Jute</th><th>Sisal</th><th>New Zealand Flax (Phormium)</th><th>Abacá</th><th>Coir</th><th>Viscose Rayon</th><th>Cuprammonium Rayon</th><th>Acetate</th><th>Casein Fibers</th><th>Soybean Fibers</th><th>Nylon</th><th>Vinyon</th></tr>
<tr><td colspan="7"></td><td>Unstained or lavender</td><td>Blue</td><td colspan="5"></td></tr>
<tr><td>Dull light brown</td><td></td><td>Light reddish brown</td><td colspan="3"></td><td>Dull yellow brown</td><td>Lilac</td><td>Reddish navy blue</td><td>Lemon yellow</td><td>Red</td><td></td><td>Dull reddish yellow</td><td>Unstained</td></tr>
<tr><td>Dark green</td><td>Light green to blue</td><td colspan="12"></td></tr>
<tr><td colspan="7"></td><td>Lavender</td><td>Dark blue</td><td>Pale greenish yellow</td><td colspan="2"></td><td>Pale greenish yellow</td><td>Pale blue</td></tr>
<tr><td>Yellow to blue</td><td>Blue</td><td>Brown</td><td>Yellow</td><td colspan="2"></td><td>Yellow</td><td>Deep blue</td><td>Light blue</td><td colspan="3">Yellow</td><td>Lavender partly dissolves</td><td></td></tr>
<tr><td>Dark brown</td><td>Bluish violet</td><td>Dark green</td><td>Bluish green</td><td colspan="2"></td><td>Green</td><td>Violet</td><td>Turbid red</td><td>Pale green</td><td colspan="2">Turbid green</td><td colspan="2"></td></tr>
<tr><td colspan="2">Blue</td><td colspan="5">Deep blue</td><td colspan="7"></td></tr>
<tr><td colspan="10">Unstained</td><td colspan="2">Red to reddish brown</td><td colspan="2">Unstained</td></tr>
<tr><td colspan="10"></td><td>Rose red</td><td>Colorless</td><td colspan="2"></td></tr>
<tr><td>Violet blue with red dots</td><td>Blue violet</td><td>Olive brown</td><td>Greenish yellow with blue markings</td><td colspan="2"></td><td>Light brown</td><td>Red violet</td><td>Deep blue</td><td>Greenish yellow</td><td colspan="2">Yellow</td><td>Greenish yellow</td><td>Pale yellow</td></tr>
<tr><td colspan="2"></td><td>Magenta</td><td colspan="3">Red</td><td colspan="8"></td></tr>
<tr><td colspan="14"></td></tr>
<tr><td colspan="3"></td><td colspan="2">Cherry red</td><td>Brown</td><td colspan="8"></td></tr>
<tr><td>Violet</td><td>Violet to blue</td><td colspan="5">Yellow to brown</td><td colspan="2">Red violet</td><td>Yellow (dissolves)</td><td colspan="2">Yellow</td><td colspan="2"></td></tr>
</table>

is added to one part of concentrated hydrochloric acid and the fibers are immersed in the mixture. Vegetable fibers will be stained pink, red, or deep violet, depending upon their lignin content.

Ruthenium Red [21]. A general reagent for the differentiation of vegetable fibers. Ammoniacal oxychloride of ruthenium is dissolved in water, giving a violet-red color. This compound is insoluble in glycerol. Therefore, after the fibers are stained they can be mounted in glycerol for later microscopic observation of the color reaction. For testing of fibers 0.1 gram of the reagent is dissolved in 10 ml of water. A drop is placed on a slide, the fibers are immersed in the liquid, and the cover glass is placed over the fibers. Raw cotton will stain pink, turning violet-red after a few hours. Raw flax and hemp stain spotty from pink to dark red. Ramie stains a light pink (rose). Bleached cotton will not stain.

Swett Test [22]. A general test for rope fibers; chiefly for the differentiation of sisal and abacá. Rinse the fibers in ether to remove any oil present. Immerse the clean fibers for 30 sec in a solution of bleaching powder (sodium hypochlorite), acidified with acetic acid. Wash in water, then alcohol, and hold over concentrated ammonium hydroxide. Jute and sisal stain bright red, abacá and phormium stain reddish brown.

Zinc Chloride Iodine Reagent (Herzberg Stain) [23]. A general reagent for vegetable fibers. Twenty grams of zinc chloride are dissolved in 10 ml of water to make solution A; 2.1 grams of potassium iodide and 0.1 gram of iodine are dissolved in 5 ml of water to make solution B. Both solutions are mixed together. When precipitates have settled, the clear liquid is drawn off and a small leaf of crystalline iodine is added. The solution has to be kept in the dark. Color reactions are given in Table 3.

SYSTEMATIC ANALYSIS OF FIBERS

Identification of fibers can be approached from two definite angles. If a sample having a presumed or stated fiber content, such as all-wool or all-cotton, is submitted for examination, it is simply a matter of checking the fibers. By mounting a few fibers from representative yarns, either stained or unstained (as best suited) and examining them under the microscope, the various characteristics typical for the fibers can be checked against the actual fibers found on the slide. The claim for the sample is confirmed if all characteristics check. If, on the other hand, some or all of the fibers exhibit characteristics quite different from those typical for the claimed fibers, the identification must be approached from a different angle.

Many of the published methods for fiber identification are simply tables or charts of macroscopic and chemical tests, by means of which the unknown fiber is identified by way of elimination. While such tests work rather well when only one or a few fiber types are present, it has been found that quicker and more accurate results are obtainable when the microscope is used for preliminary grouping of the unknown as well as the ultimate identification. Only if identification without chemical reagents and stains, as well as other tests, is impossible or doubtful should other means be employed.

By using the microscope first and chemical tests as confirmation the operator accumulates certain familiarity with fiber characteristics valuable for identification. Authentic and representative samples of all commercially used fibers are another valuable aid. For preliminary analysis of fiber groups as well as for ultimate identification of a fiber, certain definite tests of identification are associated with certain fiber groups. Thus, it should be remembered that hair fibers can be differentiated *only with the microscope,* while vegetable fibers, as well as man-made fibers, can be differentiated both with the microscope and by chemical means.

Before any fibers are mounted on the slide, it is recommended that they be examined macroscopically for length, size, color, and luster. In this manner certain groups of fibers may be eliminated at once. Thus, if the fibers are of continuous length (filaments), fine, and of high luster, it can be assumed that they are either natural silk or man-made filaments. Similarly, vegetable fibers found in ropes can usually be identified by visual observation. These observations, while not conclusive, will classify the fibers into workable groups. A suggested method for preliminary sorting out of fibers or fiber groups, found either individually or in mixture with other fibers, follows.

By Use of Microscope

From the clean, decolored sample, representative yarns are selected. A few fibers from each yarn are either dry-mounted or mounted in glycerine, and are examined under the microscope at ×100 to ×200. The basic characteristics of the common fibers are given in the various chapters on these fibers.

By Use of General and Chemical Macroscopic Tests

Tables 2 and 3, taken in part from the American Association of Textile Chemists and Colorists Yearbook (1942) and in part from the

Journal of the Textile Institute, Standardization Issue (June 1941, Identification of Fibers), will give sufficient differentiation of fiber groups, without the use of the microscope, to make definite identification easier. It should be emphasized that in this case each fiber in the representative sample should be examined as some of the tests, when applied to a blend of fibers, will give poor or erroneous results. This is especially true if burning tests are employed.

DYE STAIN IDENTIFICATION [1]

Dye stain tests offer a rapid method for identification, particularly if the fibers are undyed. If the fibers are dyed, they often can be

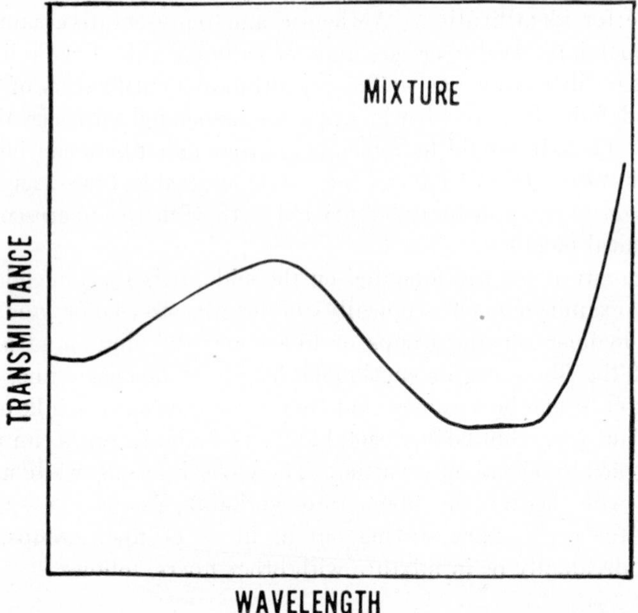

Fig. 1. Spectrophotometric curve of a typical identification stain.

bleached and then stained, but the bleaching may affect the subsequent staining. It should be noted that the undyed fibers may have been treated with chemicals such as antistatic agents, and these may affect the stain reactions. If the agents are not permanently attached to the fiber they will also have an effect on dyeing if not removed. If such is the case, the fibers should be given the same preparation or

[1] Excerpted by permission from Calco Technical *Bull.* 831, by G. L. Royer.

scouring before identification as they will be given before dyeing. It is advisable to use known fibers as a control and subject them to the same dye stain tests as are used on the unknown and include scouring or other pretreatments.

Identification stains are generally combinations of dyes which have been selected because of their specific dyeing affinity for certain fibers.

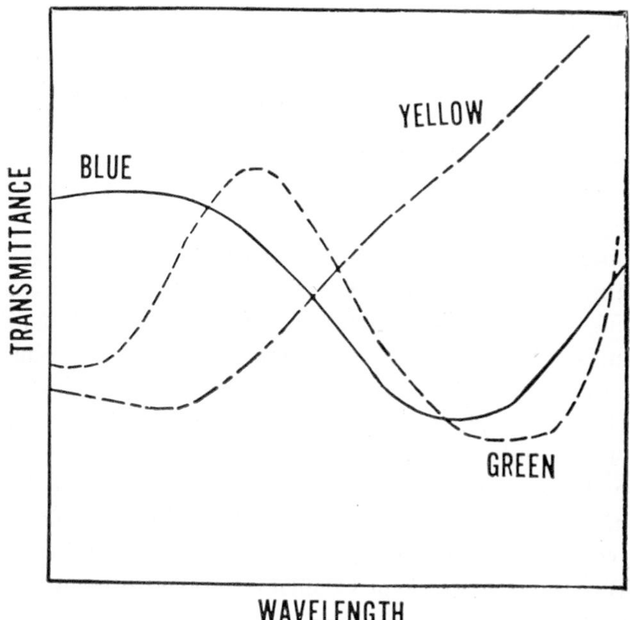

FIG. 2. Spectrophotometric curves of the components of the mixture shown in Fig. 1.

As an example of a simple identification stain, Fig. 1 shows the spectrophotometric curve of a mixture of three dyes, the individual spectro curves of which are shown in Fig. 2. The blue dye is Calcodur Blue 4GL (C.I. 533); the yellow dye is Calcosyn Yellow 5G Conc. (Pr. 245); and the green dye is Calcocid Alizarine Green CGN Ex. (C.I. 1078). The blue dye was chosen because it dyes cellulosic fibers and tends to leave the protein and acetate fibers unstained.

The green dye was chosen because it dyes protein fibers well but has little affinity for acetate or cellulosic fibers. The yellow dye is an acetate dye which, of course, dyes the acetate; however, it does stain protein fibers to some extent. It is very difficult to find an acetate dye which may not also stain wool to some extent. When acetate, cotton, and wool are placed in such a dye bath, the spectral curve for which is shown in Fig. 1, the cotton will stain blue, the acetate will stain yellow, and wool will stain green. The word "stain" is used since the period of contact with the bath is only 1 min at the boil, and this is not long enough for penetration and fixation of the dye in the fibers, which would be referred to as dyeing.

New Stains Developed

This same type of stain, of course, could be used to identify fibers other than the three mentioned above, and they would come out different shades, depending upon the differences in affinity of the fibers for these three dyes. It should be emphasized that this combination is not proposed as a practical stain, since it was chosen only to illustrate the principle of staining for identification purposes.

A number of identification stains have been developed by the dye manufacturers and others in the textile field. Each of the stains has outstanding characteristics which make it better for the identification of certain fibers than for others. Samples of the outstanding stains available were obtained and applied to the newer synthetics and a few of the well-established standard fibers.

Table 4 lists the various fibers and the colors which were obtained when the stains were applied by the recommended procedure. The color names were derived by comparing the stained samples with the Munsell color system and then changing these evaluations into the ISCC-NBS (Intersociety Color Council—National Bureau Standards) color names.

These stains were applied to the fibers as they were received from the manufacturer without any scouring or pretreatment in order to show the color reactions of the various stains on the fibers as marketed. In using these identification stain tests, it is always advisable to make a comparison with a fiber whose history is known if a more positive identification is desired. When the fibers have been blended before they are spun into the threads, it is, of course, necessary to separate the threads after staining and identify the color of the single filaments by use of a magnifier or microscope.

A more complete description of each of the identification stains is as follows:

The Interchemical Corporation Identification Stain is a product of Interchemical Corporation, Hawthorne, N. J. This stain is said to contain a mixture of:

WITH IDENTIFICATION STAINS

Identification Stain ODDA	National Aniline Stain C-63807	Texchrome Identification Stain	Testfabrics Identification Stain	Interchemical Identification Stain	Du Pont Identification Stain No. 4
Dark grayish reddish brown	Dark grayish green	Dark greenish blue	Purplish black	Blackish green	Black
Grayish red	Grayish yellow brown	Pale green	Light brown	Pale yellowish green	Light brown
Moderate pink and light grayish brown	Dark grayish yellow	Pale yellow green	Moderate reddish orange	Moderate green	Grayish reddish orange
Grayish green	Light olive	Pale green	Strong yellowish brown	Moderate yellowish green	Light brown and moderate orange
Grayish yellowish pink	Grayish yellow green	Pale blue	Grayish yellow	Strong yellow green and pale green	Moderate orange
Dark reddish grayish brown	Deep red	Strong yellow green	Deep red	Dark greenish yellow	Deep red
Light bluish green	Vivid yellow	Moderate yellow green	Vivid yellow	Vivid yellow	Strong orange
Grayish purplish red	Dark blue	Very pale blue	Blackish blue	Moderate red	Dark greenish blue
Grayish purplish red	Dark grayish green	Pale blue	Dark grayish olive green	Grayish red	Grayish green
Grayish olive with traces of dark purplish gray	Dark purplish red	Dark yellow	Dark red	Dark grayish green	Dark grayish purple
Dark grayish reddish brown	Very dark purple	Moderate yellow brown	Dark reddish purple	Blackish green	Blackish purple
Light grayish reddish brown	Dark red	Strong yellow green	Deep red	Dark green	Dark reddish orange
Moderate yellowish pink	Grayish blue	Dark greenish blue	Grayish green	Light greenish blue	Moderate yellow brown
Grayish yellowish pink	Yellowish gray	Very light bluish green	Yellowish gray	Pale blue	Brownish pink
Grayish purplish pink	Light greenish yellow	Very pale blue	Orangish green yellow	Light yellowish green	Moderate orange yellow
Dark grayish purple	Dark reddish orange	Light yellow green	Deep red	Light olive	Deep red
Very pale green	Vivid yellow	Brilliant yellow green	Vivid yellow	Vivid greenish yellow	Strong orange
Moderate purplish red	Blackish blue	Very pale purple	Blackish blue	Moderate red	Dark blue

Fibrotint GLS is a product of Ciba Company, Inc., 627 Greenwich Street, New York 14, N. Y. The undyed fibers are boiled for 3 min in a 1 per cent solution of Fibrotint GLS, rinsed well, and dried.

Identification Stains GDC and ODDA are products of General Dyestuff Corporation, 435 Hudson Street, New York 14, N. Y. The undyed fibers are boiled for 3 min in a 1 per cent solution of either stain, rinsed well, and dried. These stains should have been applied with 1 per cent acetic acid. This was not done in the experiments which are recorded in Table 4.

National Aniline Identification Stain C-63807 is a product of the National Aniline Division, Allied Chemical & Dye Corporation, 40 Rector Street, New York 6, N. Y. The undyed fibers are boiled for 3 min in a solution containing 10 ml of the prepared stain in 50 ml of water, rinsed well, and dried.

MICROSCOPICAL IDENTIFICATION

Fibers can be identified under the microscope in longitudinal view and in cross-section. Longitudinal examination is often adequate, particularly if the fibers have been treated with an identification stain and the microscope is being used to pick out the various fibers. Longitudinal examination is also very useful in identifying those fibers which have a surface structure like wool and mohair, which have scales on their surface. Mohair can be distinguished from wool by the fact that it is more circular in cross-section and has a more glossy appearance. The glossiness comes from the fact that the scales are closer together on mohair than on wool. In the case of mohair there are 5 to 6 scales per 100 μ (W. von Bergen, private communication). Here the longitudinal examination is very useful in the identification.

Cross-sectioning technique often provides a more positive method of identification than longitudinal examination, since it gives a more representative view of many fibers which are under examination. A technique for cross-sectioning which has been found to be quite useful is the so-called Hardy method. This has been described and illustrated in other publications [*J. Soc. Dyers Colourists,* **63,** 287 (1947); *Textile Research J.,* **17,** 144 (1947); *Anal. Chem.,* **21,** 442 (1949)]. Since the development of the Calco Hardy type microtome, Dr. J. I. Hardy has developed a similar but simpler type microtome (manufactured by A. M. de LaRue, 3406 Longfellow Street, Hyattsville, Md.).

When preparing cross-sections by the Hardy technique, slips are obtained as the section is cut. Normally these are mounted directly in a mounting medium on a microscope slide. If dyes or stains are to

Fig. 3. Photograph showing the staining at the "slip" stage of cross-sectioning.

be applied, however, we have found it possible to do so at this point; see Fig. 3. If the slips are put into the stain or reagent bath the ends of the fibers are available for reaction. After this they can be washed, dried, and mounted in the usual manner. This technique can be used with the identification stains for the identification of textile fibers and has been used extensively to identify and determine the location of various textile agents and resins.

One of the difficulties in the staining of the newer hydrophobic synthetic fibers is that diffusion of dye into the fibers is very slow. If the staining is made from the end of the fiber by the slip technique described above, the dye solution penetrates unobstructed and more

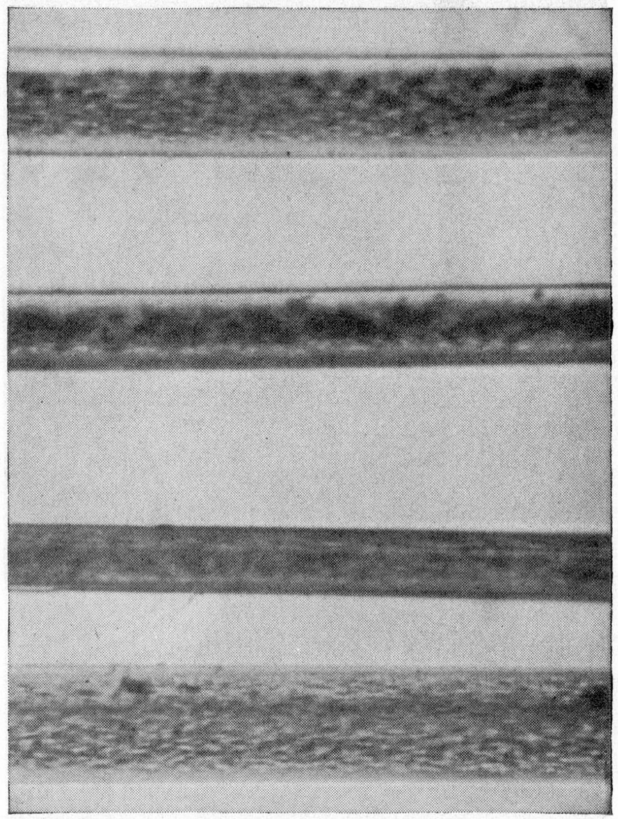

FIG. 4. Longitudinal view of Orlon acrylic fiber.

rapidly to the center of the fiber and the identification is more positive. Care does have to be taken to avoid submitting these slips to too high a temperature, since they are rather fragile. In applying the dye stain test, therefore, the bath is kept at a low temperature and not agitated except for occasional stirring.

In order to show the advantage of cross-sectional examination for identification, let us first look at two of the newer synthetics, Orlon and Dynel. If these are examined in longitudinal view, it is almost impossible to distinguish one from the other by their physical structure without very careful microscopical examination; see Figs. 4 and 5. In cross-section, however, they are readily discernible; see Figs. 6 and 7. In general, Orlon fibers appear as dumbbell-shaped fibers. More recently clover-leaf types have been observed and also some having the appearance of a boomerang. Apparently these come from

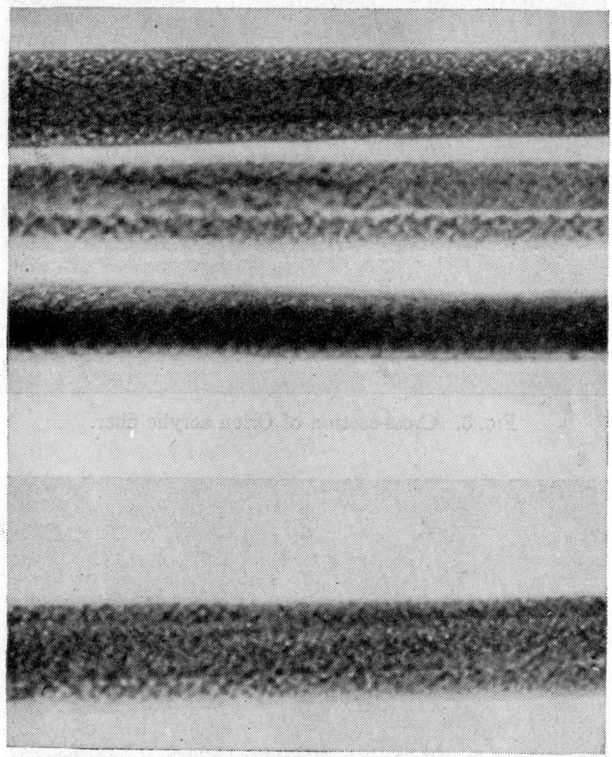

FIG. 5. Longitudinal view of Dynel.

modifications due to variations in the manufacture. The Dynel fiber is quite different. It is thin in one direction and much thicker in the other, and, therefore, it appears somewhat like a ribbon which is twisted and bent.

The X-51 fiber, being round in cross-section, is quite different from the other newer synthetics. However, there may be some difficulty distinguishing it from wool and other textile fibers which are round in shape. Solubility, dye stain, and index of refraction tests could be used for positive identification if it is only a question of the identification of the X-51 from many of the other round fibers. Of course, longitudinal views would show it to be quite different from wool since wool has scales and X-51 does not. See Fig. 8.

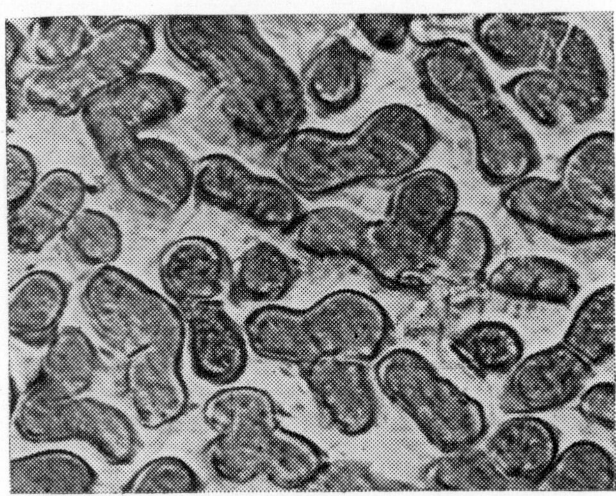

Fig. 6. Cross-section of Orlon acrylic fiber.

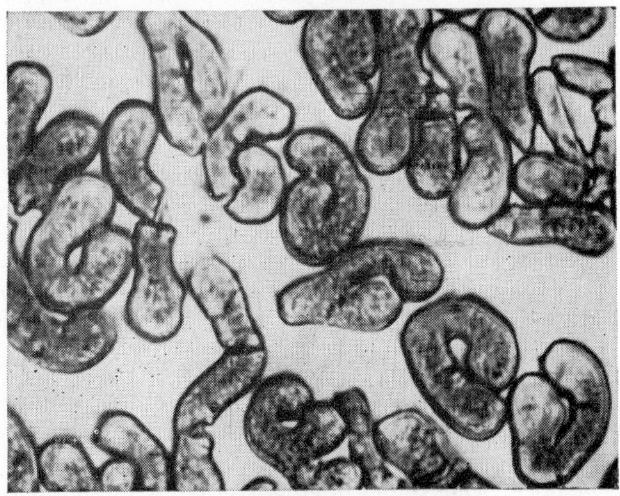

Fig. 7. Cross-section of Dynel.

Acrilan has a different appearance in cross-section (see Fig. 9) since it is a kidney-shaped fiber. Although cotton is somewhat similar in form, there would be no difficulty in telling the two apart because of the differences in size and the uniformity of the cross-section of the Acrilan.

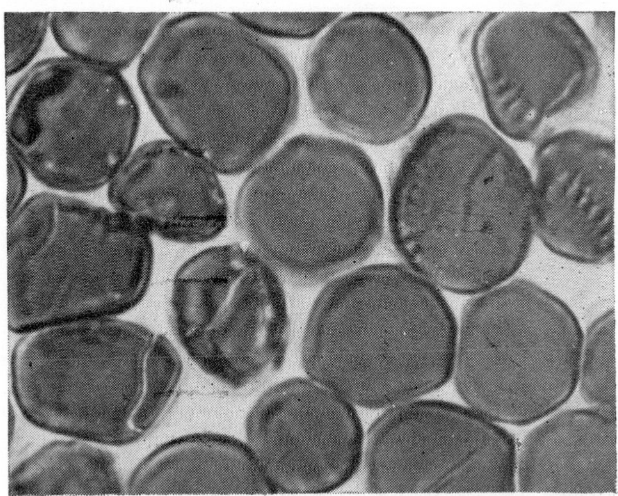

FIG. 8. Cross-section of X-51 acrylic fiber.

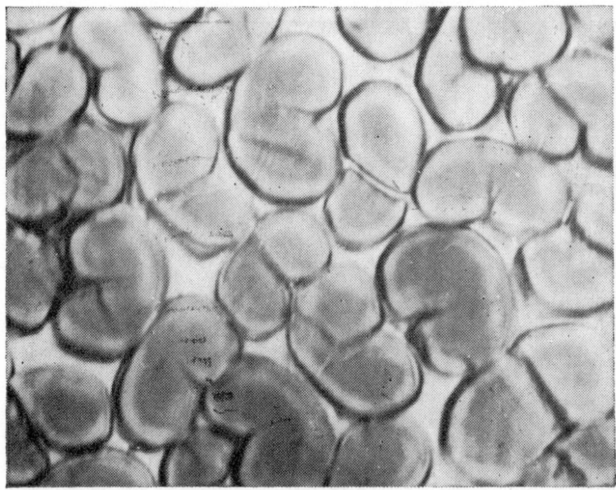

FIG. 9. Cross-section of Acrilan acrylic fiber.

Nylon is another textile fiber of round cross-section; see Fig. 10. It is more regular in size and shape than some of the newer synthetics but, here again, additional tests would have to be applied in order to distinguish it from the other round textile fibers.

Dacron (see Fig. 11) and Vicara [2] (see Fig. 12) are also round in cross-section. A combination of stain tests and cross-sectioning, how-

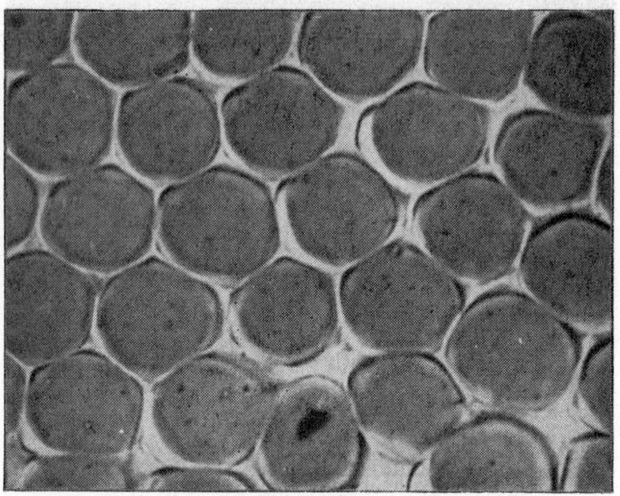

FIG. 10. Cross-section of nylon.

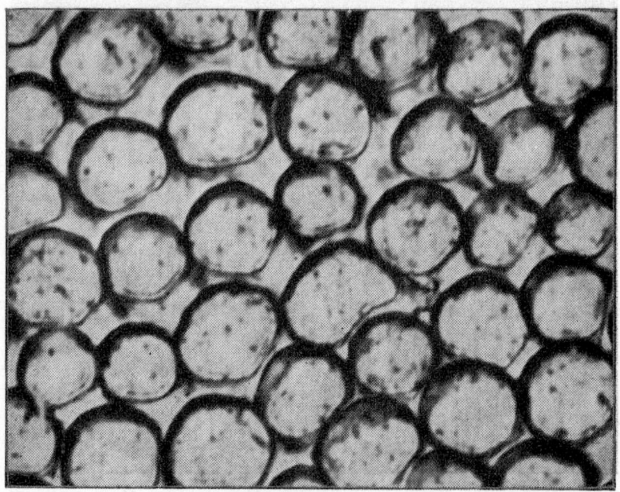

FIG. 11. Cross-section of Dacron polyester fiber.

ever, would quickly distinguish these from the others. Vicara stains readily with most identification stains and, of course, takes on the

[2] Trade mark of the manufacturer.

distinctive protein fiber color, which is quite different from that of the acrylic fibers. Dacron also can be identified with a stain test and, as

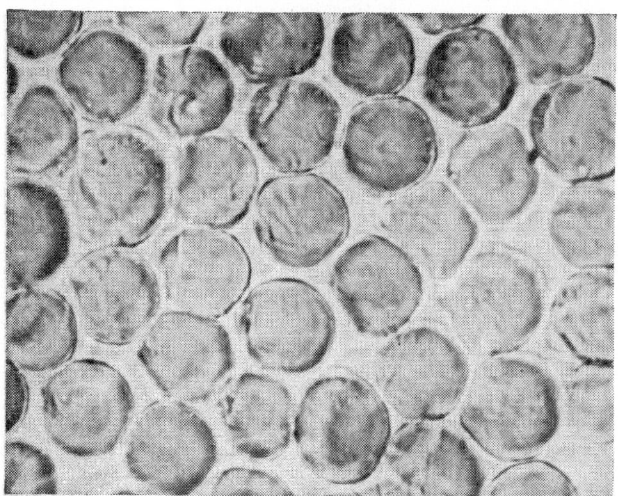

FIG. 12. Cross-section of Vicara.

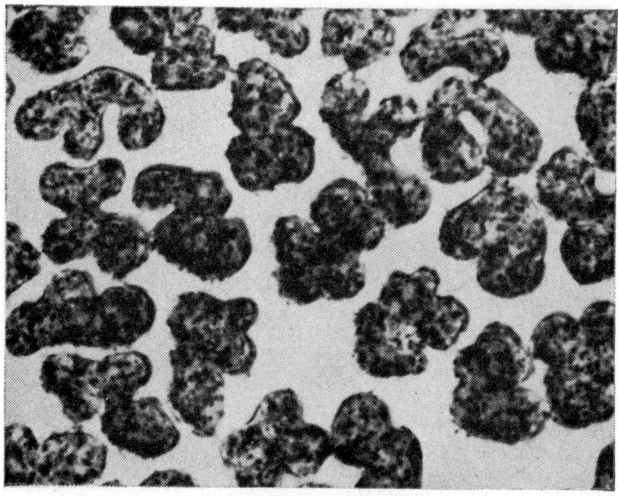

FIG. 13. Cross-section of cellulose acetate.

indicated by Mr. Wilson (*A.A.T.T. J.*, p. 29, Dec. 1952) by solubility tests.

Cellulose acetate (see Fig. 13) in cross-section might be confused with viscose rayon (see Fig. 14), but, because of its solubility in acetone, may be differentiated. In cross-section viscose rayon is quite characteristic because of its irregular shape or form. F. F. Morehead

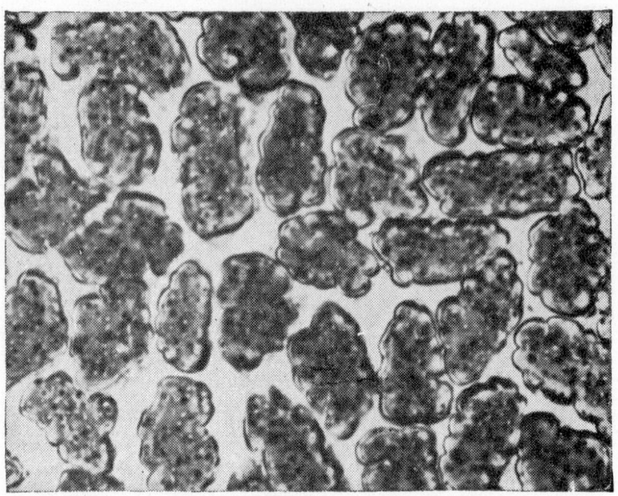

Fig. 14. Cross-section of visccse rayon.

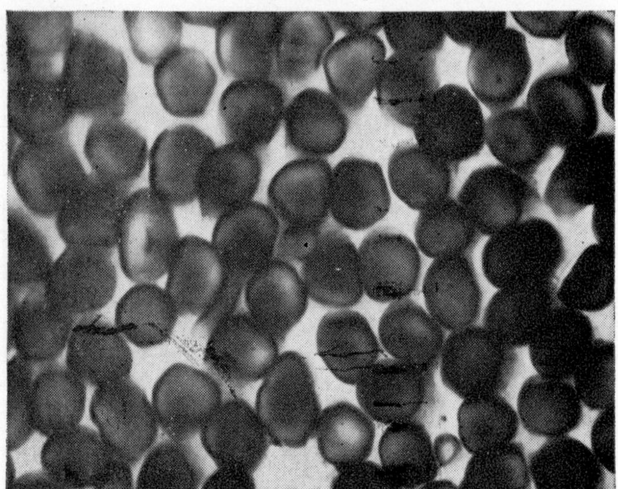

Fig. 15. Cross-section of Bemberg rayon.

of the American Viscose Company has stated (private communication) that in the early days of viscose manufacture various viscose fibers from different manufacturers were identifiable because their shapes were so characteristic. Today, however, this is no longer true, since many of the viscose rayons appear much alike in cross-section. Refractive index is useful in distinguishing differences in viscose rayons caused by variations in manufacturing procedure.

Bemberg[3] rayon is another regenerated cellulose; see Fig. 15. Until recently, it was one of the finest denier rayons and it could be identified because of its small diameter. This is no longer true, since most of the brands of rayons now appear in fine 1-denier sizes. The Bemberg fiber is a more circular fiber and in general is smaller in diameter than the average viscose rayons which are on the market.

Description is not given of the natural fibers nor of some of the synthetics which have little commercial importance at this time. The publications referred to earlier in this section have shown cross-sections of these and many of them, of course, are quite characteristic both in cross and longitudinal view, so that the microscope is the only tool needed to identify them. Cross-sectional as well as longitudinal examination can be used to detect pigments or oils that have been added for dulling or delustering of the synthetic fibers.

QUANTITATIVE FIBER ANALYSIS

After the fibers present in a textile product have been properly identified, another important step in the evaluation of such products is the quantitative determination of fibers present. In fact, the identification of the fibers present in a blend is only the preliminary step in quantitative analysis, especially in blends of the more common fibers, such as wool and cotton or cotton and rayon. The Wool Products Labeling Act [24] of 1939, the Federal Trade Commission Trade Practice Rules for the linen [25], rayon [26], and silk [27] industries, as well as other branches of the textile industry, strongly emphasize the necessity for correct disclosure of fibers in textile products. The Wool Products Labeling Act, for instance, states under Section 4 (*a*):

> A wool product shall be misbranded . . . (3) In the case of a wool product containing a fiber other than wool, if the percentages by weight of the wool contents thereof are not shown in words and figures plainly legible.

The Trade Practice Rules for the rayon industry further elaborate on this subject under Group II, Rule A—Disclosure of Proportions of Mixed Fibers:

> The practice of making full and accurate disclosure of the proportions or percentages of constituents in such mixed goods is approved as a proper prac-

[3] Trade mark of the manufacturer.

tice to the end that salespersons, dealers and other marketers of such products may have accurate information of the contents and may in turn correctly inform the purchasing and consuming public thereof, thereby avoiding confusion, misunderstanding or misrepresentation as to the content of such products . . .

That further differentiation and quantitative determination of fibers within a limited fiber group is of definite value can best be illustrated with the specialty hair fibers. While all of these fibers can be called wool according to the rules of the Wool Products Labeling Act, the disclosure and exploitation for advertising purpose of the various specialty hairs present in a blend is of definite advantage to the seller of such merchandise.

The Rules and Regulations under the Wool Act as promulgated by the Federal Trade Commission [28] comment as follows on the disclosure of specialty hairs:

Rule 18—Use of Name of Specialty Hair Fiber. In setting forth the required fiber content of a product containing any of the specialty fibers named in 2 (*b*) of the Act, the name of the specialty fiber present may be used in lieu of the word "wool," *provided* the percentage of each specialty fiber is given *and provided further* that the name of each specialty fiber so used is qualified by the word "reprocessed" or "reused" when the fiber referred to is "reprocessed wool" or "reused wool" as defined by the Act.

METHODS OF QUANTITATIVE ANALYSIS

The methods used for quantitative analysis, like those used for fiber identification, can be grouped into *three* classes, namely:

Physical fiber separation.
Chemical separation.
Microscopic determination.

Skinkle [29] suggests another class—the proximate analysis for quantitative fiber determination. Examples of this type of analysis given are:

a. Determination of specific gravity of a mixture and calculation from it of the composition.
b. Determination of the fluidity of a mixture of cotton and viscose rayon and calculating the percentages from the obtained fluidity.
c. Determination of the nitrogen content of a mixture of animal and vegetable fibers and calculation of the composition.

d. Determination of the P_2O_5 (phosphorus pentoxide) content of a mixture of wool and casein fiber and calculation of the composition.

It is pointed out that such proximate analyses tend to be inaccurate. The methods of quantitative analysis used for a specific sample are dependent upon what fibers are present, their respective chemical compositions, as well as the final result desired. *For instance,* a sample may contain wool, rayon, and cotton but only the wool content may be desired. Most of the chemical and microscopic methods used at present for percentage determination of the more common fibers are standard methods published by the National Bureau of Standards, *Commercial Standard CS 65–43,* in the Yearbook of Textile Standards of the American Society for Testing Materials, and the Yearbook of the American Association of Textile Chemists and Colorists. There are other methods, not as yet accepted as standards by trade associations, available for the chemical separation of such common fibers as wool, cotton, silk, newer synthetic fibers, and rayon; and the use of one of these methods over the others, performing similar duties, is at times purely a matter of convenience or personal preference. Most of the published methods of physical, chemical, or microscopic fiber separation are of sufficient accuracy that little or no correction of the results is needed.

Preparation of Fibers

The first step in the preparation of fibers for quantitative analysis is the proper identification of the fibers in order to determine what type of separation and what specific tests are best suited. Once this is decided, further preparation of the fibers, yarn, or fabric has to be made. The most important step is the complete removal of foreign matter from the sample, especially if chemical methods of separation have to be employed. For microscopic quantitative analysis, the removal of foreign matter is not necessary except in cases where such matter interferes with the proper identification and fiber fineness determination.

Similar to methods for quantitative analysis, many of the methods for the removal of finishing materials are standardized and can be found in the yearbooks of various textile associations. While these methods are, primarily, for the quantitative determination of the finishing materials present, it is advisable to follow them. In this manner complete removal of foreign or applied matter is insured. Unless a quantitative determination of such finishing materials is desired, it is not necessary to oven-dry and weigh the sample before removing such matter. The oven-dry weight of the clean fiber, yarn, or fabric sample has to be determined, however, before a chemical fiber separation is made.

The following procedure is taken from Tentative Methods of Quantitative Analysis of Textiles. Total sizing, finishing, and other nonfibrous materials.[4]

5. (*a*) Nature of Test. This procedure is intended for removing all nonfibrous natural constituents of the fiber and substances added by the manufacturer. Starch, china clay, soaps, some waxes, some nondrying oils, and the usual natural constituents are in this category and are removed by the procedure described. However, general directions for the removal of all possible substances which may be present cannot be included. The delustered rayons and some of the newer finishes present special problems. The analyst will have to meet special cases as they arise. When it is necessary to modify the procedure in order to completely remove nonfibrous constituents, the analyst shall make sure that purified samples of the fibers under consideration do not lose weight when subjected to the same treatment. Ordinarily, samples shall be analyzed in accordance with Paragraphs (*b*) to (*e*).

(*b*) Test Specimen. A specimen of approximately 5 g shall be tested. Particular care shall be taken to prevent the loss of fibers in the treatments. The specimen shall be dried at 105° to 110° C. to constant weight [Section 4(*c*)] to obtain the oven-dry weight of the original specimen, weight *B*.

(*c*) Procedure. Extract the dried specimen for 2 hr with carbon tetrachloride in a Soxhlet or similar extractor, syphoning over a minimum of six times. Dry specimen in the air, and wash by repeated immersion in hot distilled water, squeezing between each immersion. Immerse the specimen in an aqueous solution of a starch and protein-solubilizing enzyme preparation (3 to 5 per cent) at 50° to 60° C. or the optimum temperature range for the particular enzyme used. Squeeze the specimen while immersed, remove, and squeeze again, and repeat this treatment at least three times to insure thorough wetting of the fibers by the enzyme solution. Keep the specimen immersed for 1 hr in the enzyme solution, maintaining it at the optimum temperature range. A shorter time is permissible, if sizing is removed in a shorter time; 15 min is sufficient for some textiles. Then immerse the specimen for two 30-min periods in boiling distilled water baths, rinsing after each bath. Thorough rinsing is necessary in order to remove china clay from heavily filled fabrics. Dry the rinsed specimen at 105° to 110° C. to constant weight to obtain the oven-dry weight of clean fiber, weight *C*.

(*d*) For testing materials containing a synthetic resin finish, immerse a specimen for 10 min in gently boiling 0.1*N* HNO_3, using 200 ml of HNO_3 to 1 g of specimen. Rinse the specimen until free from acid, and dry at 105° to 110° C. to constant weight to obtain the oven-dry weight of clean fiber, weight *C*.

[4] (A.S.T.M. Designation: D629-46T.) "A.S.T.M. Standards on Textile Materials," pp. 92–93 (1950).

(*e*) Calculation. Calculate the total amount of nonfibrous constituents present from Eq. 3 to Eq. 12, Section 13, depending upon the bases on which the composition is to be expressed.

Equation 3: Nonfibrous materials per cent $= \frac{B - C}{B} \times 100$

where B = oven-dry weight of the specimen as received [Section 4(*c*)]
C = oven-dry weight of the clean fiber [Section 5(*c*)]

The following procedure is taken from Methods of Fiber Identification and Quantitative Separation. Quantitative analysis.[5]

1. *Moisture*

A sample of the material to be tested is oven dried at 105° to 110° C. for 1 to 1½ hr or until it reaches a constant weight (± 0.003 gram).

$$\text{Moisture} = \% \frac{A - B}{A} \times 100$$

where A = original weight of the sample,
B = dry weight of the sample.

2. *Total Sizing, Finishing and Other Nonfibrous Materials*

(*a*) Extract the oven-dried sample for 2 hr with carbon tetrachloride in a Soxhlet extractor, air-dry, then boil in distilled water 10 min and rinse thoroughly in hot distilled water.

(*b*) Immerse in a 3 to 5 per cent aqueous solution of a starch and protein-solubilizing enzyme preparation at 122° F. (50° C.) for 1 hr. Work frequently during immersion to insure thorough wetting of the sample. Remove and rinse 12 times in fresh portions of hot distilled water, then dry to constant weight.

If any of the newer resinous types of finishes are present special procedures must be worked out for the removal of the particular type present. This also applies to some of the waterproofing compounds.

$$\text{Per cent total sizing, etc.} = \frac{B - C}{B} \times 100$$

where B = dry weight of sample,
C = dry weight of cleaned fiber.

Physical Methods of Fiber Separation

Mechanical Separation by Raveling or Sorting. If a microscopic examination shows that different fibers are segregated in separate yarns in the sample, such as a rayon warp and a cotton filling, the yarns can be separated and sorted into groups each containing one fiber only. The various groups are then oven dried and weighed individually to give the percentages of the various components. In the case of felted

[5] 1942 Yearbook of the A.A.T.C.C., p. 277.

fabrics where it would be difficult to make a clean separation in this manner, other means of quantitative analysis should be employed.

A similar separation can be made of coarse fibers used in ropes whose identification is possible without the microscope. Mixtures of sisal and abacá have been successfully separated quantitatively by using the Swett test as means of identification. In the same manner quantitative determination of coarse vegetable fibers and animal bristles, as found in paint brushes, can be made.

Mechanical Separation by Flotation. The difference in specific gravity between wool and Lanital (Italian casein fiber) has been suggested by Larose [30] as a means for quantitative analysis. This method, a tentative standard in the A.S.T.M. Yearbook of 1950, consists of immersing the clean yarns, cut into small sections (1 mm), in a cylindrical vessel containing a separating liquid of a specific gravity of 1.310 at room temperature. The yarn sections are shaken up to separate the individual fibers, and, after standing, the fibers having a higher specific gravity (wool) will sink to the bottom of the vessel while those of a lower gravity (casein fibers) will remain floating on the surface of the liquid. The floating fibers and the sunken fibers are recovered separately, dried, and weighed and the percentage is calculated.

This method has been used with varying degrees of success on blends of wool and the American casein fiber. Microscopic methods, given below, are usually more satisfactory for such blends.

Preston and Nimkar [31] suggest the use of density-gradient tubes as a means of quantitative separation of natural as well as newer synthetic fibers.

Chemical Methods of Fiber Separation

The various methods to be discussed have either been adopted as standards by the United States Government or by technical associations or have been published in the technical journals and were found to be satisfactory. Wherever the chemicals used require special preparation, this is given along with the method. In order to follow some logical procedure, certain fiber blends are assumed. It is understood that in all cases the fibers are clean and that the oven-dry weight has been determined.

Schaeffer [32] suggests that, as fibers are blended by weight while containing the natural amount of moisture, the moisture factor should be included in any calculations of chemical separation. Thus, if a

50:50 blend of cotton and wool is determined quantitatively by removing the wool, the oven-dry weight of the cotton residue is approximately 52.6 per cent of the total oven-dry fabric weight.

Fiber Blend	Weight, Moist (grams)	Proportion (per cent)	Moisture Content (per cent)	Weight, Oven-Dry (grams)	Proportion (per cent)
Cotton	100	50	9	91	52.6
Wool	100	50	18	82	47.4
Totals	200			173	

It is suggested that, instead of weighing the clean fabric oven dry, the fabric should be conditioned at standard conditions of 70° F. and 65 per cent relative humidity and only the residue of chemical separation be weighed oven dry. The regain factor of the residue is multiplied by the oven-dry weight of the residue to give the correct proportion by weight of the fibers containing normal moisture.

Conditioned sample containing wool and cotton = 200 grams
Oven-dry residue (cotton) after chemical separation = 91 grams
Correction factor: cotton regain = 8.5 per cent

$$91 \times 1.085 = 100 \text{ grams}$$

$$\frac{100}{200} = 50 \text{ per cent cotton}$$

Howlett, Morley, and Urquhart [33] give the approximate moisture regain of the major fibers for convenience of expressing results of chemical separation on the "air-dry" basis. Table 5 is taken in part from this work.

TABLE 5. Approximate Regains of the Principal Fibers

Fibers	*Per Cent Regain*	*Fibers*	*Per Cent Regain*
Acetate (Estron)	6	Linen, bleached	7
Asbestos	1	Nylon	4
Casein fiber	13	Orlon	1
Cotton, mercerized	8	Silk, degummed	10
Cotton, scoured	6	Silk, Tussah	11
Cuprammonium rayon	11	Vicara	10
Dacron	0.4	Vinyon	0
Dynel	0.5	Viscose rayon	11
		Wool, scoured	14

The methods given on the following pages for the chemical separation of fibers are in most cases taken, with some omissions or slight changes, from accepted standards or other published methods. The changes or omissions in the text were made without changing the meaning or accuracy of the method. In cases where there are several known and tried methods performing similar duties, only the better-known methods (standard methods) are given in detail.

Although certain methods for quantitative separation of natural fiber in mixture with newer synthetic fibers have been suggested by various authors, no standard methods have been accepted.

I. Microscopic examination shows the sample contains:

Acetate (Estron)

a. Mixed with wool, silk, cotton, regenerated cellulose rayon, and synthetic fibers.

Method 1. Acetone Method.[6]

This procedure is applicable only to acetone-soluble types of acetate [Note 2]. Take the clean fiber residue obtained and agitate it vigorously for 15 min in about 50 times its weight of acetone at room temperature [Note 3]. Rinse the residue by alternate squeezing and immersing in acetone, using two fresh portions of acetone. Allow the residue to dry and immerse in water at about 70° C. Remove the excess water by squeezing, and dry the residue at 105° to 110° C. to constant weight, weight D.

Note 2. A few types of acetate are not completely soluble in acetone but are soluble in glacial acetic acid. The analyst can readily vary the method for such material and use glacial acetic acid as the solvent at this point.

Note 3. A Launder-Ometer can be used to obtain satisfactory agitation.

(*b*) Calculation. Calculate the acetate content from Eq. 4 . . .

Equation 4: $$\text{Acetate per cent} = \frac{C - D}{B} \times 100$$

where B = oven-dry weight of the specimen as received,
C = oven-dry weight of the clean fiber residue,
D = oven-dry weight of fiber residue (acetone method).

If the mixture contains Vinyon and Dynel along with acetate, these fibers will also be dissolved by the acetone method.

[6] A.S.T.M. Standards on Textile Materials, 1950, p. 93.

Method 2. Glacial Acetic Acid Method.[7] The sample is immersed in 50 times its weight in boiling glacial acetic acid and left to boil for 20 min. It is then filtered through a Gooch filter or a 100-mesh screen, washed in succession with fresh glacial acetic acid, water, dilute ammonia, and again with water. This treatment dissolves all acetate but affects other fibers, and correction factors for their loss have to be included in calculating the percentages.

Loss of Fibers in Glacial Acetic Acid Method, Per Cent

Wool, other hair fibers	1.5
Silk	5.0
Viscose rayon	3.0
Cotton	2.0

b. Mixed with Vinyon.

While it is unlikely that both acetate and Vinyon are blended together, the following method suggested by Howlett, Morley, and Urquhart[8] will dissolve acetate and viscose rayons, nylon, bleached tussah and cultivated silks and *will not attack* wool, casein fibers (Aralac), cotton, or Vinyon.

Method 3. 60 Per Cent Sulfuric Acid Method. Weigh about 0.25 gram of the sample and transfer to a conical flask (Erlenmeyer flask). Add about 20 ml of 60 per cent sulfuric acid to the flask, shake vigorously and leave for ½ hr at room temperature. Shake again and leave for another ½ hr. Shake for a third time and transfer to a weighed, fritted glass filter crucible. With a little more 60 per cent sulfuric acid, wash residue into crucible and drain crucible by applying suction.

Wash residue with about 10 ml of dilute sulfuric acid (100 ml of concentrated H_2SO_4 added to 1900 ml of distilled water), remove excess by suction; wash with about 10 ml of water, let stand for ½ hr, remove excess by suction; wash with about 10 ml of dilute ammonia (80 ml of concentrated ammonia added to 920 ml of water), let stand for 10 min, remove excess by suction, and again wash with 30 ml of water and let stand for ½ hr before removing the excess with suction.

After the final washing, dry the crucible with residue for at least 3 hr, at 110° C., cool in a desiccator, and weigh. This method dissolves the acetate but does *not* attack Vinyon, Vicara, Dacron, Orlon, or Dynel.

[7] A.A.T.C.C. Yearbook, 1942, p. 277.

[8] *J. Textile Inst.*, **33,** T87, 1942.

II. The microscopic examination shows the sample contains:

Wool and Other Hair Fibers

a. Mixed with natural vegetable fibers, acetate or regenerated cellulose rayon, silk or bleached tussah silk.

Method 4. 70 Per Cent Sulfuric Acid Method.[9] This method destroys all fibers but wool and other hair fibers. About 2 grams of the sample is immersed in 100 times its weight of boiling 1 per cent sulfuric acid for 7 to 10 min. Transfer to a Büchner or Hirsch funnel and remove the excess acid solution by suction. Allow the specimen to cool; then, if it is in the form of a fabric or tightly twisted yarn, hold over a 400-ml beaker and carefully cut into strips or shreds approximately ⅛ in. by 1 in. Add about 100 times its weight of 70 per cent sulfuric acid (70 grams of concentrated H_2SO_4 in 100 ml of solution) at 38° C. and allow to stand for 15 min, stirring the solution frequently. At the end of 15 min pour the acid solution and fibers cautiously, but quickly, into 600 ml of cold water in a 1-liter beaker. Rinse the 400-ml beaker with two 50-ml portions of cold water and add the washings to the 1-liter beaker. Filter the fibers from the solution by suction, using a tared fritted glass-bottomed filtering crucible. Rinse the residue with several portions of cold water, using suction; then with 200 ml of a cold 2 per cent solution of $NaHCO_3$, reduce the rate of filtering by reducing the suction to allow the alkaline solution to come in contact with the fibers for 5 min. Again rinse with several portions of cold water, removing excess water by suction. Dry residue to constant weight at 105° to 110° C.

The following notes are added to this method in the A.S.T.M. Standards on Textile Materials, 1950, page 96.

Note 7. Investigation had disclosed that when *reprocessed* or *reused* wool, as defined in the Wool Products Labeling Act of 1939, is present in the textile, the amount of wool determined by the sulfuric acid method may be lower than the actual amount present by as much as 4 per cent of the amount of *reprocessed* or *reused* wool present. The effect of the acid treatment appears to depend on the previous history of the wool fibers and is too uncertain to apply a correction factor. In the case of normal wool no correction factor is required.

Note 8. A 1 per cent sulfuric acid solution by weight (1 gram of H_2SO_4 in 100 grams of solution) may be prepared by adding 5.9 ml of H_2SO_4 (93 per cent) to 990 ml of water.

Note 9. Experience has shown that it is not necessary to shred the sample for the first treatment. Shredding the sample while still wet prevents any loss of

[9] Based on method of A.A.T.C.C. Yearbook, 1942, p. 278, and A.S.T.M. Standard on Textile Materials, 1950, p. 95.

fiber and prepares the sample so that it insures complete removal of the cellulosic materials by the 70 per cent acid.

Note 10. The successful use of the sulfuric acid method depends on using an accurately prepared 70 per cent acid solution (70 grams of H_2SO_4 in 100 grams of solution). This solution may be prepared from laboratory reagent H_2SO_4 (sp. gr. 1.84) or from commercial H_2SO_4 (55° Bé) which is obtainable from chemical supply houses in carboys at a very reasonable price. The acid used in preparing the 70 per cent solution should be titrated to insure making a solution of the correct strength.

Note 11. A Gooch crucible, No. 100 (149 μ) sieve, or a Büchner funnel with a cotton fabric filtering disk may also be used to collect the wool fibers.

Note 12. If the atmospheric conditions are such that difficulty is experienced in obtaining the dry weight of the residue, the filtering crucible may be placed in a covered weighing bottle to prevent absorption of moisture.

Method 5. 75 Per Cent Sulfuric Acid Method, suggested by Howlett, Morley, and Urquhart.[10] This method is similar to Method 4. About 0.25 gram of the dried sample is treated in the same manner as in Method 3 (separation of acetate and Vinyon) except that a 75 per cent solution of sulfuric acid is used instead of a 70 per cent solution. This concentration is prepared by adding 1360 ml of concentrated sulfuric acid slowly to 700 ml of water. After the solution has cooled, water is added to give a specific gravity of about 1.67. This method dissolves all but wool and other hair fibers, casein fibers, and Vinyon.

b. Mixed with cotton and other vegetable fibers and regenerated cellulose rayon only.

Method 6. Aluminum Chloride Method [34]. The sample is immersed for 10 min in a boiling solution (100 times its weight) of aluminum chloride containing 5 grams of $AlCl_3$ (or 9 grams of hydrated salt $AlCl_3 \cdot 6H_2O$) per 100 ml of water. It shall be removed from the solution and after allowing the excess liquid to drain off without squeezing the sample, it is heated in an oven at 221° to 230° F. until all the cotton or other vegetable fibers have become brown and brittle. The specimen is then placed on a 100-mesh screen and rubbed against it until all the carbonized vegetable fibers have powdered and passed through the screen. The remaining residue on the screen (wool) is placed in a 250-ml beaker and the material passed through the screen is collected and passed through again to recover any small wool fibers. The residue in the beaker is agitated in about 100 ml of diluted hydrochloric acid (one part of concentrated hydrochloric acid to nine parts of water), collected on a 100-mesh screen, rinsed with water until free of chloride, and then dried.

[10] *J. Textile Inst.,* **33,** T83, 1942.

Comparison of the sulfuric acid carbonization method (Method 3) and the aluminum chloride method (Method 6) has been made by Schaeffer [32] and Weidenhammer, Prisley, and Ryberg [35].

Method 7. Boil-Out Method with Sodium Hydroxide.[11] If the wool content has been estimated in the microscopic examination as being over one-half of the total content, the boil-out method, destroying the wool, can be used.

Immerse the sample in 100 times its weight of a boiling 5 per cent solution of sodium hydroxide for 10 min. Keep the sample completely submerged in the boiling solution during this treatment. Filter off the liquid by passing through a filtering crucible or a 100-mesh sieve. Wash the residue, first with water, then with 5 per cent acetic acid, and again with water until the water is neutral to litmus. Dry the residue at 105° to 110° C.

As cotton and regenerated cellulose rayon is partially attacked, a correction factor of 3 per cent for cotton and of 5 per cent for regenerated cellulose rayon should be included in the calculations.

c. Mixed with cultivated silk.

Method 8. Conc. Hydrochloric Acid Method.[12]

Clean, oven dry, and weigh the sample (about 2 grams). Treat with 250 ml of concentrated hydrochloric acid at room temperature for 15 min. Filter through a Gooch filter or fritted glass filter. Wash with concentrated hydrochloric acid, wash with water, wash with dilute ammonia (100 ml concentrated reagent diluted to 1 liter), wash with water. Oven dry and weigh.

This method dissolved silk but not cotton or wool; rayons and acetates are partly dissolved, and no correction factor can be given.

Method 9. Calcium Thiocyanate (sp. gr. 1.20) Method.[13] Cut the clean sample into small yarn sections, of 1 to 4 mm lengths.

Agitate the fibers vigorously for 1 hr in 200 ml of a clear aqueous solution of calcium thiocyanate [Note 4] made just acid to litmus with acetic acid, and maintain at 70 ±2° C.; precautions must be taken to prevent evaporation from the solution with consequent concentration of the thiocyanate. Collect the undissolved fibers in a small Büchner funnel, Gooch crucible, or bitumen filter, preferably with the aid of suction. When a good pad of fibers has formed on the filter, pour the hot filtrate through the filter a second time to recover all fibers on the pad. Agitate the fibers for 5 min in a fresh 200-ml portion of the thiocyanate solution. Repeat the filtration and wash the fibers with hot distilled water until free from thiocyanate. Add a drop of diluted HCl (5 to 6 N) and 1 ml of ferric sulfate solution (15 per cent in 5 N H_2SO_4) to the filtrate. A reddish coloration indicates the presence of thiocyanate.

[11] Based on A.S.T.M. Standards on Textile Materials, 1950, p. 97.

[12] A.A.T.C.C. Tentative Test Method 20-47, 1951 *Yearbook,* p. 109.

[13] From A.S.T.M. Standards on Textile Materials, 1950, p. 94.

Dry and weigh the residue. This method, like Method 8, dissolves silk but not wool.

The preparation of the calcium thiocyanate is given in the A.S.T.M. Standards on Textile Materials, 1950, page 95, as follows:

Note 4. Calcium thiocyanate may be prepared from calcium oxide and ammonium thiocyanate by the following procedure: Dissolve 1 kg of ammonium thiocyanate in 2 liters of water and bring to a boil. Add calcium oxide to the boiling solution from time to time over a period of 3 or 4 hr until 250 grams have been added. Keep the solution boiling until ammonia has ceased coming off (test vapor with litmus). Add water to the solution from time to time in order to keep the volume fairly constant. After the reaction is complete, remove the excess lime by suction, filtering through asbestos. Evaporate the resultant clear solution of calcium thiocyanate to the desired strength.

III. The microscopic examination shows the sample contains:

Silk

a. Mixed with cotton.

Method 3. 60 Per Cent Sulfuric Acid Method.
Method 7. 5 Per Cent Sodium Hydroxide Method.
Method 9. Calcium Thiocyanate (sp. gr. 1.20) Method.

b. Mixed with cotton, bast fibers, cuprammonium and viscose rayon, wool, casein fibers, Vinyon.

Method 10. 8.9 N Hydrochloric Acid Method (suggested by Howlett, Morley, and Urquhart).[14] This method will dissolve silk and leave the other fibers intact. The method is similar to Method 3 (60 per cent Sulfuric Acid Method) except that 8.9 *N* hydrochloric acid is used instead of the 60 per cent sulfuric acid and dilute hydrochloric acid (200 ml of hydrochloric acid is added to 800 ml of water) instead of the dilute sulfuric acid is used for washing.

c. Mixed with wool.

Method 4. 70 Per Cent Sulfuric Acid Method.
Method 8. Concentrated Hydrochloric Acid Method.
Method 9. Calcium Thiocyanate (sp. gr. 1.20) Method.
Method 10. 8.9 N Hydrochloric Acid Method.

d. Mixed with nylon.

Method 11. Glacial Acetic Acid Method (suggested by Howlett, Morley, and Urquhart).[15] Weigh out about 0.25 gram of the sample

[14] *J. Textile Inst.,* **33,** T91, 1942.
[15] *J. Textile Inst.,* **33,** T92, 1942.

and transfer to a 50-ml conical flask (Erlenmeyer flask). Add about 20 ml of glacial acetic acid to the flask, and about three glass beads to facilitate boiling; loosely close the neck with a pear-shaped glass stopper (or weighted-down watch glass) and heat quickly with a Bunsen burner to boiling. Boil for 5 min and transfer to a weighed fritted-glass crucible, making sure that all the beads are retained in the flask. Wash out the flask with a little hot glacial acetic acid, pour this into the crucible, and drain by applying suction.

Wash the residue with (*a*) about 10 ml of dilute acetic acid, (*b*) about 10 ml of water, (*c*) about 10 ml of dilute ammonia solution, and (*d*) about 30 ml of water.

During the washing the residue is allowed to soak in the ammonia solution for 10 min and during the operation in water for about half an hour. After each separate washing the crucible should be drained by suction. After the final washing and draining, dry the crucible for at least 3 hr at 110° C. Cool in desiccator and weigh.

IV. The microscopic examination shows the sample contains:

Regenerated Cellulose Rayons Mixed with Cotton and/or Bleached Flax

Method 12. Calcium Thiocyanate (sp. gr. 1.36) Method.[16] This method is similar in procedure to Method 9 except that the acid solution of calcium thiocyanate shall have a specific gravity of 1.35 to 1.36 at 70° C.

Method 3. 60 Per Cent Sulfuric Acid Method. If a separation of regenerated cellulose and bleached flax is made by this method a correction factor of 12 per cent has to be made for the flax, as the fibers are slightly attacked.

V. The microscopic examination shows the sample contains:

Casein Fibers (Aralac)

a. Mixed with silk, vegetable fibers, rayon, and nylon, but not wool and other hair fibers.

Method 5. 75 Per Cent Sulfuric Acid.

b. Mixed with wool and other hair fibers.

DaSchio [36] recommends the use of an 18 per cent solution of sodium hydroxide for the separation of wool and Lanital, the Italian

[16] From the A.S.T.M. Standards on Textile Materials, 1950, p. 95.

casein fiber. Cappelli and Tuffi [37] suggest the use of sodium hydroxide and sodium sulfite for this separation, but as neither of the methods has given satisfactory results with Aralac the use of microscopic methods is recommended for the quantitative analysis of such fiber blends.

Wolf [38] suggests the use of sodium hypochlorite, 40 per cent sodium hydroxide, and formic acid as solvents for quantitative analyses for mixtures containing wool, nylon, Orlon, and Dacron.

Table 6 is a summary of the various methods described and their particular application.

TABLE 6. METHODS OF FIBER SEPARATION

	Wool	Viscose rayon	Vinyon	Tussah silk	Silk	Nylon	Flax bleached	Cuprammonium rayon	Cotton	Casein (Aralac)
Acetate	1, 2	1, 2	3	1, 2	1, 2	1	1, 2	1, 2	1, 2	1, 2
Casein (Aralac)	(*)	3, 5	1	3, 5	3, 5	11	5	5	5	
Cotton	4, 5, 6, 7, 12	3, 12	1	3, 7, 8	3, 7, 8	3, 11	(*)	3, 12		
Cupram. rayon	3, 4, 5, 6, 7	(*)	1	7	7, 9	11	3, 12			
Flax bl.	4, 5, 6, 7, 12	3, 12	1	3, 7, 8	3, 7, 8	3, 11				
Nylon	4, 5, 11	11	1, 5, 10	10, 11	11					
Silk	8, 9, 10	7, 9	1	10						
Tussah silk	5, 7, 8	7	1							
Vinyon	1	1								
Viscose	3, 4, 5, 6, 7									

Method 1. Acetone.
Method 2. Glacial acetic acid.
Method 3. 60 per cent sulfuric acid.
Method 4. 70 per cent sulfuric acid.
Method 5. 75 per cent sulfuric acid.
Method 6. Aluminum chloride.
Method 7. 5 per cent sodium hydroxide.
Method 8. Concentrated hydrochloric acid.
Method 9. Calcium thiocyanate (sp. gr. 1.20).
Method 10. 8.9N hydrochloric acid.
Method 11. Glacial acetic acid (new method).
Method 12 Calcium thiocyanate (sp. gr. 1.36).

* Microscopic methods recommended.

Microscopic Determination

The use of the microscope for quantitative fiber analysis was advocated by Vétillard [39] as early as 1876 as the only means of determining quantitatively fibers of like chemical composition.

The microscope methods described below all consist, briefly, of the identification of the fibers, the numerical count of each fiber, the determination of the average diameter of each fiber type present, and, finally, the conversion of the numerical percentages into percentages by weight.

Here, as in other quantitative methods, the accuracy depends to a great extent upon proper sampling of the specimen. Here especially a maximum of sample, limited only by the time factor of its analysis, is desired. As the microscopic methods depend largely upon the skill of the operator to count correctly and measure the diameter of the various components of the sample, errors due to incorrect identification and other personal factors can be much larger than those incurred with chemical methods. Basically, there are only *two* methods of microscopic quantitative analysis, namely, the longitudinal mount method and the cross-section mount method.

Longitudinal Mount Method 1. This method is used in most cases because of its simplicity as compared with other similar methods. The method can be used for any fiber blend where chemical separation is impossible. However, if any noticeable degree of irregularity of the mixture exists Longitudinal Mount Method 2 is preferable. Sampling, as in other methods, is important. In the A.S.T.M. Tentative Method D629-42T on quantitative analysis (A.S.T.M. Standards on Textile Materials, 1942, p. 34) the following procedure for sampling is suggested for the longitudinal mount method:

> Cut a 3/16-in. square from the fabric and separate the yarns. Mount all of the yarns in glycerol (about 2 yarns per slide) and carefully separate and parallel the individual fibers. Where there is a definite repetition in design, the sampling shall cover all the yarns in the complete pattern. If the yarn is in skein form, cut off specimens 3/16 in. in length, several feet apart, mount them in glycerol, and parallel the fibers.

If yarns of like nature are present in both directions of the fabric it is usually sufficient to cut small sections from two to three yarns taken from the warp and filling of the fabric.

The mounting of the fiber sections is accomplished in a manner similar to the longitudinal mounting of fibers for identification except that here the whole yarn section should be placed upon the slide. Should the yarn be too heavy to permit mounting the entire section on one slide, two or three slides can be used, but the results obtained from the combined slides should be computed. The yarn sections are best mounted in glycerol, which does *not swell* the fibers, so that subsequent measurements of the diameter can be made on the same slides. Even with acetate rayon, which shows slight swelling in glycerol, the measurements can be made on the slide, since the error due to the swelling is not sufficiently large to interfere with the accuracy of the final result. If other mounting media or staining media are used in the longitudinal mount method to bring out characteristics for identification, the fibers should not be measured in the same media.

After the yarn sections are mounted, the slide can be examined under the microscope. By starting on one side of the cover glass, the slide is moved slowly across the field of vision, counting each fiber type present. If only two fiber types are present on the slide, the one in apparent majority can be counted by using a hand- or foot-operated counter while the other fiber type can be carried in the head of the operator. If more than two fiber types are present two of the fibers can be counted on the first trip across and the other fibers can be counted by going over the same area of the slide the second time. A multiple counter is a time-saver for such fiber blends.

Depending upon the fibers present, the magnification to be used should be either ×200 or ×500. Magnifications less than ×200 are, for commonly used fiber blends of similar chemical composition, too low to show the differentiating characteristics sufficiently.

The number of total fibers counted should be at least 1000 fibers in each direction of the fabric, i.e., fabrics containing uniform blends. In irregular blends at least 2000 fibers are needed for fairly accurate quantitative analysis.

Longitudinal Mount Method 2. In fabrics where uniformity of blends is lacking within the comparatively small sample used in the longitudinal methods, it can be compensated by taking a larger sample and giving same a thorough mixing. The sampling and mounting in this method assure uniform mixtures on the slide and thus uniform results in the determination. The method, originally developed for the quantitative analysis of fibers in part-linen fabrics, can be used successfully for other mixtures except those containing hair fibers. Representative sampling and preparing of the slide, using the new method, is done according to Krauss [40] in the following manner:

Sampling. A swatch of the fabric, measuring at least 2 by 2 in. or, in the case of a yarn sample, at least 2 yd should be available.

A. Fabrics. Count the number of threads in both the warp and the filling direction. Pull out from each direction at random a number of yarns proportionate to the thread count. The combined number of yarns of warp and filling should total at least 20.

Example:

	Thread Count	Proportion	Yarns Removed
Warp	36	½	18
Filling	20	½	10
Totals			28

B. Yarns. Cut at least 20 yarn sections of 2 in. lengths each from the yarn at reasonable intervals or, if less than 2 yd of yarn is available, cut the entire length into sections. From each yarn or yarn section selected as above, cut small sections (approximately 1 mm) until an equal amount, about 1 in., of each yarn has been sectioned. These sections are best collected on paper of contrasting color or they can be cut directly into an Erlenmeyer flask of 250 ml capacity.

Mixing. After placing the cut fibers in the flask add about 75 to 100 ml of distilled water. Stopper the flask tightly and shake the contents until a uniform fiber suspension is evident. Quick boiling of the liquid or the addition of a few glass pellets greatly facilitates the separations of the individual fiber sections.

Preparation and Staining of the Slide. Take a clean glass slide and, with a wax pencil, mark two vertical lines about 1 in. apart near the center of the slide. Draw by means of a wide mouth pipette about 0.5 ml of the well-shaken suspension and place it within the confines of the two lines on the slide. Allow the water to evaporate slowly so that no bunching of the fibers occurs. The amount of liquid drawn from the flask is dependent on the density of the suspension. If the suspension is very dense, either less liquid is placed on the slide or more water is added to the flask. A little practice is required to place just sufficient liquid on the slide so that after evaporation a thin uniform film of fibers remains . . . After all moisture has evaporated from the slide, stain the fibers with a one solution stain—Herzberg stain—and cover with a 1 by 1 in. cover glass.

For the actual counting of the fibers in the mixture, a magnification of ×200 to ×250 is preferable. A cross-hair ocular is essential.

The slide is placed in the mechanical stage having horizontal and vertical graduations. Counting is begun either near the upper or lower corners of the cover glass. The slide is moved slowly across the field of vision and all fiber sections passing the center of the cross hairs are identified and counted. After each trip across, the slide is moved 1 to 2 mm vertically and another trip across the slide is started. This is repeated until the whole slide has been covered in this manner. The fibers are then counted by moving the slide slowly vertically and spacing each trip 1 to 2 mm horizontally. The spacing after each trip is dependent upon the amount of fiber sections present on the slide. The combined horizontal and vertical counts should total at least 1000 fibers. Though some fibers are counted twice in the above manner, there are many instances where the sections lie parallel to the direction of one counting and would be missed if the slide were not counted in the other direction. If a fiber passes the crossline more than once, each passing is recorded.

Note: This method is similar to that given in the A.S.T.M. Tentative Method D629-46T.[17]

As in the other longitudinal method, the counting is best done by counting the fibers in majority by means of a hand or foot single or multiple counter, marking down the individual fiber counts after each

[17] From A.S.T.M. Standards on Textile Materials, 1950, p. 99.

trip across the slide. These figures can then be totaled for the entire slide.

For the determination of the fineness of the fibers present in the mixture, the stained slide should not be used as the fibers have swollen during both the water mixing and the staining. It is suggested that yarn sections from the fabric be mounted according to the method for fineness analysis described later.

TABLE 7. AVERAGE FIBER FINENESS IN MICRONS

U. S. Wool Top Grades

80's	18.5 to 19.5	50's	30.0 to 31.5
70's	20.0 to 21.0	48's	32.0 to 33.0
64's	21.5 to 22.5	46's	34.0 to 35.0
60's	24.5 to 25.5	44's	35.5 to 36.5
58's	26.0 to 27.0	40's	37.5 to 38.5
56's	27.5 to 29.0	38's	39.0 to 41.0

Mohair Grades

Kid	24.0 to 30.0
First	30.0 to 40.0
Second	40.0 to 50.0
Third	50.0 to 60.0

Various Vegetable Fibers

[Data from von Bergen and Krauss, *Textile Fiber Atlas.*]

Cotton	16 to 20
Kapok	21 to 30
Flax	15 to 17
Hemp	18 to 23
Ramie	25
Jute	15

Specialty Hairs, Fur Fibers and Silk Fibers

[Data from von Bergen and Krauss *Textile Fiber Atlas.*]

Alpaca, llama	26 to 28	Rabbit	12 to 14
Cashmere	15 to 16	Silk	10 to 13
Camel hair	18	Tussah	20
Goat (fine hair)	13 to 15	Vicuña	13 to 14
Muskrat	16		

Rayon Staple Fibers

[Theoretical values.]

Acetate		Viscose Rayon	
3 den.	17.8	1.5 den.	11.8
5 den.	23.0	3.0 den.	16.7
8 den.	29.1	5.5 den.	22.6
12 den.	35.7	10.0 den.	30.6
16 den.	41.2	20.0 den.	43.2
20 den.	46.1		

Cross-Section Method. This method is excellent in cases where darkly dyed fibers do not permit identification and subsequent quantitative determination; also in cases where cross-sectional microscopic characteristics for differentiation are more pronounced for the fibers involved. Sampling of the specimen is similar to that used in the Longitudinal Mount Method. About 3/16 in. of fabric is cut out and all yarns are sectioned by any of the cross-section methods described in the chapter on fiber identification. The various fiber types present can be counted directly under the microscope or by making a photomicrograph of the cross-section and then counting them. The latter means, while more convenient for the operator doing the determination, consumes too much time for routine analysis.

Fineness Determination of Fibers for Microscopic Quantitative Analysis. In order to convert the numerical percentages obtained in the above manner into percentages by weight, the factors of fineness and specific weight have to be determined and should be included in the calculations. For both longitudinal and cross-sectional determination of the fineness of fibers the A.S.T.M. Tentative Method of Test D419-50T for determining the "Fineness of Wool" (A.S.T.M. Standards on Textile Materials, 1950, p. 408) can be used.

Other statistical values may be obtained as set forth elsewhere in A.S.T.M. methods.

In routine microscopic quantitative determinations it was found that accepted average fineness measurements can be used for most vegetable fibers, silk, and some of the hair fibers. Table 7 lists the fineness measurements of the more common textile fibers. Similarly the specific weights are given in Table 8.

TABLE 8. SPECIFIC GRAVITY OF TEXTILE FIBERS

Fibers	*Specific Gravity*	*Fibers*	*Specific Gravity*
Acetate	1.32 to 1.35	Mohair	1.30
Aralac (casein)	1.29	Nylon	1.14
Cotton	1.50 to 1.55	Orlon	1.17
Cupra rayon	1.54	Ramie	1.51 to 1.52
Dacron	1.38	Silk	1.25
Dynel	1.28	Vinyon	1.34 to 1.36
Flax	1.50	Viscose rayon	1.52
Hemp	1.48	Wool	1.28 to 1.33
Jute	1.48		

Calculation of Percentage by Weight. The conversion of the numerical percentage into percentage by weight of the fibers found in the blend is the same, regardless of which one of the microscopic methods is used in the mounting, identification, and counting of the fibers.

The number of fibers of each type is multiplied by the square of the diameter of each type and by the respective specific gravity. The product of each type obtained in the above manner is divided by the total of the products of all fibers present to give the percentages by weight for each fiber type present as shown by the example below:

Fibers counted on slide

Wool: 127
Cotton: 34
Viscose rayon: 62

Average fineness measurements for each fiber

Wool: 21.0 μ
Cotton: 17.5 μ
Viscose rayon: 15.0 μ

Specific gravity for each fiber

Wool: 1.30
Cotton: 1.48
Viscose rayon: 1.52

Calculation

Wool: $127 \times 21.0^2 \times 1.30 = 72{,}809.0$
Cotton: $34 \times 17.5^2 \times 1.48 = 16{,}462.5$
Viscose rayon: $62 \times 15.0^2 \times 1.52 = 21{,}204.0$

Wool = 66 per cent
Cotton = 15 per cent
Viscose rayon = 19 per cent
Total 100 per cent

REFERENCES IN TEXT

1. von Wiesner, J., *Technische Mikroskopie,* Vienna (1867).
2. Herzog, A., *Mikrophotographischer Atlas der technisch wichtigen Faserstoffe,* Munich (1908).
3. Herzog, A., "The Determination of Cotton and Linen," *Teachers College Bull. Series* 8, *No.* 5, Columbia University.
4. Lochte, T., *Atlas der menschlischen und tierischen Haare,* Leipzig (1938).
5. Hardy, J. I., *J. Textile Inst.,* **23,** 1T (1932).
6. Manby, J., *J. Textile Inst.,* **23,** 5T (1932).
7. Reumuth, H., *Klepzig's Textil Zeitschrift,* **39,** 612 (1936).
8. Herzog, A., *Melliand Textilberichte,* **19,** 405 (1938).
9. Schwarz, E. R., *Textiles and the Microscope,* New York, McGraw-Hill (1934).
10. Hardy, J. I., *Textile Research,* **5,** 184 (1935).
11. Hardy, J. I., "A Practical Laboratory Method for Making Thin Cross-Sections of Fibers," *U. S. Dept. of Agriculture, Circ.* 378 (Nov. 1935).

12. Heermann, P., and Herzog, A., *Mikroskopische und mechanisch-technische Textil Untersuchungen,* Berlin, Springer (1930).
13. Hanausek, T. F., *The Microscopy of Technical Products,* New York, Wiley (1907).
14. *Rayon Textile Monthly,* **24,** 82 (1943).
15. Cross, C. F., and Bevan, E. J., *Textbook of Papermaking,* London (1907).
16. Davis, H. L., and Rynkiewicz, H. J., *J. Ind. Eng. Chem.,* **14,** 472 (1942).
17. *J. Textile Inst.,* **32,** S22 (1941).
18. Millon, E., *Compt. rend.,* **28,** 40.
19. Simon, W., and Tonn, W. H., *Rayon Textile Monthly,* **22,** 63 (Sept. 1941).
20. Herzog, A., and Koch, P., *Fehler in Textilien,* Heidelberg (1938).
21. Matthews, J. M., *Textile Fibers,* 4th Ed., New York, Wiley (1924).
22. Swett, C. E., *J. Ind. Eng. Chem.,* **10,** 377 (1918).
23. Federal Specifications for Paper, General Specifications UU-P-31, section IV, part 5 (March 1932).
24. Public Document 850, 76th Congress, 3rd Session, S 162.
25. Trade Practice Rules for the Linen Industry, promulgated Feb. 1, 1941.
26. Rayon and Acetate Trade Practice Rules Industry, promulgated Feb. 9, 1952.
27. Trade Practice Rules for the Silk Industry, promulgated Nov. 4, 1938.
28. "Rules and Regulations under the Wool Products Labeling Act of 1939," promulgated by the Federal Trade Commission, effective July 15, 1941.
29. Skinkle, J. H., *Textile Testing; Physical, Chemical and Microscopical,* New York (1940).
30. Larose, P., *Can. J. Research,* **16,** 61 (1938).
31. Preston, J. M., and Nimkar, M. V., *J. Textile Inst.,* **42** (11), (1950).
32. Schaeffer, A., *Melliand Textilber.,* **21,** 65 (1940).
33. Howlett, F., Morley, M. J., and Urquhart, A. R., "The Chemical Analysis of Fiber Mixtures," *J. Textile Inst.,* **33** (June 1942).
34. Mease, R. T., and Jessup, D. A., "Analysis of Textiles," *Am. Dyestuff Reptr.,* **24,** 616 (1935).
35. Weidenhammer, W. E., Prisley, F. A., and Ryberg, B. A., *Am. Dyestuff Reptr.,* **30,** 348 (1941).
36. DaSchio, E., *Rusta Rayonne,* **12,** 157 (1937).
37. Cappelli, A., and Tuffi, R., *Boll. assoc. ital. chim. tessili color,* **16,** 2 (1940).
38. Wolf, H. W., *Am. Dyestuff Reptr.,* **40** (9), 273 (1951).
39. Vétillard, M., *Études sur les fibres végétales,* Paris (1876).
40. Krauss, W., "Quantative Analysis of Linen in Part Linen Fabrics," *Rayon Textile Monthly,* **23,** 653, 713 (1942).

CHAPTER XXI

X-RAY DIAGRAMS OF NATURAL AND SYNTHETIC FIBERS

A. N. J. Heyn

The X-ray patterns produced by textile fibers are a result of the characteristic crystalline structure of their basic chemical constituents (cellulose, keratin, fibroin, etc.) and the special arrangement of these constituents in the fiber. The X-ray method, therefore, is a tool for studying (1) the molecular structure of the separate crystalline portions, and (2) the organization of these crystalline units in the aggregate of the fiber.

1. Each chemical constituent produces a characteristic X-ray pattern, and the *"basic" patterns* of these substances have been explained in terms of the *spatial arrangement of molecules inside the crystal.* As the basic patterns have been explained, it is possible to draw conclusions about the molecular structure of the fiber by recognizing the pattern without a full analysis of the diagram.

The basic patterns and their related molecular structure within the crystal are discussed in the section "Basic X-ray Patterns, etc.," below.

2. The special organization of the constituents is concerned with *microcrystalline structure of the fiber,* which includes the orientation and the distribution of the crystallites, their relative amount and relation to the noncrystalline material, their size, shape, and crystalline perfection, etc. These secondary features also include the presence of additional substances and express themselves as variations of the basic X-ray pattern of the substance. They are discussed in the section "Description and Explanation of X-ray Patterns of the Individual Natural Fibers."

The knowledge of the molecular and crystalline structure of fibers is not only of interest as a mere structural ("morphological") feature; this structure is responsible for many of the physical and physicochemical properties of the fibers. Furthermore, fibers of different chemical composition are readily identified by their X-ray diagrams, and to a certain extent it is also possible to differentiate between fibers of the same chemical composition by utilizing, secondarily, the features of their structure.

X-ray analysis is not only an important tool for investigating the molecular structure as such but also gives valuable information about certain mechanical phenomena in fibers, e.g., unfolding of molecules during stretching of wool, reorientation and slippage of crystallites during elongation; chemical reactions, e.g., mercerization, formation of derivatives by topochemical reactions, and physico-chemical phenomena, e.g., swelling, hydration; etc.

The application of the X-ray technique has been largely confined, to date, to the structure of the crystalline portion of the fiber. The technique has been used only to a negligible extent for the analysis of the structure of the noncrystalline portion of the fiber because of the more difficult experimentation and interpretation. Therefore, this chapter will deal only with the X-ray analysis of the crystalline portion of the fiber.

As an introduction to the explanation of the method a few general data will be given on the structure of crystals in general and the crystalline structure of fibers in particular.

THE STRUCTURE OF CRYSTALS AND THE CRYSTALLINE STRUCTURE OF FIBERS

A crystal may be considered as a definite grouping of atoms or molecules periodically repeated in all three dimensions. Planes imagined through the atoms and the molecules so arranged form what is called a three-dimensional *"space lattice."* The smallest and simplest repeating volume of this lattice is called the *"unit cell,"* and this unit has a fixed shape and set of dimensions and contains a constant and generally small number of atoms or molecules.

Each space lattice has many different sets of parallel imaginary planes, each set of planes being parallel within itself. (See Fig. 1.) The distances between successive parallel planes are known as *"interplanar spacings,"* and these are in general different for each set of planes.[1]

[1] The different sets of parallel planes are distinguished from each other and designated by the *Miller indices* (h, k, l, in general). They are proportional to the reciprocals of the intercepts made by each plane on the three axes of the unit cell (Fig. 1). For example, if the plane cuts off half a "unit" intercept on all three axes of the unit cell, it is designated 222, if it is parallel to the a and c axes cutting off a "unit" intercept on the b axis, it is designated 010. Intercepts of the negative direction of the axes are designated by $-$ above the index.

The majority of natural fibers are high-polymer substances of which the long-chain molecules form regions of more or less perfect crystallinity. These regions alternate with *amorphous regions* where a less regular arrangement exists. The *crystalline regions* or *microcrystallites* are very small, measuring from 50 to about a few hundred A [2] in diameter, and their length is usually many times the width. The same molecule may extend through one or more amorphous as well as crystalline regions, the crystalline areas being formed by bundling together of parts of the long molecules into parallel orientation. Also other

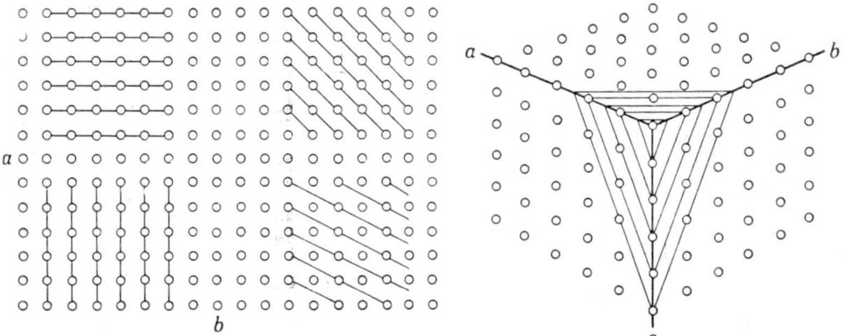

FIG. 1*a*. Two-dimensional crystal lattice and some of the lattice planes (above plane 100 and 110, below plane 010 and 210). 1*b*. Three-dimensional crystal lattice and a set of lattice planes (221). (*From A. N. J. Heyn,* 1952.)

components may be found in these *amorphous* regions, for instance, in cellulose fiber, pectins, and lignins.

The microcrystallites in a *fiber of "ideal" structure* are oriented with one of the crystallographic directions parallel to the fiber axis, whereas the other two axes have random orientation around the fiber axis. The conception of a fiber as a composite of microcrystallites (oriented in one direction and random in the other two directions) is equivalent to a single *crystal* when *rotated* during a period around one of its axes.

Unlike the "ideal" fiber, orientation of crystallites in the direction of the fiber axis is not always perfect in natural fibers, ranging from almost complete orientation to absolute randomness. The most general situation is where the crystallites fluctuate in position around an average "preferred" position. In many natural fibers the long axis of the microcrystallite forms a constant angle with the fiber axis so that the crystallites are arranged in a spiral. The pitch of the spiral varies in different fibers.

[2] An angstrom unit is 10^{-8} cm and is designated A.

ELEMENTARY X-RAY TECHNIQUE

The fibers are arranged in parallel order in a bundle, and a fine collimated beam of parallel X-rays [3] (diameter of 0.1 mm) is passed through the center of the bundle at right angles to its axis (see Fig. 2).

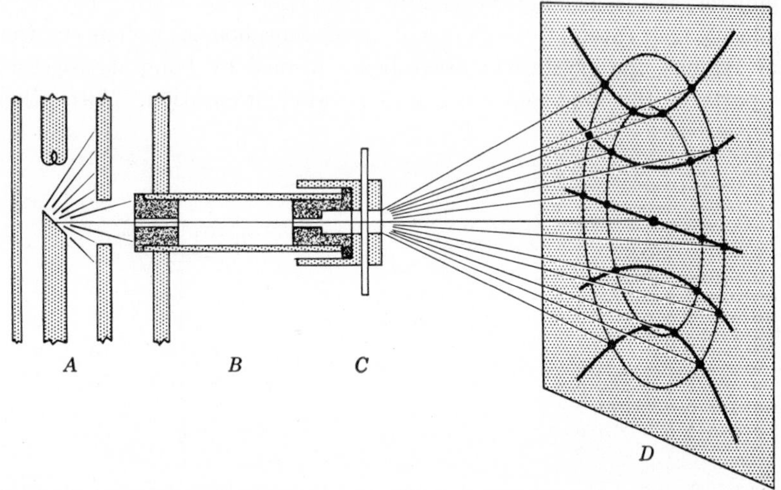

FIG. 2. Pin-hole assembly and fiber diagram schematically. The interferences, being intersections of the vertical and horizontal cones, are circles and hyperbolas on the flat film. Their intersections locate the interference spots. *A*, X-ray tube; *B*, pin-hole assembly; *C*, sample in holder; and *D*, flat film. (*From A. N. J. Heyn,* 1952.)

Part of the radiation will pass undisturbed through the bundle (primary beam), but another part will deviate from its original path and be scattered or diffracted to produce a pattern of spots and bands in

[3] X-rays are electromagnetic when a beam of electrons (accelerated by a strong electrostatic field) strikes an atom. There are *two* commercial types of X-ray tubes. The first, the Coolidge tube, contains a filament which when heated emits free electrons; it is generally highly evacuated and permanently sealed. Most commercial tubes are of this type. The *second* type is the gas tube, which has no filament, using ionization of the residual gas to obtain the electrons. Most tubes are operated between 30 and 50 kv. Complete diffraction units containing the high-voltage generator and a sealed Coolidge tube are commercially made by various firms in the United States. The wave-length distribution of the X-ray radiation consists of a continuous part of low intensity and a characteristic radiation of high intensity. This characteristic radiation is known as the K series and consists of α_1, α_2, and β components. The wave lengths of the K radiation is determined by the atomic number of the target material and is 1.537 A for copper, 2.28 A for chromium, and 1.71 A for molybdenum. For fiber research copper radiation is the most common.

a definite arrangement on a photographic plate placed behind the fiber perpendicular to the primary beam and parallel to the fiber bundle at a distance of 40 mm. The crystalline regions of the fiber diffract the X-rays to form the characteristic "interference" pattern on the photographic film, whereas the amorphous regions scatter part of the radiation to cause general scattering or fogging of the film.

The patterns of the various fibers differ in: the number of interference spots (or rings); the distance of interferences from the center (or diameter of rings); the relative intensity of interferences; the enlargements of interferences into arcs or rings; the width and diffuseness of interferences; the general scattering or background.

INTERPRETATION OF DIAGRAMS

General

Information on the crystalline and molecular structure of substances is derived in the following general way:

From the position of the interferences in the diagram, more precisely the angle between diffracted and primary beam, the interplanar spacings of the various crystalline planes are calculated. From the various spacings found and the relative orientations of some of them, the unit cell is constructed. From the chemical structure of the substances and the relative intensities of the interferences, the position of the molecules in the crystal lattice (unit cell) is calculated.

This has been done for the main components of the natural fibers, and the crystalline configuration of the molecules is known. In the section "Basic X-ray Patterns, etc.," the characteristic spacings, unit-cell dimensions, and the positions of the molecules in the unit cell (of the crystal lattice) are given.

With this knowledge at hand it is sufficient first to recognize the characteristic spacings from the diagram in order to know which component is present, and second to determine the orientation of the crystal lattice in order to know the orientation of the molecules and microcrystallites in the fiber.

The procedures for calculating the interplanar spacings, the orientation of the crystal planes in the fiber, and the size of the microcrystallites is discussed in the following sections.

Calculation from Diagram of Interplanar Spacings of the Crystal Lattice and Relative Position of Particular Lattice Planes in the Fiber

Diffraction as by Crystal Powder, "Horizontal Diffraction Cones." The distribution of the diffracted radiation as resulting from the arrangement of the molecules and atoms in a crystal lattice is expressed by *Bragg's law,* according to which the various sets of parallel planes in the crystal lattice diffract the radiation just as though they were reflected by the surface of one of the planes in a manner similar to the way a mirror reflects visible light. The only difference is that the reflection occurs here *only at definite angles, glancing angles,* θ, of the incident beam with the planes. According to Bragg the relation between these angles, the interplanar spacing d, and the wave length of the radiation λ is given by:

$$n\lambda = 2d \sin \theta \quad (1)$$

If the various sets of planes have random orientation around the primary beam, as in a crystal powder, the reflected radiation will describe a set of coaxial

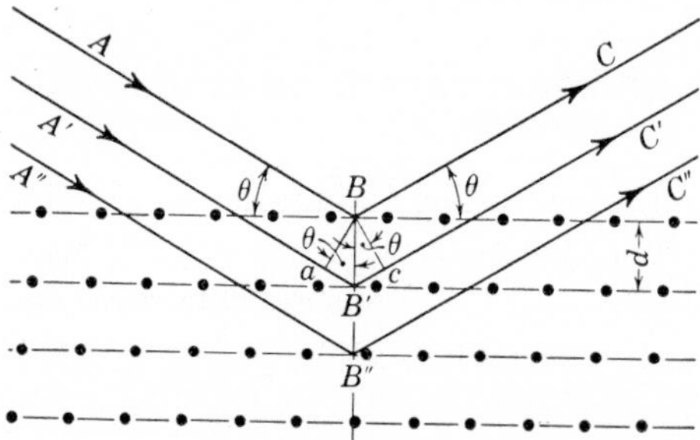

Fig. 3. Condition for reflection by a crystal lattice. The difference of path between the beam ABC and $A'B'C'$, $aB + Bc = 2d \sin \theta$, must be $n\lambda$. (*From A. N. J. Heyn,* 1952.)

cones of semi-vertical angle 2θ *around the X-ray beam.* These cones will be called here *"horizontal cones,"* as the beam has generally horizontal direction. Their record on a flat film perpendicular to the beam consists of a set of concentric circles. From the radius of these circles and the distance of the film from the specimen, the angle θ can be found, so that following equation 1 the interplanar spacing d can be calculated if the wave length is known. Figure 3 illustrates this law.[4]

Diffraction by a Row of Atoms, "Vertical Diffraction Cones." In the case of fibers (and the rotated crystal) a second specialization of the distribution of the diffracted radiation results from the already mentioned orientation of one of the axes. This orientation results in an arrangement of all the molecules and atoms in rows parallel to the fiber axis.

The radiation diffracted by a row of atoms spaced at definite distances also describes the surface of a set of coaxial cones, but this time round the direction

[4] The spacings corresponding to these glancing angles can be directly looked up in the "Internationale Tabellen zur Bestimming von Kristall Strukturen," and in the "Tables for Conversion of X-ray Diffraction Angles to Interplanar Spacing," U. S. Dept. of Commerce, Natl. Bur. of Standards, Applied Mathematics Series 10 (Sept. 1950).

of the atom row. These cones will be called here *"vertical cones."* The relation between the semi-vertical angle θ of the cone, the spacing of the atoms in the row c, and the wave length of the radiation is expressed by:

$$c \cos \theta = n\lambda \tag{2}$$

where n is an integral or whole number. This condition is illustrated in Fig. 4.

The diffractions at different values of n are termed reflections of the 1, 2, 3, and nth order. A *cylindrical* film round the row of atoms as axis will record the radiation of the cone surfaces as rings, which appear as straight lines when the cylinder is flattened out. These lines, perpendicular to the axis of the atom row, are known as *"layerlines."* The record of the cones on a *flat* film parallel to the fiber axis consists of a set of *hyperbolas* on either side of the "equator." Figures 5*A* and *B* illustrate the above.

Fiber Diagram. As the conditions under the sections on diffraction, above, must be both fulfilled in the case of fibers and a rotating crystal, the actual reflection will be limited to the intersections of the sets of horizontal and vertical cones. The result may be readily seen by considering the pattern as recorded on a flat film. Figure 2 shows the circles from the horizontal cones and the hyperbolas from the vertical cones and their intersections which indicate the position of the diffraction spots actually occurring.

The pattern is symmetrical with regard to the equator and meridian, and each interference occurs four times (once in each quadrant) with the exception of the *equatorial interferences and those on the meridian which occur only twice.* For this reason this type of diagram is often termed a *four-point diagram.*

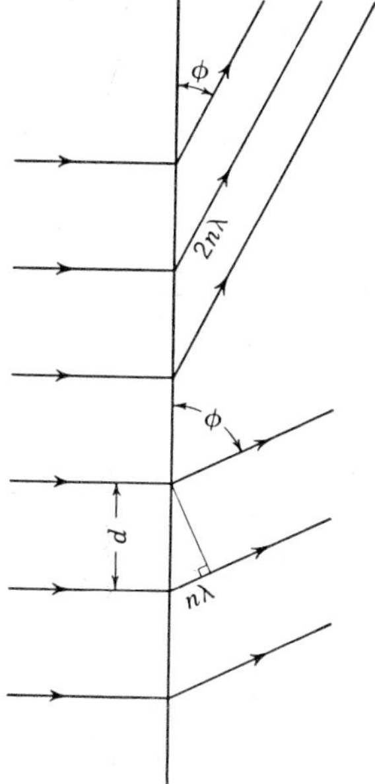

FIG. 4. Diffraction by a row of equally spaced points of distance C. The condition of diffraction of a beam perpendicular to the point row is $c \cos \phi = n\lambda$ when ϕ is the angle between the diffracted beam and the row. (*From A. N. J. Heyn,* 1952.)

From equation 2 the distance of the atoms in the direction of the row can be readily calculated. For the cylindrical film the angle θ follows from the distances of the layerlines (on which the actual diffraction spots are arranged) from the equator and the distance of the specimen from the film. For the nth layerline the equation $n\lambda = c \cos \theta$ is used.

Interference spots on the equator indicate planes parallel to the fiber axis, designated as *paratropic planes* (generally of Miller indices, 110, 010, 200). Interferences on the meridian indicate planes perpendicular to the fiber axis, designated *diatropic planes.* (The paratropic planes generally have intense interferences in high polymers as they contain the greatest amount of scattering material: the entire chain molecule.)

In conclusion it may be stated that it is possible by the above procedures to determine from the diagram various interplanar spacings of the crystallites of the fiber, and that some of these spacings can be ascribed to special crystal planes, for instance, to planes perpendicular to the fiber (fiber period) and to planes parallel to the fiber axis (paratropic planes) lateral spacings.

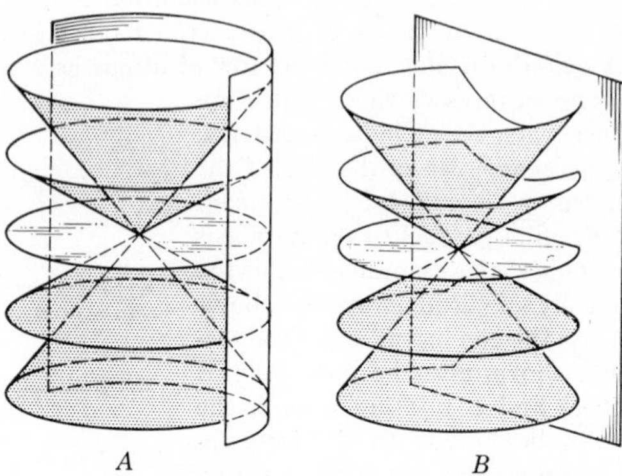

FIG. 5. The vertical diffraction cones around the point row intersect a cylindrical film as circles (*A*), and a flat film along hyperbolas (*B*). (*From A. N. J. Heyn,* 1952.)

Determination of Orientation of Crystal Lattice in Fiber and of Lateral Order of Molecules inside Crystal

The orientation of the microcrystallites refers to the alignment of the *b* or *c* axis of the crystal with reference to the fiber axis. Different crystallites do not have the same orientation but are subject to variation or fluctuation around the preferred direction. This fluctuation is expressed in the diagram by an enlargement of the interference spots (e.g., the equatorial (002) interferences in cellulose fibers) into arcs or sickles.

From the size of the arcs, conclusions can be drawn about the distribution of the crystallites around the direction of the X-ray beam. The larger the arc the larger the fluctuation; at random orientation the arcs fuse together to form complete rings. Sisson and Clark (1933) attempted to put the determination of orientation on a quantitative basis. They assumed that the angular distribution (number of crystallites) around the X-ray beam is proportional to the intensity distribution around the (002) arc or ring on the flat film. The measurement of intensity is made with a micro-densitometer equipped with a rotating stage. The orientation is expressed by curves in which the relative intensity is plotted against the angle to fiber axis. The curves so obtained have the general shape of normal frequency distribution curves.

In natural fibers the microcrystallites are often arranged in a spiral around the fiber axis, the pitch of the fibers being different in different fibers. The direction of the microcrystallites will fluctuate in the ordinary way around the spiral direction. The X-ray pattern will be principally "an X-ray projection" of the spiral on the film in the direction of the beam. As the fiber is a hollow cylinder, the pattern will be principally determined by crystallites around the two (opposite) directions of the spiral at the front and the back of the fiber, and partly, by microcrystallites in intermediate positions (the microcrystallites in the part of the wall parallel to the X-ray beam have, for instance, orientation "parallel" to the fiber axis and therefore diffract on the equator; this results in a shifting of the intensity toward the equator). The pattern will therefore principally consist of two arcs on each side of the spiral directions so that the diagram contains four arcs. At a steep spiral these two arcs will be almost completely superimposed, however, and the intensity maximum will still be found on the equator. At a less steep spiral orientation the equatorial arcs will have lower intensities at the equator with intensity maxima on each side, giving four intensity maxima in total. (This is clearly shown for instance, in Diagram 35 and 36, later in this chapter.)

For a more complete discussion reference is made to the review of Sisson (1943), and the original articles of Sisson and Clark (1933), Sisson (1935), Berkley and Woodyard (1938), Hermans (1946), Tsien (1949), and Meredith (1951*a*) for natural fibers; and Ingersoll (1946) for rayons. (See bibliography.)

The diagrams of the natural fibers can be differentiated already by the size of the arcs, without a complete intensity distribution curve being given. This procedure will be followed in the section "Description and Explanation of X-ray Patterns of the Individual Natural Fibers."

The distribution of intensity, for instance, in the (003) arc, *in the direction of the equator* gives information about the perfection of crystallinity, or lateral order of molecules, in the crystallites. The narrower the interference spots and the better defined their borders are, the more perfect the crystalline order.

A complication results from the fact that the width of interferences is also influenced by the size of the crystallites: the smaller the crystallites the wider the interference.

Long Spacings and Size, Distance, and Orientation of Microcrystallites in Fiber as Revealed by Small-Angle X-Ray Scattering

The angles under which the X-rays are diffracted in the microcrystallites of the fiber generally are above some 3°. (The main interferences of cellulose, for instance, have glancing angles of: A_1: 7.3°; A_2: 8.1°; A_4: 11.3°.) The larger the spacing in question the smaller the angle, and vice versa (*Bragg's law*).

Besides these interferences at larger angles, interferences or scattering of X-rays at very small angles close to the primary beam occur in the diagrams of many fibers.

In the case where real *discontinuous interference spots* are found, the presence of large spacings (superidentity periods) has been concluded. This type of *diffraction at small angles* has been described for many proteins, where superidentity periods (from 25 to 725 A) within the chain molecule along its axis have been related with these interferences (see in bibliography Bernal and Crowfoot, 1934; Wyckoff and Corey, 1935; Astbury and Sisson, 1935; Corey and Wyckoff, 1936; Bernal and Fankuchen, 1941; Bear, 1944).

Superidentity periods have been mainly found in such highly oriented proteins as porcupine quill and special feathers but not in natural textile fibers like wool. In a few synthetics they have been described but not explained (Hess and Kieszig, 1943 and 1944; Zahn and Kohler, 1950; and Meibohm and Smith, 1951).

In the case where a *continuous scattering* near the primary beam occurs the interpretation is different. From the radial distribution of intensity around the primary beam, important information can be obtained about the microcrystalline structure of the fiber. Scattering at small angles has been used for the determination of particle size (for instance, carbon black) by Guinier (1942) and others, and was introduced for the systematic investigation of the "micellar," "microcrystalline," or "supermolecular" structure of cellulose fibers by the author (Heyn, 1948, 1949*a*, and 1950*a* and *c*). This new X-ray method has proved an important tool for the investigation of the following features of the microcrystalline structure of fiber:

The Size of the Microcrystallites. For this purpose the distribution of intensity of the radiation in radial direction from the primary beam is determined by direct or photographic methods. The distribution curves so obtained are different for different fibers. From the shape of the curves the size (diameter) of the microcrystallites can be calculated. By this method, the size of microcrystallites in different fibers has been found to be different (Heyn, 1950*c*).

The Orientation of the Microcrystallites in the Fiber. In fibers with orientation of crystallites parallel to the long axis (hemp, jute, flax, ramie) the scattering image consists of a horizontal strip along the equator. In fibers with spiral orientation the scattering image consists of two strips intersecting each other in the center of the diagram, forming a cross at an angle equivalent to twice the angle between the axis, of the microcrystallites and the axis of the fiber. (See patterns, Plate XVIII.)

The Distance between Microcrystallites. From the scattering by the fiber in the swollen state (where the scattering by the individual particles is independent), and the scattering by the dry fiber (where the scattering by the individual particles interferes), it is possible to determine the radial distribution of microcrystallites in the fiber.

NATURAL FIBERS

Basic Diagrams of the Main Components and the Respective Molecular Configurations Derived

In this section the characteristic spacings, unit-cell dimensions, and spatial arrangements of molecules in the crystal lattice are given for the main chemical components of the natural fibers.

A characteristic feature concerning the position of the chain molecules in the crystal lattice is that the lattice is a "primary valence chain lattice": the molecules are held together in the direction of the *b* axis of the lattice by primary valence forces and in lateral directions by secondary valence forces. Another characteristic is that the unit cell corresponds only to part of the chain molecule, namely, the repeating chemical unit or a multiple thereof. (For instance, a cellobiose unit, two glucose residues—in cellulose, the CH—CO—NH group in proteins.)

Cellulose I

X-Ray Pattern. The X-ray pattern of native cellulose, *"Cellulose I,"* in the oriented state is a typical fiber diagram (four-point diagram) with distinct interference spots (for example, see Diagram 12, ramie).

The following equatorial interferences (originating from crystal planes parallel to the fiber axis—*paratropic planes*) are the most characteristic in the pattern:

A_1, Miller index (101), interplanar spacing 6.05 A

A_2, Miller index ($10\bar{1}$), interplanar spacing 5.45 A

A_4, Miller index (002), interplanar spacing 3.92 A

The fiber period calculated from the layerlines is 10.3 A.

Unit Cell. The unit cell is monoclinic (Mark and von Susich, 1929; Hengstenberg, 1928; Gross and Clark, 1938) and has the following dimensions:

$$a = 8.35 \text{ A} \qquad b = 10.3 \text{ A} \qquad c = 7.9 \text{ A} \qquad \beta = 84°$$

In fibers of high orientation the b axis of the unit cell is parallel to the fiber axis.

The Position of Molecules in the Unit Cell (Crystal Lattice). Cellulose consists of long-chain molecules of cellobiose residues, each consisting of two glucose rings. The cellobiose units measure 10.3 A in length and are placed with their long axis along the b axis of the unit cell (Sponsler, 1926*a* and *b*, 1930; Sponsler and Dore, 1926; Meyer and Mark, 1928*b*, 1929, 1930). The plane of the glucose rings is identical with the (002) plane (Meyer and Misch, 1937); the great number of atoms contained in this plane accounts for the very high intensity of the (002) interference.

It is generally accepted that in all natural fibers cellulose occurs in the native form described here.

Cellulose II

Cellulose may occur in another crystalline configuration or allotropic modification, which is termed *Cellulose II, mercerized cellulose,* or *hydrated cellulose.* The molecules arrange themselves in this different lattice when the native cellulose is mercerized or the cellulose is regenerated from solutions. Although this configuration does not occur in native fibers it is mentioned here for the sake of completeness as the process of mercerization is often applied to natural fibers.

The equatorial interferences are very intense as in native cellulose. The interplanar spacings calculated from these interferences are:

A_0	(101)	7.35 A
A_3	($10\bar{1}$)	4.5 A
A_4	(002)	4.01 A

The fiber period is the same as in native cellulose, 10.30 A.

The *unit cell* is monoclinic (Andress, 1929; Burgeni and Kratky, 1929; Weissenberg, 1929) and has the following dimensions:

$$a = 8.14 \text{ A} \qquad b = 10.30 \text{ A} \qquad c = 9.14 \text{ A} \qquad \beta = 62°$$

Each cell contains also two cellobiose units. The plane of the glucose residues coincides, however, with the $(10\bar{1})$ plane, the chains (as present in native cellulose) being rotated around their axis into the diagonal plane of the unit cell.

Cellulose T

A third modification of cellulose, "*Cellulose T*," is very similar to native cellulose and differs only in that it has a rhombic unit cell and in that the a axis is slightly shorter ($a = 8.11$ A) than in native cellulose.

This form is obtained under special conditions from Cellulose II and has been described by Meyer and Badenhuizen (1937), Kubo and Kanamaru (1937), and Hess and Kieszig (1941). According to Kubo (1940), the modification would occur in many plant fibers like *Agave*. The results of Hess and Kieszig (1941), however, are not in accordance with this conclusion.

For complete reviews of the crystalline structure of all types of cellulose, refer to Meyer and Mark (1930), Sisson (1943), and Meyer (1950).

Pectins

Pectins are long-chain molecules consisting of polymerized *a-d* galacturonic acid groups.

The pattern of commercial citrous pectin shows a diffuse X-ray ring (indicating a structure almost amorphous) corresponding to an interplanar distance of 4.17 A (Heyn, 1933). From highly oriented preparations (Wuhrmann and Pilnik, 1945; Palmer and Lotzkar, 1945; Palmer and Hartzog, 1945), a fiber period of 13–14 A has been calculated, corresponding to 3 galacturonic rings.

In the patterns of fibers containing pectin in the cell wall there appears a diffuse ring which could be attributed to pectin in the amorphous state.

Plant Waxes

The superimposition of "wax rings" in the pattern of cellulose walls was first described by Heyn (1933 and 1934) and was later explained by Hess, Trogus, and Wergin (1936). (See also Wergin, 1936, and

Gundermann, Wergin, and Hess, 1937.) The wax component in the pattern of the natural fibers has been largely overlooked to date. (Sisson, 1938, and Hess, Wergin, and Kieszig, 1942, described the presence of wax rings in young cotton fiber; Hess, Kieszig, and Wergin, 1943, described it in the pattern of seed hairs of *Eriophorum.*)

X-Ray Pattern. The X-ray pattern of natural waxes in the natural unoriented state is characterized by two very intense rings (which lie close together) of interplanar spacings of 4.2 and 3.7 A, and one or more rings of large spacing close to the primary beam.

Unit Cell. The lateral dimensions of the unit cell in which the hydrocarbons and derivatives which constitute waxes are arranged are almost consistently the following: $a = 7.45$ A, $b = 4.97$ A (Müller, 1927, 1928, 1929, 1932; Hengstenberg, 1928). The most intense diffractions are caused by the (110) planes of interplanar spacing 4.2 A and (020) planes of interplanar spacing 3.7 A.

Position of Molecules in Crystal Lattice. Natural waxes are mixtures of different long-chain hydrocarbons, higher fatty acids and alcohols; therefore, the X-ray pattern derived has a composite nature.

The hydrocarbon chain lies parallel to the c axis of the unit cell. The constant lateral dimensions of this cell indicate a constant sidewise packing of the hydrocarbon chains. The only differences occur in the long-spacing diffractions (fiber period). The basic fiber period of the hydrocarbon chain is 2.53 A, corresponding to the length of the CH group. The occurrence of a long spacing in the fiber direction is connected with the length of the total chain (which is a multiple of the basic period). Variations result from different length and tilt of the chain, and the position of substituting side groups.

The chain lengths and positions in the chain of the acid and alcohol groups have been determined in the various components of plant and animal waxes from the large spacings (see the publications of Piper, Chibnall and Williams, 1934; Chibnall, Piper, et al., 1934; and Kreger, 1951).

Lignin and Other Components of Vegetable Fibers

Special equatorial interferences of interplanar spacings 9.7 and 14.6 A in the pattern of jute fiber have been interpreted by Sen and Woods (1948) as being associated with the presence of lignin.

Many natural fibers, especially of the *Agave* and *Furcraea* groups, contain large calcium oxalate crystals which cause intense irregular interferences scattered all over the pattern of these fibers (see, for instance, Diagrams 32 and 33).

Keratin

X-Ray Pattern of α Keratin. The X-ray pattern of α keratin, the protein substance from which animal hair fibers are built up, is much less well defined and more diffused than those of the foregoing substances, but it still has the distinct features of a fiber diagram in that equatorial and meridian arcs are present. The principal characteristics of the diagram of the substance in the unstretched state ("α keratin") are equatorial interferences of interplanar spacings 9.8 A and interferences in the direction of the meridian of interplanar spacing 5.1 A. Also, faint equatorial spots of 9.3 A occur.

X-Ray Pattern of β Keratin. The explanation of the diagram of α keratin in terms of spatial arrangements of molecules was only possible after the pattern of keratin in the stretched state (termed "β keratin") had become known. The diagram obtained from a hair fiber that has been highly stretched after softening in hot water is different from the pattern of α keratin. The 9.8 A equatorial interferences are maintained, but, besides, new equatorial interferences of spacing 4.65 A are found. At full stretch (of 70 per cent) the meridian arcs of 5.1 A of the α pattern are replaced by meridian arcs of interplanar spacing of 3.34 A (at intermediate stretch, mixed patterns exist).

Unit Cell. Astbury (1936*a* and *b*) accepts a rhombic unit cell for β keratin with sides a = 9.8 A and c = 4.65 A. Meyer (1950) accepts a monoclinic cell with sides a = 10.4 A and c = 4.8 A. The fiber period (b axis) is 5.1 A in α keratin and 3.34 A in β keratin.

Position of Molecules in the Lattice. Keratins consist of polypeptide chains built up of some twenty different α amino acids. The amino acid groups combine to form the main polypeptide chain, and the free ends of the amino acids (which do not participate in the chain itself) form side chains. These side chains form cross linkages between the main chains. In this way molecular sheets or "grids" are formed.

Position of Molecules in the β Keratin Lattice. The repeat period of a stretched polypeptide chain is 3.34 A. This period agrees with the dimension of the repeating amino acid group (CO—NH—CH group) in the length direction of the polypeptide chain. This period lies along the b axis.

The lateral spacing of the chain corresponds to 4.65 A in one direction ("backbone spacing" between the molecular sheets) and 9.8 A in the other direction ("side-chain spacing" within the grid) (Astbury and coworkers, e.g., Astbury, 1933, 1936*a* and *b*, 1945; Astbury and Woods, 1930, 1933; Astbury and Street, 1931; Astbury and Sisson,

1935). The above β configuration of keratin is found in some feather proteins (Lundgren, 1948) as well as in stretched hair fibers.

Position of Molecules in the α Keratin Lattice. In α keratin, the molecular sheets are folded up somewhat in a corrugated pattern (Astbury and Bell, 1941). In this folding process the lateral "side-chain" spacings of 9.8 A are not affected, but the other lateral spacing, "backbone spacing" of 4.65 A, disappears and is replaced by a faint 9.3 A spacing in α keratin ("α keratin backbone spacing"). Principally, the chains maintain the same position in the lattice, the only difference being the folded state. As a result, the protein fiber period of the stretched molecule of 3.4 A in the β pattern is replaced by the new period, "fold spacing," of the folded chain of 5.1 A.

Although the molecular structure of α and β keratin has been largely explained by Astbury and collaborators, a few points remain to be established, especially with regard to the type of fold (Bragg, Kendrew and Perutz, 1950, reviewed all possible structures). A modified folding has been suggested by Huggins, 1943, and Pauling and Corey, 1951; and Pauling, Corey, and Branson, 1951, have suggested a new spiral model for the keratin molecule, the spiral being formed by the CO—NH—CH residues, the sidechains projecting laterally from this backbone in all directions around the spiral.

All the natural hair fibers in unstretched condition give the pattern of α keratin, so that it may be concluded that their molecules are present in the folded state.

Silk Fibroin

The X-Ray Pattern. The patterns of natural and tussah silk are very distinct fiber diagrams in which the first and second layerlines are recognized. Some interferences on the equator and on the first layerlines are very intense. The patterns of natural and tussah silk are different. The following interferences are characteristic:

Equator	A_1	9.5 A
	A_2	4.8 A
	A_3	4.3 A
First layerline	I_2	3.6 A

The equatorial interferences (A_2 and A_3) are clearly separated in tussah silk, whereas they are fused in the pattern of cultivated silk.

In cultivated silk a strong interference (I_2) is found on the first layer-line, and a weaker one near the meridian (I_1). In the pattern of tussah silk, two interferences close together occur on the first layer-line instead.

Unit Cell. The most likely unit cells (Brill, 1923, 1943*b*) have the following dimensions:

Natural silk	a = 9.65 A	b = 6.95 A	c = 10.4 A	β = 62.4°
Tussah silk	a = 9.5 A	b = 6.95 A	c = 11.8 A	β = 66°

The b axis is the fiber axis. (See also Bergmann and Niemann, 1938, Kratky and Kuriyama, 1931, Trogus and Hess, 1933, MacNicholas, 1940.)

Position of Molecules in Unit Cell. Silk fibroin is mainly built up of the amino acids, glycine, and alanine, which alternate in the chain. The main chain is built up of amino acid residues (as in keratin); the side chains are shorter than in keratin.

The fiber period of 7 A is twice the length of the amino acid residue, so that two amino acid residues ($CHR—CO—NH—CH_2$) fit along the b axis.

These parallel chains are connected sidewise by hydrogen bonds between the CO and NH groups of neighboring chains, so that a "grid" is formed in the a-b plane of lateral spacing 9.6 A. The side chains lie along the c axis in the b-c plane.

This explains why the a axis is the same in both kinds of silk whereas the c axis is different as its length depends on the length of the side chain, which is different in the two types.

Description and Explanation of X-Ray Patterns of the Individual Natural Fibers

The X-ray patterns of natural fibers of different chemical groups are very distinctive, each group being easily recognized by the basic diagram of its X-ray pattern. (The individual fiber types of man-made fibers may be easily identified by their X-ray diagrams (Heyn, 1950–51), as each of these individual types differs substantially in its chemical composition.) Among the natural fiber types within each chemical group, however, the differences are more subtle; therefore, the differentiation must be based on the details of the X-ray patterns.

The diagrams of the natural fibers reproduced in the plates in this section have been made under standardized conditions including a constant specimen distance of 40 mm, except for diagrams 52*a* and *b*, and the use of a constant weight per length of fiber bundle (a bundle of 4-cm length weighing 10 mg), so that the same amount of material was always exposed to the X-ray beam. As a result of the standardized conditions, the diagrams can be directly compared with each other. (For details of this technique refer to Heyn, 1951.) The original diagrams were reduced by one-third.

Cotton (Diagrams 1 and 2)

The main characteristic of the diagram of mature cotton fiber is the presence of three well-defined intense equatorial arcs of which the

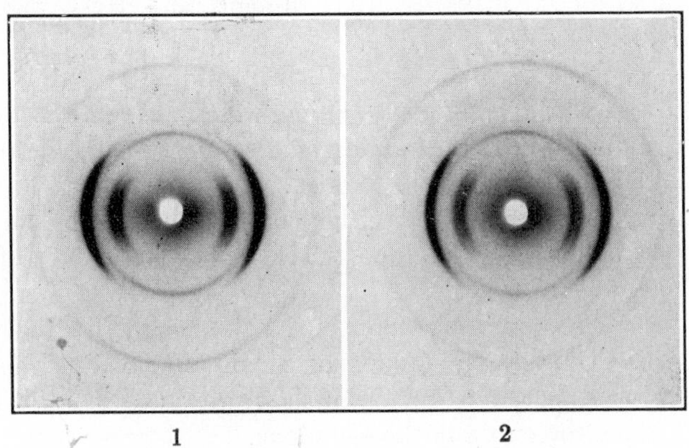

PLATE I. Cotton, *Gossypium hirsutum* L. (Malvaceae). Upland cotton. Diagram 1, Empire, X-ray angle 33.2°. Diagram 2, Coker 100 Wilt, X-ray angle 44.2°.

outer ones are the most intense and extend over a length of 50° to 70°. These equatorial interferences correspond to the A_1 (101), A_2 $(10\bar{1})$, and A_4 (002) interferences of native cellulose. Fainter arcs are present around the meridian which correspond to the (021) interferences of cellulose. On the outside of the pattern a faint ring, with highest intensity around the meridian, is found corresponding to the interplanar spacing 2.58 A, being one-fourth the fiber period of cellulose. The pattern of cotton, therefore, corresponds to the basic diagram of pure cellulose. The arcs result from spiral arrangement of the microcrystallites in the fiber.

The size of the arcs is different in different cottons (for instance, 33.2° in Diagram 1; and 44.2° in Diagram 2). For a quantitative measurement of the size of the arc, the "X-ray angle," and the explanation in terms of spiral pitch refer to the section on determination of orientation in crystal lattice.

Berkley and Woodyard (1938 and 1948) and Meredith (1951*b*) made special studies of the X-ray angles in different cottons.[5] Cotton fibers of different ages have been studied by Clark, Farr, and Pickett (1930) and Sisson (1937*a* and 1938), who found an increase of sharpness and intensity of the cellulose interferences with age.

In immature cotton fibers interferences of wax are superimposed on the pattern of cellulose. The wax pattern consists of the two characteristic (110) and (020) interferences of wax which form arcs on the meridian, at almost the same place as of the (021) cellulose arcs. An orientation of the long axis of the hydrocarbon chains of the wax perpendicular to the fiber axis may be concluded from this (Sisson, 1938; see also Hess, Wergin, and Kieszig, 1942).

In mature cotton fibers the wax pattern is not seen because the percentage of wax is lower in mature cotton (Heyn, 1949*b*), and because of the higher intensity of the cellulose interferences. An exception is the Arkansas Green Lint upland cotton (Conrad, 1941), which variety contains not less than 15 per cent of wax and from which a similar wax pattern is obtained as from immature cotton.[6]

As a result of mercerization, the basic cellulose diagram changes into the diagram of mercerized cellulose (see section "Cellulose II," above). Commercial mercerization generally does not convert all cellulose into the mercerized state, so that a superimposition of the native and mercerized diagrams results.

Bast Fibers (Diagrams 3 to 21)

The diagrams of the bast fibers differ from cotton in that the interferences, especially the ones on the equator, are broader, which indicates a lower degree of lateral order of the molecules; they are also shorter, which indicates an orientation nearly parallel to the fiber axis. In many cases wax rings are present and sometimes also vague scattering is found due to other substances, presumably lignins and pectins.

The highest crystallinity, as indicated by the sharpness of the interferences, is found in ramie, next is flax; lower crystallinity is found in the Malvaceae and sunn fibers.

[5] Berkley (1938 and 1939) correlated the X-ray angle with the strength of the cotton fiber; Meredith (1951*b*) with the number of convolutions.

[6] Unpublished results of author.

Flax (Diagrams 3 to 9)

The diagram of flax (*Linum usitatissimum*) is a clear fiber diagram in which at least four layerlines can be recognized. It differs from

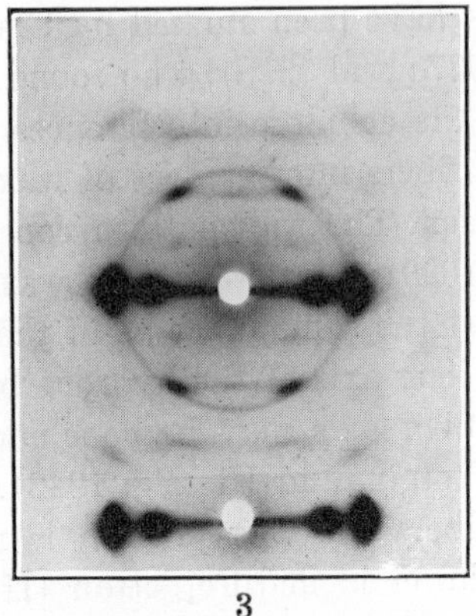

3

4 5

PLATE II. Flax, *Linum usitatissimum* (Linaceae). Diagram 3, retted fiber flax from Russia. Note double wax ring. Diagram 4, same after wax has been dissolved, proving that rings are due to presence of wax. Diagram 5, diffraction pattern of wax extracted from this fiber, showing the most prominent rings; the outer, fainter rings are not shown.

that of ramie by its more diffused and broader interferences, indicating lower lateral order and (or) smaller crystallites. The interference arcs are short, elliptically diamond-shaped, with diffused border, as in the pattern of undegummed ramie. The A_1 and A_2 interferences are nearly fused together and can be only separated in short time-exposure diagrams (Inset Diagrams 3 and 8).

The presence of continuous wax rings is a very striking feature in all samples of retted flax; the (110) and (020) wax rings are clearly

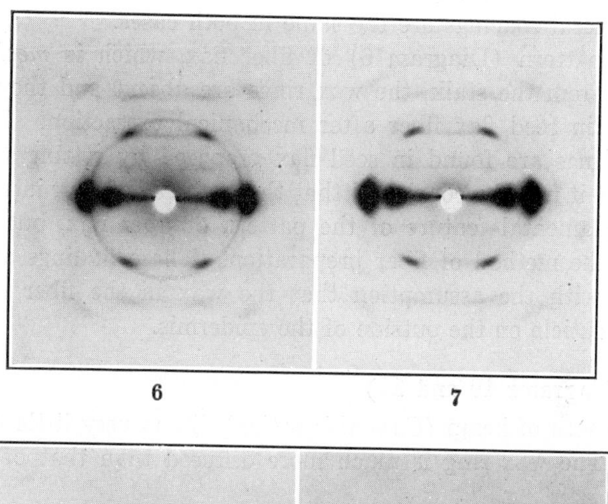

6 7

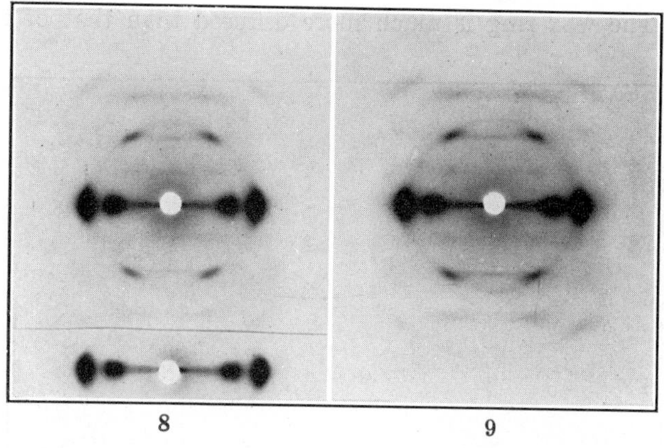

8 9

PLATE III. Flax fiber, *Linum usitatissimum* (Linaceae). Diagram 6, dew-retted fiber flax from Canada; loose fiber lifted from one single stalk. Diagram 7, unretted fiber flax from Ekusta, N. C., fiber mechanically extracted from stalk. Diagram 8, seed flax, Bison, fiber mechanically extracted from stalk. Diagram 9, seed flax, Dakota, fiber prepared by retting. Note presence of wax ring in Diagrams 6 and 8, and absence of wax ring in Diagrams 7 and 9, where fiber has been mechanically extracted.

shown in Diagrams 3, 6, and 9. In Diagram 8 of mechanically prepared seed flax these wax rings are absent.

That the rings are due to wax is proved by comparing the diagrams of normal and dewaxed samples (Diagram 4) and of the wax alone (Diagram 5). Diagram 5 clearly shows the (110) and (020) rings of flax wax. The narrow rings close to the primary beam which are due to *long spacings* is only faintly visible in this reproduction. The large spacings of cotton wax are different from those of flax wax,[7] but the lateral spacings are the same in both cases.

In the pattern (Diagram 6) of fiber flax, which is *mechanically* extracted from the stalk, the wax rings are absent and they also do not occur in seed flax fiber after mechanical extraction. Inversely, the wax rings are found in seed flax prepared by retting (Diagram 9), so that it may be concluded that the presence of wax interferences is no fundamental feature of the pattern of *fiber* flax, but rather a result of the method of fiber preparation. These findings are in accordance with the assumption that the wax in the fiber originates from the cuticle on the outside of the epidermis.

Hemp (Diagrams 10 and 11)

The pattern of hemp (*Cannabis sativa*) differs very little from that of flax. The wax ring is much more diffused than that of flax and

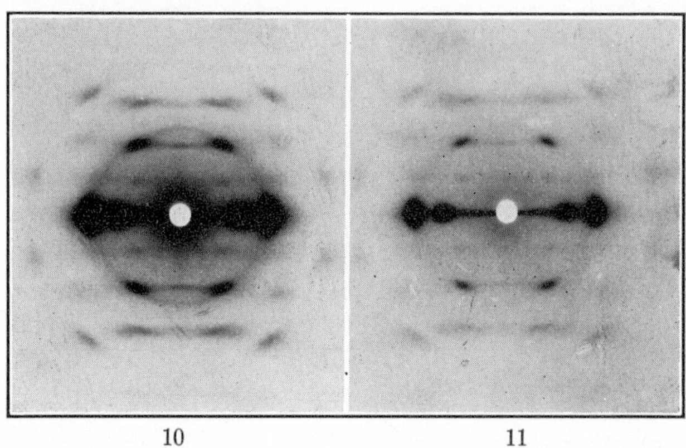

10 11

PLATE IV. Hemp, *Cannabis sativa* (Cannabaceae). Diagram 10, American hemp, prepared by retting. Note faint wax ring. Diagram 11, same as Diagram 10, shorter exposure.

generally only shows up at longer exposure (Diagram 10). The equatorial interferences are less elongated than in flax and are almost elliptical-diamond shaped, also the (021) interferences are slightly shorter than in flax. This indicates a higher degree of orientation than in flax.

[7] Unpublished results of author.

Ramie (Diagrams 12 to 14)

The diagram of ramie (*Boehmeria nivea*) is very close to the ideal fiber diagram of native cellulose. The intereferences are arranged

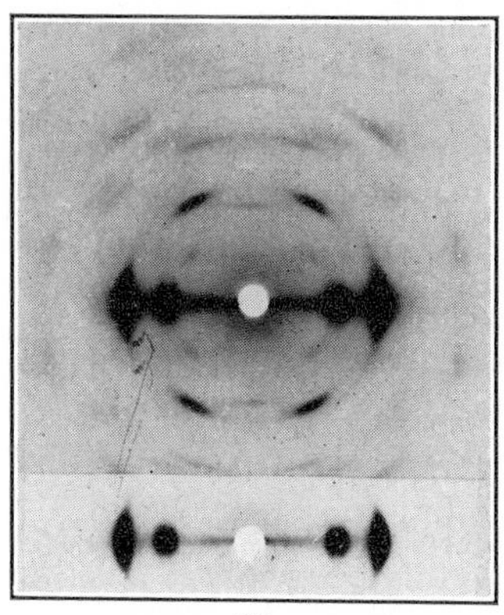

12

13 14

Plate V. Bast fiber, ramie, *Boehmeria nivea* (Urticaceae). Diagram 12, ramie degummed by Siland process. Diagram 13, ramie degummed by another process, lower degree of orientation. Diagram 14, undegummed ramie, low lateral order; note different shape of interference spots.

in clear layerlines, from which at least five can be recognized. Ramie has short and relatively narrow, well-defined equatorial arcs. The A_4 interferences have elongated diamond shape. The A_1 and A_2 interferences are clearly separated from each other.

(In most other bast fibers the interferences are more diffused and broader, having more poorly defined contours, as a result of less perfect order. The A_1 and A_2 interferences are generally fused together in the other materials.)

The different methods of growth and degumming of the fiber influence the pattern (see Diagrams 12 and 13), and in the extreme case of undegummed ramie (China grass) the diagram is almost similar to the one of jute, which has a much lower lateral order.

Malvaceae Bast Fibers (Diagrams 15 and 16)

All the patterns of the various representatives of the Malvaceae bast fibers are very similar, e.g., jute (*Corchorus capsularis*), Diagram 15*a*; devil's cotton (*Abroma augusta*), Diagram 15*b*; kenaf (Java jute, *Hibiscus cannabinus*), Diagram 15*c*; roselle (*Hibiscus sabdariffa*), Diagram 16*a*; musk "hemp," *Hibicus abelmoschus*, Diagram 16*b*; Queensland "hemp," *Sida rhombifolia*, Diagram 16*c*; Caesar weed (*Urena lobata*), Diagram 16*d*; *Malachra capitata*, Diagram 16*e*. The diagrams are more diffuse than those of the foregoing fibers, and the layerlines are less pronounced. The equatorial interferences are broad, elliptical-oblong, with diffused borders. The A_4 interferences extend 25–28° in length. The A_1 and A_2 interferences are fused together into one diffused spot and are no longer separated in short time-exposure diagrams (see Inset Diagram 16*a*). The four (021) interferences (on the diagonals) are diffused. Most patterns show a vague diffused ring in continuation of the A_4 and (021) interferences; this ring is possibly due to cellulose in random orientation, or to wax, or to other substances or to combinations of all these materials.

Sirkar and Chowdhury (1946) showed that some of the interferences in the pattern of jute become smaller and the pattern clearer as a result of bleaching. The removal of some of the amorphous material will help in producing a sharper diagram.

The pattern of *Malachra capitata*, Diagram 16*e*, is the most distinct of all Malvaceae diagrams. It is almost similar to that of hemp; faint wax rings are present.

Diffused interferences presumably associated with the presence of lignin (Sen and Woods, 1948) are present in many of the Malvaceae bast fibers.

Sunn Fiber (Diagrams 17 and 18)

The patterns of sunn fiber, *Crotalaria juncea*, and kudzu "hemp," *Pueraria phaseoloides*, are identical. The interferences are less diffused and better defined than in the Malvaceae fibers, particularly the (021) arcs on the diagonals, which are much sharper.

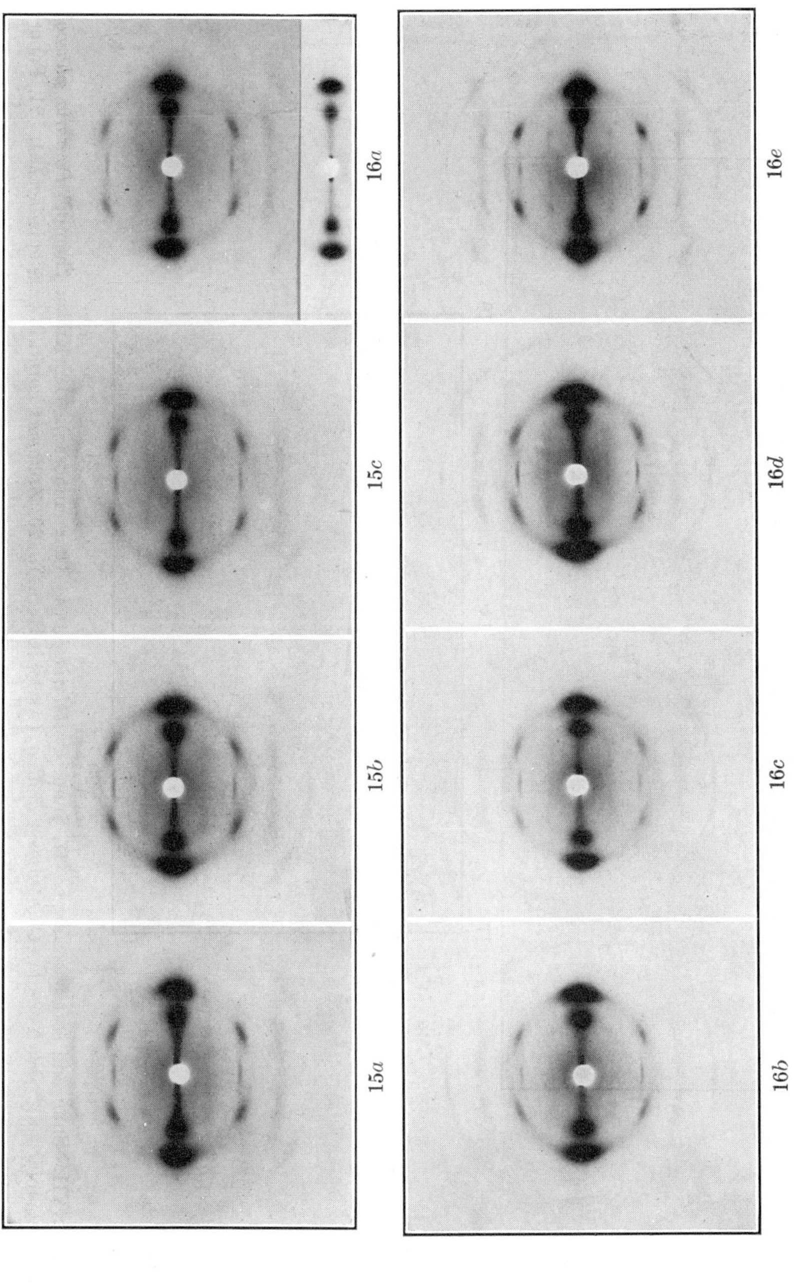

PLATE VI. Malvaceae bast fibers. 15*a*, Jute, *Corchorus capsularis*. 15*b*, Devil's cotton, *Abroma augusta* (Sterculiaceae). 15*c*, Kenaf (Java "jute"), *Hibiscus cannabinus*. 16*a*, Roselle, *Hibiscus sabdariffa*. 16*b*, Musk "hemp," *Hibiscus abelmoschus*. 16*c*, Queensland "hemp," *Sida rhombifolia*. 16*d*, Caesar weed (uacima), *Urena lobata*. 16*e*, *Malachra capitata*.

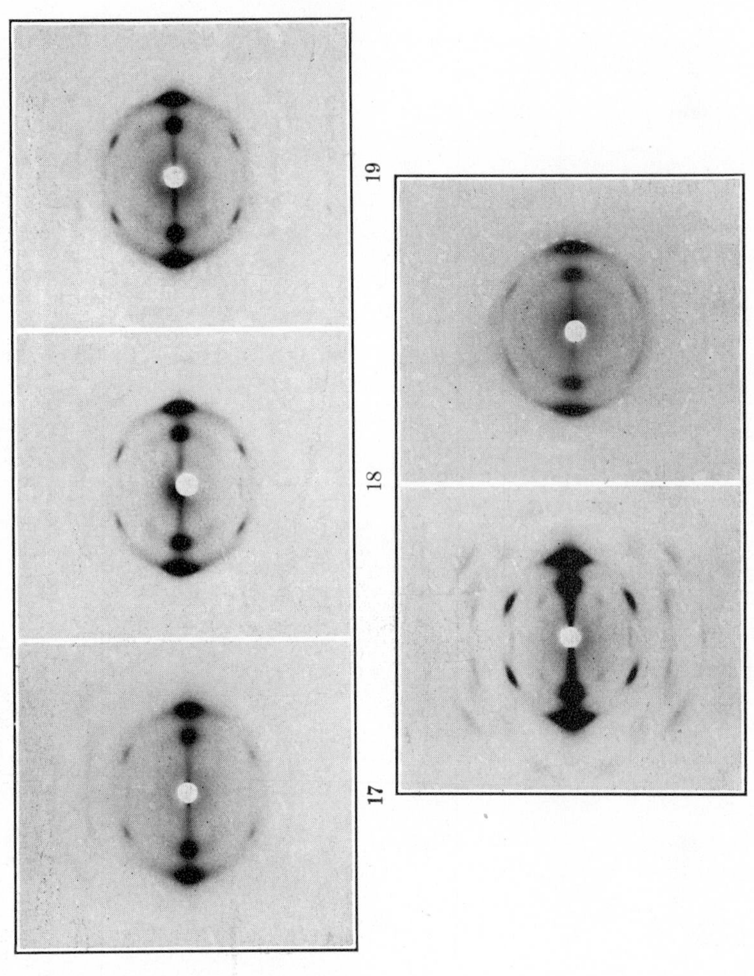

PLATE VII. Sunn and soft bast fibers. 17, Sunn, *Crotalaria juncea* (Leguminosae). 18, Kudzu "hemp," *Pueraria phaseoloides* (Leguminosae). 19. Yercum, *Calotropis gigantea* (Asclepiadaceae). 20, *Asclepias cornutii* (Asclepiadaceae). 21, Paper mulberry, *Broussonetia papyrifera* (Urticaceae).

A remarkable feature in these diagrams is the presence of a faint continuation of the A_4 interference on the same diffraction circle. This may be explained by the presence, to a small degree, of crystallites in directions other than the one around the fiber axis.

Soft Bast Fibers (Diagrams 19 to 21)

The diagram of *Crotalaria gigantea* is similar to that of the sunn fibers. The pattern of the bast fiber from *Asclepias cornutii* (Diagram 20) is completely different from that of *C. gigantea,* resembling closely the pattern of ramie (Diagrams 12–14), a very sharp, distinct cellulose fiber diagram.

The pattern of the paper mulberry fiber (*Broussonetia papyrifera,* Diagram 21) is basically a cellulose pattern with elongated, narrow equatorial arcs (A_4) with a diffuse, continuous ring.

Leaf Fibers (Diagrams 22 to 36)

The patterns of the structural or leaf fibers correspond to the diagram of cellulose in spiral orientation. The pitch of the spiral in which the crystallites are oriented is different in the different fibers, as is expressed by the differences in extension of the A_4 (002) interference arcs from the equator along the diffraction circle (see section on determination of orientation of crystal lattice, etc.).

On the basis of the sizes of the arcs in their X-ray patterns, the different leaf fibers may be separated into four groups. Note short arcs in Diagrams 22 and 23, increased arcs in Diagrams 26–28, and largest arcs in Diagram 29. Scattered fine spots in the diagrams are caused by crystals of calcium oxalate in the fibers.

1. The fibers of the *first group* have a pattern with relatively short equatorial interference arcs (A_4, 002), from 30 to 35°. They are longer than the oblong interferences found in the patterns of the Malvaceae fibers. The arcs generally fade out in an extension of very low intensity on the same diffraction circle (002).

The arc size of abacá (Manila "hemp"; *Musa textilis,* Diagram 22) is 30°, and that of phormium (New Zealand flax; *Phormium tenax,* Diagram 23) is larger, 35°. The pattern of palma pita (*Yucca treculeana,* Diagram 43) also falls in this group and is quite similar to the pattern of phormium.

The patterns of the above fibers are very similar to the ones of the Malvaceae bast fibers with the difference that the equatorial interferences are a little narrower and more arc-like.

The pattern of the pineapple fiber (*Ananas comosus* syn. *sativa*), Diagram 24, and of caroa (*Neoglazovia variegata*), Diagram 25, are

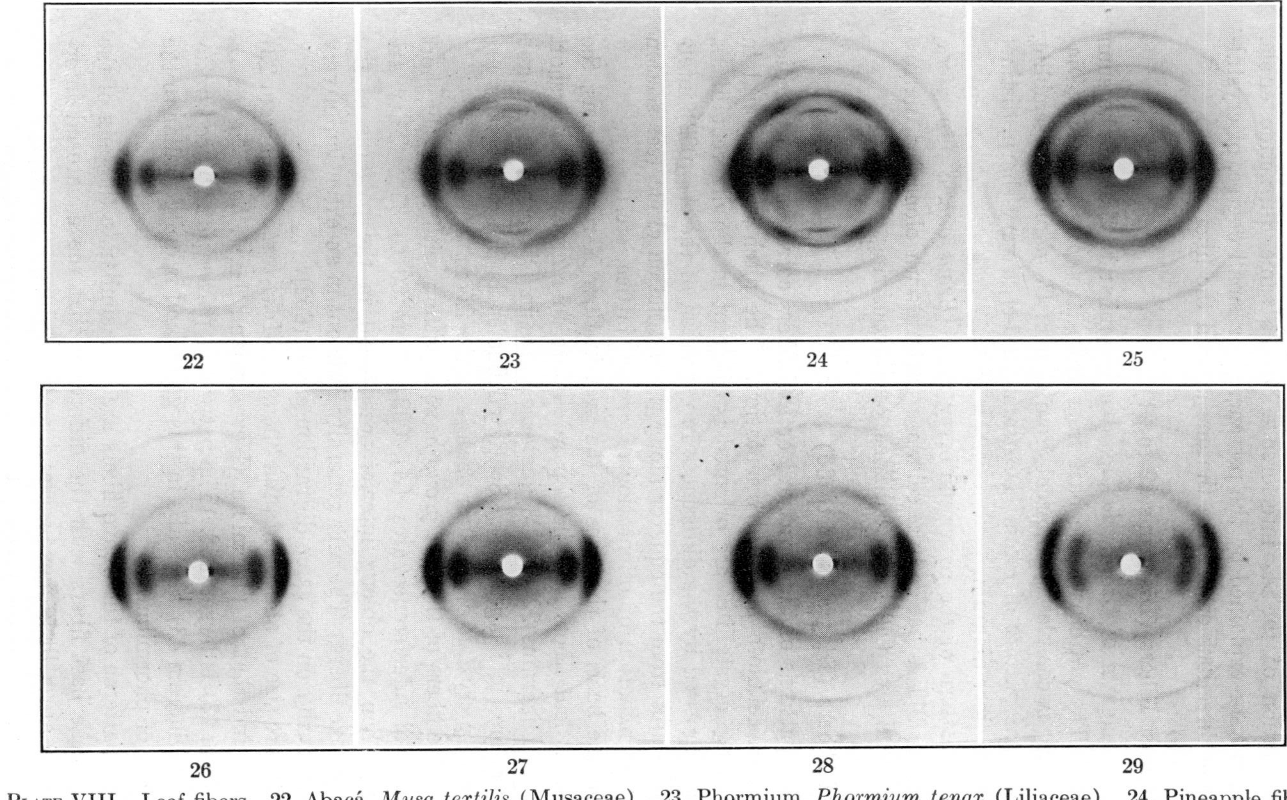

PLATE VIII. Leaf fibers. 22, Abacá, *Musa textilis* (Musaceae). 23, Phormium, *Phormium tenax* (Liliaceae). 24, Pineapple fiber, *Ananas sativa* (Bromeliaceae). 25, caroa, *Neoglazovia variegata* (Bromeliaceae). Agaves (Amaryllidaceae). 26, Sisal, *Agave sisalana*. 27, Cantala, *Agave cantala*. 28, Mexican maguey, *Agave lurida*. 29, Henequen, *Agave fourcroydes*.

characterized by a little longer arc, 40°, than the patterns of the foregoing fibers of this group. The diagram of the pineapple fiber is the sharpest one and shows very clear diagonal (021) interferences and a strong indication for the presence of wax by meridian arcs. A high degree of purity and crystallinity of the cellulose of this fiber as well as the presence of wax may be concluded from the diagram.

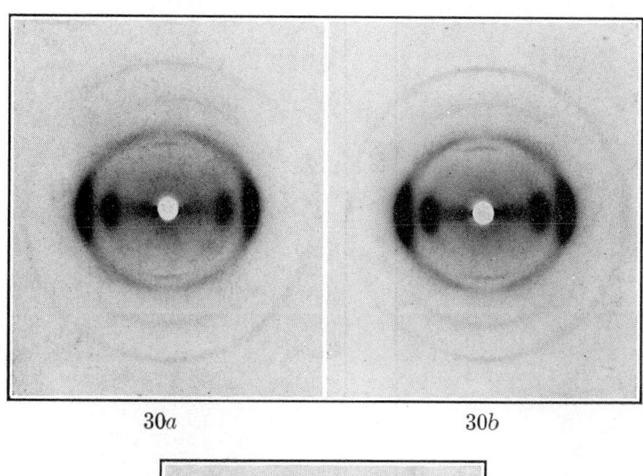

30*a* 30*b*

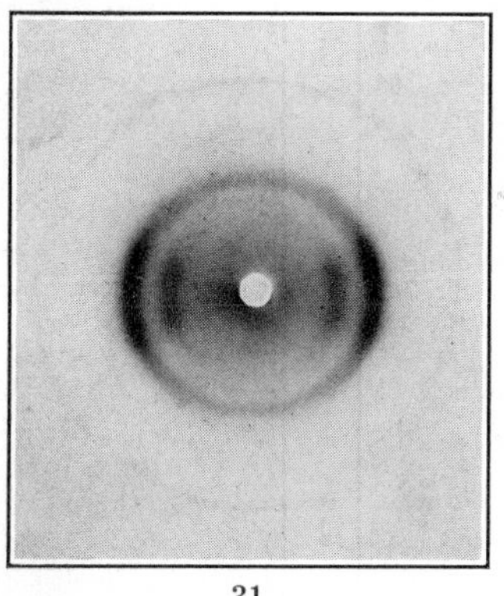

31

PLATE IX. Leaf fibers, Sansevierias (Liliaceae). Diagram 30*a*, Guinea bowstring, *Sansevieria thyrsiflora* (syn. *guineensis*). Diagram 30*b*, bowstring, *Sansevieria zeylanica*. Diagram 31, ife, *Sansevieria cylindrica*.

2. The fibers of the *second group* have patterns with longer equatorial interferences, from 43° to 55°. To this group belong the agaves and sansevierias.

The patterns of sisal (*Agave sisalana*), Diagram 26, cantala (*Agave Cantala*), Diagram 27, and of Mexican maguey (*Agave lurida*), Diagram 28, are almost identical and have arcs from 43° to 45°. The diagonal (021) interferences are very diffused in these patterns.

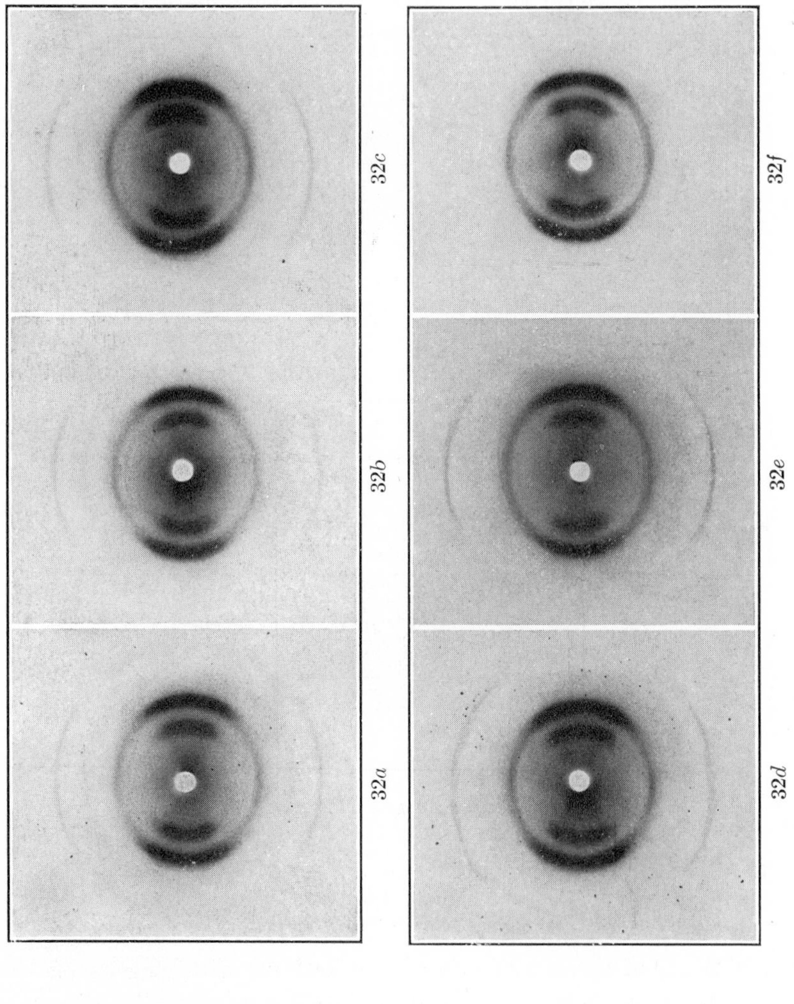

PLATE X. Leaf fibers, Furcraeas (Amaryllidaceae). 32*a*, Mauritius fiber, *Furcraea gigantea*. 32*b*, Fique, *Furcraea macrophylla*. 32*c*, *Furcraea selloa*. 32*d*, *Furcraea pubescens*. 32*e*, *Furcraea cubensis* (syn. *hexapetala*). 32*f*, *Furcraea tuberosa*.

The pattern of Mexican henequen (*Agave fourcroydes*), Diagram 29, has the longest arcs (55°) and forms a transition to the long arcs in the patterns of the Furcraeae. The (021) interferences are no longer distinct here.

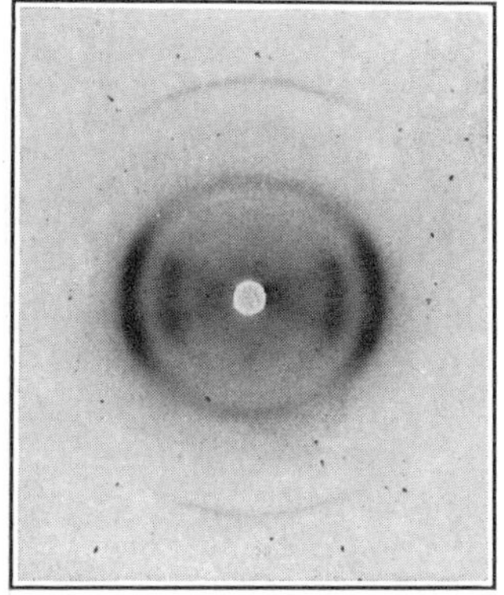

33*a*

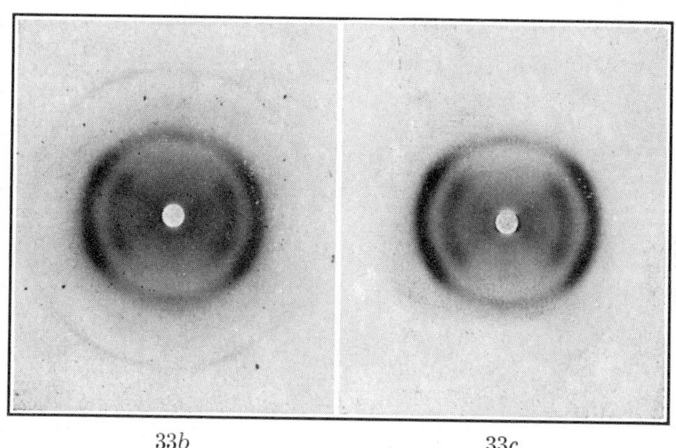

33*b* 33*c*

PLATE XI. Leaf fibers and brush fibers (Amaryllidaceae). Diagram 33*a*, sisal (*Agave*). Diagram 33*b*, ixtle de Jaumave, *Agava heterocantha*. Diagram 33*c*, tula ixtle, *Agave lophantha*. Scattered fine spots are due to presence of crystallites of calcium oxalate in fiber.

In the patterns of most agave fibers, a few irregular spots appear scattered all over the diagram; they are due to the diffraction by large calcium oxalate crystals which are found in these fibers.

The patterns of Guinea bowstring (*Sansevieria thyrsiflora* syn. *guineensis*), Diagram 30*a*, and ordinary bowstring (*Sansevieria zeylanica*), Diagram 30*b*, are almost identical. The A_4 arcs measure

50°. The pattern of ife (*Sansevieria cylindrica*), Diagram 31, has longer arcs (about 60°); this pattern is almost identical to that of *Agave fourcroydes* (Diagram 29).

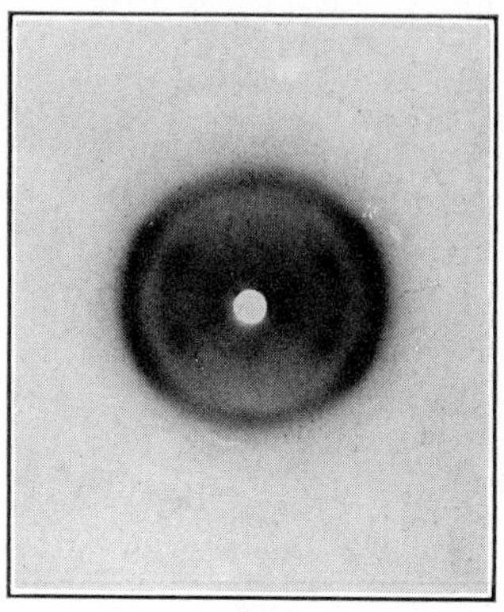

34

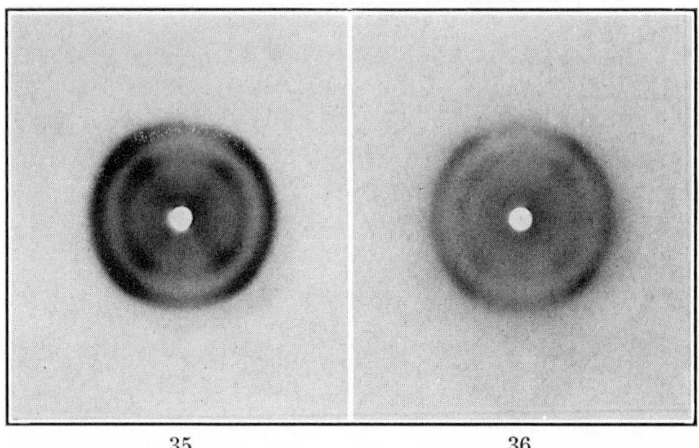

35 36

PLATE XII. Leaf fibers and brush fibers (Palmaceae). Diagram 34, Bahia piassaba, *Attala funifera*. Diagram 35, coir, *Cocos mucifera*. Diagram 36, bassine palmyra, *Borassus flabellifera*.

3. The fibers of the *third group* have patterns with still longer arcs of 55° to 80°. To this group belong the Furcraeae, Diagrams 32*a* to *f*. These have A_4 interference arcs with equal thicknesses over the entire length. Sometimes a narrower place of lower intensity occurs in the center of the arc at the equator (Diagram 32*d* and *f*). The A_1 and A_2 interferences are fused together side by side into a single arc within the A_4 arc. The arcs end rather abruptly and continue in a very

faint intensity along the diffraction ring. The diagonal (021) arcs are fused in this faint ring.

These features indicate a distinct spiral structure with relatively small fluctuation of crystallites around the direction of the spiral.

Diagram 32*d* shows many scattered diffraction spots which originate from calcium oxalate crystals in the fiber.

4. The fibers of the *fourth group* have patterns with the largest arcs, from 65° to 98°. To this group belong the brush fibers.

The pattern of the *Agave,* Diagram 33*a*, has arcs of 65° and forms a transition to the foregoing group. The pattern is very similar to that of the Furcraeae and of *Agave fourcroydes.* The patterns of the next fibers in this group have ever-increasing arcs, combined with a tendency of the arc to break down at the equator where the intensity is lower and the thickness narrower. For the discussion of breaking down of the arc into separate arcs, refer to the section on determination of orientation of crystal lattice.

The pattern of the ixtle de Jaumave (*Agave heterocantha*), Diagram 33*b* and of tula ixtle (*Agave lophantha*), Diagram 33*c*, have arcs of 85°. In the patterns of these fibers, very strong interference spots occur, scattered all over the diagram, due to diffraction by calcium oxalate crystals in the fiber. These interferences disappear after treatment of the fiber with weak hydrochloric acid.

The patterns of Bahia piassaba (*Attalia funifera*), Diagram 34, coconut fiber or coir, a seed fiber (*Cocos nucifera*), Diagram 35, and bassine palmyra (*Borassus flabellifera*), Diagram 36, have arc sizes of 80°, 90°, and 98°, respectively. The diagrams of coir and bassine show especially a clear breaking down of the equatorial arcs into four separate arcs.

Seed and Fruit Fibers (Diagrams 37 to 40)

The pattern of Java kapok (*Ceiba pentandra*), Diagram 39, and of the cattail fiber (*Typha* spp.), Diagram 40, are very similar (also the pattern of milkweed floss, see below). Both patterns are characterized by the presence of very intense, diffused scattering discs from and around the primary beam. Both diagrams have in addition a faint diffused ring at about the place of the A_4 interference of cellulose. This ring may be partly due to pectin, especially since the chemical composition of kapok differs from that of the foregoing fibers by containing only 60 per cent of cellulose and a high percentage of pentosanes (pectins) (about 25 per cent) and lignin.

The pattern of the fibers of milkweed (*Asclepias syriaca*), Diagram 37, shows the same features as above, but points of maximum intensity occur at the equator in the diffused rings, corresponding to the

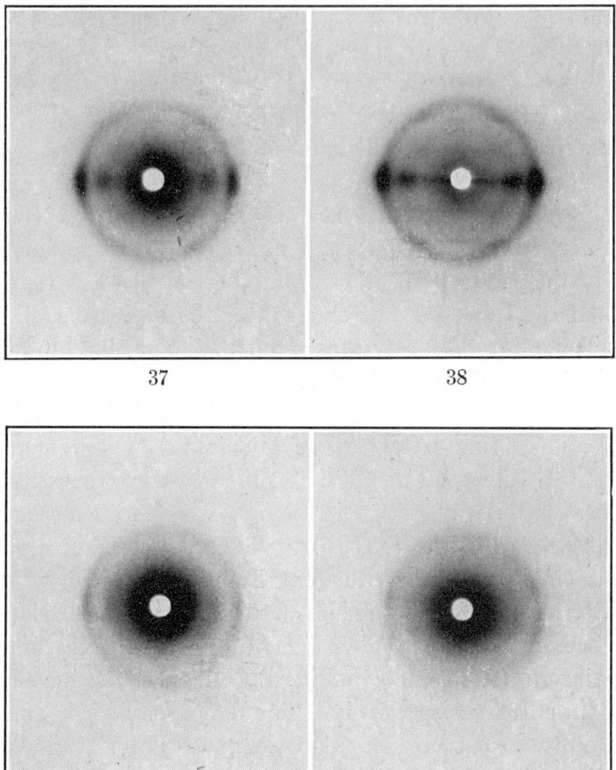

PLATE XIII. Seed and fruit fibers. Diagram 37, milkweed floss, *Asclepias syriaca* (Asclepiadaceae). Diagram 38, akund, *Calotropis gigantea* (Asclepiadaceae). Diagram 39, Java kapok, *Ceiba petandra* (Bombacaceae). Diagram 40, Cattail fiber, *Typha latifolia* (Typhaceae).

A_4 interferences of cellulose and indicating the presence of oriented cellulose in this fiber (A_1 and A_2 interferences also occur).

In the pattern of akund (the seed floss of *Calotropis gigantea*), Diagram 38, this feature is still more pronounced, and a clear pattern of cellulose appears. A remarkable feature is the presence of distinct layerlines here. In this pattern the scattering around the primary beam, found in the foregoing three patterns, is absent.

Fibers Consisting of Complete Plant Organs (Diagrams 41 to 44)

The pattern of raphia (a complete epidermis of the leaf of *Raphia pedunculata*), Diagram 41, is closest to that of the Sansevieriae (see above) but shows, in addition, a clear wax ring. The pattern of

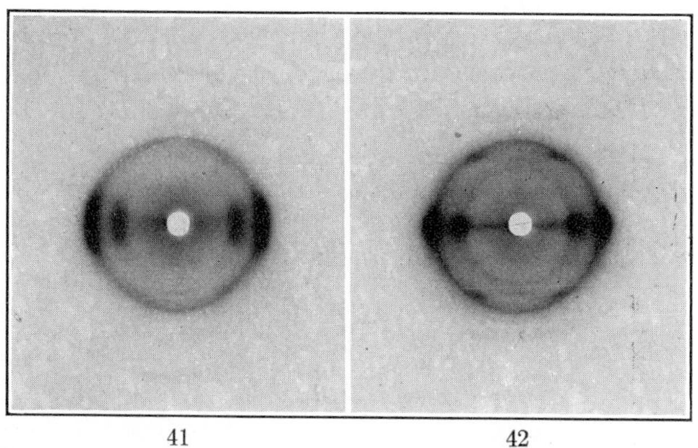

41 42

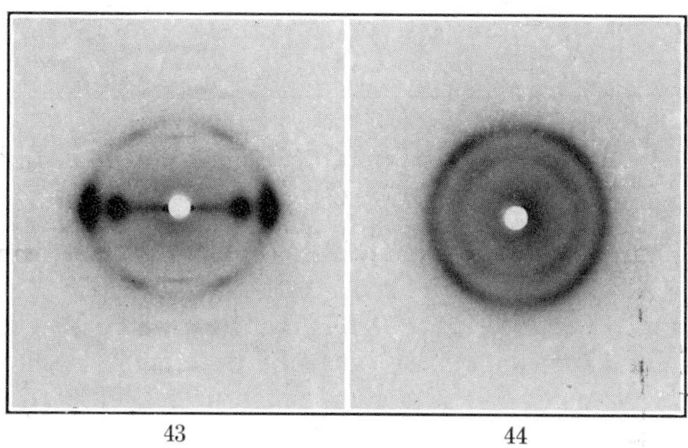

43 44

PLATE XIV. Miscellaneous plant fibers. Diagram 41, raphia, *Raphia pedunculata* (Palmaceae). Diagram 42, *Stipa tenacissima* (Gramineae). Diagram 43, palma pita, *Yucca treculeana* (Liliaceae). Diagram 44, zacaton (rice root), *Epicampes macroura* (Gramineae).

Stipa tenacissima, Diagram 42, is one of a clear cellulose pattern of the Malvaceae type with a superimposed clear wax ring and an unidentified fine inner ring, probably due to silicates.

The pattern of *rice root* or *zacaton,* a brush fiber prepared from the roots of *Epicampes macroura,* Diagram 44, has basically the same pattern as that of *Borassus,* Diagram 36, in that it shows four diagonally placed intensity maxima of the A_1, A_2, and A_4 interferences.

Animal Hair Fibers (Diagrams 45 to 49)

The patterns of the animal hair fibers are identical with the diagrams of α keratin, which is described above in the section on keratin.

Wool, mohair, alpaca, llama, cashmere, camel hair, and vicuña all give the same pattern.

The only differences are in the sharpness of the interferences; for instance, a slight difference may be observed in Diagram 45 of 36's quality wool and Diagram 46 of 60's quality wool. In Diagram 45

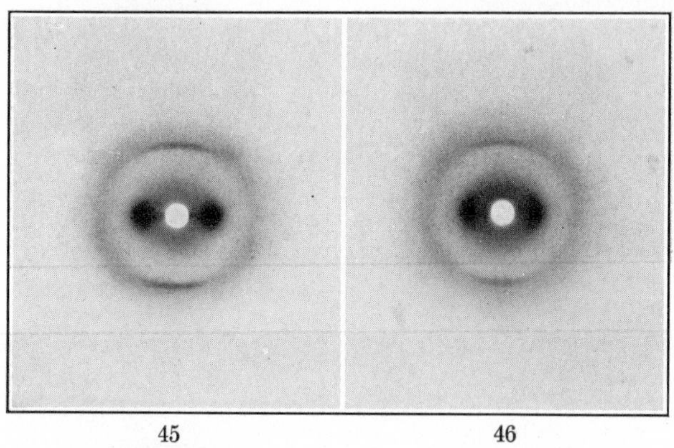

PLATE XV. Animal hair fibers; wool. Diagram 45, wool 36's. Diagram 46, wool 60's.

the meridian interferences seem a little bit more distinct than in Diagram 46. Also the equatorial spots are more distinct in Diagram 45, where they are round, than in Diagram 46, where they are more oblong. The clear diagram, 45, may be due to the larger diameter of the fiber, resulting in the showing of a smaller portion of the cuticle. Astbury (1936) found that the keratin in the cuticle may be less oriented than in the cortex, and he obtained a clearer pattern with descaled fibers. Also the background is more diffused in Diagram 46. Similar differences are found between mohair, alpaca, and llama on one hand (Diagrams 47 and 48), and cashmere, camel hair and vicuña on the other (Diagram 49). Diagrams 49 all have a diffused background.

Silk (Diagrams 50 and 51)

The patterns of natural silk and tussah silk correspond to the basic patterns described in the section "Silk Fibroin," under "Basic X-Ray Patterns, etc.," above.

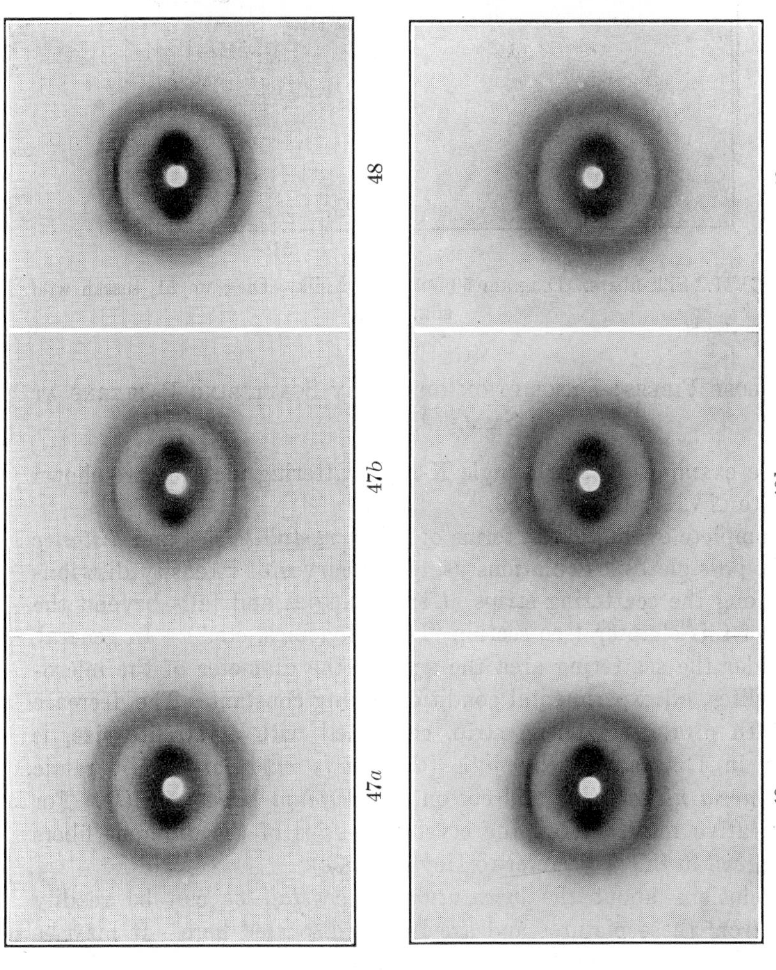

PLATE XVI. Animal hair fibers. 47*a*, Mohair. 47*b*, Alpaca. 48, Llama. 49*a*, Cashmere. 49*b*, Camel hair. 49*c*, Vicuña.

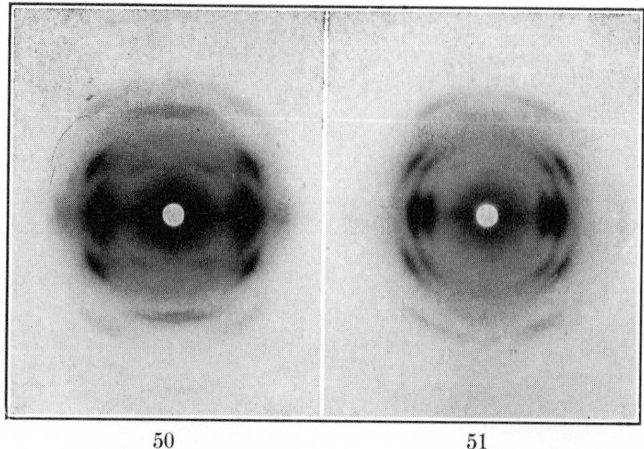

PLATE XVII. Silk fibers. Diagram 50, cultivated silk. Diagram 51, tussah wild silk.

CELLULOSE FIBERS; DESCRIPTION OF X-RAY SCATTERING PATTERNS AT SMALL ANGLES

Some examples of small-angle X-ray scattering pictures are shown in Plate XVIII, Diagram 52.

A complete evaluation in terms of *microcrystallite size* and *distance* is only possible by calculations using the curves of intensity distribution along the scattering strips at small angles and falls beyond the scope of this chapter (see section "Long Spacings, etc."). In general, the wider the scattering area the smaller the diameter of the microcrystallites, all experimental conditions being constant. The decrease in width of the scattering strip, connected with crystallite size, is shown in Diagram 52 by jute (*Corchorus capsularis*) (*j*), ramie (*Boehmeria nivea*) (*k*), and cotton (*Gossypium hirsutum*) (*l*). For quantitative results about the crystallite sizes of the different fibers determined in this way, refer to Heyn (1950*c*).

Conclusions about the *orientation of crystallites* can be readily made from these pictures and are briefly discussed here. It may be seen that the patterns lettered *g-l* consist of a horizontal scattering strip of different extension. This scattering is found with fibers of microcrystallite orientation parallel or almost parallel to the fiber axis.

Patterns *a* to *f* consist of two scattering strips which cross each other at the center of the diagram at different angles. These angles

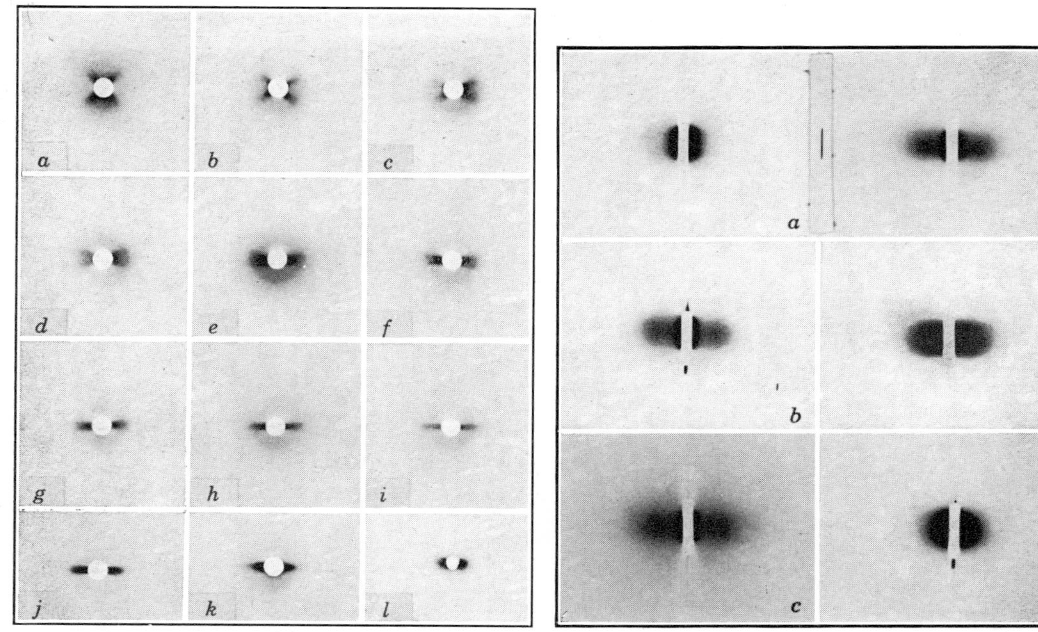

52*A* 52*B*

PLATE XVIII. Small-angle X-ray scattering. 52*A*, *a*, Coir, *Cocos nucifera; b*, tula ixtle, *Agave lophantha; c*, ixtle de Jaumave, *Agave heterocantha; d*, Mexican henequen, *Agave fourcroydes; e*, Guinea bowstring, *Sansevieria guinensis; f*, sisal, *Agave sisilana; g*, yucca; *h*, abacá, *Musa textilis; i*, pineapple fiber, *Ananias comosus; j*, jute, *Corchorus capsularis; k*, ramie, *Boehmeria nivea; l*, cotton, *Gossypium hirsutum*. 52*B*, Small-angle scattering by some rayons. Original size. Sample film distance 20 cm. *a*, Fortisan, dry state; *b, c*, same, water-swollen state; *d*, Fiber G, water-swollen state; *e*, same, swollen beyond water-swollen state; *f*, Cordura, water-swollen state. Note presence of maxima in *b, c*, and *d*.

are related to the spiral pitch of the fibers (twice the angle of the pitch). The same order is found when the different fibers are grouped according to their spiral pitch and when the X-ray scattering pictures are grouped according to the angle of the cross, namely, *a*, coir (*Cocos nucifera*); *b*, tula ixtle (*Agave lophantha*); *c*, ixtle de Jaumave (*Agave heterocantha*); *d*, Mexican henequen (*Agave fourcroydes*); *e*, Guinea bowstring (*Sansevieria thyrsiflora*); *f*, sisal (*Agave sisalana*); *g*, yucca (*Yucca* spp.); *h*, abacá (*Musa textilis*); *i*, pineapple fiber (*Ananas comosus*).

REGENERATED FIBERS

Basic Diagrams of Regenerated Cellulose and Regenerated Protein Fibers

The basic X-ray patterns of viscose and cuprammonium rayons correspond to the pattern of cellulose II (which see). The differences between the various types of rayon within this group are due to the different orientation and different degree of crystallinity and lateral order (e.g., see Ingersoll, 1946).

The basic X-ray pattern of the globular proteins, zein fibers, and soybean fibers agree essentially with the basic pattern of β keratin (which see), so that chains of these polypeptides must be packed in a way similar to the polypeptide chains of wool. Senti (1947), Senti, Eddy, and Nutting (1943), and Nutting, Hawley, Copley, and Senti (1946) demonstrated the unfolding of these globular proteins into extended polypeptide chains by converting them by heat and mechanical working into a fibrous form of high orientation. A pattern similar to that of β keratin was obtained from these materials.

The basic patterns of cellulose acetate (not a regenerated fiber in the strict sense) and of the alginate fiber have not yet been completely explained in terms of the molecular structure, although it is certain that the 10.3 A spacing in cellulose acetate corresponds to the repeat period of the chain molecule (see further under cellulose acetate). The 4.25 A spacing in alginate fiber is probably also related to the fiber period.

Description and Explanation of X-Ray Patterns of the Individual Regenerated Cellulose and Protein Fibers (Diagrams 53 to 60)

The pattern of *Fortisan* (Celanese Corporation of America), Diagram 53, a highly oriented regenerated cellulose, is the most perfect (i.e., the nearest to the "ideal" fiber) fiber pattern of all cellulosic fibers. The extremely clear layerlines and the concentration of the equatorial interferences into well-defined spots indicates almost perfect orientation. The equatorial interferences are represented separately in a picture of shorter exposure time. The repeat period in the fiber axis as calculated from the layerlines is 10.3 A, and the spacings of the paratropic planes, calculated from the equatorial reflections, are

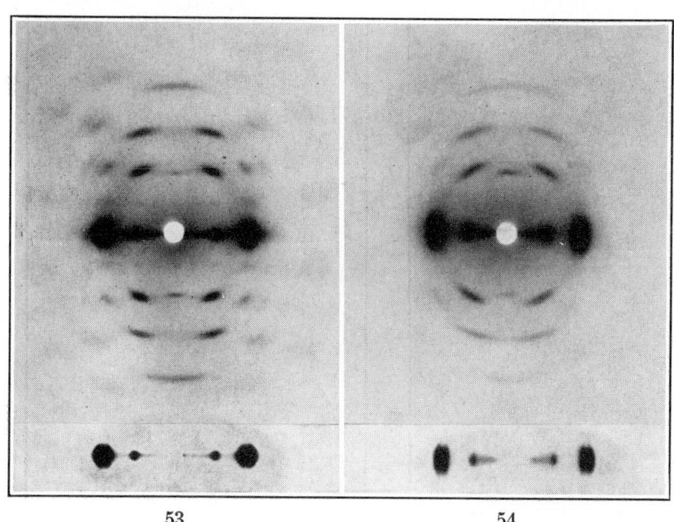

53 54

Plate XIX. Cellulose acetate fibers. Diagram 53, Fortisan 60 (Celanese Corporation of America). Diagram 54, Fiber G 1100-552 (E. I. du Pont de Nemours and Company).

7.35 A (interference A_0 or planes of Miller indices (101)), 4.5 A (A_3, planes (101)), and 4.01 A (A_4, planes (002)). (The crystallographic *b* axis is in the direction of the fiber axis here.) These spacings apply also to the regenerated cellulose fibers.

The pattern of *Fiber G* (du Pont), Diagram 54, is slightly less distinct, indicating less perfect orientation. The spots on the equator are modified into very short arcs, and the layerlines are less pronounced; the pattern still shows a very high degree of orientation, however.

The patterns of *ordinary viscose rayons* are still more diffuse. The equatorial interferences are replaced by distinct arcs or sickles of various size, indicating a further degree of disorientation. The distribution of interferences on distinct layerlines is no longer clearly

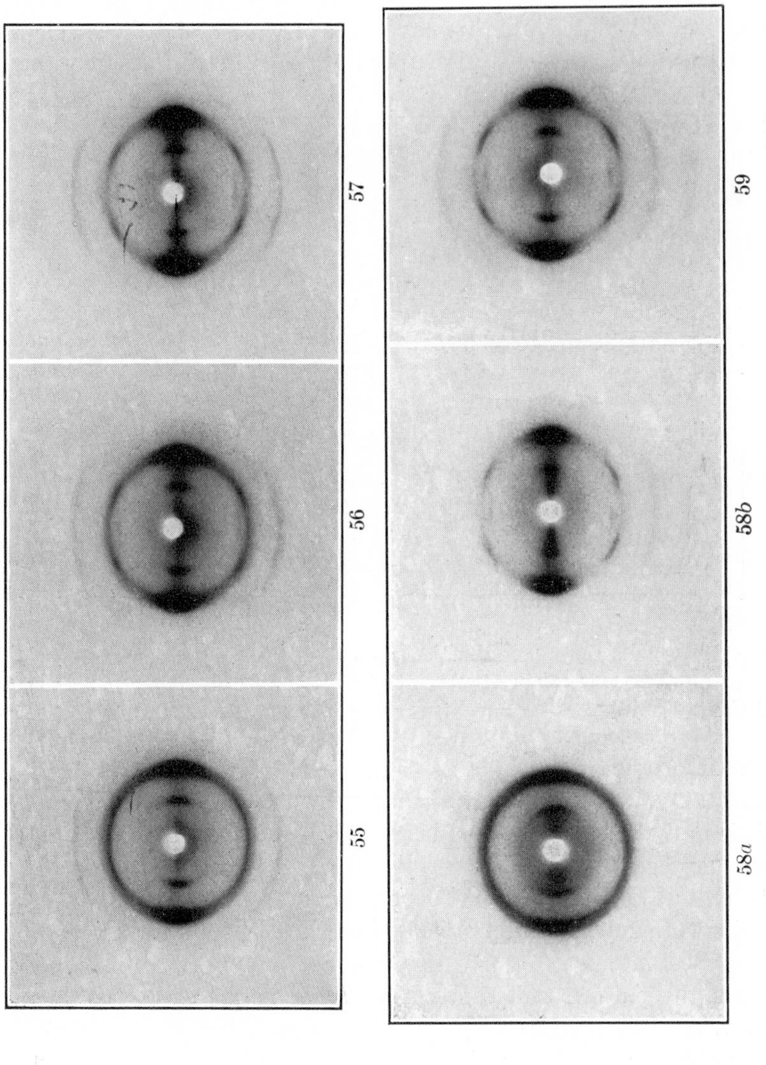

Plate XX. Regenerated rayons. 55. Narco 150-42. 56, Narco 75-100. 57, Supernarco 1100-480 (high-tenacity) (*North American Rayon*). 58*a* and *b*, Viscose rayon spun with zero % and 70% Godet stretch (experimental sample, *American Viscose*). 59, Bemberg (cuprammonium) rayon 100-74 (*Bemberg*).

observed. Generally, a vague ring continues from the equatorial arcs and includes also some of the interferences belonging to the first layer-line (for instance, the two (020) interferences).

The different degree of orientation that may be found in commercial rayons is mainly a result of the stretch in the spinning process. This relationship is conclusively shown by the diagrams of two experimental samples (courtesy of American Viscose Corporation), which are comparable in every respect except stretch. As shown in Diagram 58*a*,

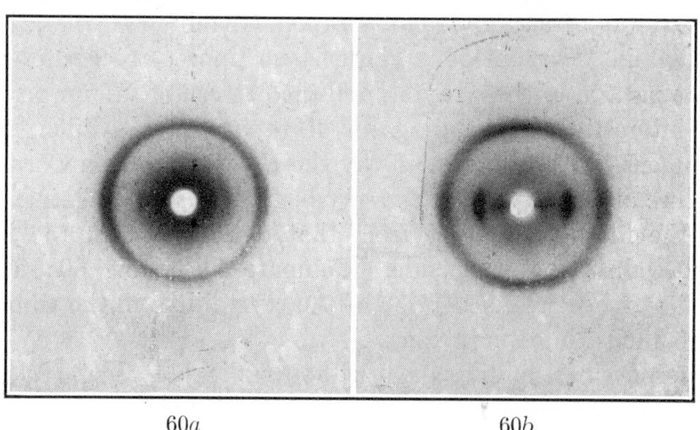

60*a* 60*b*

PLATE XXI. Specialty viscose filaments. Diagram 60, rayon ribbon monofilamen of 360 denier, so-called rayon straw (Hartford Rayon Corporation). *a*, beam perpendicular to ribbon; *b*, beam parallel to ribbon.

the sample of zero per cent Godet wheel stretch displays a pattern of continuous diffuse rings with slight concentration of intensity on the equator, indicating an almost complete random orientation. The pattern of the sample of 70 per cent Godet stretch, Diagram 58*b*, displays rings reduced to clear arcs on the equator, indicating high orientation of the fiber.

With respect to commercial samples, the differences are not so extreme as in the above experimental samples but are similar. This is illustrated in the diagrams of three commercial samples of viscose produced by North American Rayon Corporation, Diagrams 55, 56, and 57. *Narco,* 150 denier, Diagram 55, shows the lowest orientation. *Narco,* 75 denier, Diagram 56, shows a higher orientation, and the highest degree is found in *Supernarco,* tire cord, Diagram 57. The (020) interferences are modified into arcs which are fused together in the pattern of Diagram 56. The differences in orientation among all commercial types of viscose rayons are of the same nature as the

The pattern of *Vinylon,* a polyvinyl alcohol fiber developed in Japan, is very clear (Diagram 70) with main equatorial interferences of 7.93, 4.54, 3.49, and 2.78 A. The diagram has been completely evaluated by Mooney (1941), who gives the following values for the dimensions of the unit cell: $a = 7.82$; $b = 2.52$; $c = 5.60$. Each unit cell contains 2 CH_2CHOH change segments (see also Bunn, 1948, and Halle and Hoffman, 1935).

The pattern of *tetrafluoroethylene,* a fiber currently being developed, is represented in Diagram 71.

Vinyl Vinylidene Group

The pattern of *Velon,* polyvinylidene chloride (Firestone Plastics Corporation), Diagram 72, is a very clear fiber diagram with clear layerlines. The fiber period is 4.9 A, being less than the double value of the basic period of the hydrocarbon chain, which indicates that the chloride substitutes are not located in the same plane, so that the chain may be distorted. For further information see Goggin and Lowry, 1942.

The pattern of *Saran,* copolymer of vinylidene chloride and vinyl chloride (National Plastics Corporation), Diagram 73, is similar but less distinct than that of Velon, probably due to the presence of the vinyl chloride component. The presence of the raylike diffraction streaks originating from the center (probably indicating portions of incomplete crystallinity) is typical for *both* patterns. The relative intensity of these streaks compared to the well-defined diffractions is different in these two fibers, as can be seen by comparing Diagrams 70 and 71. Saran has streaks of much *higher* intensity.

Vinyon, a copolymer of vinyl chloride and vinyl acetate (American Viscose Corporation), Diagrams 74 and 75, displays patterns that are quite different from the foregoing high-polymer fibers. This may be ascribed to the presence of the very large acetate groups which disrupts the basic lateral order (see, e.g., Misch and Picker, 1937). The pattern is very indistinct and consists only of vague interference arcs as obtained from amorphous substances. Orientation is clearly indicated in the case of *Vinyon CF,* Diagram 75, whereas the unstretched product, *Vinyon HH,* shows only diffuse rings, Diagram 74.

Acrylonitrile Group

The patterns of *Vinyon N,* vinyl chloride acrylonitrile copolymer (Carbide and Carbon Chemicals Company) are represented in Diagrams 76*a* to *e*. These fibers are produced in various degrees of orientation by stretch combined or not with a heat stabilization process; the treatment is indicated by special designation. Both NEZZ and NEXX types of fibers, Diagrams 76*d* and *e,* respectively, show random orientation, indicated by very strong inner rings (5.3 A)

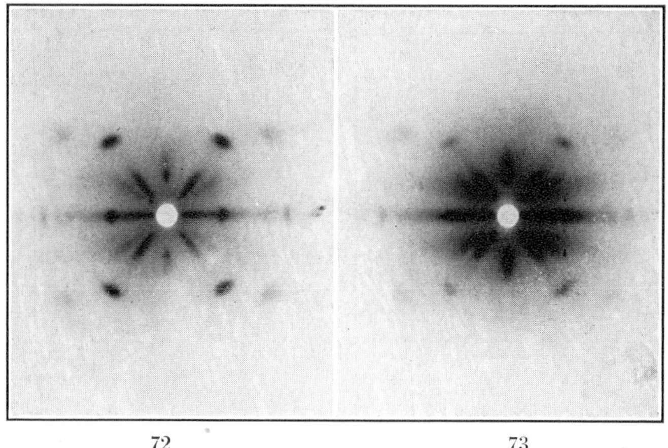

72 73

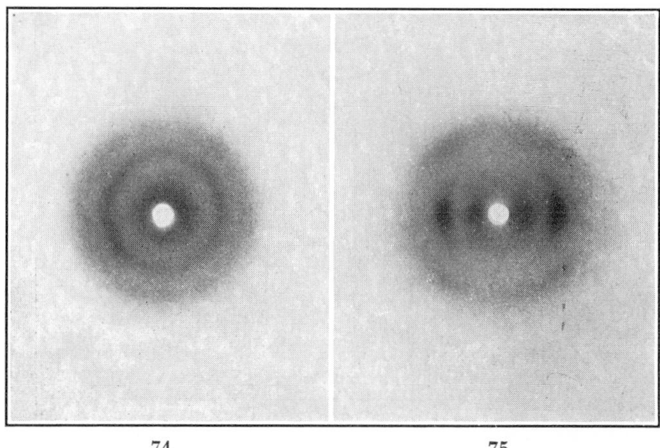

74 75

PLATE XXV. Synthetic fibers. Diagram 72, Velon, 0.2 mm (Firestone Plastics Corporation). Diagram 73, Saran (National Plastics Corporation). Diagram 74, Vinyon HH. Diagram 75, Vinyon CF, 250-216 (stretched yarn) (American Viscose Corporation).

and a more diffuse outer ring. The types NOHH, NORU and NOZZ show increased orientation indicated by arcs (5.3 A) of decreasing lengths. The inner ring is replaced by a strong distinct equatorial arc, and the broad outer ring is broken down into four diffuse scattering areas. Very interesting in the case of NOZZ type (Diagram 76*c*)

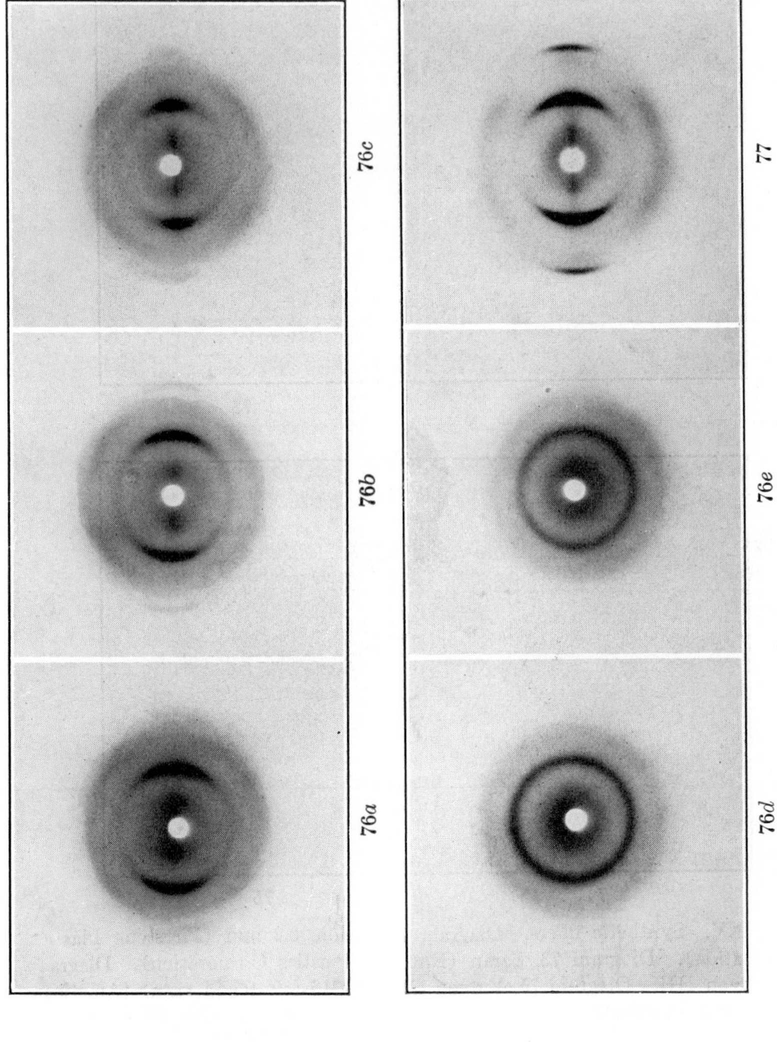

PLATE XXVI. Synthetic fibers. Diagram 76, Vinyon N (Carbide and Carbon Chemicals Company). *a*, NOHH; *b*, NORN; *c*, NOZZ; *d*, NEXX; *e*, NEZZ. Diagram 77, Orlon (E. I. du Pont de Nemours and Company).

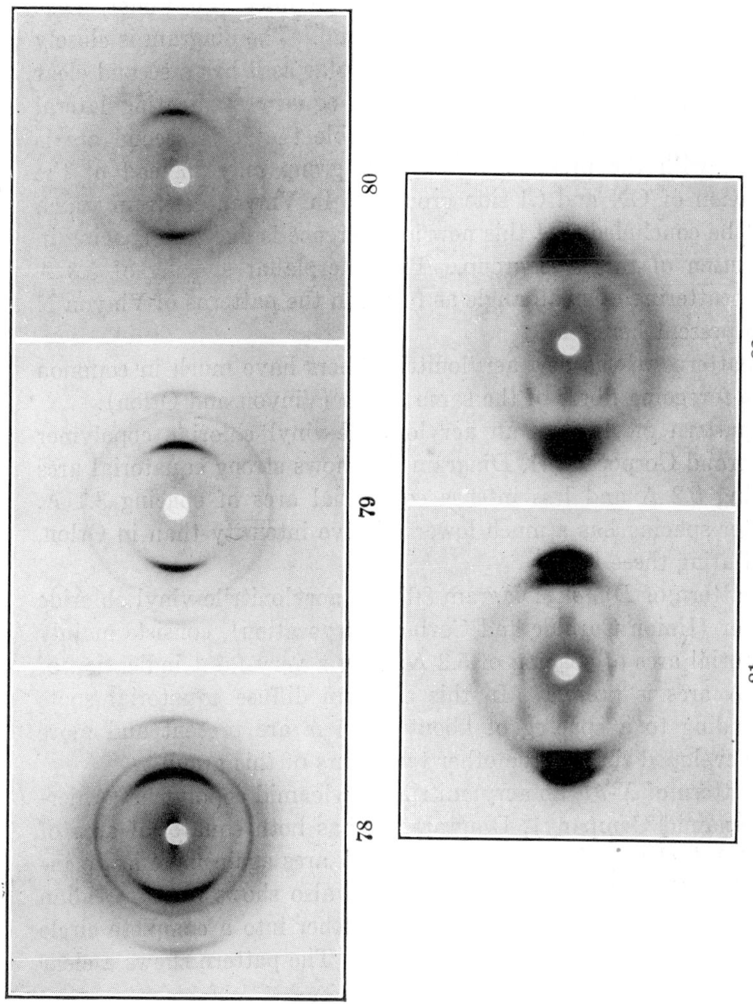

PLATE XXVII. Acrylonitrile fibers and Perlons. Diagram 78, X-51 (American Cyanamid Corporation), dull. Diagram 79, Acrilan (Chemstrand Corporation), dull. Diagram 80, Dynel (Union Carbide and Carbon Corporation). Perlons. Diagram 81, Perlon L (Bobingen). Diagram 82, Perlon U (Bayer).

is the formation of a distinct equatorial scattering area at small angles. Thus it may be concluded that, depending on the manufacturing process, this fiber can be produced in various degrees of orientation.

The pattern of *Orlon,* a polyacrylonitrile fiber (du Pont), Diagram 77, is a continuation of the above trend. The diagram is closely similar to that of Vinyon N, but differs insofar as it has a second clear interference arc of spacing 3.1 A on the equator, indicating lateral order in one more direction. It is probable that this second arc is connected with the presence of the CN group only instead of the combination of CN and Cl side groups as in Vinyon N, from which it might be concluded that this new interference is due to a spacing in the direction of this side group. The interplanar spacing of 5.3 A and the scattering at small angle as found in the patterns of Vinyon N are also present here.

The patterns of the new acrylonitrile fibers have much in common with the foregoing fibers of the same group (Vinyon and Orlon).

The pattern of *Acrilan,* an acrylonitrile-vinyl chloride copolymer (Chemstrand Corporation), Diagram 79, shows strong equatorial arcs of spacing 5.2 A and less intense equatorial arcs of spacing 3.1 A. The latter spacing has a much lower relative intensity than in Orlon, differentiating these fibers.

The pattern of *Dynel* (Diagram 80), an acrylonitrile-vinyl chloride copolymer (Union Carbide and Carbon Corporation), consists mainly of equatorial arcs of spacing of 5.2 A; only a very faint indication of the 3.1 A arcs is present. In this diagram diffuse equatorial spots corresponding to a spacing of about 10.35 A are present and more clearly developed than in the other two fibers of this group.

The pattern of *X-51,* an acrylonitrile-acryloamid copolymer (American Cyanamid Company), Diagram 78, has both equatorial arcs of 5.2 and 3.1 A clearly developed. The 3.1 A arcs again have lower intensity than the 5.2 A arcs. The diagram also shows clear meridian arcs of about 4.1 A which almost fuse together into a complete circle but have highest intensities at the equator. The pattern shows a clear equatorial small-angle scattering.

Nylon Group

The *nylon fibers,* 66, polyhexamethylene adipamide, and 610, polyhexamethylene sebacamide (du Pont), Diagrams 83 and 84, also fall within the "polyethylene group."

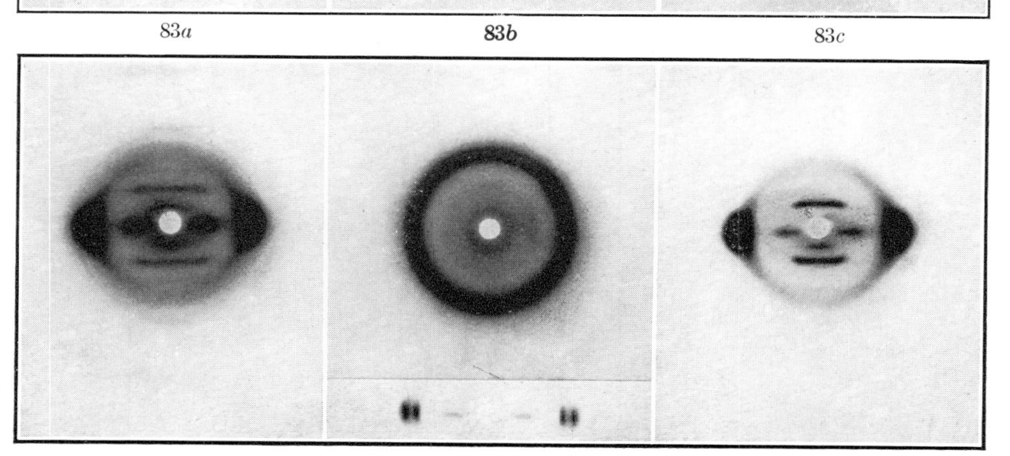

PLATE XXVIII. Nylon fibers. Diagram 83, nylon 66 (E. I. du Pont de Nemours and Company). *a*, 300 (210-34); *b*, 100 (70-34); *c*, 109 (20-20); *d*, 200 (40-34); *e*, undrawn nylon, and equatorial spots in "cold" samples. Diagram 84, nylon 610, monofilament.

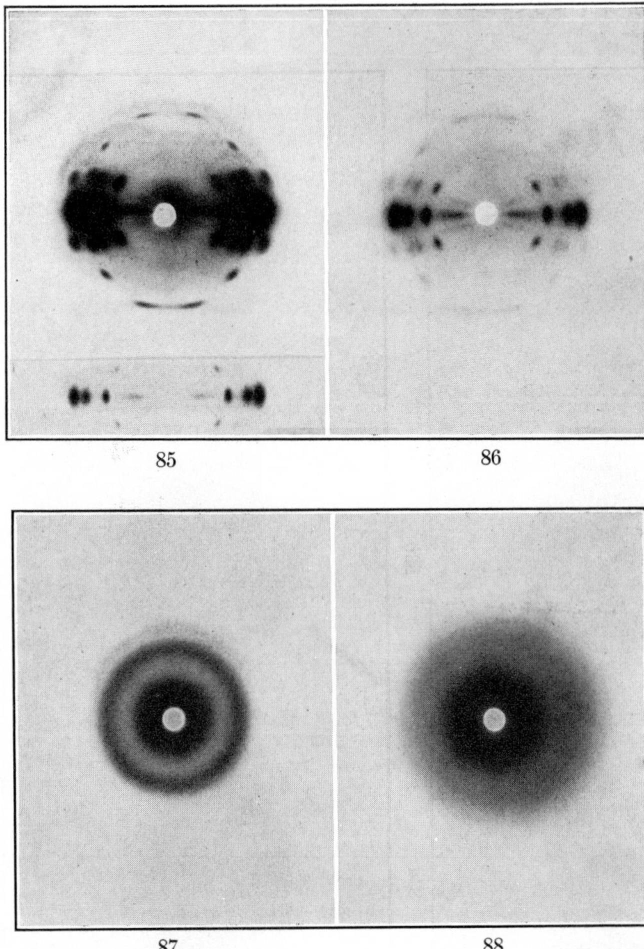

PLATE XXIX. Polyester and mineral fibers. Diagram 85, Dacron (Fiber V) (E. I. du Pont de Nemours and Company). Diagram 86, Terylene (Dacron); different exposure times and equatorial interferences separately. Diagram 87, Polyfiber (Polystyrene) (Dow Chemical Corporation). Diagram 88, fibrous glass 450-4/3 (Owens-Corning Fiberglas Corporation).

The fiber period is clearly expressed by the presence of layerlines. A period of 17.2 A may be calculated for the 66 polymer and of 22.4 A for the 610 polymer.

The lateral spacings of the paratropic planes (Diagram 83*e*, inset) agree with those typical for hydrocarbons (4.2 A and 3.7 A) and are almost as intense as in polyethylene (but less sharp). A diffuse ring inside the main equatorial interferences is present, indicating the presence also of long-chain molecules with a lower degree of lateral order and random orientation. Different diagrams are known to result in nylon, depending on the rate of cooling the material during the spinning process. Different degrees of lateral order are expressed by the width of the interferences. The different degrees of longitudinal orientation are expressed by the length of the arcs.

Diagram 83*a* of *Nylon* 66, 300, a high-tenacity nylon, shows well-defined equatorial interferences from which a high degree of orientation parallel to the fiber axis may be concluded. The patterns of the nylons of ordinary tenacity, 100 and 109, as represented in Diagrams 83*b* and *c*, show a lower degree of orientation, the interferences being a little more arc-like. The pattern of nylon before cold drawing is represented in Diagram 83*e* and consists of two predominant rings of 4.2 and 3.7 A and a few less clear rings. The diagram of monofilament of nylon 610 is represented in Diagram 84; a fiber period of 22.4 A may be calculated from this diagram.

Perlon L, the German nylon equivalent, prepared from caprolactam (which polymerizes as if it were aminocaproic acid), the "6" polymer, has a diagram very similar to the one of nylon. The equatorial spots are more arclike and better separated (Diagram 81).

Perlon U, polyurethane (ethyl ester of carbamic acid), has a diagram (82) that shows great similarity with those of nylon and Perlon L. The equatorial spots are much more diffuse than in the other diagrams (see Zahn, 1951).

Polyester Group

The fiber termed *Terylene* in England and *Dacron* in the United States is a polyester of ethylene glycol and terephthalate.

According to Astbury and Brown (1946) (see also Hardy and Wood, 1947), the unit cell has the following dimensions:

$$a = 5.5\ \text{A} \quad b = 4.1\ \text{A} \quad c = 10.8\ \text{A} \quad \alpha = 107^\circ \quad \beta = 112^\circ \quad \gamma = 92^\circ$$

The molecules are placed with their long axis along the c axis and their flat side in the $1\bar{1}0$ planes.

The pattern of both types is a very distinct fiber diagram with clear layerlines, indicating a repeat period in the fiber axis (10.8 A) different from the basic one in the foregoing groups; see Diagrams 85 and 86. Not only on the equator but also on the first layerlines are very intense interferences, as clearly shown by the short-exposure photograph, Diagram 86.

Polystyrene Group

The pattern of *Polyfiber,* polystyrene fiber (Dow Chemical Corporation), Diagram 87, displays two diffuse rings, indicating a very low degree of order and crystallinity. This is a result of the large side group which not only prevents lateral order but also causes the main chain to coil. A type of "semi-crystalline" structure like that of fluids exists here. For further information refer to Krimm and Tobolsky, 1951*b*.

Fibrous Glass

Fibrous glass produces a pattern very similar to that of amorphous substances. The glass molecules occur in a continuous random network (Zachariasen, 1932), the atoms being ordered in larger groups together (Preston, 1942). The pattern has been considered as a diffused modification of a crystalline silicate (Warren, Krutter, and Morningstar, 1936).

The pattern of *Fiberglas* (Owens-Corning Fiberglas Corporation), Diagram 88, shows a typical feature of a diagram of a fluid, only diffuse, very broad rings being present. This type pattern is typical for amorphous substances.

MINERAL FIBERS

Asbestos

Commercial asbestos comprises the fibrous varieties of the amphibole and serpentine groups of silicates. Various types of asbestos have different unit cells but generally the same fiber period (5.24 A). The unit cell of *chrysotile* is orthorhombic and has the following dimensions according to Warren and Bragg (1930) (see Warren, 1932, for a summary):

$$a = 14.6 \text{ A} \qquad b = 18.4 \text{ A} \qquad c = 5.24 \text{ A}$$

The position of the molecules in the unit cell has been established: the silicon oxygen chains are parallel to the c axis. In chrysotile double chains occur. The chains are held together laterally by calcium and magnesium atoms.

The pattern of chrysotile, Diagram 89, shows very pronounced layer-lines on which the interference spots are located. A typical "smearing out" of the spots is observed.

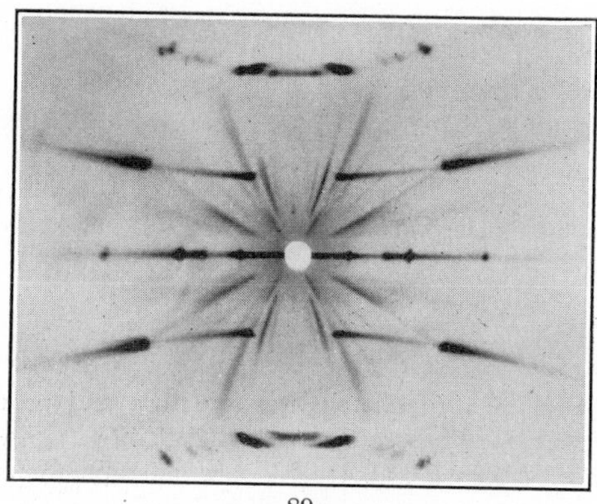

89

DIAGRAM 89. Asbestos, chrysotile.

REFERENCES

ANDRESS, K. R., "The X-ray diagrams of mercerized cellulose," *Z. physik. Chem.*, Abt. *B* (4), 190 (1929).

ASTBURY, W. T., *Fundamentals of Fiber Structure,* Oxford University Press, New York, London (1933).

ASTBURY, W. T., "Recent advances in the X-ray study of protein fibres," *J. Textile Inst.*, **27,** 282 (1936*a*).

ASTBURY, W. T., "X-ray interpretation of protein structure," *Chem Weekblad,* **33,** 778 (1936*b*).

ASTBURY, W. T., "Textile fibres under the X-rays," *Imperial Chem. Inds.*, London (1943).

ASTBURY, W. T., "The molecular structure of fibres," *J. Textile Inst.*, **36,** 154 (1945).

ASTBURY, W. T., and BELL, F. O., "X-ray data on structure of natural fibers and other substances of high molecular weight," *Tabul. biol.*, **17,** 90 (1939).

ASTBURY, W. T., and BELL, F. O., "Nature of the intramolecular fold in α-keratin and α-myosin," *Nature,* **147,** 696 (1941).

ASTBURY, W. T., and BROWN, C. J., "Structure of Terylene," *Nature,* **158,** 871 (1946).

ASTBURY, W. T., PRESTON, R. D., and NORMAN, A. G., "Lignified fibres: X-ray patterns," *Nature,* **136,** 391 (1935).

ASTBURY, W. T., and SISSON, W. A., "X-ray studies of the structures of hair, wool, and related fibers. III: The configuration of the keratin molecule and its orientation in the biological cell," *Proc. Roy. Soc. London A,* **150,** 533 (1935).

ASTBURY, W. T., and STREET, A., "X-ray studies of the structure of hair, wool, and related fibers," *Trans. Roy. Soc. London A,* **230,** 75 (1931).

ASTBURY, W. T., and WOODS, H. J., "X-ray interpretation of the structure and elastic properties of hair keratin," *Nature,* **126,** 913 (1930).

ASTBURY, W. T., and WOODS, H. J., "X-ray studies of the structure of hair, wool, and related fibers. II: The molecular structure and elastic properties of hair keratin," *Trans. Roy. Soc. London A,* **232,** 333 (1933).

BAKER, W. O., and FULLER, C. S., "Intermolecular forces and chain configuration in linear polymers—the effect of N-methylation on the X-ray structures and properties of linear polyamides," *J. Am. Chem. Soc.,* **65,** 1120 (1943).

BEAR, R. S., "X-ray diffraction studies on protein fibers," *J. Am. Chem. Soc.,* **66,** 1297, 2043 (1944).

BERGMANN, M. E., FANKUCHEN, I., and MARK, H., "A few experiments on the crystallinity of polyamides," *Textile Research J.,* **18,** 1 (1948).

BERGMANN, M., and NIEMANN, C., "On the structure of silk fibroin," *J. Biol. Chem.,* **122,** 577 (1938).

BERKLEY, E. E., "Cellulose orientation, strength, and cell wall development of cotton fibers," *Textile Research J.,* **9,** 355 (1939).

BERKLEY, E. E., "Certain variations in the structure and properties of natural cellulose fibers," *Textile Research J.,* **19,** 363 (1949).

BERKLEY, E. E., and WOODYARD, O. C., "A new microphotometer for analyzing X-ray diffraction patterns of raw cotton fiber," *Ind. Eng. Chem.,* Anal. Ed., **10,** 451 (1938).

BERKLEY, E. E., and WOODYARD, O. C., "Experimental background of X-ray method," *U.S.D.A. Tech. Bull.* 949, 3 (1948).

BERNAL, J. D., and CROWFOOT, D., "X-ray photographs of crystalline pepsin," *Nature,* **133,** 794 (1934).

BERNAL, J. D., and FANKUCHEN, I., "X-ray and crystallographic studies of plant virus preparations," *J. Gen. Physiol.,* **25,** 111 (1941).

BOSE, C. R., and AHMAD, N., "A study of some vegetable fibers by X-ray diffraction method," *Indian J. Phys.,* **20,** 105–110 (1946).

BRAGG, L., KENDREW, J. C., and PERUTZ, M. F., *Proc. Roy. Soc. London A,* **203,** 321 (1950).

BRILL, R., "Über Seidenfibroin," *Ann.* **434,** 204 (1923).

BRILL, R., "Behavior of polyamides on heating," *J. prakt. Chem.,* **161,** 49 (1943*a*).

BRILL, R., "Relations between the structures of polyamides and silk fibres," *Z. physik. Chem. B,* **53,** 61 (1943*b*).

BUNN, C. W., "Crystal structure of long-chain normal paraffin hydrocarbons. Shape of the methylene group," *Trans. Faraday Soc.,* **35,** 482 (1939).

BUNN, C. W., "Crystal structure of polyvinyl alcohol," *Nature,* **161,** 929 (1948).

BUNN, C. W., "The study of fibers by X-ray diffraction methods," *Fibre Science* (Textile Inst.), 158 (1949).

BUNN, C. W., and GARNER, E. V., "The crystal structures of two polyamides (nylons)," *Proc. Roy. Soc. London A,* **189,** 39 (1947).

BURGENI, A., and KRATKY, O., "X-ray spectrographic observations on cellulose. V: The lattice of cellulose hydrate," *Z. physik. Chem. B,* **4,** 401–430 (1929). (Röntgenspectrographische Beobachtungen an Cellulose. Über das Gitter der Hydratcellulose.)

CHIBNALL, A. C., PIPER, S. H., POLLARD, A., WILLIAMS, E. F., and SAHAI, P. N.,

"The constitution of the primary alcohols, fatty acids, and paraffins present in plant and insect waxes," *Biochem. J.,* **28,** 2189 (1934).

Clark, G. L., "Cellulose as it is completely revealed by X-rays," *Indus. Eng. Chem.,* **22,** 474 (1930).

Clark, G. L., Farr, W. K., and Pickett, L. W., "Analysis of growth and classification of cotton fibers," *Indus. Eng. Chem.,* **22,** 481 (1930).

Clark, G. L., Pickett, L. W., and Farr, W. K., "Some practical results of an X-ray analysis of cotton fibers," *Science,* **71,** 293 (1930).

Conrad, C. M., "The high wax content of green lint cotton," *Science,* **94,** 113 (1941).

Corey, R. G., and Wyckoff, R. W. G., "Long spacings in macromolecular solids," *J. Biol. Chem.,* **114,** 407 (1936).

Fankuchen, I., and Mark, H., "X-ray studies of chain polymers," *J. Appl. Phys.,* **15,** 364 (1944).

Fuller, C. S., "The investigation of synthetic linear polymers by X-rays," *Chem. Revs.,* **26,** 143 (1940).

Fuller, C. S., Baker, W. O., and Pape, N. R., "Crystalline behavior of linear polyamides. Effect of heat treatment," *J. Am. Chem. Soc.,* **62,** 3275 (1940).

Fuller, C. S., and Frosch, C. J., "X-ray investigation of the decamethylene series of polyesters," *J. Am. Chem. Soc.,* **61,** 2575 (1939).

Goggin, W. C., and Lowry, R. D., "Vinylidene chloride polymers," *Ind. Eng Chem.,* **34,** 327 (1942).

Gross, S. T., and Clark, G. L., *Z. Krist.,* **99,** 357 (1938).

Guinier, A., Thesis, "Radiocrystallography," Paris, Dunod (1942).

Gundermann, J., Wergin, W., and Hess, K., "Über die Natur und das Vorkommen der Primärsubstanz in den Zellwänden der pflänzlichen Gewebe," *Ber. deut. chem. Ges.,* **70,** 517 (1937).

Halle, F., and Hofmann, W., "Fiber diagram of polyvinyl alcohol," *Naturwissenschaften,* **23,** 770 (1935).

Hardy, D. U. N., and Wood, W. A., "Structure of Terylene," *Nature,* **159,** 673 (1947).

Hengstenberg, H. Z., "Röntgenuntersuchungen über den Bau der C-Ketten Kohlenwasserstoffen," *Z. Krist.,* **67,** 583 (1928); *see also* in K. H. Meyer and H. Mark, *Z. physik. Chem. B,* **2,** 115 (1929).

Hermans, J. J., *Contribution to the Physics of Cellulose Fibers,* Elsevier, Amsterdam (1946).

Hermans, J. J., Hermans, P. H., Vermaas, D., and Weidinger, A., "Quantitative evaluation of orientation in cellulose fibers from the X-ray fiber diagrams," *Rec. trav. chim.,* **65,** 427 (1946).

Hermans, P. H., and Weidinger, A., "The hydrates of cellulose," *J. Colloid Sci.,* **1,** 186 (1946).

Hess, K., and Kieszig, H., "Zur Kenntniss der Feinstruktur der Polyamidfasern," *Naturwissenschaften,* **31,** 171 (1943); *see also Z. physik. Chem.,* **193,** 196 (1944).

Hess, K., Kieszig, H., and Wergin, W., "Über den Aufbau der Eriophorum-Samenhaare," *Ber. deut. chem. Ges., B,* **76,** 449 (1943).

Hess, K., Trogus, C., Wergin, W., "Untersuchungen über die Bildung der pflänzlichen Zellwand," *Planta,* **25,** 419 (1936).

Hess, K., Wergin, W., and Kieszig, H., "The structure of the primary wall of the cottonseed hair," *Planta,* **33,** 151 (1942).

Heyn, A. N. J., "X-ray investigations of the cellulose in the wall of young epidermis cells," *Proc. Akad. Wetensch.*, Amsterdam, **36,** 560 (1933).

Heyn, A. N. J., "Weitere Untersuchungen über den Mechanismus der Zellstreckung und die Eigenschaften der Zellmembran. II: Das Röntgendiagramm von jungen wächsenden Zellwänden und parenchymatischen Geweben" (The X-ray diagrams of young growing cell walls and parenchymatous tissues), *Protoplasma,* **21,** 299 (1934).

Heyn, A. N. J., "Small angle X-ray scattering of various cellulose fibers," *J. Am. Chem. Soc.,* **71,** 1873 (1948).

Heyn, A. N. J., "Small angle X-ray scattering in various cellulose fibers and its relation with the micellar structure," *Textile Research J.,* **19,** 163 (1949*a*).

Heyn, A. N. J., "Relationship of wax content to maturity of cotton," *Textile Research J.,* **14,** 711 (1949*b*).

Heyn, A. N. J., "Small angle X-ray scattering by cellulose fibers: Experimental study of the orientation factor in model filaments and rayons," *J. Am. Chem. Soc.,* **72,** 2284 (1950*a*).

Heyn, A. N. J., "How to identify synthetic fibers by their X-ray diagrams," *Rayon and Synthetic Textiles,* **31,** (9); (10), 42 (1950*b*).

Heyn, A. N. J., "A quantitative evaluation of small-angle X-ray scattering by various cellulose fibers for the determination of crystallite size with special reference to the problem of interparticle interference," *J. Am. Chem. Soc.,* **72,** 5768 (1950*c*).

Heyn, A. N. J., "The identification of synthetic fibers by X-ray diffraction," *Am. Handbook of Synthetic Textiles,* Chap. 19, Textile Book Publishers, Inc., New York (1952).

Huggins, M. L., "The structure of fibrous proteins," *Chem. Revs.,* **32,** 195 (1943).

Ingersoll, H. G., "Fine structure of viscose rayon," *J. Appl. Phys.,* **17,** 925 (1946).

Kauffman, J., and Waller, G., "Load induced X-ray line broadening in nylon filaments," *J. Appl. Phys.,* **21,** 431 (1950).

Kratky, O., and Kuriyama, S., "Über Seidenfibroin" (Silk fibroin III), *Z. physik. Chem., B,* **11,** 363 (1931).

Kreger, D. R., "A comparative study of a number of waxy coatings from plants on the basis of their powder diagrams," in: Bouman, *X-ray Crystallography,* Interscience Publishers, Inc., New York (1951).

Krimm, S., and Tobolsky, A., "Quantitative X-ray studies of order in amorphous and crystalline polymers. Quantitative X-ray determination of crystallinity in polyethylene," *J. Polymer Sci.,* **7,** 57 (1951*a*).

Krimm, S., and Tobolsky, A. V., "Quantitative X-ray studies of order in amorphous and crystalline polymers scattering from various polymers and a study of the glass transition in polystyrene and polymethyl methacrylate," *Textile Research J.,* **21,** 805 (1951*b*).

Kubo, T., "Studies on the conversion of cellulose hydrate into natural cellulose. VII: The crystal structure of the product of conversion as well as of a natural cellulose preparation of the highest degree of orientation," *Z. physik. Chem. A,* **187,** 297 (1940).

Kubo, T., and Kanamaru, K., "Lyophilic properties of cellulose and its derivatives," *Z. physik. Chem. A,* **182,** 341 (1937).

KUCHINO, K., and SAKURADA, I., "Studies of synthetic polyamides by means of X-rays," *Sci. Papers, Inst. Phys. Chem. Res.* (Tokyo), **40,** 125 (1942).

LUNDGREN, H. P., STEIN, A. M., KOORN, V. M., and O'CONNELL, R. A., "Stability of synthetic keratin fibers in alcohol-water mixtures. Theoretical basis for a new method for solubilizing feather keratin," *J. Phys. & Colloid Chem.,* **52,** 180 (1948).

MACNICHOLAS, H. J., "X-ray studies of silk fibers," *Textile Research,* **11,** 1 (1940–41).

MARK, H., and VON SUSICH, G., "Über den Bau des kristallisierten Anteils der Cellulose, III," *Z. physik. Chem. B,* **4,** 431 (1929).

MEIBOHM, E. P. H., and SMITH, A. F., "Observations on small-angle interference maxima in synthetic organic polymers," *J. Polymer Sci.,* **7,** 449 (1951).

MEREDITH, R., "On the technique of measuring orientation in cotton by X-rays," *J. Textile Inst.,* **42,** T275 (1951*a*).

MEREDITH, R., "Cotton fiber tensile strength and X-ray orientation," *J. Textile Inst.,* **42,** T291 (1951*b*).

MEYER, K. H., "High polymers," *Natural and Synthetic High Polymers,* Interscience Publishers, New York (2nd Ed.) (1950).

MEYER, K. H., and BADENHUIZEN, N. P., "Transformation of hydrated cellulose into native cellulose," *Nature,* **140,** 281 (1937).

MEYER, K. H., and MARK, H., "Über den Aufbau des Seiden fibroins," *Ber. deut. chem. Ges., B,* **61,** 1932 (1928*a*).

MEYER, K. H., and MARK, H., "The structure of crystallized components of cellulose," *Ber. deut. chem. Ges., B,* **61,** 593 (1928*b*).

MEYER, K. H., and MARK, H., *Z. physik. Chem. B,* **2,** 115 (1929).

MEYER, K. H., and MARK, H., "Der Aufbau der hochpolymeren organischen Naturstoffe," *Akad. Verlagsges.,* Leipzig (1930).

MEYER, K. H., and MISCH, L., "Constitution of the crystalline part of cellulose," *Helv. Chim. Acta,* **20,** 232 (1937).

MISCH, L., and PICKER, L., "The structure of polyvinyl acetate," *Z. physik. Chem. B,* **36,** 398 (1937).

MOONEY, R. C. L., "An X-ray study of the structure of polyvinyl alcohol," *J. Am. Chem. Soc.,* **63,** 2828 (1941).

MÜLLER, A., "An X-ray investigation of certain long-chain compounds," *Proc. Roy. Soc. London A,* **11,** 542 (1927).

MÜLLER, A., "A further investigation of long-chain compounds (*n*-hydrocarbons)," *Proc. Roy. Soc. London A,* **120,** 437 (1928).

MÜLLER, A., "The connection between the zig-zag structure of the hydrocarbon chains and the alternations in the properties of odd and even numbered chain compounds," *Proc. Roy. Soc. London A,* **124,** 317 (1929).

MÜLLER, A., "An X-ray investigation of normal paraffins near their melting point," *Proc. Roy. Soc. London A,* **130,** 514 (1932).

NUTTING, G. C., HALWER, M., COPLEY, M. J., and SENTI, F. R., "Relationship between molecular configuration and tensile properties of protein fibers," *Textile Research J.,* **16,** 599 (1946).

NUTTING, G. C., SENTI, F. R., and COPLEY, M. J., "Conversion of globular to oriented fibrous proteins," *Science,* **99,** 328 (1944).

OTT, E., "High polymers, V," in: OTT, *Cellulose and Cellulose Derivatives,* Interscience Publishers, New York (1943).

Palmer, K. H., and Hartzog, M. B., "An X-ray diffraction investigation of sodium pectate," *J. Am. Chem. Soc.*, **67**, 2122 (1945).

Palmer, K. H., and Lotzkar, H., "Oriented fibers of sodium pectate," *J. Am. Chem. Soc.*, **67**, 884 (1945); cited in: *J. Polymer Sci.*, **2**, 319 (1947).

Pauling, L., and Corey, R. B., "The structure of hair, muscle, and related proteins," *Proc. Nat. Acad. Sci.*, **37**, 261 (1951).

Pauling, L., Corey, R. B., and Branson, H. R., "The structure of proteins; two hydrogen-bonded helical configurations of the polypeptide chain," *Proc. Nat. Acad. Sci.*, **37**, 205 (1951).

Piper, S. H., Chibnall, A. C., and Williams, E. F., "Melting-points and long crystal spacings of the higher primary alcohols and *n*-fatty acids," *Biochem. J.*, **28**, 2175 (1934).

Preston, E., "Structure and constitution of glass," *J. Soc. Glass Technol.*, **26**, 82 (1942).

Sakurada, I., and Funtino, K., "X-ray investigation of natural and regenerated silk," *Sci. Papers, Inst. Phys. Chem. Research* (Tokyo), **21**, 266 (1933).

Sakurada, I., and Hizawa, I., "Manufacture of nylon I–II," *J. Soc. Chem. Ind. Japan*, **43**, 348 (1940).

Sen, M. K., and Woods, H. J., "X-ray investigation of the structure of jute," *Nature*, **161**, 768 (1948).

Senti, F. R., "Structure of protein fibers," *Am. Dyestuff Reptr.* (May 5, 1947).

Senti, F. R., Eddy, C. R., and Nutting, G. C., "Conversion of globular to oriented fibrous proteins. I: By heat and mechanical working," *J. Am. Chem. Soc.*, **65**, 2473 (1943).

Sirkar, S. C., and Chowdhury, S. K., "X-ray diffraction patterns of bleached jute fiber," *Indian J. Phys.*, **20**, 31 (1946).

Sisson, W. A., "X-ray studies of crystallite orientation in cellulose fibers," *Ind. Eng. Chem.*, **27**, 51 (1935).

Sisson, W. A., "Identification of crystalline cellulose in young cotton fibers by X-ray diffraction analysis," *Contrib. Boyce Thompson Inst.*, **8**, 389 (1937*a*).

Sisson, W. A., "X-ray analysis of textile fibers. Part V: Relation of orientation to tensile strength of raw cotton," *Textile Research*, **7**, 425 (1937*b*); *see also Textile Research*, **5**, 119 (1935); **6**, 243 (1935).

Sisson, W. A., "Orientation in young cotton fibers as indicated by X-ray diffraction studies," *Contrib. Boyce Thompson Inst.*, **9**, 239 (1938).

Sisson, W. A., "X-ray studies regarding the formation and orientation of crystalline cellulose in the cell wall of *Valonia*," *Contrib. Boyce Thompson Inst.*, **12**, 171 (1941).

Sisson, W. A., "X-ray examination," in: Ott, *Cellulose and Cellulose Derivatives*, Interscience Publishers, New York (1943).

Sisson, W. A., and Clark, G. L., "X-ray method for quantitative comparison of crystallite orientation in cellulose fibers," *Ind. Eng. Chem.*, Anal. Ed., **5**, 296 (1933).

Sponsler, O. L., "X-ray diffraction pattern from plant fibers," *J. Gen. Physiol.*, **9**, 221 (1926*a*).

Sponsler, O. L., "Molecular structure of plant fibers determined by X-rays," *J. Gen. Physiol.*, **9**, 677 (1926*b*).

Sponsler, O. L., "Orientation of cellulose space lattice in the cell wall. Additional data from *Valonia* cell wall," *Protoplasma*, **12**, 241 (1930).

SPONSLER, O. L., and DORE, W. H., "The structure of ramie cellulose as derived from X-ray data," *Colloid Symposium Monograph,* **4,** 174 (1926).

TROGUS, C., and HESS, K., "Studies on natural silk and its behavior with acids and alkalies. Röntgenographic studies on proteins," *Biochem. Z.,* **260,** 376 (1933).

TSIEN, P. C., "A new method of evaluation of the crystallite orientation of cellulose fibers from X-ray data," *Textile Research J.,* **19**, 330 (1949).

WARREN, B. E., "Structure of asbestos, an X-ray study," *Ind. Eng. Chem.,* **24,** 419 (1932).

WARREN, B. E., and BRAGG, W. L., "Structure of biopside," "Structure of chrysotile," *Z. Krist.,* **69,** 168 (1928); **76,** 201 (1930).

WARREN, B. E., KRUTTER, H., and MORNINGSTAR, O., "Fourier analysis of X-ray patterns of vitreous SiO_2 and B_2O_3," *J. Am. Ceram. Soc.,* **19,** 202 (1936).

WEISSENBERG, K., "The translation lattice of hydrated cellulose," *Kaiser Wilhelm Inst. Faserstoffchemie, Berlin Dahlem. Naturwissenschaften,* **17,** 181 (1929).

WERGIN, W., "Über das Wachstum pflänzlicher Zellwände," *Angew. Chem.,* **843** (1936).

WOODS, H. J., "Structure of textile fibers. III: Fiber properties and molecular arrangement," *J. Textile Inst.,* **40,** 363 (1949).

WUHRMANN, K., and PILNIK, W., "Über Optik, und Feinbau des Pektins und seiner Derivate" (The optics and fine structure of pectin and its derivatives), *Experientia,* **1,** 330 (1945).

WYCKOFF, R. W. G., and COREY, R. B., "X-ray diffractions from haemoglobin and other crystalline proteins," *Science,* **81** (1935).

ZACHARIASEN, W. H., "The atomic arrangement in glass," *J. Am. Chem. Soc.,* **54,** 3841 (1932).

ZAHN, H., "X-ray structure of polyurethan fibers," *Melliand Textilber.,* **32,** 534 (1951).

ZAHN, H., and KOHLER, K., "Kleinwinkelinterferenzen (Langperioden) bei Polyurethanfäden," *Kolloid Z.,* **118,** Heft 2 (1950).

NOTE: The author is indebted to the Kress Foundation of Clemson College, which purchased the X-ray apparatus and some additional equipment used in this study. All the samples of synthetic fibers represented in the diagrams were graciously furnished by the various companies that manufacture these materials.

CHAPTER XXII

FIBER-TESTING METHODS

E. R. Schwarz

Fiber testing involves two types of measurements—those which evaluate the dimensional characteristics in the absence of external forces and those which indicate the behavior of the specimen under stress. Typical of the first group are determinations of staple length, fineness, and appearance. In this chapter only those measurements not primarily involving microscopical or chemical tests are considered since these are discussed elsewhere. The second group includes such evaluations as tensile strength, stretch, resilience, torsional deformation, and friction properties. Every effort has been made to achieve brevity but, at the same time, to give essential details for what are believed to be the more important or useful techniques. Fiber properties are important, not only from the standpoint of selection and quality control, but because of their profound influence upon the properties of the resulting yarns and fabrics.

It should be borne in mind that laboratory tests are suited to work in quality control, development problems (as a means of measuring changes), and in research. To be related to service, however, results of laboratory investigations are limited to correlation with the results of service tests, or to the attempt to duplicate the results of service. The only service tests that can be performed in a laboratory are confined to the performance of laboratory equipment itself.

The actual performance of textile fibers in service calls for evaluation. Just what laboratory tests should be selected or devised for this purpose is a real problem. Every effort should be made to be certain that the test actually measures the desired property, that the units of measurement are definitely known, and that the results are treated by proper statistical methods from the initial sampling all the way through to the final determination of significance and degree of correlation.

Staple Length

The cotton classer obtains a staple or bundle of fibers, squared at each end, by a series of drawing and lapping operations accompanied by discarding of fibers withdrawn when squaring the ends of the "pull." The resulting measurement is known as the classer's staple. For wool, the fiber sample is paralleled by drawing and lapping, one end of the "pull" being kept square. Withdrawals by successive "pulls" from the nonsquared ends enable the operator to draw fibers of progressively shorter lengths from the bundle. If these are laid side by side on a velvet-covered background, they form an approximation of a frequency array of lengths. The human element is very much in evidence in such tests, and a reasonably high degree of skill and judgment is required. (See Fig. 1.)

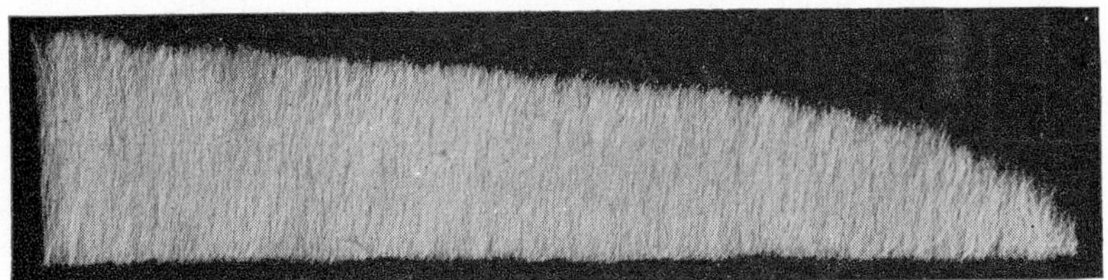

FIG. 1. Staple array of cotton fibers. (*American Cotton Handbook.*)

From a frequency array of fiber lengths the average staple (mean staple) can be obtained by dividing the area of the array by the length of the base line (both in proper units, i.e., square inches and inches, respectively). The array must be laid out with as nearly uniform fiber density as possible.

Other measures of length may also be obtained from such arrays, as

Modal length: the fiber length occurring with greatest frequency. (This may be impossible to determine if the array shows no particular fiber length of greater frequency than other lengths.)

Median length: the fiber length lying halfway along the frequency axis of the diagram.

Quartile length: the fiber length lying 25 per cent of the distance along the frequency axis (usually measured from the end of the array composed of fibers of maximum length).

Effective length: a fiber length obtained by a method suggested by Clegg [1] involving a simple geometric construction (see Fig. 2).

Although there is little agreement as to the proper length of fiber determined from a frequency distribution of length, there is increasing agreement that the frequency array itself is important. As evidence for this statement, consider the recommendation of the A.S.T.M. [2]. For cotton, the upper quartile length is suggested; for rayon staple fiber, the modal fiber length is to be reported; and for wool, the average fiber length is to be determined. The particular length chosen is probably arrived at to achieve some parity with previous results as obtained by the classer. Thus, the work of Clegg is a case of very good agreement between the effective staple and the classer's staple, when the latter is obtained by a skillful operator. Similar agreement is claimed for the

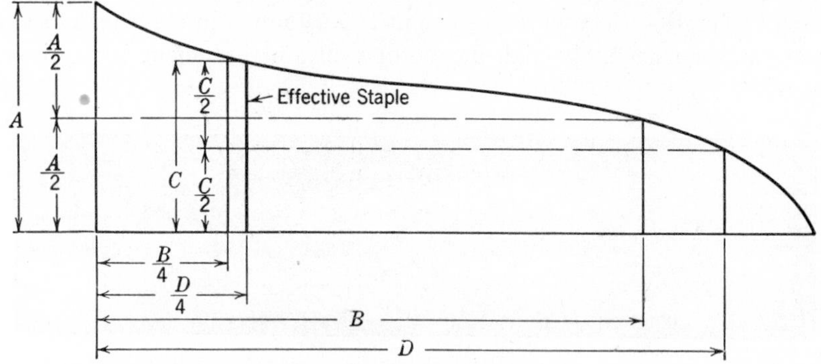

FIG. 2. Method for determining effective staple.

upper quartile length, although this must be somewhat shorter than the effective staple by the very geometry of the array. In any case, a sorting technique is employed.

For fiber sorting, a set of combs may be employed as in the Baer and Suter staplers for wool, rayon, or cotton [2] (see Fig. 3). The details of the method are given by the A.S.T.M. and in general involve the paralleling of a bunch of fibers representative of the lot being sampled. This parallel bundle is held by one set of combs while a series of small "pulls" are withdrawn, usually with forceps, and placed in a second set of combs—the gripped ends being squared off carefully at each transfer. The device is rotated through 180° and successive "pulls" are now taken with the forceps—only the longest fibers are available for each "pull." Combs are dropped out of the way one after the other as the fibers grow shorter in length. Each "pull" is transferred to the adjacent set of combs with the gripped ends again squared off evenly, and the procedure just described is repeated, save that each "pull" as it is removed is placed on a piece of black velvet to form groups of similar staple lengths for weighing—or in a continuous, uniform density array for geometric analysis.

In the former instance, the weight of bundles of similar length is taken as a measure of frequency. One difficulty of this method is that a long-fibered group of the same weight will contain fewer fibers than a short-fibered group. Turner [3] and Ahmad [4] both have noted this fact in a study of results obtained from whole fibers and cut portions. A further discussion is to be found by Richardson, Bailey, and Conrad in a bulletin of the United States Department of Agriculture [5]. For cotton the

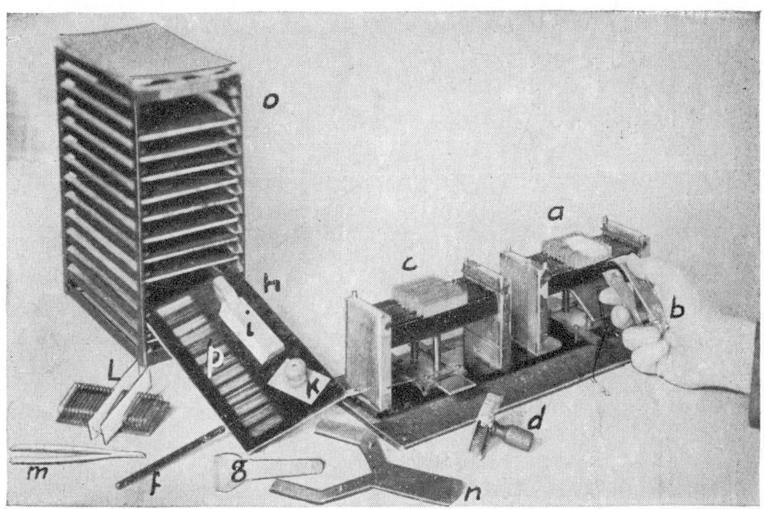

Fig. 3. Fiber staple sorter and parts. (*American Cotton Handbook.*)

difficulty due to these effects is partially offset by the fact that long fibers tend on the whole to be smaller in diameter than short fibers. For wool, however, short fibers tend to be finer than long ones, which makes the error greater.

It is possible to prepare a fiber array by a semimechanical means, such as the Balls' sledge sorter [6]. The sliver, prepared from the cotton, is fed into a pair of delivery rollers. The motion is intermittent and by alternately feeding the sliver and removing projecting fibers, the material delivered by the rollers is set out onto a background of plush as the sledge is moved forward bodily. The fibers will be deposited in the order of their group length, and the process is repeated over the same fiber deposit until a sufficient amount is laid on the plush to be easily collected and weighed in groups on a torsion balance. From these data, the frequency distribution of the staple lengths of the fibers together with other desired information can be computed.

A rapid means for determining the average staple of short fibers, such as cotton or certain types of rayon staple fiber, involves the use of a pair of scissors or a razor blade and three glass plates (usually 3×1 in. microscope slides will do). A representative bundle of fiber is paralleled by repeated drawing and lapping without discarding any fiber. This bundle is then cut cleanly into two parts (approximately in halves) and one part—the cut end nearer the left edge of the glass plate—is placed upon the first piece of glass. The second piece of glass is placed above it and the second half of the bundle—cut end nearest the right edge—is placed upon it in turn. The third piece of glass is then placed on top of all, making a sort of three-decker sandwich, with the cotton as the filling. The whole arrangement is held up to the light, and the glass plates may be moved about carrying the cotton with them until the bundle is of uniform density from edge to edge. The distance between the parallel cut edges is then the average staple.

Foster [7], referring to earlier work by Flühr [8] and Müller [9], suggests another method for obtaining average staple. A parallel bundle is formed as usual and a narrow section is cut from it and weighed (weight equals M_1) on a sensitive torsion balance. The remaining fibers are bunched and weighed (weight equals M_2). If h is the width of the cut strip, then

$$\text{Mean staple} = L = 2h\left(\frac{M_1}{M_2}\right)$$

The degree of parallelism and the uniformity of fibers axially affect the results.

A method less dependent on these factors is also suggested by Foster [7]. Here the bundle is squared off at one end and the narrow strip (width $y = \frac{1}{8}$ in.) is cut at the squared end and weights taken as before. Now

$$\text{Mean staple} = L = \tfrac{1}{2}y\left(4\frac{M_1}{M_2} + 3\right)$$

Hertel [10, 11] describes a device for obtaining staple length analyses, known as a "fibrograph." This operates on the null principle with an electrical indicator and suitable recording elements. Essentially, two balanced optical systems originate in the same light source and terminate in two separate photoelectric cells, which are connected in series. In parallel with them is a galvanometer, which indicates when the differential current is zero; in other words, when the optical systems are in balance. The light reaching the first of these cells is transmitted by a slit-exposed portion of the cotton sample, which is a squared-off tuft prepared in much the same fashion as those already discussed in the foregoing paragraphs. The light reaching the second photoelectric cell may be controlled in intensity by moving a cam over a slit, which therefore moderates the quantity of light reaching the photoelectric cell.

As the cotton is moved past the slit, which allows light to pass to the first photoelectric cell, the variation in the number of fibers will vary the intensity of light reaching the first cell. Then, in order to obtain a balance, the cam operating over the slit controlling the light striking the second cell must be moved to produce the same degree of intensity of lighting, which will be indicated by the zero reading on the galvanometer. It will be evident that the distance traveled by this cam is related to the change in the number of fibers through the shape of the cam itself, and this can be developed mathematically and empirically in order to obtain satisfactory results.

The cotton travels a distance which will correspond to the length of the fibers, since the direction of motion is parallel to the axes of the fibers. These two motions correspond to the co-ordinates of the desired length frequency curve, which is built up on the cumulative principle. The operation of the instrument is governed by two hand-operated knobs, one of which controls the cam motion and the other the motion of the bundle of fibers. The machine is autographic inasmuch as a pen moving integrally with the cotton rests upon a smooth card which is moved integrally with the cam. (See Fig. 4.)

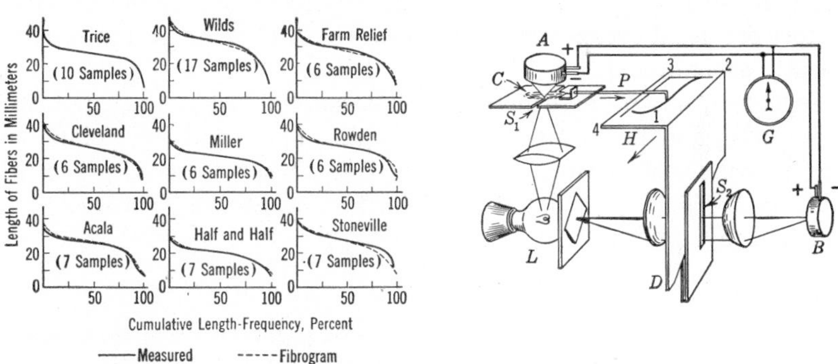

FIG. 4. Hertel fibrograph and resulting fibrograms (*Textile Research*). *A*, *B*, photocells; *C*, fiber sample; *L*, light source; *P*, recording pen; *G*, galvanometer; *D*, cam shutter and graph support; S_1, S_2, slits.

The resulting record is called a "fibrogram." When corrected for nonuniformity of diameter of cotton fibers throughout their entire length, the results are shown to compare favorably with the diagrams obtained by the usual sorting techniques. The apparatus is said to be very much faster in operation than the other sorting methods. It is pointed out by the author that a number of interesting interpretations as to settings of drawing rollers in drafting machinery and other information in regard to unevenness and its distribution throughout drafted slivers and rovings may be studied readily.

Measurements of the length of individual fibers has been considered a prohibitively tedious method. In some instances the fibers have been stretched in straightened form on the surface of a pile fabric and measured with a scale [12]. In others [13] a magnified image of the fiber was projected onto a screen and the length of the image was measured with a map reader and corrected by dividing this length by the magnification employed.

Sever [14] describes a device which makes possible the measurement of wool fibers one at a time at the rate of several hundred per hour. It consists essentially of three clamps, the middle one of which is fixed, while the other two can be traversed slowly in either direction by means of a rotating screw. Their separation at any instant can be read on a conveniently placed scale. A fiber is securely clamped near its center in the middle clamp. The fiber ends extend into and through the side clamps, which exert a mild yet insufficient pressure against the fiber to prevent slipping. The jaws are then traversed one at a time until the instant that the fiber pulls free. The clamp separation, which is the fiber length, can be noted on the scale. The apparatus conceivably might be adapted to rayon staple, but it would probably not be satisfactory for usual cotton where lengths as short as ¼ in. or less are frequently encountered.

Success by any of these methods will be conditioned by the care taken in selecting and preparing the test samples. Townend [15] points out the importance of this for wool, and the U. S. Department of Agriculture and the A.S.T.M. [2] point this out for fiber length tests on wool, cotton, and rayon alike.

Fineness

There is a growing awareness in the textile industry of the importance of the fineness of the fibers which constitute the raw material. The standards of quality for wool are based upon the frequency distribution of fiber diameters. Both the producers and users of rayon are keenly aware of the importance of denier size of the individual filaments. An important property of silk is its fineness; and a means of process control in the preparation of flax, jute, and hemp is the diameter range of fibers produced.

The direct measurement of diameter is best accomplished by the use of the microscope, but the measurement is often complicated by irregularity and departures from circularity of the fiber cross-section. Thus "ribbon width" of cotton is not a satisfactory measure. Calvert and Harland [16] suggest mercerization of cotton with an 18 per cent caustic soda solution to swell the fibers to the size they originally had in the boll. Maturity (cell-wall development) has an effect here, since the action of the caustic is to introduce convolutions into the immature fibers, where none previously existed.

Hardy [17] avoids certain of the difficulties of microscopic measurement of fiber sections by placing a tuft of fibers in a slot of known size under known tension. A sharp blade is brought down to a definite depth across the slot, cutting all but the fibers left between the cutting edge and the bottom of the slot. Müller [18] and Küsebauch [19] have modified this method. In the latter instance, instead of counting the number of fibers remaining, which will be inversely proportional to the fineness, the diameter of a bundle of 100 fibers is measured. In none of these methods is it possible to obtain a frequency distribution of fiber diameters.

Ewles [20], MacNicholas and Curtis [21], and Matthew [22] form a bundle of paralleled fibers which is used as a diffraction grating to view a slit [21] or a pair of slits [22] to produce a diffraction pattern, measurement of which can, by means of a calibration chart, determine the average fiber diameter. Very fine fibers do not give particularly good results. Again, a frequency distribution is not possible.

The gravimetric method involves the determination of weight per unit length, which is taken to be inversely proportional to fineness. For fibers which do not have a central channel—and hence a possibility of variable wall thickness—and which are substantially uniform in diameter throughout their length, such as silk or most of the man-made filaments, these methods are effective.

Peirce and Lord [23] point out that fiber weight for cotton is not a good measure of fineness unless maturity is considered. Two fibers may have the same weight per unit length, one having a large perimeter and thin walls, the other having a small perimeter and thick walls. The above have determined a relationship between fiber weight and maturity, where the latter is defined as the difference between the number of normal and the number of immature fibers in a sample of 100, or $(N - D)$. If a standard maturity is taken at +60, then the maturity ratio is

$$\frac{\text{Measured weight}}{\text{Standard weight}} = \frac{\frac{1}{2}(N - D)}{100 + 0.7}$$

The standard fiber weight is taken as comparable between samples.

A newer technique based on work of Hertel and Sullivan [24] is outlined by Grimes [25]. This is said to have the advantage of speed and simplicity of equipment. The fibers to be tested are made up into wads under controlled conditions and are inserted into a cylinder. Air is drawn through the wads, and the pressure difference required to produce steady flow is read on a manometer.

Calibration against weight per inch measurements (it is not stated whether maturity correction was made) results in the formula

$$\text{Weight per inch} = 7.8225 - 1.4608(\Delta)$$

where Δ = pressure difference in millimeters.

The A.S.T.M. [26] expresses the weight fineness for cotton in micrograms per inch determined from the weight of a definite number of whole fibers whose length has been determined by the method mentioned on page 1216 from a sorter array.

For wool, the A.S.T.M. [26] recommends the microscopic measurement by the wedge method (see page 8) and for rayon staple fiber (D540-42) either the measurement of filament denier from microscopically projected cross-section measurement

$$\text{Denier per fiber} = \frac{ASK}{M^2}$$

where A = average observed area in square millimeters,
S = specific gravity of the sample,
M = linear magnification,
K = constant of magnitude equaling 9000,

or the measurement of the weight of a definite number of fibers of known length (where the fibers are easily straightened and do not represent mixed deniers).

SINGLE FIBER TENSILE TESTERS

The strength of a textile yarn and ultimately the fabric depends to a large extent on the tensile strength of the fibers of which the yarn is composed. This is especially true of filamentous materials, such as silk, rayon, and nylon. Yarns manufactured from short-length fibers, like cotton, wool, staple rayons, hemp, jute, ramie, and other similar fibers, in the final analysis depend also on the strength of the fibers for their composite structural characteristics. The contribution of fiber strength to the completed yarn properties varies widely; it depends upon such factors as fiber friction, staple length, fineness, and yarn twist, in addition to the final fabric specifications. The fiber strength still remains the basis for strength requirements of the finished product.

Many attempts have been made to measure single fiber tensile strength. The problem at best is not an easy one. The small dimensions of the fibers alone require apparatus quite delicate in construction. When it is realized that the breaking strength is only one part of the complete problem and that of equal importance are other factors, such as elongation, yield point, plastic flow regions, modulus of elasticity, in addition to temperature and humidity effects, the apparatus becomes quite complex. From a practical point of view, simplicity of operation, low initial cost, and rapid testing procedure are additional prerequisites.

Basically, the different types of testing machines can be placed in six general classes:

(1) Hydraulic type,
(2) Balance type,
(3) Pendulum type,
(4) Spring type,
(5) Chainomatic type,
(6) Transducer type.

Some of the machines may be identified in more than one class as they involve more than one of the principles tabulated above. This will be made clear subsequently.

Hydraulic Type

Attempts to evaluate single fiber strength were made by O'Neill [27] as early as 1863. In this machine the top jaw was fixed and the lower jaw was connected to a float riding in water inside a cylinder. When a sample is placed between the two jaws and water is drained from the cylinder, the buoyant effect on the float becomes less and hence load is imparted to the sample. It follows that the amount of water drained from the cylinder before the sample breaks can be used as an indication of the fiber strength (see Fig. 5).

This machine had some very distinct disadvantages. During the test the sample elongated of course, which lowered the float relative to the fixed top jaw. It can be recognized, then, that water drained from the cylinder is not directly proportional to the load impressed on the sample. In addition, as the sample was mounted directly above the water in the cylinder, the humidity of the air surrounding the sample is an unknown quantity. Changes in the atmospheric conditions in proximity to the sample will, of course, affect the test results. Such other difficulties as surface-tension effects and time lag, resulting from the breaking of the fiber and the shutting off of the stop cocks, introduced errors which prevented the test from being a quantitative one.

Henry [28] in 1902 described a machine which represented an improvement on the O'Neill apparatus. Instead of measuring the amount of water drained from the cylinder, the inventor graduated the side of his float. The differences in the water level as noted on the graduations then indicated the difference in buoyancy effect of the float independent of the elongation of the sample. The disadvantages of lack of humidity control and difficulties in determining the end-point precisely still persisted in this apparatus.

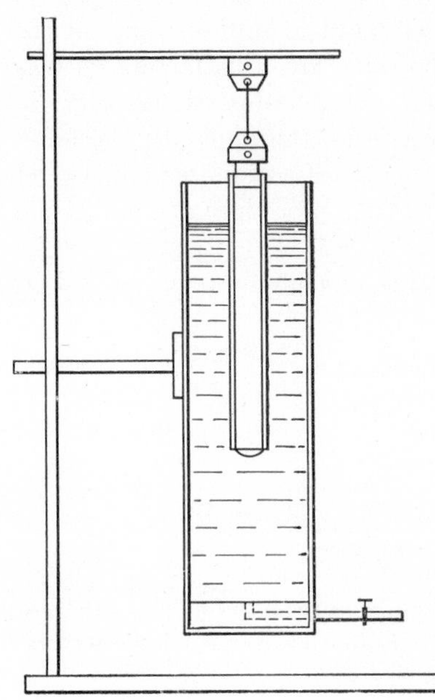

FIG. 5. O'Neill hydraulic-type fiber tester.

W. L. Balls [29] described an apparatus by Hughes which is an improvement of both the O'Neill and Henry testers. The most important modification was that the method of mounting the sample had been altered in order to straighten the fiber and to compensate for different gage lengths. Also, a capillary outlet was attached to the cylinder in order to evaluate more precisely the amount of water drained from the cylinder. Lack of humidity control and the requirement of elongation correction still existed as theoretical limitations.

A further improvement on these three machines is described by Mann and Peirce [30]. This tester also made provision for straightening the fiber without initially tensioning it unduly and modified the manner in which the sample was mounted. A calcium chloride solution was used in the cylinder in order to obtain a vapor pressure at a given temperature which resulted in essentially a 66 per cent relative humidity for the atmosphere surrounding the sample. It follows, of course, that in order to maintain this atmospheric condition, the temperature of the room must be controlled quite accurately. Correction was made for elongation so that the amount of water drained from the cylinder would be indicative of the tensile strength of the sample under test.

The general hydraulic principle was used also by Smith [31] after a suggestion by E. Schmid. The author used a balance, the left arm of which was utilized for holding the sample. A float, attached to the right arm of the balance, provided the means for loading the sample. *N*-propyl alcohol was used in the float and cylinder combination in order to avoid errors introduced by evaporation. As this fluid was then drained from the cylinder, the load due to the loss in buoyancy effect on the float was transmitted through the balance to the jaw holding the sample. Provision was made by means of a special mount to straighten the fiber without unduly tensioning it before the test. The use of the fluid in the cylinder set apart from the jaw holding the sample eliminated the effect of any changes in relative humidity in proximity to the sample.

Raybaut [32] reported a tester by Heim-Richards, which is somewhat similar in construction to the Hughes tester. Mercury instead of water was used in the cylinder in order to alleviate any difficulties encountered by changes in relative humidity. This instrument differed from any of the others in that it was made autographic to give load-elongation diagrams of the test sample.

Quite an ingenious machine for testing fiber strength was reported by Sukthanker, Ahmad, and Navkal [33]. Here, a fiber is suspended from a hook fixed to a lever arrangement in such a way that an electric circuit is completed as soon as the fiber is straightened out. The other end of the fiber is attached to a float suspended in a solution of calcium chloride contained in a U-tube. The fiber tension is applied by raising a counterpoise suspended from a string in the second arm of the U-tube. As this counterpoise is gradually raised, the level of the liquid surrounding the float falls and the pull on the fiber increases steadily until it breaks, and the float, which has been held by the fiber, drops in the U-tube. The counterpoise is raised by winding the string on a pulley, driven by a gear arrangement from a small electric motor. This same gear train records the tension applied to the fiber on two calibrated dials. The arrangement for applying and recording the tension is connected to the electric circuit and is in operation only so long as the circuit is complete. As soon as the fiber breaks, the electric circuit is interrupted and both the pointer and the counterpoise come to rest. It is possible to read the tensile strength and elongation at any load, including rupture, from the dials.

Balance Type

The balance type of instrument uses the well-known principle of moments, wherein a weight is either moved with respect to a given fulcrum, in order to increase the lever arm, or the lever arm remains constant with an increase in weight. Either of these methods will result in an increase in the moment about the fulcrum.

Bowman [34] in 1908 suggested an apparatus built around this principle. One arm of the balance was used for holding one end of the sample, and the other arm of the balance was made with a graduated beam. By moving a given weight along this arm, then, it was possible to increase the moment about the fulcrum and hence increase the tensile force on the sample under test. As the position of the weight on the arm was controlled manually, the rate of loading on the sample is something of an unknown quantity. In addition, the machine is susceptible to shock and vibration due to manual control of the weights, and there is friction at the fulcrum or pivot, which necessarily introduces errors in the testing technique.

An instrument similar to the Bowman tester is reported by Matthews [35]. The load is brought to bear upon the sample by moving a weight along the lever, except in this instance the motion of the weight is governed by a rack and pinion drive. Such an arrangement minimizes the shock or vibration resulting from manual control, but it does not eliminate the friction at the bearing.

Barratt [36] in 1922 described an apparatus in which the load is applied to the sample electrically. As before, one end of the sample is attached to a jaw on one side of a balance lever, while to the opposite side of the lever is attached a metal core penetrating into a solenoid. If, now, the solenoid current should be increased by varying a suitable rheostat, the core is drawn into the solenoid in proportion to the increased amperage flowing in the electrical circuit. Similarly, if the current flowing through the solenoid winding is decreased, the amount of load on the sample is decreased.

It is possible, then, to obtain data which the author describes as "recovery from strain." In order to interpret correctly the data from this tester, it is necessary to calibrate the machine in such a way that the current flowing through the solenoid is interpreted in terms of load on the sample. As in the preceding machine, this tester is subject to the limitations of rate of load dependent upon the rate of amperage increase or decrease and is also subject to friction in bearings.

An apparatus similar to Barratt's was built by Stetson and Jacobson [37], and it was found that one of the operational difficulties centered about the end of the test. As the sample ruptured, resistance to the penetration of the core into the solenoid was destroyed and the core was immediately drawn its full travel into the solenoid. Such an impact disturbed the machine, so that in many instances the calibration was destroyed.

Another apparatus built around the balance principle was reported by Krais [38]. Suspended from one arm of the balance is the top jaw for holding one end of the sample, while the other arm of the balance has a hook to which a bucket can be attached. The sample is mounted between the jaw described above and an adjustable jaw mounted on the

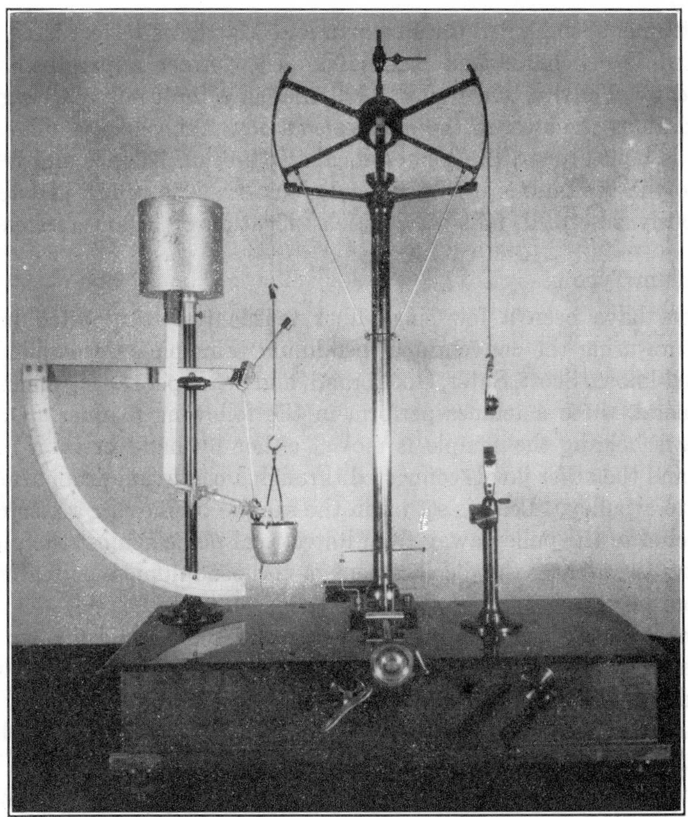

Fig. 6. Krais-Keyl balance-type fiber tester. (*Fabric Research Labs., Inc.*)

table of the apparatus. This latter jaw allows for adjustments to compensate for any crimp or curliness that might exist in the sample and also allows for adjustment for the specific gage length being employed. As the test proceeds, water is drained from a reservoir through a capillary burette into the bucket hanging on one side of the balance. The couple introduced by this greater weight is transmitted through a knife-edge bearing to the jaw holding the sample. Water is allowed to accumulate in the bucket until sufficient load is impressed upon the sample to cause rupture; the weight of this then indicates the load. The instrument can

Barker and Tunstall [46] have described an instrument built around a horizontal coil spring. The specimen is clamped between a jaw attached to a motor-driven screw and the other end of the specimen is attached to a jaw mounted on the horizontal coil spring. The load is applied by extending the spring at a constant rate through the motor drive. A float between the fiber and the spring operates switches which control the motor driving the fiber clamp. When the fiber motor runs, the stretch is taken out by movement of the clamp on that end of the fiber. A pen is attached to this clamp and moves along a drum by this motion. The spring is stretched and the drum rotated at a constant rate by the other motor, which runs continuously until shut off at the extremity of the throw. A plot of the load elongation relationship is thus obtained from rectilinear co-ordinates.

An instrument described by Smith [47] is essentially an improved type of Polanyi [44] tester. The lower jaw is mounted on a micrometer screw and the upper jaw is connected to a flat steel beam spring mounted on knife-edges. The bottom jaw is moved downward by a worm and gear arrangement, and the amount of load impressed upon the sample is read by the angular deflection of a light beam from a mirror mounted on the spring. Aoki and Atsuki [48] describe an instrument similar to Smith's, which is also of the spring type. In their arrangement, the elongation is measured photographically.

Cliff [49] has reported a method of obtaining load-extension diagrams of textile fibers employing a constant rate of load throughout each test. The novel point in the method consists in the application of the load through a spiral spring by the rotation of a torsion head at constant speed. The instrument gives diagrams in rectangular co-ordinates and can be designed with a number of capacities. In the case of single fiber testing the capacity is such that fibers can be tested below a strength of 20 grams.

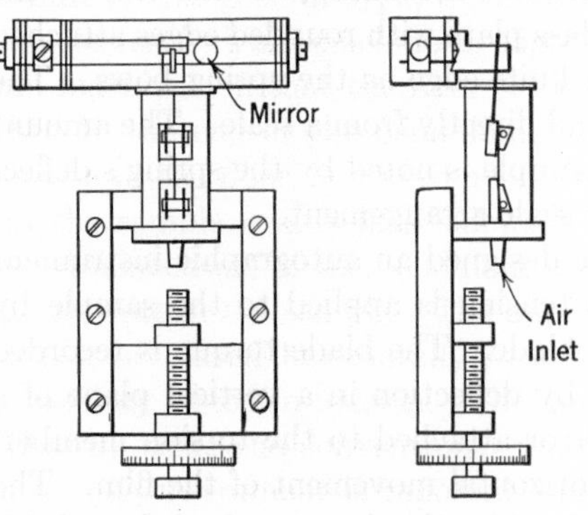

Fig. 7. Steinberger spring-type fiber tester

As a result of a Textile Foundation research project, an instrument for testing single fibers was designed by Steinberger [50] (see Fig. 7). In this instrument, the upper jaw is mounted on a cantilever beam supported on a spring formed by a pair of tuned wires. The lower jaw is mounted in a micrometer-controlled heavy slide. A mirror is also attached to the upper jaw, and the amount of load is recorded by means of a reflected light beam, with the actual reading being taken through a telescope. This instrument was also refined by Dunlop [51].

A very elaborate single fiber testing machine was reported by Osumi and Kato [52]. It is essentially of the same design as the Cliff [49] instrument; i.e., it uses a rotating head with a torsional spring, except in this case the instrument is kept in balance manually.

Chainomatic Type

A number of single fiber testing machines have been built around the so-called chainomatic principle. Some of these testers have incorporated the balance principle as well, but all accomplish the actual loading by means of a chain. In its simplest sense, the chainomatic principle involves subjecting the sample to a force resulting from smoothly hanging increasing lengths of chain from one end of the sample. The magnitude and rate of load are accomplished by considering the weight of the chain per unit length and the speed with which the chain is fed into the catenary, in part suspended from the sample. The method is simple, devoid of shock or vibration, and can be so constructed as to result in a constant rate of load.

Kropf [53] in 1931 designed, constructed, and calibrated a single fiber testing machine involving the chainomatic principle. The top jaw of this machine, which held one end of the sample, was fixed, and the bottom jaw, at the other end of the sample, was connected to one end of the chain. If different lengths of the chain were brought to bear upon the sample, it would be stressed in proportion to the length of chain introduced. The movement of the lower jaw indicates elongation of the sample and can be correlated with the length of chain on the sample to give data which will depict a load elongation diagram. If the length of chain brought to bear upon the sample was governed by an entirely independent mechanism of a constant speed unwinding type, the elongation of the sample would preclude the utilization of a constant rate of load. In order to correct for the decreased length of chain due to elongation of the sample, the author introduced compensating chains. As the sample then elongated, the compensating chain brought on a proportional amount of load to correct for the reduction of load in the main chain drive.

A machine of substantially the same principle was reported also by Demeulemeester and Nicoloff [54]. The main advantage of their instrument is that it introduces a method for obtaining load elongation diagrams direct. This is accomplished by a suitable arrangement of a photographic film drive, so that the two co-ordinates of the film would represent load and elongation. By projecting a beam of light from a reflecting mirror, it is possible to get a trace on the film depicting the characteristics of the sample under test. The authors also introduced a compensating chain in order to correct for the elongation of the sample.

Fig. 8. Chainomatic-type fiber tester. (*Rayon Textile Monthly.*)

Another instrument was described by Saxl [55] which also gives this type of loading. In his apparatus, one end of the sample is connected to a sliding micrometer jaw and the other end to one end of a light-weight lever. The chain used to test the sample is also connected to this same lever. As load is brought on by the application of more links of chain, the lever arm tends to fall because of the elongation of the sample. If, however, the micrometer jaw is adjusted so that a datum point located with respect to the lever is maintained, the movement of the adjustable jaw can then be interpreted in terms of elongation. The amount of load at the different elongation stations can be read from a calibrated scale on which is mounted a slide holding the free end of the chain. As the level of the loading chain is maintained a constant, no compensating chain need be introduced to correct for elongation.

About a year later Demeulemeester and Nicoloff [56] reported an improvement of their former instrument, in which the load elongation diagrams resulted from a photoelectric cell circuit rather than from a photographic process.

Recently Hindman and Fox [57] described an apparatus (Fig. 8) applicable to single fiber testing, which is somewhat similar to the Saxl instrument but with certain refinements. A motor drive for the chain

FIG. 9. Sookne and Rutherford fiber tester. (*Rayon Textile Monthly.*)

was incorporated in order to insure constant rate of loading, and a buzzer circuit was employed to demarcate the loading stations. In addition, provision was made for testing the sample under different conditions of temperature and humidity by enclosing the sample in a glass tube and using suitable temperature and humidification controls.

Still another single fiber tester (Fig. 9) was reported by Sookne and Rutherford [58] in 1943. This represents an improvement on the apparatus described by Sookne and Harris in 1937. The original apparatus [59] was one of the balance type and the later one incorporated the chainomatic principle and was made autographic. By the use of photoelectric controls and an automatic electronic balance, the apparatus produced a continuous record of the fiber properties when strained at a constant rate of elongation and a point-by-point diagram when stressed at a constant rate of loading. By use of a suitable reversing mechanism, the instrument could be made to yield relaxation curves as well. As in other instruments previously described, the sample could be immersed in different fluids and tested under these conditions.

Transducer Type

Use of load cells employing bonded-wire strain gages for detecting and measuring loads ranging from 2 grams full scale to 1000 lb makes the Instron Tensile Tester [60] available for testing not only yarns and fabrics but also fibers as well. The instrument can be operated at jaw speeds from 0.02 to 20 in. per min, and its operation is servo-controlled. Thus the usual machine characteristics which complicate the interpretation of the graphical record are eliminated. Since the upper jaw is attached to the load cell and since the latter is sufficiently rigid so as to have negligible deflection, the deformation of the specimen can be measured with high precision in terms of lower jaw travel. (See Fig. 10.)

A further feature of very great importance is the ability of the unit to record graphically either load relaxation (or, if desired, load restoration) for a given constant deformation of the specimen. This is a particularly revealing technique when matters of molecular structure of fibers is under investigation.

AGGREGATE FIBER TESTS

Special techniques for determining cotton fiber strength have been reported by a number of investigators. Since it has been shown that cotton fiber strength may vary widely, it is necessary to test a large number of fibers in order to characterize a given cotton with reasonable precision. This tedious process can be shortened reasonably well by testing a number of fibers at the same time, resulting in the so-called bundle or aggregate fiber tests.

Crowley [61] apparently used this general method first by selecting a suitable sample of cotton and proceeding as follows: The fibers in the sample were first parallelized by a combing technique. As the strength of the resulting flat bundle is dependent upon the number of fibers in the bundle, it is necessary to get a measure of the number of fibers being tested. One way to accomplish this is to cut all the fibers to a predetermined length and then weigh the sample under standard atmospheric conditions. If care is employed in preparing the sample of a designated length, the weight of the sample is an efficient method

Fig. 10. Instron Tester, which is easily arranged to work with individual fibers or fiber bundles. (*Courtesy Instron Engineering Corporation.*)

of estimating the number of fibers in the bundle. If the ends of the bundle are held by some type of adhesive material such as Scotch tape, the bundle can then be tested on a conventional pendulum-type testing machine.

A similar method was also employed by Bellinson [62], who compared the tensile strength of a large variety of cottons. The procedure was refined somewhat as to both method of combing and technique of trimming the sample to a given length. To effect accurate trimming, a steel clamp was made, of which the upper part was a steel bar 0.5 in. in width. The tuft of fibers was laid upon a piece of cardboard and clamped. The projecting ends of the fibers could then be easily trimmed off with a razor blade, leaving a tuft, which was always 0.5 in. long. In order to establish a finite gage length, and in order to properly mount the bundles between adhesive material, a special metal plate was prepared with four upright pins placed at the corners of a rectangle measuring 0.75 by 0.08 in. The bundle of fibers then could be placed between the pins and manipulated so that the thickness was uniform. The adhesive material such as drafting tape could then be applied by holding the square end of the tape against the pins above the fibers and lowering the tape until it was stuck to the bundle. When both projecting ends of the bundle have been attached to the tape, the entire bundle may be removed from the pins, turned over, and replaced between the pins so that additional pieces of tape may be attached to the back.

The bundle was then ready to be tested in a machine of the pendulum type. However, it was found that the jaw separation at the beginning of successive breaks was likely to vary. In order to correct for this variation, the author introduced a compensating device, built into the lower jaw of the testing machine. By varying the position of the lower jaw through this compensating mechanism, the gage length could be established with great precision. Comparable readings for several samples can be obtained by dividing the breaking load of the composite tuft by the weight of the sample.

Another method of testing fibers in groups was proposed by Chandler [63]. In this method (see Fig. 11), a bundle of approximately 10,000 fibers is broken as a unit. The fibers are parallelized by combing; the bundle is then placed in two clamps, which are separated so that the bundle is under slight tension. Ends of a piece of sewing thread are attached to the bundle at each clamp, and a weight suspended in the loop of the thread. As both clamps are rotated together, the thread is wound around the bundle. The length of thread required to wrap

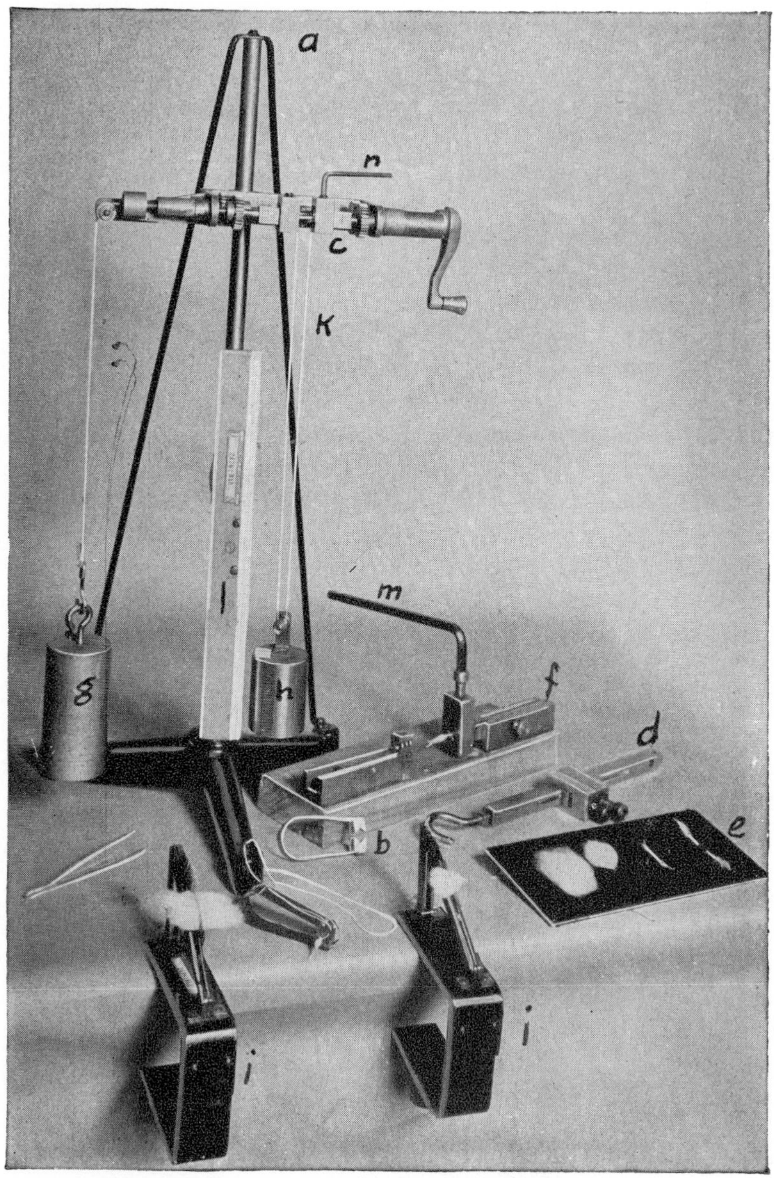

FIG. 11. Chandler bundle tester. (*American Cotton Handbook.*)

the bundle ten times is noted and used to compute the circumference. Chandler recommends a bundle the circumference of which shall be from 0.15 to 0.20 in.

As the thread is wound on the bundle, it forms a spiral and the arms of the loop travel to the center of the bundle. After they reach the center, the direction of the spiral is reversed and, although the bundle is rotated in the same direction, the arms of the loop now travel back to the ends of the bundle. As a result, the bundle is completely wound with the sewing thread, yet the center remains free. Special jaws for the break machine are clamped on each side of this center portion and, since the jaws are in contact during the clamping, the gage length is essentially zero.

It is necessary, of course, to convert the breaking strength of the bundle, either into a strength per unit fiber or a strength per unit area basis. The cross-sectional area may be determined from the weight and density of the bundle, requiring the trimming of the fibers to a uniform length, determining their weight, and then finding the density.

The latest method for testing cotton fibers by the bundle method was reported by Pressley [64]. The procedure of sample preparation is quite similar to either the flat bundle test or the Chandler test. The sample is selected and the fibers are then parallel and cut to a predetermined length. Special clamps are used by Pressley; these are mounted in a device separate from that used for breaking the sample.

The tester (see Fig. 12) is composed of a carriage mounted on rollers, which is allowed to move down a slightly inclined surface. The motion of the carriage down the track, constituting one arm of a balance, continues until a sufficient moment is set up about the fulcrum of the balance to rupture the sample, which is mounted as part of the other arm of the balance. When the sample breaks, the inclined plane track falls immediately and the motion of the carriage is arrested by a brake mechanism. By means of a graduated scale on the inclined plane track, it is possible to note the amount of force required to rupture the sample. As in other tests of this nature, the weight of the sample being tested must be obtained in order to correlate it with the breaking strength of the composite sample.

An interesting attempt was made by Denham and Lonsdale [65] in 1928 to evaluate the impact properties of a fiber bundle. The apparatus used for testing the sample was of the pendulum type with one jaw attached to the pendulum at the center of percussion and the other jaw capable of having its motion arrested by a stop on the frame of the machine. In the test, the pendulum is allowed to drop from a given distance and the amount of energy absorbed by the sample in rupturing it at the bottom of the pendulum swing is indicated by the decrease in height of the pendulum at the end of its full swing.

Greater emphasis is being given to the general phase of impact testing as it is the feeling of many textile technologists that ordinary tensile strength or so-called static tests run at the conventional 12 in. per min are a poor counterpart of many actual service conditions. In

FIG. 12. Pressley flat bundle tester.

the case of materials that are apt to be subjected to impact loading in service, it follows then that more information should be obtained regarding the properties of the different materials under laboratory conditions involving high rates of load.

COMPRESSION TESTING

In contrast to the single fiber tensile tests are a number of methods for testing masses of fiber in compression. Such testing procedures are of importance as there are many conditions under which textile fibers are subjected to such a force. Any determination which involves pressure of one unit against another involves compression; thus, the simple procedures of thickness measurement of yarn or fabric as carried out by means of the usual thickness gage having a presser foot and anvil are compression tests. Measurements of the compressibility of mattress or pillow stuffing materials, carpets, pile fabrics, or insulating pads are additional examples.

In addition to the ability of the sample to be compressed, i.e., compressibility, the recovery from compression is of considerable interest. This recovery is known as "compressional resilience" and may be elastic in nature, if the deformation resulting from the compression is instantly and completely recovered. It may be in the nature of creep, if the recovery is relatively slow. When the load is reduced or removed entirely, there will be a change in deformation of a recovery nature, which will progress systematically with time. A time-deformation curve can be plotted, and its form will give information of value regarding the resilience of the material.

There may also be nonrecoverable deformation, i.e., "permanent set," which is measurable and of interest. This "permanent set" should be thought of as a transient phenomenon, as the deformation is alterable by atmospheric changes. Textile materials in general exhibit the properties of plastic substances and are, therefore, considerably affected by the time factor in tests which involve change of shape with load application; it is necessary to consider a definite schedule of load application in order to reproduce results as well as to determine the effect of loading rates and cyclical loading histories upon the characteristics of the test sample.

It is often necessary to evaluate the resilience of a sample in terms of work done or in terms of energy rather than in the light of simple deformation. It can be understood that a specimen may be deformed from one size to another with the expenditure of considerable energy or conversely with little energy. The recovery after the deformation may require a substantial amount of work in the form of potential energy in the sample when the deformation originally occurred and which can be restored wholly or in part as the material comes back more nearly to its original condition. If the results of a compression and recovery test, i.e., loads and corresponding thicknesses, are plotted, it will be seen that between the initial and final points of either the compression or recovery curves, any number of lines may be drawn, each one indicating a certain load deformation behavior. The area beneath any one of these lines is a measure of the energy involved and will be different for each path taken.

It is not enough, therefore, simply to measure the deformation produced at any particular load and to report the resilience in terms of this deformation. It is also of importance to know how easily the recovery was accomplished or with what difficulty the compression was produced.

The difficulty of determining the initial thickness or volume of a material under no load has led to the general adoption of an initial small load on a given weight of sample. It is easier to work with a given weight of material than with a specified volume, because of differences in specific gravity of fibers, state of aggregation, and past compressional history. For masses of bulk fiber, for example, this is not particularly satisfactory. Only a partial change of volume is brought about by a small load, and it is possible to get quite different initial conditions as to bulk on repeat tests on the same or other samples of the same material. Hence, the data of the first load-deformation cycle, particularly that part produced during application of load, are uncertain.

If, however, at the end of the first cycle, the same loading and unloading are repeated, another loop will result with entirely different characteristics. As the loading and unloading are continued, the loops approach each other more closely, and usually at about the fifth or sixth cycle the loops will be practically superimposed. This repeating cycle can be thought of as a mechanically conditioned cycle; i.e., through a mechanical action, namely, compression, the material tested can be made to reproduce its characteristics.

It follows, then, that through a treatment of repeated cycles in which time is the important factor, data can be obtained which appear to be most reliable for comparing different samples or different conditions of testing on similar samples. It has been found occasionally that the number of cycles necessary to obtain the superimposed loop may be a significant measure of the difference between materials.

Test Methods

There have been several methods suggested for testing textile fibers in compression. In 1926 Hardy [66], working for the U. S. Bureau of Animal Industry, found that there was a significant relationship between the volume of raw wool under pressure and the clean wool content. His apparatus was built around an ordinary platform scale of 2000-lb capacity. Cylinders of different sizes were filled by handfuls, using care to place the stock in as uniform layers as possible. The cylinder containing the material to be tested was then placed on the scale platform and the counterbalance weight for the force to be exerted on the stock was suspended from the beam. The actual force was applied by moving a plunger, mounted in a horizontal support, into the cylinder until the tipping of the beam indicated that the desired force had been applied. At this time, the volume of the material was determined by noting the penetration of the plunger. The results of this investigation indicated that it was possible to predict the yield of raw wool within 5 per cent.

A similar investigation was reported by Burns and Johnston [67] in 1936 using Hardy's apparatus. The authors used a refined sampling technique and standardized the preparation of the sample to be tested as well as recognized the time factor as it influenced their readings. It was reported that their investigation proved conclusively that it is possible to predict the actual yield of raw wool from its density under pressure within a small margin.

A similar apparatus with some refinements was designed, built, and calibrated by Peterson and Wenberg [68]. Later Dockstader [69], using the principle of the inclined plane (constant rate of load) which was developed by the H. L. Scott Co. for use in tensile testing machines, improved the original design of Hardy's apparatus. The construction is of the cylinder and plunger type, with the load being applied automatically at a constant rate throughout the compression and recovery portions of the cycle. The M.I.T. apparatus was built with the approval of the Scott Co. and provided an autographic record in multiple of as many complete compression-recovery cycles as may be desired. From the resulting charts it was possible to measure not only linear displacements but also the areas representative of the energies involved. In addition to testing bulk fibers, this apparatus has been used on cut specimens of carpets or other fabrics in multiple.

Marsh [70] has described an instrument designed to measure the thickness of single layers of fabric at known pressures. By varying the load in increments, he was able to measure the compressional characteristics of a sample using a range from 1 mg to 100 grams per sq cm. This general principle was amplified by Schiefer [71] in an investigation at the National Bureau of Standards. His apparatus allows the study of yarns and fabrics in compression and particularly their recovery from compression. The instrument, known as a compressometer, indicates the degree of compression on a specimen by means of a standard thickness gage. A calibrated spring or other suitable device is used to produce the pressure of the foot of the instrument against the specimen. The loading is intermittent, with a 15-sec relaxation period recommended. This apparatus has also been used for evaluating the crush resistance of fabrics which have been subjected to special finishing treatments. He also found that on a pile fabric, decrease of thickness was rather gradual until the pile collapsed. When the pressure was again released, complete recovery to the original thickness was not obtained.

A rather unusual method for making measurements of compression on bulk fiber was described by Winson [72]; a balloon was used to confine the sample, and the pressure was applied in all directions rather than in one direction. The balloon was filled with a weighed sample of fiber and was attached to the end of a tube, the whole being enclosed in a glass jar. The balloon and the glass jar were then evacuated equally, their respective pressures being read from manometers. Upon readmission of air to the jar and the establishment of an equilibrium condition, the pressures inside and outside the balloon could be determined. This in turn yielded data indicative of the cubic compressional characteristics of the fiber sample.

The test was continued until the difference between the pressures within and without the balloon had some arbitrarily chosen differential. Air was then evacuated from the jar in steps until the pressures were again equalized. As the volumetric displacement of the balloon had been determined, the volume of the internal system at a given pressure was proportional therefore to the volume of the internal system at any other pressure. The differences between the pressure within and without the balloon, plotted as abscissas against the ratio of the volume of the balloon at various pressures to the volume at a standard pressure, gave a curve indicating the cubic compression of the wool against pressure. A definite hysteresis was found between the loading and unloading curves, so that the findings could be reported in terms of energy.

The principle of the cylinder and plunger was somewhat modified by Saxl [73, 74, 75], who used the platform of a simple beam balance to support a beaker of fiber. An accessory vertical support carried a rack and pinion, which controlled the movement of a plunger, the descent of which into the beaker was measured by means of graduations on the vertical support. If the plunger was then lowered into a beaker containing a weighed sample of fibers, the balance could be brought to equilibrium. The weight necessary to affect this equilibrium could be recorded and plotted against the depression of the plunger into the beaker.

In 1938, Robinson [76] reported an interesting dynamic test using the cylinder and plunger principle. In his work, a series of plant fiber samples were repeatedly compressed in a cylinder by means of a piston, which was raised and lowered rapidly by a suitable motor-driven mechanism. A record was kept of the second, third, tenth, twentieth, fiftieth, one-hundredth, and one-hundred-fiftieth compressions. It was found that as the plunger was lifted, the compressed fiber mass rose a certain amount almost instantaneously, and the remainder of the rise was gradual, taking perhaps 4 to 5 sec.

A chainomatic loading type of compressional resilience tester is described by Fox and Schwarz [77, 78], and a later development employing bonded resistance wire electric strain gages mounted on a cantilever weigh bar measures the relaxation of load at a constant volume. (See Fig. 13.)

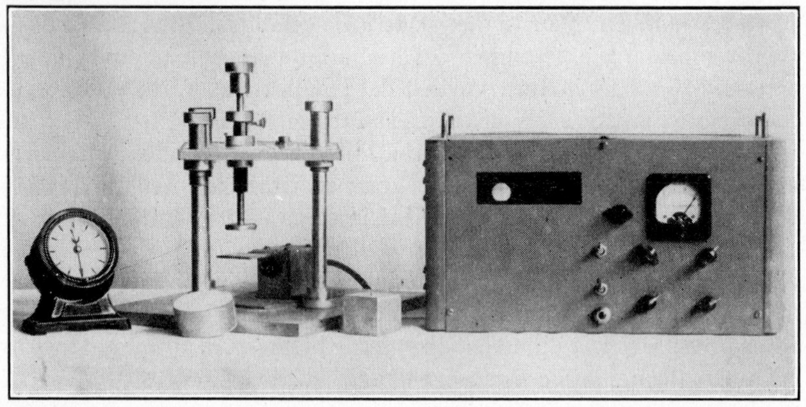

FIG. 13. Bulk fiber compressional relaxation tester. (*Courtesy M.I.T. Textile Division.*)

In order to obtain load-deformation curves on bulk fiber (or other specimens) a strain-gage load cell compression tester was developed in the M.I.T. Slater Memorial Textile Research Laboratory by Hindman and Schwarz and is described by Finch [79]. Here a presser foot is moved at any desired constant speed up and down upon the sample and the load-deformation cycles are graphed, or the rate of load relaxation or restoration at constant deformation measured. (See Fig. 14.) Additional discussion of resilience testing is given by Dillon [80].

TORSION TESTING

Inasmuch as the spinning and twisting operations necessary for the manufacture of yarn involves twisting of fibers, their resistance to torsional forces is of importance. The torsional rigidity has been defined by Peirce [81, 82] as the couple or torque required to produce a twist of one turn per centimeter of fiber length and may be measured by the method suggested by him, which consists in attaching one end of the fiber under test to a rigid support (usually by means of shellac) and then can be adapted to work with fibers which are not too fine, too short, nor too lacking in resistance to torsion. The principle involved

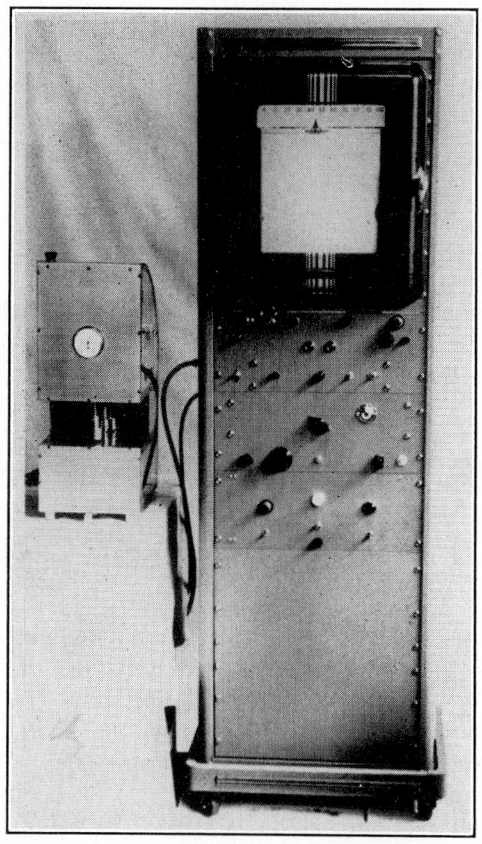

FIG. 14. Compressional resilience tester for cyclic operation as well as load relaxation or load restoration studies. (*Courtesy M.I.T. Textile Division.*)

is the attachment of a small sample under known tension to the lower end of a calibrated phosphor bronze wire. The image of a scale is viewed in a small mirror carried by the wire. A cathetometer is used for the purpose. The scale deflection can be transformed into units of torque by reference to a calibration curve. Provision is made for damping out oscillations by means of a pair of light vanes operating in an annular oil bath [83].

FIBER FRICTION PROPERTIES

The close-clinging power of cotton fibers has been measured by various investigators following work done by Adderley [84] in 1922. Navkal and Turner [85], as a part of their discussion of the foundation of yarn strength and yarn extension, used an O'Neill apparatus (see Fig. 5) to draw a bundle of 10 parallel fibers between pads of paralleled fibers pressed together by a weight-loaded lever.

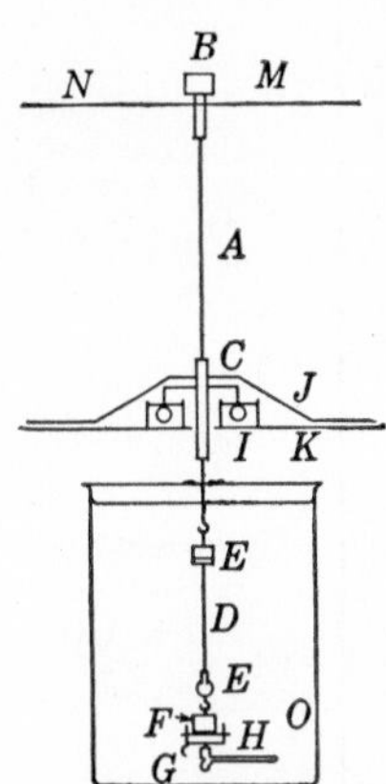

Fig. 15. Steinberger torsion apparatus [83].

Sen and Ahmad [86] built an apparatus for testing this property of cotton. A bundle of 100 parallel fibers was drawn between two pads, which were held together by air pressure acting against a rubber diaphragm. The pressure used was about 5 cm of mercury, and an average of several successive slips was taken in order to eliminate the uncertainty of the zero position of tension. The pulling force was measured with an O'Neill tester. Work has also been done by Conrad and Webb [87] on the coefficient of friction of cotton fiber.

Balls [88] referred to a method in which the strength of an untwisted roving is measured by the use of the O'Neill tester. Results were reported as "slip load per fiber." David [89] described a method for testing the coefficient of friction of yarn (conceivably this might be adapted to single filaments of rayon or silk) which involved stretching the sample under tension between clamps carried by a tilting arm. The angle of tilt necessary to cause sliding of a light rider was noted, and the errors involved in this type of instrument were indicated, one of which was the catenary form taken by the specimen.

A similar device of slightly less precision and complexity was described by Saxl [90], but again was intended primarily for yarn. Saxl also described a device involving a rotating disc against the periphery suspending a small aluminum rod from the free end of the specimen. This forms essentially a torsion pendulum. The rod used by Peirce in his experiment was approximately 2 cm long, 0.1 cm in diameter, and weighed 0.0425 gram.

The rod was twisted about one-half turn and then allowed to oscillate freely. The average time for one oscillation was determined by means of a stop-watch and recorded as the period P. The torsional rigidity was then computed from the formula

$$T_r = \frac{8\pi^3 I \cdot L}{P^2}$$

where T_r = torsional rigidity in dyne centimeters, squared.
I = moment of inertia of the rod.

$$\text{Horizontal position } I_h = \frac{W}{4}\left(r^2 + \frac{s^2}{3}\right)$$

$$\text{Vertical position } I_v = \frac{Wr^2}{2}$$

where W = weight of the rod in grams,
r = radius of the rod in centimeters,
s = length of the rod in centimeters,
L = length of the fibers in centimeters (measured with a cathetometer),
P = period of oscillation in seconds.

The modulus of rigidity in torsion (n) may be found since

$$n = \frac{T_r}{s^2} = \frac{16T_r{}^{1}}{\pi^2 d^4 e}$$

where T_r = torsional rigidity,
d = fiber diameter in centimeters,
e = form constant.

The approximate form constant may be found by reference to the following table:

Ratio of short to long diameter of fiber section	1.0	0.6	0.5	0.4	0.3	0.2
Values of e	1.0	0.9	0.8	0.7	0.6	0.4

Direct measurements of torque were made by Steinberger [83], and, although his measurements were confined to yarn, the apparatus (Fig. 15) of which the specimen was held as in a Prony brake. Use of the usual belt tension formula

$$T_1/T_2 = e^{u\theta}$$

allowed computation of the coefficient of sliding friction. Shah [91] noted that the simple belt tension formula was not quite adequate for this type of measurement. The coefficient of friction he found to vary with the tension employed and suggested the design of a chainomatic loaded device with a number of refinements of construction. The coefficient of sliding friction of fiber against fiber has not been determined by any of these workers. Activity in the study of interfiber friction by Lindberg and Gralen [92] is particularly noteworthy.

Fiber surface area measurements by use of the Arealometer are discussed by Dalla, Valle, Orr, and Cornwall [93], who give a background bibliography of other work in this field.

Measurement of sonic modulus of textile filaments by use of high-frequency sound waves yields data of importance, particularly when combined with creep tests (Fig. 16). Hamburger [94] indicates how it

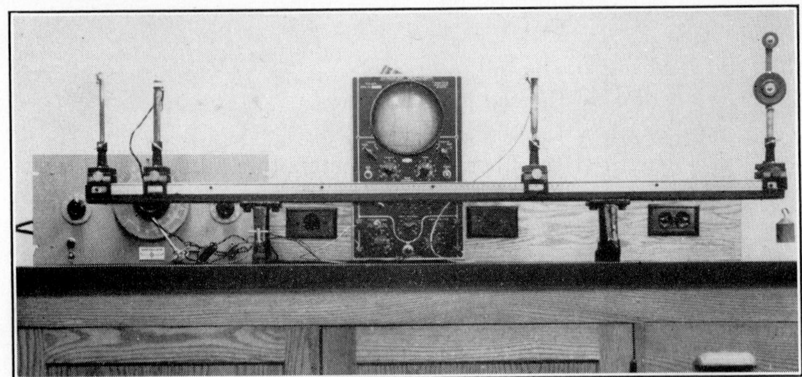

FIG. 16. Sonic modulus apparatus in simple form. (*Courtesy M.I.T. Textile Division.*)

has been possible to separate the load-deformation behavior into its rapidly recoverable, slowly recoverable, and nonrecoverable (under the conditions of test) components. This forms a background of data upon which largely depends the intelligent "engineering" of textile materials for optimum end use.

Of increasing interest to the research worker with fibers, who must necessarily accumulate a large number of observations for statistical study, is the use of punch-card techniques. As applied to the study of the physical properties of single fibers, Wakeham and Wakelin [95] have outlined important methods for carrying through such analyses as that of variance by means of automatic machines and have made evident the increased accuracy and saving of time and effort which result.

REFERENCES IN TEXT

1. CLEGG, G., *J. Textile Inst.*, **23**, T35 (1932).
2. A.S.T.M. Standards on Textile Materials (Oct. 1942), (D414-40T); (D540-42); and (D519-40).

3. Turner, A. J., Indian Central Cotton Committee Technical Series 13, *Bull. 18* (1929).
4. Ahmad, N., *ibid.*, Bull. Series A, 21 (1932).
5. Richardson, H. B., Bailey, T. L. W., Jr., and Conrad, C. M., *U. S. Dept. Agr. Tech. Bull. 545,* 41–45.
6. Balls, W. L., *A Method of Measuring the Length of Cotton Hairs,* London (1921).
7. Foster, G. A. R., *Shirley Institute Memoirs,* Series A, No. 19 (1926).
8. Flühr, H., *Ind. Text.,* **39,** 156–162 (1923).
9. Müller, E., *Leipzig. Monatschr. Textil-Ind.,* **39,** 346–347 (1924).
10. Hertel, K. L., and Zerzigon, M. G., *Textile Research,* **6** (7), 331 (May 1936).
11. Hertel, K. L., *Textile Research,* **10** (12), 510–525 (Oct. 1940).
12. Deltour, L., *Rev. Textil,* **29** (3), 313–317 (1931).
13. Cobb, N. A., U. S. Dept. Agr. (1912) (paper read before Nat. Assoc. Cotton Mfrs. (Sept. 28, 1911)).
14. Sever, W., *J. Textile Inst.,* **23** (7), 151–161 (July 1932).
15. Townend, S., *J. Textile Inst.,* **26** (4), T130–T146 (Apr. 1935).
16. Calvert, M., and Harland, S. C., *J. Textile Inst.,* **15,** T8 (1924).
17. Hardy, J. I., *Textile Research,* **3,** 189–193 (1933).
18. Müller, E., *Leipzig. Monatschr. Textil-Ind.,* **38,** 151 (1923).
19. Küsebauch, K., *Melliand Textilber.,* **12,** 21, 97 (1931).
20. Ewles, J., *J. Textile Sci.,* **2,** 100 (1928).
21. MacNicholas, H. J., and Curtis, H. J., *J. Research Natl. Bur. Standards,* **6,** 717 (1931).
22. Matthew, J. A., *J. Textile Inst.,* **23,** T55 (1932).
23. Peirce, F. T., and Lord, E., *J. Textile Inst.,* **30,** T173 (1939).
24. Hertel, K. L., and Sullivan, R. R., *Textile Research,* **11,** 30 (1940).
25. Grimes, M. A., *Textile Research,* **12,** 12 (1942).
26. A.S.T.M. Standards for Textile Materials (1950).
27. O'Neill, C., *Mem. Lit. and Phil. Soc.,* Manchester, England (Nov. 17, 1863).
28. Henry, Y., *Bull. du Jardin Colonial et des Jardins d'Essai des Colonies* (1902).
29. Balls, W. L., *The Development and Properties of Raw Cotton,* London (1915).
30. Mann, J. C., and Peirce, F. T., *J. Textile Inst.,* **17,** T82 (1926).
31. Smith, H. D. W., *J. Textile Inst.,* **22,** T158 (1931).
32. Raybaut, P., *Ind. Text.,* **49,** 246 (1932).
33. Sukthanker, S. S., Ahmad, N., and Navkal, H., *J. Textile Inst.,* **30,** T47 (1939).
34. Bowman, F. H., *Structure of the Cotton Fiber,* London (1908).
35. Matthews, J. M., *Textile Fibers,* New York (1916).
36. Barratt, T., *J. Textile Inst.,* **13,** T17 (1922).
37. Stetson, B. R., and Jacobson, J. E., M.I.T. unpublished thesis (1927).
38. Krais, P., *J. Textile Inst.,* **19,** T32 (1928).
39. Weltzien, W., and Coordt, W., *Seide,* **37,** 276 (1932).
40. Saxl, I. J., *Rayon Textile Monthly* (Sept. 1937).
41. Balls, W. L., *The Development and Properties of Raw Cotton,* London (1915).
42. Tänzer, E., *Melliand Textilber.,* **8,** 858, 938, 1013 (1927).
43. Shorter, S. H., and Hall, W. J., *J. Textile Inst.,* **14,** T493 (1923).
44. Polanyi, M., *Z. tech. Physik,* **6,** 121 (1925).
45. Denham, W. S., and Lonsdale, T., *J. Sci. Instruments,* **5,** 348 (1928).

46. Barker, S. G., and Tunstall, N., *Trans. Faraday Soc.,* **25,** 103 (1929).
47. Smith, H. D. W., *J. Textile Inst.,* **22,** T158 (1931).
48. Aoki, T., and Atsuki, K., *J. Soc. Chem. Ind. Japan,* **33,** 383B (1930).
49. Cliff, H. S., *J. Textile Inst.,* **24,** T351 (1933).
50. Steinberger, R. L., *Textile Research,* **4,** 5, 207 (1934).
51. Dunlop, D. M., unpublished M.I.T. thesis (1938).
52. Osumi, G., and Kato, E., *J. Textile Inst.,* **28,** T129 (1937).
53. Kropf, R. T., unpublished M.I.T. thesis (1931).
54. Demeulemeester, D., and Nicoloff, I., *J. Textile Inst.,* **26,** T147 (1935).
55. Saxl, I. J., *Textile Research,* **5** (12), 519 (1935).
56. Demeulemeester, D., and Nicoloff, I., *J. Textile Inst.,* **27,** T185 (1936).
57. Hindman, H., and Fox, K. R., *Rayon Textile Monthly,* **24,** 5 (1943).
58. Sookne, A. M., and Rutherford, H. A., *J. Research Natl. Bur. Standards,* **31** (July 1943).
59. Sookne, A. M., and Harris, M., *Am. Dyestuff Reptr.,* **26,** P659 (1937).
60. Hindman, H., and Burr, G. S., *Trans. A.S.M.E.,* 789 (1949).
61. Crowley, G. F., *A.S.T.M. Bull.,* 234 (1935).
62. Bellinson, H. R., *Textile Research,* **8,** 12 (1938).
63. Chandler, E. E., *U. S. Dept. Agr. Preliminary Rept.* (July 1926).
64. Pressley, E. H., *A.S.T.M. Bull.,* 13 (Oct. 1942).
65. Denham, W. S., and Lonsdale, T., *J. Sci. Instruments,* **5,** 348 (1928).
66. Hardy, J. I., *U. S. Dept. Agr. Yearbook* (1926).
67. Burns, R. H., and Johnston, A., *Proc. Am. Soc. Animal Production* (Nov. 27, 28, 1936).
68. Peterson, C. M. F., and Wenberg, C. G., unpublished M.I.T. thesis (1929).
69. Dockstader, E. K., unpublished M.I.T. thesis (1935).
70. Marsh, M. C., *J. Sci. Instruments,* **6,** 382 (1929).
71. Schiefer, H. F., *J. Research Natl. Bur. Standards,* **10,** 705 (1933).
72. Winson, C. G., *J. Textile Inst.,* **23,** T386 (1932).
73. Saxl, E. J., *Textile Research,* **8** (1), 5 (1937).
74. Saxl, E. J., *Melliand Textilber.,* **19,** 18 (Jan. 1938).
75. Saxl, E. J., *Rayon Textile Monthly,* **19,** 1 and 2 (1938).
76. Robinson, B. B., *Textile Research,* **8,** 310 (1938).
77. Fox, K. R., and Schwarz, E. R., *Textile Research,* **11** (5), 227 (1941).
78. Fox, K. R., and Schwarz, E. R., *Textile Research,* **12** (10), 2 (1942).
79. Finch, R. B., *Textile Research J.,* **3,** 165, **4,** 237 (1948).
80. Dillon, J. H., *Textile Research J.,* **4,** 207 (1947).
81. Peirce, F. T., *J. Textile Inst.,* **14,** T1 (1923).
82. Clayton, F. H., and Peirce, F. T., *J. Textile Inst.,* **20,** T315 (1929).
83. Steinberger, R. L., *Textile Research,* **7,** 83 (1936).
84. Adderley, A., *J. Textile Inst.,* **13,** T249 (1922).
85. Turner, A. J., and Navkal, H., *J. Textile Inst.,* **21,** T511 (1930).
86. Sen, K. R., and Ahmad, N., *J. Textile Inst.,* **29,** T258 (1938).
87. Conrad, C. M., and Webb, R. W., U. S. Dept. Agr., *Agr. and Cotton Marketing Bull.* (1935).
88. Balls, W. L., *Studies of Quality in Cotton,* 69, 248 (1928).
89. David, L. W., *Rayon Textile Monthly* (Feb., March, Apr. 1940).
90. Saxl, E. J., *Rayon Handbook,* 530, 531 (1939).

91. SHAH, K., unpublished M.I.T. thesis (1938).
92. LINDBERG, J., and GRALEN, N., *Textile Research J.*, **4,** 183 (1949).
93. DALLA, VALLE, J. M., ORR, C., JR., and CORNWALL, R. R., *Textile Research J.*, **10,** 676 (1950).
94. HAMBURGER, W. J., *Textile Research J.*, **12,** 705 (1948).
95. WAKEHAM, H., and WAKELIN, J. H., *Textile Research J.*, **9,** 605 (1950).

INDEX